CHEMISTRY

IN THE COMMUNITY   CHEMCOM

TEACHER'S EDITION

FIFTH EDITIONI

A PROJECT OF THE
AMERICAN CHEMICAL SOCIETY

W. H. FREEMAN AND COMPANY

ChemCom
Fifth Edition Credits

American Chemical Society

Chief Editor: Henry Heikkinen

Project Manager: Angela Powers

Revision Team: Laurie Langdon, Robert Milne, Wendy Naughton

Editors of Teacher's Edition: Angela Powers, Terri Taylor

Ancillary Materials: Susan Cooper, Joelle Lastica, Robert Milne, Wendy Naughton, Terri Taylor

ACS: Sylvia Ware, Michael Tinnesand, Terri Taylor, Helen Herlocker, Carl Heltzel, Jodi Wesemann

ACS Project Editor: Rebecca Strehlow

Technical Reviewer: Conrad Stanitski

Technical Contributors: Janet Cohen, Susan Heikkinen, Jack A. Ladson, COLOR Science Consultancy

Fourth-edition Reviewers: Kirsten Almo, Mark Beehler, Susan Berrend, Martin Besant, Regis Goode, Gary Jackson, Jane Meadows, Walt Shacklett, Terri Taylor

Teacher Contributors: Pat Chriswell, Robert Dayton, Regis Goode, Drew Lanthrum, Joelle Lastica, Steve Long, Cece Schwennsen, Barbara Sitzman, Terri Taylor

W. H. Freeman

Publisher: Susan Finnemore Brennan

Acquisitions Editor/Marketing Manager: Cindi WeissGoldner

Director of Sales and Marketing: Mike Saltzman

Developmental Editor: Rebecca Strehlow

New Media/Supplements Editors: Victoria Anderson/ Amy Shaffer

Photo Editor: Ted Szczepanski

Photo Researchers: Dena Digilio Betz, Julie Tesser

Cover Designer: Blake Logan

Text Design and Layout: Rae Grant Design

Project Editors: Katie Ostler/Denise Kadlubowski, Black Dot Group

Illustrations: Network Graphics/Black Dot Group

Composition: Black Dot Group

Printing and Binding: R.R. Donnelley/Willard

This material is based upon work supported by the National Science Foundation under Grant No. SED-88115424 and Grant No. MDR-8470104. Any opinions, findings, and conclusions or recommendations expressed in this publication are those of the authors and do not necessarily reflect the views of the National Science Foundation. Any mention of trade names does not imply endorsement by the National Science Foundation.

CORE Edition ISBN 0-7167-8505-6 (EAN: 978016785057)
Student Edition ISBN 0-7167-8919-1
Teacher's Edition ISBN 0-7167-8920-5 (EAN: 978-0-7167-8920-8)

CORE Edition Library of Congress Control Number: 2005929254
Student Edition Library of Congress Control Number: 2005938770

Printed in the United States of America
First printing 2006

ABOUT THE COVER

This is a schematic diagram of a sodium chloride crystal dissolving in water as rendered by Matt Collins of *Scientific American* magazine. For more context, please see Student Edition Figure 1.39, page 61.

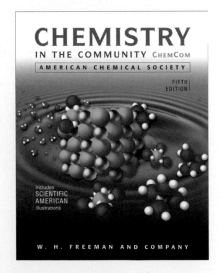

NOTE TO STUDENTS

You are likely taking a chemistry course for the first time. Of course, even if you haven't realized it, you have been immersed in chemistry all of your life. Chemical reactions are involved in foods, fuels, synthetic fabrics, and medicines. Chemistry, which is the study of matter and its changes, is responsible for materials that make up your home, transportation vehicles, what you wear—and, in fact, chemistry is also responsible for sustaining you. As someone wryly observed, you simply can't ignore chemistry, because chemistry won't ignore you.

As society increasingly depends on scientific advances, citizens will be expected to understand scientific phenomena and principles involved in making public-policy decisions. This chemistry course is designed to provide you opportunities to develop and use important chemistry concepts and skills, so you can understand the chemistry behind some issues and problems that may arise within your community.

Each unit in this course introduces a chemistry-related concern related to your life or to your community. You will complete laboratory investigations and other exercises that encourage you to apply your chemistry knowledge and skills to a particular issue or problem. You will seek solutions and weigh consequences of decisions that you and your classmates propose.

We begin with a newspaper article about a water-related emergency in Riverwood, an issue that serves as the theme for the first unit. Can chemistry help solve the problem? Welcome to the study of chemistry and to Riverwood!

IMPORTANT NOTICE

ChemCom is intended for use by high school students in the classroom laboratory under the direct supervision of a qualified chemistry teacher. The experiments described in this book involve substances that may be harmful if they are misused or if the procedures described are not followed. Read cautions carefully, and follow all directions. Do not use or combine any substances or materials not specifically called for in carrying out investigations. Other substances are mentioned for educational purposes only and should not be used by students unless the instructions specifically so indicate.

The materials, safety information, and procedures contained in this book are believed to be reliable. This information and these procedures should serve only as a starting point for good laboratory practices, and they do not purport to specify minimal legal standards or to represent the policy of the American Chemical Society. No warranty, guarantee, or representation is made by the American Chemical Society as to the accuracy or specificity of the information contained herein, and the American Chemical Society assumes no responsibility in connection therewith. The added safety information is intended to provide basic guidelines for safe practices. It cannot be assumed that all necessary warnings and precautionary measures are contained in the document or that other additional information and measures may not be required.

iii

SAFETY AND LABORATORY ACTIVITY

In *ChemCom* you will frequently complete laboratory investigations. While no human activity is completely risk free, if you use common sense, as well as chemical sense, and follow the rules of laboratory safety, you should encounter no problems. Chemical sense is just an extension of common sense. Sensible laboratory conduct won't happen by memorizing a list of rules, any more than a perfect score on a written driver's test ensures an excellent driving record. The true "driver's test" of chemical sense is your actual conduct in the laboratory.

The following safety pointers apply to all laboratory activity. For your personal safety and that of your classmates, make adherence to these guidelines second nature in the laboratory. Your teacher will point out any special safety guidelines that apply to each investigation. Two safety icons appear in your textbook. They appear at the beginning of the laboratory procedure, but apply to the entire investigation.

 When you see the goggle icon you should put on your protective goggles and continue to wear them until you are completely finished in the laboratory.

 The caution icon means there are substances or procedures requiring special care. See your teacher for specific information on these cautions.

If you understand the reasons behind them, these safety rules will be easy to remember and to follow. So, for each listed safety guideline:
- Identify a similar rule or precaution that applies in everyday life—for example in cooking, repairing or driving a car, or playing a sport.
- Briefly describe possible harmful consequences if the rule is not followed.

RULES OF LABORATORY CONDUCT

1. Do laboratory work only when your teacher is present. Unauthorized or unsupervised laboratory experimenting is not allowed.

2. Your concern for safety should begin even before the first laboratory investigation. Before starting any laboratory work, always read and think about the details of your laboratory assignment.

3. Know the location and use of all safety equipment in your laboratory. These should include the safety shower, eye wash, first-aid kit, fire extinguisher, fire blanket, exits, emergency warning system, and evacuation routes.

4. Wear a laboratory coat or apron and impact/splash-proof goggles for all laboratory work. Wear closed shoes (rather than sandals or open-toed shoes), preferably constructed of leather or similar water-impervious material, and tie back loose hair. Shorts or short skirts must not be worn.

5. Clear your bench top of all unnecessary material, such as books and clothing, before starting your work.

6. Check chemistry labels twice to ensure that you have the correct substance and the correct solution concentration. Some chemical formulas and names may differ by only a letter or a number.

7. You may be asked to transfer some chemical substances from a supply bottle or jar to your own container. Do not return any excess material to its original container unless authorized by your teacher, as you may contaminate the supply bottle.

8. Avoid unnecessary movement and talk in the laboratory.

9. Never taste any laboratory materials. Do not bring gum, food, or drinks into the laboratory. Do not put fingers, pens, or pencils in your mouth while in the laboratory.

10. If you are instructed to smell something, do so by fanning some of the vapor toward your nose. Do not place your nose near the opening of the container. Your teacher will show you the correct technique.

11. Never look directly down into a test tube; view the contents from the side. Never point the open end of a test tube toward yourself or your neighbor. Never directly heat a test tube in a Bunsen burner flame.

12. Any laboratory accident, however small, should be reported immediately to your teacher.

13. In case of a chemical spill on your skin or clothing, rinse the affected area with plenty of water. If your eyes are affected, rinsing with water must begin immediately and continue for at least 10 to 15 minutes. Professional assistance must be obtained.

14. Minor skin burns should be placed under cold, running water.

15. When discarding or disposing of used materials, carefully follow all provided instructions. Waste chemical substances usually are not permitted in the sewer system.

16. Return equipment, supplies, aprons, and protective goggles to their designated locations.

17. Before leaving the laboratory, make sure that gas lines and water faucets are shut off.

18. Wash your hands before leaving the laboratory.

19. If you are unclear or confused about proper safety procedures, ask your teacher for clarification. If in doubt, ask!

CONTENTS

BRIEF TABLE OF CONTENTS

**End of CORE FOUR Units
Begin Non-sequential Units**

FEATURES

Developing Skills

Making Decisions

Investigating Matter

Particulate-level model: sodium chloride (NaCl) dissolving in water (H₂O). A "snapshot" of the dissolving process, as sodium and chloride ions that make up a salt crystal are surrounded and carried away by water molecules. Emphasizes attractions among electrically-charged and polar molecules. **61**

Working knowledge of water softeners. Illustrates (a) softening hard water for use in the home and (b) recharging the "used" resin so that the process can be repeated. Macroscopic depictions of water flowing through resin-filled tanks are complemented by particulate-level representations of hard and soft ions involved in ion exchange on the resin. **99**

Model of a lithium (Li) atom. A cross-section of an atom illustrating the central nucleus (composed of protons and neutrons) surrounded by electron clouds. Emphasizes differences in volume and mass between an atom's nucleus and its electrons. **121**

Working knowledge of color-change paint. Illustrates a phenomenon whereby objects appear to change colors when viewed at different angles. Depicts light striking the surface of a mica-based pigment at two different viewing angles—one of which makes the paint appear blue, the other green. **201**

Model of a hydrogen (H₂) molecule. A cross-section of a molecule illustrating the bond that forms when two hydrogen atoms share two electrons. Emphasizes attractions between the shared electrons and the protons that make up each atom's nucleus. **223**

Working knowledge of hybrid gasoline–electric vehicles. Illustrates (a) how both the gasoline engine and electric storage battery contribute to powering the vehicle as it accelerates and (b) how some of that energy is captured and stored in the electric battery when the vehicle's brakes are applied. **292**

Particulate-level model of gases. A macroscopic view of a balloon flying high in the sky combined with particulate-level representations of helium atoms inside the balloon and nitrogen and oxygen molecules outside. Emphasizes the movement and spacing of gas particles. **314**

Working knowledge of aerosol spray cans. A cross-section of an aerosol can before and after the nozzle is pushed down. Shows propellant gases exerting high pressure on the walls of the can and on the liquid product inside the can. Pushing the nozzle opens a passage to the outside, allowing the gas pressure to propel the liquid up the nozzle and out of the can. **397**

Dynamic equilibrium. Depicts water levels in two transparent flasks—one stoppered and one unstoppered. Contrasts relative rates of evaporation and condensation in each flask, as depicted by arrows and particulate-level models of water molecules involved in each process. **435**

Working knowledge of rechargeable batteries. Cross sections of a nickel-metal hydride (NiMH) battery showing direction of electron flow as the battery is charged (in a recharger) and discharged (in an operating flashlight). **459**

Working knowledge of positron emission tomography (PET). Illustrates detection of gamma rays as a PET scan detects a brain tumor in a patient. The illustration zooms in to reveal the cancerous tissue, located near a blood vessel. This is then associated with a particulate-level representation of the production of gamma rays as positrons (emitted from radioisotope tracers within tagged sugar molecules) collide with electrons in cancerous cells. **530**

Nuclear fission and fusion. Particulate-level representations depict (a) smaller nuclei colliding to form a larger nucleus during fusion and (b) fission of a large nucleus into two smaller nuclei due to its collision with a neutron. Highlights energy released as mass is converted into energy during fusion and fission processes. **552**

Enzyme action. A sequence of illustrations that depicts (a) a substrate molecule approaching the active site of an enzyme molecule, (b) the substrate interacting with the enzyme, and (c) two product molecules leaving the enzyme. Emphasizes important enzyme features, including size, shape, specificity, and catalytic behavior. **613**

Working knowledge of emulsifier action. A sequence of illustrations that depicts (a) separate oil and water layers in a glass bowl, (b) addition of an egg yolk, and (c) the mayonnaise that is produced by whisking. Particulate-level representations show how lecithin molecules (contained in the egg yolk), with their nonpolar and polar regions, surround the nonpolar oil molecules and cause them to disperse among polar water molecules—an oil-in-water emulsion is created. **632**

American Chemical Society

Education Division
Sylvia A. Ware, Director

1155 SIXTEENTH STREET, NW
WASHINGTON, DC 20036-4800
Phone 800.227.5558

Dear Reader:

Welcome to *Chemistry in the Community*!

Since the early 1980s, when *Chemistry in the Community* (*ChemCom*) was first designed and released, *ChemCom* has been used successfully by over an estimated two million students and teachers in many different high school settings. Developed by the American Chemical Society (ACS) with initial funding from the National Science Foundation and several ACS sources, revision of this Fifth Edition has been guided by classroom experiences and advice of *ChemCom* teachers, advances in chemistry, new insights in chemistry teaching and learning, and—most significantly—by chemistry learning expectations highlighted by state and national science education standards.

The five goals of *ChemCom*, as they have been since its creation, are to help students

- develop an understanding of chemistry;
- cultivate problem-solving and critical-thinking skills related to chemistry;
- apply chemistry knowledge to decision-making about scientific and technological issues;
- recognize the importance of chemistry in daily life;
- understand benefits as well as limitations of science and technology.

As in previous editions of this textbook, chemistry concepts are developed on a "need-to-know" basis. That is, each unit of study starts with a significant chemistry-related concern or issue that serves as a motivational framework upon which appropriate chemistry is introduced and developed. Woven into this framework are chemical principles and skills relevant to that particular issue. Each unit is focused upon a community setting—a school, town, region, nation—and also focuses on developing specific chemistry concepts and skills. Each unit ends with a consolidating activity, where the theme is revisited and addressed, applying the chemistry introduced and learned within that unit. Student laboratory investigations, as well as decision-making opportunities and skill-building exercises, help students develop an understanding of chemistry. Although presented within a "need-to-know" context, the content encompasses all key chemical concepts and skills typically found in a first-year high school course.

The following pages will introduce users to various features of this textbook. Great care has been taken to develop the fundamental concepts of chemistry so that student interest, involvement, and learning are encouraged, supported, and cultivated.

Sincerely,

Sylvia A. Ware

Sylvia A. Ware, Director
Education Division
American Chemical Society

Welcome to the Teacher's Edition of *Chemistry in the Community*, Fifth Edition. This wraparound Teacher's Edition, along with the full *ChemCom* teaching package, offers complete, ongoing support for leading students through the *ChemCom* chemistry experience.

The Teacher's Edition

The wraparound Teacher's Edition, with reproductions of each Student Edition page, offers commentary when and where you can best take advantage of it.

Planning Guides lead into each unit of the Teacher's Edition. Organized by sections, these guide pages offer objectives, suggest class-time allotments, list special pedagogical features in the textbook, and identify relevant print and media program resources. Planning Guides also include materials lists to help you plan ahead for laboratory activities. When demonstrations are suggested in a *ChemCom* unit, the Planning Guide may provide detailed instructions and set-up photographs.

Commentary alongside Student Edition pages gives you point-of-use teaching strategies for students of various ability levels and learning styles. Preparation suggestions for student investigations appear where each investigation begins. Teacher pages also include background material, supplemental activities, references to media, computer, and print supplements, and answers to all text questions and problems. A new feature of the Teacher's Edition for *Chemistry in the Community*, Fifth Edition, is the "Using the Figures" feature. This feature, provided throughout the book, includes suggestions for using art and photographs to encourage student thought and discussion about specific ideas or concepts.

The Planning Guide lists student objectives for each section of the unit.

Section-by-section listings of specific print and media resources help you prepare class presentations.

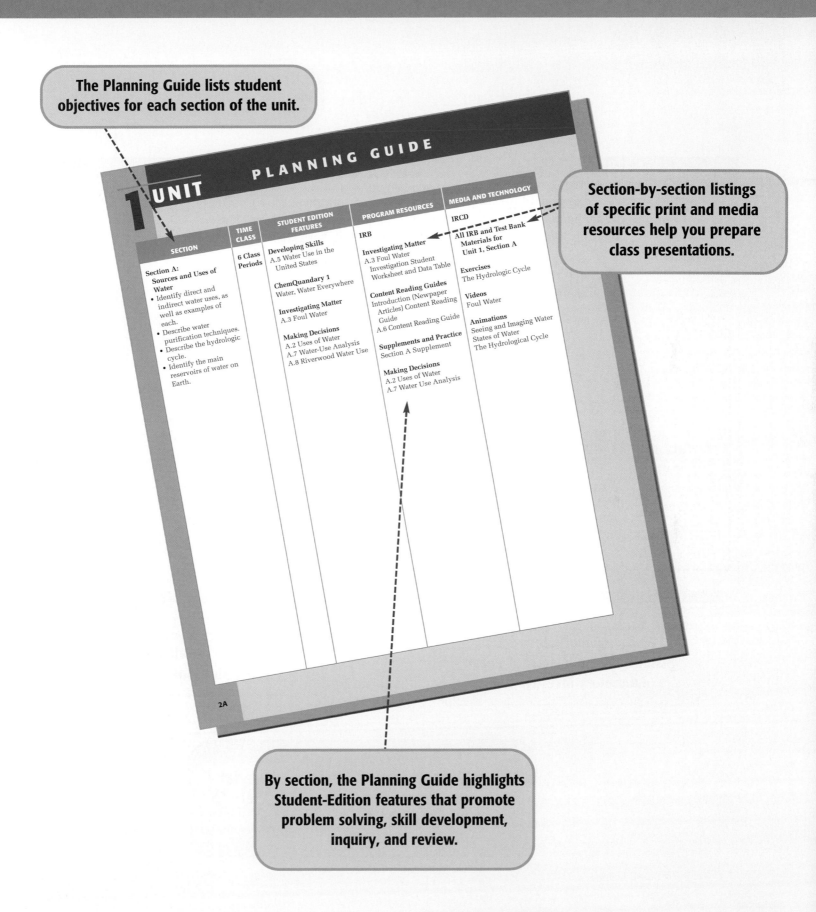

PLANNING GUIDE

UNIT 1

SECTION	TIME CLASS	STUDENT EDITION FEATURES	PROGRAM RESOURCES	MEDIA AND TECHNOLOGY
Section A: **Sources and Uses of Water** • Identify direct and indirect water uses, as well as examples of each. • Describe water purification techniques. • Describe the hydrologic cycle. • Identify the main reservoirs of water on Earth.	6 Class Periods	**Developing Skills** A.5 Water Use in the United States **ChemQuandary 1** Water, Water Everywhere **Investigating Matter** A.3 Foul Water **Making Decisions** A.2 Uses of Water A.7 Water-Use Analysis A.8 Riverwood Water Use	**IRB** **Investigating Matter** A.3 Foul Water Investigation Student Worksheet and Data Table **Content Reading Guides** Introduction (Newpaper Articles) Content Reading Guide A.6 Content Reading Guide **Supplements and Practice** Section A Supplement **Making Decisions** A.2 Uses of Water A.7 Water Use Analysis	**IRCD** All IRB and Test Bank Materials for Unit 1, Section A **Exercises** The Hydrologic Cycle **Videos** Foul Water **Animations** Seeing and Imaging Water States of Water The Hydrological Cycle

2A

By section, the Planning Guide highlights Student-Edition features that promote problem solving, skill development, inquiry, and review.

Ideas for leading into each investigation

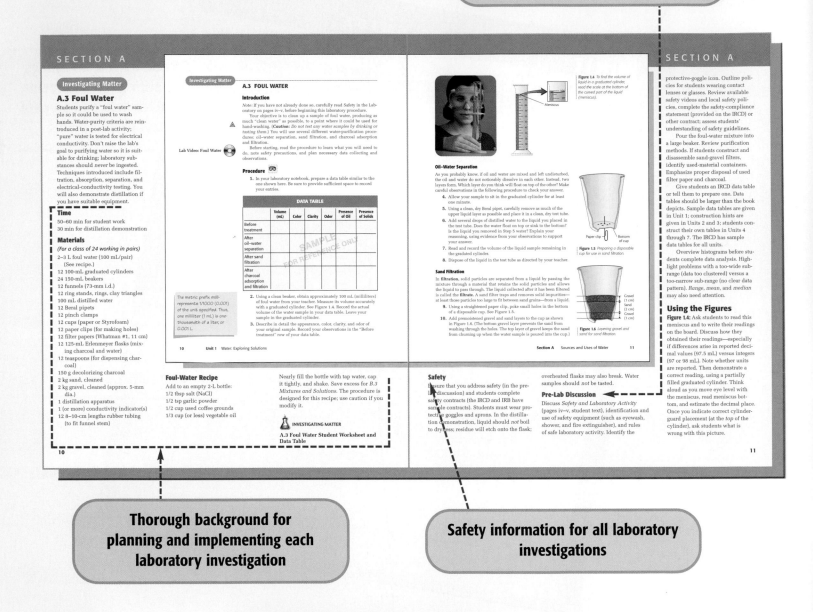

Thorough background for planning and implementing each laboratory investigation

Safety information for all laboratory investigations

Additional teacher laboratory material includes expected results and answers to all Student-Edition questions

B.1 Physical Properties of Water

This material deals with physical properties of water, including density, physical state, surface tension, boiling and freezing point, and solvent characteristics. To emphasize the unusual properties of water, you may wish to conduct demonstrations and ask students to interpret and explain the results of each.

Demonstration Ideas

1. Surface tension:

a. Float a needle or rubber band on the surface of the water. Gently lower the needle onto the surface of the water using a bent paper clip.

b. Show that more water can be added to a full glass of water. Fill a glass to the rim, then continue to add water drop by drop until it bulges well above the rim. The same effect can be demonstrated by filling a glass with water even with the rim, then asking students how many paper clips they could add to the same glass. Many more than they expect can be added due to the surface tension of the water clinging to the edge of the glass.

c. Drop water onto the surface of a penny, counting how many drops can be added before water escapes the surface. Repeat with hexane or isopropanol for contrast.

2. Density:

a. Find the mass of 20.0 mL water in a 100-mL plastic graduated cylinder. You may add food coloring to the water to make it easy to read the volumes

before and after freezing. Have students calculate the density of liquid water. Then place the cylinder in a freezer. After freezing, find the new volume and have students calculate the density of ice.

b. Create a density column: Carefully place the following materials in a large graduated cylinder (to dramatize density differences) in this order: lead sinker (11.3 g/mL), corn syrup (1.36 g/mL), glycerin (1.26 g/mL), rubber stopper

---

As the previous article indicates, water experts attribute the cause of the fish kill to something dissolved or suspended in the Snake River. What might it be? How can the search for the cause be narrowed further? Knowing the properties of water (and of substances that might be found in it) will aid in this task. To understand these properties, you will be introduced to matter at the particulate level. You will also begin to learn the language of chemistry and use it to communicate with your classmates as you investigate the fish kill. And, just like scientists and public policy decision makers, you will gather and use available evidence to make decisions about Riverwood's situation.

Figure 1.18 *Earth as seen from space. Our planet's abundant supply of water makes it unlike any other in our solar system.*

B.1 PHYSICAL PROPERTIES OF WATER

Water is a common substance—so common that we usually take it for granted. We drink it, wash with it, swim in it, and sometimes grumble when it falls from the sky. But are you aware that water is one of the rarest and most unusual substances in the universe? As planetary space probes have gathered data, scientists have learned that the great abundance of water on Earth is unmatched by any planet or moon in our solar system. Earth is usually half-enveloped by water-laden clouds, as you can see in Figure 1.18. In addition, more than 70% of Earth's surface is covered by oceans that have an average depth of more than three kilometers (two miles).

Figure 1.19 *What states of water can be observed in this winter scene?*

Unit 1 Water: Exploring Solutions

26

Water is a form of matter. See Figure 1.19. As you may recall from previous science courses, **matter** is anything that occupies space and has mass. All solids, liquids, and gases are classified as matter. Matter can be distinguished by its characteristic properties. Water has many **physical properties**—properties that can be observed and measured without changing the chemical makeup of the substance. One physical property of a sample of matter is its **density**, which is the mass of material within a given volume. The density of water as a liquid is easy to remember. Because one milliliter (mL) of liquid water at room temperature (25 °C) has a mass of about 1.00 g, the density of this water is 1.00 g/mL. One milliliter of volume is exactly equal to one cubic centimeter (1 cm³), which is pictured in Figure 1.20. Thus, the density of water at 25 °C can also be reported as 1.00 g/cm³.

The **freezing point** of water, which is another physical property, is 0 °C at normal atmospheric pressure. What other physical properties of water can you describe?

Water is the only ordinary liquid found naturally in our environment. Because so many substances dissolve readily in water, quite a few liquids are actually water solutions. Such a water-based solution is called an **aqueous solution**. Even water that seems pure is never entirely so. Surface water contains dissolved minerals as well as other substances. Distilled water used in steam irons and car batteries contains dissolved gases from the atmosphere, as does rainwater.

Pure water is clear, colorless, odorless, and tasteless. The characteristic taste and slight odor of some tap-water samples are caused by substances dissolved in the water. You can confirm this by boiling and then refrigerating a sample of distilled water. When you compare its taste with the taste of chilled tap water, you may notice that *pure* distilled water tastes flat.

Water's physical properties (see Figure 1.21) help to distinguish it from other substances. In the following activity, you will compare the density of water with the density of some other common materials.

States of Water / States of Matter

Figure 1.20 *One cubic centimeter (shown actual size). 1 cm³ = 1 mL*

The density of liquid water actually depends on its temperature—for example, the density of liquid water is 0.992 g/mL at 40 °C and 0.972 g/mL at 80 °C.

Aqueous is based on the Latin root for water (aqua).

Figure 1.21 *What properties of water might account for its sheeting action under the swimmer's right arm?*

Section B Looking at Water and Its Contaminants

27

(1.2 g/mL), ethylene glycol (1.11 g/mL), water (1.0 g/mL), plastic (0.9 g/mL), oil (cooking, mineral, or colored lamp, 0.9 g/mL), oak (0.9 g/mL), alcohol (either ethanol or 2-propanol at 0.79 g/mL), and cork (0.2 g/mL). To form discrete layers,

pour the liquids slowly down the side of the tilted graduated cylinder, or add each liquid layer using a long-stemmed funnel. Note that ethylene glycol is antifreeze. Consider coloring the water with food coloring for effect.

---

c. Place an ice cube in a graduated cylinder filled with isopropyl alcohol. The ice cube will sink rather than float because it is denser than the alcohol. Allow the cylinder to stand undisturbed for several minutes until the ice cube melts, pointing out any condensation that forms on the cylinder's outer surface. Add a second ice cube; it should float just above the bottom of the cylinder, supported by the layer of melted ice. More ice cubes can be added, and as long as the cylinder is not shaken, the alcohol and water will remain in separate layers and added ice cubes will float, farther and farther from the bottom of the cylinder.

d. In a large clear container filled with water (such as an aquarium) place a can of regular soda and a can of diet soda. The regular-soda container will sink, while the diet-soda container floats due to differences in their densities. There is much more sugar in regular soda than artificial sweetener in diet soda, resulting in a dramatic difference in mass and, subsequently, density. For a more quantitative investigation, find the mass and volume and then calculate the density of each type of soda.

Using the Figures

Figure 1.21: Sheeting action refers to the tendency of water to roll off a surface in large "sheets" rather than small separated droplets. This phenomenon is desirable, for example, when rinsing a car, dishes, or sunglasses, as it reduces spotting during drying. Water's high surface tension (and strong intermolecular forces) contributes to this phenomenon.

Demonstration ideas

Suggestions for using photographs and art to encourage student thought about issues and concepts

Answers to section summary questions at point of use.

Suggestions for additional activities

Section overviews

PREFACE

Chemistry in the Community (ChemCom) is a high-school general chemistry text. Its seven units cover a full scope of science content and process standards, developing major concepts with laboratory investigations, modeling activities, practice problems, and critical thinking exercises.

ChemCom presents chemical principles on a need-to-know basis. Each unit opens with a real-world community issue, then introduces and develops these chemical principles within this context. Each unit concludes with a consolidating activity requiring the application of all the tools and techniques learned throughout the unit.

UNIT TITLE	REPRESENTATIVE CONCEPTS	SCENARIO
1 **Water: Exploring Solutions**	Physical and chemical properties, formulas and equations, ions, solutions	Determining the cause of a fish kill
2 **Materials: Structure and Uses**	Properties, periodicity, atomic structure, the mole	Designing a new coin
3 **Petroleum: Breaking and Making Bonds**	Bonding, nomenclature, organic chemistry	Marketing an alternative-energy vehicle
4 **Air: Chemistry and the Atmosphere**	Gas laws, acid–base chemistry, kinetic molecular theory, green chemistry	Evaluating a proposed school bus-idling policy
5 **Industry: Applying Chemical Reactions**	Oxidation–reduction, kinetics, equilibrium, industrial chemistry, environmental chemistry	Choosing whether to invite an aluminum processing plant or a nitrogen fertilizer plant to the community
6 **Atoms: Nuclear Interactions**	Atomic structure, nuclear radiation, nuclear reactions, nuclear energy	Informing the public about risks and benefits of nuclear technology
7 **Food: Matter and Energy for Life**	Biochemistry, energy relationships, organic chemistry	Recommending a new vending-machine policy for the school

UNIT OPENERS

Opener images and questions stimulate thinking. How much do you already know? What are you about to discover?

INVESTIGATING MATTER

Each unit contains laboratory investigations to immerse you in the real world of chemistry. As you learn the processes of science you employ chemical principles, develop analytical skills, and use data and observations to draw conclusions.

Each investigation usually consists of an Introduction, a detailed or student-developed procedure, and Questions. Investigating Matter sections may also include Calculations, Data Analysis, and Post-Lab Activities.

NEW TO THIS EDITION

Scientific American illustrators developed selected artwork for this edition. There are two illustrations for each unit, one to deepen your conceptual understanding and one to share "working knowledge" of a device related to unit concepts. Extended captions complement these teaching visuals.

New photos abound in this edition, and line art has been refined for extra clarity. The text is completely re-designed to be inviting and easy to navigate.

MODELING CHEMISTRY

Modeling Matter activities make abstract chemical ideas easier to grasp. The activities require critiquing and creating visual representations of chemical activity, formulating and revising scientific explanations, developing manipulable models, and using logic and evidence to make decisions.

xxii   Preface

Thousands of people use chemistry every day. **Chemistry at Work** essays introduce you to some of them and show how they apply chemical processes and principles in their careers.

REAL-LIFE SKILLS AND DECISIONS

Making Decisions sections give you experience with real-life decision-making strategies—many related to the unit's organizing theme. Each Making Decisions activity asks you to collect and/or analyze data for underlying patterns, and to develop and evaluate answers based on scientific evidence and potential consequences.

ChemQuandary activities stimulate you with puzzling questions.

Developing Skills sections focus on problem-solving skills with real-world chemistry situations and practice problems.

Each lettered section in a unit concludes with a **Section Summary** organized around section learning goals. *ChemCom* poses three categories of questions. *Reviewing the Concepts* allows for practice with basic ideas. *Connecting the Concepts* asks you to identify and develop relationships among ideas. *Extending the Concepts* challenges you to seek additional information and apply chemical principles to new situations.

CHEMISTRY IN THE COMMUNITY (*CHEMCOM*) FIFTH EDITION–TEACHER AND STUDENT MEDIA, SUPPLEMENTS, AND SUPPORT

THE TEACHER'S RESOURCE BINDER

New for the Fifth Edition, the Teacher's Resource Binder offers teachers a wealth of resources to facilitate classroom and laboratory work while meeting science education standards. This Binder is a collection of three-hole punched, removable pages for key activities in the text along with supplementary material. Not only does the Teacher's Resource Binder help teachers manage a busy classroom, it can help you meet standards, student needs, and school expectations. The Teacher's Resource Binder contains the following:

Investigating Matter Student Worksheets and Data Tables—Teachers of previous editions of *ChemCom* asked for ways to prevent damage to the textbook in the laboratory. They also wanted to minimize student laboratory preparation time and maximize laboratory table space. In response, all of the Investigations that appear in the student and teacher texts appear in the TRB as reproducible worksheets. Lines are provided for students to answer the questions at the end of each investigation. Additionally, data tables have been provided at the end of each investigation for student use or as models. The data tables are at the end of the investigation to allow each teacher the flexibility to provide data tables according to student ability and readiness.

Modeling Matter Student Worksheets—All of the Modeling Matter activities that appear in the student and teacher texts are available in the TRB as student worksheets. The questions and text that characterize the Modeling Matter activities in the text are accompanied by designated space for answers on each student worksheet.

Select Making Decisions Worksheets—Some of the Making Decisions activities require students to do substantial data collection. Reproducible data tables have been provided in the TRB for select Making Decisions activities to meet the needs of students who may need this tool.

Content Reading Guides—High school students still need assistance with effective reading strategies. At an increasing rate, secondary teachers of all subjects have been required to provide support for reading across the curriculum. To meet this need, Content Reading Guides have been added to the TRB. Content Reading Guides, provided for select sections of the text, provide scaffolding and help students to interact with the text as they read.

Supplements—Supplements provide teachers and students with additional problem sets that allow students to practice their new chemistry skills and to build confidence. Supplements support individual parts of the textbook (e.g., A.1, C.1, B.7, etc…) and support entire sections (e.g., Section A, Section B, etc…). Answers are provided for supplements in the TRB Appendix.

Skill Building Supplements—The Skill Building Supplements provide teachers and their students with lessons on the mathematics required for high school chemistry classes. Skill Building Supplements guide students with diverse backgrounds toward understanding how scientific measurements can be applied in the search for understanding. Each Skill Building Supplement consists of a lesson and an accompanying practice worksheet. Skill building topics include:
   Measurement
   Dimensional Analysis
   Precision and Accuracy in Measurement
   Using Significant Figures in Calculations
   Scientific Notation
   Understanding and Interpreting Graphs and Tables
   Balancing Chemical Equations
   The Mole
   Quantitative Understanding of Formulas
   Understanding Mass Relationships in Chemical Reactions

Putting It All Together Handouts—The TRB contains reproducible student handouts and assessment tools for "Putting It All Together" sections.

Blackline Copy Masters—The TRB contains student handouts that support many of the *ChemCom* classroom activities.

THE TEACHER'S RESOURCE CD-ROM

New for the Fifth Edition, the Teacher's Resource CD-ROM offers teachers all of the content of the Teacher's Resource Binder in an electronic format. Additionally, the Teacher's Resource CD-ROM contains:

- All textbook images
- Animations, videos, tutorials, and other activities from the student CD-ROM/website

Icons referencing TRB and TRCD material can be found throughout the Teacher's Edition.

TEACHER RESOURCES

Wraparound Teacher's Edition—This new Teacher's Edition provides reduced pages from the student text with the teacher's material "wrapped around" the outer edges of these pages. Teacher annotations include answers to problems, suggested activities, and alternative teaching ideas and suggestions, as well as materials and procedures for setting up the laboratory investigations. The Teacher's Edition offers point-of-use support for both new and experienced teachers, while providing instructional strategies for students with different ability levels and learning styles. In addition, you will find background material, supplemental activities, objectives, and pacing guides for each unit, along with details of how *ChemCom* addresses the *National Science Education Standards*.

Printed Testbank—The printed testbank contains hundreds of multiple choice and short-answer questions for each unit.

Computerized Testbank—This electronic version of the testbank provides both Windows and Mac formats (on one CD), and is designed to allow teachers to add, edit, and resequence all test items.

Overhead Transparencies—The transparency package is a valuable teaching tool for introducing, clarifying, or reviewing key topics and augmenting instruction with visual learning approaches. Over 100 color transparencies provide teachers with useful graphic organizers of content and figures from the text to prompt class inquiry.

Teacher's Resource Binder—This new ancillary resource includes preliminary skill building activities, classroom handouts, practice problems, lab procedures, and lab worksheets along with reading guides, variable pacing guides, and more! All resources in this binder may be copied for class distribution and multiple uses.

Teacher's Resource CD-ROM—This is designed to help teachers create classroom presentations, enhance instructional time, build websites, and develop other resources, this CD-ROM allows users to search and export all resources listed below by key word:

- All textbook images in JPEG format
- Animations, videos, tutorials, and other interactivities from the student CD-ROM/website
- The entire contents of the Teacher's Resource Binder and other instructor materials in an electronic format.

Professional Development Workshops and Training—ACS-conducted workshops are available throughout the year in various locations. In each workshop, experienced *ChemCom* Teacher Leaders guide participants through the *ChemCom* textbook and instructional philosophy and provide hands-on experience with many laboratory investigations, modeling exercises, and culminating activities. Workshops also introduce participants to many ancillaries new to the fifth edition of *ChemCom*.

STUDENT RESOURCES

CD-ROM—This CD offers a variety of interactive student features, plus a dynamic periodic table, calculator, audio-vocabulary tool, and other useful electronic chemistry learning tools. The interface allows students to search for particular topics, key words, and terms. An auditory glossary facilitates pronunciation of these words.

Website—the *ChemCom* companion website includes all the features and tools offered on the Student CD and more! Access the site at:
www.whfreeman.com/chemcom5e

CHEMCOM AND THE *NATIONAL SCIENCE EDUCATION STANDARDS*

The *National Science Education Standards* (*NSES*) specify standards for science teaching, professional development, assessment, science content, science education programs, and science education systems. *NSES* for science content outline what all students should know, understand, and be able to do to attain scientific literacy over their K–12 education. No one science course is expected to address all of these content standards. In fact, "meeting the standards" should be an expected result of each student's total school experience. As a curriculum for first-year chemistry, *ChemCom* provides excellent student support for not only inquiry and physical science standards, but for aspects of other content standards, as well.

Within the *NSES*, each content standard is followed by "A Guide to the Content Standard." It describes the fundamental abilities, concepts, and principles underlying each content standard. The relationship of *ChemCom* to those underlying abilities, concepts, and principles is summarized in the following tables.

UNIFYING CONCEPTS AND PROCESSES STANDARD

The *National Science Education Standards* also feature a content standard addressing concepts and processes that provide connections between and among different scientific disciplines. This K–12 Unifying Concepts and Processes Standard states:

As a result of activities in grades K–12, all students should develop understanding and abilities aligned with the following concepts and processes:

- *Systems, order, and organization*
- *Evidence, models, and explanation*
- *Change, constancy, and measurement*
- *Evolution and equilibrium*
- *Form and function*

Many of these unifying concepts and processes are developed and supported throughout *ChemCom*. For instance, students are customarily asked to support conclusions and explanations with evidence from their investigations. The *Modeling Matter* feature helps students develop skills associated with modeling chemical phenomena at the particulate level and creating and evaluating appropriate physical and mental models. Equilibrium is an important concept that is introduced in Unit 4 and further developed in Unit 5.

We encourage *ChemCom* teachers to collaborate with other science teachers in their schools to ensure that these unifying concepts and processes are addressed across K–12 science curricula. The *ChemCom* student textbook is rich with applications of these concepts and processes to chemistry. One way to introduce these unifying ideas might be to organize cross-disciplinary seminars to provide students opportunities to discuss each of these unifying concepts and processes within the particular science they are currently studying. We encourage you to consult the *National Science Education Standards* for additional information on these unifying ideas.

OVERVIEW: *NSES* CONTENT STANDARDS, GRADES 9-12, VS. *CHEMCOM* COVERAGE

	A. Science as Inquiry	B. Physical Science	C. Life Science	D. Earth and Space Science	E. Science and Technology	F. Science in Personal and Social Perspectives	G. History and Nature of Science
Fundamental abilities, concepts, principles	Abilities necessary to do scientific inquiry	Structure of atoms	The cell	Energy in the earth system	Abilities of technological design	Personal and community health	Science as a human endeavor
	Understandings about scientific inquiry	Structure and properties of matter	Molecular basis of heredity	Geochemical cycles	Understandings about science and technology	Population growth	Nature of scientific knowledge
		Chemical reactions	Biological evolution	Origin and evolution of the earth system		Natural resources	Historical perspectives
		Motions and forces	Interdependence of organisms	Origin and evolution of the universe		Environmental quality	
		Conservation of energy and increase in disorder	Matter, energy, and organization in living systems			Natural and human-induced hazards	
		Interaction of energy and matter	Behavior of organisms			Science and technology in local, national, and global challenges	

LEGEND

ChemCom addresses *all* aspects of these fundamental abilities, concepts, or principles

ChemCom addresses *most* aspects of these fundamental abilities, concepts, or principles

ChemCom addresses *some* aspects of these fundamental abilities, concepts, or principles

Not typically addressed in first-year chemistry courses

A. SCIENCE AS INQUIRY STANDARD

Fundamental abilities and concepts		
Abilities and/or concepts developed in *ChemCom*	*ChemCom* **Unit(s) and Section(s)**[†]	
Abilities necessary to do scientific inquiry Addresses all abilities, including identifying questions, planning and conducting investigations, using technology and mathematics, using logic and evidence, constructing and revising explanations, evaluating alternatives, communicating results of investigations, and constructing and defending scientific arguments.	1. Water O/P A B C D 2. Materials O/P A B C D 3. Petroleum O/P A B C D 4. Air O/P A B C D 5. Industry O/P A B C 6. Atoms O/P A B C D 7. Food O/P A B C D	
Understandings about scientific inquiry Addresses all concepts, including nature of scientific investigations, reasons for conducting scientific investigations, and use of mathematical tools, logic, evidence, and scientific knowledge in conducting investigations.	1. Water O/P A B C D 2. Materials O/P A B C D 3. Petroleum O/P A B C D 4. Air O/P A B C D 5. Industry O/P A B C 6. Atoms O/P A B C D 7. Food O/P A B C D	
[†] O/P = Unit Opener and Putting It All Together		

B. PHYSICAL SCIENCE STANDARD

Fundamental concepts and principles					
Concepts and/or principles developed in *ChemCom*	*ChemCom* Unit(s) and Section(s)				

Concept	Unit	O/P	A	B	C	D
Structure of atoms — Addresses all concepts, including identity and properties of subatomic particles, electrostatic forces, nuclear model of the atom, isotopes, nuclear reactions, fission and fusion, radioactive isotopes, and radioactive decay.	1. Water	O/P	A	B	C	D
	2. Materials	O/P	A	B	C	D
	3. Petroleum	O/P	A	B	C	D
	4. Air	O/P	A	B	C	D
	5. Industry	O/P	A	B	C	
	6. Atoms	O/P	A	B	C	D
	7. Food	O/P	A	B	C	
Structure and properties of matter — Addresses all concepts, including periodic table of the elements, periodicity, elements and compounds, physical and chemical properties, ionic and covalent bonding, intermolecular forces, states of matter, structure of organic molecules, gas laws, and kinetic molecular theory.	1. Water	O/P	A	B	C	D
	2. Materials	O/P	A	B	C	D
	3. Petroleum	O/P	A	B	C	D
	4. Air	O/P	A	B	C	D
	5. Industry	O/P	A	B	C	
	6. Atoms	O/P	A	B	C	D
	7. Food	O/P	A	B	C	D
Chemical reactions — Addresses all concepts, including types of reactions (organic, oxidation/reduction, and acid/base), links to "real-world" chemical reactions (within cells, consumer chemistry, industrial processes, and environmental chemistry), kinetics (collision theory, reaction rates, activation energy, catalysis), pH scale, the mole, conservation of matter, and enthalpy.	1. Water	O/P	A	B	C	D
	2. Materials	O/P	A	B	C	D
	3. Petroleum	O/P	A	B	C	D
	4. Air	O/P	A	B	C	D
	5. Industry	O/P	A	B	C	
	6. Atoms	O/P	A	B	C	D
	7. Food	O/P	A	B	C	D
Motions and forces — Addresses some concepts, including electric forces and pressure.	1. Water	O/P	A	B	C	D
	2. Materials	O/P	A	B	C	D
	3. Petroleum	O/P	A	B	C	D
	4. Air	O/P	A	B	C	D
	5. Industry	O/P	A	B	C	
	6. Atoms	O/P	A	B	C	D
	7. Food	O/P	A	B	C	D
Conservation of energy and the increase in disorder — Addresses most concepts, including energy transfer, kinetic and potential energy, and heat as random motion.	1. Water	O/P	A	B	C	D
	2. Materials	O/P	A	B	C	D
	3. Petroleum	O/P	A	B	C	D
	4. Air	O/P	A	B	C	D
	5. Industry	O/P	A	B	C	
	6. Atoms	O/P	A	B	C	D
	7. Food	O/P	A	B	C	D
Interactions of energy and matter — Addresses all concepts, including wavelength/frequency/energy relationships, electromagnetic radiation, and conductive properties of metals, nonmetals, and metalloids.	1. Water	O/P	A	B	C	D
	2. Materials	O/P	A	B	C	D
	3. Petroleum	O/P	A	B	C	D
	4. Air	O/P	A	B	C	D
	5. Industry	O/P	A	B	C	
	6. Atoms	O/P	A	B	C	D
	7. Food	O/P	A	B	C	D

Fundamental concepts and principles Concepts and/or principles developed in *ChemCom*	*ChemCom* Unit(s) and Section(s)				
The cell Addresses some concepts, including cellular reactions involving fats, proteins, and carbohydrates, structure and synthesis of proteins from amino acids, and chemical reactions involved in photosynthesis.	1. Water O/P 2. Materials O/P 3. Petroleum O/P 4. Air O/P 5. Industry O/P 6. Atoms O/P 7. Food **O/P**	A A A A A A **A**	B B B B B **B** **B**	C C C C C C **C**	D D D D D **D**
The molecular basis of heredity Concepts not typically addressed in first-year chemistry.					
Biological evolution Concepts not typically addressed in first-year chemistry.					
Interdependence of organisms Addresses most concepts, including hydrologic, carbon and nitrogen cycles, energy flow through ecosystems, and impact of human activities on habitats and the environment.	1. Water O/P 2. Materials O/P 3. Petroleum O/P 4. Air O/P 5. Industry O/P 6. Atoms O/P 7. Food O/P	A A A A **A** A **A**	B B B **B** B B B	C C C **C** C C C	D D D **D** D D
Matter, energy, and organization in living systems Addresses most concepts, including food for energy and growth, synthesis of biomolecules, ATP and phosphate bonds, the sun as the main source of energy for life, energy involved in bond-making and bond-breaking, and the cycle of energy and matter through living and nonliving systems.	1. Water O/P 2. Materials O/P 3. Petroleum O/P 4. Air O/P 5. Industry O/P 6. Atoms O/P 7. Food **O/P**	A A A A **A** A **A**	B B **B** **B** B **B** **B**	C C C C C C **C**	D D **D** **D** **D** **D**
Behavior of organisms Concepts not typically addressed in first-year chemistry.					

D. EARTH AND SPACE SCIENCE STANDARD

Fundamental concepts and principles	ChemCom Unit(s) and Section(s)
Concepts and/or principles developed in *ChemCom*	

Energy in the earth system

Addresses most concepts, including sources of energy (solar and nuclear), Earth's energy balance, atmosphere and climate, and the greenhouse effect.

Unit	O/P	A	B	C	D
1. Water	O/P	A	B	C	D
2. Materials	O/P	A	B	C	D
3. Petroleum	O/P	A	**B**	C	**D**
4. Air	O/P	A	**B**	C	**D**
5. Industry	O/P	A	B	C	
6. Atoms	O/P	A	B	C	**D**
7. Food	O/P	**A**	B	C	D

Geochemical cycles

Addresses most concepts, including chemical reservoirs, the carbon cycle, and the nitrogen cycle.

Unit	O/P	A	B	C	D
1. Water	O/P	A	B	C	D
2. Materials	O/P	A	B	C	D
3. Petroleum	O/P	A	B	C	D
4. Air	O/P	A	**B**	C	D
5. Industry	O/P	**A**	B	C	
6. Atoms	O/P	A	B	**C**	D
7. Food	O/P	A	B	C	D

Origin and evolution of the earth system

Addresses some concepts, including radioactive isotopes for dating and half-lives.

Unit	O/P	A	B	C	D
1. Water	O/P	A	B	C	D
2. Materials	O/P	A	B	C	D
3. Petroleum	O/P	A	B	C	D
4. Air	O/P	A	B	C	D
5. Industry	O/P	A	B	C	
6. Atoms	O/P	A	B	**C**	D
7. Food	O/P	A	B	C	D

Origin and evolution of the universe

Addresses some concepts, including nuclear fusion.

Unit	O/P	A	B	C	D
1. Water	O/P	A	B	C	D
2. Materials	O/P	A	B	C	D
3. Petroleum	O/P	A	B	C	D
4. Air	O/P	A	**B**	C	D
5. Industry	O/P	A	B	C	
6. Atoms	O/P	A	B	C	**D**
7. Food	O/P	A	B	C	D

E. SCIENCE AND TECHNOLOGY STANDARD

Fundamental abilities and concepts					
Abilities and/or concepts developed in *ChemCom*	*ChemCom* Unit(s) and Section(s)				
Abilities of technological design Addresses most abilities, including using models to propose and evaluate designs, evaluating existing technologies, and presenting models and diagrams of proposed designs.	1. Water 2. Materials 3. Petroleum 4. Air 5. Industry 6. Atoms 7. Food	O/P O/P O/P O/P O/P O/P O/P	A A A A A A A	B B B B B B B	C C C C C C C	D D D D D D
Understandings about science and technology Addresses all concepts, including the role of engineers in scientific investigations, emergence of new scientific disciplines, advancement of science through new technologies, the role of creativity, imagination, and a good scientific knowledge base in science and engineering, chemical, petroleum, and nuclear technologies, nature of science and technology.	1. Water 2. Materials 3. Petroleum 4. Air 5. Industry 6. Atoms 7. Food	O/P O/P O/P O/P O/P O/P O/P	A A A A A A A	B B B B B B B	C C C C C C C	D D D D D D

F. SCIENCE IN PERSONAL AND SOCIAL PERSPECTIVES STANDARD

Fundamental concepts and principles	ChemCom Unit(s) and Section(s)					
Concepts and/or principles developed in *ChemCom*						

Personal and community health

Addresses some concepts, including potential for accidents to occur and personal choice involving food and health.

1. Water	O/P	A	B	C	D
2. Materials	O/P	A	B	C	D
3. Petroleum	O/P	A	B	C	D
4. Air	O/P	A	B	C	D
5. Industry	O/P	A	B	C	
6. Atoms	O/P	A	B	C	D
7. Food	O/P	A	B	C	D

Population growth

Addresses some concepts, including use of resources and environmental pollution.

1. Water	O/P	A	B	C	D
2. Materials	O/P	A	B	C	D
3. Petroleum	O/P	A	B	C	D
4. Air	O/P	A	B	C	D
5. Industry	O/P	A	B	C	
6. Atoms	O/P	A	B	C	D
7. Food	O/P	A	B	C	D

Natural resources

Addresses all concepts, including renewable and nonrenewable resources, uses and distribution of resources, and recycling.

1. Water	O/P	A	B	C	D
2. Materials	O/P	A	B	C	D
3. Petroleum	O/P	A	B	C	D
4. Air	O/P	A	B	C	D
5. Industry	O/P	A	B	C	
6. Atoms	O/P	A	B	C	D
7. Food	O/P	A	B	C	D

Environmental quality

Addresses all concepts, including air and water quality issues, pollution prevention, and nuclear waste.

1. Water	O/P	A	B	C	D
2. Materials	O/P	A	B	C	D
3. Petroleum	O/P	A	B	C	D
4. Air	O/P	A	B	C	D
5. Industry	O/P	A	B	C	
6. Atoms	O/P	A	B	C	D
7. Food	O/P	A	B	C	D

Natural and human-induced hazards

Addresses some concepts, including risk analysis and potential hazards associated with nuclear technology and waste.

1. Water	O/P	A	B	C	D
2. Materials	O/P	A	B	C	D
3. Petroleum	O/P	A	B	C	D
4. Air	O/P	A	B	C	D
5. Industry	O/P	A	B	C	
6. Atoms	O/P	A	B	C	D
7. Food	O/P	A	B	C	D

Science and technology in local, national, and global challenges

Addresses all concepts, including the role of scientific knowledge in making decisions, relationships among science, technology, politics, and society, risk/benefit analysis, assessing alternatives, and the complexity of decision making.

1. Water	O/P	A	B	C	D
2. Materials	O/P	A	B	C	D
3. Petroleum	O/P	A	B	C	D
4. Air	O/P	A	B	C	D
5. Industry	O/P	A	B	C	
6. Atoms	O/P	A	B	C	D
7. Food	O/P	A	B	C	D

G. HISTORY AND NATURE OF SCIENCE STANDARD

Fundamental concepts and principles					
Concepts and/or principles developed in *ChemCom*	*ChemCom* Unit(s) and Section(s)				
Science as a human endeavor Addresses most concepts, including scientific careers, interactions of scientists with society, work of individual scientists and teams of scientists, and public communication of scientific investigations.	**1. Water** O/P A **B** C **D** **2. Materials** O/P A **B** C **D** **3. Petroleum** O/P A **B** C **D** **4. Air** O/P A **B** **C** **D** **5. Industry** O/P A **B** **C** **6. Atoms** O/P A **B** **C** **D** **7. Food** O/P A **B** C **D**				
Nature of scientific knowledge Addresses most concepts, including use of evidence, logic, and scientific knowledge in constructing explanations and models, and the tentative nature of scientific knowledge.	**1. Water** **O/P** A **B** **C** D **2. Materials** O/P A B C **D** **3. Petroleum** O/P A B **C** D **4. Air** O/P **A** **B** **C** **D** 5. Industry O/P A B C **6. Atoms** O/P **A** B **C** D 7. Food O/P A B C D				
Historical perspectives Addresses most concepts, including the development of atomic theory, nuclear chemistry, and some medical technology.	1. Water O/P A B C D **2. Materials** O/P **A** **B** C **D** 3. Petroleum O/P A B C D **4. Air** O/P A B C **D** **5. Industry** O/P A **B** **C** **6. Atoms** O/P A B **C** **D** **7. Food** O/P A B C **D**				

CHEMICAL SAFETY, STORAGE, AND DISPOSAL REFERENCES

While no laboratory exercise is without some potential risk, most accidents can be prevented by basing laboratory practices and procedures on established chemical safety guidelines. The following references offer valuable background information. Since risk assessments are subject to change with new studies, you should stay up to date by reading professional journals (such as the *Journal of Chemical Education* and *The Science Teacher*) and learning about any guidelines and regulations issued in your local school district or state.

Aldrich Catalog Handbook of Fine Chemicals, Aldrich Chemical Co., P.O. Box 355, Milwaukee, WI 53201.

Chemical Catalog/Reference Manual, Flinn Scientific, Inc., P.O. Box 219, 770 Raddant Rd., Batavia, IL 60510. 630–879–6900; 800–452–1261.

Committee on Chemical Safety (ACS), *A Model Chemical Hygiene Plan for High Schools,* American Chemical Society, Washington, DC 20036, 1995. Product HS70A. 800–209–0423.

Committee on Chemical Safety (ACS), *Safety in Academic Chemistry Laboratories,* 7th edition. American Chemical Society, Washington, D.C. 20036, 2003.

Fire Protection Guide on Hazardous Materials, National Fire Protection Association, 11 Tracy Drive, Avon, MA 02322, 2001. 617–770–4543. National safety code as applied to laboratory fire prevention and protection.

Furr, A. Keith. *CRC Handbook of Laboratory Safety,* 5th edition, CRC Press, Boca Raton, FL, 2000.

The Merck Index, 13th Edition, Merck & Co., Inc., Rathway, NJ, 2001. Authoritative, brief descriptions of properties (including health hazards) of many substances.

NIOSH Pocket Guide to Chemical Hazards, U.S. Department of Health and Human Services, Centers for Disease Control, National Institute for Occupational Safety and Health, Washington D.C., 2005. A pocket summary of hazardous properties of substances regulated by NIOSH.

Prudent Practices in the Laboratory: Handling and Disposal of Chemicals, National Academy Press, Washington, D.C., 1995.

School Science Laboratories: A Guide to Some Hazardous Substances, Council of State Science Supervisors and U.S. Consumer Products Safety Commission, Washington, D.C., 1984.

School Science Safety Lecture Series/Secondary, Flinn Scientific, Inc., 770 Raddant Rd., Batavia, IL 60510, 1996. 630–879–6900; 800–452–1261. Overhead transparency masters, suggested student activities, student assessments.

Sourcebook Version 2.1, ChemSource, Inc., College of New Rochelle, New Rochelle, NY 10805, 1998. This and other ChemSource materials are available from the American Chemical Society, Washington, D.C. 20036. Contact the ACS online store (*chemistry.org*) or 800–227–5558 to order.

Starting With Safety: An Introduction for the Academic Chemistry Laboratory, American Chemical Society, Washington, D.C. 20036. 35-minute VHS videotape and teacher's guide. Product V5100. 800–209–0423.

Wood, Claire. *Safety in School Science Labs,* James A. Kaufman & Associates, Natick, MA, 1995.

CHEMICAL AND SCIENTIFIC EQUIPMENT SUPPLIERS

The following representative firms provide general supplies and equipment for all areas of science teaching, as well as specific items for chemistry teaching.

Boreal Laboratories, Ltd., 399 Vansickle Road, St. Catharines, Ontario, L2S 3T4, Canada. 905–984–3000, 800–387–9393. *www.boreal.com*

Carolina Biological Supply Company, 2700 York Rd., Burlington, NC 27215. 336–586–4333; 800–334–5551. *www.carolina.com*

Chem Scientific LLC., 1250 Washington Street, Norwood, MA 02062. 888–527–5827; 781–440–0900. *www.chemscientific.com*

Connecticut Valley Biological Supply Company, Inc., 82 Valley Rd., P.O. Box 326, Southampton, MA 01073. 413–527–4030; 800–628–7748. *www.ctvalleybio.com*

Demco, Inc., 4801 Forest Run Road, Madison, WI 53704. 608–241–1201; 800–356–1200.

Edmund Scientific, 60 Pearce Avenue, Tonawanda, NY 14150. 800–728–6999. *www.scientificsonline.com*

Educational Innovations, Inc., 362 Main Avenue, Norwalk, CT 06851. 203–229–0730; 888–912–7474. *www.teachersource.com*

Fisher Scientific Company, Educational Materials Division, 485 South Frontage Road, Burr Ridge, IL 60521. 630–655–4410. *www.fisheredu.com*

Flinn Scientific, Inc., P.O. Box 219, Batavia, IL 60510. 630–879–6900; 800–452–1261. *www.flinnsci.com*. The Flinn Chemical Catalog also provides information on chemical safety, storage, and disposal.

Frey Scientific, P.O. Box 8101, 100 Paragon Parkway, Mansfield, OH 44903. 419–589–1900; 800–225–3739. *www.freyscientific.com*

Hach Company, P.O. Box 608, Loveland, CO 80539–0608. 800–227–4224. *www.hach.com*. Test kits for environmental studies.

J.T. Baker, 222 Red School Lane, Phillipsburg, NJ 08865. 908–859–2151; 800–582–2537. *www.jtbaker.com*

Lab Safety Supply, P.O. Box 1368, Janesville, WI 53547–1368. 608–754–2345; 800–356–0783. *www.labsafety.com*. Specializes in safety equipment and supplies.

LaMotte Company, P.O. Box 329, Chestertown, MD 21620–0329. 410–778–3100; 800–344–3100. *www.lamotte.com*. Test kits for environmental studies.

Markson, P.O. Box 3616, Honolulu, HI 96811–3616. 800–528–5114. *www.markson.com*

Micro Mole Scientific, 1312 North 15th Street, Pasco, WA 99301. 509–545–4904.

Nalgene Labware Division, P.O. Box 20365, Rochester, NY 14602–0365. 585–586–8800; 800–625–4327. *www.nalgenelabware.com*. Specializes in transparent and translucent plastic laboratory equipment.

NASCO, 901 Janesville Ave., P.O. Box 901, Ft. Atkinson, WI 53538. 414–563–2446; 800–558–9595. *www.enasco.com*

Ohaus Corporation, 19A Chapin Road, P.O. Box 2033, Pine Brook, NJ 07058. 800–672–7722. *www.ohaus.com*

S17 Science Supplies & Services Co. Ltd., PMB #231, 5 Columbia Drive, Niagara Falls, NY 19305–1275. 905–709–2033; 800–288–7151. *www.S17Science.com*

Sargent–Welch/Cenco, 911 Commerce Court, P.O. Box 5229, Buffalo Grove, IL 60089–5229. 847–459–6625; 800–727–4368. *www.sargentwelch.com*

Science Kit & Boreal Laboratories, Inc., 777 E. Park Drive, P.O. Box 5003, Tonawanda, NY 14150–6782. 716–874–6020; 800–828–7777. *www.sciencekit.com*

Sigma-Aldrich, 3050 Spruce St., St. Louis, MO 63103. 800–325–3010. *www.sigmaaldrich.com*

Vernier Software, 13979 SW Millikan Way, Beaverton, OR 97005–2886. 888–837–6437. *www.vernier.com*

Wards Natural Science Establishment, Inc., 5100 West Henrietta Rd., P.O. Box 92912, Rochester, NY 14692–9012. 585–359–2502; 800–962–2660. *www.wardsci.com*

INFORMATION ON ACIDS AND BASES

	Molar mass of reagent, g/mol	Approximate strength of concentrated reagent[a]	Molarity of concentrated reagent (M)	Milliliters of concentrated reagent needed to prepare one liter of 1 M solution[b]
Acetic acid, $HC_2H_3O_2$	60.5	99.8	17.4	57.5
Hydrochloric acid, HCl	36.46	37.2	12.1	82.5
Nitric acid, HNO_3	63.01	70.4	15.9	63.0
Sulfuric acid, H_2SO_4	98.07	96.0	18.0	55.5
Aqueous ammonia, NH_3 (aq)	17.03	28.0	14.5	69.0

[a]Representative value, mass percent
[b]Rounded to nearest 0.5 mL

MATERIALS AND SUPPLIES

Quantities are for a class of 24 students working in pairs and completing all recommended *ChemCom* investigations. For information concerning actual quantities needed for specific activities, see the supply list at the beginning of each unit of the Teacher's Edition and the relevant investigation materials list.

QUANTITY	ITEM	UNIT-SECTION
50 mL	acetic acid, glacial, 17.4 M	3-C.8
100 mL	alcohol (ethyl or isopropyl)	6-B.9
12 sets	alpha, beta, and gamma radiation sets	6-B.4
12	aluminum soft drink can, empty	4-A.3
25 g	ammonium chloride (NH_4Cl)	1-C.11
7.5 g	ammonium tetrahydrate ($(NH_4)_6Mo_7O_{24} \cdot 4H_2O$)	5-A.7
0.4 g	ammonium nitrate (NH_4NO_3)	5-A.3
2.3 g	amylase	7-C.7
12.4 g	anhydrous boric acid (H_3BO_3)	7-C.7
1	apple	7-C.5
10 mL	aqueous ammonia (NH_3), concentrated, 14.8 M	4-D.6
20 g	ascorbic acid ($C_6H_8O_6$)	5-A.7
12	aspirator adaptors	4-B.9, 4-D.6
12	bags, zip-seal, pint-sized	4-C.2
12	balances	1-C.3, 2-C.11, 3-B.6, 3-D.4, 4-A.3, 4-B.6, 5-A.7, 6-A.6, 7-A.3
48	balloons, medium to large	4-A.3
1 m	bare copper wire, approx. 18 gauge	4-D.6
1.2 g	barium chloride dihydrate ($BaCl_2 \cdot 2H_2O$)	1-B.11, 5-A.3
12	batteries, 9-V or 1.5-V	2-D.8
24	beakers, 100-mL	2-C.11, 3-A.2, 3-C.8, 3-D.4, 5-A.3
12	beakers, 250-mL	2-D.5, 3-D.4, 7-C.7
36	beakers, 400-mL	1-C.3, 4-B.6, 5-A.7, 5-B.3
1	beaker, 600-mL	4-A.10
300 mL	Benedict's solution	7-C.7
140	Beral pipets	1-A.3, 1-B.11, 2-A.5, 2-B.5, 3-D.4, 4-C.2, 5-A.3, 5-C.2, 7-D.3
12	Beral pipets containing 0.1 M HCl	4-C.11
12	Beral pipets containing 0.1 M NaOH (sodium hydroxide)	4-C.11
12	Beral pipets containing 0.1 M $H_2PO_4^-$/HPO_4^{2-} buffer solution	4-C.11
12	Beral pipets containing distilled water	4-C.11
12	Beral pipets containing universal indicator	4-C.11
24	boiling chips	3-A.2, 3-C.8, 7-C.7
12	bottles, squeeze (for alcohol)	6-B.9
12	bottles, wide-mouth (or glass jars)	7-D.7

QUANTITY	ITEM	UNIT-SECTION
200 mL	bromthymol blue solution, 0.04% (m/v)	4-B.9
3	buckets, plastic, clear, 2-L	4-A.3
60 mL	buffer solution, pH 10	7-C.7
60 mL	buffer solution, pH 2	7-C.7
60 mL	buffer solution, pH 4	7-C.7
60 mL	buffer solution, pH 7	7-C.7
60 mL	buffer solution, pH 8	7-C.7
12	Bunsen burners	5-A.3, 5-A.7, 5-B.3
2.93 g	calcium chloride dihydrate ($CaCl_2 \cdot 2H_2O$)	1-D.7, 1-B.11
40 g	calcium chloride, anhydrous ($CaCl_2$)	5-B.3
1 box	Calgon (sodium hexametaphosphate)	1-D.7
12	candles, paraffin	3-B.6
12	candles, tea light or similar	4-B.9
1 lb	candy, M&Ms	7-D.7
1 lb	candy, Skittles	7-D.7
12	capillary melting point tubes	4-A.10
12	cardboard squares, 8 cm $\times$ 8 cm	4-B.6
1	cardboard, heavy, 1cm^2 (used as source of smoke)	4-D.6
100 g	cation-exchange resin	1-D.7
1 pkg	chromatography paper, 2-in wide	7-D.7
24	clamps	3-A.2, 4-B.9
12	clay triangles	1-A.3, 1-D.7
12	cloud chamber kit	6-B.9
2.37 g	cobalt(II) chloride hexahydrate ($CoCl_2 \cdot 6H_2O$)	5-B.3
12	cobalt-blue glass squares	5-A.3
12	condensers	3-A.2
4	conductivity apparatus	1-A.3, 2-A.5
12	container or box (plastic or cardboard) with lid	6-C.2
12 g	copper powder	2-B.3
12	copper strips, medium	2-D.8, 5-C.2
12	copper strips, narrow	5-C.2
12	copper strips, wide	5-C.2
6 cm	copper wire	2-B.5
0.43 g	copper(II) chloride ($CuCl_2 \cdot 2H_2O$)	2-A.5
2.53 g	copper(II) nitrate trihydrate ($Cu(NO_3)_2 \cdot 3H_2O$)	2-B.5, 5-C.2
61 g	copper(II) sulfate pentahydrate ($CuSO_4 \cdot 5H_2O$)	1-C.11, 2-D.8, 7-C.7
12	corks, size 20	7-A.3
12	crucible tongs	2-D.5, 6-B.9
12	crucibles	2-B.3
12	cups, paper or styrofoam	1-A.3
1	distillation apparatus	1-A.3
20 L	distilled water	1-A.3, 1-B.11, 1-C.11, 1-D.7, 2-C.11, 2-D.5, 3-D.4, 4-C.2, 4-C.11, 5-A.7
600 mL	distillation solution	3-A.2
12 sets	dominoes	6-D.2
2	drinking glass, plastic, clear	4-A.3
24	dropper bottles	2-A.5, 5-B.3
6	dropper bottles with liquid soap	1-D.7
48	dropper bottles for organic reactants	3-C.8

QUANTITY	ITEM	UNIT-SECTION
10 pounds	dry ice	6-B.9
12	empty soft drink cans with pull tabs, 12-oz	3-B.6, 3-D.4, 7-A.3
12	Erlenmeyer flasks, 125-mL	1-A.3
12	Erlenmeyer flasks, 250-mL	4-B.9
2	Erlenmeyer flasks, 500-mL	4-D.6
700 mL	ethanol (C_2H_5OH), 95%	1-C.11, 5-B.3
12	filter flasks, 250-mL	4-B.9
1	filter flasks, 500-mL	4-D.6
96 pieces	filter paper, Whatman #1, 11 cm diameter	1-A.3, 2-C.11, 1-D.7
12	Florence flasks, 125-mL	3-A.2
1	food coloring, blue	7-D.7
1	food coloring, green	7-D.7
1	food coloring, red	7-D.7
1	food coloring, yellow	7-D.7
12	forceps	2-A.5, 2-C.11, 6-B.4, 6-B.9
12	funnels, 73-mm inside diameter	1-A.3, 1-D.7, 4-B.9
0.5 tsp (0.5 g)	garlic powder	1-A.3
24	glass plates (about 5-cm square, 0.2-cm thick)	6-B.4
1 box	gloves, disposable	6-B.9
25 g	glucose ($C_6H_{12}O_6$)	1-C.11
12	graduated cylinders, 10-mL	1-C.11, 1-D.7, 3-C.8, 3-D.4, 5-A.7, 7-C.7, 7-D.3
12	graduated cylinders, 25-mL	2-D.5
1	graduated cylinder, 100-mL, glass	4-D.6
12	graduated cylinders, 50-mL or 100-mL	5-A.7
12	graduated cylinders, 100-mL	1-A.3, 1-C.3, 3-A.2, 3-B.6, 3-D.4, 4-B.6
20 g	granular fertilizer	5-A.7
1 package	graph paper	6-B.4
5 g	graphite pencil lead	2-A.5
2 kg	gravel	1-A.3
4	hammers, small	2-A.5
25 mL	hexane (C_6H_{14})	1-C.11
12	hot plates	1-C.3, 2-B.3, 2-C.11, 2-D.5, 3-C.8, 4-A.3, 4-B.6, 5-A.3, 7-C.5, 7-C.7
1 pkg	Hydrion (pH) paper, wide-range	4-C.2, 4-D.6
165 mL	hydrochloric acid (HCl), concentrated, 12.0 M	2-A.5, 2-C.11, 4-C.2, 4-D.6, 5-A.3
120 mL	hydrogen peroxide, 3% (H_2O_2)	7-C.5
8 lbs	ice	1-C.3, 3-B.6, 3-D.4, 4-A.3, 5-B.3, 7-A.3
12	index cards, 3" × 5" (or cut as necessary)	3-B.6, 6-B.4, 7-A.3
26 g	iodine (I_2)	1-C.11, 3-A.2
12	iron nails	2-D.8
12	iron strips	5-C.2
5 g	iron wire	2-A.5
2.8 g	iron(II) sulfate heptahydrate ($FeSO_4 \cdot 7H_2O$)	1-B.11, 5-A.3
6.0 g	iron(III) nitrate nonahydrate ($Fe(NO_3)_3 \cdot 9H_2O$)	1-B.11, 5-A.3, 5-C.2
600 mL	lamp oil	1-C.11

QUANTITY	ITEM	UNIT-SECTION
24	lead plates (about 5 cm square, 0.1 cm thick)	6-B.4
12	light, high intensity (bright flashlight)	6-B.9
1 pkg	litmus paper, blue	4-C.2
2 pkgs	litmus paper, red	4-C.2, 5-A.3
0.5 lbs	liver, raw	7-C.5
1.8 g	magnesium nitrate hexahydrate ($Mg(NO_3)_2 \cdot 6H_2O$)	2-B.5, 5-C.2
48 cm	magnesium ribbon	2-A.5, 4-C.2, 5-C.2
24	marble chips (calcium carbonate ($CaCO_3$))	4-C.2
12	marking pencils	1-C.11
12	matchbooks	3-B.6, 3-D.4, 7-A.3
12	medicine droppers	1-C.11
12	metal sample cups (empty tea candle containers)	3-D.4
12	metal samples for calorimetry experiement	4-B.6
12	meter sticks or rulers	6-B.4
224 mL	methyl alcohol	3-C.8, 3-D.4
25 g	naphthalene flakes ($C_{10}H_8$)	1-C.11
12	nichrome or platinum (Pt) wire loops with handles	5-A.3
50 mL	octyl alcohol	3-C.8
12	paper clips	1-A.3, 7-A.3
12 sheets	paper towels	4-A.10, 4-C.2
1	peeler or paring knife	4-C.2
12	pencils	3-D.4
1200	pennies	6-C.2
36	pennies, copper	2-D.5
72	pennies, post-1982	6-A.6
72	pennies, pre-1982	6-A.6
50 mL	pentyl alcohol	3-C.8
0.92 g	dipotassium monohydrogen phosphate (K_2HPO_4) (used to prepare phosphate standard)	5-A.7
12	pinch clamps	1-A.3
1	plastic bottle, clear 2- or 2-L	4-A.3
1	plastic bottle, clear 2- or 2-L with 0.5-cm hole poked in side	4-A.3
1	plastic sheet, stiff, 3×3 cm (CD jewel case or coffee can lid)	4-A.3
1	plastic wrap, 3×3 cm	4-A.3
14.1 g	potassium hydroxide (KOH)	3-D.4
1 g	potassium iodate (KIO_3)	7-D.3
1 g	potassium iodide (KI)	7-D.3
35.5 g	potassium nitrate (KNO_3)	5-A.3, 5-C.2
1.75 g	potassium thiocyanate (KSCN)	1-B.11, 5-A.3
1	potato, white or baking	7-C.5
12	radiation counter	6-B.4
12	radiation source (usually part of cloud chamber)	6-B.9
1	reagent bottle for dispensing 18 M H_2SO_4	3-C.8
2	red apples	4-C.2
24	ring stands	1-A.3, 1-D.7, 3-A.2, 3-B.6, 3-D.4, 4-B.9, 5-A.7, 5-B.3, 7-A.3
24	rings	1-A.3, 1-D.7, 3-B.6, 3-D.4, 5-A.7, 5-B.3, 7-A.3

QUANTITY	ITEM	UNIT-SECTION
250 g	rock salt	4-A.3
24	rubber bands, small orthodontic	4-A.10
12	rulers, metric	1-C.3, 4-A.10
6 g	salicylic acid	3-C.8
2.5 kg	sand	1-A.3, 1-D.7
12	sealed opaque containers (possibly film canisters)	6-A.6
5 g	silicon, lumps	2-A.5
6 cm	silver foil	2-B.5
5.7 g	silver nitrate ($AgNO_3$)	1-B.11, 2-B.5, 5-B.3
101.6 g	sodium carbonate monohydrate ($Na_2CO_3 \cdot H_2O$)	1-B.11, 1-D.7, 7-C.7
35 g	sodium chloride (NaCl)	1-A.3, 1-C.11, 5-B.3
173 g	sodium citrate dihydrate ($Na_3C_6H_5O_7 \cdot 2H_2O$)	7-C.7
6.8 g	sodium hydroxide (NaOH)	4-B.9, 5-A.3
4.3 g	sodium nitrate ($NaNO_3$)	5-A.3
40.0 g	sodium phosphate dodecahydrate ($Na_3PO_4 \cdot 12H_2O$)	5-A.3, 7-C.7
1.6 g	sodium sulfate decahydrate ($Na_2SO_4 \cdot 10 H_2O$)	5-A.3
12 g	sodium sulfite (Na_2SO_3)	4-C.2
12	space-filling or ball-and-stick model sets	3-A.7, 3-A.9, 3-C.4
12	spatulas	1-C.11, 2-B.3
1.5 g	starch solution, 1%	7-C.7, 7-D.3
1 roll (~100 g)	steel wool	2-B.5, 2-D.5, 3-D.4
24	stir rods, glass	1-C.3, 1-D.7, 2-C.11, 3-B.6, 3-D.4, 5-A.7, 7-A.3
12	stir sticks, coffee	4-C.11
12	stoppers (to fit 18-mm test tubes)	1-D.7
60	stoppers (to fit 16-mm test tubes)	7-C.7
24	stoppers (to fit 16-mm test tubes, with inserted glass tubing)	7-C.5
12	stoppers, to fit bottles (or glass jars)	7-D.7
1	stopper, 1 hole (to fit 100-mL graduated cylinder)	4-D.6
1	stopper, 1-hole (to fit 500-mL filter flask)	4-D.6
12	stoppers, 2 holes (to fit 125-mL Florence flasks)	3-A.2
12	stoppers, 2-hole (to fit 250-mL flasks)	4-B.9
2	stoppers, 2-hole (to fit 500-mL flasks)	4-D.6
12	stopwatches or timers	3-A.2
12	straws, drinking	4-B.9
36	strips of filter paper, 8 mm x 3 cm	5-C.2
24	styrofoam cups	4-B.6
120 g	succinic acid	1-C.3
5 g	sulfur	2-A.5
205 mL	sulfuric acid (H_2SO_4), concentrated, 18 M	3-C.8, 5-A.3, 7-D.3, 7-D.7
1	syringe, large (>30 mL), Luer-tip with cap	4-A.3
12	teaspoons	1-A.3
1	Tesla coil	4-D.6
12	test tube holders	1-C.3, 3-C.8, 5-A.3, 5-A.7, 7-C.7
12	test tube racks	1-C.11, 1-C.3, 1-D.7, 5-A.3, 5-A.7

QUANTITY	ITEM	UNIT-SECTION
24	test tubes (13 × 100 mm)	1-C.11
36	test tubes (15 × 125 mm)	3-C.8
60	test tubes (16 × 125 mm)	7-C.5, 7-C.7
1	test tube (18 × 150 mm)	
220	test tubes (18 × 150 mm)	1-D.7, 4-A.3, 4-B.9, 4-C.2, 5-A.3, 5-A.7, 5-B.3
72	test tubes, Pyrex or Kimax (20 × 150 mm)	1-C.3
12	thermometers, alcohol, −10 to 110 °C	1-C.3, 2-C.11, 3-A.2, 3-B.6, 3-D.4, 4-B.6, 7-A.3
12	thermometers, non-mercury, readable to 150 °C	4-A.10
5 g	tin, wire or foil	2-A.5
12	tongs	4-A.3, 4-B.6
2 boxes	toothpicks	5-A.3, 7-D.3, 7-D.7
1 roll	transparent tape	4-D.6
1	tube, thistle	4-D.6
2 pieces	tubing, glass, 90° bends approximately 20 cm apart	4-D.6
12	tubing, glass, bent	4-B.9
12	tubing, glass, straight	4-B.9
18 m	tubing, rubber	3-A.2
24	tubing, rubber, 30-cm lengths	4-B.9
12	tubing, rubber, 8-10 cm lengths	1-A.3
12	universal indicator color charts	4-C.11
5 mL	universal indicator solution	4-D.6
25 g	urea ($(NH_2)_2CO$)	1-C.11
0.5 cup (125 mL)	used coffee grounds	1-A.3
12	U-tubes with appropriate containers for support	2-D.8
1.6 L	vegetable oil	1-A.3, 3-D.4
1	Vitamin C tablets (60 or 100 mg)	7-D.3
12	voltmeter or CBL	2-D.8, 5-C.2
12	wash bottles (used to dispense distilled water)	1-D.7
12	watch glasses	2-C.11, 2-D.5
12	wellplates, 24-well	1-B.11, 2-A.5, 2-B.5, 4-C.11, 5-C.2, 7-D.3, 7-D.7
1 pair	wire cutters	4-D.6
24	wire leads with alligator clips	2-D.8, 5-C.2
12	wooden splints	3-A.2
1 pkg	yeast	7-C.5
300 mL	yellow corn oil	4-A.10
136 g	zinc chloride ($ZnCl_2$)	2-D.5
7.5 g	zinc nitrate hexahydrate ($Zn(NO_3)_2{\cdot}6H_2O$)	2-B.5, 5-C.2
12	zinc strips, medium	5-C.2
12	zinc strips, narrow	5-C.2
12	zinc strips, wide	5-C.2
36 g	zinc, granulated or foil	2-D.5
15 g	zinc, mossy or wire	2-A.5
6 cm	zinc, wire	2-B.5

SECTION	CLASS TIME	STUDENT EDITION FEATURES	PROGRAM RESOURCES	MEDIA AND TECHNOLOGY
Section A: **Sources and Uses of Water** • Identify direct and indirect water uses, as well as examples of each. • Describe water purification techniques. • Describe the hydrologic cycle. • Identify the main reservoirs of water on Earth.	**6 Class Periods**	**Developing Skills** A.5 Water Use in the United States **ChemQuandary 1** Water, Water Everywhere **Investigating Matter** A.3 Foul Water **Making Decisions** A.2 Uses of Water A.7 Water-Use Analysis A.8 Riverwood Water Use	**TRB** **Investigating Matter** A.3 Foul Water Investigation Student Worksheet and Data Table **Content Reading Guides** Introduction (Newpaper Articles) Content Reading Guide A.6 Content Reading Guide **Supplements and Practice** Section A Supplement **Making Decisions** A.2 Uses of Water A.7 Water Use Analysis	**TRCD** **All TRB and Test Bank Materials for Unit 1, Section A** **Exercises** The Hydrologic Cycle **Videos** Foul Water **Animations** Seeing and Imagining Water States of Water The Hydrological Cycle

SECTION	CLASS TIME	STUDENT EDITION FEATURES	PROGRAM RESOURCES	MEDIA AND TECHNOLOGY
Section B: **Looking at Water and Its Contaminants** • Define and identify examples of physical properties. • Classify samples of matter in terms of elements, compounds, and mixtures. • Interpret and create models that represent elements, compounds, and mixtures at the particulate level. • Distinguish among different types of mixtures (solutions, colloids, and suspensions). • Recognize, describe, explain, and distinguish among chemical symbols, formulas, and equations. • Recognize and distinguish characteristics of the basic subatomic particles: protons, neutrons, and electrons. • Describe what constitutes an ion. • Indicate the electrical charge of an ion containing a specified number of protons and electrons. • Write the formula and name of an ionic compound, given the compound's anion and cation name and electrical charge.	**7 Class Periods**	**Developing Skills** B.2 Density B.7 Symbols, Formulas, and Equations B.10 Ionic Compounds **Investigating Matter** B.11 Water Testing **Modeling Matter** B.5 Pictures in the Mind **Making Decisions** B.13 The Riverwood Water Mystery	**TRB** **Investigating Matter** B.11 Water Testing Student Worksheet and Data Table **Modeling Matter** B.5 Pictures in the Mind Student Worksheet **Content Reading Guides** Introduction (Newspaper Articles) Content Reading Guide B.1 and B.2 Content Reading Guide B.4, B.6, and B.9 Content Reading Guide **Supplements and Practice** B.9 Supplement: Ions and Ionic Compounds Section B Supplement	**TRCD** **All TRB and Test Bank Materials for Unit 1, Section B** **Exercises** Modeling Matter: Attraction between Water Molecules **Videos** Water Ions **Animations** Molecular Views of Water Modeling Matter: Attraction between Water Molecules States of Matter

SECTION	CLASS TIME	STUDENT EDITION FEATURES	PROGRAM RESOURCES	MEDIA AND TECHNOLOGY
Section C: Investigating the Cause of the Fish Kill • Define the terms *insoluble, unsaturated, saturated,* and *supersaturated.* • Quantitatively describe and predict solution variables, including concentration, volume, temperature, mass of solute, and solubility. • Use the concept of polarity to account for water's ability to dissolve many ionic solids. • Describe the properties, as well as health and environmental effects, of heavy metal ions (particularly lead and mercury). • Given the pH of a solution, classify it as acidic, basic, or neutral. • Describe the effect of intermolecular forces on a molecular substance's solubility in water. • Interpret and explain solubility curves. • Describe the effect of temperature and external pressure on the solubility of gaseous substances.	9–10 Class Periods	**Developing Skills** C.2 Solubility and Solubility Curves C.7 Describing Solution Concentrations **Investigating Matter** C.3 Constructing a Solubility Curve C.11 Solvents **Modeling Matter** C.5 The Dissolving Process **Making Decisions** C.14 Determining the Cause of the Fish Kill	**TRB** **Investigating Matter** C.3 Constructing a Solubility Curve Student Worksheet and Data Table C.11 Solvents Student Worksheet and Data Table **Modeling Matter** C.5 The Dissolving Process Student Worksheet **Content Reading Guides** C.8 Content Reading Guide C.9 Content Reading Guide C.12 Content Reading Guide **Supplements and Practice** C.1 Supplement: Solubility and Solubility Curves C.6 Supplement: Solution Concentration Section C Supplement **Skill Building Supplements** Skill Building Topic 6: Understanding and Interpreting Graphs and Tables	**TRCD** **All TRB and Test Bank Materials for Unit 1, Section C** **Exercises** Modeling Matter: Ionic Solutions **Videos** Solvents Solubility **Animations** Dissolving Ionic Compounds Modeling Matter: Ionic Solutions Solubility of Molecular Substances Temperature, Dissolved Oxygen, and Life

SECTION	CLASS TIME	STUDENT EDITION FEATURES	PROGRAM RESOURCES	MEDIA AND TECHNOLOGY
Section D: **Water Purification and Treatment** • Compare natural and municipal water purification. • Describe the problems associated with hard-water ions and the processes of softening hard water. • Assess the risks and benefits of chlorination.	**4 Class Periods**	**Making Decisions** D.3 Water Purification D.6 Bottled Water Versus Tap Water **Investigating Matter** D.7 Water Softening	**TRB** **Investigating Matter** D.7 Water Softening Student Worksheet and Data Table **Content Reading Guides** D.1 and D.3 Content Reading Guide Chemistry at Work Content Reading Guide **Supplements and Practice** Section D Supplement	**TRCD** **All TRB and Test Bank Materials for Unit 1, Section D** **Videos** Hard Water **Animations** Hard Water and Soap Scum Water Softening by Ion Exchange
Putting It All Together: **Fish Kill—Finding the Solution**	**2 Class Periods**	**Putting It All Together** • Fish Kill—Finding the Solution	**TRB** **Putting It All Together** Fish Kill—Finding the Solution Introduction Riverwood Town Council Meeting Group Worksheet 1 Riverwood Town Council Meeting Group Worksheet 2 Riverwood Town Council Meeting Evaluation Form **Black Line Masters** EPA Drinking Water Standards Scenarios 1–4: September's Data Scenarios 1–4: Last Two Year's Data **Appendix** Teacher's Background Information for Data Analysis (Determining the Cause of the Fish Kill)	**TRCD** **All TRB Materials for Putting It All Together** **Worksheets** Water Data Week Following Fish Kill (Scenarios 1–4) Water Quality Data (Scenarios 1–4)

Equipment, Expendable Items, and Unusual Materials (per 12 Student Pairs)

Sorted by Item

QUANTITY	ITEM	SECTION USED
25 g	ammonium chloride (NH_4Cl)	C.11
6	balances	C.3
50 mL	barium chloride dihydrate ($BaCl_2 \cdot 2H_2O$), 0.1 M	B.11
12	beakers, 400-mL	C.3
12	Beral pipets	A.3
140	Beral pipets	B.11
50 mL	calcium chloride dihydrate ($CaCl_2 \cdot 2H_2O$), 0.1 M	B.11
1 box	Calgon (sodium hexametaphosphate)	D.7
100 g	cation-exchange resin	D.7
12	clay triangles	A.3, D.7
1	conductivity apparatus	A.3
25 g	copper(II) sulfate pentahydrate ($CuSO_4 \cdot 5H_2O$)	C.11
12	cups	A.3
1	distillation apparatus	A.3
100 mL	distilled water	A.3
500 mL	distilled water	B.11
1 L	distilled water	C.11, D.7

Sorted by Item (continued)

QUANTITY	ITEM	SECTION USED
6	dropper bottles with liquid soap	D.7
100 mL	sodium carbonate (Na_2CO_3), 0.1 M	D.7
12	Erlenmeyer flasks, 125-mL	A.3
600 mL	ethanol, denatured alcohol (C_2H_5OH)	C.11
12 pieces	filter paper, Whatman #1, 11-cm diameter	A.3
96 pieces	filter paper, Whatman #1, 11-cm diameter	D.7
12	funnels, 73-mm inside diameter	A.3, D.7
0.5 tsp (0.5 g)	garlic powder	A.3
12	glass stirring rods, 20-cm	D.7
25 g	glucose ($C_6H_{12}O_6$)	C.11
12	graduated cylinders, 100-mL	A.3, C.3
12	graduated cylinders, 10-mL	C.11, D.7
2 kg	gravel	A.3
1.5 L	hard water, 0.01 M Ca^{2+}	D.7
25 mL	hexane (C_6H_{14})	C.11
6	hot plates	C.3
0.5 kg	ice	C.3
25 g	iodine (I_2)	C.11

Sorted by Item (continued)

QUANTITY	ITEM	SECTION USED
50 mL	iron(II) sulfate heptahydrate ($FeSO_4 \cdot 7H_2O$), 0.1 M	B.11
50 mL	iron(III) nitrate nonahydrate ($Fe(NO_3)_3 \cdot 9H_2O$), 0.1 M	B.11
600 mL	lamp oil	C.11
12	marking pencils	C.11
12	medicine droppers	C.11
25 g	naphthalene flakes ($C_{10}H_8$)	C.11
12	paper clips	A.3
12	pinch clamps	A.3
50 mL	potassium thiocyanate (KSCN), 0.5 M	B.11
72	Pyrex test tubes, 20 × 150 mm	C.3
12	ring stands	A.3, D.7
12	rings	A.3, D.7
12	rubber tubing segments, 8–10 cm	A.3
12	rulers, metric	C.3
2 kg	sand	A.3
0.5 kg	sand	D.7
50 mL	silver nitrate ($AgNO_3$), 0.1 M	B.11
50 mL	sodium carbonate (Na_2CO_3), 0.1 M	B.11

Sorted by Item (continued)

QUANTITY	ITEM	SECTION USED
0.5 tbs (5 g)	sodium chloride (NaCl)	A.3
25 g	sodium chloride (NaCl)	C.11
12	spatulas	C.11
24	stir rods, glass	C.3
12	stoppers (18-mm test tubes)	D.7
120 g	succinic acid	C.3
12	teaspoons	A.3
12	test tube holders	C.3
12	test tube racks	C.3, C.11, D.7
220	test tubes (18 × 150 mm)	D.7
24	test tubes (13 × 100 mm)	C.11
12	thermometers, alcohol –10 °C to 110 °C	C.3
25 g	urea ($(NH_2)_2CO$)	C.11
0.5 cup (125 mL)	used coffee grounds	A.3
0.3 cup (80 mL)	vegetable oil	A.3
12	wash bottles for dispensing distilled water	D.7
12	wellplates, 24-well	B.11

Equipment, Expendable Items, and Unusual Materials (per 12 Student Pairs)

Sorted by Section

QUANTITY	ITEM	SECTION USED
0.5 tbs (5 g)	sodium chloride (NaCl)	A.3
0.5 tsp (0.5 g)	garlic powder	A.3
0.5 cup (125 mL)	used coffee grounds	A.3
0.3 cup (80 mL)	vegetable oil	A.3
12	graduated cylinders, 100-mL	A.3
12	Beral pipets	A.3
100 mL	distilled water	A.3
12	cups	A.3
2 kg	sand	A.3
2 kg	gravel	A.3
12	paper clips	A.3
12 pieces	filter paper, Whatman #1, 11-cm diameter	A.3
12	clay triangles	A.3
12	rings	A.3
12	ring stands	A.3
12	funnels, 73-mm inside diameter	A.3
12	Erlenmeyer flasks, 125-mL	A.3
1	conductivity apparatus	A.3
1	distillation apparatus	A.3
12	teaspoons	A.3
12	pinch clamps	A.3
12	rubber tubing segments, 8–10 cm	A.3

Sorted by Section (continued)

QUANTITY	ITEM	SECTION USED
12	wellplates, 24-well	B.11
140	Beral pipets	B.11
500 mL	distilled water	B.11
50 mL	calcium chloride dihydrate ($CaCl_2 \cdot 2H_2O$), 0.1 M	B.11
50 mL	sodium carbonate (Na_2CO_3), 0.1 M	B.11
50 mL	iron(III) nitrate nonahydrate ($Fe(NO_3)_3 \cdot 9H_2O$), 0.1 M	B.11
50 mL	potassium thiocyanate (KSCN), 0.5 M	B.11
50 mL	silver nitrate ($AgNO_3$), 0.1 M	B.11
50 mL	iron(II) sulfate heptahydrate ($FeSO_4 \cdot 7H_2O$), 0.1 M	B.11
50 mL	barium chloride dihydrate ($BaCl_2 \cdot 2H_2O$), 0.1 M	B.11
12	beakers, 400-mL	C.3
12	thermometers, alcohol $-10\ °C$ to $110\ °C$	C.3
120 g	succinic acid	C.3
72	Pyrex or Kimax test tubes, 20×150 mm	C.3
24	stir rods, glass	C.3
12	test tube holders	C.3
12	test tube racks	C.3
6	hot plates	C.3
0.5 kg	ice	C.3

Sorted by Section (continued)

QUANTITY	ITEM	SECTION USED
12	graduated cylinders, 100-mL	C.3
12	rulers, metric	C.3
6	balances	C.3
24	test tubes, 13 × 100 mm	C.11
12	test tube racks	C.11
12	graduated cylinders, 10-mL	C.11
12	marking pencils	C.11
12	spatulas	C.11
12	medicine droppers	C.11
25 g	urea ($(NH_2)_2CO$)	C.11
25 g	iodine (I_2)	C.11
25 g	ammonium chloride (NH_4Cl)	C.11
25 g	sodium chloride (NaCl)	C.11
25 g	glucose ($C_6H_{12}O_6$)	C.11
25 g	naphthalene flakes ($C_{10}H_8$)	C.11
25 g	copper(II) sulfate pentahydrate ($CuSO_4 \cdot 5H_2O$)	C.11
25 mL	hexane (C_6H_{14})	C.11
600 mL	ethanol, denatured alcohol (C_2H_5OH)	C.11
600 mL	lamp oil	C.11

Sorted by Section (continued)

QUANTITY	ITEM	SECTION USED
1 L	distilled water	C.11
12	funnels, 73-mm inside diameter	D.7
96 pieces	filter paper, Whatman #1, 11-cm diameter	D.7
12	ring stands	D.7
12	rings	D.7
220	test tubes (18 × 150 mm)	D.7
12	test tube racks	D.7
12	glass stirring rods, 20-cm	D.7
12	graduated cylinders, 10-mL	D.7
100 mL	sodium carbonate (Na_2CO_3), 0.1 M	D.7
1.5 L	hard water, 0.01 M Ca^{2+}	D.7
6	dropper bottles with liquid soap	D.7
12	wash bottles for dispensing distilled water	D.7
1 L	distilled water	D.7
1 lb	sand	D.7
1 box	Calgon (sodium hexametaphosphate)	D.7
100 g	cation-exchange resin	D.7
12	stoppers (18-mm test tubes)	D.7
12	clay triangles	D.7

UNIT 1
WATER: EXPLORING SOLUTIONS

Introduction to the Unit

The first unit in *Chemistry in the Community* is organized around a fish kill, in the Snake River in the fictional town of Riverwood, and resulting water supply and quality issues. In the process of deciding the cause of the fish kill, students explore properties of water and aqueous solutions, learn about some of the many substances found in water, and analyze processes that purify water. In the context of the Riverwood fish-kill story, fundamental chemistry concepts and skills, including chemical formulas, nomenclature, and solubility, are introduced, developed, and applied.

The unit exemplifies the *ChemCom* approach: Create a "need to know" in the minds of students via a chemistry-related societal problem or issue, then introduce and develop chemical concepts that allow students to address and deal with the issue. One aspect of this approach is that when a concept is introduced, only the information necessary to understand the issue or problem at hand is developed. For example, concepts of acids, bases, salts, and pH are introduced in this unit. However, only a small portion of what students will ultimately learn about these topics is introduced and developed in Unit 1. It is unnecessary to present more information or to further develop these concepts now; all of these topics are revisited in subsequent units. Students "need to know" just the aspects presented in Unit 1 to address the fish-kill mystery.

UNIT 1
Water: Exploring Solutions

WHAT techniques can we use to purify water?

WHAT are the physical properties of water?

WHY do some substances readily dissolve in water and others do not?

HOW does chemistry contribute to effective water treatment?

? Fish are dying in Riverwood's Snake River. Why? What are the consequences for the community? Turn the page to find out more about this crisis and the role of water in modern life.

After the text introduces the fish-kill mystery, an initial *ChemQuandary 1* (page 8) opens a discussion of direct and indirect uses of water. Students are then asked to collect water-use information from their own homes (which they later analyze) and complete their first laboratory investigation by purifying a sample of "foul water." Within the rest of Unit 1, topics are similarly introduced. These topics include matter, properties of matter, molecular structure, atomic structure, chemical formulas, nomenclature, ionic bonding, solubility of all states of matter, solution chemistry, heavy metals, pH, acids and bases, water purification, and distillation. At the end of Section C, you will give students data (from the TRCD, *ChemCom* web site, or Black Line Masters) that will inform their decision making about the fish kill. The unit culminates in a Town Council Meeting, where students determine the cause of the fish kill, based on scientific data, and make decisions regarding responsibility, restitution, and prevention of future water-quality problems.

Using the Unit Project

Two newspaper articles introduce students to a water-quality problem in Riverwood and set the stage for the unit's main storyline. Students follow the progress of Riverwood citizens in dealing with this water crisis through a series of related newspaper articles.

You may decide to read these articles as a class, to help students become engaged with the storyline, which will serve as the "need to know" for the entire unit. After reading, try to distinguish, in small groups or as a class, factual statements from opinions in the articles. You may also elect to invite students to evaluate some quotations in the articles or think about scientific questions that would help them solve the mystery, although these issues are addressed in later activities within the text.

Fish Kill Triggers Riverwood Water Emergency

Severe Water Rationing in Effect

Soon after discovering the fish kill, Riverwood High School students returned to the river to investigate.

BY LORI KATZ
Riverwood News Staff Reporter

Citing possible health hazards, Mayor Edward Cisko announced today that Riverwood will stop withdrawing water from the Snake River and will temporarily shut down the city's water-treatment plant over water-quality concerns provoked by a massive fish kill. Starting at 6 p.m., river water will not be pumped to the plant for at least three days. If the cause of the fish kill has not been determined and corrected by that time, the shutdown will continue indefinitely.

During the plant shutdown, water engineers and chemists from the county sanitation commission and the U.S. Environmental Protection Agency (EPA) will investigate the cause of the major fish kill discovered yesterday. The fish kill extended from the base of Snake River Dam, located upstream from Riverwood, to the town's water-pumping station.

The initial alarm was sounded when Jane Abelson, 15, and Chad Wong, 16—both students at Riverwood High School—found many dead fish floating in a favorite fishing spot. "We thought maybe someone had poured poison into the reservoir," explained Wong.

Mary Steiner, a Riverwood High School biology teacher, accompanied the students back to the river. "We hiked downstream for almost a mile. Dead fish of all kinds were washed up on the banks and caught in the rocks," Abelson reported.

Ms. Steiner contacted county sanitation commission officers, who immediately collected Snake River water samples for analysis. Chief engineer Hal Cooper reported at last night's emergency meeting that the water samples appeared clear, colorless, and odorless. However, he indi-cated some concern. "We can't say for certain that the water supply is safe until the cause of the fish kill is determined. It's far better that we take no chances until then," Cooper advised.

Mayor Cisko canceled the community's "Fall Fish-In," which was scheduled to start September 15. No plans to reschedule Riverwood's annual fishing tournament were announced. "The decision was made at last night's emergency town council meeting to start investigating the situation immediately," he said.

After five hours of often-heated debate yesterday, the Riverwood town council finally reached agreement to stop drawing water from the Snake River. Council member Henry McLatchen (also a chamber of commerce member) commented that the decision was highly emotional and unnecessary. He cited financial losses

Dead fish washed up along the banks of the Snake River yesterday afternoon.

see *Fish Kill*, page 5

Fish Kill, from page 1

that motels and restaurants will suffer because of the Fish-In cancellation, as well as potential loss of future tourism dollars due to adverse publicity. However, McLatchen and other council members sharing that view were out-voted by those holding the position that the fish kill, the only one within Riverwood's recorded history, may indicate a public health emergency.

Mayor Cisko assured residents that essential municipal services will not be affected by the crisis. For example, he promised to maintain fire department access to adequate supplies of water to meet firefighting needs.

Arrangements have been made to transport emergency drinking water from Mapleton. The first water ship-ments by truck are due to arrive in Riverwood by midmorning tomorrow. Distribution points are listed in Sec-tion 2 of today's *Riverwood News,* along with guidelines on conserving water during this emergency.

All Riverwood schools will be closed Monday and possibly through Wednesday. No other closings or can-cellations have been announced. Local TV and radio will report any schedule changes as they become available.

A public meeting tonight at 8 p.m. at the town hall features Dr. Mar-garet Brooke, a water expert at State University. She will answer questions concerning water safety and use. Brooke was invited by the county san-itation commission to help clarify the situation for concerned citizens.

Asked how long the water emer-gency would last, Brooke refused to speculate, saying that she first needed to talk to other scientists conducting the investigation. EPA investigators, in addition to collecting and analyzing water samples, will examine dead fish in an effort to determine what was responsible for the fish kill. Brooke reported that trends or irregularities in water-quality data from Snake River monitoring during the past two years also will play a part in the investigation.

| **Figure 1.1** *Riverwood*

Remind students that a large problem can often be solved more easily if it is first reduced to a series of smaller, more manageable sub-problems. Students can then iden-tify some sub-problems involved in the Snake River water-quality crisis.

If you ask students to read these articles on their own, provide focus questions or reading goals to direct their attention and be certain they comprehend important points raised in this introduction to the Unit 1 theme. Some of the important points include the need for safe water, the collection of evidence (such as water samples) to support future problem solving and decision making, the economic consequences of environ-mental incidents, and the need to plan for essential uses of resources in a crisis.

Sources and Uses of Water

To help set the stage, consider conducting a brief class discussion on what students believe may have caused the fish kill and whether they think Riverwood water is safe to drink. Because you and the students may still be getting to know one another at this point, you might ask them to give their names before responding to questions. It might be helpful to ask a student to generate a summary list on a large sheet of paper as you conduct this discussion. You can use the list later to reevaluate students' thoughts on the fish kill's cause.

After the discussion, remind students that they will need to better understand chemistry (after all, that's the purpose of this course!) to address these questions completely.

A.1 Town in Crisis

Indicate that the problems in Riverwood frequently happen in real life. You may direct students to conduct a search (newspaper and Internet) to find out if this type of problem has occurred elsewhere—especially in your own community—recently. Emphasize that the questions posed here—*Can we get enough water to meet our needs?* and *Can we get sufficiently pure water?*—are major themes of the unit.

Ask students to explain where water comes from in their community and whether having enough water is a concern. After the concept of pure water is introduced, ask students whether the water they can obtain from various sources (tap, filter, bottles) is "pure" and whether they are concerned about the purity of the water that they use. Ask students to suggest what the criteria for "pure water" might be.

Townspeople React to Fish Kill and Riverwood Water Crisis

BY JUAN HERNANDEZ
Riverwood News Staff Reporter

In a series of on-the-street interviews, Riverwood citizens expressed a variety of opinions earlier today about the crisis. "It doesn't bother me," said nine-year-old Jimmy Hendricks. "I'm just going to drink bottled water and canned fruit juice."

"I knew that eventually they'd pollute the river and kill the fish," complained Harmon Lewis, a lifelong resident of Fieldstone Acres, located east of Riverwood. Lewis, who traces his ancestry to original county settlers, still gets his water from a well and will be unaffected by the water crisis. He said that he plans to pump enough well water to supply the children's ward at Community Hospital if the emergency extends more than a few days.

Bob and Ruth Hardy, co-owners of Hardy's Ice Cream Store, expressed annoyance at the inconvenience but were reas-

David Price was excited that school is canceled.

The fish kill sparked diverse reactions among Riverwood residents. Don Harris voiced concerns about health and economic impact of the fish kill.

sured by council actions. They were eager to learn the reason for the fish kill and its possible effects on water supplies. The Hardy's daughter Toni, who loves to fish, was worried that late-season fishing would be ruined. Toni and her father won first prize in last year's angling competition.

Riverwood Motel owner Don Harris expressed concern for both the health of town residents and the loss of business due to the tournament cancellation. "I always earn reasonable income from this event and, without the revenue from the Fish-In, I may need a loan to pay bills next spring."

The unexpected school vacation was "great," according to twelve-year-old David Price. Asked why he thought schools would be closed Monday, Price said that all he could think of was that "the drinking fountains won't work."

Elmo Turner, whose residential landscaping has won Garden Club recognition for the past five years, felt reassured on one point. Because of an unusually wet summer, grass watering is unnecessary; lawns are not in danger of drying out due to current water rationing.

Sources and Uses of Water

Riverwood confronts at least a three-day water shortage. The water emergency has aroused understandable concern among Riverwood citizens, town officials, and business owners. What caused the fish kill? Does the fish kill mean that Riverwood's water supply poses hazards to humans? In the following pages, you will monitor the town's progress in answering these questions as you learn more about water's properties.

A.1 TOWN IN CRISIS

Although Riverwood is imaginary, its problems are not. Residents of many communities have faced these and similar problems. In fact, two water-related challenges confront each of us every day. Can we get enough water to supply our needs? Can we get sufficiently pure water? These two questions serve as major themes of this unit, and their answers require an understanding of water's chemistry and uses.

The notion of water *purity* must be given careful consideration. See Figure 1.2. You will soon learn that the cost of producing a supply of water that is *100%* pure is prohibitively high. Is that level of purity needed—or even desirable? Communities and regulatory agencies are responsible for ensuring the availability of water of sufficiently high quality for its intended uses at reasonable cost. How do they accomplish this task?

Even the apparently simple idea of "water use" presents some fascinating puzzles, as the following *ChemQuandary* illustrates.

Figure 1.2 *This water is obviously clear, but is it pure? What is pure water?*

You may decide to post current articles about water quality and water supply on a bulletin board for the duration of the unit. These articles may be student or teacher selected. Current information on water quality and water supply will reinforce for students that the concerns in the fictional town of Riverwood are, indeed, relevant to their own lives.

Using the Figures

Throughout the book, photographs and art have been included to engage students and to help support their learning. Captions often pose questions to encourage students to think about an issue or concept more deeply. Suggestions for using figures will be provided throughout this Teacher's Guide, as will additional information regarding specific photos.

Figure 1.2: Use this photograph and caption as a springboard into the section. Ask students to think about and discuss the questions posed in the caption. This will help them anticipate ideas they will encounter in the text.

ChemQuandary 1

Water, Water Everywhere

A *ChemQuandary* is an interesting question, fact, or situation designed to stimulate open-ended thinking and additional questions. ChemQuandaries provide good opportunities to explore students' prior knowledge of the topic at hand, including any erroneous preconceptions or misconceptions.

This activity can be completed either as a teacher-led brainstorming session or as cooperative group work (3 to 4 students). In either case, begin by asking students to identify uses of water that are involved in making eggs or cans of juice available in local grocery stores.

In egg production, water is used for drinking by chickens, to grow chicken feed, to grow trees that provide wood to build chicken houses, to wash eggs, and to produce the cardboard cartons in which eggs are packaged. Students may identify many other indirect water uses.

In juice production, water is used to grow the fruit trees, to wash harvested fruit, and to process fruit into juice. The quantity of water used indirectly to produce the juice must also be considered. Mining iron ore and transporting it to steel mills requires 4 L water per can; a steel mill uses about 76 L of water to produce the metal for each can; and the rolling mill that fabricates the metal for the can consumes another 46 L of water per can. Thus, the total indirect volume of water used to fabricate one juice can is about 126 L.

One liter (1 L) is equal to a volume of approximately one quart.

ChemQuandary 1

WATER, WATER EVERYWHERE

It takes approximately 120 L of water to produce one 1.3-L can of fruit juice. It takes about 450 L of water to place one fried egg on your breakfast plate. Think of possible explanations for these two facts by listing the steps involved in producing and delivering to your home the fruit juice and the egg. Then review each step and consider where water use would occur.

As you just learned, a basic challenge that people have always faced is related to accessing water supplies of sufficiently high quality. In the following activities, you will explore these issues by first evaluating your family's typical water uses and, later, by trying to purify as much of a contaminated-water (foul-water) sample as you can. The challenges for people always remain the same—to obtain purified water at low total cost and to ensure adequate water supplies to meet all necessary uses.

Making Decisions

A.2 USES OF WATER

Keep a diary of water use in your home for three days. On a data table similar to the one shown on the next page, record how often various water-use activities occur. Ask each household member to cooperate and help you.

Check the activities listed on the chart. See Figure 1.3. If family members use water in other ways within the three-day period, add those uses to your diary. Estimate the quantities of water used by each activity.

Point out to students that while consuming canned juice may help address part of the short-term water shortage in Riverwood, it does not contribute to long-term water conservation. *Note:* 1 qt = 0.946 L.

For comparison, point out that, given the data in this activity, producing two eggs and one 1.3-L can of juice uses as much water as taking 10 showers; washing 10 loads of clothes or 25 loads of dishes; or flushing a toilet 100 times.

DATA TABLE			
Per Household	Day 1	Day 2	Day 3
Number of persons			
Number of baths			
Number of showers Average duration of a shower (min)			
Number of toilet flushes			
Number of hand-washed loads of dishes			
Number of machine-washed loads of dishes			
Number of washing-machine loads of laundry			
Number of lawn or garden waterings Average duration of a watering (min)			
Number of car washes			
Number of cups of water (estimated) for cooking and drinking			
Number of times water runs in sink Average duration of water running (min)			
Other uses and frequency			

Figure 1.3 *Will you be washing a car in the next three days? If so, record it in your water-use log.*

Section A   Sources and Uses of Water   9

ness of home water use. The activity also features information gathering as the first step in making decisions. The collected data will be analyzed later in Making Decisions *A.7 Water-Use Analysis* (page 20).

The time needed for data collection is three days. If possible, *include one weekend day*. You may decide to extend the collection interval to seven days, which provides a better estimate of average household water use, but requires longer household cooperation and more demanding student data management.

A sample data table is provided on the Teacher's Resource CD (TRCD) and in the Teacher's Resource Binder (TRB) for use with this activity. Give students this data table (or a similar one, or invite them to construct their own), and demonstrate methods for recording data in the table. You may decide to brainstorm possible household water uses with students before providing this table. It may be useful for some students to create index cards to collect data directly at the point of water use—for example, for family members to record the total minutes of showering.

The data table gives average values for water used by various appliances and processes. If the students want more accurate estimations, they can measure the water actually used for some household purposes, either directly or by observing a water-meter reading.

Making Decisions

A.2 Uses of Water

Making Decisions activities provide opportunities for students to collect or analyze data, formulate scientific questions, and develop answers and make decisions based on evidence. Throughout *ChemCom*, students are given opportunities to explore the role of chemistry in their lives. In this activity, students are asked to include all household members in their data-collection process. The activity explores and promotes aware-

9

A.3 Foul Water

Students purify a "foul water" sample so it could be used to wash hands. Water-purity criteria are reintroduced in a post-lab activity; "pure" water is tested for electrical conductivity. Don't raise the lab's goal to purifying water so it is suitable for drinking; laboratory substances should *never* be ingested. Techniques introduced include filtration, absorption, separation, and electrical-conductivity testing. You will also demonstrate distillation if you have suitable equipment.

Time

50–60 min for student work
30 min for distillation demonstration

Materials

(For a class of 24 working in pairs)

2–3 L foul water (100 mL/pair) (See recipe.)
12 100-mL graduated cylinders
24 150-mL beakers
12 funnels (73-mm i.d.)
12 ring stands, rings, clay triangles
100 mL distilled water
12 Beral pipets
12 pinch clamps
12 cups (paper or Styrofoam)
12 paper clips (for making holes)
12 filter papers (Whatman #1, 11 cm)
12 125-mL Erlenmeyer flasks (mixing charcoal and water)
12 teaspoons (for dispensing charcoal)
150 g decolorizing charcoal
2 kg sand, cleaned
2 kg gravel, cleaned (approx. 5-mm dia.)
1 distillation apparatus
1 (or more) conductivity indicator(s)
12 8–10-cm lengths rubber tubing (to fit funnel stem)

Foul-Water Recipe

Add to an empty 2-L bottle:
1/2 tbsp salt (NaCl)
1/2 tsp garlic powder
1/2 cup used coffee grounds
1/3 cup (or less) vegetable oil

A.3 FOUL WATER

Introduction

Note: If you have not already done so, carefully read Safety in the Laboratory on pages iv–v, before beginning this laboratory procedure.

Your objective is to clean up a sample of foul water, producing as much "clean water" as possible, to a point where it could be used for hand-washing. (**Caution:** *Do not test any water samples by drinking or tasting them.*) You will use several different water-purification procedures: oil–water separation, sand filtration, and charcoal adsorption and filtration.

Before starting, read the procedure to learn what you will need to do, note safety precautions, and plan necessary data collecting and observations.

Lab Video: Foul Water

Procedure

1. In your laboratory notebook, prepare a data table similar to the one shown here. Be sure to provide sufficient space to record your entries.

DATA TABLE						
	Volume (mL)	Color	Clarity	Odor	Presence of Oil	Presence of Solids
Before treatment						
After oil–water separation						
After sand filtration						
After charcoal adsorption and filtration						

The metric prefix *milli-* represents 1/1000 (0.001) of the unit specified. Thus, one milliliter (1 mL) is one-thousandth of a liter, or 0.001 L.

2. Using a clean beaker, obtain approximately 100 mL (milliliters) of foul water from your teacher. Measure its volume accurately with a graduated cylinder. See Figure 1.4. Record the actual volume of the water sample in your data table. Leave your sample in the graduated cylinder.

3. Describe in detail the appearance, color, clarity, and odor of your original sample. Record your observations in the "Before treatment" row of your data table.

Nearly fill the bottle with tap water, cap it tightly, and shake. Save excess for *B.3 Mixtures and Solutions.* The procedure is designed for this recipe; use caution if you modify it.

A.3 Foul Water Student Worksheet and Data Table

Figure 1.4 *To find the volume of liquid in a graduated cylinder, read the scale at the bottom of the curved part of the liquid (meniscus).*

Meniscus

Oil–Water Separation

As you probably know, if oil and water are mixed and left undisturbed, the oil and water do not noticeably dissolve in each other. Instead, two layers form. Which layer do you think will float on top of the other? Make careful observations in the following procedure to check your answer.

4. Allow your sample to sit in the graduated cylinder for at least one minute.

5. Using a clean, dry Beral pipet, carefully remove as much of the upper liquid layer as possible and place it in a clean, dry test tube.

6. Add several drops of distilled water to the liquid you placed in the test tube. Does the water float on top or sink to the bottom? Is the liquid you removed in Step 5 water? Explain your reasoning, using evidence from your observations to support your answer.

7. Read and record the volume of the liquid sample remaining in the gradated cylinder.

8. Dispose of the liquid in the test tube as directed by your teacher.

Sand Filtration

In **filtration**, solid particles are separated from a liquid by passing the mixture through a material that retains the solid particles and allows the liquid to pass through. The liquid collected after it has been filtered is called the **filtrate**. A sand filter traps and removes solid impurities—at least those particles too large to fit between sand grains—from a liquid.

9. Using a straightened paper clip, poke small holes in the bottom of a disposable cup. See Figure 1.5.

10. Add premoistened gravel and sand layers to the cup as shown in Figure 1.6. (The bottom gravel layer prevents the sand from washing through the holes. The top layer of gravel keeps the sand from churning up when the water sample is poured into the cup.)

Paper clip — Bottom of cup

Figure 1.5 *Preparing a disposable cup for use in sand filtration.*

Gravel (1 cm)
Sand (2 cm)
Gravel (1 cm)

Figure 1.6 *Layering gravel and sand for sand filtration.*

Safety

Ensure that you address safety (in the pre-lab discussion) and students complete safety contracts (the TRCD and TRB have sample contracts). Students must wear protective goggles and aprons. In the distillation demonstration, liquid should *not* boil to dryness; residue will etch onto the flask;

overheated flasks may also break. Water samples should *not* be tasted.

Pre-Lab Discussion

Discuss *Safety and Laboratory Activity* (pages iv–v, student text), identification and use of safety equipment (such as eyewash, shower, and fire extinguisher), and rules of safe laboratory activity. Identify the

protective-goggle icon. Outline policies for students wearing contact lenses or glasses. Review available safety videos and local safety policies, complete the safety-compliance statement (provided on the IRCD) or other contract; assess students' understanding of safety guidelines.

Pour the foul-water mixture into a large beaker. Review purification methods. If students construct and disassemble sand-gravel filters, identify used-material containers. Emphasize proper disposal of used filter paper and charcoal.

Give students an IRCD data table or tell them to prepare one. Data tables should be larger than the book depicts. Sample data tables are given in Unit 1; construction hints are given in Units 2 and 3; students construct their own tables in Units 4 through 7. The IRCD has sample data tables for all units.

Overview histograms before students complete data analysis. Highlight problems with a too-wide sub-range (data too clustered) versus a too-narrow sub-range (no clear data pattern). *Range*, *mean*, and *median* may also need attention.

Using the Figures

Figure 1.4: Ask students to read this meniscus and to write their readings on the board. Discuss how they obtained their readings—especially if differences arise in reported decimal values (97.5 mL) versus integers (97 or 98 mL). Note whether units are reported. Then demonstrate a correct reading, using a partially filled graduated cylinder. Think aloud as you move eye level with the meniscus, read meniscus bottom, and estimate the decimal place. Once you indicate correct cylinder-guard placement (at the *top* of the cylinder), ask students what is wrong with this picture.

Using the Figures

Figure 1.7: Be sure that students pay careful attention to proper techniques for folding their filter paper to avoid problems during the charcoal adsorption/filtration step.

Lab Tips

• Dispense about 100 mL of foul water to each pair. Shake the mixture first (to establish representative sampling). Remind students to record the actual volume they receive, and emphasize the level of precision you expect for their measurements.

• Encourage students to wash or rinse their graduated cylinders between steps. Residual coffee grounds and/or oil clinging to the graduated cylinder walls can contaminate their increasingly purified water samples.

• Some teachers prefer using plastic cups (instead of the paper or Styrofoam cups) so students can see the layers of sand and gravel. However, an object such as a heated paper clip or fork usually is needed to puncture rigid clear plastic cups. Puncturing the cups from the inside helps ensure better liquid flow and reduces the likelihood of clogging.

• To save time and materials, you may choose to construct the sand and gravel filters before the investigation. The filters can then be reused for several classes. If the sand-gravel filters start to slow noticeably, you can clean them by pouring a small amount of alcohol through them. (*Note:* This cleaning method is for <u>paper</u> cups only.)

• Some forms of decolorizing charcoal (especially dust) are quite messy and can be irritating if inhaled. It is helpful to prepare a thick slurry of the charcoal with water beforehand, and have students use small spoonfuls of the mixture.

11. Gently pour the sample to be filtered into the cup. Catch the filtrate in a beaker as it drains through.

12. Dispose of the used sand and gravel according to your teacher's instructions. (***Caution:*** *Do not pour any sand or gravel into the sink!*)

13. Observe the properties of the filtered water sample and measure its volume. Record your results. Save the filtered water sample for the next procedure.

Charcoal Adsorption and Filtration

Charcoal **adsorbs,** which means attracts and holds on its surface, many substances that could give water a bad taste, a cloudy appearance, or an odor.

14. Fold a piece of filter paper, as shown in Figure 1.7.

The pump system in an aquarium often includes a charcoal filter for adsorption of contaminants.

| **Figure 1.7** *Folding filter paper.*

15. Place the folded filter paper in a funnel. Hold the filter paper in position and moisten it slightly so that it rests firmly against the base and sides of the funnel cone.

16. Place the funnel in a clay triangle supported by a ring, as shown in Figure 1.8. Lower the ring so that the rubber tube extends 2 to 3 cm (centimeters) inside a 150-mL beaker.

17. Place no more than one level teaspoon of charcoal in a 125-mL or 250-mL Erlenmeyer flask.

18. Pour the water sample into the flask. Swirl the flask vigorously for several seconds. Then gently pour the liquid through the filter paper. Keep the liquid level below the top of the filter paper; liquid should not flow between the filter paper and the funnel because that might permit unwanted charcoal and other solid matter to seep into the filtrate.

19. If the filtrate is darkened by small charcoal particles, once again filter the liquid through a clean piece of moistened filter paper.

20. When you are satisfied with the appearance and odor of your charcoal-filtered water sample, pour the filtered water sample into a graduated cylinder. Record the final volume and properties of your purified sample.

| **Figure 1.8** *Funnel in clay triangle.*

Granular charcoal, used in aquariums, is a cheaper alternative to powdered charcoal. You may want to grind granular charcoal with a mortar and pestle before use. Activated charcoal works well if you remove as much oil as possible before adding the activated charcoal. Caution students that using too much charcoal will slow down the filtering process significantly.

• Do not reveal the composition of the original foul-water sample until the post-lab discussion.

• If possible, purchase a class set of graduated cylinders to dedicate to this investigation (plastic is acceptable). The mixture is quite difficult to remove completely from the graduated cylinders, especially if hot water and soap are not readily available.

21. Follow your teacher's suggestions about saving or disposing of your purified sample. Place the used charcoal in the container that is provided for that purpose.

22. Wash your hands thoroughly before leaving the laboratory.

Data Analysis

Record all calculations and answers in your laboratory notebook.

1. What percent of your original foul water sample did you recover as *purified water*? This value is called the **percent recovery.**

2. What volume of liquid (in milliliters) did you lose during the entire purification process?

3. What percent of your original foul-water sample was lost during purification?

To answer the following questions, first collect a list of percent recovery values for water samples from each laboratory group.

4. Construct a **histogram** showing the percent recovery obtained by all laboratory groups in your class. To do so, organize the data into equal subdivisions, such as 90.0–99.9%, 80.0–89.9%, and so forth. Count the number of data points in each subdivision. Then use this number to represent the height of the appropriate bar on your histogram, as illustrated in Figure 1.9. In this sample histogram, for example, you can see that three data points fell between 70.0% and 79.9%.

5. What was the largest percent recovery obtained by a laboratory group in your class? What was the smallest? The difference between the largest and smallest values in a data set is the **range** of those data points. What was the range of percent recovery data in your class?

6. What was the average percent recovery for your class? Compute an **average** value by adding all values together and dividing the sum by the total number of values. The result is also called the **mean** value.

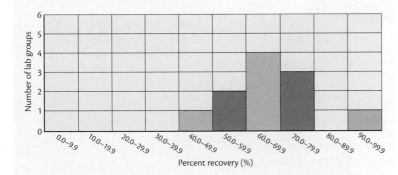

Figure 1.9 *Typical histogram of foul-water recovery data.*

• Some students may want to repeat steps—particularly the charcoal adsorption and filtration step. If time permits, this will help students to better appreciate the effort required to obtain municipal supplies of clean water. They should also find that adding more steps in water purification often results in purer water but decreased recovery.

Data Analysis

1. Percent recovery =
$$\frac{\text{final volume (purified water)}}{\text{initial volume (foul water)}} \times 100$$

2. Volume lost = initial volume (foul water) − final volume (purified water)

3. Percent lost =
$$\frac{\text{volume lost}}{\text{initial volume (foul water)}} \times 100$$

4. Histograms will vary. See **Figure 1.9** for a typical "Foul-Water Investigation" histogram—most data points will be in the 65–85% range.

5. Student answers will vary, but should be consistent across the class. Percent recovery tends not to exceed 90%. Smallest percent recoveries may be 50%, or even less if a lab team experienced a spill or was unable to filter the entire sample in the time allowed. A typical range might be 60–90% recovery.

6. The average, or mean, is found by adding all the values and dividing by the total number of values. A typical mean will be around 75% recovery.

TYPICAL RESULTS					
	VOLUME (mL)	**COLOR**	**CLARITY**	**PRESENCE OF ODOR OR OIL?**	**PRESENCE OF SOLIDS?**
Before treatment	80–100	Brownish	Cloudy	Yes	Yes
Oil-water separation	75–95	Brownish	Cloudy	Slight	Yes
Sand filtration	70–90	Yellowish	Mostly clear	No	No
Charcoal filtration	55–85	Colorless	Clear	No	No

7. The median value may be close to the mean but not necessarily so. Median values help minimize the effect of extreme values.

Post-Lab Activities

Students may think clear liquid samples with no odor are "pure," but unaided senses cannot detect some contaminants. These steps will lead students to question their sensory observations and to reevaluate criteria for water purity:

1. Demonstrate the distillation of a foul-water sample (see **Figure 3.6,** p. 215). The setup may vary depending on available equipment. Discard the initial 20% of distillate. Leave about 25% of the sample undistilled. Test the distillate for conductivity.
2. Check electrical conductivity of student-processed foul-water samples versus the foul-water distillate (or commercially sold distilled water). Distilled water should show no electrical conductivity. Student-processed samples should conduct electricity; filtering does not remove dissolved NaCl.
3. Demonstrate the Tyndall effect by placing a piece of cardboard with a pencil-size hole on an overhead-projector stage; put a beaker of water with several drops of milk over the hole. Test student-processed samples also. A laser beam can also demonstrate the Tyndall effect—pocket laser pointers work well.

Answers to Post-Lab Activity Questions

1. a. In distillation, the liquid sample is heated, causing vaporization. The vapor travels through a cooled condenser; the vapor condenses. The condensate is then collected.

Figure 1.10 *This is a typical laboratory distillation apparatus. It may differ slightly from one that your teacher demonstrates.*

Figure 1.11 *Above: Particles are suspended in the sample in the beaker on the left. The particles are too small to see, but large enough to reflect light coming from a beam to the left of the beakers. This is called the Tyndall effect. Particles in the solution in the beaker on the right are too small to reflect light. Right: The Tyndall effect is also observable in nature.*

7. The mean is a mathematical expression for the most "typical" or "representative" value for a data set. Another useful expression is the **median** value, or middle value. To find the median for percent-recovery data, list all values in either ascending or descending order. Then find the value in the middle of the list—the point where there are as many data points above as below.

Consider this data set: 1 2 2 4 5 6 7

Three values lower ↑ Three values higher
Median

If you have an even number of data points, take the average of the two values nearest the middle. What is the median percent recovery of all of your class laboratory results?

Post-Lab Activities

1. Your teacher will demonstrate distillation, which is another technique for water purification. See Figure 1.10.
   a. Write a description of the steps in distillation.
   b. Why did your teacher discard the first portion of distilled liquid?
   c. Why was some liquid purposely left in the distilling flask at the end of the demonstration?
2. Your teacher will organize a test of the **electrical conductivity** of the purified water samples obtained by your class. This test focuses on the presence of dissolved, electrically charged particles in the water. You will also compare the electrical conductivity of distilled water and tap water. (You will learn more about electrically charged particles on pages 37–38.) What do these test results suggest about the purity of your water sample? Support your answer with evidence from your observations.

When a significant vapor temperature change occurs, the collection vessel is replaced; a different substance is now vaporized, condensed, and collected.
b. The first distillate portion may contain volatile impurities.
c. Samples should not be distilled to dryness; substances may remain and decompose at high temperatures, posing possible hazards.
2. There is a substance in the purified sample that conducts electricity, but it is absent after distillation.
3. Some tiny particles suspended in water are not observed until they scatter a light beam.

3. Your teacher will test the clarity of the various water samples by passing a beam of light through each sample. Observe the results. The differences are due to the presence or absence of the *Tyndall effect*. See Figure 1.11. Referring to your observations, explain what this test suggests about the purity of your water sample.

Questions

1. Is your purified water sample *pure* water? Provide evidence to support your answer.

2. How could you compare the quality of your final water sample with that obtained by other laboratory groups? That is, how should someone judge the success of each laboratory group? Defend your answer using evidence from this investigation.

3. How could you improve the water-purification procedures you followed so that you could recover a higher percent of purified water?

4. a. Estimate the total time you spent purifying your water sample.
   b. In your opinion, did that time investment result in a large enough sample of sufficiently purified water?
   c. It is sometimes said that "time is money."
      i. If you spent twice as much time purifying your sample, would that extra time investment pay off in higher-quality water?
      ii. If you spent about ten times as much time, would that extra investment pay off? Explain your reasoning.

5. Municipal water-treatment plants do not use distillation to purify water. Why?

A.4 WATER SUPPLY AND DEMAND

Is the United States in danger of running out of water? The answer is both no and yes. The total water available is far more than enough. Each day, some 15 trillion liters (4 trillion gallons) of rain or snow falls in the United States. Only 10% is used by humans. The rest flows back into large bodies of water, evaporates into the air, and falls again as part of a perpetual *water cycle,* or *hydrologic cycle*. So, that is the *no* part of the answer. However, the distribution of rain and snow in the United States does not necessarily correspond to regions of high water use. Figure 1.12 (page 16) summarizes how available water is used in various regions of the country, organized by five major water-use categories.

A U.S. family of four (two adults, two children) uses an average of 1480 liters (390 gallons) of water daily. That approximate volume represents **direct water use**, that which can be directly measured. In addi-

> A trillion gallons is 1 000 000 000 000 gallons, or 10^{12} gallons.

3. Student answers may include procedures that might improve recovery, such as letting the sample filter longer, adding more water to premoisten the sand, or poking more holes in the cup.

4. a. Most answers should be about 25–60 min.
   b. The procedure yields little additional purified water for added time spent.
   c. i. Spending twice as much time could improve water quality, since a process that increases purity but decreases recovery (such as increase total filtration steps, reduce filter-pore size, use finer sand, or repeat some processes) requires more time.
   ii. Spending ten times longer would only lead to marginally better results than spending twice as long. Procedure limitations are more important than total time.

5. Distillation is too expensive primarily due to energy consumed. Time and equipment are also factors. Some nations with water scarcity do use solar-powered distillation to desalinate seawater.

Post-Lab Discussion

Consider the class histogram and discuss any large data variations. Ask students to explain how groups following the same procedures and using the same equipment still had different results. Make a case for repeated trials to obtain a better estimate of central tendency.

Ask students to compare mean and median values and decide which value best represents the data. Explain how and why histograms are used, if students are unfamiliar with them.

Answers to Investigation Questions

1. Students should indicate an understanding that their sample is not pure water. Evidence may include residual odor, color, lack of clarity, presence of immiscible liquids, positive Tyndall effect, and positive conductivity test.

2. Student answers will vary, but should convey understanding of how samples may differ. For instance, students may suggest that they line up samples and shine a bright light through them; look for clarity, particles, and oil; or check sample odor. Some may suggest testing pH or conductivity, or spectrophotometric analysis.

A.4 Water Supply and Demand

Students are probably already familiar with the water cycle. You can assess their prior knowledge by displaying a water-cycle model and asking them to describe or discuss steps represented. Students will learn more about natural water purification, including the hydrologic cycle (pages 86–87), so there is little need for elaboration here. For more information about key hydrologic-cycle steps, see **http://observe. arc.nasa.gov/nasa/earth/hydrocycle/ hydro1.html.**

Like energy, water is an essential behind-the-scenes component in nearly all human endeavors. U.S. industrial production—including electrical energy, primary metals, chemical products, petroleum refining, pulp and paper manufacturing, and food processing—accounts for about 51% of water use, agriculture about 40%, and the municipal sector about 9%. These activities directly use large volumes of water (U.S. average: about 316 L/person/day), but larger volumes are used behind the scenes.

The U.S. Geological Survey reports that total water withdrawn in the United States/person/day is about 1430 gallons (5420 L); however, the average withdrawn per person per day for domestic use is about 180 gallons (680 L) and per-person withdrawal by well users is about 82 gallons (310 L). See **http://water.usgs.gov/watuse/** for recent data.

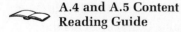 **A.4 and A.5 Content Reading Guide**

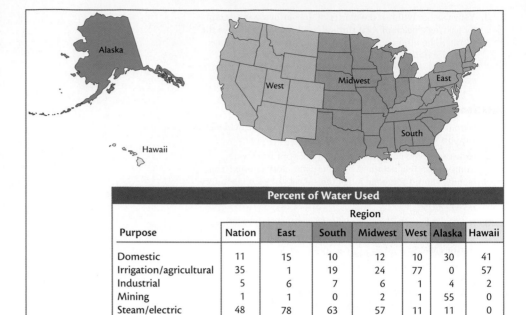

Figure 1.12 *Water use in the United States.*

	Percent of Water Used						
	Region						
Purpose	Nation	East	South	Midwest	West	Alaska	Hawaii
Domestic	11	15	10	12	10	30	41
Irrigation/agricultural	35	1	19	24	77	0	57
Industrial	5	6	7	6	1	4	2
Mining	1	1	0	2	1	55	0
Steam/electric	48	78	63	57	11	11	0

tion, there is also **indirect water use,** hidden uses of water that you may never have considered. Each time you eat a slice of pizza, some potato chips, or an egg, you are "using" water. Why? Because water was needed to grow and process the various components of each food.

Consider again *ChemQuandary 1* on page 8. At first glance, you probably thought that the volumes of water mentioned were absurdly large. How could so much water be needed to produce one fried egg or one can of fruit juice? These two examples illustrate typical indirect (hidden) uses of water. The chicken that laid the egg needed drinking water. Water was used to grow the chicken's feed. Water was also used for various steps in the process that eventually brought the egg to your home. Even small quantities of water used for these and other purposes quickly add up when billions of eggs are involved!

In a Riverwood newspaper article you read earlier, Jimmy Hendricks was quoted as saying that he would drink bottled water and canned fruit juice until the water supply was turned on again. However, drinking fruit juice from a container involves the use of much *more* water than drinking a glass of tap water. Why? Because the quantity of liquid *in* the container is insignificant when compared with the quantity of water used to *make* the container and possibly to irrigate the fruit trees and process the fruit juice. See Figure 1.13.

Fabricating a metal can, for example, is the primary source of the surprising 120 L of water mentioned on page 8. What examples of hidden water use do you encounter in daily life?

Although people depend on large quantities of water, hardly anyone is aware of how much they actually use. This lack of awareness is understandable because water normally flows freely when taps are turned on—in Riverwood or in your home. Where does all this water come from? Check what you already know about the distribution of this seemingly plentiful resource.

Figure 1.13 *Making canned juice (right) takes large quantities of water. Fruits and other crops require irrigation water, as shown in this aerial photo of a center pivot sprinkler (top). Water is also used to produce steel (bottom) for the juice can.*

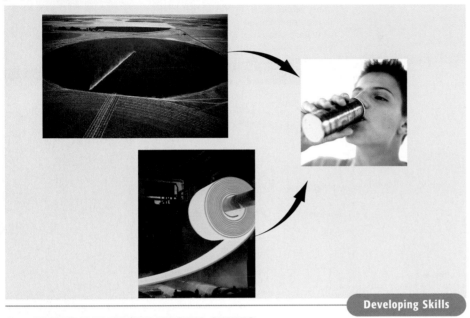

Developing Skills

A.5 WATER USE IN THE UNITED STATES

Refer to Figure 1.12 to answer the following questions.

1. For each region in the United States, name the greatest single use of water.
   a. the East   b. the South   c. the Midwest
   d. the West   e. Alaska   f. Hawaii
2. Explain the differences in how water is used in the East and the West. Think about where most people live and where most of the nation's factories and farms are located. What other regional factors help explain the general patterns of water use?
3. List two factors about the weather, economy, or culture that could explain the greatest water use within each of these six U.S. regions.

Section A   Sources and Uses of Water   **17**

Developing Skills

A.5 Water Use in the United States

Developing Skills activities give students opportunities to practice skills as the course unfolds. This practice is within a need-to-know context, and frequently includes just several problems. Many *Developing Skills* feature Sample Problems. For students who need further practice, additional problems are provided in the TRB and on the TRCD for many of these skills.

This particular activity encourages students to explore U.S. regional differences in water sources and uses. The table and map allow practice in interpreting graphics and data to seek answers to questions. If students' geographic knowledge is weak, you can discuss characteristics of U.S. regions.

Answers
1. a. Steam/electric
   b. Steam/electric
   c. Steam/electric
   d. Irrigation/agricultural
   e. Mining
   f. Irrigation/agricultural
2. Water use in the East, South, and Midwest is mainly steam/electric, due in part to large populations. U.S. industry is mainly here; electricity is used in homes and manufacturing. The West and Hawaii are engaged in major agriculture; the West is quite arid. Thus, these regions use water mainly to produce food. Alaska is sparsely populated, lightly industrialized, and does not grow many crops. It has mineral resources; mining is its main water use.
3. Students list two factors per region:
   East: humid climate, extensive manufacturing, high population.
   South: humid climate, extensive farming, high population.
   Midwest: humid climate, extensive farming, moderate population.
   West: arid climate, extensive farming, widely variable population density.
   Alaska: cold climate, plentiful mineral resources, low population.
   Hawaii: warm climate, extensive farming.

A.6 Where Is the World's Water?

 A.6 Content Reading Guide

Students may be puzzled that the largest water supply after the oceans is within glaciers and ice caps—ice that is essentially unavailable, involving costly recovery. Although U.S. total water supply profiles are good, regionalized problems exist.

Tap water is traced back to its source, supporting the idea that we have finite (but recyclable) water supplies. Students can explore water sources in your community; a field trip to a municipal pumping station can be informative.

States of matter are addressed here and later (pages 313–315); students may already be familiar with some of these ideas.

Using the Figures

Figure 1.14: What forms of water are depicted? The caption focuses on the glacier, but a lake or ocean also appears. Emphasize the photo's scale—how large is this glacier compared to the people? Even though much water is stored here, is it accessible? Could the United States obtain drinking water from here? Consider the glaciers' location—in Argentina's Patagonia area. Obvious difficulties arise in harvesting and transporting ice.

A.6 WHERE IS THE WORLD'S WATER?

You are probably not surprised to learn that most of Earth's total water (97% of it, in fact) is in the oceans. However, the next largest global water-storage place is not so obvious. Do you know what it is? If you said rivers and lakes, you and many others agree; however, that answer is incorrect. The second largest quantity of water is stored in Earth's ice caps and glaciers. See Figure 1.14. Figure 1.15 shows how the world's supply of water is distributed.

Figure 1.14 *Most of Earth's fresh water is stored in glaciers like this one.*

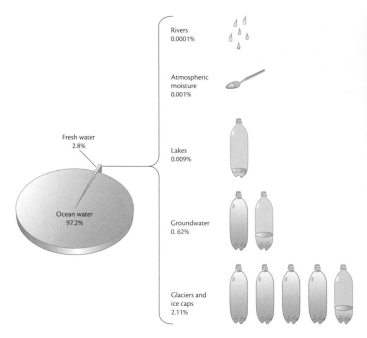

| **Figure 1.15** *Distribution of the world's water supply.*

As you know, water can be found in three different physical states at ordinary temperatures. Water vapor in the air is in the **gaseous state.** Water is most easily identified in the **liquid state**—in lakes, rivers, oceans, clouds, and rain. Ice is a common example of water in the **solid state.** What other forms of "solid water" can you identify?

At present, most of the United States is fortunate to have abundant supplies of high-quality water. You turn on the tap, use what you need, and go about your daily routine—giving little thought about how that seemingly unlimited water supply manages to reach you.

In some U.S. regions, water in the gaseous state is experienced as high humidity that contributes to summer discomfort.

City Water

If you live in a city or town, the water pipes in your home are linked to underground water pipes. These pipes bring water downhill from a reservoir or a water tower, usually located near the highest point in town, to all the faucets in the area. Water stored in the tower was previously cleaned and purified at a water-treatment plant. It may have been pumped to the treatment plant from a reservoir, lake, or river. If your home's water supply originated in a river or other body of water, you are using **surface water.** If it originated in a well, you are using **groundwater.** Groundwater must be pumped to the surface.

About one-fifth of the U.S. water supply is held as groundwater.

Rural Water

If you live in a rural area, your home probably has its own water-supply system. A well with a pipe driven deep into an **aquifer** (a water-bearing layer of rock, sand, or gravel) pumps the water to the surface. A small, pressurized tank holds the water before it enters your home's plumbing system.

Not surprisingly, neither groundwater nor surface-water samples are completely pure. When water falls as precipitation (rain, snow, sleet, or hail) and joins a stream or when it seeps far into the soil to become groundwater, it picks up small amounts of dissolved gases, soil, and rock. These dissolved materials are rarely removed from water at the treatment plant or from well water. In the amounts normally found in water, they are harmless. In fact, some minerals found in water (such as iron, zinc, or calcium) are essential in small quantities to human health, or they may actually improve the water's taste.

When the water supply is shut off, as it was in Riverwood, it is usually shut off for a short time. However, suppose a drought lasted several years; or suppose the shortage was perpetual, as it is in some areas of the world. In such circumstances, what uses of water would you give up first? Clearly, using available water for survival purposes would have priority. Nonessential uses would probably be eliminated.

Now it is time to examine your water-use data. Refer to your completed water-use diary (see page 9) to find out how much water you use in your home and for what purposes.

Demonstration

Model Earth's water supply with a 1-L beaker or graduated cylinder of water, pouring out various volumes into containers (with suitable explanatory talk) to illustrate relative distribution. For example: Start with an empty 1-L graduated cylinder, add 970 mL of water to indicate that 97% of all Earth's water comes from the oceans, add 21 mL for glaciers and ice caps, 6 mL for groundwater, 1 mL (or equivalent, roughly 20 drops) for lakes, a few drops for atmospheric moisture, and just a drop for rivers. Using water colored blue with food coloring makes for a visually appealing demonstration.

A.7 Water-Use Analysis

In this activity, students analyze data they collected earlier about daily water use by their families. Students gain useful experience transforming raw data into a form that can be compared with national averages. Data processing includes finding the total volume of water used by the family during the survey, calculating the total water use per person, and determining the average daily water use per person. Students then compare their results with average water-use data.

The activity can be completed in 25 to 45 min, depending on the level of detail in the data and students' mathematical abilities. You may decide to have each student put an average water-use-per-day value on the board to assist in compiling class data. Data sheets are provided in the TRCD/TRB. Students could use spreadsheets to analyze the data, if available. This analysis provides a good opportunity to stress keeping track of units associated with data and having well-organized data. Student-calculated water-use values will vary according to how accurately students recorded water use, family water-use habits, climate, weather conditions, and other variables.

Have sample household water-use data available for students who did not complete *Making Decisions A.2.*

Students could also compare their calculated water use with that shown on an actual water bill.

Answers

1. Student answers should match their data and should be close to (# people in household) × (3 days) × (370 L/person/day).

Table 1.1 indicates that a regular showerhead delivers 19 L each minute. In English units, that is 5 gallons per minute, or 25 gallons of water during a five-minute shower! To visualize that volume of water, think of 47 two-liter beverage bottles or five filled 5-gallon buckets.

| Table 1.1

A.7 WATER-USE ANALYSIS

Use Table 1.1 and the data you collected for Making Decisions A.2 to answer the following questions about your household's water use, as well as those of your classmates.

1. Calculate the total water volume (in liters) used by your household during the three days.
2. How much water (in liters) did one member of your household use, on average, in one day?
3. Compile the answers to Question 2 for all members of your class by creating a histogram. To review the construction of a histogram, see page 13. (*Hint:* The range in values for each histogram bar must be equal and should be selected so that there are about ten total bars.)

WATER REQUIRED FOR TYPICAL ACTIVITIES	
Activity	**Water Volume (L)**
Bathing (per bath)	130
Showering (per minute)	
Regular showerhead	19
Water-efficient showerhead	9
Cooking and drinking (per 10 cups of water)	2
Flushing toilet (per flush)	
Conventional toilet	19
Water-saving toilet	13
Low-flow toilet	6
Watering lawn (per hour)	1130
Washing clothes (per load)	170
Washing dishes (per load)	
By hand (with water running)	114
By hand (washing and rinsing in dishpans)	19
By machine (full cycle)	61
By machine (short cycle)	26
Washing car (running hose)	680
Running water in sink (per minute)	
Conventional faucet	19
Water-saving faucet	9

2. Answer should be the answer to Question 1 divided by (# people in household) divided by (3 days).
3. Student histograms within a class should show the same data. A histogram might look like this:

SAMPLE WATER-USE HISTOGRAM

Number of Households (y-axis)
Average water use per person per day (L) (x-axis): <300, 300–325, 326–350, 351–375, 376–400, 401–425, 426–450, 451–475, 476–500, >500

4. What is the range of the average daily personal water use within your class?

5. Calculate the mean and median values for the class data. Which do you think is more representative of the data set—the mean or median value? That is, which is a better expression of central tendency for these data?

6. Compare your answer from Question 2 with the estimated average volume of water, which is 370 L, used daily by each person in the United States. What reasons can you propose to explain any difference between your value and the national average value?

7. Which is closer to the national average (mean) for daily water use by each person, your answer to Question 2 or the class average in Question 5? What reasons can you give to explain why that value is closer?

Recall that the Riverwood town council arranged to truck water from Mapleton to Riverwood (see Figure 1.16) for three days to meet the needs of Riverwood residents for drinking water and cooking water. The current population of Riverwood is about 19 500.

Figure 1.16 *Emergency workers prepare to distribute bottled water.*

8. On the basis of the water-use data collected and analyzed by your class (pages 8–9 and 20–21), explain how you would estimate the total volume of water that would need to be hauled to Riverwood during the three days.

9. What additional information would help you improve your estimate in Question 8? Why?

10. What assumptions must you make to complete your estimate?

You are now quite aware of the volume of water you use daily. Suppose you had to live with much less water. How would you ration your water for survival and comfort? This is exactly the question that now confronts Riverwood residents.

7. The class average, rather than household average, is probably closer to the national average. This is due to the larger quantity of data in the class average.

8. Students could look at how much water was used for drinking and cooking for three days in the inventory. This value could be divided by the number of household members and multiplied by the population of Riverwood (19 500) to give an estimate of the volume of water needed.

9. The number of households in Riverwood, current Riverwood weather, the availability of other (non-drinkable) water, and current Riverwood water-use data.

10. Riverwood residents use amounts of water for drinking and cooking similar to amounts used by the family or class, and that the water will be used only for these purposes.

4. Range should be consistent with the histogram, typically 180–1200 L/person/day.

5. Students should report both mean and median values. Answers about which value is more representative will vary. Either answer is acceptable as long as the choice is supported.

6. Student answers might include weather conditions, excessive or inadequate showering or washing clothes/dishes, household members at/away from home during the day, (specific) unusual water needs or use of water-efficient appliances.

Making Decisions

A.8 Riverwood Water Use

This role-playing activity puts students in the place of individuals required to make difficult water-use decisions during a water shortage. Students are challenged to plan how to use a limited supply (150 L) of water for maximum benefit. This activity is appropriate for group work and takes about 15 to 20 min to complete.

Answers

1. Examples of water uses one could do without (temporarily) include bathing/showering, washing hair, washing cars, washing windows, washing pets, washing clothes, and watering plants and lawns.

2. Possible answers include flushing toilets and washing hands.

3. Water use could be reduced for washing hands, washing dishes, and flushing the toilet. Use could be reduced by washing dishes by hand in a small amount of water, flushing the toilet less often, and using small amounts of water or a waterless hand cleaner for hand cleaning.

4. a. Impure water could be used for flushing toilets and watering plants and lawns.
   b. Prior uses that would produce reusable water include washing hands, washing and preparing food, and washing dishes.

Post-Activity Discussion

It has been estimated that 30 to 50% of water used in the United States is wasted. Lead students to see how individual acts of conservation can lead to significant savings at the community or national level, where the impact is multiplied by 300 million.

Figure 1.17 *Faced with water rationing, how essential do you consider these water uses to be? Could water from one activity be reused for the other?*

Making Decisions

A.8 RIVERWOOD WATER USE

Potable water is pure enough for use in drinking and cooking. *Grey water* is left over from home use (such as showers, sinks, laundry, and dishwashers) and may sometimes be reused for other purposes, especially landscape watering. *Black water* has contacted toilet wastes and must be chemically treated and disinfected before reuse.

Riverwood authorities have severely rationed home water supplies for three days, while they investigate possible fish-kill causes. The County Sanitation Commission recommends cleaning and rinsing your bathtub, adding a tight stopper, and filling the tub with water. That water will be your family's total water supply for all uses other than drinking and cooking for up to three days. (Recall that water for drinking and cooking will be trucked in from Mapleton.)

Assuming that your household has just one tub of water (150 L, which equals 40 gal) to use and considering the typical water uses (see Figure 1.17) listed here, answer the questions that follow the list.

► washing cars, floors, windows, pets
► bathing, showering, washing hair, washing hands
► washing clothes, dishes
► watering indoor plants, outdoor plants, lawn
► flushing toilets

1. List three water uses that you could do without.
2. Identify one activity that you could *not* do without.
3. For which tasks could you reduce your water use? How?
4. Impurities added by using water for one particular use may not prevent its reuse for other purposes. For example, you might decide to save hand-washing water and use it later to bathe your dog.
   a. For which activities could you use such impure water?
   b. From which prior uses could this water be taken?

It should now be obvious that clean water is a valuable resource that must not be taken for granted. Unfortunately, water is easily contaminated. In the next section, as Riverwood deals with its water emergency, you will examine some causes of water contamination.

You may also wish to discuss the terms *potable water* (drinking water), *grey water* (used wash water), and *black water* (sewage). Question 4 introduced the idea of using grey water in households. The use of grey water is regulated in many areas, which could lead to interesting policy discussions.

Additional ChemQuandary

Ask students what Benjamin Franklin meant when he said (1746), "When the well is dry, we learn the worth of water." Discussion: Economic systems place a higher value on scarce commodities. Even though water is a renewable resource, it is possible to deplete and pollute it at a rate that exceeds natural chemical recycling processes.

SECTION A SUMMARY
Reviewing the Concepts

Both direct and indirect uses of water must be considered when evaluating water use.

1. Assume that Jimmy Hendricks drank just packaged fruit juice during the water shortage. Does that mean he did not use any water? Explain.

2. List at least three indirect uses of water associated with producing a loaf of bread.

3. The following are three water uses associated with your foul-water laboratory investigation (page 10). Classify each as either a direct or an indirect water use. Explain your answers.
   a. manufacture of the filter paper
   b. premoistening of the sand and gravel
   c. use of water to cool the distillation apparatus

Water can be purified by a variety of techniques.

4. What does it mean to "purify" water?

5. Identify at least three techniques for purifying water.

6. What was removed from your foul-water sample in each step of that investigation?

7. The procedure used in the foul-water laboratory investigation could not convert seawater to water suitable for drinking.
   a. Explain why not.
   b. What additional purification steps would be needed to make seawater suitable for drinking?

The amount of water available in Earth's hydrologic cycle is essentially fixed. The distribution of water is not always sufficient to meet local needs.

8. Has the world's total water changed in the past 100 years? The past 1 million years? Explain.

9. Rank the following locations in order of greatest to least total water abundance on Earth: rivers, oceans, glaciers, water vapor.

10. Consider this quotation: "Water, water, everywhere, nor any drop to drink." Describe a situation in which this would be true.

11. Look at Figure 1.12 on page 16. What percent of water is used in irrigation and agriculture in your U.S. region?

12. Look at Figure 1.15 on page 18. Fresh water makes up 2.8% of Earth's water supply. Calculate the percent of fresh water found in
    a. glaciers and ice caps.
    b. lakes.

Section A Summary

 Section A Supplement

Reviewing the Concepts

1. No. Indirect water use is involved in preparing a bottle of juice, from watering the fruit to manufacturing the can.

2. Possible answers include: Water is used to grow the grain, to harvest the grain, and to make machines to grind the grain into flour. Water is also used in the production of bread packaging.

3. a. Indirect: to grow trees, process lumber, and manufacture paper.
   b. Direct
   c. Direct

4. To remove non-water substances from it, including those that may be harmful or unpleasant.

5. Examples include distillation, oil–water separation, sand filtration, charcoal filtration, and reverse osmosis.

6. Oil–water separation—oil
   Sand filtration—large particles (coffee grounds, garlic powder)
   Charcoal filtration—small particles that added color and odor (coffee and garlic powder)
   Distillation (demonstration)—dissolved particles (salt)

7. a. Soluble salts, a primary "contaminant" in seawater, are not removed.
   b. Distillation or another desalination step would be required.

8. No and no; the amount of water on Earth has remained constant for billions of years.

9. Oceans, glaciers, rivers, water vapor

10. Answers could include: During a flood, or after another natural disaster, there is plenty of contaminated water; a clear mountain stream may carry disease-producing microorganisms, as might some reservoirs; very humid air might be everywhere, but atmospheric humidity is unavailable for immediate consumption; referring to the source of the quotation (Samuel Taylor Coleridge, "The Rime of the Ancient Mariner"), the oceans contain vast quantities of saltwater, unsuitable for drinking.

11. Answers depend on your region. East: 1%; South: 19%; Midwest: 24%; West: 77%; Alaska: 0%; Hawaii: 57%.

12. a. $2.11/2.8 \times 100\% = 75\%$
    b. $0.009/2.8 \times 100\% = 0.3\%$

Connecting the Concepts

13. The water used by dinosaurs is the same water that is now on Earth. The hydrologic cycle continuously redistributes water around the planet. Thus, a water molecule swallowed by a dinosaur could have been recycled through the hydrologic cycle (multiple times) and ended up in your glass of water.

14. Student answers may vary, but should be substantiated with practical considerations. For example, distillation is least practical for a city's water supply because of the energy and expense required; or oil–water separation would be the least practical because of the time and size of containers required.

15. This politician's guarantee is not likely to succeed. Even if all drinking water were distilled, which would be very expensive, it would not be 100% pure. Even distilled water will dissolve some air; it will no longer be 100% pure.

16. a. Water for beverage production must be cleaner than water for immediate use by employees. Both must be safe for drinking, but the beverage production water must meet food production standards.

    b. It is very expensive to produce high-purity water, so it is not cost-effective to provide such water where it is not needed. It is also unrealistic to create a water-transport system that could efficiently supply the entire plant.

17. 370 L represents direct use, while 4960 L is the indirect per capita use.

Connecting the Concepts

13. Explain why it might be possible that a molecule of water that you drank today was once swallowed by a dinosaur.

14. Consider oil–water separation, sand filtration, charcoal adsorption and filtration, and distillation. Which purification procedure would be *least* practical to purify a city's water supply? Why?

15. A politician campaigning for election guarantees that "every household will have 100% pure water from every tap." Evaluate this promise and predict the likelihood of its success.

16. A carbonated beverage plant has separate water supplies for various uses, such as cleaning, producing the beverage, and employee uses.

    a. How do the water purity standards differ for the various uses?

    b. Why wouldn't it be more efficient to have one water supply for the entire plant?

17. Each person in the United States uses an average of 370 L of water daily. Other sources, however, report that U.S. per capita water use is 4960 L. If both values are correct, explain this apparent discrepancy.

Extending the Concepts

18. You are marooned on a sandy island surrounded by ocean water. A stagnant, murky pond contains the only available water on the island. In your survival kit, you have the following items:

    ▶ one nylon jacket
    ▶ one plastic cup
    ▶ two plastic bags
    ▶ one length of rubber tubing
    ▶ one knife
    ▶ one 1-L bottle of liquid bleach
    ▶ one 5-L glass bottle
    ▶ one bag of salted peanuts

    Describe a plan to produce drinkable water, using only these items.

19. Charcoal-filter materials are available in various sizes—from briquettes to fine powder. List the advantages and the disadvantages of using either large charcoal pieces or small charcoal pieces for filtering.

20. Find out how much charcoal is used in a fish aquarium filter and how fast water flows through the filter. Estimate the volume of water that can be filtered by a kilogram of charcoal. What mass of charcoal would be needed to filter the daily water supply for Riverwood, population 19 500?

21. A group of friends is planning a four-day backpacking hike. Some members of the group favor carrying their own bottled water. Other members of the group wish to carry no water, instead, they will buy bottled water in towns along the trail; still others want to purchase and carry portable filters for use with stream water.

    a. What are advantages and disadvantages of each option?

    b. What additional information would the group need before deciding on a group plan?

Extending the Concepts

18. Student answers will vary. Below are two possibilities.

a. Steps: settle, decant, filter, collect, and disinfect. Construct a sand filtration device by using the knife to make a hole in the bottom of the cup. Fill about two-thirds of the cup with wet beach sand. Insert one end of the tube into the hole. Put the other end into the glass bottle. Collect water in one bag, allow time for mud to settle at bottom of the bag. Place the jacket (filter) over the cup, and pour off (decant) the water from the top of the bag into the cup. The water will go through the sand, then pass through the tube into the glass bottle. Add some bleach (about four drops per quart) to the bottle. Shake the bottle, place it in the sun (to further kill microorganisms), and increase the contact time of the bleach.

b. Make a distillation apparatus by digging a hole in a sunny area. Fill it with water (sea or pond) to a level not above the cup, put the cup in the middle of the hole, drape the nylon jacket over the hole, and place something in the middle to cause the distilled vapor to condense and drip into the cup. This process will be slow.

19. Finer powder will have more surface area available to adsorb odor and color. Large pieces of charcoal will have a smaller surface area and a reduced ability to adsorb odor and color. Charcoal that has been activated has been treated so it has increased pores on its surface. The more pores, the greater the surface area and the greater the extent of adsorption. Fine powder can be a lung irritant and can be more difficult to filter or settle. Cost may differ for various sizes of charcoal.

20. Students should check charcoal boxes and aquarium instructions for the recommended quantity of charcoal and for guidelines as to how often to change the charcoal. Research should include measuring the water flow rates through the filters and the amount of water purified for a given quantity of charcoal. Students need to determine what factor they can measure that will indicate when the charcoal in the filter has reached the end of its effectiveness. Once the data are gathered, the amount of charcoal required for the entire town can be extrapolated.

21. a.

OPTION	ADVANTAGES	DISADVANTAGES
Carry own water	Convenient; no worry about supply; can be inexpensive	Heavy and bulky
Buy bottled water	No weight; no backpack space required	Must rely on availability, market hours and locations; can be expensive
Use portable filter	Little weight; removes microorganisms	Streams must be near trails; takes time; some water will still have to be carried for immediate consumption

b. How much water will be needed? How much will the water weigh? What size containers are needed to carry the water? Where are the stores that sell water located? When are they open? Do filters remove all disease-causing microorganisms? What is the rate of production of drinkable water by the filters? Where are streams?

Looking at Water and Its Contaminants

not have to teach for mastery of each concept now. Many concepts are taught in a spiral manner, meaning students will build on their knowledge of the concept each time they encounter it in the text. You may consult the Section Summary at the end of each section to gauge the depth of student knowledge required at this time.

With more information, students go back to the newspaper articles to separate fact from opinion. Knowledge of chemistry provides a framework for posing questions about societal problems that may help lead to solutions.

MEETING RAISES FISH-KILL CONCERNS

Chemists and other authorities report their progress in the investigation of the Snake River fish kill, using water-based terms such as *dissolved oxygen*, *suspended*, and *solubility*.

Additional Activities

Students can maintain a "Chemistry in the News" bulletin board to display local, regional, and national newspaper or magazine articles, cartoons, and so on relating to the main idea of the unit being studied. For this unit, students should pay particular attention to actual reported fish kills. You may have students post articles on the bulletin board or have them present a short report to the class. For example, have students prepare a summary of the article in large print and post their summary along with the original article on the bulletin board. Post new articles on a regular basis to maintain interest.

Such activities help emphasize that Riverwood-type scenarios are not just made-up stories, but happen regularly. Chemistry-related issues appear consistently in both national and local news, and *ChemCom* topics focus on a variety of community settings and events.

Meeting Raises Fish-Kill Concerns

BY CAROL SIMMONS
Riverwood News Staff Reporter

More than 300 concerned citizens, many prepared with questions, attended a Riverwood Town Hall public meeting last evening to hear from scientists investigating the Snake River fish kill.

Dr. Harold Schmidt, a chemist with the Environmental Protection Agency (EPA), expressed regret that the fishing tournament was canceled, but he strongly supported the town council's decision, saying it was the safest course in the long run. He reported that his laboratory is still conducting tests on the river water.

Dr. Margaret Brooke, a State University water specialist, helped interpret information and answered questions. Local physician Dr. Jason Martingdale and Riverwood High School family and consumer sciences teacher Alicia Green joined the speakers for a question-and-answer session.

Brooke confirmed that preliminary water-sample analyses showed no likely cause for the fish kill. She reported that EPA chemists will collect water samples at hourly intervals today to look for any unusual fluctuations in dissolved-oxygen (DO) levels. Fish require an adequate amount of oxygen gas dissolved in water for their survival; unusual DO levels sometimes kill fish.

Concerning possible fish-kill causes, Brooke said that EPA scientists have been unable to identify any microorganisms in the fish that could have been responsible for their death. She concluded that "it must have been something dissolved or temporarily suspended in the water." If dissolved matter were involved, EPA chemists will have to consider the relative amounts of various substances that can dissolve in water, and the effect of water temperature on their solubility. Brooke expressed confidence that further studies would shed more light on the causes of the problem.

Dr. Martingdale reassured citizens that "thus far, no illness reported by either physicians or the hospital can be linked to drinking water." Ms. Green offered water-conservation tips for housekeeping and cooking to make life easier for inconvenienced citizens. The information sheet she distributed is available on the Riverwood city Web site.

Mayor Cisko confirmed that water supplies will again be trucked in from Mapleton today, and he expressed hope that the crisis will last no longer than three days.

Those attending the meeting appeared to accept the emergency situation with good spirits. "I'll never take tap water for granted again," said Trudy Anderson, a Riverwood resident. "I thought scientists would have the answers," puzzled Robert Morgan, head of Morgan Enterprises. "They don't know either! There's certainly more involved in all this than I ever imagined."

Looking at Water and Its Contaminants

B.1 and B.2 Content Reading Guide

Section B returns to Riverwood's problem through another newspaper article about the fish kill. To understand the issues, students need to know more about the chemistry of water and how substances interact with water. This section introduces some properties of water, and students learn to classify mixtures as suspensions, colloids, or solutions. A simple particulate model of matter is proposed, and the universal symbolic language of chemistry is introduced. Students distinguish *pure* water from *clean* water, and investigate the presence of dissolved ions in water samples.

This material also contains many new chemistry terms and concepts. **Remember that because these concepts will be revisited many times during this course, you do**

B.1 Physical Properties of Water

This material deals with physical properties of water, including density, physical state, surface tension, boiling and freezing point, and solvent characteristics. To emphasize the unusual properties of water, you may wish to conduct demonstrations and ask students to interpret and explain the results of each.

Demonstration Ideas

1. Surface tension:
    a. Float a needle or a rubber band on the surface of the water. Gently lower the needle onto the surface of the water using a bent paper clip.
    b. Show that more water can be added to a full glass of water. Fill a glass to the rim, then continue to add water drop by drop until it bulges well above the rim. The same effect can be demonstrated by filling a glass with water even with the rim, then asking students how many paper clips they could add to the same glass. Many more than they expect can be added due to the surface tension of the water clinging to the edge of the glass.
    c. Drop water onto the surface of a penny, counting how many drops can be added before water escapes the surface. Repeat with hexane or isopropanol for contrast.
2. Density:
    a. Find the mass of 20.0 mL water in a 100-mL plastic graduated cylinder. You may add food coloring to the water to make it easy to read the volumes

---

As the previous article indicates, water experts attribute the cause of the fish kill to something dissolved or suspended in the Snake River. What might it be? How can the search for the cause be narrowed further? Knowing the properties of water (and of substances that might be found in it) will aid in this task. To understand these properties, you will be introduced to matter at the particulate level. You will also begin to learn the language of chemistry and use it to communicate with your classmates as you investigate the fish kill. And, just like scientists and public policy decision makers, you will gather and use available evidence to make decisions about Riverwood's situation.

Figure 1.18 *Earth as seen from space. Our planet's abundant supply of water makes it unlike any other in our solar system.*

B.1 PHYSICAL PROPERTIES OF WATER

Water is a common substance—so common that we usually take it for granted. We drink it, wash with it, swim in it, and sometimes grumble when it falls from the sky. But are you aware that water is one of the rarest and most unusual substances in the universe? As planetary space probes have gathered data, scientists have learned that the great abundance of water on Earth is unmatched by any planet or moon in our solar system. Earth is usually half-enveloped by water-laden clouds, as you can see in Figure 1.18. In addition, more than 70% of Earth's surface is covered by oceans that have an average depth of more than three kilometers (two miles).

Figure 1.19 *What states of water can be observed in this winter scene?*

---

before and after freezing. Have students calculate the density of liquid water. Then place the cylinder in a freezer. After freezing, find the new volume and have students calculate the density of ice.

b. Create a density column: Carefully place the following materials in a large graduated cylinder (to dramatize density differences) in this order: lead sinker (11.3 g/mL), corn syrup (1.36 g/mL), glycerin (1.26 g/mL), rubber stopper

Water is a form of matter. See Figure 1.19. As you may recall from previous science courses, **matter** is anything that occupies space and has mass. All solids, liquids, and gases are classified as matter. Matter can be distinguished by its characteristic properties. Water has many **physical properties**—properties that can be observed and measured without changing the chemical makeup of the substance. One physical property of a sample of matter is its **density,** which is the mass of material within a given volume. The density of water as a liquid is easy to remember. Because one milliliter (mL) of liquid water at room temperature (25 °C) has a mass of about 1.00 g, the density of this water is 1.00 g/mL. One milliliter of volume is exactly equal to one cubic centimeter (1 cm³), which is pictured in Figure 1.20. Thus, the density of water at 25 °C can also be reported as 1.00 g/cm³.

The **freezing point** of water, which is another physical property, is 0 °C at normal atmospheric pressure. What other physical properties of water can you describe?

Water is the only ordinary liquid found naturally in our environment. Because so many substances dissolve readily in water, quite a few liquids are actually water solutions. Such a water-based solution is called an **aqueous solution.** Even water that seems pure is never entirely so. Surface water contains dissolved minerals as well as other substances. Distilled water used in steam irons and car batteries contains dissolved gases from the atmosphere, as does rainwater.

Pure water is clear, colorless, odorless, and tasteless. The characteristic taste and slight odor of some tap-water samples are caused by substances dissolved in the water. You can confirm this by boiling and then refrigerating a sample of distilled water. When you compare its taste with the taste of chilled tap water, you may notice that *pure* distilled water tastes flat.

Water's physical properties (see Figure 1.21) help to distinguish it from other substances. In the following activity, you will compare the density of water with the density of some other common materials.

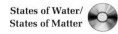

States of Water/ States of Matter

Figure 1.20 *One cubic centimeter (shown actual size). 1 cm³ = 1 mL.*

The density of liquid water actually depends on its temperature—for example, the density of liquid water is 0.992 g/mL at 40 °C and 0.972 g/mL at 80 °C.

Aqueous is based on the Latin root for *water* (aqua).

Figure 1.21 *What properties of water might account for its sheeting action under the swimmer's right arm?*

c. Place an ice cube in a graduated cylinder filled with isopropyl alcohol. The ice cube will sink rather than float because it is denser than the alcohol. Allow the cylinder to stand undisturbed for several minutes until the ice cube melts, pointing out any condensation that forms on the cylinder's outer surface. Add a second ice cube; it should float just above the bottom of the cylinder, supported by the layer of melted ice. More ice cubes can be added, and as long as the cylinder is not shaken, the alcohol and water will remain in separate layers and added ice cubes will float, farther and farther from the bottom of the cylinder.

d. In a large clear container filled with water (such as an aquarium) place a can of regular soda and a can of diet soda. The regular-soda container will sink, while the diet-soda container floats due to differences in their densities. There is much more sugar in regular soda than artificial sweetener in diet soda, resulting in a dramatic difference in mass and, subsequently, density. For a more quantitative investigation, find the mass and volume and then calculate the density of each type of soda.

Using the Figures

Figure 1.21: Sheeting action refers to the tendency of water to roll off a surface in large "sheets" rather than small separated droplets. This phenomenon is desirable, for example, when rinsing a car, dishes, or sunglasses, as it reduces spotting during drying. Water's high surface tension (and strong intermolecular forces) contributes to this phenomenon.

(1.2 g/mL), ethylene glycol (1.11 g/mL), water (1.0 g/mL), plastic (0.9 g/mL), oil (cooking, mineral, or colored lamp, 0.9 g/mL), oak (0.9 g/mL), alcohol (either ethanol or 2-propanol at 0.79 g/mL), and cork (0.2 g/mL). To form discrete layers, pour the liquids slowly down the side of the tilted graduated cylinder, or add each liquid layer using a long-stemmed funnel. Note that ethylene glycol is antifreeze. Consider coloring the water with food coloring for effect.

Developing Skills

B.2 Density

This *Developing Skills* activity reviews the concept of density through real-life applications.

Answers

1. The coffee grounds have the highest density, so they settle to the bottom; oil, which is less dense than water, floats.

2. Ice is less dense than water, which is why an ice cube floats in water. If this were reversed, ice would settle to the bottom, and in rivers and lakes in colder climates, fish could no longer bottom feed. Also, this effect might change the overall water temperature of rivers and lakes in colder climates.

3. Mass and volume would have to be determined to find the density of the copper sample. In the laboratory, a balance could be used to determine the mass. Its volume can be determined by measurement and calculation if it is regularly shaped. If it is irregularly shaped, use the water displacement method (place the object in a graduated cylinder partially filled with water and measure the change in water volume) to determine volume.

Developing Skills

Another approach to characterizing water is to consider how it reacts chemically with other substances. You will learn more about chemical properties of substances in Unit 2.

B.2 DENSITY

You may already be familiar with such physical properties of water as density, boiling point, and melting point. Use your experiences with water and other materials to answer the following questions about density:

1. In the foul-water investigation (page 10), you observed that coffee grounds settled to the bottom of the water sample, whereas oil floated on top. Explain this observation in terms of the relative densities of coffee grounds, water, and oil.

2. How does the density of ice compare with that of liquid water? What evidence can you cite to support your answer? (*Hint:* Use your everyday experiences to answer these questions.) What would happen to rivers and lakes (and fish) in colder climates if the relative densities of ice and liquid water were reversed?

3. Suppose you were given a small cube of copper metal. What measurements would you need to make to determine its density? How would you make these measurements in the laboratory?

B.3 MIXTURES AND SOLUTIONS

How can you decide if a water sample is not clean enough to drink? How can dissolved or suspended substances in water be separated and identified? Answers to these questions will be helpful in understanding, and possibly solving, the fish-kill mystery.

When two or more substances combine, and yet the substances retain their individual properties, the result is called a **mixture.** The foul water that you purified earlier is an example of a mixture because it contained coffee grounds, garlic powder, oil, and salt. As you discovered, the components of a mixture can be separated by physical means, such as filtration and adsorption.

When you first examined your foul-water sample, did it look uniform throughout? Most likely, the coffee grounds had settled to the bottom and were not distributed evenly throughout the liquid. The foul water is an example of a **heterogeneous mixture** because its composition is not the same, or uniform, throughout. One type of heterogeneous mixture is called a **suspension** if the solid particles are large enough to settle out or can be separated by using filtration. Water plus coffee grounds and water plus small pepper particles are examples of suspensions.

A heterogeneous mixture's composition varies from sample to sample.

Figure 1.22 *Milk is an example of a colloid.*

If the particles are smaller than those in a suspension, they may not settle out and, therefore, they may cause the water to appear cloudy. Recall what happened when your teacher shined a light through your sample of purified water. The scattering of the light, known as the **Tyndall effect** (see Figure 1.11, page 14), indicated that small, solid particles were still in the water. This type of mixture is called a **colloid.**

A more familiar example of a colloid is whole or low-fat milk (see Figure 1.22), which contains small butterfat particles dispersed in water. These colloidal butterfat particles are not visible to the unaided eye; the mixture appears homogeneous—uniform throughout. Under high magnification, however, individual butterfat globules can be observed suspended in the water. Milk no longer appears homogeneous.

Particles far smaller than colloidal particles also may be present in a mixture. When small amounts of table salt are mixed with water, as in your foul-water sample, the salt dissolves in the water. That is, the salt crystals separate into particles so small that they cannot be seen even at high magnification, nor do the particles exhibit the Tyndall effect when a light beam is passed through the mixture. These particles become uniformly mingled with the particles of water, producing a **homogeneous mixture,** or a mixture that is uniform throughout. All **solutions** are homogeneous mixtures. In a salt solution, the salt is the **solute** (the dissolved substance) and the water is the **solvent** (the dissolving agent). All solutions consist of one or more solutes and a solvent. See Figure 1.23.

Figure 1.23 *Sugar cubes dissolve in tea. In this case, tea is the solvent and sugar is the solute.*

B.3 Mixtures and Solutions

This material introduces types and classification of mixtures, with emphasis on water mixtures. You can use a sample of foul water from *Investigating Matter A.3* as an effective visual aid—the initial foul water is a heterogeneous mixture with colloidal properties. Demonstrate the heterogeneity by pointing out the coffee grounds on the bottom and oil on top. The Tyndall effect can demonstrate the colloid characteristics of both the original foul water and the mixture following the oil–water separation and sand-gravel filtration. The final student-processed samples are still solutions, which can be shown by using a conductivity detector to suggest that electrically charged particles (ions) remain.

This section introduces several chemical concepts. The terms are probably familiar to students, so focus on helping students understand water solutions and their application to solving the fish-kill mystery.

Using the Figures

Figure 1.24: Food analogies can be helpful in illustrating this chart; for instance, gelatin is a solution, while gelatin with fruit is a heterogeneous mixture. Ask students to provide other examples of mixtures (using food or other analogies). Although the "substances" branch of the diagram is not addressed until the next section, students probably know about elements and compounds.

After you address the "Substances" branch of this classification scheme, you may want to give students a list of common materials—milk, orange juice, mayonnaise, lemonade, copper, sodium chloride, sugar—and challenge them to classify each according to this figure.

Such questions are ideal for informally assessing students' understanding of the classification of matter. Asking students where pure water fits on this chart is a way to lead into *B.4 Particulate View of Water.*

Demonstration Ideas

Many demonstrations illustrate and contrast the types of matter:

1. Use several drops of whole milk in a beaker of water to display a colloidal suspension.

2. The Chemical Sunset demonstration, found in *Chemical Demonstrations: A Sourcebook for Teachers, Volume 1*, Demonstration 96 on page 163, illustrates solutions and colloidal suspension mixtures. For large groups, illuminate the solution with an overhead projector.

Evidence that something was still dissolved in your purified water sample came from the results of the conductivity test. The positive result (the bulb lit up) indicated that electrically charged particles were dissolved in the mixture. Figure 1.24 contains a summary flowchart of the various types of mixtures, as well as types of substances, which will be discussed next.

| **Figure 1.24** *Classification of matter*

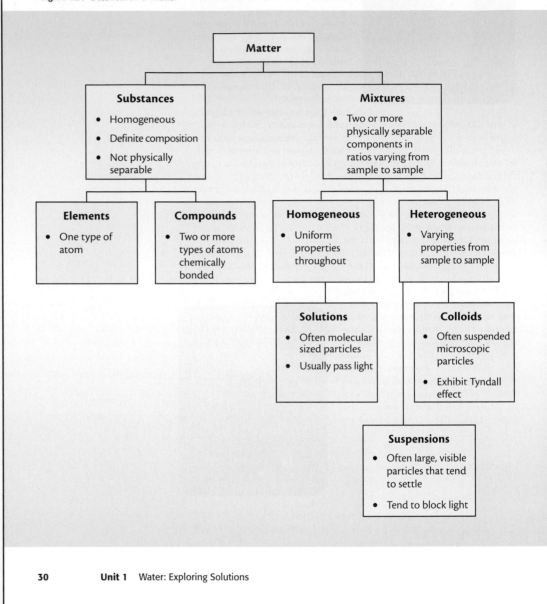

B.4 PARTICULATE VIEW OF WATER

So far in your exploration of water, you have focused on properties that are observable with your unaided senses. Have you wondered why water's freezing point is 0 °C or why certain substances such as salt dissolve in water? To understand why water has its specific properties, you must investigate it at the **particulate level;** that is, at the level of its atoms and molecules.

All matter is composed of atoms. **Atoms** are often called the building blocks of matter. Matter that is made up of only one kind of atom is known as an **element.** For example, oxygen is considered an element because it is composed of only oxygen atoms. Because hydrogen gas contains no atoms other than hydrogen atoms, it, too, is an element. Approximately ninety different elements are found in nature, each having its own type of atom and identifying properties.

What type of matter is a sample of water? Is it an element? A mixture? As you probably know already, water contains atoms of two elements—oxygen and hydrogen. Thus, water is not an element. And, because water's properties are different from those of oxygen and hydrogen, and the oxygen and hydrogen contained in water cannot be readily separated, water cannot be classified as a mixture, either.

Instead, water is an example of a **compound**—a substance that is composed of the atoms of two or more elements linked together chemically in certain fixed proportions. To date, chemists have identified more than 24 million compounds. Compounds and elements are represented by **chemical formulas.** In addition to water (H_2O), some other compounds and formulas with which you may be familiar include table salt (NaCl), ammonia (NH_3), baking soda ($NaHCO_3$), chalk ($CaCO_3$), sugar ($C_{12}H_{22}O_{11}$), and octane (C_8H_{18}).

Each element and compound is considered a **substance** because each has a uniform and definite composition, as well as distinct properties. The smallest unit of a molecular compound that retains the properties of that substance is a **molecule.** Atoms of a molecule are held together by chemical bonds. You can think of chemical bonds as the "glue" that holds atoms of a molecule together. Oxygen is an example of an *element* typically found in molecular form—two oxygen atoms bonded to one another (O_2)— while water is a molecular *compound.* One molecule of water is composed of two hydrogen atoms bonded to one oxygen atom, hence H_2O. An ammonia molecule (NH_3) contains three hydrogen atoms bonded to one nitrogen atom. Figure 1.25 shows representations of some atoms and molecules.

The next activity will give you the opportunity to apply a particulate viewpoint to a variety of common observations.

> **Seeing and Imagining Water**

> An element cannot be broken down into any simpler substances.

Figure 1.25 *Top row: hydrogen (H), oxygen (O), and nitrogen (N) atoms. Bottom row: hydrogen (H_2), water (H_2O), and ammonia (NH_3) molecules. Models similar to these are used throughout this book to depict atoms and molecules.*

 B.4, B.6, and B.9 Content Reading Guide

B.4 Particulate View of Water

One goal of introductory chemistry as developed by *ChemCom* is that students interrelate and move among three representations of chemistry— *macroscopic, particulate,* and *symbolic.* This section helps students make the transition from observable properties of water to a particulate model of water and consideration of atoms and molecules. The IRCD contains simulations that can help support this transition.

This section *introduces* ideas about atoms and molecules; it is not necessary to go into great detail. Even though chemical bonds are introduced, it is not appropriate at this time to discuss the different types of chemical bonds. These topics will be revisited later in this and other units.

The term *matter* is presented with the assumption that students have prior knowledge of its meaning. Remind students that everything (every *thing*) around us is made of matter and that matter has mass and occupies space (volume).

You may wish to show students molecular models of water to illustrate its "bent" shape. Indicate that this bent shape is key to understanding many of water's chemical and physical properties.

Additional ChemQuandary

Could there be an *impure substance?* Could there be a *pure material* that is not a *substance?*
Discussion: *Pure substance* is a redundant term. A substance contains only one type of smallest unit (atom or molecule) and is thus pure by definition. Ask students why people often use both parts of the term. An *impure substance* would, in reality, be a *mixture.*

Modeling Matter

B.5 Pictures in the Mind

**B.5 Pictures in the Mind
Student Worksheet**

Modeling Matter activities provide opportunities to explore chemistry using visual representations that may be two- or three-dimensional. This is useful for all students, particularly those who learn primarily through visual or kinesthetic modes. Students' sketches and physical models also help you identify misconceptions that are not obvious through their verbal answers. Students need considerable practice recognizing, describing, and creating good particulate-level models. *Modeling Matter* activities and particulate-level figures throughout the text help students develop their ability to "think molecularly."

In this initial *Modeling Matter* activity, students first encounter models of types of mixtures, and then draw their own models. Students also evaluate models and consider the models' limitations.

Answers

1. This drawing should depict three different element gases. Element gases can be monatomic (single atom), such as the noble gases, or diatomic (two bonded atoms), as in oxygen and chlorine. Diatomic sketches should clearly indicate that the two atoms are identical. The molecules should be separated and uniformly distributed to indicate the gaseous state.

Modeling Matter

B.5 PICTURES IN THE MIND

You live in a **macroscopic** world—a world filled with large-scale *(macro)*, readily observed things. As you experience the properties and behavior of bulk materials, you probably give little thought to the particulate world of atoms and molecules. If you wrap leftover cake in aluminum foil, it is unlikely that you think about how the individual aluminum atoms are arranged in the wrapping material. It is also unlikely that you consider what the mixture of molecules making up air looks like as you breathe. And you probably seldom wonder about atomic and molecular behavior when you observe water boiling or an iron nail rusting.

Nevertheless, having a sense of how atoms and molecules might look and behave in substances and mixtures can help you explain everyday phenomena. To develop this sense, it is useful to construct and evaluate **models**, or representations, of atoms and molecules.

Sample Problem: *Draw a model of two gaseous compounds in a homogenous mixture.*

A homogeneous mixture is uniform throughout, so the two compounds should be intermingled and evenly distributed. Also compounds are composed of atoms of two or more different elements linked together by chemical bonds.

Suppose a molecule of one of these compounds contains two different atoms. To represent this molecule, you could draw two differently shaded or labeled circles to denote atoms of the two elements and a line connecting the atoms to indicate a bond, like this:

Now, suppose that the other compound is composed of molecules made up of three atoms, and that two atoms are of the same element. You now need to decide on the order in which the atoms should be connected: the unique atom (Y) could be in the middle, X–Y–X, or on the end, X–X–Y. As long as you draw this imaginary compound the *same way every time,* it does not matter which way you draw it for this activity. However, the way in which atoms are connected in real compounds does, in fact, make a difference; X–Y–X would be quite a different molecule than X–X–Y.

a   b   c

---

2. This model represents a gaseous, heterogeneous mixture of two molecular substances, each of which consists of two types of atoms.

3. a. The particles should be spread far apart and mixed uniformly throughout the space available, with several molecules of each of two gases. The gases could both be monatomic or diatomic, as discussed in Answer 1.

b. The compound is linear. The atoms should be depicted as distinctly different and bonded together.

Examine models a, b, and c in the illustration on page 32. Which best represents a homogeneous mixture of the two compounds just described? You are correct if you said that model b is the best visual model. The two types of molecules are uniformly mixed, and the atoms are colored to indicate that they represent different elements. In model a, the mixture is not homogeneous because the molecules are not uniformly mixed. Model c contains three different compounds instead of two. Notice that in model a, bonded atoms in each molecule are connected by lines. In models b and c, bonded atoms just touch each other. Both representations are used by chemists; either one is acceptable in this activity.

Now it is your turn to create and evaluate various visual models of matter.

1. Draw a model of a homogeneous mixture composed of three different gaseous elements.

2. What kind of matter does the following model represent? Explain your answer.

3. Draw a model of a container of each of the following samples of matter. Write a description of key features of each model.

a. a mixture of gaseous elements X and Z

b. a two-atom compound of X and Z

c. a four-atom compound of X and Z

d. a solution composed of a solvent that is a two-atom compound of L and R, and a solute that is a compound composed of two atoms of element D and one atom of element T

4. Compare each visual model that you created in Question 3 with those of your classmates.

a. Although the models may look a little different, does each set depict the same type of sample? Comment on any similarities and differences.

b. Do the differences help or hinder your ability to visualize the type of matter that is depicted? Explain.

5. The element iodine (I) has a greater density in its solid state than in its gaseous state. Draw models that depict and account for this difference at the particulate level. Iodine normally exists as a two-atom molecule.

Section B   Looking at Water and Its Contaminants   **33**

c. There are multiple ways to connect the atoms. Any combination that connects four atoms with at least one atom each of X and Z is acceptable. The essen-

tial idea for students to depict is that every molecule has the same number of each kind of atom connected in exactly the same way.

d. There should be many two-atom molecules of L and R. There should be fewer molecules of the solute consisting of D and T, all of which should be identical. The solute particles should be uniformly distributed throughout the solvent and separated from each other.

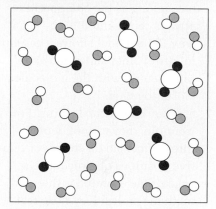

4. a. Student answers will vary. Most will find that their models are similar but differ in size, color, and number of atoms/molecules depicted. The three- and four-atom molecules may differ in the order that the atoms are connected.
   b. Student answers will vary, but they may indicate that the differences helped them identify any errors and recognize underlying concepts.

5. In the solid, iodine would appear as diatomic molecules (I_2) in relatively close contact with each other. As a gas, the I_2 molecules would still be diatomic, but spread much farther apart.

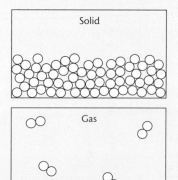

6. It is a reasonable model of a mixture of an element and a compound, representing the element as a diatomic molecule (as in H_2 or O_2). It would also be acceptable to have the element as single free atoms. This student has represented the compound with two atoms. Other structures are possible as long as the compound is always represented in the same way. This model shows a gaseous mixture; other states could be represented with the molecules closer together.

7. a. They can be misleading. For example, they cannot depict three-dimensional shapes or relative positions of molecules in space. One example is the methane molecule, whose real shape is tetrahedral. In student drawings it almost always looks flat. Another limitation of two-dimensional representations is the inability to depict complex twists or cross-links in large molecules.
   b. Good models reflect the nature of the concept they represent. Models should be clear and easy to visualize and understand. Good models extend understanding by revealing interactions and relationships.

| Table 1.2

COMMON ELEMENTS	
Name	**Symbol**
Aluminum	Al
Bromine	Br
Calcium	Ca
Carbon	C
Chlorine	Cl
Cobalt	Co
Copper	Cu
Fluorine	F
Gold	Au
Hydrogen	H
Iodine	I
Iron	Fe
Lead	Pb
Magnesium	Mg
Mercury	Hg
Nickel	Ni
Nitrogen	N
Oxygen	O
Phosphorus	P
Potassium	K
Silver	Ag
Sodium	Na
Sulfur	S
Tin	Sn

6. A chemistry student at Riverwood High School was asked to draw a model of a mixture composed of an element and a compound:

Comment on the usefulness of the student's drawing.

7. You have been interpreting and creating two-dimensional models of three-dimensional molecules.
   a. What are some limitations of flat, two-dimensional models?
   b. What are some characteristics that good models of matter should have?

As you continue to study chemistry, you will encounter visual models of matter similar to those in this activity. When you see them, think about their usefulness as well as their possible limitations.

B.6 SYMBOLS, FORMULAS, AND EQUATIONS

An international "chemical language" for use in oral and written communication was developed to represent atoms, elements, and compounds. The *letters* in this language's alphabet are **chemical symbols,** which are understood by scientists throughout the world. Each element is assigned a chemical symbol. Only the first letter of the symbol is capitalized; all other letters are lowercase. For example, C is the symbol for the element carbon, and Ca is the symbol for the element calcium. Symbols for some common elements are listed in Table 1.2.

All known elements are organized into the **periodic table of the elements,** which is one of the most useful tools in a chemist's work. A few examples of elements found in the periodic table are shown in Figure 1.26. As you continue your study of chemistry, you will learn more about this table. For now, become familiar with this chart by locating each element listed in Table 1.2 on the periodic table found on page 124.

Words in the language of chemistry are composed of letters (which represent elements) from the periodic table. Each *word* is a **chemical formula,** which represents a different chemical substance.

In the chemical formula of a substance, a chemical symbol represents each element present. A **subscript** (a number written below the normal line of letters) indicates how many atoms of the element just to the left of the subscript are in one unit of the substance.

For example, as you already know, the chemical formula for water is H_2O. The subscript 2 indicates that each water molecule contains two hydrogen atoms. Each water molecule also contains one oxygen atom. However, the subscript 1 is "understood" in the absence of any subscript and is therefore not included in chemical formulas.

2 Atoms of hydrogen   1 Atom of oxygen

Sample Problem: *The chemical formula for propane, a compound commonly used as a fuel, is C_3H_8. What elements are present in a molecule of propane, and how many atoms of each element are there?*

You are correct if you said each propane molecule consists of *three* carbon atoms and *eight* hydrogen atoms.

3 Atoms of carbon   8 Atoms of hydrogen

If formulas are words in the language of chemistry, then **chemical equations** can be regarded as chemical *sentences*. Each chemical equation summarizes the details of a particular chemical reaction. **Chemical reactions** entail the breaking and forming of chemical bonds, causing atoms to become rearranged into new substances. These new substances have different properties from those of the original materials.

The expression for the formation of water from its elements

shows that two hydrogen molecules (2 H_2) and one oxygen molecule (O_2) react to produce ($\rightarrow$) two molecules of water (2 H_2O). The original (starting) substances in a chemical reaction are called **reactants;** their formulas are always written on the left side of the arrow. The new substance or substances formed from the rearrangement of the reactant atoms are called **products;** their formulas are always written on the right side of the arrow. Note that this equation, like all chemical equations, is *balanced*—the total number of each type of atom (four H atoms and two O atoms) is the same for both reactants and products.

Figure 1.26 *(top) People use aluminum to make a variety of products including foil, cans, and lightweight construction materials. (middle) Silicon has properties that lie between those of metals and nonmetals. It is classified as a metalloid. One of its primary uses is in electronic devices. (bottom) Sulfur is a nonmetal used in products such as fungicides and rubber for automobile tires.*

B.6 Symbols, Formulas, and Equations

This material introduces students to symbols, formulas, and equations and to the significance of subscripts and coefficients. Emphasize the importance of a common, worldwide chemical language. Emphasize the relationship between symbolic representations (formulas such as H_2O, C_3H_8, and O_2) and particulate-level representations. The periodic table is also introduced.

These topics are further developed in Unit 2. It is not necessary for students to memorize any symbols or learn to balance equations now. Instead, show students where (the periodic table) to find all the symbols and element names. Tell students that an equation represents a chemical reaction that happens or that someone predicts might happen.

During discussion of symbols and chemical names, students may wonder why some elements have symbols that differ so fully from their names. The symbols for many elements are derived from their names in other languages. *Extending the Concepts Question 35* in the Section Summary also explores this issue.

SECTION B

Developing Skills

B.7 Symbols, Formulas, and Equations

This activity reinforces concepts and skills by giving students opportunities to practice recognizing and interpreting symbols, formulas, and equations. The equations are intended to introduce students to using an "atom inventory" prior to balancing chemical equations. It is unnecessary to discuss types of chemical reactions or to balance these equations. Students will learn more about chemical equations—including how to balance them—in Unit 2.

Answers

1. a. i. phosphorus   v. bromine
   ii. nickel   vi. potassium
   iii. copper   vii. sodium
   iv. cobalt   viii. iron

   b. phosphorus, nickel, cobalt, bromine

   c. An element's symbol. Names are specific to the language, but for scientists to communicate worldwide, a consistent system of symbols (as shown in the periodic table) was established. See **www.webelements.com** for examples.

2. a. 2 hydrogen atoms, 2 oxygen atoms

   b. 1 calcium atom, 2 chlorine atoms

   c. 1 sodium atom, 1 hydrogen atom, 1 carbon atom, 3 oxygen atoms

   d. 2 hydrogen atoms, 1 sulfur atom, 4 oxygen atoms

3. a. Methane and oxygen react to form carbon dioxide and water.
   b. Oxygen is an element. Methane, carbon dioxide, and water are compounds.

"GEN-U-INE DIATOMICS" serves as a useful memory device for all common diatomic elements. The names of all diatomic elements end in GEN or INE, and U should remember them!

Perhaps you noticed that in the chemical equation for the formation of water from its elements the reactants hydrogen and oxygen are written with subscripts (H_2 and O_2). Most uncombined elements in chemical equations are represented as single atoms (Cu, Fe, Na, and Mg, for example). A handful of elements are **diatomic molecules**; they exist as two bonded atoms of the same element. Oxygen gas and hydrogen gas are two examples of diatomic molecules. Table 1.3 lists all the common elements that exist as diatomic molecules at normal conditions. It will be helpful for you to remember these elements. Find the diatomic elements in the periodic table. Where are they located?

| Table 1.3

ELEMENTS THAT EXIST AS DIATOMIC MOLECULES			
Element	**Formula**	**Element**	**Formula**
Hydrogen	H_2	Chlorine	Cl_2
Nitrogen	N_2	Bromine	Br_2
Oxygen	O_2	Iodine	I_2
Fluorine	F_2		

Developing Skills

B.7 SYMBOLS, FORMULAS, AND EQUATIONS

1. a. Name the element represented by each of these symbols.
   i. P   v. Br
   ii. Ni   vi. K
   iii. Cu   vii. Na
   iv. Co   viii. Fe

   b. Which elements in Question 1a have symbols that correspond to their English names?

   c. Which is more likely to be the same throughout the world—an element's symbol or its name? Explain.

2. For each formula, name the elements and give the number of atoms of each element indicated.
   a. H_2O_2 Hydrogen peroxide   Antiseptic
   b. $CaCl_2$ Calcium chloride   Sidewalk deicer
   c. $NaHCO_3$ Sodium hydrogen carbonate   Baking soda
   d. H_2SO_4 Sulfuric acid   Battery acid

Sample Problem: *Complete an "atom inventory" of this chemical equation:*

$$N_2 \quad + \quad 3\,H_2 \quad \longrightarrow \quad 2\,NH_3$$

2 N atoms   +   6 H atoms   ⟶   2 N atoms and 6 H atoms

Note that the total number of atoms of N (nitrogen) and H (hydrogen) does not change during this chemical reaction.

---

c. 1 C atom and 4 H atoms + 4 O atoms →

1 C atom and 2 O atoms + 4 H atoms and 2 O atoms

d.

CH_4 + $2\,O_2$ ⟶ CO_2 + $2\,H_2O$

Next, interpret the equation in terms of molecules:

$$N_2 + 3 H_2 \longrightarrow 2 NH_3$$

1 N_2 molecule   3 H_2 molecules $\longrightarrow$ 2 NH_3 molecules

One molecule of N_2 reacts with three molecules of H_2 to produce two molecules of the compound NH_3, called ammonia.

3. The following chemical equation represents the burning of methane, CH_4, to form water and carbon dioxide:

$$CH_4 + 2 O_2 \longrightarrow CO_2 + 2 H_2O$$

a. Write a sentence describing the equation in terms of molecules.
b. Identify each molecule as either a compound or an element.
c. Complete an atom inventory for the equation.
d. Provide a visual model (picture in your mind) of the chemical reaction.

Let ⬭ represent CH_4. Let ⬭ represent CO_2.

Use the model of an H_2O molecule depicted in Figure 1.25 (page 31) to draw a molecule of H_2O similar to that for CH_4 and CO_2 shown here.

> Household ammonia is made by dissolving gaseous ammonia in water.

B.8 THE ELECTRICAL NATURE OF MATTER

Previously, you were introduced to the concept of atoms and molecules. How do the atoms in molecules stick together to form bonds? Are atoms made up of even smaller particles? The answers to these questions require understanding the electrical properties of matter.

You have already experienced the electrical nature of matter, most probably without realizing it. Clothes often display static cling when taken from the dryer. The pieces of fabric stick firmly together and can be separated only with effort. The shock that you sometimes receive after walking across a rug and touching a metal doorknob is another reminder of matter's electrical nature. And if you rub two inflated balloons against your hair, both balloons will attract your hair but repel each other, a phenomenon best seen when the humidity is low. See Figure 1.27.

Figure 1.27 *Rubbing a balloon against your hair results in static electricity. The balloon attracts your hair, even when you hold it away from your head.*

B.8 The Electrical Nature of Matter

This material introduces the following concepts: interactions among charges, specifically the attraction of opposite charges and repulsion of like charges; protons and electrons as sources of electrical charges within atoms and molecules, and neutrons as electrically neutral particles; the relative numbers of protons and electrons determine the electrical charge on an atom; and that attractions between the protons in one atom and electrons in another hold molecules together. Do not discuss or drill these concepts in great detail now, as students will learn more about subatomic particles later.

Demonstration Ideas

Rub two inflated balloons with a dry wool cloth. The balloons will acquire extra electrons and repel one another. It may be easiest to show this by attaching each balloon to a string.

Alternatively, rub an inflated balloon on your hair and then use the balloon to make your hair stand up. In this demonstration, the hair transfers electrons to the balloon, so the hair and balloon become oppositely charged and attract one another.

Extra Practice Items (for B.7 Question 2)

Note: The TRB/TRCD offers additional practice problems.

a. Ethylene glycol (automobile antifreeze): $C_2H_6O_2$—2 carbon atoms, 6 hydrogen atoms, 2 oxygen atoms

b. Ammonium phosphate (a fertilizer): $(NH_4)_3PO_4$—3 nitrogen atoms, 12 hydrogen atoms, 1 phosphorus atom, 4 oxygen atoms

c. Iron(III) oxide (common rust): Fe_2O_3—2 iron atoms, 3 oxygen atoms

SECTION B

B.9 Ions and Ionic Compounds

This material introduces and discusses naming ionic compounds.

Be sure students understand that ionic crystals are composed of regular arrangements of positive and negative ions. The formula NaCl thus represents the one-to-one ratio of cations to anions in the structure, while $CaCl_2$ represents a one-to-two ratio of cations to anions.

The source of ionic charges is again briefly considered.

Polyatomic (many-atom) ions are introduced here. **Table 1.4** provides the names and symbols for many common ions. It may be useful for students to bookmark this page for future reference. Students need not memorize the ions in this table, as they will become familiar with them through repeated use. Point out that there are two types of copper and iron ions in this table and that they (and many other metal ions) must always be distinguished by their Roman numerals, indicating their ionic charge.

A "criss-cross method" can be used to write formulas of ionic compounds: The charge from the cation becomes the subscript of the anion, and the charge of the anion becomes the subscript of the cation. This produces an electrically neutral formula unit. Caution students about mindlessly applying the criss-cross method without remembering the ultimate goal of identifying the *simplest ratio of ions* in an overall electrically neutral compound. Remind students to treat polyatomic ions as a single unit and to enclose them within parentheses when applying a subscript.

The electrical properties of matter can be summarized as follows:

What are these positive and negative charges? How do they relate to the idea of atoms and molecules? Every electrically neutral (uncharged) atom contains equal numbers of positively charged particles called **protons** and negatively charged particles called **electrons.** For instance, an electrically neutral sodium atom contains 11 protons and 11 electrons. An electrically neutral chlorine atom contains 17 protons and 17 electrons.

In addition to protons and electrons, most atoms contain one or more electrically neutral particles called **neutrons.** Positive–negative attractions between protons in one atom and electrons in another atom provide the attachment that holds atoms together. This "sticky force" (glue) is the chemical bond you read about on page 31.

These ideas will be used in later sections and in future units to explain the properties of substances, the process of dissolving, and chemical bonding. Now you will combine these ideas with your knowledge of atoms, chemical symbols, and chemical names to learn about a class of compounds that generally dissolve to some extent in water. It is possible that one or more of these compounds might be the cause of the Riverwood fish kill.

B.9 IONS AND IONIC COMPOUNDS

Earlier in this unit (page 31), you learned about molecules. Molecules make up one type of compound. Another type of compound is composed of **ions,** which are electrically charged atoms or groups of atoms. Atoms gain or lose electrons to form negative or positive ions, respectively. For instance, a sodium atom can easily lose one electron, resulting in an ion containing 11 protons and 10 electrons. A chlorine atom readily gains one electron. Summing protons and electrons reveals the resulting electrical charge for these two ions:

Sodium ion: 11 protons (11+ charge)
+ 10 electrons (10− charge)
Sodium ion (1+ charge); thus, Na^+

Chloride ion: 17 protons (17+ charge)
+ 18 electrons (18− charge)
Chloride ion (1− charge); thus, Cl^-

Ionic compounds are substances that are composed of positive and negative ions. An ionic compound has no net electrical charge; it is neutral because the positive and negative electrical charges offset each other. The most familiar example of an ionic compound is table salt, sodium chloride (NaCl).

38   **Unit 1**   Water: Exploring Solutions

 B.9 Supplement; Ions and Ionic Compounds

Figure 1.28 *You probably use sodium chloride, NaCl, to salt your food (left). A scanning electron micrograph shows the cubic structure of NaCl crystals (center). A space-filling model of NaCl (right) provides information about how the individual chloride ions (Cl⁻) and sodium ions (Na⁺) are arranged within the salt crystal. What else does this model suggest about sodium and chloride ions?*

Solid sodium chloride, NaCl(s), consists of equal numbers of positive sodium ions (Na⁺) and negative chloride ions (Cl⁻) arranged in a three-dimensional network called a *crystal*. In solid ionic compounds, such as table salt, the ions are held together in crystals by attractions among the negative and positive charges. See Figure 1.28. When an ionic compound dissolves in water, its individual ions separate from each other and disperse throughout the water. The designation (aq) following the symbol for an ion, as in Na⁺(aq), indicates that the ions are dissolved in water (aqueous) solution.

A negatively charged ion is called an **anion,** and a positively charged ion is called a **cation.** An ion can be a single atom, such as a sodium cation (Na⁺) or a chloride anion (Cl⁻); or a group of bonded atoms, such as an ammonium cation (NH₄⁺) or a nitrate anion (NO₃⁻). An ion consisting of a group of bonded atoms is called a **polyatomic** (*many atom*) **ion.** Table 1.4 (page 40) lists the formulas and names of common cations and anions.

The ionic compound calcium chloride, CaCl₂, presents a picture similar to NaCl. However, unlike sodium ions, calcium ions (Ca²⁺) each have a charge of 2+.

You can write formulas for ionic compounds by following two simple rules.

▶ Write the cation first, then write the anion.

▶ The correct formula will contain the fewest positive and negative ions needed to make the total electrical charge zero.

Why are the numbers of chloride ions different in sodium chloride (NaCl) and calcium chloride (CaCl₂)? In sodium chloride, the ion charges are 1+ and 1−, thus one cation and one anion result in a total charge of zero. So, the formula for sodium chloride must be NaCl.

When cation and anion charges do not add up to zero, ions of either type must be added until the charges are the same. In calcium chloride, one calcium ion (Ca²⁺) has a charge of 2+. Each chloride ion (Cl⁻) has a charge of 1−; two Cl⁻ ions are needed to balance a charge of 2+. Thus, two chloride ions (2 Cl⁻) are needed for each calcium ion (Ca²⁺). The subscript 2 written after chlorine's symbol in the formula indicates this. The correct formula for calcium chloride is CaCl₂.

recrystallized in the process of distilling water. The magnification is ×70 of its 35-mm size (so we've zoomed in from the top photo). Despite some irregularities, this SEM clearly shows the cubic crystal structure of NaCl(s).

To zoom in even further (to the point of visualizing individual ions that make up NaCl crystals) we must draw a particulate-level sketch that depicts the arrangement of Na⁺ and Cl⁻ ions.

Some features this model suggests are: Sodium and chloride ions are arranged in an alternating pattern; Na⁺ ions are smaller than Cl⁻ ions; ions pack closely together (in all ionic solids); ions are arranged in a large crystal, not as individual units like H₂ or H₂O molecules. Students may also state that the model suggests that Cl⁻ ions are green and Na⁺ ions are gray. This is a limitation of such models; color is used only to help distinguish types of atoms—individual atoms and ions are not colored. (Color is a property of bulk matter, not of individual atoms that make up the material.) The model also suggests that ions have a hard surface, like a billiard ball. In reality, boundaries are much fuzzier, as they consist of electron clouds. Discussing these limitations explicitly with your students may help them develop their ability to critique and create particulate-level models. It can also serve as a way to talk about characteristics of models in general.

Using the Figures

Figure 1.28: Emphasize relationships among representations of sodium chloride in this figure. Students are most familiar with the top photo. Get them to think about what they know about properties of table salt. Ask: What happens if you crush salt crystals with the back of a spoon? What happens when you add salt to water? What do you see? How can you confirm that the salt is still there? How would you recover the salt?

The middle photograph is a scanning electron micrograph (SEM) of pure salt

| Table 1.4

COMMON IONS

Cations

1+ Charge		2+ Charge		3+ Charge	
Formula	Name	Formula	Name	Formula	Name
H^+	hydrogen	Mg^{2+}	magnesium	Al^{3+}	aluminum
Na^+	sodium	Ca^{2+}	calcium	Fe^{3+}	iron(III)*
K^+	potassium	Ba^{2+}	barium		
Cu^+	copper(I)*	Zn^{2+}	zinc		
Ag^+	silver	Cd^{2+}	cadmium		
NH_4^+	ammonium	Hg^{2+}	mercury(II)*		
Li^+	lithium	Cu^{2+}	copper(II)*		
		Pb^{2+}	lead(II)*		
		Fe^{2+}	iron(II)*		

Anions

1− Charge		2− Charge		3− Charge	
Formula	Name	Formula	Name	Formula	Name
F^-	fluoride	O^{2-}	oxide	PO_4^{3-}	phosphate
Cl^-	chloride	S^{2-}	sulfide	P^{3-}	phosphide
Br^-	bromide	SO_4^{2-}	sulfate		
I^-	iodide	SO_3^{2-}	sulfite		
NO_3^-	nitrate	CO_3^{2-}	carbonate		
NO_2^-	nitrite				
OH^-	hydroxide				
HCO_3^-	hydrogen carbonate (bicarbonate)				
$HOCl^-$	hypochlorite				
SCN^-	thiocyanate				

*Some metal atoms form ions with one charge under certain conditions and another charge under different conditions. To specify the electrical charge for these ions, Roman numerals are used in parentheses after the metal's name.

Formulas for compounds that contain polyatomic ions, such as Na_2CO_3 (sodium carbonate), follow these same rules. However, if more than one polyatomic ion is needed to bring the total charge of the compound to zero, the formula for the polyatomic ion is enclosed in parentheses before the needed subscript is written. For instance, calcium nitrate is composed of Ca^{2+} ions and NO_3^- ions. Its correct formula, written to balance electrical charges, is $Ca(NO_3)_2$. Ammonium sulfate is composed of ammonium (NH_4^+) and sulfate (SO_4^{2-}) ions. *Two* ammonium cations with a total charge of 2+ are needed to match the 2− charge of *one* sulfate anion. Thus, the formula for ammonium sulfate is $(NH_4)_2SO_4$. Note that the entire ammonium ion symbol is enclosed in parentheses; the subscript 2 indicates that *two* cations are needed to complete the formula of ammonium sulfate.

The written name of an ionic compound is composed of two parts. The cation is named first, then the anion. As Table 1.4 suggests, many cations have the same name as their original elements. Anions composed of a single atom, however, have the last few letters of the element's name changed to the suffix *-ide*. For example, the anion formed from fluorine (F) is fluor*ide* (F^-). Thus, KF is named potassium fluor*ide.* The following activity will provide practice in expressing names and writing formulas for ionic compounds, according to the universal language of chemistry.

B.10 IONIC COMPOUNDS

Developing Skills

Sample Problem: *What is the composition of potassium chloride, the primary ingredient in table-salt substitutes used by people on low-sodium diets?*

Refer to Table 1.4. The compound described in the sample problem and those described in Statements 1 through 6 should be entered in a table similar to this one:

	Cation	Anion	Formula	Name
Sample	K^+	Cl^-	KCl	potassium chloride
	(Complete this chart for substances 1 through 6.)			

1. $CaSO_4$ is a component of plaster.
2. A substance composed of Ca^{2+} and PO_4^{3-} ions is found in some brands of phosphorus-containing fertilizer.
3. Ammonium nitrate, a rich source of nitrogen, is often used in fertilizer mixtures.
4. $Al_2(SO_4)_3$ is a compound sometimes used to help purify water.
5. Magnesium hydroxide is sometimes called *milk of magnesia* when it is mixed with water.
6. Limestone and marble (see photo) are two common forms of the compound calcium carbonate.

Developing Skills

B.10 Ionic Compounds

This activity provides practice in recognizing, naming, and writing formulas for ionic compounds. Remind students to use the ionic charges and names from **Table 1.4**.

ANSWERS			
CATION	**ANION**	**FORMULA**	**NAME**
K^+	Cl^-	KCl	potassium chloride
1. Ca^{2+}	SO_4^{2-}	$CaSO_4$	calcium sulfate
2. Ca^{2+}	PO_4^{3-}	$Ca_3(PO_4)_2$	calcium phosphate
3. NH_4^+	NO_3^-	NH_4NO_3	ammonium nitrate
4. Al^{3+}	SO_4^{2-}	$Al_2(SO_4)_3$	aluminum sulfate
5. Mg^{2+}	OH^-	$Mg(OH)_2$	magnesium hydroxide
6. Ca^{2+}	CO_3^{2-}	$CaCO_3$	calcium carbonate

Investigating Matter

B.11 Water Testing Student Worksheet and Data Table

B.11 Water Testing

In this investigation, students test water samples for the presence of dissolved ions—iron(III) and calcium cations, and chloride and sulfate anions. The qualitative-analysis procedures are based on a "confirming-test" approach. Emphasize that a negative test does *not* necessarily mean that the ion was absent, only that it may not have been present in detectable amounts.

Students also analyze natural water samples. They can test samples from wells, streams, lakes, oceans, or bottled water. You can simulate ocean water by dissolving sea salt in water.

Time

50 min

Materials

(For a class of 24 working in pairs)

12 24-well microplates

144 Beral pipets containing test solutions and reference-ion solutions

Test Solutions

50 mL 0.5 M KSCN (potassium thiocyanate, 2.4 g/50 mL) [SCN^- source]

50 mL 0.1 M Na_2CO_3 (sodium carbonate, 0.53 g/50 mL) [CO_3^{2-} source]

50 mL 0.1 M $AgNO_3$ (silver nitrate, 0.85 g/50 mL) [Ag^+ source]

50 mL 0.1 M $BaCl_2$ (barium chloride, 0.735 g $BaCl_2$·H_2O/50 mL) [Ba^{2+} source]

B.11 WATER TESTING

Introduction

How do chemists detect and identify certain substances or ions in water solutions? This investigation will allow you to use a method that chemists, including those investigating the Riverwood fish kill, use to detect the presence of specific ions in water solutions.

The tests that you will conduct are **confirming tests.** That is, a positive test confirms that the ion in question is present. In each confirming test, you will look for a change in solution color or for the appearance of an insoluble material called a **precipitate**. See Figure 1.29. A negative test (no color or precipitate) means one of two things: either the ion is not present, or the ion is present in such low amounts that the chemical test involved is unable to produce a confirming result.

You will conduct **qualitative tests,** which are tests that identify the presence or absence of a particular substance in a sample. In contrast, **quantitative tests** determine the *amount* of a specific substance present in a sample. Most likely, both types of tests would be used to determine the cause of the Snake River fish kill.

You will test for the presence of iron(III) (Fe^{3+}) and calcium (Ca^{2+}) cations, as well as chloride (Cl^-) and sulfate (SO_4^{2-}) anions. These ions often are found in groundwater and tap water. Although you are familiar with the names and symbols for Ca^{2+}, Cl^-, and SO_4^{2-}, the name for Fe^{3+}—iron(III)—may look strange to you. Some elements can form cations with different charges. Iron atoms can lose either two electrons to form Fe^{2+} cations or three electrons to form Fe^{3+} cations. Thus, the name "iron cation" is not helpful enough; it does not distinguish between Fe^{2+} and Fe^{3+}. For this reason, Roman numerals are added to the name to indicate the charge on the ion. Examples of other cations that must include Roman numerals in their names are copper(I), copper(II), cobalt(II), and cobalt(III). The formulas and equations that accompany each of the following tests are provided so that you can see how chemists describe these confirming reactions.

You will complete each confirming test on several different water samples. The first solution will be a distilled-water *blank*—one known not to contain any ions of interest. The second is a **reference solution** (a solution of known composition used as a comparison)—one known to contain the sought ion.

Next, you will test an unknown solution that may contain one or more of the ions. The other samples to test are tap water and the natural water samples that you or your teacher collected. These solutions may or may not contain the ions. To determine whether these

Technologies are available for detecting ions when their amounts are so small that a confirming test cannot produce a positive result.

Figure 1.29 *A bright yellow precipitate forms when you add a solution of potassiium iodide, KI, to a solution of lead(II) nitrate, $Pb(NO_3)_2$. The precipitate is lead(II) iodide, PbI_2.*

Lab Video: Water Testing

Reference-Ion Solutions

50 mL 0.1 M $Fe(NO_3)_3$ (2.02 g $Fe(NO_3)_3$· 9 H_2O/50 mL) [Fe^{3+} source]

50 mL 0.1 M $CaCl_2$ (5.9 g $CaCl_2$· 2H_2O/50 mL) [Ca^{2+} and Cl^- source]

50 mL 0.1 M $FeSO_4$ (1.4 g $FeSO_4$· 7H_2O/50 mL) [SO_4^{2-} source]

Safety

Students should wear protective goggles and aprons throughout the investigation. Caution students that silver nitrate solution stains skin.

solutions contain the ions, you will compare the results you obtained with the behavior of your reference samples and with the distilled-water blank.

In your laboratory notebook, prepare four data tables (one for each ion) similar to the one shown. Add rows if you are testing more than one natural-water sample. Note the source of each natural-water sample.

DATA TABLE: *(Name of ion)*		
Solution	**Observations (color, precipitate, etc.)**	**Result (Is ion present?)**
Reference		
Control		
Tap water		
Natural water from ___ *(source)*		

The following suggestions will help guide your ion analysis:

1. If the ion is present in tap water or natural water, it will probably be present in a smaller amount than in the same volume of reference solution. Therefore, the quantity of precipitate or color produced in the tap-water or natural-water sample will be lower than in the reference solution.

2. When completing an ion test, mix the contents of the well thoroughly, using a toothpick or small glass stirring rod. Do not use the same toothpick or stirring rod in other samples without first rinsing it and wiping it dry.

3. In a confirming test based on color change, so few color-producing ions may be present that it is difficult to determine if the reaction actually took place. Here are two ways to decide whether the expected color is actually present:
   ▶ Place a sheet of white paper behind or under the wellplate to make any color more visible.
   ▶ Place the wellplate on a black or dark surface to make a precipitate more visible.

Before starting, read the procedure to learn what you will need to do, note safety precautions, and plan necessary data collecting and observations.

Procedure

If the ion of interest is present, a confirming chemical reaction will occur, producing either a colored solution or a precipitate. The chemical equations for the reactions are provided for each ion.

Advance Preparation

You can minimize student movement around the laboratory if you label pipets, fill them with solutions, and distribute them upside-down in a wellplate or cassette tape case. You can use the same pipets and solutions for several classes. After the investigation, empty, rinse, and store the pipets for future use.

Using the Figures

Figure 1.29: Ask students: What color is potassium iodide solution? (colorless) What color is lead(II) nitrate solution? (colorless) What color is solid lead(II) iodide? (yellow) Emphasize that color changes are useful for detecting the presence of particular ions, and also generally for detecting chemical changes.

SECTION B

Pre-Lab Discussion

Focus on the confirming-test approach, which provides a positive result if the ion is present and no change if the ion is not present (or undetectable). Discuss examples of common "confirming tests" (swimming-pool and well-water test kits, urine tests, pregnancy tests). Explain that distilled water is used as a *blank*, a system in which the ion of interest is known to be absent, while *reference solutions* are known to contain the ion of interest. Both blanks and reference solutions are used for comparing unknown-sample test results.

It may be helpful to model the procedure before students start the investigation or to complete the first confirming test as a class. Ask questions throughout this process to ensure that students understand the role of each solution.

Remind students that although small quantities are used in this investigation, they must exercise care in handling all materials in the laboratory. Remind them to clean their wellplates immediately after use to avoid staining.

Lab Tips

• In some areas, tap water does not contain detectable levels of the ions of interest in this investigation. You may elect to "manufacture" alternative tap water by dissolving a small amount of sodium chloride or calcium or sulfate salts in distilled water.

• If a test color is too dark, students may add small amounts of distilled water to observe the color more easily. To observe faint precipitates, students may need to use both white and dark paper.

• If several classes use the same wellplates, encourage students to rinse their wellplates and stirring rods thoroughly with distilled water following (or prior to) the investigation. Residues in a wellplate or on a stirring rod may cause false positives in subsequent investigations.

• Students are often confused about using the same solution for both Ca^{2+} and Cl^- ions. Remind them that $CaCl_2$ dissolves to supply *both* ions.

• Students often have difficulty identifying precipitates. Remind students that precipitate formation at times may be as subtle as the appearance of cloudiness in their wellplates.

Answers

1. A reference solution is used so that the appearance of a positive test can be identified, while a blank shows the effect of a negative test.

2. The concentration of some ions may be too low to detect; the test for one ion may interfere with or mask the behavior of another ion, giving false-positive or false-negative results; and the tests cannot determine the amount of ion present.

3. Ions may be present at levels below those that would cause an observable positive result.

4. Ions could have remained on them and produced false-positive results.

Post-Lab Discussion

Focus on student answers to questions. These questions help develop reasoning skills in interpreting laboratory data. Reinforce the idea that qualitative chemical tests rely on formation of a recognizable product by the reference ion. Also stress the idea that a negative qualitative test does not necessarily suggest that the ion is not present; the ion may not

Only ions taking part in the reaction are included in this type of equation, called a net ionic equation.

Figure 1.30 *Adding drops to a 24-well wellplate.*

Calcium Ion (Ca^{2+}) Test

$$Ca^{2+}(aq) \quad + \quad CO_3{}^{2-}(aq) \quad \longrightarrow \quad CaCO_3(s)$$

Calcium ion   Carbonate ion   Calcium carbonate precipitate

Follow these steps for each sample (distilled-water blank, Ca^{2+} reference, unknown, tap water, and natural water):

1. Place 20 drops of solution into a well of a 24-well wellplate.
2. Add three drops of sodium carbonate (Na_2CO_3) test solution to the well. See Figure 1.30.
3. Record your observations, including the color and whether a precipitate formed.
4. Decide whether Ca^{2+} cations are present and record your results.
5. Repeat for the remaining samples.
6. Discard the contents of the wellplate as directed by your teacher.

Iron(III) Ion (Fe^{3+}) Test

$$Fe^{3+}(aq) \quad + \quad SCN^-(aq) \quad \longrightarrow \quad [FeSCN]^{2+}(aq)$$

Iron(III) ion   Thiocyanate ion   Iron(III) thiocyanate ion (reddish color)

Follow these steps for each sample (distilled-water blank, Fe^{3+} reference, unknown, tap water, and natural water):

1. Place 20 drops of solution into a well of a 24-well wellplate.
2. Add one or two drops of potassium thiocyanate (KSCN) test reagent to the well.
3. Record your observations, including the color and whether a precipitate formed.
4. Decide whether Fe^{3+} cations are present and record your results.
5. Repeat for the remaining samples.
6. Discard the contents of the wellplate as directed by your teacher.

Chloride Ion (Cl^-) Test

$$Cl^-(aq) \quad + \quad Ag^+(aq) \quad \longrightarrow \quad AgCl(s)$$

Chloride ion   Silver ion   Silver chloride precipitate

Follow these steps for each sample (distilled-water blank, Cl^- reference, unknown, tap water, and natural water):

1. Place 20 drops of solution into a well of a 24-well wellplate.
2. Add three drops of silver nitrate ($AgNO_3$) test reagent to the well.
3. Record your observations including the color and whether a precipitate formed.
4. Decide whether Cl^- anions are present and record your results.
5. Repeat for the remaining samples.
6. Discard the contents of the wellplate as directed by your teacher.

be present in sufficient concentration to be detected by that particular test. Some students may be interested to know that in an analytical-chemistry laboratory, researchers can complete different confirming tests (of varying sensitivities) for the same species to definitively confirm its presence.

EXPECTED POSITIVE RESULTS		
REFERENCE SOLUTION	COLOR	PRECIPITATE?
Fe^{3+}	Red	No
Ca^{2+}	White	Yes
Cl^-	White	Yes
$SO_4{}^{2-}$	White	Yes

Sulfate Ion (SO$_4$$^{2-}$) Test

$$SO_4^{2-}(aq) \quad + \quad Ba^{2+}(aq) \quad \longrightarrow \quad BaSO_4(s)$$

Sulfate ion   Barium ion   Barium sulfate precipitate

Follow these steps for each sample (distilled-water blank, SO$_4$$^{2-}$ reference, unknown, tap water, and natural water):

1. Place 20 drops of solution into a well of a 24-well wellplate.
2. Add three drops of barium chloride (BaCl$_2$) test reagent to the well.
3. Record your observations, including the color and whether a precipitate formed.
4. Decide whether SO$_4$$^{2-}$ anions are present and record your results.
5. Repeat for the remaining samples.
6. Discard the contents of the wellplate as directed by your teacher.

Questions

1. Why were a reference solution and a blank used in each test?
2. What are some possible problems associated with the use of qualitative tests?
3. These tests cannot absolutely confirm the absence of an ion. Why?
4. How might your observations have changed if you had not cleaned your wells or stirring rods thoroughly after each test?

B.12 PURE AND IMPURE WATER

Now that you have learned about water's properties and about some of the substances that can dissolve in water, you are ready to return to the problem of Riverwood's fish kill. Recall that Riverwood residents had different ideas about the cause of the problem. For example, Harmon Lewis was sure the cause was pollution of the river water.

> What is the difference between clean water and pure water?

Families in most U.S. cities and towns receive an abundant supply of clean, but not absolutely pure, water at an extremely low cost. You can check the water cost in your own area; if you use municipal water, your family's water bill will contain the current water cost.

It is useless to insist on absolutely pure water. The cost of processing water to make it absolutely pure would be prohibitively high. Even if cost were not a problem, it would still be impossible to have absolutely pure water. The atmospheric gases nitrogen (N$_2$), oxygen (O$_2$), and carbon dioxide (CO$_2$) will always dissolve in the water to some extent. See Figure 1.31.

Figure 1.31 *Although distilled water (right) is purer than water gushing from this discharge pipe (left), it still contains dissolved gases and thus is not "100%" pure.*

B.12 Pure and Impure Water

This discussion helps students distinguish pure water from clean water. Substances that dissolve naturally in water supplies are also considered.

This offers a good opportunity to consider world water supplies and consequences of unclean water. See **http://www.who.int/water_ sanitation_health/en/, http://www. epa.gov/safewater/dwhealth.html** or **http://www.nlm.nih.gov/medlineplus/ drinkingwater.html** for more information.

Most water suppliers provide annual reports detailing the quality of the water they provide. You may have students examine one of these reports (see **http://www. denverwater.org/waterquality/ TreatedWQSummaryReport2003. pdf** for an example) in the context of discussing pure versus clean water.

Making Decisions

B.13 The Riverwood Water Mystery

This activity introduces students to a particular aspect of a scientific approach to solving problems—distinguishing facts from opinions.

Have students reread all newspaper articles in Unit 1 as homework. In class, assign students to groups of 4 or 5 to work on this activity, after which the class can compare and discuss each group's answers. (The entire activity can also be assigned as homework if students have requisite skills and motivation.) You may wish to get students started by finding several facts in the articles as a class. Suggest that groups review chemistry knowledge they gained in previous text material to help them form questions and eliminate fish-kill causes.

1. No question; students should reread the articles.
2. Facts/data include:

   Dead trout and other fish were floating from near the base of the Snake River dam to the town's water-pumping station.

   Preliminary tests looked for substances dissolved in the water that might be responsible for the fish kill.

   Early evidence seems to point to something dissolved in the water as the cause.

   The substance and its origin are still undetermined.

   The Fall Fish-In has been canceled.

   The town council voted to shut down the water plant for three days.

Making Decisions

B.13 THE RIVERWOOD WATER MYSTERY

At the beginning of this unit, you read newspaper articles describing the Riverwood fish kill and the reactions of several citizens. Among those interviewed were Harmon Lewis, a longtime resident of Riverwood, and Dr. Margaret Brooke, a water-systems scientist. These two people had very different reactions to the fish kill. Harmon Lewis was certain that human activity—probably some sort of pollution—had caused the fish kill. Dr. Brooke refused to speculate about the cause of the fish kill until she had conducted some tests.

Which of these two opinions comes closer to your own reaction at this point? Complete the following activities to investigate the fish-kill issue further.

1. Reread the fish-kill newspaper reports at the start of Sections A and B (pages 4–6 and page 25).
2. As a group, generate a list of all the fish-kill facts (not opinions) in these articles. Scientists often refer to facts as data. **Data** are objective pieces of information. They do not include interpretation. Figure 1.32 depicts the beginning of a "fact list," and provides some examples to get your group started.
3. As you have read and thought about Riverwood's fish kill, have any questions occurred to you? Perhaps you wish you had more information about the situation. List at least five factual questions you would like to have answered before you decide on the possible causes of the fish kill. Some typical questions might be: Do barges or other commercial boats travel on the Snake River? Were any shipping accidents on the river reported recently?
4. Look over your two lists—one of facts and the other of questions. Although you probably still have unanswered questions about the Riverwood fish kill, perhaps you have some hunches about what did or did not cause it.

   a. Based on the information you now have, list at least two possible fish-kill causes that you consider unlikely. Explain your reasoning.

   b. Can you suggest a probable cause for the fish kill? Be as specific as possible.

   Later in this unit, you will have the opportunity to check the reasoning you used in answering these questions.

Figure 1.32 *Some possible Riverwood fish-kill facts.*

Fish-Kill Facts
1) Chad and Jane found many dead fish.
2) All kinds of dead fish were washed up.

Arrangements have been made to transport emergency drinking water from Mapleton.

Dead fish will be examined.

Riverwood has had an unusually wet summer.

Water samples will be collected hourly to monitor dissolved oxygen.

No microorganisms that could have been responsible have been identified in the dead fish.

B.14 WHAT ARE THE POSSIBILITIES?

The activities that you just completed (gathering data, seeking patterns or regularities among the data, and suggesting possible explanations or reasons to account for the data) are typical of the approaches scientists take in attempting to solve problems. Such scientific methods are a combination of systematic, step-by-step procedures and logic, as well as occasional hunches and guesses.

A fundamental, yet difficult, part of a scientist's work is knowing what questions to ask. You have listed some questions that might be posed concerning the cause of the fish kill. Such questions help focus a scientist's thinking. Often a large problem can be reduced to several smaller problems or questions, each of which is easier to manage and solve.

The number of possible causes for the fish kill is large. Scientists investigating this problem must find ways to eliminate some causes and focus on the more promising causes. They try to disprove all but one cause or they produce conclusive proof in support of a specific cause.

As you recall, water specialist Dr. Brooke studied possible causes of the Snake River fish kill. She concluded that if the actual cause were water-related, it would have to be the result of something dissolved or suspended in the water.

In Section C, you will examine several categories of water-soluble substances and consider how they may be implicated in the fish kill. The mystery of the Riverwood fish kill will be confronted at last!

3. Student questions will vary, but could include:
What types of substances might be dissolved in water?
Could contaminants enter below the dam?
What possible emission sources are upstream from the dam?
What happens to water as it goes over the dam?
Do any additional substances dissolve in the water?
What substances might harm fish?
Could the fish have died from a deficiency or overdose of a naturally occurring and necessary substance?

4. a. Student answers will vary, but some possible unlikely causes at this point include a visible water contaminant, a storm or other meteorological cause (drought, heat wave), and microorganisms.
b. Student answers will vary, but may suggest a dissolved or suspended contaminant or name a specific contaminant.

B.14 What Are the Possibilities?

This material relates the processes students have experienced to the typical work of scientists. It is a bridge to Section C, where students investigate types of substances that can be dissolved or suspended in water and determine which are potentially harmful to aquatic life.

Knowledge of scientific facts, theories, laws, and principles helps working scientists form questions or hypotheses, just as chemistry knowledge helps students reject some possible causes as improbable.

Soon you will need to decide which evidence you will provide to students for Section C and Putting It All Together. Four sets of data have been prepared, each with a different cause for the fish kill. These data and an explanation of the scenario behind each set are in the TRB/TRCD and on the *ChemCom* web site. Students will analyze the data and use evidence from the data to determine the cause. You may want to use a different set of data with each class you teach, or vary the cause from one year to the next.

CHEMISTRY AT WORK

The *Chemistry at Work* feature provides opportunities for students to become familiar with careers that involve applications of chemistry. Throughout the text, students should gain understanding of the varied types of work that chemists do.

This *Chemistry at Work* spotlights Wayne Crayton, an environmental specialist with the U.S. Army Corp of Engineers in Alaska. Crayton and his team assess damage to wildlife and coordinate cleanup if necessary. This is a good opportunity to remind students about the water-testing investigation they completed and to remind them of the fish-kill problem in Riverwood.

CHEMISTRY at Work

Environmental Cleanup: It's a Dirty Job...But That's the Point

Wayne Crayton spends his summers touring exotic islands in the Aleutian Islands chain off the coast of Alaska. But it is not just an adventure that he embarks on; it is also his job.

As an Environmental Contaminants Specialist with the U.S. Army Corps of Engineers, Alaska District, Wayne investigates areas that were formerly used as military bases and fueling stations. Wayne and his teammates review and assess the damage (if any) that contaminants have done to key areas used by wildlife. Based on their findings, they then develop plans to fix these problems.

Wayne works in an office in Anchorage during the rest of the year, analyzing and interpreting data and test results from the field investigations.

As part of investigation planning, the team reviews information to determine what they might find at a given site. For example, historical documents about the site will indicate whether the team members should be looking for petroleum residues or other contaminants. Aerial photography and records from earlier investigations will help to identify specific areas that are potential sites of contamination.

At the site, the team collects soil, sediment, and water samples from the exact location where a contaminant was originally introduced to the environment plus samples from the area over which the contaminant might have spread. The team may also collect small mammals or fish that have been exposed to the contaminants. After collecting the necessary samples, the team members return home quickly because some of the collected samples can degrade or change characteristics soon after collection.

Wayne works in an office in Anchorage during the rest of the year, analyzing and interpreting data and test results from the field investigations. He and his colleagues calculate concentrations of hazardous substances, including organochlorines, polychlorinated biphenyls (PCBs), pesticides, petroleum residues, and trace metals. Then they determine whether any of these substances present a risk to humans or the surrounding ecosystems.

Solving Scientific Problems . . .

This icon indicates an opportunity to consult resources on the World Wide Web. See your teacher for further instructions.

Scientists often solve problems in unique ways—ways that are different from the methods used in other areas of academic research.

- Outline the problem-solving steps that Environmental Contaminants Specialists use in planning their investigations.

- Compare the steps used by these scientists with the steps that you have used in completing laboratory investigations.

- Conduct a World Wide Web search for any U.S. Army Corps of Engineers or U.S. Environmental Protection Agency investigations or projects that might be underway in your community.

Using these results, the team recommends procedures for removing and treating contaminated soil and other material. In some situations, they might decide that the best solution is to do nothing; the cleanup itself could destroy wetlands, disturb endangered wildlife, or have other negative effects on the environment. The U.S. Army Corps of Engineers uses the team's recommendations to direct the work of the contractor performing the actual cleanup.

Section B Summary

 Section B Supplement

Reviewing the Concepts

1. A property that can be observed and measured without changing the chemical makeup of the substance.

2. Physical properties of water include density of 1.0 g/mL at 25 °C; freezing point of 0 °C; clear; colorless; odorless; tasteless; high surface tension.

3. Solid water (ice) is less dense than liquid water.

4. Student answers will vary, but they might describe a winter scene where some ice was melting and some was subliming, or a summer scene with a glass of ice water and humidity in the air.

5. Heterogeneous mixtures vary in composition; samples taken from different parts of the mixture will have different properties. Homogeneous mixtures are uniform throughout; samples taken from different parts of the mixture will have the same properties.

6. Their densities

7. Solution: d. Suspension: a, b, e. Colloid: c, f

8. Suspension. Most dust particles would eventually settle to the floor, or could be removed using an air filter. The particles and their behavior in air are inconsistent with those of a colloid or solution.

9. Student sketches will vary, but should show a solution as a mixture with evenly interspersed particles and a suspension as a mixture with occasional suspended particles and some solid particles on the bottom.

SECTION B SUMMARY
Reviewing the Concepts

| Substances can be distinguished, in part, by their physical properties.

1. What is a physical property?
2. Identify three physical properties of water.
3. How does the density of solid water compare to the density of liquid water?
4. Describe a setting where you might observe water as a solid, a liquid, and a gas all at the same time.

| Physically combining two or more substances produces a mixture. Mixtures can be either heterogeneous or homogeneous.

5. How are heterogeneous and homogeneous mixtures different?
6. When gasoline and water are poured into the same container, they form two distinct layers. What do you need to know to predict which liquid will be on top?
7. Identify each of the following materials as a solution, a suspension, or a colloid.
   a. a medicine accompanied by instructions to "shake before using"
   b. Italian salad dressing
   c. mayonnaise
   d. a cola soft drink
   e. an oil-based paint
   f. milk

8. You notice beams of light passing into a darkened room through the blinds on a window. Does this demonstrate that air in the room is a solution, a suspension, or a colloid? Explain.
9. Sketch a visual model on the molecular level, similar to those you drew in the Modeling Matter activity (page 32), that represents each of the following types of mixtures. Label and explain the features of each sketch.
   a. a solution   b. a suspension
10. Suppose you have a clear, red liquid mixture. A beam of light is observed as it passes through the mixture. Over a period of time, no particles settle to the bottom of the container. Classify this mixture as a solution, a colloid, or a suspension, and provide evidence to justify your choice.

| An element is composed of only one type of atom; compounds consist of two or more types of atoms. Both elements and compounds are considered substances.

11. Define the term *substance* and give two examples.
12. Classify each of the following substances as an element or a compound.
    a. CO   c. HCl   e. $NaHCO_3$ g. I_2
    b. Co   d. Mg   f. NO
13. Draw a model of a molecular compound made up of two atoms of A and one atom of D.

14. Look at these models:

   a. Which models represent elements?
   b. Which models represent compounds?

---

10. Colloid: The beam of light indicates that it is either a colloid or a suspension, and the fact that no particles settle out eliminates the possibility of it being a suspension.

11. A substance is a sample of matter that has a uniform and definite composition, as well as distinct properties. Both ele-

ments and compounds are examples of substances. (Students may give more specific examples, such as sodium chloride or water. Either type of example is acceptable.)

12. Elements: b, d, g Compounds: a, c, e, f

13. Students should draw several identical three-atom molecules made up of two

> A chemical formula indicates the composition of a substance. A chemical equation represents a reaction of one or more substances to form one or more new substances.

15. What two pieces of information does a chemical formula provide?

16. Name the elements and list the number of each atom indicated in the following substances:

a. phosphoric acid, H_3PO_4 (used in soft drinks)
b. sodium hydroxide, NaOH (found in some drain cleaners)
c. sulfur dioxide, SO_2 (an air pollutant)

17. Represent each chemical equation by drawing the molecules and their component atoms. Use circles of different sizes, colors, or shading for atoms of each element. Let ●●●● represent a hydrogen peroxide molecule, H_2O_2.

a. $H_2(g) + Cl_2(g) \longrightarrow 2\ HCl(g)$
b. $2\ H_2O_2(aq) \longrightarrow 2\ H_2O(l) + O_2(g)$

c. Using complete sentences, write word equations for the chemical equations given in Questions 17a and 17b. Include the numbers of molecules involved.

18. Write chemical equations that represent the following word equations:

a. Baking soda ($NaHCO_3$) reacts with hydrochloric acid (HCl) to produce sodium chloride, water, and carbon dioxide.
b. During respiration, one molecule of glucose, $C_6H_{12}O_6$, combines with six molecules of oxygen gas to produce six molecules of carbon dioxide and six molecules of water.

> An atom is composed of smaller particles (protons, neutrons, and electrons), each possessing a characteristic mass and electrical charge. An electrically neutral atom has equal numbers of protons and electrons.

19. For each of the following elements, identify the number of protons or electrons needed for an electrically neutral atom.

a. carbon: 6 protons   __ electrons
b. aluminum: __ protons   13 electrons
c. lead: 82 protons   __ electrons
d. chlorine: __ protons   17 electrons

20. Decide whether each of the following atoms is electrically neutral.

a. sulfur: 16 protons   18 electrons
b. iron: 26 protons   24 electrons
c. silver: 47 protons   47 electrons
d. iodine: 53 protons   54 electrons

> Ionic compounds are composed of positively and negatively charged ions (atoms that have lost or gained electrons), combined to give the compound no net electrical charge.

21. Classify each of the following as an electrically neutral atom, an anion, or a cation.

a. O^{2-} c. Cl   e. Hg^{2+}
b. Li   d. Ag^+

22. For each particle in Question 21, indicate whether the electrical charge or lack of electrical charge was from a neutral atom gaining electrons, losing electrons, or neither.

23. Write the symbol and show the electrical charge (if any) on the following atoms or ions:

a. hydrogen with 1 proton and 1 electron
b. sodium with 11 protons and 10 electrons
c. chlorine with 17 protons and 18 electrons
d. aluminum with 13 protons and 10 electrons

24. Write the name and formula for the ionic compound that can be formed from these cations and anions:

a. K^+ and I^- d. Ba^{2+} and OH^-
b. Ca^{2+} and S^{2-} e. NH_4^+ and PO_4^{3-}
c. Fe^{3+} and Br^- f. Al^{3+} and O^{2-}

Section Summary   51

c. i. One molecule of hydrogen gas and one molecule of chlorine gas react to form two molecules of gaseous hydrogen chloride.

ii. Two molecules of aqueous hydrogen peroxide (or dihydrogen dioxide) react to form two molecules of liquid water and one molecule of oxygen gas.

18. a. $NaHCO_3 + HCl \rightarrow NaCl + H_2O + CO_2$
b. $C_6H_{12}O_6 + 6\ O_2 \rightarrow 6\ CO_2 + 6\ H_2O$

19. a. 6
b. 13
c. 82
d. 17

20. a. Not electrically neutral (-2 charge)
b. Not electrically neutral ($+2$ charge)
c. Electrically neutral
d. Not electrically neutral (-1 charge)

21. Electrically neutral atom: b, c, Anion: a   Cation: d, e

22. Gaining: a   Neither: b, c Losing: d, e

23. a. H
b. Na^+
c. Cl^-
d. Al^{3+}

24. a. KI
b. CaS
c. $FeBr_3$
d. $Ba(OH)_2$
e. $(NH_4)_3PO_4$
f. Al_2O_3

atoms of the same type (A) and one that is different (D).

14. a. (i)   (ii)   (iv)   (vi)

b. (iii)   (v)

15. The identity and number of each type of element in a substance

16. a. 3 hydrogen atoms, 1 phosphorus atom, and 4 oxygen atoms
b. 1 sodium atom, 1 oxygen atom, and 1 hydrogen atom
c. 1 sulfur atom and 2 oxygen atoms

17. a.

H_2 + Cl_2 ⟶   2 HCl

b.

$2\ H_2O_2$ ⟶ $2\ H_2O$ + O_2

25. Qualitative tests identify the presence or absence of a particular substance in a sample, while quantitative tests determine the amount of a specific substance in a sample.

26. A test in which a positive result confirms that the ion in question is present.

27. a. The reference solution is known to contain the sought ion and thus is an example of a positive test.

b. The distilled-water blank is known not to contain any ions of interest and thus is an example of a negative test.

28. No. The test used is a confirming test and will give a positive result if enough iron is present. It is impossible to know from a negative result whether the iron is absent or simply undetectable.

Connecting the Concepts

29. a. (i) Examine the mixture to determine whether it is clear throughout, (ii) look for particles that settle to the bottom of the container, and (iii) pass a light beam through the mixture to see whether the light is visible within the mixture.

b. i. Suspensions and colloids tend to appear cloudy.

ii. Particles that settle at the bottom of the container indicate a suspension.

iii. Suspensions and colloids show the Tyndall effect; the light beam is visible within the mixture.

30. The bottle probably contains a suspension, so some ingredients settle to the bottom. The bottle must be shaken (re-suspending the ingredients) to ensure that the patient receives a complete mixture of ingredients.

52

Substances dissolved in water can be identified by specific chemical tests.

25. Describe differences between qualitative and quantitative tests.

26. What is a confirming test?

27. In the water-testing investigation (pages 42–45), what was the purpose of

a. the reference solution?
b. the distilled-water blank?

Connecting the Concepts

29. Given an unknown mixture,

a. what steps would you follow to classify it as a solution, a suspension, or a colloid?

b. describe how each step would help you to distinguish among the three types of mixtures.

30. Explain the possible risks in failing to follow the direction "shake before using" on the label of a medicine bottle.

Extending the Concepts

34. Compare the physical properties of water (H_2O) with the physical properties of the elements from which it is composed.

35. Some elements in Table 1.2 (page 34) have symbols that are not based on their modern names (such as K for potassium). Look up their historical names and explain the origin of their symbols.

36. The symbols of elements are accepted and used by chemists in all nations, regardless of the country's official language. However, the name of an element often depends on language. For example, the element N is *nitrogen* in English, but *azote* in French. The element H is *hydrogen* in English, but *Wasserstoff* in German. Investigate the names of some common elements in a foreign language of your choice. What are the meanings or origins of the foreign element names that you find? How do those meanings or origins compare with those for the corresponding English element names?

28. Using the procedure outlined in the water-testing investigation, a student tests a sample of groundwater for iron and observes no color change. Should the student conclude that no iron is present? Explain your answer.

31. Why is it useful for element symbols to have international acceptance?

32. Draw a model of a solution in which water is the solvent and oxygen gas (O_2) is the solute.

33. Is it possible for water to be 100% "chemical free?" Explain.

37. Investigate and report on why 100% pure water would be unsuitable for long-term human consumption—even if taste were not a consideration.

38. Using an encyclopedia or an Internet search, compare the maximum and minimum temperatures naturally found on the surfaces of Earth, the Moon, and Venus. The large amount of water on Earth is one of the factors limiting the natural temperature range on the planet. Suggest ways that water accomplishes this. As a start, find out what *heat of fusion, specific heat capacity,* and *heat of vaporization* mean.

39. Look up the normal freezing point, boiling point, heat of fusion, and heat of vaporization of ammonia (NH_3). If a planet's life forms were made up mostly of ammonia rather than water, what special survival problems might those life forms face? What temperature range would an ammonia-based planet need to support those life forms?

31. Chemicals for research, analysis, medications, and manufacturing are transported throughout the world, and scientists throughout the world communicate their discoveries to other scientists.

32.

33. No, all water has some gases dissolved in it. Water is itself a chemical compound, and all matter can be regarded as composed of chemical substances.

Extending the Concepts

34. At room temperature, water is a clear liquid; hydrogen and oxygen are colorless gases. Water boils at 100 °C and freezes at 0 °C; hydrogen boils at −252 °C and freezes at −259 °C; oxygen boils at −183 °C and freezes at −218 °C. The density of water is 1g/mL; of hydrogen, 0.00008 g/mL, and of oxygen, 0.0013 g/mL. Both hydrogen and oxygen are flammable; water is not.

35. Symbols for some elements are derived from the Latin name for the element.

ELEMENT	SYMBOL	LATIN ORIGIN OF SYMBOL
Gold	Au	*aurum;* "shining dawn"
Iron	Fe	*ferrum;* "iron" or "firmness"
Lead	Pb	*plumbum;* "lead"
Mercury	Hg	*hydrargentum;* "liquid silver"
Potassium	K	*kalium;* "alkali"
Silver	Ag	*argentum;* "silver" or "money"
Sodium	Na	*natrium;* "soda"
Tin	Sn	*stannum; meant silver/lead alloy before tin was recognized as an element*

36. Student answers will vary. Webelements (www.webelements.com) is a useful resource. Looking up the names of elements in foreign languages can be a good way to introduce interdisciplinary lessons. Some examples: Sodium (Na) in English originated in Latin as *natrium;* copper (Cu) in Latin is *cyprium* and in Late Latin is *cuprum;* chlorine (Cl) in Spanish is *cloro,* in Greek is *chlòros,* in French is *chlore,* and in German is *Chlor.*

37. Student answers will vary, but they should indicate (with supporting details) that some substances or ions commonly dissolved in water participate in chemical reactions in the human body. For example, fluoride prevents tooth decay and iodide prevents goiter. This is also a good topic to lead to a discussion of the quality of information available on the Internet and the value of becoming an informed consumer of information.

38. *Minimum and maximum temperatures:* Earth, −14 and 58 °C; moon, −233 and 123 °C; Venus, −45 and 500 °C. *Heat of fusion* is the thermal energy needed to melt (or that must be withdrawn to freeze) a certain quantity of a substance. *Specific heat capacity* is the quantity of thermal energy needed to raise the temperature of 1 g of a material by 1 °C. *Heat of vaporization* is the thermal energy needed to convert a certain quantity of substance from liquid to gas at its normal boiling point. Water, which covers over 70% of Earth, absorbs much of the sun's radiation because of its high specific heat capacity. It takes significant quantities of thermal energy to raise water's temperature appreciably, thus limiting the natural temperature range of the planet. Its high heat of vaporization means water does not vaporize readily (it generally remains in liquid state at 25 °C) and is able to absorb incoming solar radiation, again limiting the natural temperature range on the planet's surface.

39. Normal freezing point = −78 °C
Normal boiling point = −33.5 °C
Heat of fusion = 331.37 J/g
Heat of vaporization = 1371.2 J/g
Specific heat capacity = 4.70 J/g·°C
The required temperature range would have to be substantially lower than the range on Earth. Using Earth's temperature range as a guide, the range could be somewhere between −85 °C and −50 °C.

Investigating the Cause of the Fish Kill

The challenge facing investigators of the Riverwood fish kill is to decide what was present in the Snake River water that caused this crisis. In this section, you will learn about water as a solvent, how water solutions behave and are described, and the types of substances that dissolve in water. This background will ensure that you have the knowledge and skills needed to evaluate Snake River water data and, finally, to determine the cause of the fish kill.

C.1 SOLUBILITY OF SOLIDS IN WATER

What Is Solubility?

Could something that dissolved in the Snake River have caused the fish kill? As you already know, a variety of substances can dissolve in natural waters. To decide whether any of these possible substances could harm fish, it will be helpful to know how water solutions form and are described. For example, how much of a certain solid substance will dissolve in a given amount of water?

Imagine preparing a water solution of potassium nitrate, KNO_3. As you stir the water, the solid white crystals dissolve. The resulting solution remains colorless and clear. In this solution, water is the solvent, and potassium nitrate is the solute.

What will happen if you add a second scoopful of potassium nitrate crystals and stir? These crystals also may dissolve. However, if you continue adding potassium nitrate without adding more water, eventually some potassium nitrate crystals will remain undissolved—as a solid—on the bottom of the container, no matter how long you vigorously stir. At this point, the solution is said to be **saturated.** The maximum quantity of a substance that will dissolve in a certain quantity of water (for example, 100 g) at a specified temperature is called its **solubility** in water. In this example, the solubility of potassium nitrate might be expressed as "grams potassium nitrate per 100 g water" at a specified temperature.

From everyday experience, you probably know that both the size of the solute crystals and the vigor and duration of stirring affect how long it takes for a sample of solute to dissolve at a given temperature. But, with enough time and stirring, will even more potassium nitrate dissolve in water? It turns out that the solubility of a substance in water is a characteristic of the substance and cannot be changed by any extent of stirring over time.

In a solution, the solvent is the dissolving agent, and the solute is the dissolved substance.

SECTION C

Section C: Investigating the Cause of the Fish Kill

Remind students that they are investigating the possible cause or causes of the Riverwood fish kill. The evidence points to something dissolved in the water. Water is a unique substance that can dissolve many solutes. To better investigate, we need to understand the solubility of substances in water. This section discusses the behavior of ionic compounds, heavy metals, acids and bases, molecular substances, and gases (particularly oxygen) in water.

C.1 Solubility of Solids in Water

 C.1 Supplement: Solubility and Solubility Curves

 Understanding and Interpreting Graphs and Tables

C.1 presents vocabulary and concepts related to solubility: solute, solvent, solution, saturation, and solubility curve. The effect of temperature on the solubility of solids is explained. A solubility curve is introduced and used to help clarify the terms *saturated*, *unsaturated*, and *supersaturated*. It may be helpful to work through the text's examples based on the solubility curve as a class. Point out to students that saturated solutions usually include some undissolved solute. Ask students if they know how to prepare a supersaturated sugar solution (add the sugar to hot water and then cool the solution) or prepare a supersaturated sugar solution as a demonstration.

SECTION C

Demonstration Ideas

You can demonstrate the concept of *supersaturation* by adding 160 g sodium acetate trihydrate, $NaC_2H_3O_2 \cdot 3H_2O$, to a clean, dry Erlenmeyer flask. As you add sodium acetate to the flask, ensure that no crystals cling to the flask's inner walls. Add 30 mL distilled water and heat the mixture until all solid dissolves. Allow the solution to cool to room temperature. The cooling process can take some time. Add a single crystal of sodium acetate to the cooled solution and observe the crystallization. You can reuse the solution by reheating to dissolve the solid. Be sure to keep the container clean and undisturbed to prevent premature recrystallization (move the solution as little as possible before adding the seed crystal). Beakers can also be used, but the smaller opening in the Erlenmeyer flask helps minimize exposure to airborne particles that might trigger premature recrystallization. See **http://www.stevespanglerscience. com/experiment/00000078** for a description and video.

Reusable hand-warming packets contain the same substance and work quite well for demonstrations. They can be reused by placing them in boiling water to redissolve crystallized sodium acetate. These hand-warmer packets are available from outdoor equipment or sporting goods stores such as **http://www.rei.com**.

Additional Background Information

The solubility of a solute in a solvent (water in the present discussion) depends on the relative strengths of solute–solute and solute–solvent attractions. When a

Figure 1.33 *Relationship between solute solubility in water and temperature.*

Temperature and Solubility

So what *does* affect the actual quantity of solute that dissolves in a given amount of solvent? As you can see from Figure 1.33, the mass of solid solute that will dissolve in 100 g water varies as the water temperature changes from 0 °C to 100 °C. The graphical representation of this relationship is called the solute's **solubility curve.**

Each point on the solubility curve indicates a solution in which the solvent contains as much dissolved solute as it normally can at that temperature. Such a solution is called a *saturated solution*. Thus, each point along the solubility curve indicates the conditions of a saturated solution. Look at the curve for potassium nitrate (KNO_3) in Figure 1.33. Locate the intersection of the potassium nitrate curve with the vertical line representing 40 °C. Follow the horizontal line to the left and read the value. According to the solubility curve, the solubility of potassium nitrate in 40 °C water is 60 g KNO_3 per 100 g water.

Sample Problem 1: *At 50 °C, how much potassium nitrate will dissolve in 100 g water to form a saturated solution?*

This value from Figure 1.33—80 g KNO_3 per 100 g water—represents the solubility of potassium nitrate in 50 °C water. By contrast, the solubility of potassium nitrate in cooler 20 °C water is only about 30 g KNO_3 per 100 g water. (Ensure that you can read this 30-g value from the Figure 1.33 graph.)

Note that the solubility graph for sodium chloride (NaCl) is nearly a horizontal line. What does this mean about the solubility of sodium chloride as temperature changes? Compare the curve for sodium chloride with the curve for potassium nitrate (KNO_3), which rises steeply as temperature increases. You should be able to conclude that for some solutes, such as potassium nitrate (KNO_3), solubility in water is greatly affected by temperature, whereas for others, such as sodium chloride (NaCl), the change is only slight.

Sample Problem 2: *Consider a solution containing 80 g potassium nitrate in 100 g water at 60 °C. Locate this point on the graph. Locate where this temperature falls in relation to the solubility curve. What does this information tell you about the level of saturation of the solution?*

Because each point on the solubility curve represents a saturated solution, any point on a graph *below* a solubility curve must represent an unsaturated solution. An **unsaturated solution** is a solution that contains less dissolved solute than the amount that the solvent can normally hold at that temperature.

Sample Problem 3: *What would happen if you cooled this solution to 40 °C?*

Follow the line representing 80 g to the left. You should expect that some solid KNO_3 crystals would form and fall to the bottom of the beaker. In fact, this is likely to occur. Sometimes, however, you can

54 **Unit 1** Water: Exploring Solutions

substance dissolves, solute–solute and solvent–solvent attractions are interrupted and broken (endothermic change). New solute–solvent attractions form (exothermic change).

For some solids, the overall process of dissolving is endothermic because more

energy is needed to overcome solute–solute attractions than is released when solute–solvent attractions are formed. In this case, adding thermal energy by raising the solvent temperature will help interrupt solute–solute attractions and thus permit more solid to dissolve. For other solids, the

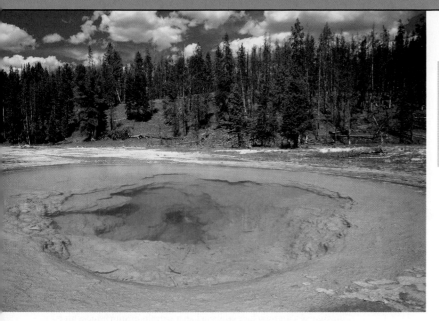

Figure 1.34 *As the water in Emerald Pool (Yellowstone National Park) cools and evaporates at the edges, it becomes supersaturated and precipitates begin to form.*

cool a saturated solution without causing any solid crystals to form, producing an unstable solution that contains more solute than could usually be dissolved at that temperature. This type of solution is called a **supersaturated solution.** (Note that this new point lies *above* the solubility curve for potassium nitrate.) Merely agitating a supersaturated solution or adding a "seed" crystal to the solution often causes the *extra* solute to appear as solid crystals and settle to the bottom of the beaker, or precipitate. The remaining liquid then contains the amount of solute that represents a stable, saturated solution at that temperature.

One example of crystallization from a supersaturated solution may be familiar to you—making rock candy. Here is how it is done: A water solution is first supersaturated with sugar. When seed crystals are added to the supersaturated solution, they cause excess dissolved sugar to crystallize from the solution onto a string hanging into the liquid.

Mineral deposits around a hot spring are another example of crystallization from a supersaturated solution. See Figure 1.34. Water emerging from a hot spring is saturated with dissolved minerals. As the solution cools, it becomes supersaturated. The rocks over which the solution flows act as seed crystals, causing the formation of more mineral deposits.

> Developing Skills

C.2 SOLUBILITY AND SOLUBILITY CURVES

Sample Problem 1: *What is the solubility of potassium nitrate at 70 °C?*
The answer is found from the solubility curve for potassium nitrate given in Figure 1.33. The solubility of potassium nitrate in 70 °C water is about 134 g KNO_3 per 100 g water.

Demonstration Ideas

To demonstrate the energy changes that accompany dissolving, dissolve some NH_4NO_3 in water to illustrate an endothermic process. Dissolve some $CaCl_2$ in water to demonstrate an exothermic process. Use a thermometer to identify the initial and final temperatures in both processes.

Using the Figures

Figure 1.34: Although most yellow observed in Emerald Pool is due to colonies of bacteria, have students consider why minerals would precipitate around the perimeter of this pool. Inform students (or they may be able to guess, based on prior knowledge and experiences) that sulfur and many sulfur-containing substances are typically yellow. This is an opportunity to review the concept of physical versus chemical properties.

> Developing Skills

C.2 Solubility and Solubility Curves

This activity provides students opportunities to practice interpreting solubility curves such as those in **Figure 1.33.** Students can use Figure 1.33 or proportional reasoning to answer the questions. This activity could be completed in small groups and used to enhance a class discussion.

overall reaction is exothermic—more energy is released when solvent–solute bonds are formed than is required to break solute–solute bonds. Adding thermal energy does not tend to increase the solubility of such substances significantly. All substances represented in **Figure 1.33** have endothermic dissolving processes, but the dissolution of KNO_3 is much more endothermic than are either KCl or NaCl. Pressure has no appreciable effect on the solubility of solids; grinding and stirring change the rate of dissolving but do not affect how much solid will ultimately dissolve.

Answers

1. a. 105 g (from graph)
   b. 45 g (from graph)

2. a. 45 g at saturation − 25 g in already = about 20 g more to add

   b. $\dfrac{25 \text{ g KNO}_3}{x \text{ g water}} = \dfrac{45 \text{ g KNO}_3}{100 \text{ g water}}$

   $x = \dfrac{25 \text{ g KNO}_3}{45 \text{ g KNO}_3} \times 100 \text{ g water} =$

   56 g water

3. a. 150 g KNO$_3$ − 95 g KNO$_3$ (saturated mass at 55 °C) = 55 g precipitated KNO$_3$

   b. $\dfrac{150 \text{ g KNO}_3}{x \text{ g water}} = \dfrac{95 \text{ g KNO}_3}{100 \text{ g water}}$

   $x = \dfrac{150 \text{ g KNO}_3}{95 \text{ g KNO}_3} \times 100 \text{ g water} =$

   160 g water

   60 g of water must be added to the original 100 g.

> Investigating Matter

C.3 Constructing a Solubility Curve

C.3 Constructing a Solubility Curve Student Worksheet and Data Table

Divide students into pairs or groups, with each group collecting solubility data at a different temperature (45 °C, 55 °C, or 65 °C). At each temperature, tell students to place a known mass of water and succinic acid into a test tube, then stir and heat the mixture. After the appropriate temperature is reached, the solution and undissolved solute should be separated by decanting, after which the solution is cooled to precipitate the remaining solute. Students can then estimate the relative quantity of solute dissolved during heating by measuring the height of precipitate.

Sample Problem 2: *At what temperature will the solubility of potassium nitrate be 25 g per 100 g water?*

Think of the space between 20 g and 30 g on the y-axis in Figure 1.33 as divided into two equal parts, then follow an imaginary horizontal line at "25 g/100 g" to its intersection with the curve. Follow a vertical line down to the x-axis. Because the line falls halfway between 10 °C and 20 °C, the desired temperature must be about 15 °C.

As you have seen, the solubility curve is quite useful when you are working with 100 g water. For example, the solubility curve indicates that 60 g potassium nitrate will dissolve in 100 g water at 40 °C. But what happens when you work with other quantities of water?

Sample Problem 3: *How much potassium nitrate will dissolve in 150 g water at 40 °C?*

You can reason the answer in the following way. The quantity of solvent (water) has increased from 100 g to 150 g—1.5 times as much solvent. That means that 1.5 times as much solute can be dissolved. Thus: 1.5 × 60 g KNO$_3$ = 90 g KNO$_3$.

The answer can also be expressed as a simple proportion, which produces the same answer once the proportion is solved for *x*:

$$\frac{60 \text{ g KNO}_3}{100 \text{ g H}_2\text{O}} = \frac{x \text{ g KNO}_3}{150 \text{ g H}_2\text{O}}$$

$$150 \text{ g H}_2\text{O} \times 60 \text{ g KNO}_3 = 100 \text{ g H}_2\text{O} \times x \text{ g KNO}_3$$

$$x \text{ g KNO}_3 = 150 \text{ g H}_2\text{O} \times \frac{60 \text{ g KNO}_3}{100 \text{ g H}_2\text{O}} = 90 \text{ g KNO}_3$$

Refer to Figure 1.33 when answering the following questions.

1. a. What mass (in grams) of potassium nitrate (KNO$_3$) will dissolve in 100 g water at 60 °C?
   b. What mass (in grams) of potassium chloride (KCl) will dissolve in 100 g water at the same (60 °C) temperature?

2. a. You dissolve 25 g potassium nitrate in 100 g water at 30 °C, producing an unsaturated solution. How much more potassium nitrate (in grams) must be added to form a saturated solution at 30 °C?
   b. What is the minimum mass (in grams) of 30 °C water needed to dissolve 25 g potassium nitrate?

3. a. A supersaturated solution of potassium nitrate is formed by adding 150 g KNO$_3$ to 100 g water, heating until the solute completely dissolves, and then cooling the solution to 55 °C. If the solution is agitated, how much potassium nitrate will precipitate?
   b. How much 55 °C water would have to be added (to the original 100 g water) to just dissolve all of the KNO$_3$?

To construct a solubility curve, each data point should represent an average of at least three trials.

Time

50 min

Materials

(For a class of 24 working in pairs)

72 Pyrex® or Kimax® test tubes, 20 × 150 mm

24 glass stirring rods

C.3 CONSTRUCTING A SOLUBILITY CURVE

Introduction

In this investigation, you will collect experimental data to construct a solubility curve for succinic acid ($C_4H_6O_4$), which is a molecular compound. Before you proceed, think about how your knowledge of solubility can help you gather data to construct a solubility curve.

▶ How can you use the properties of a saturated solution?

▶ What solvent temperatures can you investigate?

▶ How many times should you repeat the procedure to be sure of your data?

Discuss these questions with your partner or laboratory group. Your teacher will then discuss with the class how you will gather data and will demonstrate safe use of the equipment and materials involved.

Before starting, read the following safety and procedure sections to learn what you will need to do, note safety precautions, and plan necessary data collecting and observations. For guidance, refer to the sample data table.

DATA TABLE	
Trial	Crystal Height (mm)
1	
2	
...	
Average	

Safety

Keep the following precautions in mind while completing this laboratory investigation.

▶ Succinic acid is slightly toxic if ingested by mouth. Wash your hands thoroughly at the end of the investigation.

▶ Avoid spilling any succinic acid crystals or solution on the hot plate; its products are acrid smoke and irritating fumes.

▶ Never stir a liquid with a thermometer. Use a stirring rod.

▶ Use insulated tongs or gloves to remove a hot beaker from a hot plate. Hot glass burns bare fingers!

▶ Dispose of all wastes as directed by your teacher.

Procedure

1. To prepare a warm-water bath, add approximately 300 mL water to a 400-mL beaker. Heat the beaker, with stirring, either to 45 °C, 55 °C, or 65 °C, as agreed upon in your prelab class discussion. Ensure that each student team sharing your hot plate is investigating the same temperature. Using gloves or beaker tongs, carefully remove the beaker when it reaches the desired temperature. (*Note:* Do not allow the water-bath temperature to rise more than 5 °C above the temperature you have chosen.) Return the beaker to the hot plate as needed to maintain the appropriate water-bath temperature.

Lab Video:
Constructing a Solubility Curve

12 test-tube holders	6 hot plates
12 alcohol thermometers, −10 °C to 110 °C	120 g succinic acid
12 graduated cylinders	12 metric rulers
12 test-tube racks	Ice
12 400-mL beakers	Balances

SECTION C

Safety

• Succinic acid is slightly toxic (LD_{50} = 2.3 g/kg) if ingested by mouth: Students should wash hands thoroughly at the close of the investigation.

• Students should avoid spilling succinic acid crystals or solution on the hot plate; at such high temperatures, acrid smoke and irritating fumes will form.

• Remind students to gently "tap off" the stirring rod and thermometer onto the test tube's inner wall before removing them from the test tube, so that they do not drip succinic acid solution on the hot plate.

• Students should never stir a liquid with a thermometer. They should use a stirring rod. Tell students to carefully stir the succinic acid solution. Aggressive stirring can cause the bottom of the test tube to break.

• Students should use insulated tongs or gloves to remove a hot beaker from a hot plate. Hot glass burns skin even when the glass does not appear hot. Remind students that hot and cold glass are indistinguishable; care should be taken in handling all glassware.

• Instruct students on the disposal (or, more likely, collection) of wastes. The succinic acid should be reclaimed for future use, but you may also wash it down the drain with copious volumes of water.

• Students should wear protective goggles and aprons throughout the laboratory activity.

• If mercury thermometers are used, tell students in the event of breakage not to touch the thermometer or mercury beads. Instead, they should promptly notify you; use a special mercury-disposal kit to clean up the mercury.

SECTION C

Pre-Lab Discussion

Remind students about the environmental context of this investigation: The solubility of materials in water (as in agricultural runoff or industrial waste) depends on water temperature, and dissolved materials will have different environmental effects than undissolved materials. Review the terms *unsaturated*, *saturated*, and *supersaturated* within the context of this investigation.

Lab Tips

• If you have not already done so, this would be a good time to instruct students in the use and care of balances.

• Before the investigation, demonstrate how to decant a solution from a test tube. Supervise student use of hot plates carefully.

• Assign each pair or group a particular temperature for which to collect data. Each pair/group should report the average of its two trials at one specified temperature—45 °C, 55 °C, or 65 °C—to the class.

• Using temperatures lower than 45 °C may result in insufficient crystal formation. Using temperatures higher than 65 °C poses a potential safety hazard.

• When students are finished, provide a labeled beaker for reclaiming the succinic acid. You may decant the excess solution or leave it to evaporate. Remaining crystals may be reused.

Figure 1.35 *Stirring a test tube in a water bath.*

Figure 1.36 *Decanting a solution from a test tube.*

A millimeter is 1/10 of a centimeter.

| **Figure 1.37** *Measuring crystal height.*

2. Place between 4 g and 5 g succinic acid in each of two test tubes. (*Caution: Be careful not to spill any succinic acid crystals or solution. If you do, clean up and dispose of the succinic acid as directed by your teacher.*) Add 20 mL distilled water to each test tube.

3. Place each test tube in the warm-water bath and take turns stirring the succinic acid solution with a glass stirring rod every 30 s for 7 min (Figure 1.35). Each minute, place the thermometer in the test tube and monitor the temperature of the succinic acid solution, ensuring that it is within 2 °C of the temperature that you have chosen.

4. At the end of seven minutes, carefully decant the clear liquid from each test tube into a separate, empty test tube, as demonstrated by your teacher and as shown in Figure 1.36.

5. Carefully pour the hot water from the beaker into the sink.

6. Prepare an ice bath by filling a new 400-mL beaker with water and ice.

7. Place the two test tubes containing the clear liquid in the ice bath for two minutes. Stir the liquid in each test tube gently once or twice. Remove the test tubes from the ice water. Allow the test tubes to sit at room temperature for 5 min. Observe each test tube carefully during that time. Record your observations.

8. Tap the side of each test tube and swirl the liquid once or twice to cause the crystals to settle evenly on the bottom of the test tube.

9. Measure the height of crystals collected in millimeters (mm). See Figure 1.37. Have your partner or laboratory group measure the same crystal sample height and compare your results. Report the average crystal height for your two test tubes to your teacher.

Answers

1. It is useful to collect data from more than one trial, since individual trials are subject to error. Repeated trials allow for averaging such random error, thus decreasing its effect.

2. The heated solution of succinic acid is a saturated solution for that temperature. The cooled succinic acid solution is also a saturated solution for its temperature. The amount of solid succinic acid that precipitates represents the difference in solubility between the two temperatures.

10. Rinse the succinic acid crystals from the test tubes into a collection beaker designated by your teacher. Make sure that your laboratory area is clean.

11. Wash your hands thoroughly before leaving the laboratory.

Data Analysis

1. Find the mean crystal height obtained by your entire class for each temperature reported.

2. Plot the mean crystal height in millimeters (*y*-axis) versus the water temperature in degrees Celsius (*x*-axis).

Turn to page 13 to review how to calculate a mean.

Questions

1. Why is it useful to collect data from more than one trial at a particular temperature?

2. How did you make use of the properties of a saturated solution at different temperatures?

3. Did all the succinic acid that originally dissolved in the water crystallize out of the solution? Provide evidence to support your answer.

4. Given pooled class data, did you have enough data points to make a reliable solubility curve for succinic acid? Would the curve be good enough to make useful predictions about succinic acid solubility at temperatures you have not yet investigated? Explain your answers.

5. What procedures in this investigation could lead to errors? How would each error affect your data?

6. Using your knowledge of solubility, propose a different procedure for gathering data to construct a solubility curve.

C.4 DISSOLVING IONIC COMPOUNDS

You have just investigated a compound dissolving in water. What you observed is called a *macroscopic* phenomenon. However, chemistry is primarily concerned with what happens at the *particulate* level—atomic and molecular phenomena that cannot be easily observed. You have seen that temperature, agitation, and time all contribute to dissolving a solid material. But how do the atoms and molecules of solute and solvent interact to make this happen?

Experiments indicate that although the entire water molecule is electrically neutral, the electrons are not evenly distributed throughout its structure. A **polar molecule** has an uneven distribution of electrical charge, which means that each molecule has a partial positive region at one end and a partial negative region at the other end.

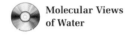 **Molecular Views of Water**

---

5. Some procedures include stirring, thermometer use, decanting, and temperature control. Students will obtain a faulty *low* average (less precipitate than they should) if they forget to tap the stirring rod or thermometer after use, spill some solution during decanting, or fail to cool the solution adequately. Students will obtain a faulty *high* average (more precipitate than they should) if they heat the solution to a temperature higher than their assigned value. Students may propose additional, acceptable reasons for error.

6. Accept reasonable answers that adequately describe solution preparation and recovery of the dissolved solute.

C.4 Dissolving Ionic Compounds

Emphasize that dissolving can be thought about as requiring two separate steps—(1) overcoming solute–solute (and solvent–solvent) attractive forces and (2) forming new solute–solvent attractive forces.

Discuss how the polarity of water makes it an effective solvent for many ionic compounds. The idea of partial charges may be new to students. Point out that the δ symbol does not indicate the magnitude of the partial charge. In water, the partial negative electrical charge on the oxygen must balance the two partial positive electrical charges on the hydrogens.

Use the *Scientific American* illustration, Figure 1.39 on page 61, to explain the dissolving process.

---

3. Some succinic acid is still dissolved in the water at room temperature. The quantity of succinic acid that crystallized is visibly less than the original quantity of succinic acid used. This suggests that some succinic acid remains dissolved in the room-temperature water.

4. A reliable solubility curve can be constructed, and it is appropriate to interpolate using the data collected. Extrapolation may not be possible, since succinic acid solubility for temperatures outside the range investigated is unknown.

Figure 1.38 *Polarity of a water molecule. The* δ⁺ *and* δ⁻ *indicate partial electrical charges.*

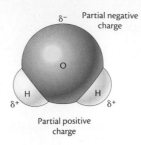

Partial negative charge

δ⁻

O

H   H

δ⁺   δ⁺

Partial positive charge

Evidence also verifies that a water molecule has a bent or V-shape, as illustrated in Figure 1.38, rather than a linear, sticklike shape as in H–O–H. The *oxygen end* is an electrically negative region that has a greater concentration of electrons (shown as δ⁻) compared with the two *hydrogen ends,* which are electrically positive (shown as δ⁺). The Greek symbol δ (delta) means "partial"—thus, partial positive and partial negative electrical charges are indicated. Because these charges are equal and opposite, the molecule as a whole is electrically neutral.

Polar water molecules are attracted to other polar substances and to substances composed of electrically charged particles. These electrical attractions make it possible for water to dissolve a great variety of substances. Many solid substances, especially ionic compounds, are crystalline. In ionic crystals, positively charged cations are surrounded by negatively charged anions, with the anions likewise surrounded by cations. The crystal is held together by attractive forces between the cations and the anions. The substance will dissolve only if its ions are so strongly attracted to water molecules that the water molecules can "tug" the ions away from the crystal.

Modeling Matter: Attraction Between Particles

Water molecules are attracted to ions located on the surface of an ionic solid, as shown by the models in Figure 1.39. The water molecule's negative (oxygen) end is attracted to the crystal's cations. The positive (hydrogen) ends of other water molecules are attracted to the anions of the crystal. When the attractive forces between the water molecules and the surface ions are strong enough, the bonds between the crystal and its surface ions become strained, and the ions may be pulled away from the crystal. Figure 1.39 uses models of water molecules and solute ions to illustrate the results of water tugging on solute ions. The detached ions become surrounded by water molecules, producing an ionic solution.

Using the description and illustrations of this process, can you decide which factors influence whether an ionic solid will dissolve in water? Because dissolving entails competition among three types of attractions—those between solvent and solute particles, between solvent particles themselves, and between particles within the solute crystals—properties of both solute and solvent determine whether two substances will form a solution. Water is highly polar; therefore, it is effective at dissolving charged or ionic substances. However, if positive–negative attractions between cations and anions within the crystal are sufficiently strong, a particular ionic compound may be only slightly soluble in water.

The water solubility of some ionic compounds is extremely low, indeed. For example, at room temperature, solid lead(II) sulfide (PbS) has a solubility of only about 10^{-14} g (0.000 000 000 000 01 g) per liter of water solution or 0.000 01 parts per billion (ppb).

Scientific American Conceptual Illustration

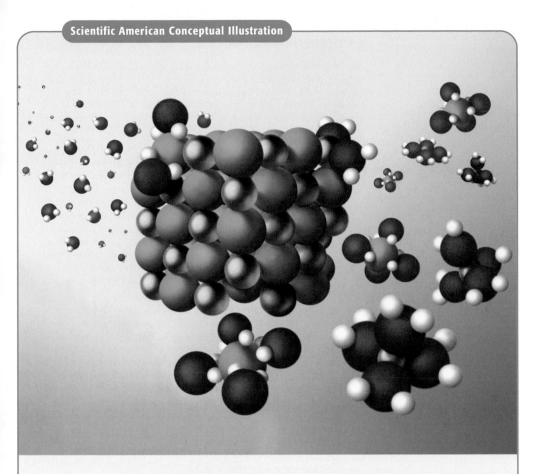

Figure 1.39 *Particulate-level model of sodium chloride (NaCl) dissolving in water (H₂O).* Sodium chloride crystals (common table salt) consist of positively-charged sodium ions (Na⁺, gray spheres) and negatively-charged chloride ions (Cl⁻, green spheres). Every water molecule is polar; the oxygen (red) side has partial negative electrical charge and the hydrogen (white) side has partial positive electrical charge. Thus, as water molecules approach the sodium chloride crystal, hydrogen attracts chloride ions and oxygen attracts sodium ions. Several water molecules surround each ion and carry it away from the crystal.

As you study this two-dimensional representation, try to visualize it in three dimensions and put the dissolving process "in motion." Think about these ions and molecules interacting at different times, such as immediately after the crystal drops into the water, after the crystal seems to disappear completely, or if the water has fully evaporated.

Section C   Investigating the Cause of the Fish Kill   **61**

What do the dissolved ions have in common with each other? They are all solvated—surrounded—by water molecules.

How are the dissolved ions different? Direct attention to the orientation of the water molecules. The H ends of the molecules are oriented toward negative chloride ions, while the O ends of the molecules are oriented toward positive sodium ions.

On the particulate level, what would evaporating water imply for this system? With fewer water molecules to overcome ion–ion attractive forces, the crystal lattice would begin to reform, or recrystallize.

This illustration is a useful way to help visualize the dissolving process at the particulate level. When you discuss the concept of dissolving (dissociation), ask students to point out ways that this visual model falls short of thoroughly representing the process. Also, point out that not all of the water molecules are shown. Atoms are not hard spheres. Individual atoms are not colored. This static particulate model does not depict molecules/ions in motion. It does not take into account constant motion that actually occurs during the dissolving process. The *Chem-Com* CD and website offer animated views of this process, addressing this limitation.

Scientific American **Conceptual Illustration**

Use this illustration to highlight the forces involved in the process of dissolving an ionic substance in water. Guide student discussion using prompts such as these:

What forces hold the ionic lattice together? Opposing ionic charges

Why do the water molecules interact with ions? Water's molecular polarity allows it to interact with both positive and negative ions.

Modeling Matter

C.5 The Dissolving Process

 C.5 The Dissolving Process Student Worksheet

You may wish to demonstrate dissolving 40 g KCl in 100 g water at 70 °C to prompt students' thinking about this activity. Before doing so, ask students to decide whether this mass of KCl will dissolve in 100 g water at 70 °C. This information cannot be determined directly from the graph provided, so students will need to infer the result based on trends in the data.

Answers

1. a. At 50 °C, 40 g KCl will completely dissolve in 100 g water. As the solution cools, the solute will remain in solution at least down to 40 °C. Below that, some solute is likely to begin crystallizing out of solution. At 25 °C, only 35 g KCl will remain dissolved, so about 5 g of solute would be expected to precipitate.

b. The drawings (see below) should represent the solution—unsaturated at 50 °C and saturated at 40 °C. At any temperature below 40 °C, some precipitate would be expected, so some KCl crystals should be shown at the bottom of the container.

25 °C

2. a. The drawings should show the solution as unsaturated, similar to

---

Modeling Matter

C.5 THE DISSOLVING PROCESS

Figure 1.40 *Solubility curve for potassium chloride.*

Dissolving Ionic Compounds

Modeling Matter: Ionic Solutions

You have now learned about solubility, solubility curves, and the process of dissolving ionic compounds in water. As part of these discussions, visual models, such as those presented in Figure 1.39 (page 61), have helped to describe the process of dissolving. In this activity, you will combine these models with your knowledge of solubility curves to create new models of ions dissolved in water.

1. Suppose you dissolved 40 g potassium chloride (KCl) in 100 g water at 50 °C. You then let the solution cool to room temperature, about 25 °C.

   a. What changes would you see in the beaker as the solution cooled? See Figure 1.40.

   b. Draw models of what the contents in the beaker would look like at the particulate level at 50 °C, 40 °C, and 25 °C. Keep these points in mind:

You should consider whether the sample at each temperature is *saturated* with excess precipitate present, *unsaturated,* or *supersaturated,* and draw the model accordingly. The solubility curve in Figure 1.40 and the particles depicted in Figure 1.39 will be helpful. It is impossible to draw all the ions and molecules in this sample. The ions and molecules you draw will represent a simpler version of what happens.

2. An unsaturated solution will become more concentrated if you add more solute. Decreasing the total volume of water in the solution (such as by evaporation) also increases the solution's concentration. Consider a solution made by dissolving 20 g KCl in 100 g water at 40 °C.

   a. Draw a model of this solution.

   b. Suppose that while the solution was kept at 40 °C, one-fourth of the water evaporated.

   i. Draw a model of this final solution and describe how it differs from your model of the original solution.

   ii. How much water must evaporate at this temperature to create a saturated solution?

3. A solution may be diluted (made less concentrated) by adding water.

   a. Draw a model of a solution containing 10.0 g KCl in 100 g water at 25 °C.

   b. Suppose you diluted this solution by adding another 100 g water with stirring. Draw a model of this 25 °C new solution.

   c. Compare your models in Questions 3a and 3b. What key feature is different in the two models? Why?

(with about half as many ions as) the first drawing for Question 1b.

---

b. i. The model should show an unsaturated solution. The container size should not change, but the amount of water should be reduced by 1/4. Thus, the concentration of the solution is higher, but the solution is still not saturated.

C.6 SOLUTION CONCENTRATION

The general terms *saturated* and *unsaturated* are not always adequate to describe the properties of solutions that contain different amounts of solute. A more precise description of the quantity of solute in a solution is needed—a quantitative expression of concentration.

Solution **concentration** refers to how much solute is dissolved in a specific quantity of solvent or solution. You have already worked with one type of solution concentration expression: The water-solubility curves in Figure 1.33 (page 54) reported solution concentrations as the mass of a substance dissolved in a particular mass of water.

Another way to express concentration is with **percent** values. For example, dissolving 5 g table salt in 95 g water produces 100 g solution with a 5% salt concentration (by mass). "Percent" means parts solute per hundred total parts (solute plus solvent). So, a 5% salt solution could also be reported as a five parts per hundred salt solution (5 pph salt). However, percent is much more commonly used.

For solutions containing considerably smaller quantities of solute (as are found in many environmental water samples, including those from the Snake River), concentration units of **parts per million** (**ppm**) are sometimes useful. As you might expect, for very low concentrations, **parts per billion** (**ppb**) is often used. For example, the maximum concentration of nitrate allowed in drinking water is much too low to be conveniently written as a percent (it is 0.0010%); instead, it is written as 10 ppm.

Sample Problem: *What is the concentration of a 1% salt solution expressed in ppm?*

Because 1% of 1 million is 10 000, a 1% salt solution is 10 000 ppm (parts per million).

Although you might not realize it, the notion of concentration is part of daily life. For example, preparing beverages from premixed concentrate, adding antifreeze to water in an automobile radiator, and mixing pesticide or fertilizer solutions all require the use of solution concentrations. The following activity will help you review solution concentration, as well as gain experience with the chemist's use of this concept.

> Just as *percent* means "for every hundred," *per million* means "for every million." To express a concentration using parts per million (ppm), divide the mass of solute by the mass of solvent and multiply by 1 000 000.

> Nitrates are anions commonly found in natural waters as a result of fertilizer runoff. The EPA has established a maximum concentration limit of nitrates in drinking water at 10 ppm to prevent undesirable health effects resulting from elevated nitrate levels in the body.

Developing Skills

C.7 DESCRIBING SOLUTION CONCENTRATIONS

Sample Problem 1: *A common intravenous saline solution used in medical practice contains 4.5 g NaCl dissolved in 495.5 g sterilized distilled water. What is the concentration of this solution, expressed as percent by mass?*

Because this solution contains 4.5 g NaCl and 495.5 g water, its total mass is 500.0 g. Expressing a solution's concentration in *percent by mass* involves taking the mass of solute and dividing it by the mass of solution, then multiplying by 100. In the sample problem, that means dividing 4.5 g by 500.0 g and then multiplying by 100 to get 0.90%.

b. Student drawings should show twice as many water molecules as in the answer to Question 3a.

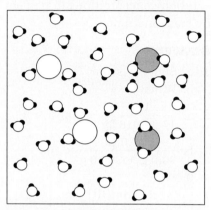

c. The ratio of solute to solvent particles would be different. The second solution is half as concentrated as the first solution.

C.6 Solution Concentration

C.6 Supplement: Solution Concentration

This material introduces quantitative means of describing solution concentration, including percent concentration (parts per hundred, pph), parts per million (ppm), and parts per billion (ppb). Students may have seen the expressions *ppm* or *ppb* in news articles about environmental pollution. Ensure that students remember that the total mass of solution also includes the mass of solute. Discuss the relevance of *solution concentration* to environmental chemists.

---

ii. To cause KCl crystals to form, 50 g of water would need to evaporate at 40 °C:

$$\frac{40 \text{ g KCl}}{100 \text{ g water}} = \frac{20 \text{ g KCl}}{x \text{ g water}}$$

$$x = \frac{20 \text{ g KCl}}{40 \text{ g KCl}} \times 100 \text{ g water} =$$

50 g water

3. a. Drawings should show an unsaturated, homogeneous solution. At 25 °C, 10 g KCl would completely dissolve in 100 g H_2O, since about 35g KCl will dissolve in 100 g of 25 °C water.

You might note that *ppm* and *ppb* are not acceptable SI units, because names for numbers such as *million* and *billion* differ among languages.

Developing Skills

C.7 Describing Solution Concentrations

In this activity, students calculate solution concentrations in percent by mass and ppm.

Answers

1. a. Sucrose (sugar)
  b. Water

2. a. $\dfrac{17 \text{ g}}{17 \text{ g} + 183 \text{ g}} \times 100\% = 8.5\%$

  b. $\dfrac{30.0 \text{ g}}{30.0 \text{ g} + 300.0 \text{ g}} \times 100\% = 9.09\%$

3. a. i. $\dfrac{x \text{ g iron(III) ions}}{1\,000\,000 \text{ g water}} = \dfrac{0.0020 \text{ g iron(III) ions}}{500.0 \text{ g water}}$

  $x = \dfrac{0.0020 \text{ g iron(III) ions}}{500.0 \text{ g water}} \times 1\,000\,000 \text{ g water} = 4.0 \text{ ppm}$

  ii. $\dfrac{x \text{ g calcium ions}}{1\,000\,000 \text{ g water}} = \dfrac{0.25 \text{ g calcium ions}}{850.0 \text{ g water}}$

  $x = \dfrac{0.25 \text{ g calcium ions}}{850.0 \text{ g water}} \times 1\,000\,000 \text{ g water} = 290 \text{ ppm}$

  b. 8.5% = 85 000 ppm and 9.09% = 90 900 ppm

4. a. $\dfrac{45 \text{ g KCl}}{100 \text{ g} + 45 \text{ g}} \times 100\% = 31\%$ KCl by mass

  b. $\dfrac{45 \text{ g KCl}}{100 \text{ g} + 45 \text{ g} + 155 \text{ g}} \times 100\% = 15\%$ KCl by mass

5. Students may answer that they would first need to know the water temperature, and then use the solubility curve to determine the mass of solute needed to prepare a saturated solution, meas-

$$\text{Percent by mass} = \frac{4.5 \text{ g}}{500.0 \text{ g}} \times 100\% = 0.90\%$$

Another way to look at it is to remember that *percent* means "per hundred." How many grams of NaCl do you have for each 100 g solution? Because there are 500 g solution, we are dealing with 5 times as much material as in 100 g of solution. If there are 4.5 g NaCl in 500.0 g solution, there must be 1/5 that much NaCl in 1/5 of the solution—1/5 of 4.5 g NaCl is 0.90 g NaCl. That means there are 0.90 g NaCl per 100 g solution, or that the solution is 0.90% NaCl by mass, which is the same answer we arrived at previously.

Sample Problem 2: *One teaspoon of sucrose, with a mass of 10.0 g, is dissolved in 240.0 g water. What is the concentration of the solution, expressed as grams sucrose per 100 g solution? As percent sucrose by mass?*

This solution contains 10.0 g sucrose and 240.0 g water; therefore, its total mass is 250.0 g. Because 100.0 g solution would contain 2/5 as much solution, it would also contain 2/5 as much solute, or 4.0 g sucrose. Thus, 100.0 g solution contains 4.0 g sucrose, a concentration of 4.0 g sucrose per 100.0 g solution. To express this concentration in the form of a percent by mass,

$$\text{Percent by mass} = \frac{4.0 \text{ g}}{100.0 \text{ g}} \times 100\% = 4.0\%$$

Now answer the following questions.

1. One teaspoon of sucrose is dissolved in a cup of water. Identify
   a. the solute.   b. the solvent.
2. What is the concentration of each of these solutions expressed as percent sucrose by mass?
   a. 17 g sucrose dissolved in 183 g water
   b. 30.0 g sucrose dissolved in 300.0 g water
3. a. What is the concentration of each of these solutions expressed as ppm?
      i. 0.0020 g iron(III) ions dissolved in 500.0 g water
      ii. 0.25 g calcium ions dissolved in 850.0 g water
   b. Expressed in ppm, what is the concentration of each solution in Question 2?
4. A saturated solution of potassium chloride is prepared by dissolving 45 g KCl in 100.0 g water at 60 °C.
   a. What is the concentration of this solution?
   b. What would be the new concentration if 155 g water were added?
5. How would you prepare a *saturated solution* of potassium nitrate (KNO_3) at 25 °C?

Sucrose, $C_{12}H_{22}O_{11}$, is ordinary table sugar.

ure this mass, and dissolve it in the specified quantity of water. A better answer would be to add solute to water until no more solute dissolves; a small quantity of solute remains on the bottom of the container. This method does not depend on accurate measurement of temperature and volume, or the accuracy and precision of the solubility curve, or measure-

ment of the mass of solute (as does the other method). This question helps to extend the conceptual definition of saturated to real-world notions of saturation. That is, you know you have a saturated solution if, after extended stirring, some solid solute still remains.

Now that you know how solutions of ionic compounds are formed and described, it is time to consider some possible causes of the Riverwood fish kill. The following information will suggest some possible "culprits"—substances that can dissolve or be suspended in water and harm living things. These substances include heavy metals, acids, bases, and other substances—even dissolved oxygen gas. Although many of these substances are naturally found in water sources, their concentration levels can positively or negatively affect aquatic life.

C.8 INAPPROPRIATE HEAVY-METAL ION CONCENTRATIONS?

Many metal ions, such as iron(II) (Fe^{2+}), potassium (K^+), calcium (Ca^{2+}), and magnesium (Mg^{2+}), are essential to the health of humans and other organisms. Humans obtain these ions primarily from foods, but the ions may also be present in drinking water.

Not all metal ions that dissolve in water are beneficial, however. Some **heavy-metal ions,** called "heavy metals" because their atoms have greater masses than those of essential metallic elements, are harmful to humans and other organisms. Among heavy-metal ions of greatest concern in water are cations of lead (Pb^{2+}) and mercury (Hg^{2+}). Lead and mercury are particularly likely to cause harm because they are widely used and dispersed in the environment. Heavy-metal ions are toxic because they bind to proteins in biological systems (such as in your body), preventing proteins from performing their normal tasks. As you might expect, because proteins play many roles in the body, heavy-metal poisoning effects are severe. They include damage to the nervous system, brain, kidneys, and liver, which can even lead to death.

Unfortunately, heavy-metal ions are not removed as waste as they move through the food chain. They become concentrated within the bodies of fish and shellfish, even when their abundance in the surrounding water is only a few parts per million. Such aquatic creatures then become hazardous for humans and other animals to consume.

In very low concentrations, heavy-metal ions are hard to detect in water, and they are even more difficult and costly to remove. So, how can heavy-metal poisoning be prevented? An effective way is to prevent heavy-metal ions from entering water systems in the first place. This prevention can be accomplished by producing and using alternate materials that do not contain these ions and, thus, are not harmful to health or the environment. Such practices, which prevent pollution by eliminating the production and use of hazardous substances, are examples of **Green Chemistry.** These practices are applicable to heavy metals and to many other types of pollution.

Introduction to Possible Causes

The remaining material in Unit 1 explores possible causes of the Riverwood fish kill and involves students in solving this mystery. Four possible fish-kill causes are introduced: inappropriate concentrations of heavy-metal ions, inappropriate pH, inappropriate concentrations of molecular substances, and inappropriate dissolved oxygen levels. Each possible cause leads to additional chemistry content, developed on a need-to-know basis. Students analyze Snake River data related to these potential causes and then decide on the cause of the fish kill based on data.

Four data sets are provided in the TRB/TRCD and on the W. H. Freeman *ChemCom* web site. Different chemistry classes can analyze different Snake River data, leading to different conclusions about the cause of the fish kill. The data sets include disclosure (for your information) of the fish-kill cause with which they are associated. However, students may come up with a different cause or a combination of causes. If students can support sensible chemical conclusions with evidence, their reasoning is appropriate.

C.8 Inappropriate Heavy-Metal Ion Concentrations?

C.8 Content Reading Guide

This section features lead and mercury ions (Pb^{2+} and Hg^{2+}), discussing their chemistry, historical and current commercial uses, and toxic effects. Heavy metals are particularly dangerous because they accumulate in the body and have serious health consequences.

Emphasize that metal *ions,* not metal *atoms,* dissolve in water. Metal atoms *can* exist in water as suspensions, if they are scoured up from bottom sediments by strong water flow. Also note that some metal ions form directly by metallic oxidation in water.

Discuss the idea of allowable or regulatory limits (some are provided with the Snake River data). What do such limits imply about the safety of the associated levels of exposure?

Using the Figures

Figure 1.41: Ask students to brainstorm how lead-based paint can pose a health hazard. Specifically, ask them to study the figure and suggest ways that such paint could end up in a person's body. A hint to offer students: According to the EPA, lead-based paint in good condition does not usually pose a health hazard.

The main ways people get lead in their bodies are:
• Placing their fingers or other objects covered with lead dust in their mouths
• Eating paint chips that contain lead
• Inhaling lead dust (some dust is not even visible)

Lead dust forms when lead-based paint is dry scraped, dry sanded, or heated (for instance, during building renovation), or as painted surfaces rub together (such as when windows are repeatedly opened and closed). Settled lead dust can re-enter the air when people vacuum, sweep, or walk through it (**http://www.epa.gov/lead/**).

Lead affects both adults and children. It poses a greater hazard to children because they have greater tendency to put objects into their mouths, their bodies absorb more lead, and their nervous systems are more sensitive to lead toxicity.

Figure 1.41 *Lead is a soft metal, as demonstrated when a lead weight is squeezed (Left and center). Paints containing lead compounds were used in houses until the government banned such use in 1978 (right).*

Some urban home construction included lead pipes through the 1930s; lead solder was even used, at times, until the early 1970s, posing health challenges within some homes.

Gasoline containing tetraethyl lead was known as "leaded gasoline."

Lead Ions (Pb^{2+})

Lead is probably the heavy metal most familiar to you. Its symbol, Pb, is based on the element's original Latin name *plumbum;* it is also the basis of the word *plumber.* Water pipes in ancient Rome were commonly made of lead.

Lead and lead compounds (see Figure 1.41) have been, and in some cases still are, used in pottery, automobile electrical storage batteries, solder, cooking vessels, pesticides, and paints. One compound of lead and oxygen, red lead (Pb_3O_4), is the primary ingredient in paint that protects bridges and other steel structures from corrosion.

Although lead water pipes were used in the United States in the early 1800s, they were replaced by iron pipes after people discovered that water transported through lead pipes could cause lead poisoning. In modern homes, copper or plastic water pipes are now used to prevent any contact between household water and lead.

Until the 1970s, the molecular compound *tetraethyl lead,* $Pb(C_2H_5)_4$, was added to gasoline to produce a better-burning automobile fuel. Unfortunately, the lead entered the atmosphere through automobile exhaust as lead oxide. Although the phaseout of leaded gasoline reduced lead emissions, lead contamination remains in soil surrounding heavily traveled roads. In some homes built before 1978 and not since repainted, the flaking of old leaded paint is another source of lead poisoning, particularly among children who may eat the flaking paint (see Figure 1.41).

Mercury Ions (Hg^{2+})

Mercury is the only metallic element that is a liquid at room temperature (see Figure 1.42). In fact, its symbol comes from the Latin *hydrargyrum,* meaning quicksilver or liquid silver.

Mercury has several uses, some due specifically to its liquid state. It is an excellent electrical conductor; therefore, it is used in "silent" light switches. People also use it in medical and weather thermometers, thermostats, mercury-vapor street lamps, fluorescent light bulbs, and some paints. Elemental mercury can be absorbed directly through the skin, and its vapor is quite hazardous to health. At room temperature, some mercury vapor will always be present if liquid mercury is exposed to air; therefore any mercury spill should be reported and carefully cleaned up.

Because mercury compounds are toxic, they are useful in eliminating bacteria, fungi, and agricultural pests when used in antiseptics, fungicides, and pesticides. In the 18th and 19th centuries, mercury(II) nitrate, $Hg(NO_3)_2$, was used in making felt hats, popular at that time (see Figure 1.42). After unintentionally absorbing this compound through their skin for several years, hatmakers often suffered from mercury poisoning. Their symptoms included numbness, staggered walk, tunnel vision, and brain damage, thus giving rise to the expression "mad as a hatter."

Figure 1.42 *Like other metals, mercury is very shiny. Unlike other metals, mercury is a liquid at room temperature (left). During the 18th and 19th centuries, people used mercury compounds to make felt hats (below).*

The sudden release of a large amount of heavy-metal ions might cause a fish kill, depending on the particular metal ion involved, its concentration, the species of fish present, and other factors. Was such a release responsible for the Riverwood fish kill? As you read about other possible causes of the fish kill, keep in mind questions that are relevant to all potential culprits, such as:

▶ Is there a source of this material along the Snake River within 15 km of Riverwood?

▶ What concentration of this solute would be toxic to various species of fish?

SECTION C

Additional Background Information on Mercury

Mercury is found in three main forms—methyl mercury, elemental mercury, and inorganic mercury compounds—all of which are toxic and have different effects on health. Students may have some prior knowledge about mercury concentrations in fish and/or mercury spilled in school laboratories.

Methyl mercury is found in fish and fish products; elemental mercury is found in some thermometers, thermostats, and lightbulbs. Inorganic mercury compounds are most relevant to this discussion, as they will dissolve in water, releasing mercury ions. In the past, inorganic mercury compounds were used for reasons stated in the text and also in laxatives, skin lightening treatments, and latex paints (to prevent bacterial and fungal growth). In the early 1990s, many products containing inorganic mercury compounds were removed from the market due to their toxicity.

For more information, see **http://www.cdc.gov/lead/,** **http://www.epa.gov/safewater/lead/,** **http://www.atsdr.cdc.gov/cxcx3.html,** **http://www.atsdr.cdc.gov/tfacts46.html,** and **http://water.usgs.gov/wid/FS_216-95/FS_216-95.html.**

C.9 Inappropriate pH Levels?

Acidity and alkalinity (basicity) play a major role in water quality and survival of aquatic life. This unit introduces students to the pH scale, some characteristic properties of acids and bases, and uses of some common acids and bases. The pH scale is presented as a way to distinguish acids from bases and express their relative acidity or alkalinity. Students may already have encountered these terms outside the classroom; you may want to elicit and discuss their prior knowledge (perhaps including shampoo/soap advertisements or hot tub/swimming pool maintenance).

The development of pH and acid–base concepts here illustrates the *ChemCom* philosophy— chemistry ideas are introduced only when (and to the appropriate depth!) required; this spiral curriculum strategy ensures that the text will revisit and extend introduced concepts later. Accordingly, *students will learn more about acids and bases later in the course.* Avoid introducing additional acid–base content at this point.

For more information on the pH of drinking water, see **www.epa.gov/safewater/mcl.html**.

Using the Figures

Figure 1.43: Based on the examples of acids and bases shown here, encourage students to list other household products they could categorize as acids or bases. Students may suggest items whose pH is not easy to measure due to their negligible water solubility, such as butter or oil. This could help review the role of polarity in the dissolving process.

C.9 INAPPROPRIATE pH LEVELS?

You have probably heard the term *pH* used before, perhaps in connection with acid rain or hair shampoo. What is pH, and could it possibly help account for the fish kill in Riverwood?

The **pH scale** is a convenient way to measure and report the acidic, basic, or chemically neutral character of a solution. Nearly all pH values are in the range from 0 to 14, although some extremely acidic or basic solutions may be outside this range. At room temperature, any pH value less than 7.0 indicate an acidic condition; the lower the pH, the more acidic the solution. Solutions with pH values greater than 7.0 are basic; the higher the pH, the more basic the solution. Basic solutions are also called **alkaline** solutions.

Quantitatively, a change of one pH unit indicates a *tenfold* difference in acidity or alkalinity. For example, lemon juice, with a pH of about 2, is about 10 times as acidic as some soft drinks, which have a pH of about 3.

Acids and bases, some examples of which are listed in Table 1.5 and shown in Figures 1.43a and 1.43b, exhibit certain characteristic properties. For example, the vegetable dye *litmus* turns blue in basic solution and red in acidic solution. Both acidic and basic solutions conduct electricity. Each type of solution has a distinctive taste and a distinctive feel on your skin. (**Caution:** *Never test these sensory properties in the laboratory.*) In addition, concentrated acids and bases are able to react chemically with many other substances. You are probably familiar with the ability of acids and bases to corrode materials, which is a type of chemical behavior.

Most **acids** are made up of molecules including one or more hydrogen atoms that can be released rather easily in water solution. These *acidic* hydrogen atoms are usually written first in the formula for an acid. See Table 1.5.

> Vinegar is an acid you probably have tasted; that common kitchen ingredient is considered a dilute solution of acetic acid.

Figure 1.43a *Vinegar contains acetic acid, and some soft drinks contain both carbonic acid and phosphoric acid. Many fruits and vegetables also contain acids.*

 C.9 Content Reading Guide

NAMES, FORMULAS, AND COMMON USES OF SOME ACIDS AND BASES

Name	Formula	Common Uses
Acids		
Acetic acid	$HC_2H_3O_2$	In vinegar (typically a 5% solution of acetic acid)
Carbonic acid	H_2CO_3	In carbonated soft drinks
Hydrochloric acid	HCl	Used in removing scale buildup from boilers and for cleaning materials
Nitric acid	HNO_3	Used in making fertilizers, dyes, and explosives
Phosphoric acid	H_3PO_4	Added to some soft drinks to give a tart flavor; also used in making fertilizers and detergents
Sulfuric acid	H_2SO_4	Largest-volume substance produced by the chemical industry; used in automobile battery fluid
Bases		
Calcium hydroxide	$Ca(OH)_2$	Present in mortar, plaster, and cement; used in paper pulping and removing hair from animal hides
Magnesium hydroxide	$Mg(OH)_2$	Active ingredient in milk of magnesia
Potassium hydroxide	KOH	Used in making some liquid soaps
Sodium hydroxide	NaOH	A major industrial product; active ingredient in some drain and oven cleaners; used to convert animal fats into soap

| **Table 1.5**

Many **bases** are ionic substances that include hydroxide ions (OH^-). Sodium hydroxide, NaOH, and barium hydroxide, $Ba(OH)_2$, are two examples. Some bases, such as ammonia (NH_3) and baking soda (sodium hydrogen carbonate, $NaHCO_3$), contain no OH^- ions, but they still produce basic solutions because they react with water to generate OH^- ions, as illustrated by the following equation:

$$NH_3(g) \; + \; H_2O(l) \; \longrightarrow \; NH_4^+(aq) \; + \; OH^-(aq)$$

| **Figure 1.43b** *Milk of magnesia and oven cleaner contain bases. Use Table 1.5 to identify the bases contained in these and other common household items.*

Section C Investigating the Cause of the Fish Kill   69

Demonstration Ideas

Before any demonstrations, you may wish to challenge students to classify common materials as acids or bases. This encourages students to access their prior knowledge and also provides opportunities for you to identify misconceptions. You can use demonstrations such as these to check their understandings (or guesses) about the acidic/basic nature of various substances.

Test the pH of common materials such as vinegar, citrus fruits, ammonia, baking soda, and antacids, using red and blue litmus paper, pH paper, and, if available, a pH meter. Relate the concept of pH to students' everyday lives.

Red cabbage juice contains a pigment you can use as an excellent pH indicator. To prepare the indicator solution, add boiling water to chopped red cabbage, let it steep for 10 min, and then filter out the cabbage. For a dramatic demonstration, place the red cabbage juice into a 1000-mL graduated cylinder and add a few chunks of dry ice. As the dry ice liberates $CO_2(g)$, the pH of the indicator solution changes, producing a pleasing progression of colors.

Following these demonstrations, ask students to create a list that compares acid properties and base properties, based on their observations during the demonstrations and their prior knowledge of similarities among the materials.

SECTION C

C.10 Inappropriate Molecular Substance Concentrations?

This material defines molecular substances, describes them, and contrasts them with ionic substances. The polarity of water is discussed to establish a structural basis for determining why some substances dissolve in water. This explanation for solubility can be summarized with the phrase "like dissolves like," which suggests that polar solvents will dissolve polar solutes, while nonpolar solvents will dissolve nonpolar solutes. Thus, the familiar saying, "oil and water don't mix," has a chemical basis. The student CD contains several simulations that illustrate this concept.

| Figure 1.44 The pH values of some common materials.

Expert freshwater anglers sometimes plan to fish in water with pH between 6.5 and 8.2.

What about substances that display neither acidic nor basic characteristics? Chemists classify these substances as chemically *neutral*. Water, sodium chloride (NaCl), and table sugar (sucrose, $C_{12}H_{22}O_{11}$) are all examples of chemically neutral compounds.

At 25 °C, a pH of 7.0 indicates a chemically neutral solution. The pH values of some common materials are shown in Figure 1.44.

As you can see in Figure 1.44, rainwater is naturally slightly acidic. This is because the atmosphere contains some substances—carbon dioxide (CO_2) for one—that produce acidic solutions when dissolved in water. Both acidic and basic solutions have effects on living organisms—effects that depend on their pH (Figure 1.45). When the pH of rivers, lakes, and streams is too low (meaning high acidity), fish-egg development is impaired, thus hampering the ability of fish to reproduce. Bodies of water with low (acidic) pH values also tend to increase the concentrations of metal ions in natural waters by leaching metal ions from surrounding soil. These metal ions can include aluminum ions (Al^{3+}), which are toxic to fish when present in sufficiently high concentration. High pH (basic contamination) is a problem for living organisms primarily because alkaline solutions are able to dissolve organic materials, including skin and scales.

The EPA requires that drinking water be within the pH range of 6.5 to 8.5. However, most fish can tolerate a slightly wider pH range, from about 5.0 to 9.0, in lake or river water.

On a normal day, the pH of Snake River water in Riverwood ranges between 7.0 and 8.0, nearly optimal for freshwater fishing. Could the pH have changed abruptly, killing the fish? If so, was acidic or basic contamination responsible for the Riverwood crisis?

| Figure 1.45 Testing the pH of an aquarium.

C.10 INAPPROPRIATE MOLECULAR SUBSTANCE CONCENTRATIONS?

Until now, substances considered suspects in the Riverwood fish kill have been ionic compounds that dissolve in water, releasing ions. Do other types of substances dissolve in water and possibly present a hazard to aquatic life? Some substances, such as sugar and ethanol, dissolve in water, but not as ions. These substances belong to a category known as **molecular substances** because they are composed of molecules.

Unlike ionic substances, which are crystalline solids at normal conditions, molecular substances are found as solids, liquids, or gases at room temperature. Some molecular substances, such as oxygen (O_2) and carbon dioxide (CO_2), have little attraction among their molecules and are, thus, gases at normal conditions. Molecular substances such as ethanol (ethyl alcohol, C_2H_5OH) and water (H_2O) have larger between-molecule attractions, which cause these "stickier" molecules to form liquids at normal conditions. Other molecular substances with even greater between-molecule attractions—succinic acid ($C_4H_6O_4$), for example—are solids at normal conditions. Stronger attractive forces hold these molecules together more tightly, in effect determining in which state the substance can be found at normal conditions.

Ions and ionic compounds were introduced on page 38.

You investigated the solubility behavior of succinic acid earlier. See page 57.

| Oxygen gas (O_2) | Carbon dioxide (CO_2) | Water (H_2O) | Succinic acid ($C_4H_6O_4$) | Ethanol (C_2H_5OH) |

What determines the solubility of a molecular substance in water? The attraction of a substance's molecules for each other compared to their attraction for water molecules plays a major part. But what causes these attractions? The distribution of electrical charge within molecules has a great deal to do with it.

Most molecular compounds contain atoms of nonmetallic elements. As you learned earlier, these atoms are linked together by the attraction of one atom's positively charged nucleus for another atom's negatively charged electrons. If differences in electron attraction between atoms are large enough, electrons move from one atom to another, forming ions. This is what happens in a reaction between a metallic atom and a nonmetallic atom as an ionic compound is formed. The ability of an element's atoms to attract shared electrons when bonding within a compound is known as the element's **electronegativity.** In molecular substances, these differences in electron attraction, or electronegativity, are not large enough to cause ions to form, but they may cause the electrons to be unevenly distributed among the atoms.

Solubility of Molecular Substances

Demonstration Ideas

An effective demonstration is dissolving Styrofoam (packing peanuts or cups) in a large 1-L beaker partially filled with 100 mL acetone (nail polish remover). Enough of the Styrofoam quickly dissolves, reducing the volume of packing peanuts or cups, to create a dramatic demonstration of solubility. Some students may need to see (or be reminded) that Styrofoam will not dissolve in water. You can emphasize rates of dissolving, solubility, and types of molecules that would affect the dissolution rate.

A useful extension to this demonstration is dissolving starch-based packing peanuts in a large beaker that is almost filled with water. Have the class discuss differences between these two packing materials and the advantages of one type over the other, based on these differences.

Using the Figures

Figure 1.46: This figure relates chemistry concepts to students' everyday lives. Invite students to brainstorm other examples of situations where the "like dissolves like" principle applies. Some examples: (a) Vinaigrette salad dressings often separate into two layers and must be shaken to mix (but not dissolve) the oil and water; (b) "dry cleaning" involves using nonpolar solvents to remove oily (nonpolar) stains; (c) shampoo removes oil from hair that is not easy to wash away with water alone.

> **Investigating Matter**

C.11 Solvents

 C.11 Solvents Student Worksheet and Data Table

In this investigation, students explore the concept of "like dissolves like" by testing the solubility of several substances in water, ethanol, and lamp oil, representing polar, slightly polar, and nonpolar solvents. Begin by discussing toxic solutes that might have been in the Snake River at the time of the fish kill, such as pesticides, fertilizers, preservatives, paints, mining wastes, and solvents. In addition, using the Riverwood map on page 5, discuss where they might find particular substances in the river, based on locations of facilities in and around Riverwood.

Students test solubility of various substances. Those in the materials list represent just a suggestion. Choose solutes for their varied solubility behavior in water, ethanol, and lamp oil and safe use in the laboratory. Solutes that are potential contaminants in the Snake River would be particularly interesting. The suggested solutes exhibit a range of behavior from ionic to polar to nonpolar.

Students design their own procedures for this investigation. Offer suggestions about reasonable quantities, appropriate vessels, mixing procedures, and disposal. Remind students that their procedures must control variables and generate interpretable data on the solubility of each substance. An

Figure 1.46 *A painter must use paint thinner—a nonpolar solvent—to clean oil-based paint (also nonpolar) from this paintbrush. Water, a polar solvent, will not dissolve the paint. This is an example of "like dissolves like."*

You already know that the oxygen end of a water molecule is electrically negative compared with its positive hydrogen end. This is because oxygen is more electronegative than is hydrogen; thus, electrons are partially pulled away from the two hydrogen atoms toward the oxygen atom. The result is a *polar molecule*. Water molecules are polar, and water is a common example of a polar solvent. Such charge separation (and resulting molecular polarity) is found in many molecules whose atoms have sufficiently different electronegativities.

Polar molecules tend to dissolve readily in polar solvents, such as water. For example, water is a good solvent for sugar or ethanol, which are both composed of polar molecules. On the other hand, nonpolar liquids are good solvents for nonpolar molecules. Nonpolar cleaning fluids are used to dry-clean clothes because they readily dissolve nonpolar body oils found in fabric of used clothing. By contrast, nonpolar molecules (such as those of oil and gasoline) do not dissolve well in polar solvents (such as water or ethanol).

This pattern of solubility behavior—polar substances dissolve in polar solvents, nonpolar substances dissolve in nonpolar solvents—is often summarized in the generalization "like dissolves like." This rule also accounts for why nonpolar liquids are usually ineffective in dissolving ionic and polar molecular substances. See Figure 1.46.

Were dissolved molecular substances present in the Snake River water where the fish died? Most likely *yes*, at least in small amounts. Were they responsible for the fish kill? That depends on which molecular substances were present and at what concentrations. And that, in turn, depends in part on how each solute interacts with water's polar molecules.

In the following investigation, you will compare the solubility behavior of some typical molecular and ionic substances.

> **Investigating Matter**

C.11 SOLVENTS

Introduction

The *Riverwood News* reported that Dr. Brooke believes a substance dissolved in the Snake River is one likely fish-kill cause. She based her judgment on her chemical knowledge and experience. Dr. Brooke also has a general idea about which contaminating substances she can initially rule out: those that cannot dissolve appreciably in water. Such background knowledge helps Dr. Brooke (and other chemists) reduce the number of water tests required in the laboratory.

To investigate possible solutes in the Snake River, we need to be sure we know what the terms *soluble* and *insoluble* mean. Is anything truly *insoluble* in water? It is likely that at least a few molecules or ions of any substance will dissolve in water. Thus, the term *insoluble* actually refers to substances that are only very, very slightly soluble in water. An earlier margin note (page 60) revealed that lead(II) sulfide

> Various molecular substances may normally be present at very low concentrations—so low that we observe no harm to living things.

activity sheet provided in the TRB/TRCD can help organize student plans, which you should approve *before* students complete any solubility tests. An acceptable plan should include uniform sample size (for both solutes and solvents), a procedure for mixing, and a method for assigning relative solubility. Student procedures must include only safe laboratory practices.

(PbS), which is technically considered insoluble, actually has a very low solubility of about 10^{-14} g (0.000 000 000 000 01 g) per liter of water at room temperature. Also, chalk is considered insoluble in water, even though 1.53 mg calcium carbonate ($CaCO_3$), which is the main ingredient in chalk, can dissolve in 100 g water at 25 °C.

In this investigation, you will first address the solubilities of various molecular and ionic solutes in water. These solubility data, along with toxicity data, will help you rule out some solutes as probable causes of the fish kill. You will then test other solvents and examine solubility data for any general patterns that may be apparent.

Your teacher will tell you which solutes to investigate. List them in your laboratory notebook.

You will plan your own procedure and construct your own data table for recording your data and observations. See Figure 1.47. There are no absolute rules for constructing data tables. However, scientists follow basic guidelines when organizing their laboratory data and observations. For instance, your data table should be well-organized and clear. It must be comprehensible to someone who has not completed the investigation. Keep this in mind as you plan your procedure and data collection.

> 1.53 mg = 0.001 53 g

Figure 1.47 *Planning a procedure for investigating solubility.*

Part I: Designing a Procedure for Investigating Solubility in Water

Your teacher will direct you to discuss with either the entire class or your laboratory partner a procedure for testing the room-temperature solubilities of substances listed in your laboratory notebook. (If you have conducted solubility tests before, it might be useful to recall how you completed them.) With your partner, design a step-by-step procedure to determine whether each solute is soluble (S), slightly soluble (SS), or insoluble (I) in room-temperature water.

The following questions will help you design your procedure.

1. What particular observations will allow you to judge how well each solute dissolves in water? That is, how will you decide whether to classify a given solute as soluble, slightly soluble, or insoluble in water?
2. Which variables will you need to control? Why?
3. How should the solute and solvent be mixed—all at once or a little at a time? Why?

In designing your procedure, keep these concerns in mind.

▶ Avoid any direct contact of your skin with any solutes.
▶ Follow your teacher's directions for waste disposal.

> In this investigation, *insoluble* (I) means that solubility is so low that you could observe no solute dissolving.

Time

30 min

Materials

(For a class of 24 working in pairs)

24 test tubes (assuming tubes are reused), 13 × 100 mm
12 test-tube racks
12 marking pencils
12 spatulas
12 medicine droppers
12 10-mL graduated cylinders
25 mL hexane, C_6H_{14}
600 mL ethanol (denatured alcohol), C_2H_5OH
600 mL lamp oil
1 L distilled water, H_2O
Optional solutes: 25 g each of: urea, $CO(NH_2)_2$; iodine, I_2; ammonium chloride, NH_4Cl; sodium chloride, NaCl; glucose, $C_6H_{12}O_6$; naphthalene flakes, $C_{10}H_8$; copper(II) sulfate, $CuSO_4 \cdot 5H_2O$

Safety

Students should wear protective goggles and aprons throughout the investigation. Hexane is highly flammable; ethanol and naphthalene are flammable. Ensure that there are no open flames in the room. Dispense hexane inside an operating fume hood.

Remind students not to touch any solutes (particularly iodine) or solvents, to use a spatula or splint to transfer solids, and to discard all wastes in teacher-designated containers. Iodine and naphthalene are toxic; supervise student investigation carefully. Due to the volatility and toxicity of iodine, you may elect to demonstrate tests of its solubility.

Lab Tips

• You may decide to make stirring rods available, depending on students' procedures.
• Provide labeled containers for discarded hexane samples.
• If students obtain differing results, encourage them to retest the solubility of substances in question. (Use this as an opportunity to emphasize the value of conducting multiple trials.)

Answers

Part I

1. Observations include whether the substances mix (miscibility) and the quantity of solute that does not dissolve.
2. Controlled variables include temperature, quantities of solute and solvent, and stirring time and method.
3. Always mix solute and solvent together slowly, usually while stirring, to observe partial solubility.

Part II

1. The optional solutes naphthalene, hexane, and iodine—the water-insoluble solutes—would not be expected to dissolve in the river. Any solute that did not dissolve in water would probably not dissolve in the Snake River.

2. Students should report differences revealed in class discussion of the results. Criteria for distinguishing solubility or differing ratios of solvent to solute may account for these differences. The table below summarizes expected student data.

Part III

3. a. Ethanol's behavior as a solvent for NaCl is similar to that of water. Both dissolve NaCl.
   b. Ethanol dissolves NaCl better than does lamp oil.

4. a. and b. Answers will vary according to what students may have expected.

5. In general, substances that are soluble in water are insoluble in lamp oil, and vice versa. Students may note that more solutes are soluble or partially soluble in ethanol than in either water or lamp oil.

6. a. Solutes that dissolved in lamp oil will also dissolve in hexane.
   b. Ethylene glycol (antifreeze) has solvent properties similar to those of ethanol, so solutes that dissolved in ethanol would also dissolve in ethylene glycol.

7. a. Solutes that dissolve only in water—urea, ammonium chloride, copper(II) sulfate, and

When you and your partner have agreed upon a written procedure and an accompanying data table, ask your teacher to check and approve your written plans.

Part II: Investigating Solubility in Water

Follow your teacher-approved procedure to investigate the water solubility of each specified solute. Record all data in your data table.

Part III: Investigating Solubility in Ethanol and Lamp Oil

The task of determining what may have caused the fish kill can be simplified somewhat by focusing on substances that will dissolve appreciably in water. However, in dealing with other solubility-based problems, chemists sometimes find it helpful to use solvents other than water. Ethanol and lamp oil serve that role in this investigation.

You and your partner will investigate the solubility in ethanol and lamp oil of some or all solutes from Part II.

In addition, test the solubility of water in ethanol and in lamp oil. Gaining experience with three liquid solvents—lamp oil, ethanol, and water—will allow you to recognize some general patterns about solubility behavior.

Can you use the same procedure you designed for Part II? If not, what parts of that procedure should be revised? In considering your Part III procedure, keep the questions listed in Part I in mind. Write down the procedure and construct the data table or tables that you plan to use for this investigation. (*Note:* Before starting this task, be sure to read the next paragraph completely.)

Have your written procedure and data table or tables approved by your teacher. Before you start the laboratory work, test your interpretation of the Part II results by predicting what you think will be observed about solubility in each case. Include these predictions in your data table for Part III. Then collect and record data for both solvents.

Wash your hands thoroughly before leaving the laboratory.

Questions

Part II

1. According to your data, which of the solutes tested are *least* likely to be dissolved in the Snake River? Explain, and support your explanation with evidence from your completed investigation.

2. Compare your data with those of the rest of the class. Are there any differences? If so, how can you explain those differences?

Part III

3. a. How does the behavior of ethanol as a solvent for sodium chloride compare with that of water?
   b. How does ethanol's behavior compare with that of lamp oil?

Lab Video: Solvents

SOLUTE	WATER	ETHANOL	LAMP OIL
Urea, $CO(NH_2)_2$	Soluble	Soluble	Insoluble
Ammonium chloride, NH_4Cl	Soluble	Soluble	Insoluble
Naphthalene, $C_{10}H_8$	Insoluble	Soluble	Soluble
Iodine, I_2	Insoluble	Soluble	Soluble
Copper(II) sulfate, $CuSO_4$	Soluble	Soluble	Insoluble

SOLUTE	WATER	ETHANOL	LAMP OIL
Ethanol, C_2H_5OH	Soluble	Soluble	Soluble
Sodium chloride, NaCl	Soluble	Soluble	Insoluble
Hexane	Insoluble	Soluble	Soluble
Water	Soluble	Soluble	Insoluble
Lamp oil	Insoluble	Soluble	Soluble

4. a. Were any of your solubility observations unexpected?
   b. If so, explain what you expected, why you expected it, and how your expectations compare with what you actually observed.

5. Based on your data, what general pattern of solubility behavior can you summarize and describe?

6. Predict the solubility behavior of each solid solute you tested in
   a. hexane, a liquid that is essentially insoluble in water.
   b. ethylene glycol, a liquid that is very soluble in ethanol.

7. a. Given that water is a polar solvent and lamp oil is a nonpolar solvent, classify each molecular solute tested as polar or nonpolar.
   b. How did you decide?

> The familiar saying "oil and water do not mix" has a sound chemical basis!

8. How useful is the rule "like dissolves like" for predicting solubility? Explain your answer on the basis of your results.

9. In Part II, water was the solvent, but in Part III, it was a solute.
   a. How can it be both?
   b. How can you decide whether a substance is a solute or a solvent?

You now know about the solubility of some solids and liquids in water. As you read further to learn about the behavior of gases in natural waters, consider the possibility that the presence or absence of a dissolved gas was responsible for the Snake River catastrophe.

C.12 INAPPROPRIATE DISSOLVED OXYGEN LEVELS?

You have noted that the solubility of ionic and molecular solids in water usually increases when the water temperature is increased. Does this phenomenon extend to gases dissolved in solution? To build an understanding of the dissolving behavior of gases, look at Figure 1.48, which shows the solubility curve for oxygen gas plotted as milligrams oxygen gas dissolved per 1000 g water.

What is the solubility of oxygen gas in 20 °C water? In 40 °C water? As you can see, increasing the water temperature causes the gas to be less soluble! Note also the magnitude of the values for oxygen solubility. Compare these values with those for solid solutes, as shown in Figure 1.33 (page 54). At 20 °C, about 30 g potassium nitrate will dissolve in 100 g water. In contrast, only about 9 mg (0.009 g) oxygen gas will dissolve in 10 times more water (1000 g) at this temperature. It should be clear that most gases are far less soluble in water than are many ionic solids.

Figure 1.48 Solubility curve for O_2 gas in water in contact with air.

---

substance in *lesser* quantity is the solute. The solute is sometimes thought to be the substance that undergoes a change in its form—if an observable change takes place.

C.12 Inappropriate Dissolved Oxygen Levels?

C.12 Content Reading Guide

Although the terms *solute, solvent,* and *saturated* apply to solutions of gases in liquids, the solubility behavior of gases differs from that of solids. In general, the solubility of gases decreases as the solution temperature increases, and gas solubility increases as solution temperature decreases. This material explores the relationship between gas solubility and gas pressure on the solution. These concepts are readily illustrated by carbonated soft drinks. Most students already know about the "fizz effect" (rapid release of CO_2) that can occur when they open a warm carbonated soft drink, and that carbonated beverages "go flat" after the seal is broken. The first is a result of reduced gas solubility in warm solvent, and the second results from a reduction in the pressure of CO_2 on the solution as it is opened to the atmosphere (carbonated beverages are bottled under as high as 10 atm CO_2 pressure).

---

sodium chloride—are polar or ionic. Solutes that dissolve only in lamp oil—naphthalene and iodine—are nonpolar.
b. Polarity can be deduced from the generalization that "like dissolves like." Substances that dissolve in polar solvents are polar, while those that dissolve in nonpolar solvents are nonpolar.

8. "Like dissolves like" is useful in predicting solubility; see Answer 7.

9. a. In Part II, water was used to dissolve other substances, and is thus the solvent. In Part III, an attempt was made to dissolve water in ethanol and lamp oil, so water is the solute.
   b. According to convention, the substance in *greater* quantity is the solvent, and the

The process of dissolving a gas is accompanied by the release of energy and is thus exothermic. Energy is not required to overcome attractive forces between gas "solute molecules," since there are virtually no attractive forces among the molecules before dissolving. Thus, the only energy exchange is the release of energy as intermolecular solute–solvent links occur.

Demonstration Idea

Open two bottles of club soda, one very cold and one warm. Ask: Which event results in the greater release of gas? This demonstrates the relationship between temperature and gas solubility (as solvent temperature increases, gas solubility decreases).

Additional ChemQuandary

One 40-L aquarium is kept at 25 °C, while a second, identical aquarium is kept at 20 °C. Which aquarium can support a larger population of fish? Why?

Discussion: Fish require dissolved oxygen to survive. The fish tank at the lower temperature will contain more dissolved oxygen and support a larger fish population.

C.13 Temperature, Dissolved Oxygen, and Life

The relationship between solvent temperature and dissolved oxygen (DO) is important. Emphasize that increasing water temperature has multiple effects on fish survival. Less oxygen is able to dissolve than at lower temperatures, while at the same time fish metabolism (and

Figure 1.49 *Relationship between solubility and pressure of O_2 at 25 °C.*

The modernized metric unit for pressure is the pascal (Pa): 1 atmosphere (atm) = 101 325 Pa.

Figure 1.50 *Carbon dioxide in a carbonated soft drink.*

When you investigated the solubility of molecular and ionic solids, you found that solubility depended on two factors—temperature and the nature of the solvent. The solubility of a gas depends on these two factors as well. But it also depends on gas pressure. Referring to Figure 1.49, note what happens to oxygen's solubility as the pressure of oxygen gas above it is increased. Does more or less gas dissolve in the same amount of water? What happens if the O_2 gas pressure is doubled? For example, look at the solubility of O_2 at one atmosphere and at two atmospheres of gas pressure. Also consider the shape of the graph line. What type of relationship does a linear graph line indicate?

As you have deduced by now, gas solubility in water is directly proportional to the pressure of that gaseous substance on the liquid. You see one effect of this relationship every time you open a can or bottle of carbonated soft drink. As the carbon dioxide (CO_2) gas pressure on the liquid is reduced by opening the container to the air, some dissolved CO_2 gas escapes from the liquid in a rush of bubbles.

Because not very much $CO_2(g)$ is present in air, carbon dioxide gas from a high-pressure tank must be forced into the carbonated beverage just before the beverage container is sealed. This increases the amount of carbon dioxide that dissolves in the beverage. After saturating the beverage with carbon dioxide under a very high pressure of CO_2, pressure is quickly reduced when the can or bottle is opened, and the beverage solution now becomes supersaturated with CO_2. As a result, CO_2 gas quickly begins to leave the solution (hence, you observe fizzing) and continues to leave the solution (see Figure 1.50) until the solution is again saturated with CO_2, now in relation to the lower CO_2 pressure in the atmosphere above the liquid. In other words, dissolved CO_2 escapes from the liquid until the gas reaches its lower solubility at this lower pressure. When fizzing stops, you might describe the beverage as having gone flat. Actually, excess dissolved CO_2 has simply escaped into the air; the resulting "flat" beverage is still saturated with CO_2 at the new conditions.

C.13 TEMPERATURE, DISSOLVED OXYGEN, AND LIFE

On the basis of what you know about the effect of temperature on solubility, you may wonder if the temperature of the Snake River had something to do with the fish kill. As you just learned, water temperature affects how much oxygen gas can dissolve in the water. Various forms of aquatic life, including the many fish species, have different requirements for the concentration of dis-

metabolism of other water creatures) increases, causing competition for the decreased concentration of DO. The minimum concentration of DO required for fish survival varies somewhat with species, but is sometimes generically stated as 4 ppm.

The table, pg 77, gives DO requirements for some common freshwater fish. Some reasons for changes in lake or river water temperatures can be traced to human activity, such as discharge of cooling water from power or manufacturing plants.

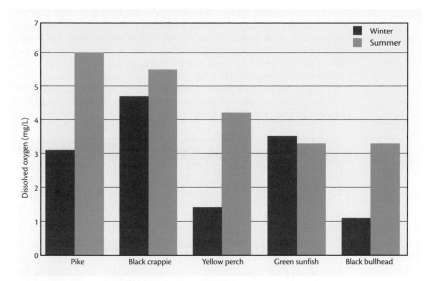

solved oxygen needed to survive. Figure 1.51 provides this information for selected fish species.

How, then, does a change in the temperature of natural waters affect fish internally? Fish are *cold-blooded* animals; their body temperatures rise and fall with the surrounding water temperature. If the water temperature rises, the body temperatures of fish also rise. This increase in body temperature, in turn, increases fish metabolism, a complex series of interrelated chemical reactions that keep fish alive. As these internal reaction rates speed up, the fish eat more, swim more, and require more dissolved oxygen. With rising temperatures, the rate of metabolism also increases for other aquatic organisms, such as aerobic bacteria, that compete with fish for dissolved oxygen.

As you can see, an increase in water temperature affects fish by decreasing the amount of dissolved oxygen in the water and by increasing the oxygen consumption of fish. A long stretch of hot summer days sometimes results in large fish kills, where hundreds of fish literally suffocate because of insufficient dissolved oxygen. Table 1.6 summarizes the maximum water temperatures at which selected fish species can survive.

Figure 1.51 *Dissolved-oxygen requirements of various fish.*

 Temperature, Dissolved Oxygen and Life

| Table 1.6

MAXIMUM WATER TEMPERATURE TOLERANCE FOR SOME FISH SPECIES (24-HOUR EXPOSURE)

	Maximum Temperature	
	°C	°F
Trout (brook, brown, rainbow)	24	75
Channel catfish	35	95
Lake herring (cisco)	25	77
Largemouth bass	34	93
Northern pike	30	86

DISSOLVED OXYGEN (DO) REQUIREMENTS FOR ADDITIONAL FISH SPECIES

FISH SPECIES	DO LEVEL (mg/L)
Northern pike	4.2
Trout (rainbow, brown, lake)	4.1
Salmon (chinook, coho, sockeye)	3.9
Channel catfish	3.2
Largemouth bass	2.5
Yellow perch	2.2

The average minimum dissolved oxygen level to maintain fish health is:
Cold-water species (trout, salmon)— 7 mg/L
Warm-water species (bass, bluegill, catfish)—5 mg/L

The concept of *percent saturation* is another way to express DO. Percent saturation is the ratio of the amount of DO in a water sample to the amount that would be present in a saturated solution. Percent saturation is sometimes used as a measure of stream "health." Values above 112% can be dangerous to fish.

The reason is related to the cause of "the bends," a condition scuba divers experience if they ascend too rapidly. Nitrogen gas, which is dissolved along with oxygen, is present at supersaturated concentrations and when DO percent saturation exceeds 100%. When conditions change (such as increases in temperature or decreases in pressure), the nitrogen may come out of solution as gas bubbles, which can cause gas-bubble trauma. This phenomenon involves formation of bubbles within various biological systems, such as the cardiovascular system (leading to a disruption of blood flow) and the gills or lungs (leading to a disruption of oxygen flow in fish) and decompression illness—"the bends" in humans. For more information, see *ChemMatters* magazine, February 2001, "Scuba: The Chemistry of an Adventure" and **http://wlapwww.gov.bc.ca/wat/wq/ BCguidelines/tgp/tgptextonly.htm, http://www.sdm.scot.nhs.uk/ decompression_illness/index.htm, http://www.merck.com/ mrkshared/mmanual/section20/ chapter285/285b.jsp,** or **http://www. diversalertnetwork.org/medical/ articles/article.asp?articleid=65.**

Demonstration Idea

You can again demonstrate the effect of solvent temperature on gas solubility. Chill a bottle of carbonated drink (colored beverages show the result better) to just above 0 °C. Prepare three beakers of water—one at 0 °C (ice-water bath), one at room temperature, and the third at about 40 °C. Open the chilled bottle and pour soda gently to fill three test tubes. Close each tube with a one-hole stopper and, with your finger over the stopper hole, invert the tube and immerse it into one of the water baths. Do the same with the other two. Ask two students to assist you, so that all three tubes are inverted and immersed simultaneously. In the water at room temperature and 40 °C, carbon dioxide is released from the solution as bubbles in the test tube. The relative quantity of bubbles liberated demonstrates that the solubility of CO_2 is, indeed, lower at higher temperatures.

Using the Figures

Figure 1.53: The unintentional side effect of saturating (or supersaturating) water with dissolved oxygen and nitrogen via this dam is also an *intentional* step in the water purification process described in Section D (page 88). It may be useful to draw students' attention to Figure 1.53 now, so that you can refer to it later when discussing aeration.

Sometimes hot summer days are not to blame. Often, high lake or river temperatures can be traced to human activity. Many industries, such as electrical power generation, depend on natural bodies of water to cool heat-producing processes. Cool water is drawn from lakes or rivers into an industrial or power-generating plant, and devices called *heat exchangers* transfer thermal energy (heat energy) from the processing area to the cooling water. The heated water is then released back into the lakes or rivers, either immediately or after the water has partly cooled, as shown in Figure 1.52.

| **Figure 1.52** Power plant cooling water is often returned to lakes or streams.

There is a lower limit on the amount of dissolved oxygen needed for fish to survive. Is there an upper limit? Can too much dissolved oxygen be a problem for fish? In nature, both oxygen and nitrogen gas are present in the air at all times. When oxygen gas dissolves, so does nitrogen gas. This fact turns out to be significant when considering the upper limit for dissolved gases. When the total amount of dissolved gases—primarily oxygen and nitrogen—reaches between 110% and 124% of saturation (a state of supersaturation), a condition called *gas-bubble trauma* may develop in fish.

This situation is dangerous because the supersaturated solution causes gas bubbles to form in the blood and tissues of fish. Oxygen-gas bubbles can be partially utilized by fish during metabolism, but nitrogen-gas bubbles block capillaries within the fish. This blockage results in the death of the fish within hours or days. Gas-bubble trauma can be diagnosed by noting gas bubbles in the gills of dead fish if they are dissected promptly after death. Supersaturation of water with

Figure 1.53 *Froth at the base of a dam can trap large quantities of air. This can result in water that is supersaturated with dissolved oxygen and nitrogen gas.*

nitrogen and oxygen gases can occur at the base of a dam or a hydroelectric project, as the released water forms "froth," trapping large quantities of air, as shown in Figure 1.53.

So, back to the original question: *What caused the Riverwood fish kill?* You have considered several possible causes. How will you decide which was the actual cause? You will start by examining water-related measurements collected by scientists and engineers on the Snake River. From these data and what you have learned, you will decide the actual cause of the fish kill.

Making Decisions

C.14 DETERMINING THE CAUSE OF THE FISH KILL

Snake River watershed data have been collected and monitored since the early 1900s. Although some measurements and methods have changed during that time, excellent data have been gathered, particularly in recent years (see Figure 1.54, page 80). Data are available for the following factors:

▶ water temperature and dissolved oxygen
▶ rainfall
▶ water flow
▶ dissolved molecular substances
▶ heavy metals
▶ pH
▶ nitrate and phosphate levels
▶ organic carbon

Making Decisions

C.14 Determining the Cause of the Fish Kill

In this activity, students work cooperatively to analyze data relating to the Riverwood fish kill. Data can be found in the Black Line Masters (TRB) and on the TRCD. Give each group a complete set of data and have each group graph data regarding one or more of these water-quality factors: water temperature, dissolved oxygen, rainfall, water flow, dissolved molecular substances (pesticides, PCBs), heavy metals (lead, cadmium, mercury, arsenic), pH, nitrate, orthophosphates, and organic carbon. Students will then analyze their graphs, looking for relationships and/or irregularities. Groups should share their graphs and interpretations with the rest of the class. You may designate an area in the classroom to post the graphs for the remainder of this unit, since they will help students prepare for the town meeting. You may want to assign roles for the town council at this point. See the TRB/TRCD for guidance.

Plan to employ cooperative learning strategies with this activity. For example, assign roles to each student in a group. Roles such as a material person, resource person, recorder, and presenter promote positive interdependence.

You may want to consider allowing students to use computers or calculators to graph and analyze the data. Ensure that any approach will result in printable graphs for future reference.

Four scenarios are presented in the TRB/TRCD. Each scenario corresponds to a likely fish-kill cause, including gas bubble trauma (too much DO in the river), pesticide contamination (molecular substances in the river), heavy-metal contamination (heavy metals from sediment in the river), and inadequate DO in the water. See the TRB/TRCD for more information. All student groups in one class should receive data for the same scenario. You may decide to use different data sets for different classes. (This prevents students who attend class earlier in the day from sharing materials with students whose classes meet later in the day.)

Some of the water-quality factors graphed in this activity may be unfamiliar to students. Use the following background information as appropriate.

Water temperature—affects DO and fish metabolism, discussed in C.13

Dissolved oxygen—discussed in C.12 and C.13

Rainfall—affects water flow and can increase potentially hazardous runoff from farms, mines, etc.

Water flow—affects dilution of contaminants and can indicate recent rainfall or snow melt

Dissolved molecular substances:

pesticides—include organophosphates, carbamates, organochlorines, and pyrethroids. Often applied to soils, lawns, gardens, and crops to prevent, destroy, repel, or mitigate pests, including insects and other plants

PCBs—polychlorinated biphenyls, chlorinated organic compounds with many uses, including as plasticizers (in paints) and insulators (in electrical equipment) before 1977

Your teacher will assign you to a group to study some of the data just listed. Each group will complete data-analysis procedures for its assigned data. After the groups have finished their work, they will share their analyses and the class will draw conclusions about factors possibly related to the fish kill.

The following background information will help you complete the analysis of data assigned to you by your teacher.

Data Analysis

Interpreting graphs of environmental data requires a slightly different approach from the one you used to interpret a solubility curve. Rather than seeking a predictable relationship, you will be looking for regularities or patterns among the values. Any major irregularity in the data may suggest a problem related to the water factor being evaluated. The following suggestions will help you prepare and interpret such graphs.

▶ Choose your scale so that the graph is large enough to fill most of the available space on the graph paper.

▶ Assign each regularly spaced division on the graph paper a convenient, constant value. The graph-paper line interval value should be easily divided by eye, such as 1, 2, 5, or 10; rather than awkward values, such as 6, 7, 9, or 14.

Figure 1.54 *Researchers monitor water quality by checking for methane emissions (left) and measuring dissolved oxygen (right). Similar procedures provided the Snake River data.*

► An axis scale does not have to start at *zero*, particularly if the plotted values cluster in a narrow range not near zero.

► Label each axis with the quantity and unit being plotted.

► Plot each point. Then draw a small symbol around each point, like this: ⊙. If you plot more than one set of data on the same graph, distinguish each by using a different color or small geometric shape to enclose the points, such as ⊡, ▽, or △.

► Give your graph a title that will readily convey its meaning and purpose to readers.

► If you use technology—such as a graphing calculator or computer software—to prepare your graphs, ensure that you follow the guidelines just given. Different devices and software have different ways to process data. Choose the appropriate type of graph (scatter plot and bar graph, for example) for your data.

Next, follow the steps listed below when preparing and plotting your graphs, and answer the questions that follow.

1. Prepare a graph for each of your group's Snake River data sets. Label the *x*-axis (independent axis) with the consecutive months indicated in the data. Label the *y*-axis (dependent axis) with the water factor measured, accompanied by its units.

2. Plot each data point, and connect the consecutive points with straight lines.

3. Is any pattern apparent in your group's plotted data?

4. Can you offer possible explanations for any pattern or irregularities that you detect?

5. What arguments might someone make to challenge your explanation?

6. How might fish be adversely affected by the pattern or patterns that your group has identified?

7. Do you think the data analyzed by your group might help account for the Snake River fish kill? Why? How?

8. Prepare to share your group's data-analysis findings in a class discussion. During the class discussion, take notes on key findings reported by each data-analysis group. Also note and record significant points raised in the data-analysis discussions.

Your class will reassemble several times during your study of Section D to discuss and consider implications of the water-analysis data you have just processed. In particular, guided by the patterns and irregularities found in your analysis of Snake River data, your class will seek an explanation or scenario that accounts for the observed data and for the resulting Riverwood fish kill. Good luck!

SECTION C

Heavy metals:
   lead—discussed in C.8
   cadmium—used primarily in batteries, pigments, and coatings
   mercury—discussed in C.8
   arsenic—used in wood preservation
pH—discussed in C.9
Nitrates—nitrogen- and oxygen-containing compounds used primarily as fertilizers
Orthophosphates—measure of phosphate available to algae and plants; increased phosphates can lead to low DO
Organic carbon—measure of organic matter (contaminants such as agricultural chemicals and natural wastes) in water that indicates general suitability for aquatic life. Often called TOC (total organic carbon)

Answers

1–4. The graphs will vary by variable. Review the graphs on the IRCD to compare student graphs for accuracy. In general, be sure students make valid interpretations of data and support their conclusions with evidence.

SECTION C SUMMARY

 Section C Supplement

Reviewing the Concepts

1. The solubility of sugar in water increases as the temperature of the water increases.

2. Referring to **Figure 1.33**, the maximum is ~ 48 g.

3. a. $\dfrac{2.0 \text{ g sugar}}{1 \text{ mL water}} \times 100.0 \text{ mL water} =$

   200 g sugar

   b. 710 g sugar

   c. 1900 g sugar

4. a. At 20 °C: NaCl, KCl, KNO_3

   b. At 80 °C: KNO_3, KCl, NaCl

5. A saturated solution contains the maximum quantity of solute that can be dissolved in a stable solution at that temperature, while an unsaturated solution is any solution that contains less than that maximum quantity of solute.

6. a. About 32 g

   b. At 30 °C, approximately 45 g KNO_3 will normally dissolve in 100 g water, so this solution is supersaturated.

   c. At 75 °C, 150 g KNO_3 will dissolve. At 40 °C, a saturated solution contains about 60 g KNO_3. The difference, 150 g − 60 g = 90 g, indicates the mass of precipitate that will form.

7. a. The crystal will dissolve (stirring may be required).

   b. The crystal will probably settle to the container bottom.

   c. The crystal will initiate crystallization of "excess" solute.

8. $\dfrac{35 \text{ g ethanol}}{(115 \text{ g water} + 35 \text{ g ethanol})} \times$ $100\% = 23\%$ ethanol by mass

SECTION C SUMMARY
Reviewing the Concepts

The solubility of a substance in water can be expressed as the quantity of that substance that will dissolve in a certain quantity of water at a specified temperature.

1. Explain why three teaspoons of sugar will completely dissolve in a serving of hot tea, but will not dissolve in an equally sized serving of iced tea.

2. What is the maximum mass of potassium chloride (KCl) that will dissolve in 100.0 g water at 70 °C?

3. If the solubility of sugar (sucrose) in water is 2.0 g/mL at room temperature, what is the maximum mass of sugar that will dissolve in
   a. 100.0 mL water?
   b. 355 mL (12 oz) water?
   c. 946 mL (1 qt) water?

4. Rank the substances in Figure 1.33 (page 54) from most soluble to least soluble at
   a. 20 °C.   b. 80 °C.

Solutions can be classified as unsaturated, saturated, or supersaturated. In quantitative terms, the concentration of a solution expresses the relative quantities of solute and solvent in a particular solution.

5. Distinguish between the terms *saturated* and *unsaturated*.

6. Using the graph on page 54, answer these questions about the solubility of potassium nitrate, KNO_3:
   a. What maximum mass of KNO_3 can dissolve in 100 g water if the water temperature is 20 °C?
   b. At 30 °C, 55 g KNO_3 is dissolved in 100 g water. Is this solution saturated, unsaturated, or supersaturated?
   c. A saturated solution of KNO_3 is formed in 100.0 g water at 75 °C. If some solute precipitates as the saturated solution cools to 40 °C, what mass (in grams) of solid KNO_3 should form?

7. You are given a solution of KNO_3 of unknown concentration. What will happen when you add a crystal of KNO_3, if the solution is
   a. unsaturated?   b. saturated?
   c. supersaturated?

8. A 35-g sample of ethanol is dissolved in 115 g water. What is the percent concentration of the ethanol, expressed as percent ethanol by mass?

9. Calculate the masses of water and sugar in a 55.0-g sugar solution that is labeled 20.0% sugar by mass.

10. The EPA maximum standard for lead in drinking water is 0.015 mg/L. Express this value as parts per million (ppm).

The polarity of water helps explain its ability to dissolve many ionic solids.

11. What makes a water molecule polar?

12. Draw a model that shows how molecules in liquid water generally arrange themselves relative to one another.

13. Which region of a polar water molecule will be attracted to a
    a. K^+ ion?   b. Br^- ion?

9. $\dfrac{20.0 \text{ g sugar}}{100.0 \text{ g solution}} \times 55.0 \text{ g solution} =$

   11.0 g sugar

   55.0 g solution − 11.0 g sugar =

   44.0 g water

10. $\dfrac{0.015 \text{ mg lead}}{1 \text{ L water}} \times \dfrac{1 \text{ L water}}{1000 \text{ g water}} \times$

    $\dfrac{1 \text{ g water}}{1000 \text{ mg water}} = \dfrac{0.015 \text{ mg lead}}{1\,000\,000 \text{ mg water}} =$

    0.015 ppm lead

11. Unequal electrical charge distribution. The oxygen end is more negative; the hydrogen ends are more positive.

Heavy-metal ions can be useful resources, but some are toxic if introduced into biological systems, even in small amounts.

14. Why are heavy metals called *heavy*?

15. List three symptoms of heavy-metal poisoning.

16. List two possible sources of human exposure to
a. lead.　　　b. mercury.

Solutions can be characterized as acidic, basic, or chemically neutral on the basis of their observed properties.

17. What ion is found in many bases?

18. What element is found in most acids?

19. Classify each sample as acidic, basic, or chemically neutral:
a. seawater (pH = 8.6)
b. drain cleaner (pH = 13.0)
c. vinegar (pH = 2.7)
d. pure water (pH = 7.0)

20. Using Figure 1.44 on page 70, decide which is more acidic:
a. a soft drink or a tomato
b. black coffee or pure water
c. milk of magnesia or household ammonia

21. How many times more acidic is a solution at pH 2.0 than a solution at pH 4.0?

22. List three negative effects of inappropriate pH levels on aquatic organisms.

The solubility of a molecular substance in water depends on the relative strength of solute–water attractive forces, compared to competing solute–solute and water–water attractive forces.

23. Distinguish between polar and nonpolar molecules.

24. Would you select ethanol, water, or lamp oil to dissolve a nonpolar molecular substance? Explain.

25. Why does table salt (NaCl) dissolve in water but not in cooking oil?

26. Explain the phrase "like dissolves like."

27. Explain why you cannot satisfactorily clean greasy dishes with just plain water.

The solubility of a gaseous substance in water depends on the water temperature and the external pressure of the gas.

28. With increasing water temperature, how does the solubility of oxygen change?

29. How many milligrams of O_2 will dissolve in 1000.0 g water at 2.5 atm? (*Hint:* Use Figure 1.49 on page 76.)

30. As scuba divers descend, the pressure increases on the gases they breathe. How does the increasing pressure affect the amount of gas dissolved in their blood?

31. Given your knowledge of gas solubility, explain why a bottle of warm cola produces more fizz when opened than does a bottle of cold cola.

32. Using the graph on page 77, determine
a. which type of fish requires more dissolved oxygen in water in the winter than in the summer.
b. how much more dissolved oxygen in water is required by yellow perch in the summer than in the winter.

Section Summary　　83

19. Acidic: c.　Basic: a, b.　Neutral: d.

20. a. A soft drink
b. Coffee
c. Milk of magnesia

21. 100 times more acidic

22. Impaired fish-egg development, increased concentrations of toxic metals, and dissolution of skin and scales

23. Polar molecules have uneven distribution of electrical charge; nonpolar molecules have uniform distribution of electrical charge.

24. Lamp oil; nonpolar solvents dissolve nonpolar solutes

25. NaCl is an ionic substance whose charged particles are attracted by and dissolved in polar solvents, like water, but not in nonpolar solvents, like cooking oil.

26. Polar solvents tend to dissolve polar and ionic solutes, due to the attraction of charged particles and partially charged molecules. Nonpolar solvents and solutes tend to mix in the dissolving process.

27. Water molecules are polar; they cannot dissolve and remove nonpolar grease from dishes.

28. It decreases.

29. About 20 mg

30. It causes a corresponding increase in the amount of dissolved gas in their blood.

31. The solubility of CO_2 in cola decreases as the cola temperature increases. As a result, there is a greater release of excess dissolved CO_2 from warmer cola than from colder cola.

32. a. Green sunfish
b. About 2.8 mg/L more

12. Molecules are close to each other, with the H end of one molecule adjacent to the O end of another.

13. a. The oxygen region
b. The hydrogen region

14. They are more dense and have larger molar masses than metals.

15. Damage to the nervous system, kidneys, and liver; mental retardation; numb-

ness; staggered walk; tunnel vision; brain damage; and death.

16. a. Paint, water pipes, and leaded-gasoline—contaminated soil.
b. Broken thermometers, thermostats, fluorescent lightbulbs, and coal-fired power plant emissions.

17. Hydroxide (OH^-) ions

18. Hydrogen

Connecting the Concepts

33. a. They are likely to contain nonpolar materials.
   b. Because they can dissolve nonpolar greases and oils
34. a. A river with rapids, which promote mixing water with air
   b. The lake in spring; it would be cooler, thus increasing the solubility of oxygen.
   c. Overall, black crappies require more oxygen than black bullheads to survive. Therefore, the lake containing the black crappies probably has more dissolved oxygen.
35. Hydrogen, because the electron density would be larger around fluorine due to its higher electronegativity
36. Tank B, because the lower temperature would allow for a greater concentration of dissolved oxygen
37. a. Approx. 9 mg/1000 g water
   b. $\dfrac{9 \text{ mg O}_2}{1000 \text{ g water}} \times$
   $\dfrac{1 \text{ g water}}{1000 \text{ mg water}} =$
   $\dfrac{9 \text{ mg O}_2}{1\,000\,000 \text{ mg water}} = 9\,\text{ppm O}_2$

Extending the Concepts

38. Baking powder contains a dry powdered acid called *cream of tartar*; baking soda is 100% sodium bicarbonate ($NaHCO_3$). When water is added to baking powder, the acid and bicarbonate react to produce CO_2 gas bubbles. By contrast, baking soda requires the addition of an acid to liberate CO_2 gas bubbles.
39. Dissolve the mixture of the two substances in a minimum quantity of hot water. Reduce the temperature until one precipitates. Quickly filter the mixture

Connecting the Concepts

33. Many mechanics prefer to use waterless hand cleaners to clean their greasy hands. Explain
   a. what kind of materials are likely to be found in these cleaners.
   b. why using these cleaners is more effective than washing with water.
34. From each of these pairs, select the water source more likely to contain the higher concentration of dissolved oxygen. Give a reason for each choice.
   a. a river with rapids or a calm lake
   b. a lake in spring or the same lake in summer
   c. a lake containing only black crappie fish or a lake containing only black bullhead fish

Extending the Concepts

38. Read the label on a container of baking soda. Compare it with the label on a container of baking powder. Which one contains an acid ingredient? Suggest a reason for including the acid in the mixture.
39. Describe how changes in solubility due to temperature could be used to separate two solid, water-soluble substances.

35. Fluorine has the highest electronegativity of any element. Fluorine and hydrogen form a polar bond. Which atom in HF would you expect to have a partial positive charge? Explain.
36. Suppose there are two identical fish tanks with identical conditions except for temperature. Tank A is maintained at a temperature 5 °C higher than is Tank B. Which tank could support the greater number of similar fish? Explain.
37. Using Figure 1.48 on page 75,
   a. determine the solubility of oxygen at 20 °C.
   b. express the answer you obtained in ppm.

40. The continued health of an aquarium depends on the balance of the solubilities of several substances. Investigate how this balance is maintained in a freshwater aquarium.
41. The pH of rainwater is approximately 5.5. Rainwater flows into the ocean. The pH of ocean water, however, is approximately 8.7. Investigate the reasons for this difference in pH.

and collect the less-soluble substance in the filter paper. Then further cool the filtrate until the second substance crystallizes.
40. Student answers will vary, but should address adjusting pH, aeration, and water temperature.

41. The rainwater originally interacts with gases in the atmosphere that make it slightly acidic. When rainwater reaches the ocean, it becomes quite diluted. The ocean contains basic solutes, which also neutralize acidic rainwater.

Water Purification and Treatment

SECTION

D

Section D: Water Purification and Treatment

The newspaper editorial sets the stage for the town council meeting being held to establish responsibility for the Riverwood fish kill. In Section C, students considered the possible cause or causes of the fish kill. Now, after analyzing Snake River data, students will decide whether the fish kill was an act of nature or if human activity was involved. They will also consider whether the fish kill could have been prevented, and who should bear the costs of emergency water and monetary losses due to cancellation of the fishing tournament.

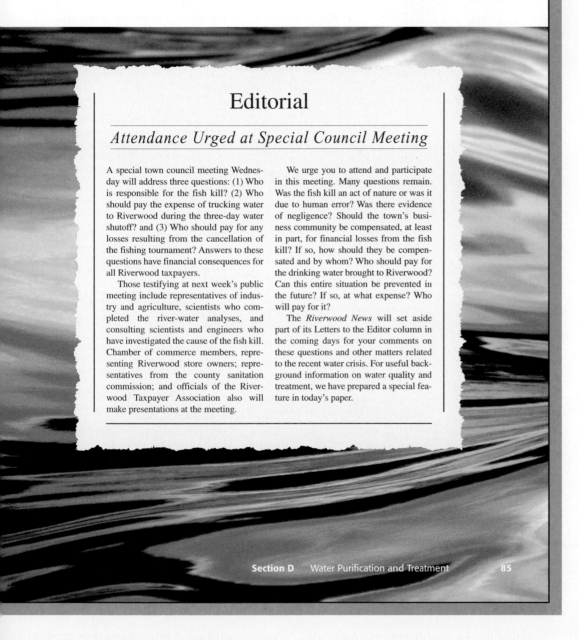

Editorial

Attendance Urged at Special Council Meeting

A special town council meeting Wednesday will address three questions: (1) Who is responsible for the fish kill? (2) Who should pay the expense of trucking water to Riverwood during the three-day water shutoff? and (3) Who should pay for any losses resulting from the cancellation of the fishing tournament? Answers to these questions have financial consequences for all Riverwood taxpayers.

Those testifying at next week's public meeting include representatives of industry and agriculture, scientists who completed the river-water analyses, and consulting scientists and engineers who have investigated the cause of the fish kill. Chamber of commerce members, representing Riverwood store owners; representatives from the county sanitation commission; and officials of the Riverwood Taxpayer Association also will make presentations at the meeting.

We urge you to attend and participate in this meeting. Many questions remain. Was the fish kill an act of nature or was it due to human error? Was there evidence of negligence? Should the town's business community be compensated, at least in part, for financial losses from the fish kill? If so, how should they be compensated and by whom? Who should pay for the drinking water brought to Riverwood? Can this entire situation be prevented in the future? If so, at what expense? Who will pay for it?

The *Riverwood News* will set aside part of its Letters to the Editor column in the coming days for your comments on these questions and other matters related to the recent water crisis. For useful background information on water quality and treatment, we have prepared a special feature in today's paper.

D.1 Natural Water Purification

 D.1–D.3 Content Reading Guide

The processes of natural water purification are discussed within the format of newspaper articles. The articles review three basic steps of nature's water-purification system—*evaporation, bacterial action,* and *filtration.* They also briefly introduce the issue of dissolved minerals in some water supplies (hard water), which will be discussed later in Section D. You may elect to review the hydrologic cycle with students or conduct a class discussion to determine the extent of students' prior knowledge about the hydrologic cycle and natural water purification.

Teaching the Hydrologic Cycle

You can think of the hydrologic cycle as a global water-purification system, powered and kept in constant motion by solar energy (and, to a much smaller extent, thermal energy from within Earth's crust) and gravitational forces. Through this dynamic system, water is continuously collected, purified, and distributed worldwide. In this analogy, the *oceans* are the primary water source, the *atmosphere* is the principal carrier of water, and *land* is the location of major water users.

The major processes of *evaporation* (and transpiration), *condensation, precipitation, infiltration,* and *runoff* characterize the cycle. Overall, within the cycle, water is neither lost nor gained. The specific water volume available at any particular place or time can vary.

Purifying Water Through the Hydrologic Cycle

 The Hydrologic Cycle

BY RITA HIDALGO
Riverwood News Staff Reporter

Riverwood residents want to know how clean their water is. It should not take a crisis to focus attention on their concerns.

This article provides details on how natural water-purification systems work. A companion article in today's *News* examines municipal water-treatment methods—procedures that mimic, in part, water-purification processes at work in nature's water cycle.

Until the late 1800s, Americans obtained water from local ponds, wells, and rainwater holding tanks. Wastewater and even human wastes were discarded into holes, dry wells, or leaching cesspools (pits lined with broken stone). Some wastewater was simply dumped on the ground.

By 1880, about one-quarter of U.S. urban households had flush toilets, and municipalities were constructing sewer systems. However, as recently as 1909, sewer wastes were often released without treatment into lakes and streams, from which water supplies were drawn at other locations. Many community leaders believed that natural waters would purify themselves indefinitely.

Waterborne diseases increased as the concentration of intestinal bacteria in drinking water rose. As a result, water filtering and chlorination soon began. However, municipal sewage—the combined waterborne wastes of a community—remained generally untreated. Today, sewage treatment is part of every U.S. municipality's water-processing procedures.

Nature's water cycle, the hydrologic cycle, includes water-purification steps that address many potential threats to water quality. Thermal energy from the Sun causes water to evaporate from oceans and other water sources. Dissolved heavy metals, minerals, or molecular substances do not evaporate and, thus, are left behind.

This natural process accomplishes many of the same results as distillation. Water vapor rises, condenses into tiny droplets in clouds, and—depending on the temperature—eventually falls as rain or snow. Raindrops and snowflakes are nature's purest form of water, containing only dissolved atmospheric gases. However, human activities release a number of gases into the air, making today's rain less pure than it used to be.

When raindrops strike soil, the rainwater collects impurities. Organic substances deposited by living creatures become suspended or dissolved in the rainwater. A few centimeters below the soil surface, bacteria feed on these substances, converting them into carbon dioxide, water, and other simple compounds. Such bacteria thus help repurify the water.

As water seeps farther into the ground, it usually passes through gravel, sand, and even rock. Waterborne bacteria and suspended matter are filtered out. Thus, three processes make up nature's water-purification system.

- Evaporation, followed by condensation, removes nearly all dissolved substances.
- Bacterial action converts dissolved organic contaminants into a few simple compounds.
- Filtration through sand and gravel removes nearly all suspended matter.

see *Purifying Water*, page 5

> Environmentalists sometimes remark that "we are all downstream from someone else."

Students can readily connect particular hydrologic-cycle stages to laboratory water-purification steps they completed (*Investigating Matter A.3*, page 10) or to municipal water-purification procedures they study in this section. These natural-purification processes include steps that resemble:

Purifiying Water, from page 3

Given appropriate conditions, people could depend solely on nature to purify their water. *Pure* rainwater is the best natural supply of clean water. If water seeping through the ground encountered enough bacteria for a long enough period of time, all organic contaminants could be removed. Flowing through sufficient sand and gravel would remove suspended matter from the water. However, nature's system only works well if it is not overloaded.

If slightly acidic groundwater (pH less than 7.0) passes through rocks that contain slightly soluble compounds, such as magnesium and calcium minerals, chemical reactions with these minerals may add substances to the water rather than remove substances in the water. In this case, the water may contain an increased concentration of dissolved minerals.

Hydrologic Cycle: Earth's water-purification system. The Sun provides energy for water to evaporate (yellow arrows). Evaporation leaves behind minerals and other dissolved substances. Water vapor condenses and falls as precipitation (red arrows), which runs off the land (blue arrows) to join surface water sources (lakes, streams, and rivers) or groundwater sources beneath Earth's surface. Both surface water and groundwater are sources of municipal and agricultural water. Any water—when returned to the surface—can evaporate and continue flowing through the hydrologic cycle. Throughout the cycle, evaporation, bacterial action, and filtration purify water.

Other processes at work include *crystallization,* formation of ice crystals from ocean water resulting in relatively pure water, and *oxidation* of complex organic matter to simpler, benign molecules.

You can also model the hydrologic cycle as consisting of water simultaneously entering and leaving various reservoirs (hydrologic compartments), where it is stored for short times or for decades or centuries. Model a reservoir using an open water container with a hole in its bottom, continually adding water to it (input) as water streams out of the hole (output). Introduce the concept of *residence time:* In the atmosphere, on average, water is completely replaced once every eight days, while water's residence time in glaciers and ice caps ranges from 20 to 100 years. The reservoirs with lowest water capacity tend to have the shortest residence time, since their inputs and outputs are relatively large compared to their capacity.

Average residence times in typical reservoirs include 1 to 2 months as soil moisture, 2 to 6 months as seasonal snow cover, 100 to 200 years as shallow groundwater, and up to about 10 000 years as deep groundwater. You could say that deep groundwater, such as the enormous Ogallala aquifer in the central and western United States, holds "fossil" water, mostly deposited during earlier, wetter climates.

- *distillation,* the evaporation of water, leaving behind dissolved ions and impurities
- *aeration* of surface water as it trickles over rocks, promoting growth of organisms that consume water contaminants
- *sedimentation,* the separation of solid particles from slow-moving water in streams and lakes
- *filtration,* silt and clay particle removal as water infiltrates sandy soil

D.2 Municipal Water Purification

The major steps in municipal water purification—screening, prechlorination, flocculation, settling, sand filtration, post-chlorination, and optional further treatment—are discussed and diagrammed within the format of a newspaper article.

An example of attempting to enhance drinking water to benefit the community is highlighted by a common procedure—adding fluoride ions to treated water. Students may have read articles about controversies over adding fluoride to municipal water. In many communities, about 1 ppm of fluoride ion is added to the water to reduce tooth decay. Medical evidence for side effects is minimal, and the benefit to dental health is well documented.

Many municipalities add other steps to their water-treatment processes, such as filtration, carbon adsorption, distillation, and reverse osmosis. Also, biological treatment can be employed to reduce concentrations of nitrogen and phosphorus in water.

This is an excellent opportunity to organize a field trip to a local water-treatment plant or a waste-treatment plant, if possible. The processes discussed and diagrammed in the text are found in most local and regional water-treatment plants.

For more information, see **http://www.epa.gov/safewater/index.html** or **http://www.awwa.org/Advocacy/learn/info/HistoryofDrinkingWater.cfm.**

Purifying Water Supplies by Municipal Pre-Use Treatment

BY **RITA HIDALGO**
Riverwood News Staff Reporter

Today, many rivers—such as the Snake River in Riverwood—are both a source of municipal water and a place to release wastewater (sewage). Therefore, the water is cleaned twice, both before and after the water is used. *Pre-use purification,* often called *water treatment,* takes place at a municipal filtration and treatment plant. It is the focus of this article.

A typical water-treatment process begins when intake water flows through metal screens that prevent fish, sticks, beverage containers, and other large objects from entering the water-treatment plant.

Plant operators may add chlorine, which is a powerful disinfecting agent, during the treatment process to kill disease-causing organisms. This step is known as *prechlorination.* Operators add crystals of alum—aluminum sulfate, $Al_2(SO_4)_3$—and slaked lime—calcium hydroxide, $Ca(OH)_2$—to remove suspended particles, such as colloidal clay, from the water. (Suspended particles can give water an unpleasant, murky appearance.) The alum and slaked lime react to form aluminum hydroxide, $Al(OH)_3$, which is a sticky, jellylike material that

Municipal Treatment: A human-made water-purification system. Surface water is commonly cleaned at a municipal water-treatment plant before being distributed to homes and businesses. Various steps in the cleaning process remove suspended materials, kill disease-causing organisms, and may remove odors or adjust pH levels.

see *Municipal Treatment,* page 6

Making Decisions

Municipal Treatment, from page 3

traps and removes the suspended particles, a process called *flocculation*. Operators then allow the aluminum hydroxide (holding trapped particles from the water) and other solids remaining in the water to settle to the tank bottom. They remove any suspended materials that do not settle out by filtering the water through sand.

In the *post-chlorination* step, operators adjust the chlorine concentration in the water to ensure that a low, but sufficient, concentration of chlorine remains in the water, thereby protecting the water from bacterial infestation.

One or more additional steps may take place, depending on community proce-

dures. Some plants spray water into the air to remove odors and improve its taste, a process known as *aeration*.

Water may sometimes be acidic enough to slowly dissolve metallic water pipes. This process not only shortens pipe life, but it may also cause copper (Cu^{2+}), as well as cadmium (Cd^{2+}) and other undesirable ions, to enter the home water supply. A plant may add lime—calcium oxide (CaO), a basic substance—to neutralize such acidic water, thus raising its pH to a proper level.

As much as about 1 ppm of fluoride ion (F^-) may be added to the treated water in a process known as *fluoridation*. Even at this low concentration, fluoride ions can reduce tooth decay.

Making Decisions

D.3 WATER PURIFICATION

Refer to the two water-treatment articles by Rita Hidalgo (pages 86 and 88) to answer the following questions.

1. Compare natural water-treatment steps to the treatment steps in municipal wastewater systems.

   a. What are key similarities?
   b. What are key differences?

2. After reading the two water-treatment articles, a Riverwood resident wrote a letter to the *Riverwood News* proposing that the town's water-treatment plant be shut down. The reader pointed out that this would save taxpayers considerable money because "natural water treatment can meet our needs just as well." Do you support the reader's proposal? Explain your answer.

Chlorine is probably the best known and most common substance used for water treatment; it is found not only in community water supplies but also in swimming pools. The following article provides background on the role of chlorine in water treatment.

Making Decisions

D.3 Water Purification

Answers

1. a. Natural and municipal water purification are similar; both include filtration and treatment that remove or render harmless organic materials.

   b. Evaporation is not a common step in municipal water treatment, but it is a key step in the natural water-treatment process. Bacterial action is not part of municipal water treatment, but is important in natural water treatment (and municipal sewage treatment). Municipal water treatment adds substances, such as chlorine, to water, while natural water treatment primarily removes substances from the water.

2. The primary problem is that natural water purification is much slower than municipal water purification. While natural water purification does produce drinkable water, current withdrawal rates would result in dry wells and depleted reservoirs before natural processes could complete adequate water purification.

D.4 Chlorination of Water

Use a whole-class discussion to uncover students' personal experiences with chlorinated water, which may include swimming pools or fish tanks. The article describes three methods of chlorination; students may be familiar with other methods.

On a worldwide basis, enough rain and snow fall each year to cover Earth's total land area to a depth of 83 cm. And yet, uneven distribution and inadequate technology make high-quality freshwater a major constraint on economic growth, food production, and general health in many nations. This is especially true of Asian and African countries, where periodic droughts and famines lead to the deaths of millions. Even when water is available in adequate quantities, it may be of poor quality. It has been estimated that 80% of all the world's sickness is caused by contaminated water and that persons with waterborne diseases occupy half of the world's hospital beds and die at a rate of 25 000 per day. Using chlorination and modern municipal water-treatment techniques could prevent many of these health issues.

For further information see **http://c3.org/chlorine_knowledge_center/index.html, http://www.awwa.org/Advocacy/govtaff/chldrpap.cfm,** or **http://www.nesc.wvu.edu/ndwc/pdf/OT/TB/TB1_Disinfection.pdf.**

D.5 Chlorination and THMs

A potential problem with chlorination is unintended production of trihalomethanes (THMs), known carcinogens. Before students read this, you might challenge them to think of ways other than chlorination to

Chlorine in Public Water Supplies

BY RITA HIDALGO
Riverwood News Staff Reporter

The single most common cause of human illness in the world is unhealthful water supplies. Without a doubt, adding chlorine to public water supplies has helped save countless lives by controlling waterborne diseases. In water, chlorine kills disease-producing microorganisms.

In most municipal water-treatment systems, chlorination, which is the addition of chlorine to the water supply to kill harmful organisms, often takes place in several different ways:

- Chlorine gas, Cl_2, is bubbled into the water. This substance is not very soluble in water. Chlorine does react with water, however, to produce a water-soluble, chlorine-containing compound.

- A water solution of sodium hypochlorite, $NaOCl$, which is the active ingredient in household bleach, is added to the water.

- Calcium hypochlorite, $Ca(OCl)_2$, is dissolved in the water. Available as both a powder and small pellets, calcium hypochlorite is often used in swimming pools. It is also a component of some solid household products sold as bleaching powder.

Regardless of how chlorination takes place, chemists believe that chlorine's most active form in water is hypochlorous acid (HOCl). This substance forms whenever chlorine, sodium hypochlorite, or calcium hypochlorite dissolves in water.

Unfortunately, a potential problem is associated with adding chlorine to municipal water. Under some conditions, chlorine in water can react with organic compounds produced by decomposing animal and plant matter to form substances that, if in sufficiently high concentrations, can be harmful to human health.

One group of such substances is known as the *trihalomethanes* (THMs). A common THM is chloroform ($CHCl_3$), a *carcinogen,* which is a substance that is known to cause cancer.

Because of concern about the possible health risks associated with THMs, the Environmental Protection Agency has placed a current limit of 80 parts per billion (ppb) on total THM concentration in municipal water-supply systems.

Possible risks associated with THMs must be balanced, of course, against the benefits of chlorinated water.

Flocculator–clarifier units at a municipal water-treatment facility.

D.5 CHLORINATION AND THMs

Operators of municipal water-treatment plants have several options for eliminating possible THM health risks highlighted in the newspaper article that you just read. However, each method has its disadvantages.

- ▶ They can pass treatment-plant water through an activated charcoal filter. Activated charcoal can remove most organic compounds from water, including THMs. *Disadvantage:* Charcoal filters are expensive to install and operate. Disposal also poses a problem because it is hard to clean used filters of contamination. Filters must be replaced relatively often.

- ▶ They can completely eliminate chlorine and use ozone (O_3) or ultraviolet light to disinfect the water. *Disadvantage:* Neither ozone nor ultraviolet light protects the water once it leaves the treatment plant. Treated water can be infected by bacteria—through faulty water pipes, for example. In addition, ozone can pose toxic hazards if not handled and used properly.

- ▶ They can eliminate prechlorination. Chlorine would be added only once, after filtering the water and removing much of the organic material. *Disadvantage:* The chlorine added in post-chlorination can still promote formation of THMs, even if to a lesser extent than with prechlorination. Additionally, a decrease in chlorine concentration might allow bacterial growth in the water.

Making Decisions

D.6 BOTTLED WATER VERSUS TAP WATER

Water that has been chlorinated sometimes has a characteristically bad taste. In general, when people do not like the taste of tap water or they think that the available water is unsafe to drink or they do not have access to other sources of fresh water, or just for convenience, they may buy bottled water (see Figure 1.55). This bottled water may come from a natural source, such as a mountain spring, or it may be processed at the bottling plant.

Is this water any better for you than tap water that has been processed by a municipal water treatment plant or that comes directly from ground or surface water?

Figure 1.55 *Which is better, bottled water or tap water? Why?*

---

control waterborne disease. Sometimes, technological solutions to problems create new problems. The formation of THMs, such as chloroform ($CHCl_3$) from chlorination is one example.

Alternative strategies such as using ozone and ultraviolet light are introduced as a way to disinfect water. Mention that these methods are already in use in some public water supplies, but that they are expensive. Additionally, these modes of disinfection involve on-site generation of the ozone or ultraviolet light and appropriately equipped facilities. You may decide to revisit the question (addressed in *Investigating Matter A.3*) of the time and expense needed to obtain safe, clean water.

Making Decisions

D.6 Bottled Water versus Tap Water

With a bottle of spring water in hand, introduce this activity by asking students if they believe this water to be pure, clean, and better than ordinary tap water. Then ask them to defend their answers. Encourage them to provide evidence or data to support their conclusion. Ask small groups of students to brainstorm for a few minutes and come up with three ways they could test the water to determine whether it is better and safer to drink than regular tap water.

Resources: **http://www.fda.gov/fdac/features/2002/402_h2o.html**, **http://www.waterandhealth.org/newsletter/new/summer-2002/bottled.html**, and **http://www.nrdc.org/water/drinking/bw/bwinx.asp**.

Answers

1. Student answers will vary, but might include safety, presence of bacteria, presence of ions, pH, cost, source, and presence of organic substances.

2. Possible factual information includes:

Safety—EPA safety limits and levels of various substances within each type of water

Presence of bacteria—EPA safety limits and detected levels within each type of water

Presence of ions—EPA safety limits and measured levels within each type of water

pH—prescribed limits and measured levels within each type of water

Cost—cost of bottled water and household tap water

Source—location from which bottled water is drawn, whether tap water is from ground or surface water, etc.

Presence of organic substances—EPA safety limits and measured levels within each type of water

---

Could it possibly be harmful? What determines water quality? How can the risks and benefits of drinking water from various sources be assessed?

As usual, answering challenging questions requires gathering reliable data and information, weighing alternatives, and making informed decisions. Working with a partner, answer the following questions:

1. In your view, what two or three factors should you consider in deciding whether to drink tap water or bottled water?

2. For each factor listed in your answer to Question 1, what factual information would be needed to establish the advantages and disadvantages of drinking bottled water rather than tap water?

Investigating Matter

Lab Video: Water Softening

D.7 WATER SOFTENING

Introduction

The goal of municipal water-treatment facilities is to provide water that is safe to drink, it is not to produce completely pure water. One aspect—water hardness—is not usually addressed at the municipal-treatment level.

Water containing an excess of dissolved calcium (Ca^{2+}), magnesium (Mg^{2+}), or iron(III) (Fe^{3+}) ions is known as **hard water.** Hard water does not form a soapy lather easily. River water usually contains low concentrations of hard-water ions. However, as groundwater flows over limestone, chalk, and other minerals that contain calcium, magnesium, and iron, it often gains higher concentrations of these ions, thus producing hard water. See Table 1.7 and Figure 1.56.

In this investigation, you will explore several ways of softening water by comparing three possible water treatments and determining

> The formula $CaSO_4 \cdot 2H_2O$ indicates there are two molecules of water for every unit of $CaSO_4$ contained in this solid crystal.

| Table 1.7

SOME MINERALS CONTRIBUTING TO WATER HARDNESS		
Mineral	**Chemical Composition**	**Chemical Formula**
Limestone or chalk	Calcium carbonate	$CaCO_3$
Magnesite	Magnesium carbonate	$MgCO_3$
Gypsum	Calcium sulfate	$CaSO_4 \cdot 2H_2O$
Dolomite	Calcium carbonate and magnesium carbonate combination	$CaCO_3 \cdot MgCO_3$

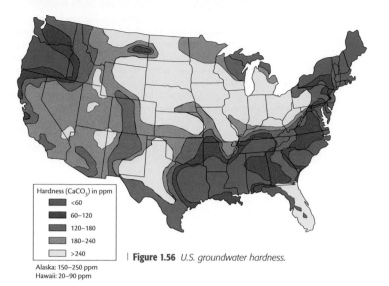

Hardness (CaCO₃) in ppm

	<60
	60–120
	120–180
	180–240
	>240

Figure 1.56 *U.S. groundwater hardness.*

Alaska: 150–250 ppm
Hawaii: 20–90 ppm

whether they remove calcium ions from a hard-water sample: (1) sand filtration, (2) treatment with Calgon, and (3) treatment with an ion-exchange resin.

Calgon, which contains sodium hexametaphosphate ($Na_6P_6O_{18}$), and similar commercial products remove hard-water cations, including calcium ions, by causing them to become part of larger, soluble anions. For example:

$$2\ Ca^{2+}(aq)\quad +\quad (P_6O_{18})^{6-}(aq)\quad \longrightarrow\quad [Ca_2(P_6O_{18})]^{2-}(aq)$$

Calcium ion   Hexametaphosphate ion   Calcium hexametaphosphate
from hard water   from $Na_6P_6O_{18}$ anion

Calcium hexametaphosphate is a water-soluble anion that binds calcium ions and prevents them from forming insoluble compounds. Calgon also contains sodium carbonate (Na_2CO_3), which softens water by removing hard-water cations as precipitates, such as calcium carbonate ($CaCO_3$). The equation for this reaction follows. Solid calcium carbonate particles are washed away with the rinse water.

$$Ca^{2+}(aq)\quad +\quad CO_3^{2-}(aq)\quad \longrightarrow\quad CaCO_3(s)$$

Calcium ion   Carbonate ion   Calcium carbonate
from hard   from sodium   precipitate
water   carbonate

Another water-softening method relies on **ion exchange.** Hard water is passed through an ion-exchange resin, such as that found in home water-softeners. The resin consists of millions of tiny, insoluble, porous beads capable of attracting and binding cations.

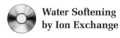 **Water Softening by Ion Exchange**

Using the Figures

Figure 1.56: Ask students to use this map to estimate the level of water hardness where you live. Ask if any students have traveled to areas of the nation where water hardness differed from what they were familiar with, according to the map. At that time, did they notice any differences in the quality of the water? (For instance, washing one's hair feels different, depending on water hardness.) Caution students that this map shows only regional levels of calcium carbonate (hardness) that are *naturally* occurring. Individual businesses, residences, and even municipalities use various technologies to alter the hardness or softness of their water supplies. Thus, students might have noticed the water was very "soft" in a region where the water supply contains high levels of calcium ions, and vice versa.

Investigating Matter

D.7 Water Softening

 D.7 Water Softening Student Worksheet and Data Table

In this investigation, students explore and compare three methods of softening hard water.

Time

50 min

Materials

(For 24 students working in pairs)

12 funnels, 73-mm inside diameter

12 ring stands

12 rings

12 clay triangles

96 pieces of 11-cm filter paper (Whatman No. 1)

220 test tubes (18 × 150 mm) [fewer required with intermediate cleaning]

12 test-tube stoppers

12 test-tube racks

12 20-cm glass stirring rods

12 10-mL graduated cylinders

1.5 L hard water, containing 0.01 M Ca^{2+} (2.2 g $CaCl_2 \cdot 2H_2O$/1.5 L)

1 L distilled water, preferably in dispensing bottles

100 mL 0.1 M sodium carbonate in dropper bottles (1.2 g $Na_2CO_3 \cdot H_2O$/100 mL)

Liquid soap solution, Ivory or equivalent, preferably in dropper bottles

1 lb sand

1 box Calgon (containing sodium hexametaphosphate) or sodium hexametaphosphate

100 g cation-exchange resin, ionic form Na^+ DOWEX 50 WX8 or equivalent, 50–100 mesh

Safety

Students should wear protective goggles and aprons throughout this investigation.

Advance Preparation

Prepare the ion-exchange resin as a water slurry: Add 2 parts water to 1 part resin in a beaker. Decant excess water. Soak the resin overnight before using it. Purchase Calgon or equivalent water softener. Ensure that your water softener contains sodium hexametaphosphate for bath use, *not* sodium sesquicarbonate for dishes. This type of Calgon may be difficult (or even impossible) to find in some regions due to its phosphate content. Alternately, sodium hexametaphosphate can be purchased from chemical-supply houses.

Rinse the sand thoroughly with distilled water to remove dirt, hard-water ions, etc., that might interfere with hard-water testing.

Pre-Lab Discussion

Emphasize that hard water is caused by excess concentrations of calcium, magnesium, and/or iron(III) ions in water. Point out that water softeners are installed in many homes and will be discussed later.

Lab Tips

• The exchange resin contains 40–50% moisture and, thus, must be stored in a sealed container to prevent drying. The ion-exchange resin and sand can be reused from period to period. The resin can be regenerated for future use by washing it three times in a beaker with 1 M NaCl, and then three times with distilled water.

• An alternative to using liquid Ivory soap is to prepare a small quantity of Ivory flakes: Place about 1/8 bar of Ivory soap in a microwave oven and heat it until it no longer expands. Allow the bar to cool and then crumble it into soap flakes. Use only several small flakes in each test tube.

Hard-water ions are retained on the ion-exchange resin, while soft-water ions are released from the resin to replace the hard-water ions in the solution. Thus, an ion-exchange resin must be recharged occasionally when all the soft-water ions have been displaced by hard-water ions. You will learn more about water-softening procedures after you have completed this investigation.

Two laboratory tests will help you decide whether your original hard-water sample has been softened. The first test is the reaction between hard-water calcium cations and carbonate anions (added as sodium carbonate, Na_2CO_3, solution) to form a calcium carbonate precipitate. The equation for this reaction is described on page 93. The second test is to observe the effect of adding soap to the water sample, forming a lather.

Before starting, read the procedure to learn what you will need to do, note safety precautions, and plan necessary data collecting and observations.

Procedure

1. In your laboratory notebook, prepare a data table similar to the one that follows.

DATA TABLE								
Test	Filter Paper		Filter Paper and Sand		Filter Paper and Calgon		Filter Paper and Ion-Exchange Resin	
	Distilled Water	Hard Water	Distilled Water	Hard Water	Distilled Water	Hard Water	Distilled Water	Hard Water
Reaction with sodium carbonate (Na_2CO_3)								
Degree of cloudiness (turbidity) with Ivory soap								
Height of suds (mm)								

2. Prepare the lab setup as shown in Figure 1.57. Lower the tip of the funnel stem into a test tube supported in a test-tube rack.

3. Fold a piece of filter paper; insert it in the funnel.

4. You will repeat Steps 5 through 7 several times. This first time, your funnel should contain only the filter paper; it serves as the control.

5. Pour about 10 mL of distilled water into the funnel. Do not pour any water over the top of the filter paper or between the filter paper and the funnel wall. Collect the filtrate in the test tube.

6. Divide the filtrate into two equal volumes of approximately 5 mL, using two clean test tubes. Add 10 drops of sodium carbonate (Na_2CO_3) solution to one of the test tubes. Does a precipitate form? Record your observations. A cloudy precipitate indicates that the Ca^{2+} ion (a hard-water cation) was not removed. Clean the test tube thoroughly with tap water and rinse with distilled water.

7. Take the second test tube containing 5 mL of filtrate and add one drop of Ivory liquid hand soap (*not* liquid detergent). Label the test tube and set it aside for Steps 12 through 15.

8. Repeat Steps 5 through 7, using 10 mL of hard water instead of distilled water.

9. Install a new piece of filter paper and fill it one-third full of sand. Repeat Steps 5 through 7 by pouring distilled water through the sand; then repeat Steps 5 through 7, pouring hard water through the sand. Dispose of the filter paper as directed by your teacher.

10. Install a new piece of filter paper and fill it one-third full of Calgon. Repeat Steps 5 through 7 for distilled water and hard water. Dispose of the solids held in your filter paper as directed by your teacher. (*Note:* The Calgon-treated filtrate may appear blue due to other softener additives. They will not cause a problem. However, if the filtrate appears cloudy, which means that some Calgon powder passed through the filter paper, use a new piece of filter paper and filter the test-tube liquid again.)

11. Install a new piece of filter paper and fill it one-third full of ion-exchange resin. Repeat Steps 5 through 7 for each type of water tested. Dispose of the solids held in your filter paper as directed by your teacher.

12. Take each test tube from Step 7 and stir gently. Wipe the stirring rod before inserting it into another test tube.

13. Compare the cloudiness of the soap solutions. Record your observations. The greater the cloudiness, the greater the quantity of soap that dispersed. The quantity of dispersed soap determines the cleaning effectiveness of the solution.

14. Stopper each test tube and then shake vigorously, as demonstrated by your teacher. The more suds that form, the softer the water. Measure the height of suds in each test tube and record your observations.

| **Figure 1.57** *Filtration setup.*

Labels: Filter paper, Metal ring, Clay triangle, Ring stand, Funnel, Test tube, Test tube rack

Section D   Water Purification and Treatment   95

EXPECTED RESULTS				
REACTANT	**FILTER PAPER**	**FILTER PAPER + SAND**	**FILTER PAPER + CALGON**	**FILTER PAPER + ION-EXCHANGE RESIN**
Sodium carbonate	Cloudy	Cloudy	No reaction	No reaction
Degree of cloudiness	Very clear	Very clear	Blue and turbid	Very turbid
Height of suds	None	None	1–2 mm	1–2 mm

Answers

1. The ion-exchange resin should remove hard-water ions best, but students may report that Calgon was a better water softener. As long as the determination is supported by evidence (degree of cloudiness or height of suds), either answer is acceptable. Possible reasons for this being the best method include removing the hard-water ions (ion-exchange resin) or trapping the hard-water ions (Calgon).

2. As the concentration of Ca^{2+} remaining in the filtrate increases (that is, as the water hardness increases), the soap will become increasingly less dispersed.

3. The cleaning action of soap depends on how dispersed or dissolved it is in water. As more soap molecules are bound to hard-water ions such as Ca^{2+}, fewer soap molecules are available for cleaning.

Post-Lab Discussion

Organize your post-lab discussion around the questions provided. You may ask students to interpret their observations. Consider mentioning that ion-exchange procedures are used in most home water-softener systems. Ask any students who happen to have these systems in their homes to describe the maintenance they require.

Recently, some communities have banned salt-based ion-exchange systems, employing mixed-bed H^+ and OH^- resins instead. The mixed-bed resin appears to be equally effective, but not as easily recharged. Instead, the resin is "exchanged" by the water-softening company. Challenge students to think about health-related reasons that can account for banning salt-based resins in some places.

---

15. Clean the test tubes thoroughly with tap water and rinse with distilled water.
16. Wash your hands thoroughly before leaving the laboratory.

Questions

1. Which was the most effective water-softening method? Support your answer with evidence from observations and data you gathered. Suggest why this method worked best.
2. What relationship can you describe between the amount of hard-water ion (Ca^{2+}) remaining in the filtrate and the dispersion (cloudiness) of Ivory liquid hand soap?
3. What effect does this relationship have on the cleansing action of the soap?

D.8 WATER AND WATER SOFTENING

Hard Water and Soap Scum

Hard water causes some common household problems. It interferes with the cleaning action of soap. As you observed, when soap mixes with soft water, it disperses to form a cloudy solution topped with a sudsy layer. In hard water, however, soap reacts with hard-water ions to form insoluble compounds (precipitates). These compounds appear as solid flakes or a sticky scum. The precipitated soap is no longer available for cleaning. Worse yet, soap curd can deposit on clothes, skin, and hair. The structural formula for this substance, the product of the reaction of soap with calcium ions, is shown in Figure 1.58.

If hydrogen carbonate (bicarbonate, HCO_3^-) ions are present in hard water, boiling the water causes solid calcium carbonate ($CaCO_3$) to form. The reaction removes undesirable calcium ions and, thus, softens the water. However, the solid calcium carbonate can produce rocklike scale inside tea kettles, household hot-water heaters, and even power-plant boilers. This scale (the same compound found in marble and limestone) acts as thermal insulation, partly blocking heat flow to the water. More time and energy are required to heat the water. Such

Figure 1.58 *Structural formula of a typical soap scum. This substance is calcium stearate.*

Figure 1.59 *In the 1960s and early 1970s, detergent molecules not decomposed by microorganisms caused some waterways to fill with sudsy foam, such as shown here. The development of biodegradable detergent molecules put an end to this unusual kind of water pollution.*

deposits can also form in home water pipes. In older homes with this problem, water flow can be greatly reduced.

Fortunately, it is possible to soften hard water by removing some dissolved calcium, magnesium, or iron(III) ions. Adding sodium carbonate to hard water (as you did in the preceding investigation) was an early method of softening water. Sodium carbonate (Na_2CO_3), known as *washing soda,* was commonly added to laundry water along with the clothes and soap. Hard-water ions, precipitated as calcium carbonate ($CaCO_3$) and magnesium carbonate ($MgCO_3$), were washed away in the rinse water.

Water-softening substances in common use today include borax, trisodium phosphate, and sodium hexametaphosphate (as in Calgon). As you learned, Calgon does not tie up hard-water ions as a precipitate, but rather as a new, soluble ion that does not react with soap.

Most cleaning products sold today contain *detergents* rather than soap. Synthetic **detergents** act like soap, but they do not form insoluble compounds with hard-water ions. Unfortunately, many early detergents were not easily decomposed by bacteria in the environment; that is, they were not biodegradable. At times, "mountains" of foamy suds were observed in natural waterways. See Figure 1.59. These early detergents also contained phosphate ions (PO_4^{3-}) that encouraged extensive algae growth, choking lakes and streams. Because most of today's detergents are biodegradable and phosphate free, they do not cause these problems.

D.8 Water and Water Softening

This material identifies sources of hard-water ions and explains common problems hard water causes. The section also covers common methods used to soften hard water, such as sodium carbonate, borax, and water softeners (ion-exchange resins).

Resources: **http://www.mortonsalt. com/faq/faq_wate.asp** and **http://home.howstuffworks.com/ question99.htm.**

Using the Figures

Figure 1.58: Challenge students to apply what they know about polar and nonpolar molecules to a class of molecules about which they are likely to be unfamiliar: *emulsifiers.* Suggest to students that soap's molecular structure is related to its usefulness. Ask them to conjecture how soap's structure facilitates its job (enabling oil from our skin and hair to be washed away with water). The long hydrocarbon tail of a soap molecule is a nonpolar region to which oil on our skin is attracted, while negatively charged oxygen atoms of soap molecules are attracted to the partially positive hydrogen ends of water molecules. This allows soap molecules to "pull off" the oil from our skin and, eventually, carry it away in water down the drain. Emulsifiers are further discussed in Unit 7, pages 630 and 632.

Scientific American Working Knowledge Illustration

This illustration shows how a common home water softener works. The drawing on the left shows normal operation, with hard water going in and soft water going out. As the hard-water ions encounter the ion-exchange resin, they displace sodium ions due to their greater (2+) electrical charge. On the right is the regeneration cycle, with concentrated sodium chloride solutions entering and hard-water ion solutions exiting. As the sodium ions encounter the ion-exchange resin, they displace—through higher concentration—hard-water ions, which then are discharged down the drain. If you deem it helpful, remind/inform students that solutions are always charge-balanced. For example, a hard-water solution contains enough anions (typically chloride ions) to equal (or electrically balance) the positive charge of hard-water cations.

Additional Background Information

The following equation summarizes the reaction that occurs in water softeners. R represents an ion-binding site in the resin:

$$2\ NaR + Ca^{2+} \rightarrow CaR_2 + 2\ Na^+$$

The resin is prepared by rinsing it thoroughly with solutions containing sodium ions, which bind to the

If you live in a hard-water region, your home plumbing may include a **water softener** (see Figure 1.60). Hard water flows through a tank containing an ion-exchange resin similar to the one that you used in the water-softening investigation. Initially, the resin is filled with sodium cations (Na^+). Calcium and magnesium cations in the hard water are attracted to the resin and become attached to it. At the same time, sodium cations leave the resin and dissolve in the water. Thus, undesirable hard-water ions are exchanged for sodium ions, which do not react to form soap curd or water-pipe scale.

As you might imagine, the resin eventually fills with hard-water ions and must be regenerated. Concentrated salt water (containing sodium ions and chloride ions) flows through the resin, replacing the hard-water ions held on the resin with sodium ions. Released hard-water ions wash down the drain with excess salt water. Because this process takes several hours, it is usually completed at night. After the resin has been regenerated, the softener is again ready to exchange ions with incoming hard water.

Water softeners are most often installed in individual homes. Other water treatment is done at a municipal level, both in Riverwood and in other cities.

HARD WATER IN

SOFT WATER OUT

CONCENTRATED SODIUM CHLORIDE SOLUTION IN

HARD-WATER IONS OUT

Figure 1.60 *Home Water Softener* *Hard water, containing excess calcium (Ca^{2+}), magnesium (Mg^{2+}), or iron(III) (Fe^{3+}) cations, prevents soap from lathering easily and can cause scale to build up inside pipes. Thus, where hard water poses a problem, many people install home water softeners. Water softeners contain ion-exchange resin, depicted here as orange beads. Left: Initially, sodium ions (Na^+, depicted as black dots in the magnified portion) are attached to the resin. As hard water flows into the tank, hard-water cations such as Mg^{2+} and Ca^{2+} (yellow triangles and red squares) become attached to the resin, releasing Na^+ ions into the water. This softened water flows through pipes to faucets, water heaters, and washing machines. Right: Eventually, all Na^+ ions are replaced by hard-water ions; no further ion exchange can occur. Then, the resin is "recharged" with Na^+ ions (black dots) by passing concentrated sodium chloride solution through the system. This displaces hard-water ions (yellow triangles and red squares) from the resin; they flow from the water softener into a drain. Thus, regenerated resin—with Na^+ ions again attached—is ready to soften hard water again.*

anion sites. When hard water containing calcium or magnesium ions is filtered through the resin, the more highly charged ions have a greater attraction to the anion sites, replacing the sodium ions, which are then discharged with the flow of the liquid through the resin. The resin is regenerated by washing it with a concentrated sodium ion solution (sodium chloride solution). Hard water is prepared with these types of resins.

The concept of charge balance is illustrated in this equation. The notion is simply that the total electrical charge must remain constant on the resin and in the water. Here two Na^+ ions are freed for each Ca^{2+} ion bound to the resin.

Additional ChemQuandary

Ion-exchange water-softening units substitute sodium ions for hard-water ions such as Ca^{2+}. Does this create any new problems? Discussion: Yes, because the water now contains higher concentrations of sodium ions. People with high blood pressure who need to restrict their sodium intake must find alternate sources of drinking water. Many houses have small reverse-osmosis units or other high-performance filtration systems for drinking and cooking water.

Chemistry at Work Content Reading Guide

Chemistry at Work

This Chemistry at Work introduces Phil Noe of Island Water Association in Florida and the process of water desalination. The benefits of reverse osmosis allow the residents of Florida's Sanibel and Captiva islands to use water from their salty aquifers.

CHEMISTRY at Work

Purifying Water Means More Than Going with the Flow

When you drink from a water fountain, do you ever wonder where the water comes from? In some parts of the country, drinking water is provided by people such as Phil Noe.

Phil is the Production Manager at Island Water Association (IWA), which provides water for Florida's Sanibel and Captiva islands. "We have a limited supply of fresh water," says Phil, "so we built a plant that lets us use water from our aquifers." Aquifers are underground layers of permeable (porous) sand and limestone that contain large quantities of water.

After pumping the brackish, undrinkable water from the Suwanee Aquifer to IWA's processing plant, Phil and his coworkers remove most of the salt and minerals, producing water that is purer than many mountain streams through a process known as *reverse osmosis*. The accompanying illustration is a comparison of osmosis with reverse osmosis. The level of

> **"We have a limited supply of fresh water," says Phil, "so we built a plant that lets us use water from our aquifers."**

OSMOSIS

Salt solution — Flow ← — Pure water

Semipermeable membrane

REVERSE OSMOSIS

Pressure

Salt solution — Flow → — Pure water

Semipermeable membrane

CROSS SECTION OF PURIFYING TUBE

Semipermeable membrane

Water molecules forced through membrane

Salty water feed/Input (Water under pressure)

Permeate (Purified water to user)

Even saltier waste water to drain

Unwanted contaminant molecules left behind

Top Left: *Osmosis occurs naturally when water in a dilute solution passes through the semipermeable membrane into a concentrated solution.*
Top Right: *In reverse osmosis, pressure must be applied to a concentrated solution to force water through the semipermeable membrane, producing purified water.*

After filtering to remove the larger solids, the water passes through equipment where reverse osmosis is used to produce purified water.

Saving up for a windy day.

Aquatic wildlife is unaffected by the salt water left over from the reverse osmosis process.

pressure applied in reverse osmosis must exceed the osmotic pressure, which tends to move the water from a region of higher vapor pressure to one of lower vapor pressure. Because osmotic pressure depends only on the concentration of the salt solution, it is known as a *colligative property.*

Aquifers are located at depths ranging between 240 and 310 m (700–900 ft). Water pumped from these aquifers contains an average of 3000 ppm total dissolved solids (TDS). Feed water is pumped through long stretches of pipes that contain salt-filtering membranes. In the process, the purified water, called the *permeate,* separates from the salts and other dissolved solids. Eventually, the water is purified to levels as low as 100 ppm TDS.

Because Florida is subject to hurricanes and other tropical storms, Sanibel Island's water system maintains 15 million gallons of purified water in storage. As a result, island customers can manage without the plant in operation during brief periods of severe weather with no more inconvenience than several weeks without lawn sprinklers.

Web Search . . .

- Search the World Wide Web for other communities that rely on reverse osmosis for all or part of their water supply.

- Most communities use rivers, lakes, or wells to supply their water needs. Search the Web for information about municipal water-supply systems that use alternative water purification processes.

- What other kinds of water purification systems are in use in the United States?

- Use the Web to gather information about the cost of water for household use in various parts of the United States. Is there a connection between the cost of water and the location of the community? For example, is water more expensive in the desert than it is near the ocean?

Section D Water Purification and Treatment **101**

SECTION D SUMMARY

 Section D Supplement

Reviewing the Concepts

1. Student diagrams should show evaporation, precipitation, runoff, streams, and aquifers.

2. Evaporation separates water from minerals and other dissolved substances. Bacterial action converts dissolved organic contaminants into simple compounds. Filtration removes suspended matter.

3. Aluminum hydroxide forms a jellylike material—created by an aqueous reaction of aluminum sulfate (alum) with calcium hydroxide (slaked lime)—that traps colloidal particles within a heavy matrix that drops to the bottom of the settling pond.

4. CaO, a basic substance, is used to neutralize water. Acidic water corrodes metallic water pipes and causes release of heavy-metal ions.

5. About 1 ppm, to prevent tooth decay

6. It does not contain disease-causing microorganisms that might live in untreated water.

7. Yes. Chlorine can react with organic compounds in water to form carcinogenic THMs.

8. Even a clear mountain stream may contain disease-causing microorganisms.

9. Charcoal filtration, ozone treatment, and ultraviolet light.

10. Formation of soap scum, formation of scale, and interference with soap cleansing.

11. Ca^{2+}, Mg^{2+}, Fe^{3+}

12. The precipitate ($CaCO_3$) indicates the presence of Ca^{2+} ions.

SECTION D SUMMARY
Reviewing the Concepts

Water can be purified through the actions of the hydrologic cycle or through municipal treatment.

1. Make a diagram of the hydrologic cycle and label all processes.

2. List three major processes that occur in natural water purification and, for each, identify the contaminants that the process removes.

3. How are the properties of aluminum hydroxide related to the process of flocculation?

4. Why is calcium oxide (CaO) sometimes added in the final steps of municipal water treatment?

5. Fluoride, an ingredient in many types of toothpaste, is sometimes added to municipal water supplies in the last stage of water treatment. How much fluoride is added and what is its purpose?

Chlorination is commonly used to treat and purify water for human consumption.

6. What are advantages of chlorinated drinking water compared to untreated water?

7. Is there a disadvantage to using chlorination in water treatment? Explain.

8. Water from a clear mountain stream may require chlorination to make it safe for drinking. Explain.

9. List two alternatives to the use of chlorination in municipal water treatment.

Hard water can be softened by removing hard-water ions as a precipitate or as large soluble ions.

10. What are two problems associated with the use of hard water?

11. Identify three common hard-water ions.

12. When a sample of well water was mixed with a few drops of sodium carbonate solution, a precipitate formed. What does the formation of a precipitate indicate about the water sample?

13. Hard water often tastes better than distilled water. Explain.

14. Which water source in a given locality would probably have harder water, a well or a river? Explain.

15. Sketch two molecular-level representations of an ion-exchange resin bead—one bead before and one bead after treatment of hard water.

13. Hard-water ions often give water a pleasant taste.

14. A well. Well water originally percolated through soil and rock, dissolving hard-water ions.

15. The "before" bead should show sodium ions attached, while the "after" bead should show hard-water ions attached.

Connecting the Concepts

16. Hard-water ions bind with soap molecules, preventing formation of suds. Soap sud formation is inversely related to water hardness.

17. Hard water causes buildup of scale in boiler pipes, reducing the flow of water and steam and thus reducing efficiency.

Connecting the Concepts

16. A simple test of water hardness is to add soap to the water sample and shake. Explain how you can measure the quantity of soap suds to assess the relative hardness of the water.

17. Explain why hard water can decrease the efficiency of a boiler in a steam-generated, electric power plant.

18. Explain what would happen to Earth's hydrologic cycle if water evaporation suddenly stopped.

19. One unique characteristic of water is that it is present in all three physical states (solid, liquid, and gas) in the range of temperatures found on Earth. How would the hydrologic cycle be different if this were not true?

20. Why does the EPA limit the concentration of THMs to 80 ppb instead of requiring their total elimination from municipal water supplies?

21. Compare how the various processes used in the foul-water investigation (page 10) are similar to steps in the natural purification of water.

22. Some physicians recommend consuming about 2 L of water daily. Municipal water supplies may contain up to 1 ppm fluoride. Assume that you drink 2 L of water per day. At 1 ppm fluoride, how many grams of fluoride ion would you consume in

a. one day? b. one week? c. one year?

Extending the Concepts

23. How much water would you need to drink to get your minimum daily requirement of calcium from water that contains 300 ppm Ca^{2+}?

24. Explain why we find hard-water stains in old sinks around hot-water faucets more often than around cold-water faucets.

25. Research the sources and production of a brand of bottled water. Report on its origin and identify the substances that are removed and added before the water is bottled and sold.

26. Discuss the health effects associated with sodium-based ion-exchange resins used in home water softening systems.

27. Compare activated charcoal with reverse osmosis in home water filtration systems.

28. Describe and evaluate the practicality of two desalination processes for making seawater suitable for drinking.

Section Summary   103

amount of naturally occurring THMs, or the relatively small health risks linked to 80 ppb THMs compared to high risks associated with untreated water.

21. Oil–water separation is similar to evaporation; phases are physically separated. Sand-gravel filtration is essentially identical to natural filtration. Charcoal absorption is also similar to filtration.

22. a. $\dfrac{1 \text{ g F}^-}{1\,000\,000 \text{ mg water}} \times$

$\dfrac{2 \text{ L}}{1 \text{ day}} \times \dfrac{1000 \text{ g water}}{1 \text{ L water}} \times$

$\dfrac{1000 \text{ mg water}}{1 \text{ g water}} \times 1 \text{ day} =$

2 mg F^-

b. $\dfrac{2 \text{ mg F}^-}{\text{day}} \times 7 \text{ days} = 14 \text{ mg F}^-$

c. 700 mg F$^-$

Extending the Concepts

23. 1200 mg for 15- to 18-year-olds is the RDA.

$1200 \text{ mg} \times \dfrac{1 \text{ L water}}{300 \text{ mg Ca}^{2+}} =$

4 L water

24. Hard-water ions are more soluble in hot than in cold water, so the hot-water faucet delivers water with a higher concentration of hard-water ions, especially stain-producing Fe^{3+}; the ions are deposited when they contact the colder surface of the sink.

25. Answers will vary depending on the brand.

26. Sodium ion-exchange resins release sodium ions, which may affect the health of some people. Students should provide details.

27. Students should list advantages and disadvantages, as well as the mode of operation of each technique.

28. Students should address techniques that may include reverse osmosis and distillation.

18. Precipitation and runoff would cease once all atmospheric moisture was released. Widespread drought would probably result.

19. Without gaseous water, problems like those described in Question 18 could result. Evaporation and precipitation would not be possible. Without such steps, concentrations of dissolved substances in water could increase over time.

Solid water serves as a reservoir for fresh water. Its absence would affect water levels throughout the cycle.

The hydrologic cycle could not operate without liquid water. Oceans, rivers and lakes would not exist.

20. Possible reasons include the need for extremely accurate measurement, the cost and difficulty associated with removing all THMs, the possible threat of a small

PUTTING IT ALL TOGETHER: FISH KILL—FINDING THE SOLUTION

 Putting It All Together: Riverwood Town Council Meeting Group Worksheets and Evaluation Form

The final newspaper clipping in this unit announces a town council meeting to discuss who is responsible for the fish kill and who should pay for costs associated with the problem.

At this simulated town council meeting, students present data to support a particular point of view. There may be some disagreements about how to address these issues. This promotes presentation skills, using data to support an argument, expressing ideas scientifically, and citizenship skills.

The purpose of this culminating activity is to encourage students to use the chemistry they have learned to analyze real-world problems resembling those they may encounter as voting adults. The preparation and actual meeting should require no more than three 50-min periods of in-class work. You can reduce this time requirement by assigning more preparation as homework.

Student groups prepare statements, develop presentations that express the viewpoint of groups they represent, and prepare questions for other groups. You might assign individual students to write an editorial or conduct an interview about the Riverwood problem.

This activity helps students recognize that while science does not provide absolute answers to social problems, they can often use scientific principles to help formulate

PUTTING IT ALL TOGETHER

FISH KILL—FINDING THE SOLUTION

Fish Kill Cause Identified

Meeting Tonight

BY ORLANI O'BRIEN
Riverwood News Staff Reporter

Mayor Edward Cisko announced at a news conference earlier today that the cause of the fish kill in the Snake River has been determined. The details of the accident cause will be released at a town council meeting tonight. As of today, levels of all dissolved materials in the river are normal and the water should be considered safe.

Accompanying Mayor Cisko was Dr. Harold Schmidt of the Environmental Protection Agency. Schmidt dissected fish taken from the river within a few hours of their death. He also directed the team that analyzed accumulated river-water data in efforts that led to determining the cause of the fish kill. Schmidt gave assurances that the town's water supply is "fully safe to drink."

Mayor Cisko refused to elaborate on the reasons for the accident. How-

ever, he invited the public to the special council meeting at 8 p.m. tonight at the town hall. The council will discuss events that caused the fish kill and how costs associated with the three-day water shutoff will be paid. Several area groups, as well as invited experts, plan to make presentations at tonight's meeting.

Mayor Cisko announced that the fish-kill mystery has been solved.

TOWN COUNCIL MEETING

Your teacher will assign you to one of the following Riverwood groups that will participate in the special town council meeting (similar to Figure 1.61), and will give you some background information about your group's viewpoints on the impact of the fish kill:

▶ Agricultural cooperative representatives
▶ Consulting engineers
▶ Consulting scientists

possible solutions to these problems. Different people can reach different conclusions from the same facts, based on their own perspectives and values. Although scientific knowledge provides information about many problems, decisions to take action involve additional considerations from social, economic, political, moral, and related perspectives. This activity is

intentionally open-ended. There is no "right" answer for the class to reach, only one that is supported by facts and data.

Pre-Activity Preparation and Discussion

Students can be assigned to one of eight "special interest" groups who will testify at the special meeting of the Riverwood town

- ▶ County sanitation commission members
- ▶ Mining company representatives
- ▶ Power company officials
- ▶ Riverwood Chamber of Commerce members
- ▶ Riverwood Taxpayer Association members
- ▶ Riverwood Town Council members

Meeting Rules and Penalties for Rule Violations

1. The presentation order is decided by council members and announced at the start of the meeting.
2. Each group will have a specified time for its presentation. Time cards will notify each speaker of time remaining.
3. If a member of another group interrupts a presentation, the offending group will be penalized thirty seconds for each interruption, to a maximum of two minutes. If the group has already made its presentation, it will forfeit its rebuttal time.

Figure 1.61 *A town meeting in session in New Jersey. Open meetings such as this encourage citizen involvement in discussions of local issues and in related decision-making challenges.*

LOOKING BACK AND LOOKING AHEAD

The Riverwood water mystery is solved! In the end, scientific data and analysis provided the answer. Now, human ingenuity will provide strategies to prevent the recurrence of such a crisis. In the course of solving the problem, the citizens of Riverwood learned about the water that they take for granted—abundant, clean water flowing steadily from their taps—and gained a greater appreciation for it.

Although Riverwood and its citizens exist only on the pages of this textbook, their water-quality crisis could be very real. The chemistry-related facts, principles, and procedures that clarified their problem and its solution have applications in your own home and community.

Although the fish-kill mystery has been solved, your exploration of chemistry has only just begun. Many issues related to chemistry in the community remain; water and its chemistry are only one part of a larger story.

Putting It All Together   **105**

---

council. Adjust the number of groups according to your class size. Relevant background information for individual special-interest groups is given here, and additional information is included in the TRB/TRCD. Have students regard these suggestions as a starting point, not as the only source of information supporting their presentations. Encourage students to use scientific principles and refer to the Snake River data in their presentations.

You may decide to give students time to research and organize their presentations. Each group has a limited time to present its position and to refute opposing positions. Failure to stay within presentation time limits may result in loss of rebuttal time. Students assigned to the town council group

will serve as timekeepers and manage the discussion.

Assign roles well in advance of the meeting. For instance, you could assign roles when students analyze Snake River data at the close of Section C. Consider student personalities when you assign town council roles: These students need leadership ability.

If you decide to form smaller groups or allow for more speakers, just add special-interest groups to the meeting. For example, there could be two groups of engineers: one as a source of information, and the other representing the original designers of the dam. The Riverwood Corporation, manufacturing a fictitious product, could be represented. The only limits to this culminating activity are time and your imagination.

Encourage students to bring appropriate props, such as hard hats or lab coats, to enhance group identities. Each interest group can design a logo to wear on a badge or name tag. Encourage students to apply their skills from other subject areas—art, graphics, computer science, business, drama, and journalism—to create an authentic town meeting atmosphere. If possible, arrange classroom tables and chairs to resemble a meeting room. A microphone adds realism to the setting. Videotaping the meeting lends an element of the theater, and students thoroughly enjoy seeing themselves on tape. Some teachers have even used the school auditorium or a vacant room in the local city hall to evoke the appropriate atmosphere.

Following the meeting, you may wish to have each group (or, alternatively, each student) write a letter to the editor of the *Riverwood News* that addresses questions posed about responsibility for the fish kill or adequacy of the decisions made in the town council meeting. See the TRB/TRCD for additional resources for organizing this activity.

Post-Activity Discussion

Following completion of this activity, discuss it as a class. At this point, students should abandon their assigned roles and analyze the entire decision-making process. Consider focusing on points such as these:

• Point out that informed decisions about any problem should take into account opposing views; don't jump to conclusions.

• Ask students to identify points in the debate where chemistry knowledge was essential.

• Highlight benefits and consequences of seeking consensus solutions to complex issues. Discourage students from viewing the debate merely in terms of winning or losing.

• With students' help, identify examples of factual, opinion-based, emotional, and logical arguments in the debate.

• Emphasize that each group contributed worthwhile viewpoints to the debate. The real-life resolution to such debates often becomes a compromise among different group views.

Your evaluation of student performance in this activity should include both individual and group grades. You may base group grades on the oral presentation or the simulated interview. It is helpful to prepare in advance a list of items to evaluate during the meeting. You may share and critique the list with students before the debate begins. Items to consider include active participation in group work, effective use of facts, use of persuasive arguments, adherence to time requirements, and evidence of research beyond the text. You may wish to generate your own scoring rubric, perhaps with student input. A sample evaluation is available at the back of this book and also in the TRB/TRCD. Requiring students to write individual letters to the *Riverwood News* editor enables you to evaluate individual work.

Town Council Meeting

Meeting Rules and Penalties for Rule Violations

1. The order of presentations is decided by council members and announced at the start of the meeting.
2. Each group is allowed a specified time for its presentation. Time cards will notify the speakers of time remaining.
3. If a member of another group interrupts a presentation, the offending group will be penalized 30 seconds for each interruption, to a maximum of one minute. If the group has already made its presentation, it forfeits all of its rebuttal time.

Town Council Members: Background Information

Your group is responsible for conducting the meeting in an orderly manner. Be prepared to:

1. Decide and announce the order of presentations. Groups presenting factual information should come before groups voicing opinions.
2. Decide on the physical arrangement of the presentation area—where to position town council members who control the meeting, presenters, and groups and observers.
3. Explain the meeting rules and penalties for violating those rules.
4. Recognize each group at its assigned presentation time.
5. Enforce established presentation time limits by preparing time cards with "one minute," "30 seconds," and "time is up" written on them. Place these cards in the speaker's line of sight to provide useful warnings.
6. Control rebuttal discussions and open-forum speeches.
7. Summarize the options after group testimony has been completed.
8. Conduct a vote of all town council members.
9. Report the results of the vote and future actions it mandates.

Power Company Officials: Background Information

The power plant includes a dam and reservoir that provide an adequate supply of cooling water. Your company's engineers control the rate of water release from the dam back into the Snake River.

Normally, only relatively small volumes of water are released at any particular time. However, releasing large, controlled quantities of water from the dam is a standard way to prevent flooding. The last time such a large volume of water was released from the dam was 30 years ago. A fish kill was reported then, but the cause remained unknown. On that occasion, Riverwood and surrounding areas had experienced an unusually wet summer.

The dam, constructed in the 1930s, incorporated the most current design thinking of that time. Since then, its basic structure has not been modified.

Agricultural Cooperative Representatives: Background Information

Cooperative members in the Snake River valley include farmers and ranchers managing a variety of crops and livestock. Your agricultural cooperative informs its members of current best practices and regulations regarding the use of agrochemicals and management of wastes and runoff from fields and pastures.

Heavy rains pose a problem for farmers. Although rain benefits crops, it can wash away recently applied fertilizers and pesticides. This is not only costly, but can create problems as some of these agrochemicals enter the watershed.

Mining Company Representatives: Background Information

Riverwood originated as a mining town on the Snake River, which provided early residents with a convenient source of water. Your company intensely mined the hills surrounding Riverwood during the 1930s and 1940s, particularly for zinc and silver.

All by-products of mining and metal-ore processing were collected in storage ponds built in compliance with the specifications and regulations in effect during that era.

In average-rainfall seasons, runoff from these ponds contains heavy-metal ions at levels within values specified by your company's EPA permit. Your company monitors effluent values and keeps all ponds secured. Your structural engineers are responsible for maintaining the storage ponds at abandoned mine sites. However, during heavy rainfall, people have observed some underground settling in the mines and small landslides in hilly areas near the Snake River.

Scientists: Background Information

You are responsible for explaining how the analyzed Snake River data indicate the proposed cause of the fish kill. You should be prepared to explain what the data mean and why data fluctuations are noted from month to month or year to year. You may be asked to explain ideas such as pH, solubility of molecular and ionic substances, units of concentration, water-purification techniques, the hydrologic cycle, and other water-related concepts. Help council members and other attendees understand how the analyzed data document the cause of the fish kill.

Consulting Engineers: Background Information

Your consulting firm was hired to conduct a detailed examination of the cause of the fish kill. Your assignment was to determine whether accident, human error, negligence, or an unforeseen circumstance was responsible. In addition, you were asked to prepare scenarios or suggest improvements that would prevent recurring fish kills.

Your presentation should include proposed solutions to the fish-kill problem, main costs and benefits of each solution, and a detailed analysis of the fish-kill cause. You may be unfamiliar with cost analyses and estimates for major projects, but try to make feasible cost estimates.

Chamber of Commerce Members: Background Information

Canceling the annual fishing tournament cost you and other Riverwood merchants a lot of money. Close to 1000 out-of-town tournament participants were expected. Many would have rented rooms for at least two nights and eaten at local restaurants and fast-food establishments. In anticipation of this business, extra food supplies and support services were ordered. Fishing and sporting goods stores stockpiled extra fishing supplies. Some businesses have already applied for short-term loans to help pay for their unsold inventories.

Local churches and Riverwood High School planned family social activities as revenue-makers during the tournament weekend. For example, the school band scheduled a benefit concert that would have raised money to send band members to the spring band competition.

People are likely to remember the fish kill for many years. Tournament organizers predict that future fishing competition revenues in Riverwood will be substantially reduced due to this year's adverse publicity. Thus, total financial losses resulting from the water emergency may be much higher than most current estimates predict.

You should discuss how merchants and businesses were affected by this event and summarize the availability of support (as well as lack of support) to help resolve the issues.

County Sanitation Commission Members: Background Information

You are responsible for the protection and safety of the Snake River's water supply. You represent the commission that completes routine water testing and data gathering for Riverwood drinking water.

You should know the meaning of standards specifying the quality of drinking water and be able to explain how water testing is completed. You should report maximum contamination levels (MCLs) for hazardous water contaminants. You should also know the allowable limits or expected ranges for other analyzed water data.

Riverwood Taxpayer Association Members: Background Information

Your organization is concerned with the financial effects of the fish kill on Riverwood citizens. Thus, your presentation should include some important questions:
• Who will pay for the water brought into Riverwood during the water shutoff?
• Will taxes be increased to compensate local businesspeople for their financial losses? (Keep in mind that local merchants themselves are likely to be Riverwood taxpayers!)
• If the organization responsible for the fish kill implements measures to prevent its recurrence, will its costs be passed on to consumers? If so, how?

LOOKING BACK AND LOOKING AHEAD

Many issues involving *Chemistry in the Community* remain; water and its chemistry are only part of a much larger story. Students are invited to explore connections between chemistry and their lives and to move further along in their study of chemistry.

SECTION	CLASS TIME	STUDENT EDITION FEATURES	PROGRAM RESOURCES	MEDIA AND TECHNOLOGY
Section A. **Why We Use What We Do** **Objectives:** • Distinguish between chemical and physical properties and between chemical and physical changes. • Classify specific examples as either chemical or physical properties. • Classify specific examples as either chemical or physical changes. • Classify selected elements as metals, nonmetals, or metalloids based on observations of chemical and physical properties. • Use the periodic table to (a) predict physical and chemical properties of an element. (b) identify elements by their atomic masses and atomic numbers. (c) locate periods and groups (families) of elements. • Distinguish between isotopes based on their total neutrons and/or mass numbers. • Calculate the mass number for an atom based on its total protons and neutrons. • Explain how an element's chemical and physical properties are associated with the number and arrangement of electrons in its atoms.	**6 Class Periods**	**Developing Skills** A.2 Physical and Chemical Properties A.9 Periodic Variation in Properties A.11 Predicting Properties **Investigating Matter** A.5 Metal or Nonmetal? **Making Decisions** A.7 Grouping the Elements A.13 It's Only Money	**TRB** **Investigating Matter** A.5 Metal or Nonmetal Student Worksheet and Data Table **Content Reading Guides** A.1 through A.3 Content Reading Guide **Supplements and Practice** A.1 Supplement: Physical and Chemical Properties A.4 Supplement: Chemical Elements Project A.8 Supplement: The Pattern of Atomic Numbers A.11 Supplement: Predicting Properties Section A Supplement **Black line Masters** Periodic Table Trends in Chemical Property and Boiling Point	**TRCD** **All TRB and Test Bank Materials for Unit 2, Section A** **Videos** Metal or Nonmetal? **Animations** Representing Atoms and Ions Trends and Variation in the Periodic Table Properties of Metals

SECTION	CLASS TIME	STUDENT EDITION FEATURES	PROGRAM RESOURCES	MEDIA AND TECHNOLOGY
Section B. **Earth's Mineral Resources** **Objectives:** • Describe Earth's atmosphere, hydrosphere, and lithosphere, including the distribution of resources among them. • Describe or recognize factors that determine the feasibility of mining an ore at a specific site. • Explain why minerals of more active metals are more difficult to refine and process than minerals of less active metals. • Define oxidation and reduction in terms of apparent electron loss or gain. • Identify and distinguish between oxidation and reduction processes. • Represent oxidation and reduction processes using chemical equations and electron-dot structures. • Describe three common methods for separating metals from their ores (electrometallurgy, pyrometallurgy, hydrometallurgy).	**6 Class Periods**	**Developing Skills** B.7 Trends in Metal Activity **Investigating Matter** B.3 Converting Copper B.5 Relative Reactivities of Metals **Making Decisions** B.2 Production versus Use **ChemQuandary 1** Discovery of Metals **Modeling Matter** B.9 Electrons and Redox Processes	**TRB** **Investigating Matter** B.3 Converting Copper Student Worksheet and Data Table B.5 Relative Reactivities of Metals Student Worksheet and Data Table **Modeling Matter** B.9 Electrons and Redox Processes Student Worksheet **Content Reading Guides** B.8 Content Reading Guide **Supplements and Practice** B.8 Supplement: Electrons and Redox Processes Section B Supplement	**TRCD** **All TRB and Test Bank Materials for Unit 2, Section B** **Exercises** Relative Reactivities of Metals **Videos** Converting Copper Relative Reactivities of Metals **Animations** A Copper Redox Reaction Relative Reactivities of Metals

SECTION	CLASS TIME	STUDENT EDITION FEATURES	PROGRAM RESOURCES	MEDIA AND TECHNOLOGY
Section C. **Conserving Matter** **Objectives:** • State and apply the Law of Conservation of Matter. • Relate balanced chemical equations to the Law of Conservation of Matter. • Write and explain balanced chemical equations. • Explain the usefulness of the mole concept in chemistry. • Calculate the molar mass of a compound, given its formula and atomic weights of its elements. • Calculate the quantities of reactants or products involved in a chemical reaction, given its balanced chemical equation. • Calculate the percent composition by mass of a specified element in a given compound. • Distinguish between renewable and nonrenewable resources. • Identify methods of conserving Earth's resources.	**9 Class Periods**	**Developing Skills** C.2 Accounting for Atoms C.4 Writing Chemical Equations C.6 Molar Masses C.8 Molar Relationships C.10 Percent Composition C.15 Copper Life-Cycle Analysis **Investigating Matter** C.11 Retrieving Copper **Making Decisions** C.13 Rethinking, Reusing, Replacing, and Recycling C.16 Designing a Coin	**TRB** **Investigating Matter** C.11 Retrieving Copper Student Worksheet and Data Table **Content Reading Guides** C.1 through C.5 Content Reading Guide C.12 Content Reading Guide **Supplements and Practice** C.1 Supplement: Keeping Track of Atoms C.3 Supplement: Balancing Equations C.5 Supplement: Molar Masses C.7 Supplement: Equations and Molar Relationships I C.7 Supplement: Equations and Molar Relationships II C.9 Supplement: Percent Composition Section C Supplement **Skill Building Supplements** Skill Building Topic 2: Dimensional Analysis Skill Building Topic 7: Understanding and Balancing Equations Skill Building Topic 8: The Mole Skill Building Topic 9: A Quantitative Understanding Of Formulas Skill Building Topic 10: Understanding Mass Relationships In Chemical Reactions	**TRCD** **All TRB and Test Bank Materials for Unit 2, Section C** **Exercises** Interpreting a Balanced Equation Modeling Matter: A Hypothetical Reaction **Videos** Retrieving Copper

SECTION	CLASS TIME	STUDENT EDITION FEATURES	PROGRAM RESOURCES	MEDIA AND TECHNOLOGY
Section D. Materials: Designing for Desired Properties **Objectives:** • Explain allotropes in terms of the bonding and arrangement of an element's atoms. • Illustrate how alloys and their constituent elements differ in their chemical and physical properties. • Describe how the electrical conductivity of a material can be changed. • Describe and differentiate among methods for surface treatment of materials (coatings, electroplating, thin films).	**5 Class Periods**	**Developing Skills** D.2 Linking Properties to Structure **ChemQuandary 2** A Case of Elusive Identity **ChemQuandary 3** Five Cents' Worth **Investigating Matter** D.5 Striking It Rich D.8 Copper Plating **Making Decisions** D.4 Alternatives to Metals D.9 More Coin Design Considerations **Chemistry at Work** All That's Gold Doesn't Glitter . . . Or Does It?	**TRB** **Investigating Matter** D.5 Striking it Rich Student Worksheet and Data Table D.8 Copper Plating Student Worksheet and Data Table **Content Reading Guides** D.6 Content Reading Guide D.7 Content Reading Guide Chemistry at Work Content Reading Guide: All That's Gold Doesn't Glitter . . . or Does it? **Supplements and Practice** Section D Supplement	**TRCD** **All TRB and Test Bank Materials for Unit 2, Section D** **Videos** Striking It Rich Copper Plating **Animations** Striking It Rich Copper Plating **Exercises** Structure and Properties: Allotropes
Putting It All Together: Making Money		**Putting It All Together** • Making Money— Selecting the Best Coin Design	**TRB** **Putting It All Together** Making Money: Selecting the Best Coin Rubric	**TRCD** **All TRB Materials for Unit 2, PIAT**

Equipment, Expendable Items, and Unusual Materials (per 12 Student Pairs)

Sorted by Item

QUANTITY	ITEM	SECTION USED
12	balances	C.11
12	batteries, 9-V or 1.5-V	D.8
24	beakers, 100-mL	C.11
24	beakers, 250-mL	D.5
24	Beral pipettes or dropper bottles	A.5
4	conductivity testers	A.5
36	copper pennies	D.5
12 g	copper powder	B.3
12 cm	copper wire	B.5
25 mL	copper(II) chloride ($CuCl_2 \cdot 2H_2O$), 0.1 M	A.5
10 mL	copper(II) nitrate ($Cu(NO_3)_2 \cdot 3H_2O$), 0.2 M	B.5
100 mL	copper(II) sulfate pentahydrate ($CuSO_4 \cdot 5H_2O$), 0.75 M, and sulfuric acid (H_2SO_4), 0.75 M	D.8
12	copper, strips	D.812
12	crucible tongs	D.5
12	crucibles	B.3
3 L	distilled water	C.11, D.5
24 pieces	filter paper, Whatman #1, 11-cm diameter	C.11
12	forceps	A.5, C.11
12	graduated cylinders, 25-mL	D.5
5 g	graphite pencil lead	A.5

Sorted by Item (continued)

QUANTITY	ITEM	SECTION USED
4	hammers, small	A.5
12	hot plates	B.3, C.11, D.5
25 mL	hydrochloric acid (HCl), 0.5 M	A.5
1000 mL	hydrochloric acid (HCl), 1 M	C.11
12	iron nails	D.8
5 g	iron, wire	A.5
10 mL	magnesium nitrate ($Mg(NO_3)_2 \cdot 6H_2O$), 0.2 M	B.5
12 cm	magnesium ribbon	A.5
12 cm	magnesium ribbon	B.5
48	pipets	B.5
5 g	silicon, lumps	A.5
12 cm	silver foil	B.5
10 mL	silver nitrate ($AgNO_3$), 0.2 M	B.5
12	spatulas	B.3
200 g	steel wool	B.5, D.5
12	stir rods, glass	C.11
5 g	sulfur	A.5
12	thermometers, alcohol −10 to 110 °C	C.11
5 g	tin, wire or foil	A.5
12	U-tubes with appropriate containers for support	D.8

Sorted by Item (continued)

QUANTITY	ITEM	SECTION USED
12	voltmeter or CBL	D.8
12	watch glasses	C.11, D.5
12	wellplates, 24-well	A.5, B.5
24	wire leads with alligator clips	D.8
350 mL	zinc chloride ($ZnCl_2$), 1 M	D.5
10 mL	zinc nitrate ($Zn(NO_3)_2 \cdot 6H_2O$), 0.2 M	B.5
36 g	zinc, granulated or foil	D.5
12 g	zinc, mossy or foil	C.11
15 g	zinc, mossy or wire	A.5
12 cm	zinc, wire	B.5

Equipment, Expendable Items, and Unusual Materials (per 12 Student Pairs)

Sorted by Section

QUANTITY	ITEM	SECTION USED
24	Beral pipettes or dropper bottles	A.5
4	conductivity testers	A.5
25 mL	copper(II) chloride ($CuCl_2 \cdot 2H_2O$), 0.1 M	A.5
12	forceps	A.5
5 g	graphite pencil lead	A.5
4	hammers, small	A.5
25 mL	hydrochloric acid (HCl), 0.5 M	A.5
5 g	iron, wire	A.5
12 cm	magnesium ribbon	A.5
5 g	silicon, lumps	A.5
5 g	sulfur	A.5
5 g	tin, wire or foil	A.5
12	wellplates, 24-well	A.5
15 g	zinc, mossy or wire	A.5
12 g	copper powder	B.3
12	crucibles	B.3
12	hot plates	B.3
12	spatulas	B.3
12 cm	copper wire	B.5
10 mL	copper(II) nitrate ($Cu(NO_3)_2 \cdot 3H_2O$), 0.2 M	B.5
10 mL	magnesium nitrate ($Mg(NO_3)_2 \cdot 6H_2O$), 0.2 M	B.5
12 cm	magnesium ribbon	B.5

Sorted by Section (continued)

QUANTITY	ITEM	SECTION USED
48	pipets	B.5
12 cm	silver foil	B.5
10 mL	silver nitrate (AgNO$_3$), 0.2 M	B.5
100 g	steel wool	B.5
12	wellplates, 24-well	B.5
10 mL	zinc nitrate (Zn(NO$_3$)$_2$·6H$_2$O), 0.2 M	B.5
12 cm	zinc, wire	B.5
12	balances	C.11
24	beakers, 100-mL	C.11
1 L	distilled water	C.11
24 pieces	filter paper, Whatman #1, 11-cm diameter	C.11
12	forceps	C.11
12	hot plates	C.11
1000 mL	hydrochloric acid (HCl), 1 M	C.11
12	stir rods, glass	C.11
12	thermometers, alcohol −10 to 110 °C	C.11
12	watch glasses	C.11
12 g	zinc, mossy or foil	C.11
24	beakers, 250-mL	D.5
36	copper pennies	D.5

Sorted by Section (continued)

QUANTITY	ITEM	SECTION USED
12	crucible tongs	D.5
2 L	distilled water	D.5
12	graduated cylinders, 25-mL	D.5
12	hot plates	D.5
100 g	steel wool	D.5
12	watch glasses	D.5
350 mL	zinc chloride ($ZnCl_2$), 1 M	D.5
36 g	zinc, granulated or foil	D.5
12	batteries, 9-V or 1.5-V	D.8
100 mL	copper(II) sulfate pentahydrate ($CuSO_4 \cdot 5H_2O$), 0.75 M and sulfuric acid (H_2SO_4), 0.75 M	D.8
12	copper, strips	D.8
12	iron nails	D.8
12	U-tubes with appropriate containers for support	D.8
12	voltmeter or CBL	D.8
24	wire leads with alligator clips	D.8

UNIT 2
MATERIALS: STRUCTURE AND USES

Introduction to the Unit

Unit 2 introduces concepts including chemical and physical properties and changes; chemical symbols and formulas; periodicity and the periodic table; metal reactivity; oxidation–reduction reactions; conservation of matter and energy; and writing and balancing chemical equations. Students also learn to calculate molar mass and percent composition. Investigations include exploring the properties of metals and nonmetals, comparing metal reactivities, and transforming metals into compounds and alloys. In the culminating unit activity, students use their knowledge of properties of materials to design a coin.

UNIT 2
Materials: Structure and Uses

HOW can chemists explain the chemical and physical properties of matter?

SECTION A
Why We Use What We Do (page 110)

WHERE do we find mineral resources and how are they processed?

SECTION B
Earth's Mineral Resources (page 134)

WHAT information do chemical equations convey about matter and its changes?

SECTION C
Conserving Matter (page 153)

HOW can chemists modify matter to make it more useful?

SECTION D
Materials: Designing for Desired Properties (page 184)

? Your congresswoman has invited you and your classmates to submit a design for a new half-dollar coin. What will be the coin's composition? What makes a material best suited for its intended use? Turn the page to learn the answers—perhaps you can become the design winner.

Using the Unit Project

Unit 2 continues the *ChemCom* approach—using a societal problem or issue to establish chemistry concepts and skills on a need-to-know basis. The scenario in Unit 2 is a design competition for a proposed new half-dollar coin. The competition, sponsored by Congresswoman Gonzales, is to stimulate interest in a bill that authorizes the U.S. Mint to produce a new half-dollar coin. Students will apply knowledge gained in this unit to design the best possible coin. You can read about procedures at the U.S. Mint at **http://www.usmint.gov**.

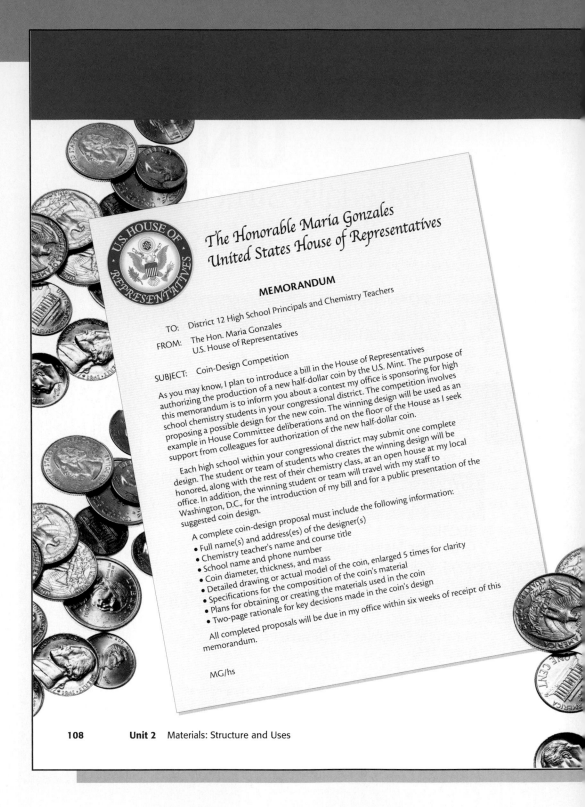

U.S. HOUSE OF REPRESENTATIVES

The Honorable Maria Gonzales
United States House of Representatives

MEMORANDUM

TO: District 12 High School Principals and Chemistry Teachers

FROM: The Hon. Maria Gonzales
U.S. House of Representatives

SUBJECT: Coin-Design Competition

As you may know, I plan to introduce a bill in the House of Representatives authorizing the production of a new half-dollar coin by the U.S. Mint. The purpose of this memorandum is to inform you about a contest my office is sponsoring for high school chemistry students in your congressional district. The competition involves proposing a possible design for the new coin. The winning design will be used as an example in House Committee deliberations and on the floor of the House as I seek support from colleagues for authorization of the new half-dollar coin.

Each high school within your congressional district may submit one complete design. The student or team of students who creates the winning design will be honored, along with the rest of their chemistry class, at an open house at my local office. In addition, the winning student or team will travel with my staff to Washington, D.C., for the introduction of my bill and for a public presentation of the suggested coin design.

A complete coin-design proposal must include the following information:
- Full name(s) and address(es) of the designer(s)
- Chemistry teacher's name and course title
- School name and phone number
- Coin diameter, thickness, and mass
- Detailed drawing or actual model of the coin, enlarged 5 times for clarity
- Specifications for the composition of the coin's material
- Plans for obtaining or creating the materials used in the coin
- Two-page rationale for key decisions made in the coin's design

All completed proposals will be due in my office within six weeks of receipt of this memorandum.

MG/hs

Encouraged by the success of the recent quarter coin series featuring each state, Congressional Representative Maria Gonzales plans to introduce a bill authorizing the U.S. Mint to produce a new half-dollar coin. To solicit unique coin-design ideas from her community, she is sponsoring a contest for high school chemistry students in her district to propose coin designs.

Representative Gonzales realizes that her congressional colleagues will request information about the proposed coin. Thus, as her memo suggests, every aspect of the half-dollar coin—from its appearance to its size and composition—is to be included in the design. Because only one design can be submitted from each school, your class will decide which team's coin proposal will be submitted for this competition.

As you consider your coin's design, you will learn about Earth's mineral resources and how nations use them. You will learn why certain materials are used for particular new products, such as coins, and how those materials are obtained from available resources. Throughout this unit, keep in mind how such chemical knowledge can help guide your design of the new coin.

Before you introduce students to the challenge of designing a coin, decide whether you would like students to work individually or in small groups. Outline your expectations for the project (see the Putting It All Together section for guidance). Knowing the overriding expectations helps to establish a need-to-know learning environment.

In each section, students will revisit the coin-design scenario through *Making Decisions* activities. You may decide to create a folder for each student (or each small group) to keep results of the *Making Decisions* activities and any brainstorming sessions. This approach gives students a handy resource (of their own creation) to consult when they begin work managing their own coin design.

Why We Use What We Do

In Section A students distinguish chemical and physical properties and changes; explore patterns in properties of the elements; are introduced to the periodic table; and consider using materials based on their properties.

 A.1–A.3 Content Reading Guide

A.1 Properties Make the Difference

This material introduces chemical and physical properties and changes in the context of coins. Emphasize that physical changes affect the form of a substance without changing its identity, while chemical changes result in the transformation of a substance into one or more different substances.

 A.1 Supplement: Physical and Chemical Properties

Using the Figures

Figure 2.1: Ask students to compare and contrast the international coins in this photo. For instance, all of these coins are made of metal. What properties of metals make them good materials for coins? Do all metals have these properties? What other materials might we consider when designing a coin? What other design features does this photo show, and what might their function be?

Demonstration Ideas

To clarify the differences between physical and chemical properties and changes, ask students to observe each event in the following demonstrations carefully and record evidence before deciding whether the change is chemical or physical.

Why We Use What We Do

Every produced object, old or new, is composed of materials selected for their specific properties. What makes a particular material best for a particular use? You can begin to answer this question by exploring some properties of materials.

A.1 PROPERTIES MAKE THE DIFFERENCE

Properties of Metals

In this unit, you will consider the design of something that you use every day—money in the form of coins. Throughout history, people have used many different items as money: beads, stones, printed paper, and precious metals, to name a few. See Figure 2.1. What characteristics make a material suitable or useful to produce coins? How important is appearance or cost? What other characteristics or properties can you suggest?

As you already know, every substance has characteristic properties that distinguish it from other substances. These characteristic properties include **physical properties** such as color, density, and odor—properties that can be determined without altering the chemical makeup of the material. Physical properties and the ability (or inability) of a material to undergo physical changes, such as melting, boiling, and bending, often influence the use of that material. In a **physical change,** the material remains the same, although its form appears to have changed.

When a substance changes into one or more *new* substances, it has undergone a **chemical change.** A substance's **chemical properties,** which

Figure 2.1 *What properties should you consider when you design a coin?*

110　　**Unit 2**　Materials: Structure and Uses

Physical Properties and Changes

1. Place a peanut-sized piece of dry ice (CO_2) in an uninflated balloon and tie the opening. As the dry ice warms, the balloon will expand. **Sublimation.** *Safety precautions:* Be careful not to let the balloon explode. Direct contact with dry ice will cause frostbite. Do not allow students to handle dry ice without appropriate precautions and supervision.

2. Allow several egg-sized chunks of dry ice to sublime in an aquarium or other large transparent container. Blow soap bubbles into the tank. The air-filled bubbles will float on the layer of gaseous carbon dioxide in the aquarium. **Density**. *Safety precautions:* See #1.

3. Heat a 20-cm (or longer) bimetallic strip (thin strips of two metals bonded together) in a burner flame. Because the

Figure 2.2 *Examples of physical and chemical changes involving copper. Bending does not alter the chemical identity of the copper (left), but allowing the copper to react with nitric acid (right) does. What evidence can you find in the photos to support these conclusions?*

relate to any kind of chemical changes it undergoes, often determine the substance's usefulness. Consider the common chemical change of iron rusting. The tendency of a metal to form an oxide, such as when iron rusts, is the chemical property that accounts for this chemical change. You can often detect a chemical change by observing one or more indications of a change, such as the formation of a gas or solid, a permanent color change, or a temperature change, which indicates that thermal energy has been absorbed or given off. Figure 2.2 illustrates some physical and chemical changes of copper.

In the following activity, you will classify some characteristics of common materials as either physical or chemical properties.

A.2 PHYSICAL AND CHEMICAL PROPERTIES

Developing Skills

Sample Problem 1: *Consider this statement: Copper compounds are often blue in color. Does the statement describe a physical or chemical property?*

To answer this, first ask yourself a question: Was the substance chemically changed as its color was observed? If the answer is *no,* then the statement describes a physical property; if the answer is *yes,* then the statement describes a chemical property. You can observe this property—color—without changing the chemical makeup of a copper compound. Color is a characteristic physical property of many compounds.

Sample Problem 2: *Consider this statement: Oxygen gas supports the burning of wood. Does the statement refer to a physical or chemical property of oxygen gas?*

If you apply the same key question—is there a change in the identity of the wood and the oxygen?—you will arrive at the correct

metals have different rates of expansion/contraction with temperature, the strip will bend when exposed to changes in temperature. Bimetallic strips are used in some refrigerators and thermostats. Some demonstrations are also available online; for instance, visit **http:// hyperphysics.phy-astr.gsu.edu/hbase/ thermo/bimetal.html** or **http://demoroom. physics.ncsu.edu/html/demos/37.html**.

Expansion. *Safety precautions:* Use tongs to hold the strip.
4. Shake and then open a warm can or bottle of soft drink. The carbon dioxide dissolved in the soda will be released with the change in pressure. **Release from solution**. *Safety precautions:* Point the opening of the can or bottle away from students and yourself.

Chemical Properties and Changes

1. Place a few calcium turnings (Ca metal) in 200 mL of water in a 400-mL beaker. Hydrogen gas is evolved, which is even more noticeable if you place the beaker on an overhead projector. For added effect, place a few drops of phenolphthalein in the water. The phenolphthalein will cause the solution to turn pink as the reaction progresses.

   The reaction taking place is $Ca + 2\ H_2O \rightarrow Ca(OH)_2 + H_2$.

   Video clips are also available online, including at **http://www. angelo.edu/faculty/kboudrea/demos/ calcium_H2O/calcium_H2O.htm**. *Safety precautions:* There should be no open flames in the room during this demonstration.

2. Burn a candle. This is especially effective if you place the candle on a digital balance and note the apparent loss of mass.
   Extension: Set several candles of varying height in the aquarium from Physical Properties demonstration 2 and light them before placing dry ice in the aquarium. As the dry ice sublimes, the candles will be extinguished in order of height. *Safety precautions:* Be aware of long hair and loose clothing around open flames. Direct contact with dry ice will cause frostbite. Do not allow students to handle the dry ice without appropriate precautions and supervision.

3. Crack a raw egg into a beaker of boiling water or into 100 mL of concentrated HCl. In either demonstration, the egg "cooks"; its proteins are denatured (unraveled) then tangled with other proteins and components of the egg to form a gel-like product (the cooked egg). *Safety precautions:* Concentrated HCl is corrosive. In this demonstration, only the instructor should handle it.

111

4. Obtain a pre-1982 penny and a post-1982 penny. Use a file to scratch the edge off of both pennies in several spots, exposing the fresh copper and inner zinc, respectively. Gently lower the two pennies into a beaker containing 100 ml of 0.5 M HCl. Place the beaker onto an overhead projector to help students observe the bubbles coming from one penny and not the other. The pure copper penny is unreactive toward HCl, while the zinc is oxidized by the hydrogen ions in HCl. Leave the pennies in the HCl overnight. Carefully remove the pennies with tongs, and rinse them with water. The post-1982 penny's core should have completely reacted, leaving the copper coating. Invite students to propose explanations. *Safety precautions:* The HCl used is corrosive. The amount required for this demonstration should only be handled by the instructor.

Developing Skills

A.2 Physical and Chemical Properties

In this activity, students practice identifying physical and chemical properties. Remind students that chemical properties are observed when one substance is transformed into a new substance, whereas physical properties (such as melting point, boiling point, thermal and electrical conductivity, density, color, and hardness) are observed without a change in the substance's identity. Remind students that physical and chemical properties help identify the best substance for a particular use. Cost and availability are also factors.

answer. As you have no doubt noted, the ash left over from a campfire looks nothing like the original wood that was burned. In fact, the burning—or **combustion**—of wood involves chemical

reactions between wood and oxygen that change both reactants. The reaction products of ash, carbon dioxide, and water vapor are very different from wood and oxygen. Thus, the statement refers to a chemical property of oxygen (as well as of wood).

Wood burning

Now it's your turn. Classify each of the following statements as describing either a physical property or a chemical property. (*Hint:* Decide whether the chemical identity of the material does or does not change when the property is observed.)

1. Pure metals have a high **luster** (are shiny and reflect light).
2. The surfaces of some metals become dull when exposed to air.
3. Nitrogen gas, which is a relatively nonreactive element at room temperature, can form nitrogen oxides at the high temperatures of an operating automobile engine.
4. Milk turns sour if left too long at room temperature.
5. Diamonds are hard enough to be used as a coating for drill bits.

Metallic luster

6. Metals are typically **ductile** (can be drawn into wires).
7. Leavened bread dough increases in volume if it is allowed to rise before baking.
8. Unreactive argon gas, rather than air, is used to fill many light bulbs to prevent the metal filament wire inside the bulb from being destroyed through oxidation.

Bread rising

9. Generally, metals are better conductors of heat and electricity than are nonmetals.

Answers

1. Physical—metals are lustrous in the absence of other substances and without changing their identity.
2. Chemical—metals react with oxygen from air and form metal oxides.
3. Chemical—nitrogen reacts with oxygen in high-temperature environments.
4. Chemical—microbes convert milk sugar (lactose) to lactic acid, which coagulates the milk protein and sours the milk. The acids are converted to non-acid products, and the protein is converted into ammonia products by more microbes.
5. Physical—diamonds are hard in the absence of other substances and without changing their identity.

A.3 PROPERTIES MATTER: DESIGNING THE PENNY

As you might imagine, you must weigh many considerations when selecting materials for a specific use. A material with properties well suited to a purpose may be either unavailable in sufficient quantity or too expensive. Alternatively, a material may have undesirable physical or chemical properties that can limit its use. In these and other situations, you can often find another material with most of the sought-after properties and use it instead.

The cost of a material is a concern when manufacturing coins and printed currency. Just imagine what would happen if the declared value of a coin were less than the cost of its component metals. How would this affect the production and circulation of the coin? This situation nearly occurred in the United States about one-quarter century ago. In the early 1980s, copper became too expensive to be used as the primary metal in pennies. In other words, the cost of the copper composing a penny was becoming just about as great as the face value of the penny. Zinc, another metallic element, was chosen to replace most of the copper in all post-1982 pennies. Zinc is about as hard as copper, and it has a density (7.13 g/cm^3) that is close to the density of copper metal (8.96 g/cm^3). Zinc is also readily available, and it is less expensive than copper.

Unfortunately, zinc is also more chemically reactive than copper. During World War II, copper metal was in short supply. To conserve that resource, zinc-plated steel pennies—known to coin collectors as "white cents" or "steel cents"—were created in 1943. The new pennies quickly corroded. As you can see in Figure 2.3, these pennies also looked considerably different from traditional copper pennies. The production of zinc-plated pennies ended within a year.

The problems associated with using zinc in pennies were solved in the early 1980s. In the new design, the properties of copper were used where they were most needed—on the coin's surface—and the properties of zinc were used where they were useful, within the coin's body. All post-1982 pennies are 97.5% zinc. They are composed of a zinc core surrounded by a thin layer of copper metal, which is added to increase the coin's durability and maintain its familiar appearance. Figure 2.4 shows a cross-section of a post-1982 penny.

Every substance has its own set of physical and chemical properties. However, with millions of substances available, how can anyone identify the *best* substance or material to meet a given need? Fortunately, all substances are made of a relatively small number of building blocks—the atoms of the different chemical elements. Knowing the similarities and differences among atoms of elements and among combinations of those atoms can greatly simplify the challenge of matching a substance to appropriate uses.

Figure 2.3 *Zinc–copper and copper pennies (top); "new" and corroded zinc-plated steel pennies (bottom).*

Thin copper outer layer

Zinc core

Figure 2.4 *Cross-section showing the structure and composition of a post-1982 penny.*

A.3 Properties Matter: Designing the Penny

This section introduces challenges associated with designing a coin. Designers must consider a material's cost as well as its physical and chemical properties. Challenges surrounding the composition of the United States penny lay the groundwork for students' coin-design process.

Historical information about coins and materials used to produce them can be found at the American Numismatic Association Website **www.money.org** and the National Numismatic Collection of the Smithsonian Institute site **http://americanhistory.si.edu/collections/numismatics/**.

Demonstration Idea

If you did not previously do so, demonstrate the reactivity of metals that make up pre- and post-1982 pennies according to directions provided in A.1 (demonstration 4 under Chemical Properties and Changes). If you completed this demonstration earlier, A.3 provides a good opportunity to display and discuss the results.

6. Physical—forming wires happens in the absence of other substances without changing identity.

7. Chemical—bread dough rises because yeast produce CO_2—a chemical reaction.

8. Chemical—argon is used because it does not react with the filament to form other substances.

9. Physical—metals are good conductors in the absence of other substances and without changing their identity.

A.4 The Chemical Elements

The substances that make up our world are all composed of chemical elements. Although over 100 elements are known, only a small proportion make up humans and the materials that surround us. Elements are grouped into three major classes—metals, nonmetals, and metalloids—based on their properties. **Table 2.1** gives the names and symbols of some of the elements. Remind students that an element's symbol is always written with an initial capital letter, followed by lowercase second and third letters (if present). You may point out the elements whose symbols derive from languages other than English, such as: sodium (Na, Latin, natrium), potassium (K, Latin, kalium), iron (Fe, Latin, ferrum), copper (Cu, Latin, cuprum), silver (Ag, Latin, argentum), tin (Sn, Latin, stannum), antimony (Sb, Latin, stibium), tungsten (W, German, wolfram), gold (Au, Latin, aurum), mercury (Hg, Latin, hydrargyrum), and lead (Pb, Latin, plumbum).

 A.4 Supplement: Chemical Elements Project

Additional Activities

Element(al) Activities

A popular activity for making elements more familiar to students is selecting an Element of the Week. Each day then has a small activity pertaining to that week's element. In a variation, each student "adopts" an element, prepares a report on it, and serves as the class expert on this element for the rest of the school year. You may have students prepare large-scale periodic tables: Ask each student (several classes may be needed) to construct a block for an

COMMON ELEMENTS AND THEIR SYMBOLS	
Name	**Symbol**
Aluminum	Al
Antimony	Sb
Argon	Ar
Barium	Ba
Beryllium	Be
Bismuth	Bi
Boron	B
Bromine	Br
Cadmium	Cd
Calcium	Ca
Carbon	C
Cesium	Cs
Chlorine	Cl
Chromium	Cr
Cobalt	Co
Copper	Cu
Fluorine	F
Gold	Au
Helium	He
Hydrogen	H
Iodine	I
Iron	Fe
Krypton	Kr
Lead	Pb
Lithium	Li
Magnesium	Mg
Manganese	Mn
Mercury	Hg
Neon	Ne
Nickel	Ni
Nitrogen	N
Oxygen	O
Phosphorus	P
Platinum	Pt
Potassium	K
Radon	Rn
Silicon	Si
Silver	Ag
Sodium	Na
Sulfur	S
Tin	Sn
Tungsten	W
Uranium	U
Zinc	Zn

| **Table 2.1**

A.4 THE CHEMICAL ELEMENTS

You learned in Unit 1 that all matter is composed of atoms. One element differs from another because its atoms have properties that differ from those of other elements. See Figure 2.5. More than 100 chemical elements are now known. Table 2.1 lists some common elements and their symbols. An alphabetical list of all elements (names and symbols) can be found on pages 128–129.

Elements can be classified in several ways, according to the similarities and the differences in their properties. Two major classes of elements are *metals* and *nonmetals*. **Metals** include such elements as iron (Fe), tin (Sn), zinc (Zn), and copper (Cu). Carbon (C) and oxygen (O) are examples of **nonmetals.** Everyday experience has given you some knowledge of metallic and nonmetallic properties. The upcoming investigation will let you further explore common properties of metals and nonmetals.

Several elements, called **metalloids,** have properties that are intermediate to those of metals and nonmetals. That is, metalloids exhibit both metallic and nonmetallic properties. Examples of metalloids include silicon (Si) and germanium (Ge), which are commonly used in the computer industry.

What properties of matter can we use to distinguish metals, nonmetals, and metalloids? The next investigation will help you find out.

Figure 2.5 *Each of these elements (clockwise from top right: sulfur, antimony, iodine, phosphorus, copper, and bismuth) is composed of chemically identical atoms. Which elements appear metallic? Which appear nonmetallic?*

element on notebook-sized colored paper. **www.webelements.com** is a useful site for finding chemical and physical data about elements.

Tom Lehrer's "The Elements"

Available at **http://www.privatehand. com/flash/elements.html**, this clever animation is done to Lehrer's classic tune about the elements.

A.5 Metal or Nonmetal?

 A.5 Metal or Nonmetal Student Worksheet and Data Table

In this investigation, students examine and test the appearance, conductivity, malleabil-

A.5 METAL OR NONMETAL?

Investigating Matter

Introduction

In this investigation, you will explore several properties of seven elements and then decide whether each element is a metal, a nonmetal, or a metalloid. You will examine the color, luster, and form of each element, and you will also attempt to crush each sample with a hammer. In addition, you or your teacher (as a demonstration) will test the substance's ability to conduct electricity. Finally, you will determine the reactivity of each element with two solutions: hydrochloric acid, $HCl(aq)$, and copper(II) chloride, $CuCl_2(aq)$.

Before starting, read the procedure to learn what you will need to do, note safety precautions, and plan necessary data collecting and observations. In your data table, create six columns: one column will be used to list the elements tested, and the other five columns will be used to record each result for appearance, conductivity, crushing, reactivity with copper(II) chloride, and reactivity with acid.

Procedure

1. Construct a data table appropriate for recording the data you will collect in this investigation.

2. *Appearance:* Observe and record the appearance of each element, including physical properties such as color, luster, and form. You can record the form as nonmetallic (like table salt, NaCl, or baking soda, $NaHCO_3$) or metallic (like iron, Fe).

3. *Conductivity:* If an electrical conductivity apparatus is available, use it to test each sample. (**Caution:** *Avoid touching the bare electrode tips; some may deliver an uncomfortable electric shock.*) Touch both electrodes to the element sample, but do not allow the electrodes to touch each other. See Figure 2.6. If the bulb lights, even dimly, electricity is flowing through the sample. Such a material is called a **conductor.** If the bulb fails to light, the material is a **nonconductor.**

Figure 2.6 *Testing a sample for electrical conductivity.*

Lab Video: Metal or Nonmetal

The symbol (aq) means that the substance is dissolved in water; thus, it indicates an aqueous solution.

---

ity, reactivity with hydrochloric acid, and reactivity with copper(II) chloride solution of seven elements. Students then group the elements based on similarities and differences in their properties and use these results to classify them as metals, nonmetals, and metalloids.

Time

50 min

Materials

(For 24 students working in pairs)

Several hammers
Several conductivity testers
12 pipets or dropper bottles for HCl
12 pipets or dropper bottles for $CuCl_2$
12 wellplates
12 forceps
25 mL 0.5 M hydrochloric acid solution (1 mL conc. HCl/25 mL)

---

25 mL 0.1 M copper(II) chloride solution (0.43 g $CuCl_2 \cdot 2\ H_2O$/25 mL)

Coded samples of seven elements:

Code A: 5 g carbon (C) pencil lead

Code B: 12 cm magnesium (Mg) ribbon, cut to 1-cm lengths

Code C: 5 g silicon (Si), 12 small lumps

Code D: 5 g tin (Sn), 12 small pieces tin wire or tin foil [*Note:* Can substitute copper (Cu) wire or foil]

Code E: 5 g sulfur (S), 12 small lumps

Code F: 5 g iron (Fe), 1-cm pieces of thin wire (for conductivity)

Code G: 15 g zinc (Zn), 12 small pieces mossy zinc or 12 1-cm pieces wire (for conductivity)

Safety

Some people have allergies to sulfur. Check with students to see if any have known sulfur allergies. If so, either eliminate the sulfur for all or excuse the allergic students from this investigation.

Students should wear protective goggles and aprons throughout the activity.

Pre-Lab Discussion

Require that students draft a data table before beginning the investigation. Either review their data tables individually or allow them to critique one another's tables prior to your evaluation. Data tables are available in the TRB/TRCD if students are not quite ready to create their own. Caution students to handle the element samples using forceps rather than their hands. Review the procedures for using acids safely. The reactions with HCl and $CuCl_2$ may be slow to occur. Encourage students to record their immediate observations and then to record further observations after a few minutes have passed.

Lab Tips

• Do not allow students access to larger amounts than specified samples of active metals such as Mg. Be sure that students do not collect and/or remove larger quantities of magnesium ribbon for unauthorized and highly dangerous "experimentation" outside of class.

• A 9-V conductivity tester with light-emitting diodes is recommended **(Figure 2.6, page 115).** These testers are considered safe for student use. (See below.)

• If a 110-V apparatus is used, you should demonstrate the activity.

• Consider having students "hammer" their samples on their metallic ring-stand base with a metal support ring; this spares the lab countertop and does not require hammers. Alternately (or additionally) place laboratory paper towels under the sample to be hammered to contain fragments and powders (see **Figure 2.7**).

• If there are fewer hammers than groups, students can take turns or you can demonstrate this part of the activity to the class.

Constructing a Safe Conductivity Apparatus

Instructions for constructing a safe student conductivity apparatus from a 9-V battery, resistors, and LEDs available from electronic supply stores are found in the reference below. A commercial version is also available from Flinn Scientific. See Katz, D. and Willis, C., *Journal of Chemical Education,* 1994, p. 330.

Figure 2.7 *Testing a sample for malleability.*

4. *Crushing:* Gently tap each element sample with a hammer as shown in Figure 2.7. Based on the results, decide whether the sample is **malleable,** which means it flattens without shattering when struck, or **brittle,** which means it shatters into pieces.

5. *Reactivity with copper(II) chloride.*
   a. Label seven wells of a clean wellplate *A* through *G.*
   b. Place a sample of each element in its well. The ribbon or solid wire samples provided by your teacher will be less than 1 cm in length. Other samples should be between 0.2 g and 0.4 g. You can estimate that mass as being no larger than the size of a match head.
   c. Add 15 to 20 drops of 0.1 M copper(II) chloride ($CuCl_2$) to each sample.
   d. Observe each system for three to five minutes—changes may be slow. A change in a sample's appearance may indicate a chemical reaction. Decide which elements reacted with the copper(II) chloride and which did not. Record these results.
   e. Discard the wellplate contents as instructed by your teacher.

6. *Reactivity with acid.*
   a. Repeat Steps 5a and 5b.
   b. Add 15 to 20 drops of 0.5 M HCl to each well that contains a sample. (**Caution:** *0.5 M hydrochloric acid (HCl) can chemically attack skin if allowed to remain in contact for a long time. If any hydrochloric acid accidentally spills on you, ask a classmate to notify your teacher immediately. Wash the affected area immediately with tap water and continue rinsing for several minutes.*)
   c. Observe and record each result. The formation of gas bubbles may indicate that a chemical reaction has occurred. Decide which elements reacted with the hydrochloric acid and which did not. Record these results.
   d. Discard the wellplate contents as instructed by your teacher.

7. Wash your hands thoroughly before leaving the laboratory.

				EXPECTED RESULTS		
CODE	ELEMENT	APPEARANCE	CRUSHING	CONDUCTIVITY	REACTIVITY WITH ACID	REACTIVITY WITH CuCl₂(aq)
A	C	Gray, dull	Brittle	Yes	No	No
B	Mg	Shiny, silver	Malleable	Yes	Yes, bubbles	Yes, darkens
C	Si	Gray, shiny	Brittle	Yes	No	No
D	Sn	Shiny, silver	Malleable	Yes	Yes, bubbles	Yes, darkens

Questions

1. Classify each property tested in this investigation as either a physical property or a chemical property.
2. Sort the seven coded elements into two groups based on similarities in their physical and chemical properties.
3. Which element or elements could fit into either group? Why?
4. Using the following information, classify each tested element as a metal, a nonmetal, or a metalloid:
   ▶ Metals have a luster, are malleable (can be hammered into sheets), and conduct electricity.
   ▶ Many metals react with acids; many metals also react with copper(II) chloride solution.
   ▶ Nonmetals are usually dull in appearance, are brittle, and do not conduct electricity.
   ▶ Metalloids have some properties of both metals and nonmetals.

You have been introduced to one classification scheme for elements: metals, nonmetals, and metalloids. However, the quantity of detailed information about all the elements is enormous. When you are choosing or designing materials for specific uses, the more information you have about the elements (including the similarities and the differences among them), the better your decisions will be. Where is knowledge about the elements conveniently organized? You have already been introduced to one answer—the *periodic table*. Now you will explore its origins and gain a greater understanding of the chemical information that the periodic table conveys.

A.6 THE PERIODIC TABLE

By the mid-1800s, chemists had identified about 60 elements. Five of these elements were nonmetals that are gases at room temperature: hydrogen (H), oxygen (O), nitrogen (N), fluorine (F), and chlorine (Cl). Two liquid elements were also known, the metal mercury (Hg) and the nonmetal bromine (Br). The rest of the known elements were solids with widely differing properties.

To organize information about the known elements, several scientists tried to place elements with similar properties near one another in a chart. Such an arrangement is called a *periodic table*.

	EXPECTED RESULTS (CONTINUED)					
CODE	ELEMENT	APPEARANCE	CRUSHING	CONDUCTIVITY	REACTIVITY WITH ACID	REACTIVITY WITH CuCl$_2$(aq)
D (alt)	Cu	Shiny, orange-brown	Malleable	Yes	Yes, bubbles	No
E	S	Yellow, dull	Brittle	No	No	No
F	Fe	Gray, shiny	Malleable	Yes	Yes, bubbles	Yes, darkens
G	Zn	Shiny, silver	Malleable	Yes	Yes, bubbles	Yes, darkens

Answers

1. Physical: appearance, crushing/ malleability, conductivity
   Chemical: reaction with acid, reaction with CuCl$_2$(aq)
2. Group 1: Elements B, D, F, and G (Mg, Sn/Cu, Fe, Zn); Group 2: Elements A, C, and E (C, Si, S).
3. Element C (Si). It is shiny and conductive but brittle.
4. Metals—Elements B, D, F, and G (Mg, Sn/Cu, Fe, Zn); nonmetals— Elements A and E (C, S); metalloids—Element C (Si). Students may also classify carbon as a metalloid based on its conductivity.

Additional Information

Some everyday uses of the elements in this investigation:

Carbon as graphite—steel making, lubricants, brake linings, pencils

Carbon as diamond—gemstone, abrasive

Carbon as activated carbon— decolorizing and purifying agent

Magnesium—high-strength/ low-weight alloys, flares, fireworks

Silicon—transistors, semiconductors, solar cells

Tin—alloys (solder, bronze, pewter)

Sulfur—producing sulfuric acid, matches, gunpowder, vulcanized rubber

Iron—structural metal (steel)

Zinc—coating (galvanizing), alloys (brass), dry cell batteries

A.6 The Periodic Table

You may wish to point out that (unlike the 1800s atomic mass scale) the modern atomic mass scale of the elements is based on a particular kind of carbon atom—the isotope carbon-12, which is defined as having an atomic mass of exactly 12. This material describes the development of the periodic table as a search for patterns and regularities.

Using the Figures

Figure 2.8:

• The caption asks students to identify the information on the stamp, which includes the symbols and atomic weights for aluminum, gallium, and indium. Ask students to locate these elements on the periodic table in the back cover of the book. Where are they in relation to one another? (They are all in the same "column." Noting this may help prepare students for learning about the organization of the periodic table.)

• Some of the writing on the stamp is in black and some is in red. Ask students what the significance of this might be. Black writing signifies Mendeleev's best estimates at one point in time; red writing signifies corrections and/or additions based on further investigations and discoveries. Note that gallium had not yet been discovered when Mendeleev first reasoned that—according to his organization scheme—an element should appear "between" aluminum and indium, with an estimated atomic weight of 68. Later, the element was discovered and named, and its atomic weight was found to be closer to 69 than the proposed 68 (thus the correction). It is unnecessary to discuss these details now—you could return to this figure and discuss it when students are working on *Developing Skills A.11*.

Figure 2.9:
The caption asks students to think of other common periodic examples. These could include school class schedules, a woman's menstrual cycle, and appearances of Halley's Comet, to name a few.

Dimitri Mendeleev, a Russian chemist, published a periodic table in 1869. We use such a table today. In some respects, the periodic table has a pattern that resembles a monthly calendar, in which weeks repeat on a regular (periodic) seven-day cycle. Figure 2.8 shows a stamp honoring Mendeleev, and Figure 2.9 shows a moon-phase chart, another type of periodic behavior.

Figure 2.8 *Dimitri Mendeleev (1834–1907) studied trends in the physical and chemical properties of elements. This stamp's left field includes 19th century data on aluminum, gallium, and indium. What particular information does the stamp provide about these elements?*

The periodic tables of the 1800s were organized according to two characteristics of elements. First, chemists knew that atoms of different elements have different masses. For example, hydrogen atoms have the lowest mass, oxygen atoms are about 16 times more massive than hydrogen atoms, and sulfur atoms are about twice as massive as oxygen atoms (making them about 32 times more massive than hydrogen atoms). Based on such comparisons, an *atomic weight* was assigned to each element in Mendeleev's periodic table. This atomic weight then became one of the two criteria for arranging elements.

The other criterion for organizing elements was their respective "combining capacity" with other elements, such as chlorine and oxygen. Atoms of various elements differ in the way that they combine with atoms of another element. For example, one atom of potassium (K) or cesium (Cs) combines with only one atom of chlorine (Cl) to produce the compound KCl or CsCl. Such one-to-one compounds can be represented as ECl, where E stands for the element combining with chlorine.

One atom of magnesium (Mg) or of strontium (Sr) combines with *two* atoms of chlorine to produce the compound $MgCl_2$ or $SrCl_2$, which can be represented in general terms as ECl$_2$. Atoms of other elements may combine with three or four chlorine atoms to produce compounds with the general formula ECl$_3$ or ECl$_4$.

January

February

Figure 2.9 *Several phenomena exhibit periodicity—the moon's phases, the seasons, and the calendar. Can you think of other common periodic examples?*

In the first periodic table, elements with similar chemical properties were placed in the same vertical column. Horizontal arrangements were based on the increasing atomic weights of the elements. In the activity that follows, you will develop a classification scheme for some elements in much the same way that Mendeleev did.

See the modern periodic table, page 124.

A.7 GROUPING THE ELEMENTS

Making Decisions

You will receive a set of 20 element data cards. Each card lists some properties of a particular element.

1. Arrange the cards in order of increasing atomic weight.

2. Try sorting the cards into several different groups. Each group should include elements with similar properties. You might need to try several methods of grouping according to properties before you find one that makes sense to you.

3. Examine the cards within each group for any patterns. Arrange the cards within each group in some logical sequence. Again, trial and error may be a useful method for accomplishing this task.

4. Observe how particular element properties vary from group to group.

5. Arrange all the card groups into some logical sequence.

6. Select the most reasonable and useful patterns within and among the card groups. Then tape the cards onto a sheet of paper to preserve your pattern for later classroom discussion.

Section A   Why We Use What We Do   **119**

Making Decisions

A.7 Grouping the Elements

Data cards (available on the TRCD and in the TRB) containing selected chemical and physical properties of 20 elements are used to classify the elements according to similarities in their properties, an approach employed by Mendeleev (who worked with 63 elements and similar data). You may duplicate the cards to make a copy for each student (or small group). This works well as a group project in class. Groups can display their "periodic tables" and be ready to describe how patterns they used are useful in organizing and predicting. Tell students that their arrangement must make sense in more than one direction, that is, that columns and rows must both have a pattern. Allow students to use arrangements of the elements that are different from the modern periodic table as long as they can explain and justify their arrangements.

If students have difficulty getting started, consider giving them hints such as "mass must increase going across" or "chemical properties must remain the same going down." Refrain from giving hints unless students are clearly unable to proceed—the activity is most useful when students arrange the elements according to their own patterns.

Students should understand that a dash on a data card is interpreted as a "zero"—indicating that the element does not combine with the specified substance to form a compound.

Students will use these cards again in *Developing Skills A.9.*

A.8 The Pattern of Atomic Numbers

This material revisits subatomic particles (considered in greater detail in Unit 6) and relates the number of protons in an atom to an element's placement on the periodic table. Emphasize that the atomic number (number of protons) determines the identity of the element and its position on the table. Distinguish atomic number and atomic weight—used to organize early periodic tables—stressing that atomic weight also includes neutrons and the negligible weight added by electrons. Discuss the limitation of organizing by atomic weight by noting that there are multiple elements with atomic weight 40 in the element data cards (*Making Decisions A.7*).

This material introduces the concept of isotopes. You may wish to briefly discuss how isotopes lead to the values for atomic mass on the periodic table, which are weighted averages of the natural distribution of isotopes of each element. Isotopes are revisited in greater detail in Unit 6.

 A.8 Supplement: The Pattern of Atomic Numbers

A.8 THE PATTERN OF ATOMIC NUMBERS

Creators of early periodic tables were unable to explain the similarities in properties found among neighboring elements. For example, we know now that all elements in the leftmost column of the periodic table are very reactive metals. All elements listed in the rightmost column are unreactive (noble) gases. See Figure 2.10. The reason for such patterns, which were discovered more than 50 years after Mendeleev's work, serves as the basis for the modern periodic table.

As you will recall from Unit 1, all atoms are composed of smaller particles, including equal numbers of positively charged protons and negatively charged electrons. The number of protons in an atom, called the **atomic number,** distinguishes atoms of different elements. For example, each sodium atom (and only atoms of sodium) contains 11 protons; the atomic number of sodium is 11. Each carbon atom contains 6 protons. If the number of protons in an atom is 9, it is a fluorine atom; if 12, it is a magnesium atom. Thus, the atomic number identifies each atom as a particular element.

In the modern periodic table of the elements, elements are placed in sequence according to their increasing atomic number (number of *protons*). However, because electrically neutral (uncharged) atoms contain equal numbers of protons and electrons, the periodic table is also sequenced by the number of *electrons* contained in neutral atoms of each element.

Early periodic tables, much like the one you just constructed, used atomic weights to organize the elements. Although this method produces reasonable results for elements with relatively small atomic weights, it does not work well for more massive atoms. The reason for this is the existence of another small particle that also contributes to the atomic weight, the electrically uncharged *neutron*. The total mass of an atom is largely determined by the combined mass of protons and neutrons in its nucleus. The **nucleus** is a concentrated region of positive charge (due to protons) in the center of an atom. See Figure 2.11.

The total number of protons and neutrons in the nucleus of an atom is called the **mass number.** Electrons make up the rest of an atom; however, because each electron is about 1/2000 the mass of a proton or neutron, the total mass of electrons does not contribute significantly to the mass of an atom.

While all atoms of a particular element have the same number of protons, the number of neutrons can differ from atom to atom of an element. For example, carbon atoms always contain 6 protons, but they

Figure 2.10 *When excited by an external energy source, neon's electrons produce brilliant orange-red light emissions. Other excited gases or inner coatings on the tube allow the emission of light of many distinctive colors.*

Mass number and atomic number are not the same.

Scientific American Conceptual Illustration

Figure 2.11 *Model of a lithium (Li) atom.* *Each electrically neutral lithium atom contains three protons, three electrons, and either three or four neutrons. In this model, the protons and three neutrons reside in the Li nucleus (center). Electrons are not depicted as individual particles; they occupy "electron clouds" around the nucleus. Two electrons (yellow cloud) remain close to the nucleus; the third electron (fainter cloud) is relatively further away. Electron clouds occupy most of an atom's volume; the nucleus accounts for nearly all the atom's mass.*

Note that an atom does not have a distinctly defined "outer edge," but, instead, has a rather fuzzy outer region.

may contain 6, 7, or 8 neutrons. Thus, individual carbon atoms can have mass numbers of 12, 13, or 14. For example, 6 protons + 7 neutrons – mass number 13. Atoms with the same number of protons but different numbers of neutrons, such as these carbon atoms, are called **isotopes.** In other words, isotopes are atoms of the same element with different mass numbers.

Is there a connection between the atomic numbers used to organize the modern periodic table and the properties of elements used by nineteenth-century chemists to create their periodic tables? If there is, what is that connection? Continue reading to explore the relationship between atomic numbers and the properties of elements.

> Isotopes are the major reason for fractional atomic weights found on the periodic table. For example, the atomic weight of chlorine is listed as 35.45. These values represent the average mass of all of the atoms of an element.

Section A   Why We Use What We Do   **121**

Using the Figures

Figure 2.10: As the caption states, excited neon gas produces an orange-red light emission. Internal phosphor coatings (like those used in fluorescent tubes) can be used with neon (or gases such as mercury and argon) to produce other colors commonly seen in "neon" signs. The phosphor coating absorbs neon's (or mercury's) weak short-wave UV emissions and fluoresces, emitting a different color. Thus, a blue-emitting phosphor combines with neon's red-orange glow to produce hot pink. A clear tube containing mercury and argon gases glows light blue.

Scientific American Conceptual Illustration

It is common for students to visualize an atom in terms of electrons orbiting the nucleus, like planets orbiting the Sun. However, this is no longer an accepted model. A better model is of electron "clouds" surrounding the nucleus. You may want to point out some limitations of this particular representation to your students. For instance, "edges" on atoms are fuzzier than depicted here. Also, the nucleus as drawn is much too large (which allows students to identify and count protons and neutrons). In reality, an atom's diameter is about 10 000 times the diameter of its nucleus.

Developing Skills

A.9 Periodic Variation in Properties

In this activity, students produce graphs illustrating the periodic relationships of elemental properties. After discovering the cyclic (periodic) trends, students relate their interpretations to the modern periodic table.

To begin, students should label each element card from *Making Decisions A.7* with the appropriate atomic number, using the periodic table for guidance. Discuss the term *mass number*—the sum of the protons and neutrons in an atom. Mass number can be loosely estimated by rounding atomic weight to the nearest whole number. The numbers labeled "atomic mass" on the element cards are more accurately called mass numbers.

Students often have difficulty with the two cards that show a mass number of 40. Students should use properties of the elements to decide which is argon (18, an inert gas) and which is calcium (20, a reactive solid).

Students will need to convert boiling points on each card from degrees Celsius to kelvins. The resulting bar graph is easier to interpret, since all boiling points will be above zero. Refer students to the margin note on page 123 for guidance.

Developing Skills

Trends and Variations in the Periodic Table

Follow the graphing guidelines you learned in Unit 1 (pages 80–81).

A.9 PERIODIC VARIATION IN PROPERTIES

Your teacher will assist you in identifying the atomic numbers of the twenty elements you considered earlier in this unit. Use these atomic numbers and information about each element's properties to prepare the two graphs described below. Look for patterns between atomic numbers and element properties as you construct the plots.

Graph 1: Trends in a Chemical Property

1. On a sheet of graph paper, draw a set of axes, and title the graph "Trends in a Chemical Property."
2. Label the x-axis "Atomic Number of *E*." What is the range of possible numbers that you will need to display on your graph? Scale your x-axis with these values in mind.
3. Label the y-axis "Oxygen Atoms per Atom of *E*." What is the range of possible numbers that you will have to display on your graph? Scale your y-axis with these values in mind.
4. Construct a bar graph, as demonstrated in Figure 2.12, by plotting the oxide data from the element cards. For example, if no oxide forms, the height of the bar will be 0 because oxygen atoms do not form a compound with atoms of *E*. If E_2O (1 oxygen atom for 2 *E* atoms) forms, the height of the bar is 0.5, which is the number of oxygen atoms for each *E* atom in the compound. Similarly, the heights of the graph bars for other oxides are 1 for *EO*, 1.5 for E_2O_3, 2 for EO_2, and 2.5 for E_2O_5. Do you understand why?

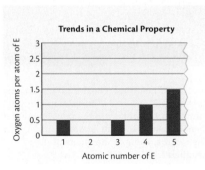

Figure 2.12 *Sample bar graph for oxide data.*

5. Label each bar with the actual symbol of the element *E* involved in that compound.

MASS NUMBER	ATOMIC NUMBER	ELEMENT	SYMBOL	BOILING POINT (K)	MASS NUMBER	ATOMIC NUMBER	ELEMENT	SYMBOL	BOILING POINT (K)
1	1	Hydrogen	H	21	12	6	Carbon	C	4620
4	2	Helium	He	4	14	7	Nitrogen	N	77
7	3	Lithium	Li	1600	16	8	Oxygen	O	90
9	4	Beryllium	Be	2780	19	9	Fluorine	F	85
10	5	Boron	B	2800	20	10	Neon	Ne	27

Graph 2: Trends in a Physical Property

6. On a separate sheet of graph paper, draw a set of axes, and title the graph "Trends in a Physical Property."

7. Label the *x*-axis "Atomic Number" and number it from 1 to 20. What range of possible numbers will you have to display on your graph? Scale your *x*-axis with these values in mind.

8. Label the *y*-axis "Boiling Point (K)." What range of possible numbers will you have to display on your graph? Scale your y-axis with these values in mind. Use as much of the graph paper as possible to plot these kelvin temperatures. (*Hint:* See the margin note to learn how to convert temperature values from degrees Celsius to kelvins.)

9. Construct a bar graph as in Step 4, this time using the boiling point data from the element cards, as shown in Figure 2.13. (*Note:* Do not include data for the element with atomic number 6. The boiling point of this element (carbon) would be quite far off the graph paper.)

10. Label each bar with the actual symbol of the element it represents.

After your graphs are completed, answer the following questions.

1. Does either bar graph reveal a repeating, or cyclic, pattern? (*Hint:* Focus on elements represented by very large or very small values.) Describe any patterns you observe.

2. Are these graphs consistent with patterns found in your earlier grouping of the elements? Explain.

3. Based on these two bar graphs, why is the chemist's organization of elements called a *periodic* table? (*Hint:* Look up the meaning of *periodic* in the dictionary.)

4. Where are elements with the highest *oxide numbers* located on the periodic table?

5. Where are elements with the highest *boiling points* located on the periodic table?

6. Explain any trends you noted in your answers to Questions 4 and 5.

7. Predict which element should have the lowest boiling point: selenium (Se), bromine (Br), or krypton (Kr). Use evidence from your graphs to explain how you decided.

8. Using your graphs, predict the pattern in boiling points and oxide numbers for the next 5 to 8 elements, starting with gallium (Ga).

> Temperature in kelvins (K) is related to temperature in degrees Celsius (°C) by K = 273.16 + °C. You will learn more about the kelvin temperature scale in Unit 4.

Figure 2.13 *Sample bar graph for boiling point data.*

You may wish to discuss the reasons for using bar graphs in this activity. In general, line graphs are used for continuous data, so even if data are available only for discrete points, the assumption is that intermediate points would have intermediate values. There are no intermediate atomic numbers—an element is, for instance, nitrogen (7) or oxygen (8), not atomic number 7.5. Thus, it is not appropriate to use a graph that suggests data are continuous.

Answers to A.10 appear on Teacher Edition page 124.

MASS NUMBER	ATOMIC NUMBER	ELEMENT	SYMBOL	BOILING POINT (K)	MASS NUMBER	ATOMIC NUMBER	ELEMENT	SYMBOL	BOILING POINT (K)
23	11	Sodium	Na	1162	32	16	Sulfur	S	718
24	12	Magnesium	Mg	1390	36	17	Chlorine	Cl	239
27	13	Aluminum	Al	2600	40	18	Argon	Ar	87
28	14	Silicon	Si	2950	39	19	Potassium	K	1030
31	15	Phosphorus	P	553	40	20	Calcium	Ca	1760

Answers to A.10 (page 123)

1. Both graphs show repeating patterns. Minimum values appear at the noble gases for both. Numbers of O in oxide are maximized for column 15 (nitrogen family) elements. Carbon family elements (column 14) have highest boiling points.

2. Answers will vary. If student groupings were similar to the periodic table, they will find high correlations between the patterns in these graphs and their groupings. If their groupings did not correlate well to the graphs, they should try to explain why not.

3. Physical characteristics of the elements tend to repeat after a certain number of elements, forming an interval or period.

4. Toward the right side of the periodic table, in the carbon and nitrogen families

5. Toward the left side of the periodic table, in the beryllium, boron, and carbon families

6. Answers will vary and may include that O in oxide increases across the period, then decreases and/or that boiling point increases on the left side of the periodic table, then decreases on the right side.

7. Krypton: Boiling points decrease on the right side of the periodic table, and krypton is the rightmost of these three elements.

8. Student answers should indicate trends similar to those observed for atomic numbers 13–20.

Variations and Extensions

• If graphing calculators are available, use them to complete this activity or use a spreadsheet such as Microsoft® Excel.

• Students could also, or alternately, plot the Number of Chlorine Atoms per Atom of E or the melting point versus atomic number.

• Students could also refer to the American Chemical Society's interactive periodic table (visit http://chemistry.org and choose Periodic Table on the Quick Find menu) to further investigate periodic trends. Users can generate graphs for a wide range of properties including melting point, boiling point, and atomic radius.

PERIODIC TABLE OF THE ELEMENTS

A.10 ORGANIZATION OF THE PERIODIC TABLE

When the first 20 elements are listed in order of increasing atomic numbers and grouped according to similar properties, they form horizontal rows called **periods.** This **periodic relationship** among elements is summarized in the modern periodic table shown on page 124. To become more familiar with the periodic table, locate the 20 elements you grouped earlier. How do their relative positions compare with those shown on your chart?

Each vertical column in the periodic table contains elements with similar properties. Each of these columns is called a **group** or **family** of elements. For example, the **alkali metal family** consists of the six elements (starting with lithium) in the first column at the left of the table. See Figure 2.14. Each element (E) in this family is a highly reactive metal that forms an ECl chloride and an E_2O oxide. By contrast, at the right side of the table, the **noble gas family** consists of very unreactive (or even chemically inert) elements; only xenon (Xe) and krypton (Kr) are known to form any compounds under normal conditions. The group containing fluorine, chlorine, and bromine—in the column just to the left of noble gases—is called the **halogen family.** Halogens readily form 1− ions; as anions, they are a component of many ionic compounds.

The arrangement of elements in the periodic table provides an orderly summary of the key characteristics of each element. By knowing the major properties of a certain chemical family, you can predict some properties of any element in that family. This knowledge can be very helpful when evaluating elements for possible uses. All elements are also listed alphabetically in Table 2.2 (pages 128–129).

Figure 2.14 *Sodium is an alkali metal. All alkali metals have similar physical and chemical properties, so they are placed in the same column (family) in the periodic table.*

Like sodium chloride (NaCl), all chlorides and oxides of alkali metal elements are ionic compounds.

A.11 PREDICTING PROPERTIES

Developing Skills

Some element properties can be estimated by averaging the respective properties of the elements located just above and just below an element on the periodic table. That is how Mendeleev predicted the properties of several elements unknown in his time. He was so convinced these elements existed that he purposely left gaps for them in his periodic table, along with a prediction of some of their properties. When those elements were discovered shortly thereafter, they fit exactly as expected. Mendeleev's fame rests largely on the accuracy of these predictions.

For example, germanium (Ge) was not known when Mendeleev proposed his periodic table. However, in 1871 he predicted the existence of germanium, calling it *ekasilicon*. Not only did Mendeleev predict germanium's existence, he also accurately predicted many of its chemical and physical properties, based on known properties of other elements in its same family.

Eka- means "standing next in order."

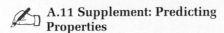

A.11 Supplement: Predicting Properties

A.10 Organization of the Periodic Table

Students should have gained some insight into the organization of the periodic table based on *Developing Skills A.9.* Vocabulary and nomenclature related to the periodic table are introduced here. Review with students the structure of the periodic table. In particular, note several groups or families that are useful in explaining chemical behavior (the noble gases, halogens, alkali metals).

Developing Skills

A.11 Predicting Properties

Dmitri Mendeleev's unique contribution was in declaring that discontinuities in the patterns of the known elements indicated the existence of elements yet to be discovered. This activity allows students to practice using the periodic table to estimate properties of elements, much as Mendeleev did.

Suggest that students review **Figure 2.8** (the Mendeleev postage stamp on page 118). If you have not already discussed some of the details in Figure 2.8, this is a good opportunity to do so.

A good resource on Mendeleev and his ideas about the periodic table is **http://en.wikipedia.org/wiki/Mendeleev**.

As an extension, students could investigate and compare the known properties of scandium and gallium to the predictions Mendeleev made of these properties.

Answers

1. Krypton should have a boiling point between that of argon (87 K) and xenon (161 K) of about 124 K (actual is 120 K).

2. a. Rubidium should have a melting point between that of potassium (337 K) and cesium (302 K) of about 320 K (actual is 312 K).
   b. Higher; melting points decrease within the family from top to bottom (actual is 370.8 K). The card-organizing activities provide data that show this trend.

3. (EkaSi)Cl$_4$ (actually GeCl$_4$)

4. a. CF$_4$
   b. Al$_2$S$_3$
   c. KCl
   d. CaBr$_2$
   e. SrO

A.12 What Determines Properties?

This material gives a brief overview of some characteristics that help determine chemical and physical properties:

• Number of protons determines identity and essential properties of an element.

• Number and arrangement of electrons determine many chemical properties.

• Interatomic attractions determine some physical properties (such as melting point), particularly of metals.

• Intermolecular forces determine some physical and chemical properties of compounds.

Students will learn more about electron arrangements and intermolecular forces in Unit 3.

Sample Problem: *Given that the density of silicon (Si) is 2.3 g/cm³ and the density of tin (Sn) is 7.3 g/cm³, estimate the density of germanium (Ge).*

These three elements are in the same group in the periodic table. Germanium is below silicon and above tin. (You can verify this by locating these elements in the periodic table.) Thus, the predicted density of germanium can be estimated by averaging the densities of silicon and tin, arriving at a calculated value of 4.8 g/cm³.

When germanium was discovered in 1886, its density was found to be 5.3 g/cm³, which is within about 10% of the earlier estimated density. The periodic table helped guide Mendeleev (and now you, too) to make a useful prediction.

Formulas for chemical compounds can also be predicted from relationships established in the periodic table. For example, carbon and oxygen form carbon dioxide (CO_2). What formula would be predicted for a compound of carbon and sulfur? The periodic table indicates that sulfur (S) and oxygen (O) are in the same family. Knowing that carbon and oxygen form CO_2, a logical—and quite correct—prediction would be CS_2 (carbon disulfide). Now it's your turn:

1. The element krypton (Kr) was not known in Mendeleev's time. Given that the boiling point of argon (Ar) is −186 °C and of xenon (Xe) is −112 °C, estimate the boiling point of krypton.

2. a. Estimate the melting point of rubidium (Rb). The melting points of potassium (K) and cesium (Cs) are 337 K and 302 K, respectively.
   b. Do you expect the melting point of sodium (Na) to be higher or lower than that of rubidium (Rb)? Explain. On what evidence did you base your answer?

3. Mendeleev knew that silicon tetrachloride ($SiCl_4$) existed. Using his periodic table, he correctly predicted the existence of *ekasilicon*, an element just below silicon in the periodic table. Predict the formula for the compound formed by Mendeleev's *ekasilicon* and chlorine.

4. Here are formulas for several known compounds: NaI, $MgCl_2$, CaO, Al_2O_3, and CCl_4. Using that information, predict the formula for a compound formed from:
   a. C and F   c. K and Cl   e. Sr and O
   b. Al and S   d. Ca and Br

A.12 WHAT DETERMINES PROPERTIES?

While any atom is uniquely identified by the number of protons contained in its nucleus, the physical and particularly the chemical properties of that atom (how it interacts with other atoms) are governed largely by the number and arrangement of the atom's electrons.

A major difference between the atoms of metals and nonmetals is that metal atoms lose electrons much more easily than do nonmetal atoms. Under suitable conditions, one or more outer electrons may be removed from a metal atom. This results in metallic elements forming positive ions (cations) because the number of positively charged protons remains unchanged while the total number of negatively charged electrons has been decreased.

Some physical properties of metals depend on attractions among their atoms. For example, stronger attractions among atoms of a metal result in higher melting points. The melting point of magnesium is 650 °C, whereas that of sodium is 98 °C. Thus, attractions among the atoms in magnesium metal must be stronger than those in sodium metal.

Chemical and physical properties of nonmetals and compounds are also explained by the makeup of their atoms, ions, or molecules and by attractions among these particles. As you learned in Unit 1, the abnormally high melting and boiling points of water are due to the strong attractions among water molecules.

Understanding the properties of atoms is the key to predicting, and even manipulating, the behavior of materials. Combined with a bit of imagination, this information allows chemists to find new uses for materials and to create new chemical compounds to meet specific needs.

> Chemists synthesize several thousand new compounds each year.

Making Decisions

A.13 IT'S ONLY MONEY

Based on what you have learned so far, you can start to make some decisions about your coin design. A good first step is to specify some characteristics that are *necessary* or *desirable* in the material you will use. (For example, a high-melting-point material is *required;* after all, who would want their coins to melt in hot sunlight? However, a metallic luster is only *desirable*.) Apply your knowledge of existing coins, as well as what you have learned about the properties of elements, to answer the following questions:

1. What physical properties must the coin material have?

2. What other physical properties are desirable?

3. What chemical properties are required of the coin's material?

4. What other chemical properties are desirable?

5. Which would make the best primary material for the new coin: a metal, a nonmetal, or a metalloid? Explain.

6. What factors or desirable coin characteristics did you consider when you answered Question 5?

Save your answers to these questions; they will help guide your coin-design work later in this unit.

A RECOMMENDED TABLE TO LIST CHARACTERISTICS FOR COIN MATERIALS:		
PROPERTIES	**NECESSARY**	**DESIRABLE**
Physical		
Chemical		

Making Decisions

A.13 It's Only Money

Students should work in small groups to begin making design decisions about the new coin that they will propose.

1. High melting point, conductivity, malleability, and an identifiable color

2. An appropriate size and shape (relatively round) to work in coin-operated machines and a pleasing design

3. Resistance to corrosion or the ability to form alloys

4. Nonreactivity with metals (and other materials) used in other coins and machine parts and compatibility with potential coatings

5. Answers will vary, but will probably favor metals. Gaseous nonmetals are not feasible, and other nonmetals tend to lack the appropriate physical properties. Metalloids tend to have at least one poor property for use as primary substance in a coin, such as reactivity, brittleness, or lack of conductivity.

6. Answers will vary but may include durability, lack of reactivity, or use in coin-operated machines.

One idea for managing the data collected in answering these questions is for students to make a chart like the one below. Remind students that they need to retain their work on this activity for their coin-design project. You may wish to require that each student (or group) maintain a folder for activities (such as A.13) that lead up to the actual coin design.

Table 2.2

CHART OF THE ELEMENTS

Element	Symbol	Atomic Number	Atomic Weight	Element	Symbol	Atomic Number	Atomic Weight
Actinium	Ac	89	[227]	Erbium	Er	68	167.26
Aluminum	Al	13	26.98	Europium	Eu	63	151.96
Americium	Am	95	[243]	Fermium	Fm	100	[257]
Antimony	Sb	51	121.76	Fluorine	F	9	19.00
Argon	Ar	18	39.95	Francium	Fr	87	[223]
Arsenic	As	33	74.92	Gadolinium	Gd	64	157.25
Astatine	At	85	[210]	Gallium	Ga	31	69.72
Barium	Ba	56	137.33	Germanium	Ge	32	72.64
Berkelium	Bk	97	[247]	Gold	Au	79	196.97
Beryllium	Be	4	9.012	Hafnium	Hf	72	178.49
Bismuth	Bi	83	208.98	Hassium	Hs	108	[277]
Bohrium	Bh	107	[264]	Helium	He	2	4.003
Boron	B	5	10.81	Holmium	Ho	67	164.93
Bromine	Br	35	79.90	Hydrogen	H	1	1.008
Cadmium	Cd	48	112.41	Indium	In	49	114.82
Calcium	Ca	20	40.08	Iodine	I	53	126.90
Californium	Cf	98	[251]	Iridium	Ir	77	192.22
Carbon	C	6	12.01	Iron	Fe	26	55.85
Cerium	Ce	58	140.12	Krypton	Kr	36	83.80
Cesium	Cs	55	132.91	Lanthanum	La	57	138.91
Chlorine	Cl	17	35.45	Lawrencium	Lr	103	[262]
Chromium	Cr	24	52.00	Lead	Pb	82	207.2
Cobalt	Co	27	58.93	Lithium	Li	3	6.941
Copper	Cu	29	63.55	Lutetium	Lu	71	174.97
Curium	Cm	96	[247]	Magnesium	Mg	12	24.31
Darmstadtium	Ds	110	[281]	Manganese	Mn	25	54.94
Dubnium	Db	105	[262]	Meitnerium	Mt	109	[268]
Dysprosium	Dy	66	162.50	Mendelevium	Md	101	[258]
Einsteinium	Es	99	[252]	Mercury	Hg	80	200.59

Table 2.2

CHART OF THE ELEMENTS (CONTINUED)							
Element	Symbol	Atomic Number	Atomic Weight	Element	Symbol	Atomic Number	Atomic Weight
Molybdenum	Mo	42	95.94	Samarium	Sm	62	150.36
Neodymium	Nd	60	144.24	Scandium	Sc	21	44.96
Neon	Ne	10	20.18	Seaborgium	Sg	106	[266]
Neptunium	Np	93	[237]	Selenium	Se	34	78.96
Nickel	Ni	28	58.69	Silicon	Si	14	28.09
Niobium	Nb	41	92.91	Silver	Ag	47	107.87
Nitrogen	N	7	14.01	Sodium	Na	11	22.99
Nobelium	No	102	[259]	Strontium	Sr	38	87.62
Osmium	Os	76	190.23	Sulfur	S	16	32.07
Oxygen	O	8	16.00	Tantalum	Ta	73	180.95
Palladium	Pd	46	106.42	Technetium	Tc	43	[98]
Phosphorus	P	15	30.97	Tellurium	Te	52	127.60
Platinum	Pt	78	195.08	Terbium	Tb	65	158.93
Plutonium	Pu	94	[244]	Thallium	Tl	81	204.38
Polonium	Po	84	[209]	Thorium	Th	90	232.04
Potassium	K	19	39.10	Thulium	Tm	69	168.93
Praseodymium	Pr	59	140.91	Tin	Sn	50	118.71
Promethium	Pm	61	[145]	Titanium	Ti	22	47.87
Protactinium	Pa	91	231.04	Tungsten	W	74	183.84
Radium	Ra	88	[226]	Uranium	U	92	238.03
Radon	Rn	86	[222]	Vanadium	V	23	50.94
Rhenium	Re	75	186.21	Xenon	Xe	54	131.29
Rhodium	Rh	45	102.91	Ytterbium	Yb	70	173.04
Roentgenium	Rg	111	[272]	Yttrium	Y	39	88.91
Rubidium	Rb	37	85.47	Zinc	Zn	30	65.41
Ruthenium	Ru	44	101.07	Zirconium	Zr	40	91.22
Rutherfordium	Rf	104	[261]				

Note: A value in square brackets is the mass number of the isotope with the longest half-life.

Section A   Why We Use What We Do   **129**

SECTION A SUMMARY

 Section A Supplement

Reviewing the Concepts

1. Chemical: b, c Physical: a, d
2. Chemical: c Physical: a, b, d
3. Chemical: a, c Physical: b, d
4. Chemical: a, b Physical: c, d
5. a. The color change
   b. Energy has been produced by the system. *Note:* Students may have difficulty with this, because although new substances have been formed within the battery, they are not evident.
   c. No new substances are formed.
   d. No new substances are formed.
6. a. Step 1: Measure and mix sugars, oils, and eggs; Step 2: Stir in dry ingredients (flour, baking soda, salt); Step 3: Stir in chocolate chips; Step 4: Drop onto cookie sheet; Step 5: Bake 8–10 min until light brown.
   b. Steps 1–4 are physical changes; Step 5 is a chemical change.
7. Metal: a Nonmetals: b, c Metalloid: d
8. Metals: a, d Metalloid: b Nonmetal: c
9. Metalloids include boron (B), silicon (Si), germanium (Ge), arsenic (As), antimony (Sb), tellurium (Te), and polonium (Po).
10. a. It would break into pieces.
    b. It would flatten.
    c. It would break into pieces.
    d. It would flatten.
11. Brittleness and nonconductivity
12. Malleability, conductivity, luster, and lack of reactivity.
13. a. Period
    b. Family or group
14. Elements, other than lithium, in the alkali metal family include: sodium (Na), potassium (K), rubidium (Rb), cesium (Cs), and francium (Fr).

SECTION A SUMMARY
Reviewing the Concepts

The physical properties of a substance can be determined without altering the substance's chemical makeup; physical changes alter a substance's physical properties. Chemical properties describe how a substance reacts chemically through its transformation into one or more different substances.

1. Classify each of the following as a chemical or a physical property:
   a. Copper has a reddish brown color.
   b. Propane burns readily.
   c. CO_2 gas extinguishes a candle flame.
   d. Honey pours more slowly than does water.

2. Classify each of the following as a chemical or a physical property:
   a. Metal wire can be bent.
   b. Ice floats in water.
   c. Paper is flammable.
   d. Sugar is soluble in water.

3. Classify each of the following as a chemical or a physical change:
   a. A candle burns.
   b. An opened carbonated beverage fizzes.
   c. Hair curls as a result of a "perm."
   d. As shoes wear out, holes appear in the soles.

4. Classify each of the following as a chemical or a physical change:
   a. A cut apple left out in the air turns brown.
   b. Flashlight batteries lose their "charge" after extended use.
   c. Dry cleaning removes oils from clothing.
   d. Italian salad dressing separates over time.

5. For each of your answers in Question 4, give evidence for your classification as a chemical or physical change.

6. a. List the steps involved in making chocolate chip cookies from scratch.
   b. Classify each step in Question 6a as involving either a chemical change or a physical change.

Elements can be classified as metals, nonmetals, or metalloids according to their physical and chemical properties.

7. Classify each property as characteristic of metals or nonmetals:
   a. shiny in appearance
   b. does not react with acids
   c. shatters easily
   d. electrically conductive

8. Classify each of these elements as a metal, a nonmetal, or a metalloid:
   a. tungsten   c. krypton
   b. antimony   d. sodium

9. List the names and symbols of two elements that are metalloids.

10. What would you expect to happen if you tapped a sample of each of the following elements with a hammer?
    a. iodine   c. phosphorus
    b. zirconium   d. nickel

11. List two properties that make nonmetals unsuitable for electric wiring.

12. List three properties that make metals suitable for use in coins.

---

15. a. On the right-hand side
    b. All are gases at normal temperatures.
    c. All are chemically inert.
16. a. MgF_2
    b. GaP
17. ($98\ °C + 39\ °C)/2 = 68.5\ °C.$ (Actual melting point is $63.4\ °C.$)
18. Looking at the trends in the halogen family, boiling points tend to increase moving down the column. (At room temperature fluorine and chlorine are gases, bromine is a liquid, and iodine is a solid.) Since chlorine is above iodine in the column, its boiling point would be lower. (A theoretical explanation involves the fact that chlorine molecules have fewer electrons than iodine molecules, resulting in weaker forces of attraction among molecules [Van der Waals or dispersion forces], thus leading to a lower boiling point.)

Elements are arranged in the periodic table based on their properties. Elements with similar chemical properties are placed in the same columns. Physical properties vary in predictable patterns across rows and down columns.

13. Give another term for each of these features of the periodic table:

a. row   b. column

14. Give the names and symbols of two elements other than lithium in the alkali metal family.

15. Consider the noble gas family:

a. Where are noble gases located on the periodic table?

b. Name one physical property that noble gases share.

c. Name one chemical property that noble gases share.

16. Given a periodic table and the formulas $BeCl_2$ and AlN, predict the formula for a compound containing

a. Mg and F   b. Ga and P

17. The melting points of sodium (Na) and rubidium (Rb) are 98 °C and 39 °C, respectively. Estimate the melting point of potassium (K).

18. Would you expect the boiling point of chlorine to be higher or lower than that of iodine? Explain.

The mass number of an atom is the sum of its number of protons and neutrons. The number of protons in an atom (the atomic number) of a given element distinguishes it from atoms of all other elements.

19. Copy and complete the following table for each electrically neutral atom.

Element Symbol	Number of Protons	Number of Neutrons	Number of Electrons
a	6	6	6
b	6	7	6
Ca	*c*	21	*d*
e	*f*	117	78
U	*g*	146	*h*

20. Using Figure 2.11 (page 121) as a model, illustrate the number of protons, neutrons, and electrons in an atom of:

a. beryllium   b. nitrogen   c. neon

21. A student is asked to explain the formation of a lead(II) ion (Pb^{2+}) from an electrically neutral lead atom (Pb). The student says that a lead atom must have gained two protons to make the ion. How would you correct this student's mistaken explanation?

20. a.

b.

c.

21. If a neutral lead atom (atomic number 82) gained two protons, it would become an atom of polonium (atomic number 84). To form a lead(II) ion, the neutral lead atom must lose two electrons, resulting in a net positive charge.

Section Summary   131

19.

ELEMENT SYMBOL	NUMBER OF PROTONS	NUMBER OF NEUTRONS	NUMBER OF ELECTRONS
a. C	6	6	6
b. C	6	7	6
Ca	c. 20	21	d. 20
e. Pt	f. 78	117	78
U	g. 92	146	h. 92

22. a.

NAME	MASS NUMBER
C	12
C	13
Ca	41
Pt	195
U	238

b. Carbon

23. No. A mass number does not define an element. Different elements can have the same mass number. A new element would be defined by its atomic number.

24. It is about 1/2000 as large.

25. a. 12, b. 12
c. 12, d. 13
e. 12, f. 14

26. Metallic elements

27. They are highly unreactive.

28. Anion: c, e, h Cation: a, b, d, f, g

Connecting the Concepts

29. b. Oxygen with mass number 16 and oxygen with mass number 18 are more chemically similar. Though they have different numbers of neutrons, they have the same number of electrons and behave identically in chemical reactions.

30. 205 picometers (the average of the diameters of Mg^{2+} and Sr^{2+}; the actual diameter of Ca^{2+} is 187.6 pm)

31. Answers will vary; everyday examples include:
a. Chemical: red litmus turns blue; physical: a wire becomes red hot
b. Chemical: burning candle; physical: cooling due to evaporation of a liquid
c. Chemical: production of gas when baking soda and vinegar react; physical: carbon dioxide coming out of solution from a carbonated beverage

---

The mass of an atom depends largely on the number of protons and neutrons contained within its nucleus. Atoms containing the same number of protons but different numbers of neutrons are considered isotopes.

22. Refer to the table provided for Question 19:
a. Calculate the mass number for each element in the table.
b. Which element has two isotopes in the table?

23. A scientist announces the discovery of a new element. The only characteristic given in the report is the element's mass number of 266. Is this information sufficient, by itself, to justify the claim of the discovery of a new element? Explain.

24. How does the mass of an electron compare to the masses of a proton and a neutron?

25. How many protons and neutrons are needed for each magnesium isotope in this table?

ISOTOPES OF MAGNESIUM

Isotope Symbol	Mass Number	Number of Protons	Number of Neutrons
Mg-24	24	*a*	*b*
Mg-25	25	*c*	*d*
Mg-26	26	*e*	*f*

The properties of an element are determined largely by the number and arrangement of electrons in its atoms.

26. Which are more likely to lose electrons, metallic elements or nonmetallic elements?

27. Noble gas elements rarely lose or gain electrons. What does this indicate about their chemical reactivity?

28. Predict whether each of the following elements would be more likely to form an anion or a cation: (*Note:* Anions are *negatively* charged; cations are *positively* charged.)
a. Na   c. F   e. O   g. Sn
b. Ca   d. Cu   f. Li   h. I

Connecting the Concepts

29. Which pair is more similar chemically? Defend your choice:
a. copper metal and copper(II) ions
or
b. oxygen with mass number 16 and oxygen with mass number 18

30. The diameter of a magnesium ion (Mg^{2+}) is 156 pm (picometers, where 1 pm = 10^{-12} m); the diameter of a strontium ion (Sr^{2+}) is 254 pm. Estimate the diameter of a calcium ion (Ca^{2+}).

31. Three kinds of observations that may indicate a chemical change appear in the following list. However, a physical change may also result in each observation. Describe a possible chemical cause and a possible physical cause for each observation:
a. change in color
b. change in temperature
c. formation of a gas

32. a. Bromine
b. Silicon

33. Students should indicate that in both situations, people used data/evidence to solve a mystery. However, Mendeleev was constructing a model organization of consistent naturally occurring substances, while students tried to find the cause of a one-time, presumably human-caused event.

34. Ar(18/39.95) and K(19/39.10);
Co(27/58.93) and Ni(28/58.69);
Te(52/127.60) and I(53/126.90);
Th(90/232.0) and Pa(91/231.0);
U(92/238.0) and Np(93/(237));
Pu(94/(244)) and Am(95/(243))

32. Identify the element that is described by each of the following statements:
    a. This element is a nonmetal. It forms anions with a 1− charge. It is in the same period as the metals used in a penny.
    b. This element is a metalloid. It is in the same period as the elements found in table salt.

33. Compare your use of the Snake River data to solve the fish-kill mystery in Unit 1 to Mendeleev's use of element data to create the periodic table.

Extending the Concepts

35. How is mercury different from other metallic elements? Using outside resources, describe some applications that take advantage of the unique properties of metallic mercury.

36. Depending on how iron is heated and cooled, it can either be hard and brittle or malleable. Explain how the same metal can have both characteristics.

34. Mendeleev arranged elements in his periodic table in order of their atomic weights. In the modern periodic table, however, elements are arranged in order of their atomic numbers. Cite two examples from the periodic table for which these two schemes would produce a different ordering of adjacent elements.

37. Construct a graph of the price per gram of an element versus its atomic number for each of the first 20 elements. Can the current cost of those elements be regarded as a periodic property? Explain. (*Hint:* Use a chemical supply catalog or the Web to locate the current price of each element.)

38. Classify the components of one or more pieces of jewelry you might possibly wear as being composed of metals, nonmetals, or metalloids.

Extending the Concepts

35. Answers will vary, but should indicate that mercury is extremely dense and is the only metal that is a liquid at room temperature. It is used in mercury barometers, thermometers, manometers, electric relays, electrodes for some batteries, and dental amalgams. Mercury is very toxic as a vapor and in many compounds, especially organomercury compounds.

36. The rate of heating and cooling determines the arrangement of atoms. This, in turn, determines brittleness or malleability.

37. The cost per gram is not a periodic property. The following sample graph is based on 2004 prices:

A useful resource: **http://minerals.er.usgs.gov/minerals/pubs/commodity/**.

38. Jewelry is made primarily of metals—they can be drawn into wire and hammered into shape. Alloys of metals are also useful because they are resistant to corrosion. Jewelry may also contain nonmetals such as carbon (diamonds); and compounds of nonmetals and metals, such as calcium carbonate (pearls) and aluminum oxide (ruby and sapphire).

Earth's Mineral Resources

Section B begins highlighting Earth's metals and minerals. Using copper as an example, students explore the sources, properties, processing, and uses of metals. Oxidation–reduction reactions (redox) are also introduced to explain the behavior of metals and their reduction from ores.

B.1 Sources and Uses of Metals

This material introduces the Earth's stores of resources—the atmosphere, hydrosphere, and lithosphere. The text identifies resources of the lithosphere, including petroleum and metal ores, as most varied. **Figure 2.15** shows reservoirs graphically and identifies some resources found in each.

One concept to emphasize in this section is that mineral resources are widely distributed among the world's nations, without regard to land area or population. Thus, most nations, including the United States, must import many mineral resources. Use this idea and **Table 2.3,** page 136, to discuss the need for trade among nations.

Among Earth's resources, metals—and the minerals from which they are extracted—have long been used by humans. Those uses have ranged from tool making, energy transmission, and construction to works of art, decoration, and coin making. In this section, you will explore properties and uses of minerals and metals. Using copper as a case study, you will learn about Earth's mineral resources and how some minerals are converted to useful metals.

B.1 SOURCES AND USES OF METALS

Earth's Mineral Resources

Human needs for resources—whether to create a new coin, make clothing, construct a space-vehicle rocket engine, or fertilize food crops—must all be met by chemical supplies currently present on Earth. These supplies of resources are often cataloged by where they are found. The table in Figure 2.15 indicates the chemical makeup of Earth.

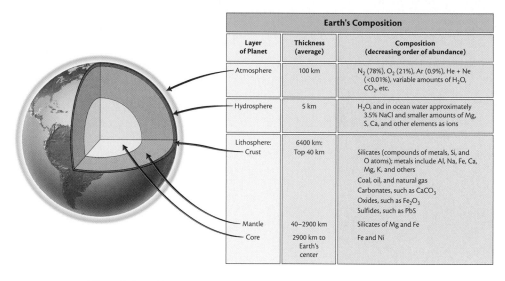

Earth's Composition		
Layer of Planet	**Thickness (average)**	**Composition (decreasing order of abundance)**
Atmosphere	100 km	N_2 (78%), O_2 (21%), Ar (0.9%), He + Ne (<0.01%), variable amounts of H_2O, CO_2, etc.
Hydrosphere	5 km	H_2O, and in ocean water approximately 3.5% NaCl and smaller amounts of Mg, S, Ca, and other elements as ions
Lithosphere: Crust	6400 km: Top 40 km	Silicates (compounds of metals, Si, and O atoms); metals include Al, Na, Fe, Ca, Mg, K, and others Coal, oil, and natural gas Carbonates, such as $CaCO_3$ Oxides, such as Fe_2O_3 Sulfides, such as PbS
Mantle	40–2900 km	Silicates of Mg and Fe
Core	2900 km to Earth's center	Fe and Ni

Figure 2.15 *Earth's composition. From what layer do most resources come that support human activities?*

Earth's atmosphere, hydrosphere, and outer layer of the lithosphere supply resources for all human activities. The **atmosphere** provides nitrogen, oxygen, neon, and argon. From the **hydrosphere** come water and some dissolved minerals. The **lithosphere,** which is the solid part of Earth, provides the greatest variety of chemical resources. For example, petroleum and metal-bearing ores are found in the lithosphere. An **ore** is a naturally occurring rock or mineral that can be mined and from which it is profitable to extract a metal or other material. An ore contains a mixture of components. Of these, **minerals** are the most important. They are naturally occurring solid compounds containing the element or group of elements of interest.

The deepest mines on Earth barely scratch the surface of its crust. If Earth were the size of an apple, all accessible resources of the lithosphere would be located within the apple's skin. From this thin band of soil and rock, we obtain the major raw materials needed to build homes, automobiles, appliances, computers, DVDs, and sports equipment—in fact, all manufactured objects.

As you can see from Table 2.3 (page 136), many of Earth's resources are not uniformly distributed. There is no relationship between a nation's supply of these resources and either its land area or its population. A particular region may be the predominant supplier of certain metals to industry. For example, Africa holds most of the world's known reserves of chromium (95%), cobalt (52%), and manganese (80%).

The growth of the United States as a major industrial nation has been facilitated, in part, by the quantity and diversity of its chemical resources. Yet, in recent years, the United States has imported increasing quantities of some chemical resources. For example, about 73% of the nation's tin (Sn) is imported. See Figures 2.16 and 2.17 (page 137) for examples of minerals and mining.

The greatest challenge regarding mineral resources is deciding on the wisest uses of available supplies. For example, is it worthwhile to mine a certain metallic ore at a particular site? The answer to this depends on several considerations, such as:

▶ the quantity of useful ore found at the site

▶ the percent of metal in the ore

▶ the type of mining and processing needed to extract the metal from its ore

▶ the distance between the mine and metal-refining facilities and markets

▶ the metal's supply-versus-demand status

▶ the environmental impact of the mining and metal processing

Copper, one of the materials you might think of using in your coin, provides an example of a vital chemical resource. In this section, you will first consider worldwide sources of copper and how copper-bearing materials are converted to pure copper. Later, you will explore some possible substitutes for this resource.

Another meaning of mineral refers to *dietary minerals*. These are elements required by living organisms (see Unit 7).

Using copper as an example, the section also considers the advisability of mining an ore at a particular site. Earth's resources are ultimately limited. Factors to consider in determining whether to mine a particular metallic ore at a particular site include

• Quantity of useful ore
• Metal content of the ore
• Types of mining and processing required (and their environmental impact)
• Mine's location relative to refining and markets
• Market demand for the metal

Emphasize that a site where mining is not profitable today may become a feasible site later, as supply and demand fluctuate.

Section B Earth's Mineral Resources **135**

Additional Activity

Have students use **Table 2.3** to answer these questions:

1. What metal might Australia wish to obtain from the United States?

2. What metal could Australia trade to the United States to obtain the metal in Question 1?

3. From which nation would you expect the United States to obtain nickel? Why?

4. Give examples of two trade agreements by which China could obtain iron ore in exchange for a metal it has in abundance.

5. What metals might Canada seek to obtain through trade?

Answers

1. Lead or copper

2. Nickel or iron

3. Canada, because it is the closest large producer of nickel.

4. China could trade aluminum to Brazil for iron ore or copper to Australia for iron ore. (Other relationships are possible—see Table 2.3.)

5. Copper, lead, silver, iron, or tin

| Table 2.3

PRODUCTION OF SELECTED METALS WORLDWIDE, 2002			
Metal	**Nation**	**Percent Production**	**Production (10³ metric tons)**	**World Total Production (10³ metric tons)**
Aluminum	China	17	4300	25 900
	Russia	13	3347	
	Canada	10	2709	
	United States	10	2707	
	Australia	7	1836	
Copper	Japan	13	1499	11 500
	China	13	1490	
	Chile	13	1439	
	Russia	7	860	
	United States	6	683	
Iron ore	Brazil	21	125 300	592 700
	Australia	19	113 548	
	China	13	76 200	
	India	8	51 200	
	Russia	8	49 000	
Lead	United States	22	1380	6390
	China	20	1250	
	Germany	6	390	
	United Kingdom	6	370	
	Japan	4	290	
Nickel	Russia	23	310	1340
	Australia	16	211	
	Canada	13	178	
	Indonesia	9	122	
	New Caledonia	7	100	
Silver	Mexico	14	2.8	20
	Peru	14	2.7	
	China	13	2.5	
	Australia	10	2	
	United States	7	1.4	
Tin	China	33	93	278
	Indonesia	19	53	
	Peru	13	36	
	Malaysia	11	30	
	Thailand	8	21	
Zinc	China	24	2100	8910
	Canada	9	793	
	Japan	8	671	
	Australia	6	572	
	Republic of Korea	6	510	

Figure 2.16 *Some minerals among these samples are mined and processed to yield useful metals.*

Copper is one of the most familiar and widely used metals in modern society. Among all the elements, it is second only to silver in electrical conductivity. This property and copper's relatively low cost, corrosion resistance, and **ductility** (ease of being drawn into thin wires) make copper the world's most common metal for electrical wiring. Copper is also used to produce brass, bronze, and other alloys; a variety of copper-based compounds; jewelry; and works of art. Table 2.4 summarizes copper's physical and chemical properties.

The first copper ores mined were relatively rich in copper—from 35% to 88%. Such ores are no longer available; however, ores less rich in copper can be used. In fact, it is now economically possible to mine ores containing less than 1% copper. Copper ore is chemically processed to produce metallic copper, which is then transformed into a

Figure 2.17 *Mining metal ores has economic and environmental consequences. What impact might mining have on a local community?*

| Table 2.4

PROPERTIES OF COPPER	
Malleability and ductility	High
Electrical conductivity	High
Thermal conductivity	High
Chemical reactivity	Relatively low
Resistance to corrosion	High
Useful alloys formed	Bronze and brass, for example
Color and luster	Reddish, shiny

Section B   Earth's Mineral Resources   **137**

B.2 Production versus Use

In this activity, student groups investigate the production/consumption cycle of metals in **Table 2.3** (page 136).

Answers

1. Answers will vary, but should include history, locations of major deposits, processing methods, and at least three current uses. Some useful Web resources:

   All metals: **http://minerals.usgs. gov/minerals/** and
   http://pearl1.lanl.gov/periodic/ default.htm
   Aluminum: **www.aluminum.org**
   Copper: **www.copper.org**
   Iron ore: **http://www.worldsteel. org/usteel.php**
   Lead: **http://www.ldaint.org/ default.htm**
   Nickel: **www.nickelinstitute.org**
   Silver: **http://www.silverinstitute. org/index.php**
   Tin: **http://minerals.usgs.gov/ minerals/pubs/commodity/tin/**
   Zinc: **www.zincworld.org**

2. Answers will vary, but should include a data table similar to Table 2.4 on page 137.

3. and **4.** Answers will vary—see resources above.

Figure 2.18 *The life cycle of copper includes mining copper ores, reducing the ore to obtain the metal, fashioning the metal for final use, and then either recycling the metal or discarding it. What effect does recycling have on the energy these processes require?*

variety of useful materials. Figure 2.18 summarizes the life cycle of copper from sources to common uses to waste products.

Earth's accessible deposits of this valuable resource are destined to become depleted. Will future developments increase or decrease the need for copper? What copper substitutes are available? The following activity will help you address these questions.

B.2 PRODUCTION VERSUS USE

Table 2.3 (page 136) provides information about the worldwide production of several selected metals. Note that the quantity of each metal produced varies. For example, nearly 100 times more aluminum is produced worldwide than tin. Why is this? Is aluminum more abundant than tin, or is there more demand and use for aluminum than for tin? How do the physical and chemical properties of these metals affect their production and eventual use?

Your teacher will divide the class into several groups. Each group will research one of the metals from Table 2.3 and will share what it learns with the class. Table 2.3 provides some initial information about the production quantity of each metal, as well as locations where each metal is produced.

As you learn more about your selected metal, use library and Internet resources to answer the following questions:

1. Investigate the cycle of production, consumption, and use for your metal (such as the copper life cycle in Figure 2.18). Generate a list of *at least* three current uses for your metal.

Research the history of your metal, as well. Perhaps, in years past, it replaced another metal for certain uses or was itself replaced. Note such information.

2. Investigate the metal's properties (both physical and chemical). Create a summary table similar to Table 2.4 (page 137).

3. For each use of your metal from the list created in Question 1, identify particular properties that make your metal an appropriate choice. If there were a replacement of your metal or if your metal replaced another metal for a particular use, what role did your metal's properties play in the transition?

4. How abundant is your metal? Are the uses and demand for your metal adequately met by the production of your metal, as noted in Table 2.3 (page 136)?

Investigating Matter

B.3 CONVERTING COPPER

Introduction

You have seen many chemical reactions in your lifetime. Some, such as a fireworks display, are memorable. Others, such as the slow process of rusting, are far less dramatic. Have you ever stopped to think about what happens to the atoms involved in those reactions? Are the materials that made up the fireworks still there after they are launched into the sky and ignited? What about the iron that turns into rust?

During this investigation, you will work with a powdered sample of elemental copper. As you observe its chemical behavior, think about why its properties make copper a good candidate for use in a coin.

Before starting, read the procedure to learn what you will need to do, note safety precautions, and plan necessary data collecting and observations. You will record several masses (in grams) throughout this investigation; it will be important to distinguish among them. The left column of your data table should be used to identify the objects for which mass is determined (for example, *crucible alone* or *crucible and copper before heating*). In the right column, you will record the measured masses.

Procedure

1. Construct a data table suitable for recording the observations and measurements you will make in this investigation.

2. Measure and record the mass of a clean, empty crucible. Add approximately 1 g copper powder to the crucible. Record the mass of the crucible with copper powder in it within the nearest 0.1 g. Find the actual mass of copper powder by subtracting the mass of the empty crucible from this value. Record the mass of copper powder.

3. Which properties of copper can you directly observe? Record your observations of the copper powder.

Section B Earth's Mineral Resources **139**

Lab Video:
Converting Copper

B.3 Converting Copper Student Worksheet and Data Table

Time

30 min

Materials

(For a class of 24 students working in pairs)

12 crucibles

12 g copper powder

12 hot plates

12 spatulas

12 crucible tongs

Safety

Students should wear protective goggles and aprons throughout the laboratory activity. They should not touch hot crucibles with their hands.

Lab Tips

• Check the quality of your copper powder supply. Older supplies may have become oxidized. If the copper powder appears black, it has probably oxidized and should be replaced by a fresher supply. Copper turnings are *not* recommended as a lab substitute for copper powder. Copper powder produces a more complete reaction in less time due to its greater surface area.

• Ensure that students use crucible tongs and know how to use them correctly: Use only the *tips* of tongs to lift the crucible and do not allow the tongs to "criss-cross." It is possible to stir continuously while holding the crucible with the crucible tongs. Ensure that students do not break up the solid copper oxide in the crucible too aggressively. Crucibles may break if students complete this process incorrectly.

• **Save the CuO (black powder) to use in *Investigating Matter C.11.***

SECTION B

Answers

1. a. Its contents changed color from reddish brown to black.
   b. Yes. Nothing was observed escaping from the crucible.
2. a. Chemical
   b. A new product formed with different properties.
3. a. It increased.
   b. Copper reacted with oxygen from the air.

Post-Lab Discussion

To convince students that the powdered copper is actually copper metal despite its dull appearance, it is possible to "burnish" a sample of powdered copper to show its luster. With the flat surface of a metal spatula, press a small mound of powdered copper down on a piece of paper. Rub gently, then more firmly with the spatula blade. The characteristic shiny, metallic luster of copper will appear.

You may wish to review types of evidence for chemical change, including production of a gas, temperature change, disappearance of a substance, solid formation, color change, and odor production.

---

4. Set the crucible on a hot plate. The crucible lid should be left slightly ajar.
5. Set the hot plate on High.
6. Heat the crucible and its contents for two minutes. Use tongs to place the crucible on a ring-stand base or other heat-resistant surface. Hold the crucible with tongs while you *gently* use a spatula (a hot crucible is quite fragile) to break up the solid in the crucible to expose as much remaining copper metal as possible. (**Caution:** *Avoid touching the hot crucible or the hot-plate surface.*)
7. Continue heating for about 10 minutes more, removing the crucible from the hot plate and breaking up the solid with a spatula every one to two minutes.
8. When you have finished Step 7, turn off the hot plate and allow the crucible and its contents to cool to room temperature. Answer Questions 1 and 2 while you are waiting.
9. After the crucible and its contents have cooled, determine their mass. Use this value and the mass of the empty crucible to calculate the mass of the contents. Record these values in your data table.
10. Label a clean, 100-mL beaker with your name, your class period, and the mass of copper product obtained. Transfer your product to the 100-mL beaker. Store the labeled beaker and product as indicated by your teacher.
11. Wash your hands thoroughly before leaving the laboratory.

> You will use your copper product later, during Investigating Matter C.11.

Questions

1. a. Describe changes you observed as you heated the copper.
   b. Did the copper atoms remain in the crucible? Explain, using evidence from your observations.
2. a. Were the changes you observed physical changes or chemical changes?
   b. What observational evidence leads you to that conclusion?
3. a. How did the mass of the crucible contents change after you heated the copper?
   b. Explain why the mass of the crucible contents changed in that manner.

Relative Reactivities of Metals

B.4 METAL REACTIVITY

As you just observed, when copper metal is heated, it gradually reacts with oxygen gas in the air to produce a black substance. The equation is:

$$2\,Cu(s) \quad + \quad O_2(g) \quad \longrightarrow \quad 2\,CuO(s)$$

Copper   Oxygen   Copper(II) oxide

Although it reacts to form copper(II) oxide when heated, at room temperature the metal remains relatively unreactive in air. You are probably familiar with this fact from observing that copper wire and the copper surface on pennies do not turn black under normal conditions.

Magnesium metal also reacts with oxygen gas. However, unlike copper metal, magnesium heated in air ignites and produces a brief flash of light. See Figure 2.19. The equation for this reaction is:

$$2\,Mg(s) \quad + \quad O_2(g) \quad \longrightarrow \quad 2\,MgO(s)$$
Magnesium   Oxygen   Magnesium oxide

By contrast, gold (Au) does not react with any components of air, including oxygen gas. This is one reason gold is highly prized in long-lasting decorative objects, such as jewelry. Gold-plated electrical contacts, such as those used for automobile air bags and audio cable connectors, are very dependable because nonconducting oxides do not form on the gold-plated contact surfaces.

Observing how readily a certain metal reacts with oxygen provides information about the metal's chemical reactivity. If we rank elements in relative order of their chemical reactivities, the ranking is called an **activity series.** Based on what you have just learned about gold and magnesium and what you already know about copper, how would you rank the three metals in terms of their relative chemical reactivity?

Two common compounds of copper and oxygen are CuO and Cu_2O. Because the name "copper oxide" could be applied to both, a Roman numeral is added to indicate copper's ionic charge. Copper(I) oxide is Cu_2O because it contains Cu^+ ions; copper(II) oxide is CuO; it contains Cu^{2+} ions.

In writing chemical formulas for substances, the symbols for solid (s), liquid (l), gas (g), and aqueous solution (aq) are sometimes added. These symbols indicate the physical state of each reactant or product under conditions of the reaction.

Figure 2.19 *Magnesium and oxygen react so spectacularly that small samples of magnesium are used in some fireworks.*

B.4 Metal Reactivity

The text refers students to *Investigating Matter B.3* to introduce the reactivity of copper with oxygen. It then compares relative reactivities of copper, magnesium, and gold with oxygen and introduces the activity series of metals. At this point, explain the activity series as a way to organize metals according to how readily they react. *Investigating Matter B.5* further develops the concept of a metal activity series.

Section B   Earth's Mineral Resources   **141**

B.5 Relative Reactivities of Metals

B.5 Relative Reactivities of Metals Student Worksheet and Data Table

This activity demonstrates the relative reactivities of copper, magnesium, zinc, and silver metals. Emphasize that a more reactive metal will replace a less reactive metal in a compound. In this case, the compounds are all aqueous, so the more reactive metal forms dissolved ions and thus goes into solution.

Time

50 min

Materials

(For 24 students working in pairs)

12 24-well wellplates

48 labeled pipets (or dropper bottles) for dispensing metal nitrate solutions

12-cm magnesium ribbon cut into 1-cm lengths

12-cm zinc wire cut into 1-cm lengths

12-cm copper wire cut into 1-cm lengths

Steel wool (for cleaning metals)

Silver metal (optional)

10 mL 0.2 M $Mg(NO_3)_2$ solution (5.1 g $Mg(NO_3)_2 \cdot 6\ H_2O/100.$ mL solution)

10 mL 0.2 M $Cu(NO_3)_2$ solution (4.8 g $Cu(NO_3)_2 \cdot 3\ H_2O/100.$ mL solution)

10 mL 0.2 M $Zn(NO_3)_2$ solution (6.0 g $Zn(NO_3)_2 \cdot 6\ H_2O/100.$ mL solution)

10 mL 0.2 M $AgNO_3$ solution (3.4 g $AgNO_3/100.$ mL solution)

B.5 RELATIVE REACTIVITIES OF METALS

 Lab Video: Relative Reactivites of Metals

Introduction

In this investigation, you will observe the reactions of the metals copper, magnesium, and zinc with four different solutions. Each solution contains a particular metal cation. The solutions you will use are copper(II) nitrate, $Cu(NO_3)_2$ (containing Cu^{2+}); magnesium nitrate, $Mg(NO_3)_2$ (containing Mg^{2+}); zinc nitrate, $Zn(NO_3)_2$ (containing Zn^{2+}); and silver nitrate, $AgNO_3$ (containing Ag^+).

Before starting, read the procedure to learn what you will need to do, note safety precautions, plan necessary data collecting and observations, and design a suitable data table. Because this investigation involves combining various ionic solutions to determine their relative reactivities, your data table should clearly indicate which materials you combined and the observed results.

Procedure

Devise a systematic procedure that will allow you to observe the reaction (if any) between each metal and each of the four ionic solutions. You will conduct each reaction in a separate well of your wellplate, using 10 drops of 0.2 M solution and a small strip of metal. See Figure 2.20. How many different combinations of metals and solutions will you need to observe? How will you arrange things so you can complete your observations efficiently, yet keep track of which metal and which solution are in each well?

1. After considering the task described, construct a data table appropriate for recording the observations that you will make in this investigation. Keep the questions posed in the preceding paragraph in mind as you plan your data table.

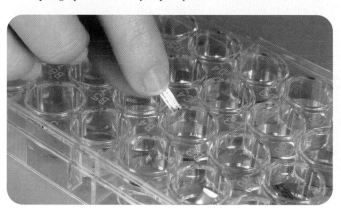

Figure 2.20 *Metal strips and metal nitrate solutions should be arranged in an orderly manner in the wellplate.*

Safety

Students should wear protective goggles and aprons throughout the laboratory activity. Silver nitrate solution stains skin (and clothing). Students should avoid direct contact with it. Keep a bottle of Spray & Wash in the lab to help remove any Ag^+ that may accidentally contact students' hands.

Pre-Lab Discussion

Observing reactions of metals with solutions of metal ions permits comparison of relative reactivity. The more reactive the metal, the more likely it is to react with the solutions. Evidence for reaction includes formation of a solid, appearance or disappearance of the solution color, formation of a gas, or changes in temperature.

2. Obtain 1-cm strips of each of the metals to be tested. Clean the surface of each metal strip by rubbing it with sandpaper or emery paper. See Figure 2.21. Record your observations of each metal's appearance.

3. Begin your planned procedure. If you observe no reaction, write "NR" in your data table. If a reaction occurs, record the changes you observe. (**Caution:** *Avoid allowing the AgNO₃ solution to come in contact with skin or clothing because it causes dark, nonwashable stains.*)

4. Dispose of all solid samples and wellplate solutions as directed by your teacher.

5. Wash your hands thoroughly before leaving the laboratory.

Questions

1. Which metal reacted with the most solutions?

2. Which metal reacted with the fewest solutions?

3. Assuming that you did not test silver metal, with which solutions (if any) would you expect silver metal to react? Explain your answer, citing evidence from your data and observations.

4. List the metals (including silver) in order, placing the most reactive metal first (the one reacting with the most solutions) and the least reactive metal last (the one reacting with the fewest solutions).

5. Refer to your "metal activity series" list from Question 4. Write a brief explanation of why the outside surface of a penny is made of copper instead of zinc.

6. a. Which of the four metals mentioned in this investigation might be an even better choice than copper for the outside surface of a penny? What observational evidence supports your conclusion?

   b. Why do you think that the particular metal that you identified in Question 6a is not used as the outside surface of a penny?

7. Given your new knowledge about the relative chemical activities of these four metals,

   a. which metal is *most* likely to be found in an uncombined, or "free," (metallic) state in nature?

   b. which metal is *least* likely to be found chemically uncombined with other elements?

8. Reconsider your experimental design for this investigation:

   a. Would it have been possible to eliminate one or more of the metal-solution combinations and still obtain all the information needed to create chemical activity ratings for the four metals?

   b. If so, which combination or combinations could have been eliminated? Why?

Figure 2.21 *Clean each metal strip with sandpaper or emery paper.*

- If you have or can borrow dissecting microscopes, they are very useful in making some hard-to-detect reactions visible. Alternatively, use a video microscope to project images of these reactions.

- Results for reaction of silver metal, Ag, can be provided if silver is unavailable. Small pieces of Ag can often be obtained from flea markets or jewelers at low cost and can be reused from year to year.

- Interactions involving a metal with its own metal-ion solution—such as Cu(s) with Cu(NO3)2(aq)—have intentionally been left open for investigation by students. You can either say nothing about these interactions or ask students whether all combinations need to be investigated.

Answers

1. Magnesium

2. Silver

3. None

4. Magnesium, zinc, copper, silver

5. Because it reacts with fewer substances than zinc

6. a. Silver, because of its lower chemical reactivity.

   b. Silver is much more expensive than copper.

7. a. Silver

   b. Magnesium

8. a. Yes

   b. The metal in a solution of its ions: Cu in Cu(NO₃)₂(aq), Mg in Mg (NO₃)₂(aq), etc.

Expected results are shown on page 144.

Students should clean the surface of each metal to be tested with steel wool. Surfaces of all metals should have luster before the investigation begins. Remind students to record initial appearances of the metal samples (after Step 2) in their data tables. Encourage students to make observations immediately after the metal is added to the solution and a few minutes later. Some reactions, particularly that of magnesium metal and zinc nitrate solution, are difficult to detect.

Lab Tips

- Record-keeping is easier if combinations in the wellplate correspond to those in the data table.

SECTION B

Post-Lab Discussion

Resolve differences in results among groups. When students disagree, ask them for evidence supporting their claims. If necessary, repeat a reaction as a demonstration (using a video microscope if possible) to show the differences. Differences often result when students fail to remove oxide coatings from the metal strips.

B.6 Metals: Properties and Uses

The discovery that fire could be used to extract a metal from its ore led to the transformation of metals into useful materials. Students may ask how natural fibers served as components of ancient tools. You can point out that people used fiber-based cords to bind stone cutting heads to their handles.

Students should understand that although most elements are found in nature, many are not found in the uncombined state. Metals are usually found in the form of a metallic ore, also known as a mineral—a compound of the metal.

If you have access to samples of both ores and metals, let students see a sample of an ore as it is found in nature along with a sample of the element in its metallic state. You may wish to refer back to **Figures 2.16 (page 137) and 2.18 (page 138)**.

Figure 2.22 *These stone, bronze, and iron tools represent three major ages of civilization. Different materials impart different properties to tools, which affects their usefulness.*

Stone

Bronze

Iron

B.6 METALS: PROPERTIES AND USES

Humans have been described as toolmakers. Readily available stone, wood, and natural fibers were the earliest materials used in tools such as hammers, chisels, knives, spears, and grinding devices. The discovery that fire could transform materials in certain rocks into strong, malleable metals triggered dramatic advances in the growth of tool making and of civilization.

Gold and silver, found as free elements rather than in chemical combination with other elements, were probably the first metals humans used. They formed these metals into decorative and useful objects and, later, into coins. The metals' relative lack of reactivity made them excellent materials for those uses.

It is estimated that copper has been used for tools, weapons, utensils, and decorations for about 10 000 years. Bronze, an alloy of copper and tin, was developed about 3800 BC. Consequently, humans advanced from the Stone Age into the Bronze Age.

Eventually, early people developed *iron metallurgy,* the extraction of iron from its ores. This led to the start of the Iron Age more than 3000 years ago. In time, as humans learned more about chemistry and fire, they transformed various metallic ores into increasingly useful metals. Figure 2.22 portrays tools used in the three major ages of civilization.

ChemQuandary 1

DISCOVERY OF METALS

Copper, gold, and silver are far from being the most abundant metals on Earth. Aluminum, iron, and calcium, for example, are all much more plentiful. Why, then, were copper, gold, and silver among the first metallic elements discovered?

Copper crystals

EXPECTED RESULTS					
METAL	APPEARANCE	$Cu(NO_3)_2$	$Mg(NO_3)_2$	$Zn(NO_3)_2$	$AgNO_3$
Cu	Shiny, copper	—	NR	NR	Becomes silvery
Mg	Shiny, silver	Darkens	—	Flaky coating	Becomes silvery
Zn	Shiny, silver	Darkens	NR	—	Becomes silvery
Ag	Shiny, silver	NR	NR	NR	—
NR = no reaction					

METAL ACTIVITY SERIES			
Element (in order of decreasing reactivity)	Metal Ions Found in Minerals	Process Used to Obtain the Metal	Metal
Lithium (Li)	Li^+	Pass direct electric current through the molten mineral salt (electrometallurgy)	Li(s)
Potassium (K)	K^+		K(s)
Calcium (Ca)	Ca^{2+}		Ca(s)
Sodium (Na)	Na^+		Na(s)
Magnesium (Mg)	Mg^{2+}		Mg(s)
Aluminum (Al)	Al^{3+}		Al(s)
Manganese (Mn)	Mn^{2+}, Mn^{3+}	Heat mineral with coke (C) or carbon monoxide (CO) (pyrometallurgy)	Mn(s)
Zinc (Zn)	Zn^{2+}		Zn(s)
Chromium (Cr)	Cr^{3+}, Cr^{2+}		Cr(s)
Iron (Fe)	Fe^{3+}, Fe^{2+}		Fe(s)
Lead (Pb)	Pb^{2+}	Heat (roast) mineral in air (pyrometallurgy) or find the metal free (uncombined)	Pb(s)
Copper (Cu)	Cu^{2+}, Cu^+		Cu(s)
Mercury (Hg)	Hg^{2+}		Hg(l)
Silver (Ag)	Ag^+		Ag(s)
Platinum (Pt)	Pt^{2+}		Pt(s)
Gold (Au)	Au^{3+}, Au^+		Au(s)

Table 2.5

You have explored some chemistry of metals and know, for example, that copper metal is more reactive than silver but less reactive than magnesium. A more complete activity series is given in Table 2.5. The table also includes brief descriptions of common methods for retrieving each metal from its ore.

You can use such an activity series to predict whether certain reactions may occur. For example, you observed in Investigating Matter B.5 that zinc metal, which is more reactive than copper, reacted with copper ions in solution. However, zinc metal did not react with magnesium ions in solution. Why? Zinc is less reactive than magnesium. In general, a *more* reactive metallic element (higher in the activity series) will cause ions of a *less* reactive metallic element (lower in the activity series) to change to their corresponding metal.

The activity series of metals is reintroduced and expanded in this section. Use **Table 2.5** to illustrate the idea that more reactive metals are more difficult to release from their compounds. Thus, alkali and alkaline earth metals (Groups I and II) must be melted and then subjected to electric current to form pure metal, while other, less reactive metals may require only heating in air, or may be found in nature in their uncombined state. **Table 2.5** may be a good launching point for discussing why we choose certain metals for certain purposes (plumbing, jewelry, coinage, etc.).

Emphasize again that a more reactive metal can cause a less reactive metal to change to its uncombined state, while the more reactive metal forms a compound (or ions). The reverse, a less reactive metal causing a more reactive metal to change to its uncombined state, does not occur spontaneously. Use student data from *Investigating Matter B.5* to reinforce this point.

ChemQuandary 1

Discovery of Metals

Due to their low chemical activity, copper, silver, and gold are often found uncombined in nature. People discovered them before aluminum, iron, and calcium, which, though more plentiful, are almost always combined with other elements in nature.

SECTION B

Developing Skills

B.7 Trends in Metal Activity

This exercise familiarizes students with the activity series of metals and relates the activity series to the periodic table. It also helps students relate activity-series concepts to metal behavior.

Answers

1. a. It generally decreases.
   b. On the left side
   c. The middle
2. a. Yes
   b. No
   c. Iron is more reactive than lead, according to the metal activity series, and will displace lead ions from a solution. Platinum is less reactive than lead and cannot displace lead from solution.
3. a. The least-reactive metals—including silver, platinum, and gold—are not the cheapest, despite having the lowest production costs.
   b. Overall availability of the metal (for instance gold, silver, and platinum are much less abundant on Earth than aluminum and iron), demand for the metal due to its desirable properties (low reactivity is one of the attractive features of gold, silver, and platinum), and ease of retrieval

B.8 Mining and Refining

 B.8 Content Reading Guide

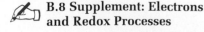 B.8 Supplement: Electrons and Redox Processes

This material defines and explains oxidation and reduction and presents the main techniques for separating metals from their compounds in ores.

Developing Skills

B.7 TRENDS IN METAL ACTIVITY

Use Table 2.5 (page 145) and the periodic table (page 124) to answer the following questions:

Sample Problem: *Will Pb metal react with Ag⁺ ions?*
Yes; according to Table 2.5, lead is a more active metal than silver, so lead will reduce Ag^+ to $Ag(s)$.

1. a. What trend in metallic reactivity is apparent as you move from left to right across a horizontal row (period) of the periodic table? (*Hint:* Compare the reactivity of sodium with that of magnesium and aluminum.)
   b. In which part of the periodic table are the most-reactive metals found?
   c. Which part of the periodic table contains the least-reactive metals?
2. a. Will iron (Fe) metal react with a solution of lead(II) nitrate, $Pb(NO_3)_2$?
   b. Will platinum (Pt) metal react with a lead(II) nitrate solution?
   c. Explain your answers to Questions 2a and 2b.
3. Use specific examples from the metal activity series in Table 2.5 in your answers to the following two questions:
   a. Are the least-reactive metals also the cheapest metals?
   b. If not, what other factor or factors might influence the market value of a metal?

B.8 MINING AND REFINING

As shown in Table 2.5 (page 145), most metals are not found free in nature. Instead, they are found combined with other elements within more stable compounds. These compounds must be mined from the lithosphere and refined to produce the free metal. The process of converting a combined metal (usually a metal ion) in a mineral to a free metal involves a particular kind of chemical change. For example, converting a copper(II) cation to an atom of copper metal requires the addition of two electrons.

Formation of Copper Metal: Reduction

In general, to convert metallic cations to atoms of pure metal, each cation must gain a particular number of electrons:

$$Cu^{2+} \ + \ 2\,e^- \ \longrightarrow \ Cu$$
Copper(II) ion   Copper metal

Chemists classify any chemical change in which a reactant can be considered to gain one or more electrons as a **reduction.** Thus, the conversion of copper(II) cations to copper metal is a reduction reaction, and we say that copper cations were **reduced.** You can convince yourself that this is a reduction reaction by examining the preceding equation.

Oxidation and reduction tend to be challenging topics for beginning chemistry students. Clearly define oxidation as a loss of electrons and reduction as a gain of electrons. "Reduction is gain" may be counterintuitive, but emphasize that the terms developed in the context of oxygen compounds, before atomic structure was well understood. Originally, reduction referred to the partial or complete removal of oxygen from a compound—a pile of metal ore would be "reduced" to a smaller amount of the pure metal.

Formation of Copper(II) Ions: Oxidation

Chemists classify the *reverse* reaction, in which an ion or other species can be considered to lose one or more electrons, as an **oxidation:**

$$Cu \longrightarrow Cu^{2+} + 2e^-$$

Copper   Copper(II)
metal   ion

Any reactant that appears to lose one or more electrons is said to be **oxidized.** In this case, a copper atom is oxidized to a copper(II) ion by loss of two electrons.

Oxidation–Reduction Reactions

Whenever one reactant loses electrons, another reactant must simultaneously gain them. In other words, oxidation and reduction reactions never occur separately. Oxidation and reduction occur together in what chemists call **oxidation–reduction reactions** or, to use a common chemical nickname, **redox reactions.**

You have already observed redox reactions in the laboratory. During Investigating Matter B.5 (pages 142–143), copper metal reacted with silver ions. The following equation shows the oxidation–reduction reaction you observed:

$$Cu(s) + 2Ag^+(aq) \longrightarrow Cu^{2+}(aq) + 2Ag(s)$$

Copper   Silver ion   Copper(II) ion   Silver
metal   (colorless)   (blue)   metal

> One easy way to remember this is OIL RIG: Oxidation Is Loss (of electrons), Reduction Is Gain (of electrons).

Each metallic copper atom (Cu) was oxidized (converted to a Cu^{2+} ion by losing two electrons) and each silver ion (Ag^+ from $AgNO_3$ solution) was reduced (converted to an Ag atom by gaining one electron). What you *actually* observed in Investigating Matter B.5 was the formation of a solid (silver) and the solution becoming blue because of the formation of colored $Cu^{2+}(aq)$ ions; these observable changes indicated a redox reaction was occurring, even though you did not actually *see* the transfer of electrons.

In the same investigation, you found that copper ions could be recovered from a solution as metallic copper by allowing the copper ions to react with magnesium metal, an element more active than copper. Magnesium atoms were *oxidized;* copper ions were *reduced.* Do you see why?

$$Cu^{2+}(aq) + Mg(s) \longrightarrow Cu(s) + Mg^{2+}(aq)$$

Copper(II) ion   Magnesium   Copper   Magnesium ion
(blue)   metal   metal   (colorless)

Note that the total electrical charge on both sides of this equation is the same. Electrical charges—as well as atoms—must balance within a correctly written chemical equation. For instance, the net electrical charge on both the reactant side and the product side is 2+ in that equation.

In some circumstances, that reaction might be a useful way to obtain copper metal. However, as is often the case, the desired copper metal could only be obtained at the expense of using up another highly valuable material—in this case, magnesium metal.

A Copper Redox Reaction

Section B   Earth's Mineral Resources   **147**

Reinforce the idea that an agent *does* the oxidizing (or reducing) and thus is itself reduced (or oxidized).

Remind students that the metal with the most attraction (pull) for electrons is the least reactive—as they saw in *Investigating Matter B.5.* Silver "holds tightly" to its electrons and does not react easily. Likewise, elemental gold is sometimes found in streams, but metallic sodium is not.

Emphasize that oxidation and reduction always go together; electrons, like all matter, cannot be created nor destroyed and thus must have both source and sink in each reaction system. The loss of electrons (oxidation) cannot occur without a simultaneous gain of electrons (reduction). This concept has biological implications. All aerobic organisms depend on the oxidation of carbohydrates and fats for energy. The electrons lost by carbohydrates and fats are accepted by oxygen. If the electrons cannot be transported to the oxygen (as in cyanide poisoning) or there is no oxygen present (as in carbon monoxide poisoning) to accept electrons, the whole process shuts down, and the organism dies.

Use the connection of oxidation with reduction to point out that the three reduction processes for obtaining a metal from its ore all require some sort of electron source—either electricity or a substance (reducing agent) that will lose electrons easily—and thus are technically redox processes.

Remind students that electrons are negatively charged particles. This often helps them process the changes in charge that result from the gain or loss of electrons.

Two mnemonics for oxidation–reduction are "LEO says GER" "Lose Electrons Oxidation—Gain Electrons Reduction" and "OIL RIG," as in the margin note. Encourage students to choose a mnemonic that works for them.

Another confusing point for students is the idea of oxidizing and reducing agents.

B.9 Electrons and Redox Processes

Point out that in chemical reactions depicted here, it is possible to find copper (metallic Cu atoms) being oxidized, as well as copper (Cu^{2+} ions) being reduced.

Remind students (again) that a more reactive metal has a greater tendency than a less reactive metal to give up electrons.

Electron-dot structures are introduced to illustrate redox processes. Help students realize, as they use these structures, that there is a relationship between electronic structure and chemical and physical properties.

This is a challenging activity for students, since they have not used electron-dot structures previously and are just considering redox reactions. Working in small groups under teacher guidance promotes student confidence and success.

 B.9 Electrons and Redox Processes Student Worksheet

Many metallic elements are found in minerals in the form of cations because they combine readily with other elements to form ionic compounds. Obtaining a metal from its mineral requires energy and a source of electrons. A reactant that provides electrons is known as a **reducing agent**.

Using Redox Reactions to Obtain Pure Metals

Look again at Table 2.5 (page 145). The table lists several techniques that metallurgists use to reduce metal cations or, in other words, to supply one or more electrons to each cation. The specific technique chosen depends on the metal's reactivity and the availability of inexpensive reducing agents and energy sources.

Two approaches summarized in the table are electrometallurgy and pyrometallurgy. As the table suggests, **electrometallurgy** involves using an electrical current to supply electrons to metal ions, thus reducing them. This process is used when no adequate chemical reducing agents are available or when very high-purity metal is sought. **Pyrometallurgy,** the oldest ore-processing method, involves treating metals and their ores with heat (thermal energy), as in a blast furnace. Carbon (coke) and carbon monoxide are common reducing agents in pyrometallurgy: They provide electrons; metal ions are thus reduced to form metal atoms. An active metal can be used if neither of these reducing agents will do the job.

A third approach to obtaining metals from their ions is **hydrometallurgy,** which involves treating ores and other metal-containing materials with reactants in a water solution. You used such a procedure when you observed the reactivity of different metals in Investigating Matter B.5. Hydrometallurgy is used to recover silver and gold from old mine tailings (the mined rock left after most of the sought mineral is removed) by a process known as *leaching*. As higher-grade ores become scarcer, it will become economically feasible to use hydrometallurgy and other "wet processes" on metal-bearing minerals that can dissolve in water.

B.9 ELECTRONS AND REDOX PROCESSES

The processes of oxidation (the apparent loss of one or more electrons) and reduction (the apparent gain of one or more electrons) can be clarified by visual representations of these events. To develop such representations, you will consider atoms of each of the metals you encountered during Investigating Matter B.5 (page 142).

First, however, here is a review of some key details about an atom's composition. Magnesium (Mg), which is an active metal, formed Mg^{2+} ions in several reactions you observed during Investigating Matter B.5. The atomic number of Mg is 12, indicating that an electrically neutral atom of magnesium contains 12 protons and 12 electrons. Recall why those numbers must be equal for a neutral atom.

If magnesium is to form a Mg^{2+} ion, two negatively charged electrons must be removed from each magnesium atom. The bookkeeping involved can be summarized as

$$Mg \longrightarrow Mg^{2+} + 2\,e^-$$

Mg	Mg^{2+}	2 e$^-$
12 protons (+)	12 protons (+)	
12 electrons (−)	10 electrons (−)	2 electrons (−)
Net charge: 0	Net charge: 2+	Net charge: 2−

To build a useful picture of this process in your mind, it is necessary to keep track of only the two electrons *released* by each magnesium atom, rather than monitoring all 12 of the atom's available electrons. (In fact, in any normal chemical reaction, a magnesium atom is not observed to release any of its other 10 electrons.)

Thus, for bookkeeping purposes, an atom of Mg will be depicted this way: Mg: (the element symbol with two dots attached). Each dot represents one of magnesium's two readily removable electrons. The symbol Mg represents the remaining parts of a magnesium atom, including its remaining ten electrons. The resulting expression for Mg is called an **electron-dot structure** or a **dot structure**. The equation for oxidation of Mg atoms can be represented this way in electron-dot terms:

$$Mg: \longrightarrow Mg^{2+} + 2\,e^-$$

1. Construct a similar electron-dot expression for the change that occurred during Investigating Matter B.5 (page 142) when each of the following events took place:

   a. An atom of zinc, Zn, was converted to a Zn^{2+} ion. (*Hint:* Zn has two readily removable electrons.)

   b. A silver ion, Ag^+, was converted to a metallic silver atom, Ag(s).

2. Apply the definitions of *oxidation* and *reduction* to your two equations in Question 1, and label each reaction appropriately.

Now consider one of the complete reactions you observed during Investigating Matter B.5. When you immersed a sample of copper metal, Cu, in silver nitrate solution, $AgNO_3$, a blue solution containing Cu^{2+} formed, as well as crystals of solid Ag. The redox reaction that occurred is

$$Cu(s) + 2\,Ag^+(aq) \longrightarrow Cu^{2+}(aq) + 2\,Ag(s)$$

Using dot structures, this redox reaction can be represented as

$$Cu: + Ag^+ + Ag^+ \longrightarrow Cu^{2+} + Ag\cdot + Ag\cdot$$

3. Which reactant (Cu or Ag^+) is reduced?

4. Why is only one Cu atom needed for each two Ag^+ ions that react?

Each copper atom involved in this reaction loses two electrons. Thus, copper atoms must be oxidized in this redox reaction. It is clear from the dot structures that the two electrons lost by copper are gained by the two Ag^+ ions. So, Ag^+ is the *agent* that caused the removal of electrons from Cu, resulting in oxidation of Cu. The species involved in removing electrons from the oxidized reactant is called the **oxidizing agent**—in this case, Ag^+ ions.

> Lewis structure is another commonly used term for an electron-dot structure.

Answers

1. a. $Zn: \rightarrow Zn^{2+} + 2\,e^-$ (oxidation)
   b. $Ag^+ + e^- \rightarrow Ag\cdot$ (reduction)
2. a. Zn metal (Zn:) was oxidized to the Zn^{2+} ion (oxidation is a loss of electrons).
   b. Ag^+ ion was reduced to Ag metal (Ag·) (reduction is a gain of electrons).
3. Ag^+ is reduced.
4. Cu gives up two electrons; each Ag^+ can accept only one electron.

5. a. A reducing agent is involved in supplying electrons to the reactant that is reduced.

   b. Copper

6. $Zn: + Cu^{2+} \rightarrow Zn^{2+} + Cu:$

   a. Zinc

   b. Copper ion

7. a. Copper ion

   b. Zinc

8. The substance that loses electrons is oxidized and ends with a more positive charge. The substance that is oxidized is the reducing agent.

9. Zn^{2+} is reduced (oxidizing agent). Mg is oxidized (reducing agent).

10. $Mg: + Ag^+ + Ag^+ \rightarrow Mg^{2+} +$ Ag· + Ag·

    Mg is oxidized (reducing agent).

    Ag^+ is reduced (oxidizing agent).

---

5. a. Given the preceding explanation of an oxidizing agent, how would you define a reducing agent?

   b. What must be the reducing agent in the reaction between Cu(s) and Ag^+ ions?

6. Now consider the following reaction, which you observed during Investigating Matter B.5:

$$Zn(s) + Cu^{2+}(aq) \longrightarrow Zn^{2+}(aq) + Cu(s)$$

Draw an electron-dot representation of this reaction.

   a. Which reactant is oxidized?

   b. Which reactant is reduced?

7. Identify the following in the reaction represented in Question 6:

   a. the oxidizing agent

   b. the reducing agent

8. Consider both of the oxidation–reduction reactions you analyzed in this activity. What general features of an oxidation–reduction reaction would allow you to answer Questions 6 and 7 *without* drawing electron-dot representations?

9. Now consider a new oxidation–reduction reaction. Answer Questions 6 and 7 for the following equation:

$$Zn^{2+}(aq) + Mg(s) \longrightarrow Zn(s) + Mg^{2+}(aq)$$

10. Return to Investigating Matter B.5 and write an oxidation–reduction equation for the reaction of silver ions with magnesium atoms. Answer Questions 6 and 7 for this equation.

The chemical properties of elements can be understood in terms of their respective electron arrangements, as you have seen. In Section C, you will further explore the composition and properties of common materials composed of these elements.

SECTION B SUMMARY

 Section B Supplement

Reviewing the Concepts

1. Answers may include:

   Atmosphere: N_2, O_2, Ne, Ar

   Hydrosphere: H_2O, Na, S, Ca, Mg

   Lithosphere: petroleum, silicates, and ores containing minerals and metals

2. a. The lithosphere consists of the crust, the top 40 km composed of silicates, metals, and other compounds; the mantle, from 40–2900 km and composed of silicates of Mg and Fe; and the core, 2900 km to the earth's center, composed of Fe and Ni.

   b. The crust

SECTION B SUMMARY
Reviewing the Concepts

The resources for all human activities must be obtained from Earth's atmosphere, hydrosphere, and outer layer of its lithosphere. These resources are not uniformly distributed.

1. List two resources typically found in each of the three major "spheres" of Earth.

2. a. List and briefly describe three major parts of the lithosphere.
   b. Which layer serves as the main storehouse of chemical resources used in manufacturing consumer products?

3. Identify the nation that produces the most
   a. silver.   b. copper.   c. tin.

4. According to the information in Table 2.3 on page 136, which of these four nations—the United States, Australia, China, or Brazil—produces the largest masses of the eight listed resources in the table?

The feasibility of mining and extracting a mineral resource depends, in part, on how easily a particular metal can be processed and used, which depends on its chemical reactivity. Active metals are more difficult to process than are less active metals and tend to corrode more quickly.

5. How do minerals differ from ores?

6. What factors determine the feasibility of mining a particular metallic ore at a certain site?

7. A nineteenth-century gold mine, inactive for over 100 years, has recently reopened for further mining. What factors may have influenced the decision to reopen the mine?

8. What is meant by referring to the quantity of "useful ore" at a site?

9. Why are active metals more difficult to process and refine than are less active metals?

10. Based on your results from Investigating Matter B.5 (page 142), which metals involved in that investigation would be the easiest to process? Why?

11. Why do most metals exist in nature as minerals rather than as pure metallic elements?

12. Which of these reactions is more likely to occur? Why? (Refer to Table 2.5, page 145.)
    a. calcium metal with chromium(III) chloride
    b. chromium metal with calcium chloride

13. Consider the following two equations. Which equation represents a reaction that is more likely to occur? Why?
    a. $Zn^{2+}(aq) + 2\ Ag(s) \longrightarrow Zn(s) + 2\ Ag^+(aq)$
    b. $2\ Ag^+(aq) + Zn(s) \longrightarrow 2\ Ag(s) + Zn^{2+}(aq)$

14. a. Why would it be a poor idea to stir a solution of lead(II) nitrate with an iron spoon? (Refer to Table 2.5, page 145.)
    b. Write a chemical equation to support your answer.

The processes of oxidation and reduction occur together, resulting in oxidation–reduction (redox) reactions.

15. Define oxidation and reduction in terms of electron transfer.

16. Write an equation for each of the following processes:
    a. the *reduction* of gold(III) ions to gold metal
    b. the *oxidation* of elemental vanadium to vanadium(IV) ions
    c. the *oxidation* of Cu^+ to Cu^{2+} ions

17. Identify each of the following equations as representing either an oxidation reaction or a reduction reaction:
    a. $Fe^{2+} + 2\ e^- \longrightarrow Fe$
    b. $Cr \longrightarrow Cr^{3+} + 3\ e^-$
    c. $Al^{3+} + 3\ e^- \longrightarrow Al$

Section Summary   151

7. New technology may allow a more economical method of extracting the metal from its ore, or demand for the metal may have increased enough to make its mining profitable.

8. It is ore that can be removed and has a percent metal high enough to make mining and refining profitable.

9. Because they require more energy to become released from their compounds

10. Copper and silver, because they are less reactive than zinc and magnesium

11. Most metals are chemically reactive and combine with other elements in minerals.

12. Reaction a: Calcium is more active than chromium and will release chromium from its compounds.

13. Reaction b: Zinc metal can reduce silver ion to silver metal because zinc is more active.

14. a. Since iron is more reactive than lead, it would displace lead in solution; lead metal would precipitate.
    b. $Fe(s) + Pb^{2+}(aq) \rightarrow Pb(s) + Fe^{2+}(aq)$

15. Oxidation is the loss of electrons, and reduction is the gain of electrons.

16. a. $Au^{3+} + 3\ e^- \rightarrow Au$
    b. $V \rightarrow V^{4+} + 4\ e^-$
    c. $Cu^+ \rightarrow Cu^{2+} + e^-$

17. a. Reduction: a, c Oxidation: b

3. a. Mexico
   b. Japan
   c. China

4. Australia
   (1 836 + 113 548 + 211 + 2 + 572 = 116 169 thousand metric tons)

5. A *mineral* is the substance that contains a metal of interest in a combined state.

An *ore* is the rock throughout which the mineral is distributed.

6. Factors include percent of metal in the ore, the type of mining and processing required, the quantity of useful ore at the site, the distance of the mine to processing facilities, and the metal's supply and demand.

18. a. Zn: Each zinc metal atom lost two electrons.
b. Ni^{2+}: Each nickel ion gained two electrons.
c. Zinc metal.

19. a. K: Each potassium metal atom lost one electron.
b. Hg^{2+} ion: Each mercury ion gained two electrons.
c. Mercury ion.

20. a. $Al(s) + Cr^{3+}(aq) \rightarrow Al^{3+}(aq) + Cr(s)$
b. $Mn^{2+}(aq) + Mg(s) \rightarrow Mn(s) + Mg^{2+}(aq)$

21. a. Metal cations gain electrons from a cathode.
b. Coke or carbon monoxide acts as a reducing agent to reduce metal cations.
c. Metal cations are treated in solution with a more active metal, which reduces metal cations.

22. a. electrometallurgy
b. pyrometallurgy

Connecting the Concepts

23. A nation's wealth depends on availability of raw materials and resources that have economic value at that time. For example, nations in the Middle East enjoy tremendous income from selling petroleum. Mineral resources allow a nation flexibility to produce many products from these resources or to sell them to other nations.

18. Consider the following equation:

$$Zn(s) + Ni^{2+}(aq) \longrightarrow Zn^{2+}(aq) + Ni(s)$$

a. Which reactant has been oxidized? Explain your choice.
b. Which reactant has been reduced? Explain your choice.
c. What is the reducing agent in this reaction?

19. Consider the following equation:

$$2 K(s) + Hg^{2+}(aq) \longrightarrow 2 K^+(aq) + Hg(s)$$

a. Which reactant has been oxidized? Explain your choice.
b. Which reactant has been reduced? Explain your choice.
c. What is the oxidizing agent in this reaction?

20. Write an equation for
a. the oxidation of Al metal by Cr^{3+} ions.
b. the reduction of Mn^{2+} ions by Mg metal.

Metal cations can be converted to metal atoms by electrometallurgy, pyrometallurgy, or hydrometallurgy.

21. Explain how each of the following processes converts metal cations to metal atoms:
a. electrometallurgy
b. pyrometallurgy
c. hydrometallurgy

22. What processes would be most useful in obtaining the following elements from their ores?
a. magnesium
b. lead

Connecting the Concepts

23. How does access to mineral resources contribute to a nation's economic success? Explain.

24. In building ships, common practice is to attach a piece of magnesium to the hull to act as a "sacrificial anode." In terms of metal activity, explain how this helps to prevent the corrosion of other metal parts of the ship.

25. There are thousands of tons of gold in sea water. Explain why it is unlikely that sea water will ever be "mined" for gold.

26. At one time, food cans were made with tin and soldered with lead. What kinds of health hazards were posed by this design?

27. Is there any connection between the process used to reduce a metal cation and the position of that element on the periodic table?

Extending the Concepts

28. Although aluminum is a more reactive metal than is iron, it is often used to build outdoor products. Investigate why this use is feasible.

29. Find and describe an historical example of uneven distribution of mineral resources and its impact on relations among nations.

30. What conclusions about materials can be drawn from a study of substances used for currency in ancient civilizations? Explain your ideas by citing examples.

31. History documents that copper has been used by humans for ten thousand years, whereas aluminum has been used for only about 100 years. Suggest and explain some reasons for this time difference.

32. The reactive metal aluminum is often used in containers for acidic beverages. Investigate and describe the technology that makes this possible.

33. What is a *patina*? Explain its value both aesthetically and chemically.

24. In a solution of ions, such as sea water, the presence of two electrically connected dissimilar metals will result in flow of electrons from the more active metal to the less active metal. The more active metal then gradually oxidizes to ions in the electrolyte (it is sacrificed), while the less active metal receives electrons, protecting it from corrosion (oxidation).

25. Gold occurs at a concentration of 0.1 to 2 mg/ton sea water. To extract it, sea water would be pumped and gold selectively separated from the water. Both processes require energy and other resources that are worth much more than the value of gold extracted.

26. In lead-soldered cans, which are still used in some countries, lead can leach into the food. Lead exposure can cause anemia, abdominal problems, irritability, kidney failure, decreased cognitive development in children, and miscarriage or stillbirth.

27. Yes. Alkali and alkaline earth metals and aluminum must be reduced electrochemically, since they are so active. Elements around the lower center of the periodic table are more easily reduced by pyrometallurgy or hydrometallurgy.

Extending the Concepts

28. Aluminum oxidizes to form a protective coating, which prevents it from further oxidation.

29. Answers will vary. Some examples include: Shortages of iron and steel were partially responsible for Germany's participation in World War I. Japan's participation in World War II related to seeking rich mineral resources of East and Southeast Asia to support industrial expansion.
    Japan and the Philippines had a major trade crisis in 1974 over Japan's cutback in purchase of Philippine copper.

Congo has experienced continual conflict over its resources with Angola, Namibia, Zimbabwe, Uganda, and Rwanda.
Diamonds in Sierra Leone and Angola are a continuing source of conflict.

30. Answers will vary. Valued materials that were available locally, such as beaver pelts, stones, and beads, were early forms of currency in North America. In ancient Asian and African civilizations, cowry shells, obtained from mollusks native to the Indian Ocean, were commonly used as currency. Silver and gold were used by ancient civilizations, since they occur uncombined in nature and scarcity enhanced their value. It would seem that early currency took the form of available and/or personally useful materials, and later took the form of easily traded, but less useful, metals and gems.

31. An inexpensive method of extracting aluminum by electrolysis from its ore, bauxite, was not devised until 1886 (by Hall and Heroult). Aluminum is usually found in combination with other elements and was not separable before this development. Copper is less reactive and sometimes found uncombined. Copper can also be refined by simply heating its ore in air (pyrometallurgy).

32. Aluminum cans are coated on the inside by a thin layer of plastic or lacquer.

33. A patina is a product of corrosion, forming a crust or film, usually on bronze or copper. The green-blue color is often aesthetically valued as an ornamental enhancement. The patina also protects the metal underneath from further corrosion.

Conserving Matter

In some chemical reactions, matter seems to be created—as a nail rusts, a new material appears; in other reactions, matter seems to disappear—a sheet of paper burns and apparently vanishes. In terms of fundamental particles, neither creation nor destruction of matter actually occurs. In this section, you will learn what happens to atoms in chemical reactions and how the atoms can be tracked through the use of chemical equations. This information will help you consider the fate of Earth's resources, as well as the fate of the materials and products developed from them.

C.1 KEEPING TRACK OF ATOMS

Think for a moment about what happens to molecules in gasoline as they burn in an automobile engine (Figure 2.23). The carbon and hydrogen atoms that make up these molecules react with oxygen atoms in air to form carbon monoxide (CO), carbon dioxide (CO_2), and water (H_2O). These products are released as exhaust and disperse in the atmosphere. Thus, atoms of carbon, hydrogen, and oxygen originally present in gasoline and air have not been destroyed; rather, they have become rearranged into different molecules.

In short, "using things up" means that materials are chemically changed, not destroyed. The **law of conservation of matter,** like all scientific laws, summarizes what has been learned by careful observation of nature: In a chemical reaction, matter is neither created nor destroyed. Molecules can be converted and decomposed by chemical processes; but atoms are forever. In a chemical reaction, matter—at the level of individual atoms—is always fully accounted for.

Because chemical reactions cannot create or destroy atoms, chemical equations representing such reactions must always be balanced. What does a "balanced equation" mean? Recall your introduction to chemical equations in Unit 1 (pages 34–37). Formulas for the reactants are placed on the left of the arrow; formulas for the products are placed on the right. In a **balanced chemical equation,** the number of atoms of each element is the same on the reactant and product sides.

Consider burning coal as an example. See Figure 2.24 (page 154). Coal is mostly carbon (C). If carbon burns completely, it combines with oxygen gas (O_2) to produce carbon dioxide (CO_2). Here is a representation of the atoms and molecules involved in this reaction:

C   + O_2 ⟶ CO_2
1 Carbon   1 Oxygen   1 Carbon dioxide
atom (C)   molecule (O_2)   molecule (CO_2)

Figure 2.23 *When a car's gas tank empties, where do the atoms in the gasoline go?*

 Interpreting a Balanced Chemical Equation

Section C   Conserving Matter   153

Conserving Matter

This section uses the law of conservation of matter to introduce the skills of tracking atoms and balancing chemical equations.

 C.1 through C.5 Content Reading Guide

C.1. Keeping Track of Atoms

The burning of coal and copper's reaction with oxygen illustrate the law of conservation of matter and its representation through correctly written chemical equations.
Emphasize:

• Each time a chemical equation is correctly balanced, the law of conservation of matter applies.

• Scientific laws are generalizations of countless observations. Therefore, the law of conservation of matter is a generalization that arose from observations of materials undergoing chemical or physical change.
• Coefficients should be written in *front* of symbols and formulas. Balancing equations is not automatic; students really need to think about what the reaction represents.
• Coefficients of "1" are not written—in the absence of any coefficient, a value of "1" is understood.
• Students may need clarification on differences between *coefficients* and *subscripts*. Coefficients are used to balance equations, consistent with the law of conservation of matter. Subscripts indicate the total atoms present in a given compound or formula unit.
• The symbols (s) for solid, (aq) for aqueous, (l) for liquid, and (g) for gas specify states of reactants and products.
• A formula unit is the smallest unit of an ionic substance. The term *molecule* applies only to molecular, or covalently bonded, substances.

Using the Figures

Figures 2.23 and 2.24: Gasoline burning in an automobile engine (or coal burning) is converted to colorless, odorless gaseous substances, rather than simply "disappearing." Students often have difficulty recognizing that substances may be present when they are not visible (such as dissolved substances in water or molecules in air). Ask students to share evidence that verifies new products form as a result of gasoline or coal combustion. For instance, some students probably know that a car engine should not run in a closed garage, because it produces toxic carbon monoxide gas.

SECTION C

Using the Figures

Figure 2.25: One challenge in chemistry teaching involves encouraging students to connect what they observe on the macroscopic level with atoms and molecules. Chemical reactions are recognized as changes in mass, volume, color, and temperature. However, even carefully describing such changes cannot account for what occurs at the particle level, so chemists devise symbolic representations and models. In this figure, the reaction that produces copper(II) oxide is shown on all three levels. Encourage students to discuss how each corner of the triangle is linked to the other two. Also, remind students that chemists constantly think about and describe unseen phenomena they infer from what they observe. As George Pimentel once noted, *chemists see one thing and think another.*

Figure 2.26: This figure lets students observe a chemical reaction at the macroscopic level before describing that same reaction at symbolic and particulate levels. In the following activity, it may be helpful to use demonstrations or graphics to illustrate each reaction on the macroscopic level, before students practice communicating and visualizing reactions at the particulate level with models and symbols.

Figure 2.24 *When a pile of coal burns, what becomes of the atoms that made up the coal?*

It is standard procedure to imply but not write the coefficient "1."

Look at the periodic table to recall which elements are metals and which are nonmetals.

Note that the numbers of carbon and oxygen atoms on the reactant side equal the numbers of carbon and oxygen atoms on the product side. This indicates that the equation is balanced.

The representation of the coal-burning reaction shows that one carbon atom reacts with one oxygen molecule to form one carbon dioxide molecule:

$$C(s) \quad + \quad O_2(g) \quad \longrightarrow \quad CO_2(g)$$

| Carbon (in coal) | and | Oxygen gas | React to produce | Carbon dioxide gas |

The chemical reaction from Investigating Matter B.3 (page 139), where you heated powdered copper in air, provides another example. Copper metal (Cu) reacts with oxygen gas (O_2) to form copper(II) oxide (CuO). Look at the following representation:

| 2 Copper atoms (Cu) | 1 Oxygen molecule (O_2) | $\longrightarrow$ | 2 Copper(II) oxide formula units (CuO) |

Again, note that the numbers of copper and oxygen atoms on the reactant side equal the respective numbers of copper and oxygen atoms on the product side. Written as a chemical equation, the reaction is

$$2\ Cu(s) \quad + \quad O_2(g) \quad \longrightarrow \quad 2\ CuO(s)$$

| Copper metal | and | Oxygen gas | React to produce | Copper(II) oxide |

You may have noticed that numbers have been placed in front of the copper and copper(II) oxide formulas. A "one" is also implied for the O_2. These numbers are called *coefficients.* **Coefficients** indicate the relative number of units of each substance involved in the chemical reaction. Reading this equation from left to right, you would say, "Two copper atoms react with one oxygen molecule to produce two formula units of copper(II) oxide."

Why is the term *formula unit* used instead of *molecule*? Compounds of a metal and a nonmetal are ionic. (*Note:* It might be helpful to review pages 38–41 of Unit 1.) Ionic compounds are not found as individual molecules. Rather, they form large crystals made up of arrays of ions. Chemists use the term **formula unit** when referring to the smallest unit of an ionic compound.

Study Figure 2.25, which represents the copper–oxygen reaction in three ways. The photograph shows what you observed during Investigating Matter B.3, representing this reaction at a large-scale (macroscopic) level. The particulate-level drawing models individual atoms and molecules for the reactants, and formula units within the ionic crystal of the product, with the chemical equation representing this reaction symbolically. The ability to think about particles involved in chemical reactions and to represent reactions with symbols will help you link your observations to what you cannot see (that is, what happens with atoms, ions, and molecules) and to keep track of reactants and products.

 C.1 Supplement: Keeping Track of Atoms

Figure 2.25 *Chemists describe the reaction between copper and oxygen in several ways: through* symbolic *equations, through models of what occurs at the* particulate *level, and through* macroscopic *descriptions of the observed properties of reactants and products.*

Macroscopic level

Copper(II) oxide

Particulate level

Solid copper + Oxygen gas → Solid copper(II) oxide

Symbolic level

$2 \, Cu(s) + O_2(g) \longrightarrow 2 \, CuO(s)$

In the following activity, you will practice recognizing and interpreting chemical equations.

Developing Skills

C.2 ACCOUNTING FOR ATOMS

Sample Problem: *The combustion reaction between propane (C_3H_8) and oxygen gas (O_2) is a common source of heat for campers, recreational-vehicle users, and others using tanks of propane fuel. See Figure 2.26. A chemical statement showing the reactants and products is*

$$C_3H_8(g) + O_2(g) \longrightarrow CO_2(g) + H_2O(g)$$

Interpret this reaction in terms of (a) words, (b) molecular models, and (c) an atom inventory. (d) Is this a balanced chemical equation?

This chemical reaction produces thermal energy (heat), which can also be considered a product.

Figure 2.26 *In what ways could you describe the reaction of propane with oxygen?*

Developing Skills

C.2 Accounting for Atoms

In this activity, students learn how to recognize a balanced equation. Learning to account for all atoms represented in a symbolic expression for a reaction is a skill to master before balancing equations. Reinforce the idea that each balanced equation represents a chemical reaction. Using the first example, it may be helpful to model the thinking involved in (1) writing the chemical statement in words, (2) drawing a representation of the chemical statement, and, finally, (3) completing an atom inventory. You may ask students to model the equations using model kits, colored paper clips, or gumdrops and toothpicks as well as drawings. Some students may benefit from using colored pencils to differentiate among and count atoms and determine whether the chemical statement is balanced.

SECTION C

1. a. Methane gas reacts with oxygen gas to produce carbon dioxide gas and water vapor.

b.

$$CH_4 + 2\,O_2 \rightarrow CO_2 + 2\,H_2O$$

c.

Reactants:	Products:
1 carbon atom	1 carbon atom
4 hydrogen atoms	4 hydrogen atoms
4 oxygen atoms	4 oxygen atoms

d. The respective numbers of carbon, hydrogen, and oxygen atoms are the same in the reactants and the products. The original statement is balanced.

2. a. Hydrobromic acid reacts with magnesium to produce hydrogen gas and magnesium bromide.

b.

$$HBr + Mg \longrightarrow H_2 + MgBr_2$$

c.

Reactants:	Products:
1 hydrogen atom	2 hydrogen atoms
1 bromine atom	2 bromine atoms
1 magnesium atom	1 magnesium atom

d. The respective numbers of hydrogen and bromine atoms are different in reactants and products. The original statement is not properly written. It is not balanced.

3. a. Solid silver reacts with hydrogen sulfide gas and oxygen gas to form solid silver sulfide and liquid water. (This is the reaction responsible for silver tarnishing and explains why silver bowls should not be used to heat sulfur-containing foods, such as eggs.)

b.

$$4\,Ag + 4\,H_2S + O_2 \longrightarrow 2\,Ag_2S + 4\,H_2O$$

See page 61 in Unit 1 to view a representation of an ionic crystal structure.

a. Interpreting this statement in words, "Propane gas reacts with oxygen gas to produce carbon dioxide gas and water vapor."

b. Using ⬤ to represent a propane molecule, the chemical statement can be represented as

$$C_3H_8 + O_2 \longrightarrow CO_2 + H_2O$$

1 Propane molecule (C_3H_8)	1 Oxygen molecule (O_2)	1 Carbon dioxide molecule (CO_2)	1 Water molecule (H_2O)

c. Counting the atoms on each side of the equation gives this atom inventory:

Reactant Side	**Product Side**
3 carbon atoms	1 carbon atom
8 hydrogen atoms	2 hydrogen atoms
2 oxygen atoms	3 oxygen atoms

d. The respective numbers of carbon, hydrogen, and oxygen atoms are different in reactants and products. Thus, the original statement is not a properly written chemical equation. That is, it is not balanced.

For each of the following chemical statements,

a. write an interpretation of the statement in words,
b. draw a representation of the chemical statement (some structures are provided),
c. complete an atom inventory of the reactants and products, and
d. decide whether the expression, as written, is balanced.

1. Many people use natural gas as a source of household heat. Natural gas contains methane (CH_4), which burns with oxygen gas (O_2) in air according to the equation

$$CH_4 + 2\,O_2 \longrightarrow CO_2 + 2\,H_2O$$

Let ⬤ represent a methane molecule.

2. When an acid reacts with a metal, hydrogen gas and an ionic compound are often formed. An expression for hydrobromic acid (HBr) reacting with magnesium metal to form hydrogen gas and magnesium bromide ($MgBr_2$) is

$$HBr + Mg \longrightarrow H_2 + MgBr_2$$

Let ⬤ represent a formula unit of magnesium bromide ($MgBr_2$). (*Note:* Formula units are potentially misleading because, under ordinary circumstances, ionic compounds are not found as individual molecules, but as large crystals made

c.

Reactants:	Products:
4 silver atoms	4 silver atoms
8 hydrogen atoms	8 hydrogen atoms
4 sulfur atoms	2 sulfur atoms
2 oxygen atoms	4 oxygen atoms

d. The respective numbers of sulfur and oxygen atoms are different in reactants and products. The expression is not balanced.

up of many ions. Thus, this and similar representations of ionic compounds are technically inaccurate; however, for an atom inventory, they will suffice. Keep these limitations in mind.)

3. Hydrogen sulfide (H_2S) and metallic silver react in air to form silver sulfide (Ag_2S), commonly known as silver tarnish, and water:

$$4\ Ag + 4\ H_2S + O_2 \longrightarrow 2\ Ag_2S + 4\ H_2O$$

Let represent a hydrogen sulfide molecule and represent a formula unit of silver sulfide.

Try Questions 4 and 5 without drawing representations. (Why might this be a good decision?)

4. Wood or paper, composed mainly of cellulose, $C_6H_{10}O_5$, can burn in air to form carbon dioxide and water vapor:

$$C_6H_{10}O_5 + 6\ O_2 \longrightarrow 6\ CO_2 + 5\ H_2O$$

5. Nitroglycerin, $C_3H_5(NO_3)_3$, the active constituent of dynamite, decomposes explosively to form N_2, O_2, CO_2, and water.

$$2\ C_3H_5(NO_3)_3 \longrightarrow 3\ N_2 + O_2 + 6\ CO_2 + 5\ H_2O$$

> There are nine oxygen atoms in one $C_3H_5(NO_3)_3$ molecule. Can you see why?

C.3 NATURE'S CONSERVATION: BALANCED CHEMICAL EQUATIONS

The law of conservation of matter is based on the notion that atoms are indestructible. All chemical changes observed in matter can be interpreted as rearrangements among atoms. Correctly written (balanced) chemical equations represent such changes. In the preceding activity, you practiced recognizing balanced chemical equations. Now you will learn how to write them.

As an example, consider the reaction of hydrogen gas with oxygen gas to produce gaseous water. First, correctly write the reactant formula or formulas to the left of the arrow and the product formula or formulas to the right of the arrow, keeping in mind that hydrogen and oxygen gas are diatomic (*two*-atom) molecules.

> The law of conservation of matter holds under normal circumstances. You may be familiar with the equation $E = mc^2$, which indicates that small quantities of matter (mass) can be converted to energy within events such as nuclear reactions.

$$H_2(g) \quad + \quad O_2(g) \quad \longrightarrow \quad H_2O(g)$$

Check the following expression by completing an atom inventory: Two hydrogen atoms appear on the left side and two on the right. Thus, hydrogen atoms are balanced. However, two oxygen atoms appear on the left side and only one on the right. Because oxygen is not balanced, the expression requires additional work.

> For a complete listing of the elements found as diatomic molecules, see page 36.

C.3 Nature's Conservation: Balanced Chemical Equations

The law of conservation of matter is used to develop stepwise procedures for balancing chemical equations. There are many different ways to teach students to balance equations: All can benefit from the approach taken here. It views balancing from both particulate and symbolic perspectives. Depending on students' learning styles, it might be useful to show several ways to balance equations. An algebraic approach to balancing equations, if your students are mathematically inclined, is described on the TRCD and in the Skill Building Supplement Section of the TRB.

4. a. Cellulose reacts with oxygen gas to form carbon dioxide gas and liquid water.
   b. Drawing is not required.
   c. Reactants: Products:
      6 carbon atoms   6 carbon atoms
      10 hydrogen atoms 10 hydrogen atoms
      17 oxygen atoms   17 oxygen atoms
   d. This is a correctly balanced equation.

5. a. Nitroglycerin decomposes to form nitrogen gas, oxygen gas, carbon dioxide gas, and water vapor.
   b. Drawing is not required.
   c. Reactants: Products:
      6 carbon atoms   6 carbon atoms
      10 hydrogen atoms 10 hydrogen atoms
      6 nitrogen atoms   6 nitrogen atoms
      18 oxygen atoms   19 oxygen atoms
   d. The expression is not balanced.

Some points to stress with students are:

• Once a formula is written correctly, do not change its subscripts. For instance, NaCl is the correct formula for sodium chloride; do not write NaCl$_2$ to balance an equation.

• Use coefficients to balance the number of atoms of an element on both sides of the equation.

• Coefficients affect every atom in the substance that they precede. A subscript only affects the atom (or polyatomic ion in parentheses) to its immediate left.

• Polyatomic ions (when they appear in both reactants and products) can often be treated as intact units rather than separate atoms when balancing equations—this simplifies procedures significantly.

• Hydrogen and oxygen should be balanced last in any equation including water.

• It is often easiest to balance compounds first, leaving elements (not in compounds) for balancing last, since changing an element's coefficient affects only one element's atom inventory.

• Always double-check atom counts.

Here is an *incorrect* way to complete the equation:

$$H_2(g) \quad + \quad O_2(g) \quad \longrightarrow \quad H_2O_2(g) \quad \textbf{Incorrect!}$$

1 Hydrogen molecule   1 Oxygen molecule   1 Hydrogen peroxide molecule

Although this chemical statement meets an atom-inventory check (there are two hydrogen and two oxygen atoms on both sides), this chemical expression is *quite wrong*. By changing the subscript of O from 1 to 2 in the product, the identity of the product has been changed from water (H_2O) to hydrogen peroxide (H_2O_2). Because hydrogen peroxide is *not* produced by this reaction, the chemical expression is incorrect. When balancing chemical equations, *subscripts* remain unchanged once correct formulas have been written for reactants and products. *Coefficients* (the numbers placed in front of formulas) must be adjusted to balance equations instead.

Additional hydrogen, oxygen, and water molecules must be added to the appropriate sides of the equation to balance the numbers of oxygen and hydrogen atoms. Another oxygen atom is needed on the product side to bring the number of oxygen atoms on both sides to two. Therefore, a water molecule is added:

$$H_2 \quad + \quad O_2 \quad \longrightarrow \quad H_2O \quad + \quad H_2O$$

1 Hydrogen molecule   1 Oxygen molecule   2 Water molecules

As a result, two oxygen atoms appear on each side of the equation. Unfortunately, hydrogen atoms are no longer balanced: Now there are two hydrogen atoms on the left side and four atoms on the right. How can two hydrogen atoms be added to the reactant side? You are correct if you said by adding one hydrogen molecule to the left side:

$$H_2 \quad + \quad H_2 \quad + \quad O_2 \quad \longrightarrow \quad H_2O \quad + \quad H_2O$$

2 Hydrogen molecules   1 Oxygen molecule   2 Water molecules

The atoms are now balanced. Count the atoms to verify that!

This information is usually summarized in a chemical equation:

$$2\ H_2(g) + O_2(g) \longrightarrow 2\ H_2O(g)$$

Under certain conditions, H_2 reacts with O_2 in a violent explosion. However, the reaction can be controlled and, in fact, it powers some types of rockets. See Figure 2.27. Used in fuel cells, this reaction can generate electricity.

Figure 2.27 *Some rockets are propelled by the thrust generated when liquid hydrogen and liquid oxygen react to form gaseous water.*

C.3 Supplement: Balancing Equations

This equation can be interpreted as indicating, "Two molecules of hydrogen gas react with one molecule of oxygen gas to produce two molecules of water vapor."

The following additional suggestions may help you as you write correctly balanced chemical equations:

▶ If polyatomic ions, such as NO_3^- and CO_3^{2-} appear as both reactants and products, treat them as units, rather than balancing their atoms individually.

▶ If water is involved in the reaction, balance hydrogen and oxygen atoms last.

▶ Recount all atoms after you think an equation is balanced—just to be sure!

C.4 WRITING CHEMICAL EQUATIONS

The reaction of methane gas (CH_4) with chlorine gas (Cl_2) occurs in sewage treatment plants and often in chlorinated water supplies (Figure 2.28). Common products are liquid chloroform ($CHCl_3$) and hydrogen chloride gas (HCl). A chemical statement describing this reaction follows. As you can see from a quick glance, the equation is not balanced:

$$CH_4(g) \ + \ Cl_2(g) \ \longrightarrow \ CHCl_3(l) \ + \ HCl(g)$$
Methane　　Chlorine　　　Chloroform　　Hydrogen chloride

To complete the chemical equation, you can follow this line of reasoning: *One* carbon atom appears on each side of the arrow, so carbon atoms balance. Thus, the coefficients in front of CH_4 and $CHCl_3$ are regarded (at least for the moment) as "1." We will write it in explicitly, just as a reminder, but the coefficient 1 is removed from the final equation:

$$1 \ CH_4 \ + \ Cl_2 \ \longrightarrow \ 1 \ CHCl_3 \ + \ HCl$$
Methane　　Chlorine　　Chloroform　　Hydrogen chloride

Four hydrogen atoms are on the left, but only two hydrogen atoms are on the right (one in $CHCl_3$, a second in HCl). To increase the number of hydrogen atoms on the product side, the coefficient of HCl can be adjusted. Because two more hydrogens are needed on the right, the number of HCl molecules must be changed from 1 to 3. This gives four hydrogen atoms on the right:

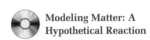
Modeling Matter: A Hypothetical Reaction

Figure 2.28 *A water-treatment plant, a portion of which is shown here, often uses chlorine to purify municipal water.*

For convenience, the symbols (g) and (l) are removed. They will reappear in the final equation.

This activity lets students practice balancing equations. The sample equations represent actual reactions in resource processing or chemical manufacturing.

Reinforce the need to count atoms on both sides of the equation. Consider using physical models such as paper clips or molecular models in addition to the drawings. When learning to balance equations, students typically progress at different speeds. Providing class time for students to work through balancing equations with instructor assistance can contribute to student confidence. Although students who grasp the balancing concept more quickly may recognize shortcuts in the balancing process, remind students that taking accurate atom inventories is the best way to ensure success.

Answers

1. a. $2\ C(s) + O_2(g) \rightarrow 2\ CO(g)$

b. $Fe_2O_3(s) + 3\ CO(g) \rightarrow 2\ Fe(l) + 3\ CO_2(g)$

2. $2\ CuO(s) + C(s) \rightarrow 2\ Cu(s) + CO_2(g)$

3. $2\ O_3(g) \rightarrow 3\ O_2(g)$

4. $4\ NH_3(g) + 7\ O_2(g) \rightarrow 4\ NO_2(g) + 6\ H_2O(l)$

5. $Cu(s) + 2\ AgNO_3(aq) \rightarrow Cu(NO_3)_2(aq) + 2\ Ag(s)$

6. $2\ C_8H_{18}(l) + 25\ O_2(g) \rightarrow 16\ CO_2(g) + 18\ H_2O(g)$

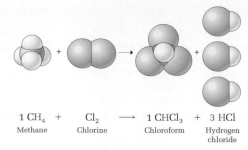

$$1\ CH_4 + Cl_2 \longrightarrow 1\ CHCl_3 + 3\ HCl$$
Methane   Chlorine   Chloroform   Hydrogen chloride

Now both carbon and hydrogen atoms are balanced. What about chlorine? Two chlorine atoms appear on the left and six on the right side. These six chlorine atoms (three in $CHCl_3$, three in 3 HCl) must have come from three chlorine (Cl_2) molecules. Thus, 3 must be the coefficient of Cl_2.

The chemical equation appears to be balanced. An atom inventory verifies that the equation is complete and correct as written:

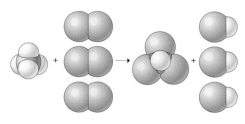

$$CH_4(g) + 3\ Cl_2(g) \longrightarrow CHCl_3(l) + 3\ HCl(g)$$
Methane   Chlorine   Chloroform   Hydrogen chloride

Reactant Side	Product Side
1 C atom	1 C atom
4 H atoms	4 H atoms (1 in $CHCl_3$, 3 in HCl)
6 Cl atoms (in 3 Cl_2)	6 Cl atoms (3 in $CHCl_3$, 3 in HCl)

Copy the following chemical expressions onto a separate sheet of paper, and balance each if needed. For Questions 1 through 4, draw a representation of your final equation to verify that it is balanced. Structures unfamiliar to you will be provided.

1. Two blast furnace reactions are used to obtain iron from its ore:
a. $C(s) + O_2(g) \longrightarrow 2\ CO(g)$
b. $Fe_2O_3(s) + CO(g) \longrightarrow Fe(l) + 3\ CO_2(g)$

Let represent a formula unit of Fe_2O_3.

Let represent a molecule of CO_2.

> Chloroform is one of the trihalomethanes (THMs) mentioned in Unit 1 (page 90).

Skill Building Topic 7: Understanding and Balancing Equations

2. The final step in the refining of a copper ore is:

$$CuO(s) + C(s) \longrightarrow Cu(s) + CO_2(g)$$

Let ⚪⚫ represent a formula unit of CuO.

3. Ozone (O_3) can decompose to form oxygen gas (O_2):

$$O_3(g) \longrightarrow O_2(g)$$

Let ⚫⚫⚫ represent an ozone molecule.

4. Ammonia (NH_3) in the soil reacts continuously with oxygen gas (O_2):

$$NH_3(g) + O_2(g) \longrightarrow NO_2(g) + H_2O(l)$$

5. Copper metal reacts with silver nitrate solution to form copper(II) nitrate solution and silver metal:

$$Cu(s) + AgNO_3(aq) \longrightarrow Cu(NO_3)_2(aq) + Ag(s)$$

(*Hint:* Look at the formula for copper(II) nitrate, $Cu(NO_3)_2$. The subscript of two outside the parentheses indicates that this formula contains two nitrate (NO_3^-) anions. Therefore, one formula unit of $Cu(NO_3)_2$ contains one copper ion, two nitrogen atoms, and six oxygen atoms.)

6. Combustion of gasoline in an automobile engine can be represented by the burning of octane (C_8H_{18}):

$$C_8H_{18}(l) + O_2(g) \longrightarrow CO_2(g) + H_2O(g)$$

C.5 INTRODUCING THE MOLE CONCEPT

The Mole

In Question 2 of the previous activity, you analyzed the chemical equation

$$2\,CuO(s) + C(s) \longrightarrow 2\,Cu(s) + CO_2(g)$$

As you know, one interpretation of this equation is as follows: Two formula units of copper(II) oxide and one atom of carbon react to produce two atoms of copper and one molecule of carbon dioxide. Although correct, this interpretation involves such small quantities of material that a reaction on that scale would be completely unnoticed. Such information would not be very useful, for example, to a metal-processing company interested in how much carbon is needed to react with a large amount of copper(II) oxide to produce metallic copper.

Chemists have devised a counting unit called the **mole** (symbolized *mol*) that can help to solve the metal-processing company's problem. You are familiar with other common counting units, such as *pair* and *dozen*. The mole can be thought of as the chemist's *dozen*.

A *pair* of water molecules is two water molecules. One *dozen* water molecules is the same as 12 water molecules. One *mole* of water molecules is 602 000 000 000 000 000 000 000 water molecules. This special number—the number of particles or "things" in one mole—is more conveniently written as 6.02×10^{23}. Either way, this is a very large number!

The number 6.02×10^{23} is commonly known as Avogadro's number.

C.5 Introducing the Mole Concept

Emphasize that the *mole* is a counting unit, similar but much larger than the *dozen*. Other common counting units include *pair, ream,* and *gross.* The concept of a mole is generally elusive for students; so concrete activities help them develop a thorough understanding.

Students readily grasp the concept of a dozen; access this prior knowledge by asking students to define *dozen.* Follow this by asking them to identify the number of atoms in a dozen atoms, the number of cars in a dozen cars, the number of bottles in a dozen bottles. Elicit from students *similarities* in a "dozen" of any item. Also elicit *differences* in a "dozen of any item." Answers should include mass, weight, volume, and appearance. At this point, you may introduce the definition of a mole and pose the same series of questions. Start from where students are (with the concept of a dozen) and lead them to this new concept (the mole).

Remind students that Avogadro's number is large because the units being counted (atoms and molecules) are so small. Approximations that emphasize the enormity of 6.02×10^{23} include that it is approximately the number of grains of sand on all the beaches of the world or the number of glasses of water in all the oceans.

The mole concept is based on the idea that if the mass of one particle is known, then we can calculate the mass of a thousand, million, or billion particles. Conversely, if the mass of a collection of these particles is known, we can calculate the number of particles. Thus, knowing the mass of one unit enables us to "count by weighing." Students may be able to think of some everyday examples of this method. For instance, arcades that award tickets for winning often weigh the tickets instead of bothering to count them. Similarly, chemists "count" the number of particles in macroscopic samples of matter by weighing them, rather than actually counting the number of atoms, molecules, or ions.

Display one mole of a variety of substances—sugar, salt, aluminum, copper, water—to reinforce the idea that the mass of one mole varies with the substance.

The atomic weights on the periodic table represent the molar masses for each element in grams. The mole is formally defined as the amount of substance that contains as many elementary entities as there are atoms in exactly 0.012 kg carbon-12—Avogadro's number of atoms.

Tell students that they can calculate the molar mass of any compound if they know its formula and sum each element's atomic weight multiplied by the total atoms of that element in the formula.

Chemical Equations and Molar Relationships Help students understand that the coefficients in an equation can refer to molecular size units (atoms, molecules, ions, formula units) or moles, since the conversion involves simply multiplying by 6.02×10^{23}. Molar masses can be used to create conversion factors, which can then be used to solve stoichiometric problems (related to quantitative relationships in chemical reactions). You can decide to provide more practice in chemical calculations at this point, especially if your content standards emphasize stoichiometry—but *don't overdo it;* students will practice these skills in later units.

Using the Figures

Figure 2.29: The primary reason one mole of each of these substances occupies a different volume relates to the type of bonding interactions involved and to the actual three-dimensional packing of the atoms/molecules—that is, to the "packing efficiency" of the particles. This packing factor accounts for the observation that the volume occupied by one mole of liquid water is smaller than the volume occupied

Figure 2.29 One mole each of copper, table salt, and water. If these samples each represent one mole of substance, why do they occupy different volumes?

The mole concept permits us literally to *count* by weighing.

To help you get a better idea of the size of a mole, consider this analogy: Imagine stringing one mole of paper clips (6.02×10^{23} paper clips) together and wrapping the paper-clip string around the world. It would circle the world about 400 trillion (4×10^{14}) times! Even if you connected a million paper clips each second, it would take you 190 million centuries to finish stringing together one mole of paper clips.

As large as one mole seems, however, drinking one mole of water molecules would leave you quite thirsty on a hot day. One mole of water is *less than one-tenth of a cup* of water—only 18 g (or 18 mL) of water. Because atoms and molecules are so very small, the amount of those tiny building blocks needed to make up the "stuff" we see is nearly countless.

That is the reason the mole is so useful for work in chemistry. It represents a number of atoms, molecules, or formula units large enough to be conveniently weighed or measured in the laboratory. Furthermore, the atomic weights of elements can be used to find the mass of one mole of any substance, a value known as the **molar mass** of a substance. Figure 2.29 shows one mole of several familiar substances.

Molar Mass

Because mass is a readily measured quantity, molar mass can be used to count particles by simply measuring the mass of a substance. Specific examples will help you to better understand this powerful idea. See Figure 2.30. Suppose you need to find the molar masses of carbon (C) and of copper (Cu). In other words, you want to know the mass of one mole of carbon atoms (6.02×10^{23} C atoms) and the mass of one mole of copper atoms (6.02×10^{23} Cu atoms). Rather than counting that collection of atoms onto a laboratory balance, you can quickly get the correct quantities from atomic-weight data. The atomic weight of each element is found on the periodic table. Carbon's atomic weight is 12.01 and copper's is 63.55. If the unit *grams* is attached to these numbers, the resulting values represent their molar masses:

$$1 \text{ mol C} = 12.01 \text{ g C} \qquad 1 \text{ mol Cu} = 63.55 \text{ g Cu}$$

In summary, the mass (in grams) of one mole of an element's atoms equals the numerical value of that element's atomic weight. Any element's molar mass can be easily found from the periodic table.

Figure 2.30 One mole of carbon (left) and copper (right). What do the different samples have in common?

by one mole of solid water (ice)—the higher density of the liquid reflects the closer packing of water molecules in the liquid state, compared to the three-dimensional lattice of ice, with its characteristic open structure.

Figure 2.30: The caption asks students what the samples have in common. It may also be useful to discuss what *differences* exist between the two samples. This line of discussion provides another opportunity to emphasize that moles are a *counting unit* and not a unit of mass or volume.

The molar mass of a diatomic element, such as O_2, is *twice* the mass given in the periodic table. Can you explain why this is so?

The molar mass of a compound is simply the sum of the molar masses of its component atoms. For example, consider two compounds of importance to metal-processing companies interested in refining large amounts of copper—carbon dioxide, CO_2, and the copper-containing mineral malachite, $Cu_2CO_3(OH)_2$.

One mole of CO_2 molecules contains one mole of C atoms and two moles of O atoms. Adding the molar mass of carbon and twice the molar mass of oxygen gives

$$1 \text{ mol C} \times \frac{12.01 \text{ g C}}{1 \text{ mol C}} = 12.01 \text{ g C}$$

$$2 \text{ mol O} \times \frac{16.00 \text{ g O}}{1 \text{ mol O}} = 32.00 \text{ g O}$$

Molar mass of CO_2 = (12.01 g + 32.00 g) = 44.01 g CO_2

> Recall that *mol* is the symbol for the unit *mole*.

The molar mass of malachite is found in a similar way. However, we must carefully count the atoms of each element in more complex compounds such as this.

One mole of malachite, $Cu_2CO_3(OH)_2$, contains 2 mol Cu, 1 mol C, 5 mol O, and 2 mol H. (Can you see where five oxygen atoms are found in the formula?)

$$2 \text{ mol Cu} \times \frac{63.55 \text{ g Cu}}{1 \text{ mol Cu}} = 127.1 \text{ g Cu}$$

$$1 \text{ mol C} \times \frac{12.01 \text{ g C}}{1 \text{ mol C}} = 12.01 \text{ g C}$$

$$5 \text{ mol O} \times \frac{16.00 \text{ g O}}{1 \text{ mol O}} = 80.00 \text{ g O}$$

$$2 \text{ mol H} \times \frac{1.008 \text{ g H}}{1 \text{ mol H}} = 2.016 \text{ g H}$$

Molar mass of $Cu_2CO_3(OH)_2$ = 221.1 g $Cu_2CO_3(OH)_2$

C.6 MOLAR MASSES

Developing Skills

Find the molar mass of each of the following substances:

1. nitrogen atoms, N
2. nitrogen molecules, N_2
3. sodium chloride (table salt), NaCl
4. sucrose (table sugar), $C_{12}H_{22}O_{11}$
5. chalcopyrite (a copper-containing mineral), $CuFeS_2$
6. magnesium phosphate, $Mg_3(PO_4)_2$
7. caffeine, $C_8H_{10}N_4O_2$
8. calcium hydroxyapatite (a mineral found in teeth), $Ca_{10}(PO_4)_6(OH)_2$
9. alunite (an aluminum mineral), $KAl_3(SO_4)_2(OH)_6$
   (*Hint:* Verify that this formula includes 14 mol of oxygen atoms.)

> The term *one mole of nitrogen* is not helpful. It could refer to one mole of N *atoms* or to one mole of N_2 *molecules*. Thus, it is important to specify clearly which substance is involved.

 C.5 Supplement: Molar Masses

 Skill Building Topic 8: The Mole

Developing Skills

C.6 Molar Masses

When students understand the mole concept, ask them to complete these calculations. Caution students about the implications of parentheses in counting atoms and in calculating molar mass. Consider discussing rules for rounding and significant figures, depending on your content standards. Resources for these topics can be found in the Student Edition appendices and on the TRCD. You may also need to remind students of the importance of units as they complete these calculations and prepare to use their skills to perform calculations based on molar relationships in equations and percent composition.

Answers

1. 14.01 g/mol
2. 14.01 g/mol $\times$ 2 = **28.02 g/mol**
3. 22.99 g/mol + 35.45 g/mol = **58.44 g/mol**
4. (12.01 g/mol $\times$ 12) + (1.008 g/mol $\times$ 22) + (16.00 g/mol $\times$ 11) = **342.30 g/mol**
5. 63.55 g/mol + 55.85 g/mol + (32.01 g/mol $\times$ 2) = **183.42 g/mol**
6. (24.31 g/mol $\times$ 3) + (30.97 g/mol $\times$ 2) + (16.00 g/mol $\times$ 8) = **262.87 g/mol**
7. (12.01 g/mol $\times$ 8) + (1.008 g/mol $\times$ 10) + (14.01 g/mol $\times$ 4) + (16.00 g/mol $\times$ 2) = **194.20 g/mol**
8. (40.08 g/mol $\times$ 10) + (30.97 g/mol $\times$ 6) + (16.00 g/mol $\times$ 26) + (1.008 g/mol $\times$ 2) = **1004.64 g/mol**
9. 39.10 g/mol + (26.98 g/mol $\times$ 3) + (32.07 g/mol $\times$ 2) + (16.00 g/mol $\times$ 14) + (1.008 g/mol $\times$ 6) = **414.23 g/mol**

SECTION C

C.7 Equations and Molar Relationships

This material introduces students to a fundamental idea in chemistry—that chemical equations describe not only quantitative relationships among molecular-scale particles, but also their macroscopic relationships. The coefficients in a chemical equation work on several levels. At the particulate level, they indicate the number of each kind of particle required or produced. Remind students of their recent introduction to the mole, which enables us to scale up to useful macroscopic quantities using the ratios implied in a chemical equation.

Students will use several relationships—molar mass, molar volume, and molar concentration—to move among "lab-based" quantities of mass and volume and particulate-level relationships described in chemical equations.

2 mol CuO, containing 2 mol Cu atoms as well as 2 mol O atoms, has a mass of 159.10 g, which is twice the molar mass of CuO.

Figure 2.31 *Following reduction from its oxide ore, molten aluminum metal is poured into a mold. The United States produces over two million metric tons of aluminum annually.*

C.7 EQUATIONS AND MOLAR RELATIONSHIPS

Why are chemical equations and molar masses useful in answering questions about large-scale reactions? The coefficients in a chemical equation show both the relative numbers of individual molecules (or formula units) of reactants and products and the relative numbers of moles of these same substances.

Consider again the copper-refining example. The mole "counting unit" makes it relatively easy to find the mass of carbon dioxide released during refining:

$$2\ CuO(s)\ +\ C(s)\ \longrightarrow\ 2\ Cu(s)\ +\ CO_2(g)$$

| 2 Formula units CuO | 1 Atom C | 2 Atoms Cu | 1 Molecule CO_2 |

Alternatively,

$$2\ mol\ CuO\ +\ 1\ mol\ C\ \longrightarrow\ 2\ mol\ Cu\ +\ 1\ mol\ CO_2$$

Thus, for every *two* moles of CuO that react, *one* mole of CO_2 is produced. The molar masses of all four substances can be used to interpret the equation in terms of the masses involved:

$$2\ CuO(s)\ +\ C(s)\ \longrightarrow\ 2\ Cu(s)\ +\ CO_2(g)$$

2 mol CuO	1 mol C	2 mol Cu	1 mol CO_2
79.55 g CuO + 79.55 g CuO	12.01 g C	63.55 g Cu + 63.55 g Cu	44.01 g CO_2
159.10 g CuO	12.01 g C	127.10 g Cu	44.01 g CO_2

Compare the total mass of products to the total mass of reactants. This illustrates the law of conservation of matter. Note that the total mass of reactants (159.10 g + 12.01 g) equals the total mass of products.

Metal processing companies typically work with quantities much larger than several grams; therefore, they produce much more than one or two moles of material. See Figure 2.31. The refiners must rely on their understanding of the molar relationships represented in equations such as the one above to complete the needed calculations involved in their large-scale reactions.

Sample Problem: *A refiner needs to convert 955.0 g CuO to pure Cu. What mass of C is needed for this reaction?*

The previous equation indicates that 1 mol C is needed to refine 2 mol CuO. But how many moles of CuO are represented by 955.0 g CuO? One mol CuO has a mass of 159.1 g, therefore

$$\frac{1 \text{ mol CuO}}{159.1 \text{ g CuO}} = \frac{x \text{ mol CuO}}{955.0 \text{ g CuO}}$$

$$955.0 \text{ g CuO} \times 1 \text{ mol CuO} = 159.1 \text{ g CuO(s)} \times x \text{ mol CuO}$$

$$x = 955 \text{ g CuO} \times \frac{1 \text{ mol CuO}}{159.1 \text{ g CuO}} = 6.00 \text{ mol CuO}$$

We started solving this sample problem with a proportion; however, in rearranging the proportion we created a **conversion factor.** The top and the bottom of this conversion factor—1 mol CuO/159.1 g CuO—both refer to the same number of particles, which are expressed in different units. This fraction allows us to convert from one unit, in this case, *grams,* to another unit, *moles,* by describing the relationship between the two units of measurement.

The refiner now knows that there are 6.00 mol CuO in 955.0 g CuO. How many moles of C are needed? Based on the equation on page 164, which states 1 mol C is required to react with 2 mol CuO, how many moles of C are needed to refine 6.00 mol CuO?

While it is quite possible to solve this problem using proportions, it is often faster and more efficient to create a conversion factor relating the quantities in question (which you would do, anyway, by solving the proportion expression).

In this case, the relevant conversion factor would be 1 mol C for every 2 mol CuO, based on the coefficients in the chemical equation. Notice, as in the previous example, we write the conversion factor to allow the appropriate units to divide and cancel:

$$6.00 \text{ mol CuO} \times \frac{1 \text{ mol C}}{2 \text{ mol CuO}} = 3.00 \text{ mol C}$$

Once this information is known, it is possible to find the mass of C needed to refine 955.0 g of CuO, again using an appropriate conversion factor:

$$3.00 \text{ mol C} \times \frac{12.01 \text{ g C}}{1 \text{ mol C}} = 36.0 \text{ g C}$$

Identify the conversion factor in the last calculation. Where did the information contained in the conversion factor come from? Once the molar masses and molar relationships involved are known, chemists can predict reactions involving any amount of material they may need or may wish to produce.

Skill Building Topic 8: The Mole

C.7 Supplement: Equations and Molar Relationships I

C.7 Supplement: Equations and Molar Relationships II

C.8 Molar Relationships

In this activity, students practice conversions using molar ratios derived from coefficients in the equation. Remind students that the absence of a coefficient implies a value of "1." Also, encourage them to use units that include the substances involved in conversion factors and final answers (for example, "1 mol CuO" rather than "1" or "1 mol").

Answers

1. CuO, 79.54 g/mol;
HCl, 36.46 g/mol;
$CuCl_2$, 134.45 g/mol;
H_2O, 18.02 g/mol

2. a. 1.0 mol HCl = 36 g HCl

b. $5.0 \text{ mol HCl} \times \dfrac{36.46 \text{ g HCl}}{1 \text{ mol HCl}} =$
180 g HCl

c. $0.5 \text{ mol CuO} \times \dfrac{79.54 \text{ g CuO}}{1 \text{ mol CuO}} =$
40 g CuO (with appropriate significant figures)

3. a. $941.5 \text{ g CuCl}_2 \times$
$\dfrac{1 \text{ mol CuCl}_2}{134.45 \text{ g CuCl}_2} = 7.000 \text{ mol CuCl}_2$

b. $201.6 \text{ g CuCl}_2 \times$
$\dfrac{1 \text{ mol CuCl}_2}{134.45 \text{ g CuCl}_2} = 1.500 \text{ mol CuCl}_2$

c. $73.0 \text{ g HCl} \times \dfrac{1 \text{ mol HCl}}{36.46 \text{ g HCl}} =$
2.00 mol HCl

4. a. 4 mol HCl will react with 2 mol
CuO; $4 \text{ mol HCl} \times \dfrac{1 \text{ mol CuO}}{2 \text{ mol HCl}} =$
2 mol CuO.

b. 4 mol CuO will react with 8 mol HCl; $4 \text{ mol CuO} \times$
$\dfrac{2 \text{ mol HCl}}{1 \text{ mol CuO}} = 8 \text{ mol HCl}.$

C.8 MOLAR RELATIONSHIPS

Base your answers to the following questions on this equation:

$$CuO(s) + 2 \, HCl(aq) \longrightarrow CuCl_2(aq) + H_2O(l)$$

1. Find the molar mass of each reactant specified in the equation.
2. Find the mass (in grams) of each of the following substances:
   a. 1.0 mol HCl
   b. 5.0 mol HCl
   c. 0.50 mol CuO
3. Find the number of moles of substance that are represented by
   a. 941.5 g $CuCl_2$
   b. 201.6 g $CuCl_2$
   c. 73.0 g HCl
4. a. How many moles of CuO are needed to react with 4 mol HCl?
   b. How many moles of HCl are needed to react with 4 mol CuO?

C.9 COMPOSITION OF MATERIALS

One decision you will make when designing your coin is whether to use only one material or a combination of materials. If your design uses more than one material, you will need to specify how much of each material will be present in the coin. The percent by mass of each material found in an item such as a coin is called its **percent composition.**

In Section A, you learned that the composition of the U.S. penny has changed several times. During 1943, it was made of zinc-coated steel. After this date and up until 1982, the penny was made mostly of copper. Since 1982, U.S. pennies have been made primarily of zinc.

Sample Problem: *A post-1982 penny with a mass of 2.500 g is composed of 2.4375 g zinc and 0.0625 g copper. What is its percent composition?*

The percent composition of the penny can be found by dividing the mass of each constituent metal by the total mass of the penny and multiplying by 100%.

$$\dfrac{2.4375 \text{ g zinc}}{2.500 \text{ g total}} \times 100\% = 97.50\% \text{ zinc}$$

$$\dfrac{0.0625 \text{ g copper}}{2.500 \text{ g total}} \times 100\% = 2.50\% \text{ copper}$$

The idea of percent composition helps geologists describe how much metal or mineral is present in a particular ore. They can then evaluate whether the ore should be mined and how it should be processed.

Figure 2.32 *Ores of copper include (left to right) chalcocite, chalcopyrite, and malachite.*

A compound's formula indicates the relative number of atoms of each element present in the substance. For example, one common commercial source of copper metal is the mineral chalcocite, copper(I) sulfide (Cu_2S). Its formula indicates that the mineral contains twice as many copper atoms as sulfur atoms. The formula also reveals how much copper can be extracted from a certain mass of the mineral, which is an important consideration in copper mining and production.

Why are the ideas of molar mass and percent composition useful in determining how much copper can be obtained from copper-containing minerals and ores? Some copper-containing minerals are listed in Table 2.6 and shown in Figure 2.32. The percent of copper in chalcocite can be found, based on what you know about molar masses.

The formula for chalcocite indicates that one mole of Cu_2S contains two moles of Cu, or 127.10 g Cu and one mole of S, or 32.07 g S. The molar mass of Cu_2S is $(2 \times 63.55 \text{ g}) + 32.07 \text{ g} = 159.17 \text{ g}$. Therefore,

$$\% \text{ Cu} = \frac{\text{Mass of Cu}}{\text{Mass of Cu}_2\text{S}} \times 100\%$$

$$\frac{127.10 \text{ g Cu}}{159.17 \text{ g Cu}_2\text{S}} \times 100\% = 79.85\% \text{ Cu}$$

A second calculation indicates that Cu_2S contains 20.15% sulfur. The sum of the percent copper and the percent sulfur equals 100.00%. Why?

Knowing the percent composition of metal in a particular mineral helps us decide whether a particular ore should be mined; however, it is not the sole criterion. What else do we need to consider?

Suppose an ore contains the mineral chalcocite, Cu_2S. Because nearly 80% of this mineral is Cu (see the calculation), it seems likely that this ore is worth mining for copper. However, we must also consider the quantity of mineral actually contained in the ore. All other factors being equal, an ore that contains only 10% chalcocite would be a less desirable copper source than one containing 50% chalcocite. Thus, two factors must be taken into account when deciding on the quality of a particular ore source: (1) the percent mineral in the ore and (2) the percent metal in the mineral.

| Table 2.6 |

SOME COPPER-CONTAINING MINERALS	
Common Name	**Formula**
Chalcocite	Cu_2S
Chalcopyrite	$CuFeS_2$
Malachite	$Cu_2CO_3(OH)_2$

C.9 Composition of Materials

In considering whether an ore is a useful source of a metal, the percent composition of the ore is a key factor. Since separating a metal from its ore can be costly (both energetically and financially), it is desirable to identify ores with the highest percent of metal for mining and processing. Three ores of copper are considered as examples.

Remind students that, in this context, percent composition is usually based on mass. They must first find the molar mass of the compound, then determine what percent of this total mass is made of each constituent. For instance, carbon dioxide has a molar mass of $[12.01 \text{ g/mol} + (2 \times 16.00 \text{ g/mol}) =] 44.01 \text{ g/mol}$. Of this total, 12.01 g/mol are carbon; $12.01/44.01 \times 100\% = 27.29\%$ carbon. Oxygen makes up $32.00/44.01 \times 100\% = 72.71\%$ of the mass of carbon dioxide. Note that the percent values total 100%. Remind students that a total of 100% represents a good check of their calculations; however, rounding the percent values of each component may skew this total slightly from 100%.

Hint: If students have difficulty calculating percent composition, you might also express it as parts per hundred. Remind students to set up percent problems as "part over whole times 100%."

 C.9 Supplement: Percent Composition

 Skill Building Topic 9: A Quantitative Understanding of Formulas

Using the Figures

Figure 2.33: The final paragraphs of C.9 highlight two levels of percent composition in the context of mining—the percent composition of *metal in the ore* and the percent composition of *ore in the rock or soil*. Help students to keep these ideas distinct. Students will be asked to draw similar diagrams in Question 3 of *Developing Skills C.10*.

> ### Developing Skills

C.10 Percent Composition

Students calculate the percent composition of some metal ores. You may wish to model some simple percent composition problems before asking students to complete this activity.

Answers

1. $Cu_3(CO_3)_2(OH)_2$ contains (per formula unit) 3 Cu atoms, 2 C atoms, 8 O atoms, and 2 H atoms.

2. a. The molar mass of chalcopyrite, $CuFeS_2$, is 63.55 g + 55.85 g + (2 × 32.07 g) = 183.54 g.

$$\% \text{ Cu} = \frac{\text{Mass Cu}}{\text{Mass CuFeS}_2} \times 100 =$$

$$\frac{63.55 \text{ g}}{183.54 \text{ g}} \times 100 = 34.62\%$$

b. The molar mass of malachite, $Cu_2CO_3(OH)_2$ = (2 × 63.55 g) + 12.01 g + (5 × 16.00 g) + (2 × 1.008 g) = 221.13 g

$$\% \text{ Cu} = \frac{\text{Mass Cu}}{\text{Mass Cu}_2\text{CO}_3(\text{OH})_2} \times$$

$$100 = \frac{(2 \times 63.55) \text{ g}}{221.13 \text{ g}} \times 100 =$$

57.48%

c. Chalcocite has the highest percent copper and would be the most profitable.

3. Calculate (for simplicity) based on a 100.0-g sample of ore.

Figure 2.33 *The large square represents the total ore sample. (left) Each square within the large square represents 1% of the sample. The ten colored squares indicate an ore that contains 10% chalcocite. (right) 80% of each chalcocite square is colored to show the percent copper in chalcocite. Overall, only 8% of the total ore sample is copper.*

Diagrams may be useful in understanding how these two values relate to the total metal found in a particular ore. Consider an ore containing 10% chalcocite. Look at Figure 2.33. Suppose the larger box in Figure 2.33 represents a piece of this ore. According to this box, 10% of the ore is composed of the mineral chalcocite. (Ten squares are colored to show this.) You know that chalcocite itself is approximately 80% copper by mass. To represent this, 80% of each chalcocite box is colored in Figure 2.33 (one box is enlarged to show the detail). This representation may help estimate visually how much copper is in this particular ore. How might similar diagrams represent an ore that is 50% chalcocite?

> ### Developing Skills

C.10 PERCENT COMPOSITION

Figure 2.34 *Hematite (Fe_2O_3, top) and magnetite (Fe_3O_4, bottom) are two iron-containing ores. If all other factors were equal, which ore would you mine for iron? Why?*

1. The chemical formula for azurite, a copper-containing mineral, is $Cu_3(CO_3)_2(OH)_2$. Complete an atom inventory for this compound. Use the material contained in Developing Skills C.2 (page 155) as a model.

2. Use Table 2.6 (page 167) to answer the following. In your calculations, assume that each mineral is present at the same concentration in an ore. Also assume that copper metal can be extracted from a given mass of any ore at the same cost. (*Note:* The percent copper in chalcocite was calculated on page 167.)

   a. Calculate the percent copper in chalcopyrite.
   b. Calculate the percent copper in malachite.
   c. Which of these minerals—chalcocite, chalcopyrite, or malachite—could be mined most profitably?

3. Suppose you have the choice either to mine ore that is 20% chalcocite (Cu_2S) or ore that is 30% chalcopyrite ($CuFeS_2$). Assuming all other factors are equal, which would you choose? Draw diagrams similar to those in Figure 2.33 to support your answer.

4. Two common iron-containing minerals are hematite (Fe_2O_3) and magnetite (Fe_3O_4). (Refer to Figure 2.34.) If you had the same mass of each mineral, which sample would contain the larger mass of iron? Support your answer with calculations.

For 20% chalcocite: 100.0 g × 20 g/100 g × 0.7984 = 15.97 g Cu
For 30% chalcopyrite: 100.0 g × 30 g/100 g × 0.3462 = 10.39 g Cu
An ore of 20% chalcocite contains more copper per 100 g than an ore of 30% chalcopyrite and would be a better choice. Drawings should show that stu-

dents understand the two-step calculations. For each ore, they should draw a 10 × 10 grid showing the percent mineral in the ore and expand one square from the grid into a second 10 × 10 grid to indicate the percent Cu in the mineral.

C.11 RETRIEVING COPPER

Introduction

While completing Investigating Matter B.3 (pages 139–140), you heated metallic copper, producing a black powder, copper(II) oxide (CuO). Because atoms are always conserved in chemical reactions, the original copper atoms must still exist. In this investigation, you will attempt to recover those atoms of metallic copper.

Before starting, read the procedure to learn what you will need to do, note safety precautions, and plan necessary data collecting and observations. Prepare a table in your lab notebook where you can record the various masses measured in this investigation, and clearly label what those data represent.

Procedure

Part I: Separating Copper(II) Oxide (CuO) from the Sample

Most likely, during Investigating Matter B.3, not all the original copper powder reacted with oxygen gas when you heated the copper in air. Some copper metal probably is still mixed in with the black copper(II) oxide. The first steps now involve separating this mixture into copper and copper(II) oxide. To do this, you will add dilute hydrochloric acid (HCl) to the black powder. Copper metal does not react with hydrochloric acid, so it will remain as a solid. The black copper(II) oxide, however, reacts with hydrochloric acid to produce copper(II) chloride (CuCl$_2$) and water, as shown in the following equation:

$$CuO(s) \ + \ 2\,HCl(aq) \ \longrightarrow \ CuCl_2(aq) \ + \ H_2O(l)$$

Copper(II) oxide   Hydrochloric acid   Copper(II) chloride   Water

1. Obtain your beaker containing the black powder from Investigating Matter B.3. Look closely at its contents. Is the material uniform throughout? If not, why not?

2. Construct a data table appropriate for recording the data you will collect in this investigation.

3. Add 50 mL of 1 M HCl to the beaker containing the copper oxide mixture. Record your observations of the solution. (**Caution:** *1 M hydrochloric acid may damage your skin. If some HCl does spill on your skin, ask another student to notify your teacher immediately. Begin rinsing the affected area with tap water immediately.*)

4. Gently heat the mixture to about 40 °C on a hot plate, and maintain at that temperature for 15 minutes, stirring every few minutes with a glass rod.

5. Remove the beaker from the hot plate. Turn off the hot plate. Allow any unreacted copper metal still remaining to settle to the bottom of the beaker. Then slowly decant the liquid into a second, empty 100-mL beaker.

> **Investigating Matter**

Lab Video:
Retrieving Copper

> Based on what you learned about mixtures on page 28, how would you classify the sample in your beaker?

> The symbol M, as in 1 M HCl, stands for molar concentration. A 1 M solution contains one mole of solute (in this case, HCl) dissolved in one liter of solution.

---

4. Magnetite contains the greater mass of iron for a given mass of mineral.

% Fe in hematite $= \dfrac{\text{Mass Fe}}{\text{Mass Fe}_2\text{O}_3} \times$

$100 = \dfrac{(2 \times 55.85)\text{g}}{[(2 \times 55.85)\text{g} + (3 \times 16.00)\text{g}]} \times$

$100 = \dfrac{111.7 \text{ g}}{159.7 \text{ g}} \times 100 = 69.94\%$

% Fe in magnetite $= \dfrac{\text{Mass Fe}}{\text{Mass Fe}_3\text{O}_4} \times$

$100 = \dfrac{(3 \times 55.85)\text{g}}{[(3 \times 55.85)\text{g} + (4 \times 16.00)\text{g}]} \times$

$100 = \dfrac{167.55 \text{ g}}{231.55 \text{ g}} \times 100 = 72.36\%$

SECTION C

Using the Figures

Figure 2.34: Magnetite contains 72.3% iron by mass; hematite contains 69.9%. Magnetite would be the more profitable.

Developing Skills

C.11 Retrieving Copper

C.11 Retrieving Copper Student Worksheet and Data Table

Students retrieve copper from the copper(II) oxide they produced in *Investigating Matter B.3* (p. 139). Remind students that desired metals are not always available in the form in which they will be most useful; often, they are found in ores and need to undergo processing. In this investigation students process an ore to obtain a metal: They extract copper from copper(II) oxide.

Time

Part I: 45 min (and overnight drying time)

Part II: 45 min (and overnight drying time)

Materials

(For a class of 24 students working in pairs)

CuO powder from *Investigating Matter B.3*

1000 mL 1 M HCl

12 hot plates

12 stirring rods

12 thermometers

24 100-mL beakers

1 L distilled water

24 circles filter paper, Whatman #1, 11-cm diameter

12 balances

12 watch glasses

12 forceps

12-g zinc pieces, mossy or foil

Safety

Students should wear protective goggles and aprons during this investigation. Hydrochloric acid may damage skin. Wash immediately with water if it is spilled on the skin.

Lab Tips

• Help students review the procedure to identify data to record in their data table and think through how entries should be organized.
• Students will probably not be familiar with decanting. Demonstrate proper decanting procedure before students begin. *Remind students not to discard their decanted liquid*, as they will need it for Part II.
• Students should transfer copper to the weighed filter paper using a stirring rod or, if available, a stirring rod with a rubber attachment (sometimes called a rubber policeman). They can use a small amount of water to rinse out remaining copper, if necessary. The zinc and copper chloride system may take considerable time to react.

Post-Lab Discussion

Use this investigation to illustrate the activity series of metals: Only a more reactive metal could release the copper from solution. Additionally, use this investigation to make students more aware of the significant investment of materials, effort, and time to extract a metal from its ore.

Figure 2.35 *Transferring copper metal from a beaker to filter paper.*

To **decant**, let the solid material settle to the bottom of the beaker, and gently pour the liquid into a separate container. Pour carefully so that solid material doesn't transfer over with the liquid.

6. Wash the solid copper remaining in the first beaker several times by swirling it gently with approximately 10 mL of distilled water. Slowly decant the liquid into the second beaker, adding it to the liquid you collected in Step 5. Set aside the collected liquid contained in the second beaker (approximately 60 mL) for Step 9.

7. Measure and record the mass of a piece of filter paper. Transfer the solid copper to the paper, as shown in Figure 2.35, and allow it to dry overnight.

8. After the sample and filter paper have dried, find the mass of the solid copper. This represents the portion of the original copper powder that failed to react to form CuO. Record this mass in your laboratory notebook.

Part II: Converting Copper(II) Chloride (CuCl$_2$) to Copper (Cu)

The final step in this investigation is to convert the dissolved copper(II) chloride (CuCl$_2$) to copper metal. Perhaps you already have an idea how to do this. Recall the metal activity series that you devised during Investigating Matter B.5 (pages 142–143). By adding solid metal samples to solutions that contain other metal ions, you compared the chemical activity of each metal. Review your observations from that earlier investigation. Which of the tested metals are more active than copper? Try to predict the result of placing one of those more active metals in your copper(II) chloride solution. Check your prediction by completing these steps.

Figure 2.36 *Adding zinc metal to a copper(II) chloride solution. How does the resulting chemical reaction relate to your earlier consideration of the activity series?*

9. Obtain a watch glass that can completely cover the top of the beaker containing copper(II) chloride (CuCl$_2$) solution from Step 6. For each gram of copper powder that you started with from Investigating Matter B.3, add about one gram of zinc metal to the CuCl$_2$ solution. See Figure 2.36.

10. Immediately cover the beaker with the watch glass, and allow it to stand for several minutes. Record your observations.

11. After the reaction has subsided, remove the watch glass and gently dislodge the solid copper that has formed on the surfaces of the zinc pieces.

12. Continue to dislodge the copper from the zinc until you are convinced that the zinc has stopped reacting with the solution. (How can you decide?) Then, add 10 mL of 1 M HCl to the beaker and carefully remove any large pieces of solid zinc from the beaker with forceps. Follow your teacher's instructions for discarding the solid zinc. Replace the watch glass on the beaker. Record your observations.

13. After a few minutes, carefully decant as much of the liquid as possible into another empty beaker. Follow your teacher's instructions for discarding the liquid.

14. Wash the solid copper several times with distilled water.

15. Transfer the copper to a preweighed piece of filter paper, and allow the copper to dry overnight.

16. After the sample and filter paper have dried, find the mass of copper metal. This represents the copper that you recovered from the copper(II) chloride solution.

17. Follow your teacher's instructions for disposing of waste materials.

18. Wash your hands thoroughly before leaving the laboratory.

> Note the caution about hydrochloric acid in Step 3.

Questions

1. During Investigating Matter B.3, not all of the original copper powder reacted when you heated it in air.
   a. What observational evidence leads you to think that the reaction was incomplete?
   b. How would you revise the procedure so that more copper(II) oxide could form?

2. During Investigating Matter B.3 (page 139),
   a. what mass of the original powdered copper sample reacted when you heated it? (*Hint:* Refer to the original mass of copper you used during this investigation and the mass of copper residue found in Step 8 to calculate this.)
   b. what percent of the total copper sample reacted?

3. In the reaction between copper(II) chloride ($CuCl_2$) solution and zinc metal, in Investigating Matter B.5 (page 142), each Cu^{2+} ion gained two electrons to form an atom of copper metal. Each zinc metal atom lost two electrons to form a Zn^{2+} ion:
   a. Write a balanced chemical equation that represents this process. (*Hint:* To review how, turn to pages 148–150.)

Answers

1. a. Small copper flecks could still be observed in the black powder (product), indicating that not all the copper metal had reacted.
   b. One could stir the copper more often, or start with more finely divided powder. Students may have other good suggestions, which are acceptable as long as they address the issue of providing more surface area for contact between copper and oxygen.

2. a. Mass of copper reacted = (Original mass of copper used in B.3) − (Mass of copper recovered in Part I). Students should complete the calculation and obtain a value between 0 g and ~1 g.
   b. Percent of copper reacted = (Mass of copper reacted)/(Original mass of copper used in B.3) × 100%. Students should complete the calculation and obtain a value between 0 and 100%.

3. a. $Cu^{2+} + Zn \rightarrow Cu + Zn^{2+}$

Section C   Conserving Matter   **171**

b. i. Zinc

ii. Copper(II) ions

iii. Zinc

iv. Copper(II) ions

4. a. The blue became less intense.

b. Zinc is more reactive than copper. Zinc replaces copper in solution, while copper is removed from solution. Removal of Cu^{2+} ions results in a less-blue solution.

c. When the color of the solution disappears, (essentially) all copper(II) ions have been removed.

5. a. Zinc

b. Zinc entered the solution as Zn^{2+}, replacing copper(II) ions.

C.12 Conservation in the Community

 C.12 Content Reading Guide

Depleting Resources

This material explains renewable and nonrenewable resources as resources that can and cannot be readily replenished. Although atoms are always conserved, atoms and molecules can be transformed into other substances that may be less useful to humans. "Running out" of a resource can mean either that it has been transformed into a less useful substance or that it has become too dispersed for economical use.

Ask students to explain how changes in composition of post-1982 U.S. pennies relate to the idea of depleted resources.

b. Based on the chemical equation you wrote in Question 3a, identify

i. the reactant that was *oxidized*.

ii. the reactant that was *reduced*.

iii. the *reducing* agent.

iv. the *oxidizing* agent.

4. Adding HCl to CuO, in Investigating Matter B.3, resulted in the formation of a blue solution. This color is due to the presence of Cu^{2+}(aq) ions. Consult your observations when answering the following questions:

a. Describe what happened to the solution color after you added zinc (see Steps 9 and 10) in this investigation.

b. What caused the changes you observed in the solution?

c. How can the color of the solution be used to indicate when the zinc metal has removed the Cu^{2+} ions from the solution?

5. To recover Cu metal from the $CuCl_2$ solution, you had to use other resources:

a. What resources were "used up" in this recovery process?

b. Where (to what location) did each resource finally go?

C.12 CONSERVATION IN THE COMMUNITY

Depleting Resources

In some ways, Earth is like a spaceship. The resources "on board" are all that are available to the ship's inhabitants. Some resources—such as fresh water and air, fertile soil, plants, and animals—can eventually be replenished by natural processes. These are called **renewable resources.** As long as natural cycles are not disturbed too much, supplies of renewable resources can be maintained indefinitely. Other materials—such as metals, natural gas, coal, and petroleum—are considered **nonrenewable resources** because they cannot be readily replenished. If atoms are always conserved, why do some people say that a resource may be "running out"? Can a resource actually "run out"?

The answer can be found by first remembering that *atoms* are conserved in chemical processes, but *molecules* might not be. For example, the current production of new petroleum molecules in nature is much, much slower than the current rate at which petroleum molecules are being burned to release thermal energy, as well as carbon dioxide, water, and other molecules. Thus, the total inventory of petroleum on Earth is declining, but the total number of carbon and hydrogen atoms on Earth remains constant.

A resource—particularly a metal—can be depleted in another way. As you have learned, profitable mining depends on finding an ore with at least some minimal metal content. This minimum level depends on the metal and its ore: from as low as 1% for copper or 0.001% for gold to as high as 30% for aluminum.

> Resources such as petroleum are regarded as nonrenewable resources because they can be formed only over millions of years.

Once ores with high metal content are depleted, lower grade ores with less metal content are processed. Meanwhile, atoms of the metal that were previously concentrated in rich deposits in limited parts of the world gradually become spread out (dispersed) over wider areas of Earth. Eventually, the mining and extraction of certain metals may become prohibitively expensive, thus making the metal too costly for general use. At that time, for practical purposes, the supply of that resource can be considered depleted.

Conserving Resources

Can such depletion scenarios be avoided? Can Earth's mineral resources be conserved? One strategy for conservation is to slow the rate at which resources are used. This can be best addressed by considering the four Rs—*rethinking, reusing, replacing,* and *recycling.*

Part of this strategy includes rethinking personal and societal habits and practices involving resource use. Such rethinking can involve decisions such as whether it is better to use paper or plastic bags in grocery stores or, as is practiced in some nations, if it is even better to consider reusing your grocery bags.

Rethinking can take the form of reexamining old assumptions, identifying resource-saving strategies, and perhaps uncovering new solutions to old problems. A fundamental part of rethinking resource conservation and management is to consider the most direct option—source reduction. That simply means decreasing the amount of resources used. If fewer resources are used now, the more remain available for future generations.

Another approach is replacing a resource by finding substitute materials with similar properties, preferably from renewable resources. In addition, some manufactured items can be refurbished or repaired for reuse, rather than sent to a landfill. Common examples include car parts and printer cartridges, both of which can often be reused after rebuilding or refilling. Finally, certain items can be recycled, or gathered for reprocessing. Such recycling allows the resources present in the items to be used again. Figure 2.37 (page 174) illustrates the steps involved in recycling aluminum cans.

However, even recycling can create environmental problems. For example, aluminum scrap, excluding cans, may contain up to 1% magnesium. The magnesium must be removed before the aluminum is processed into other products. One conventional method to remove magnesium requires adding chlorine gas, which requires special handling in the workplace and can contribute to air pollution.

Dealing with Waste

Ultimately, some items will be discarded if they are no longer wanted or needed. Each person in this country throws away an average of about 2 kg (4 lb) of unwanted materials (waste) daily. Some products, such as yesterday's newspaper, become waste after they fulfill their initial

Minimum profitability levels for mining depend not only on the metal's abundance in the ore, but also on the metal's chemical activity. Less active metals (such as gold) are often found in their native, or uncombined, state. In compounds, less active metals are more readily released from their compounds than are more active metals (such as aluminum). Thus, mining richer ores of active metals is usually more profitable.

Green chemistry is an approach that aims to eliminate pollution in industrial settings by preventing it from happening in the first place through enactment of one or more of the four Rs.

In some nations, most glass bottles are cleaned and refilled, not discarded.

Conserving Resources
Conservation often refers to managing resources. This discussion outlines conservation options aimed at reducing resource demand—replacing, reusing, recycling, and rethinking.

Dealing with Waste
This material addresses the final step in a product's life cycle, disposal. Disposal alternatives include recycling, using landfills, and burning wastes to produce energy.

Using the Figures

Figure 2.37: To answer the question in the caption, students may need to create a similar diagram of steps in producing cans starting from aluminum ore. Remind students of their recent investigation (where they generated copper metal from a mixture containing copper(II) oxide). **Figure 2.18** (page 138) may also help students create a diagram of the aluminum ore-to-aluminum can process. Aluminum refining (and its tremendous energy requirements) is explored in greater depth in Unit 5.

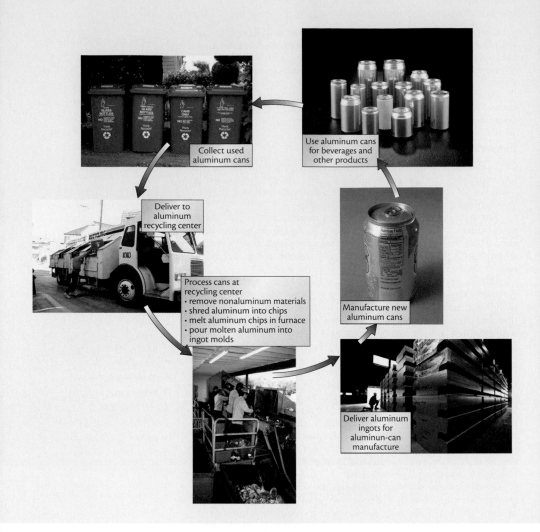

Collect used aluminum cans

Use aluminum cans for beverages and other products

Deliver to aluminum recycling center

Process cans at recycling center
• remove nonaluminum materials
• shred aluminum into chips
• melt aluminum chips in furnace
• pour molten aluminum into ingot molds

Manufacture new aluminum cans

Deliver aluminum ingots for aluminun-can manufacture

Figure 2.37 *Why does recycling aluminum require less energy than producing aluminum from its ore?*

purpose. Others, such as telephones and computers, become waste when they are discarded in favor of newer models. Combined, materials discarded by U.S. citizens and businesses represent about two kilograms (over four pounds) per person per day.

As you can see in Figure 2.38, the largest fraction of municipal solid waste in the U.S. is paper. While recycling reduces this fraction somewhat, the market for recycled paper is limited. Paper that is not recycled leaves a high proportion of combustibles as waste, which has made *waste-to-energy plants* an increasingly attractive option. Approximately 100 waste-to-energy plants currently operate in the United States, burning about 97 000 tons of solid waste per day. Each ton of garbage that serves as "fuel" in these plants produces about a third of the energy released by a similar quantity of coal.

Although waste-to-energy plants produce some fly ash and solid residues, such plants can allow the use of materials that otherwise would be disposed of as part of an unwanted product. In addition, waste-to-energy plants tend to increase recycling, both on-site and in the communities in which they are located.

Recycling, landfills, and combustion for energy production are three options for the final step in the life cycle of a material—a topic you will now consider as you prepare to select a material for your coin design.

Total Waste Generated in the United States before Recycling, 2000

Category	Weight (million tons)	Percent of waste
Paper	86.7	37.4
Yard waste	27.7	12.0
Plastics	24.7	10.7
Metals	18.0	7.8
Wood	12.7	5.5
Food waste	25.9	11.2
Glass	12.7	5.5
Other	23.2	9.9

Total generation: 231.9 million tons

Net Waste Generated in the United States after Recycling, 2000

Category	Weight (million tons)	Percent of net waste
Paper	48.9	29.2
Yard waste	12.0	7.4
Plastics	23.4	14.4
Metals	11.6	7.2
Wood	12.2	7.5
Food waste	25.5	15.0
Glass	9.8	6.1
Other	20.4	12.7

Total waste disposal: 162 million tons

Source: Municipal Solid Waste in the United States: 2000 Facts & Figures, U.S. EPA, Washington, DC.

Figure 2.38 *Composition of the U.S. municipal waste stream before and after recycling.*

Using the Figures

Figure 2.38: These pie charts offer an opportunity for students to interpret graphical information. Some questions that could be used with the charts include the following:

1. Is the percent paper a greater fraction of the total waste before or after recycling? Explain.
2. Which component shows the greatest reduction (as a fraction of the total waste) after recycling?
3. How many million tons of plastics waste were generated? How many million tons were recycled?
4. Which components make up a greater percent of waste after recycling than before recycling?

Making Decisions

C.13 Rethinking, Reusing, Replacing, and Recycling

This activity can stimulate students to explore their personal decisions and think more critically about material use and conservation. You may structure it as a class discussion or as an individual assignment; students may also complete the activity in small groups. Challenge students to come up with multiple options for disposing of the newspaper as well as corresponding benefits and drawbacks to their decisions.

Answers

1. Answers should refer to the principles of conservation introduced in *Section C.12.* Answers will probably include recycling the paper, throwing it away, and using it to wrap packages.
2. Students should suggest benefits and drawbacks based on their answers to Question 1.

C.14 The Life Cycle of a Material

In designing a new product, people must think through the full life cycle of the material, from mining to refining, designing a useful material, then recovering and reusing the material. Final stages may also include discarding it in landfills.

NSTA Press (**www.nsta.org**) publishes a book, *The Life Cycle of Everyday Stuff* by Mike Reeske and Shirley Wa Ireton (Product Number: PB154X, ISBN: 0873551877, Copyright: 2001), that may be useful in conjunction with this discussion.

Some additional resources include **http://www.gdrc.org/uem/lca/lca-for-cities.html** and **http://www.ilea.org/**.

176

Making Decisions

C.13 RETHINKING, REUSING, REPLACING, AND RECYCLING

Deciding between paper, plastic, or your own reusable grocery bags is just one of many decisions you face on a daily basis regarding material use and conservation.

1. Consider when your family is finished reading the daily newspaper (Figure 2.39). What choice would you decide to make for disposing of the newspaper?
2. Why did you decide on that choice?
   a. What are *benefits* of your decision?
   b. What are *drawbacks* of your decision?

Figure 2.39 *What are some options for disposing of a newspaper?*

C.14 THE LIFE CYCLE OF A MATERIAL

In designing a new product for human use, we must consider the full life cycle of the materials involved. A material's *life cycle* has several distinct stages. Raw materials are first obtained and then refined and synthesized into the desired material. That material is then used to make the product designed for a particular use. When the product is no longer useful, the materials may be recovered and reused, or they may become scattered in landfills. Figure 2.40 illustrates this general life cycle.

In every step of the cycle, energy and resources are used. Investigating Matter B.3 (Converting Copper) and Investigating Matter C.11 (Retrieving Copper) are good examples of this fact. Recall that thermal energy (from the hot plate) and chemical resources (hydrochloric acid and zinc metal) first were used to convert the copper metal to other copper-containing substances, and then they were also used to recover

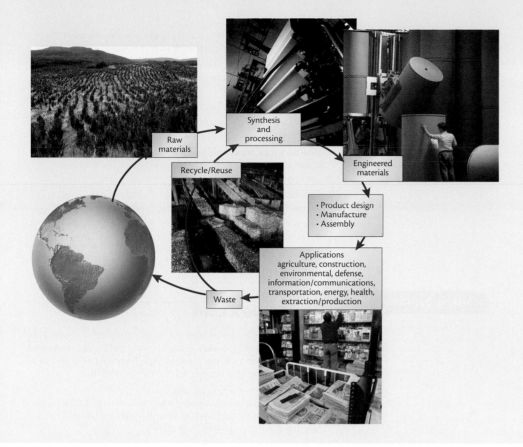

Synthesis and processing

Raw materials

Recycle/Reuse

Engineered materials

• Product design
• Manufacture
• Assembly

Applications
agriculture, construction,
environmental, defense,
information/communications,
transportation, energy, health,
extraction/production

Waste

C.15 Copper Life-Cycle Analysis

This activity lends itself well to small group work. Have student groups discuss the questions and record their answers, then gather for a full-class discussion.

Steps in the life cycle of copper water pipes include:
• Mining copper ore
• Reducing copper ore
• Molding and casting copper to make pipes
• Designing and installing copper pipe systems
• Using copper pipes for water systems
• Recycling pipes that are removed
• Disposing of pipes that cannot be recycled

the copper metal. Because energy and resource use affect economics as well as the environment, each step in the life cycle of a material becomes a factor to consider when we design a new product.

The next activity will allow you to model this process for a familiar material—copper.

Figure 2.40 *A material's life cycle. Paper, for example, has a life cycle with several distinct stages.*

C.15 COPPER LIFE-CYCLE ANALYSIS

Imagine that you are involved in designing copper water pipes. Use Figure 2.18 (page 138) and Figure 2.40 to conduct a life-cycle analysis for the copper metal in your pipes. Based on these figures, make a list of the steps involved in the life cycle of the copper used to make the pipes. Consider how each step will affect your final copper water-pipe design by answering the following questions:

Answers

1. Mining requires energy to remove and transport ore from the mine. Reduction requires energy to supply electrons. Molding and casting require energy to melt copper and operate machinery. Recycling requires energy to melt down the pipes.

2. Reduction and molding/casting

3. Purchase it from a supplier.

4. a. The pipes would need to be disassembled and removed from the sites where they were installed and then transported to a recycling site. The copper would have to be melted and separated from any other substances that had been added.
   b. It could be used for electrical applications, jewelry, cookware, or coins. Students may suggest other uses.

5. a. The energy required to process copper affects the eventual price of pipes. An increase in energy costs will increase the cost of the pipes.
   b. Such a program might decrease the eventual cost of copper pipes by "shortcutting" the process of creating new pipes—no mining or reduction would be necessary.

Making Decisions

C.16 Designing a Coin

Student groups will begin designing their coins. They do not need to complete their research at this point; they will continue their design work in Section D.

1. Which steps in the life cycle of copper consume energy? For each step, explain the particular energy needs.

2. Which life-cycle steps (such as the reduction of a mineral in an ore to produce the metal) require the use of other materials?

3. How will you obtain the copper for your water pipes?

4. People may one day want to replace their copper water pipes with pipes composed of a new material.
   a. What steps would be needed to recycle the copper?
   b. What potential uses can you think of for the recycled copper?

5. Consider your answers to the previous questions.
   a. How does each decision influence the cost of your copper water pipes?
   b. How might an effective national copper recycling program affect the eventual cost of copper water pipes?

Making Decisions

C.16 DESIGNING A COIN

By now, you have a good idea of some properties your new half-dollar coin should possess. Perhaps you have even narrowed the range of materials you are considering. To prepare for the final phase of your coin design, answer the following questions:

1. Look at the list of required and desired physical and chemical properties that you developed on page 127 of Section A. Revise and update your list using what you have learned since completing that activity.

2. Coins are traditionally made of metals.
   a. What alternative materials might you consider?
   b. What are advantages or disadvantages of these alternatives?

3. Construct a table similar to the one on the next page. Enter all needed and desirable properties from your revised list in Question 1. Then list the materials you are considering for your coin. If you have not already done so, begin researching the properties of these materials. Indicate whether each material meets each criterion. For example, you might check the box if it does, and place an "x" in the box if it does not.

	Materials				
	A	B	C	D	E
Necessary properties					
Desirable properties					

SAMPLE
FOR REFERENCE ONLY

4. Consider the design of your coin:

   a. What images are you considering for the obverse (heads) and reverse (tails) sides of the coin?
   b. What anticounterfeiting features will you include in your design?
   c. How large should this coin be?
   d. What should be its mass?

5. Consider the cost of materials in your design:

   a. What would happen if the materials in the coin were worth more than the face value of the coin (fifty cents)?
   b. What materials, if any, have you already ruled out because of this concern?

6. What other costs should you consider as you design your coin?

7. Consider the life cycle of your coin:

   a. How will the coin materials be obtained and processed?
   b. How long do you expect each coin to stay in circulation?
   c. What will happen to the materials when used coins are removed from circulation?
   d. How might the impact on the environment be addressed at each stage of the coin's life cycle?

Section C   Conserving Matter   **179**

Answers

1. Answers will vary, but should include durability, low reactivity, and availability.

2. a. Alternatives include plastics and ceramics.

   b. Advantages include cost and ease of production. Disadvantages include lack of durability or other desirable properties and ease of counterfeiting.

3. Student tables will vary.

4. a. Answers will vary.

   b. Intricate details and hard-to-duplicate images

   c. Answers should be comparable to coins currently in use—18–30 mm in diameter.

   d. Answers should be comparable to coins currently in use—2–11 g.

5. a. The coins may disappear from circulation.

   b. Silver, gold, and platinum (students may add other costly metals)

6. The costs of mining, refining, and forming the material

7. a. Mining new material or recycling

   b. The average lifetime for a coin in circulation is about 30 years.

   c. They should be reprocessed into other coins or useful objects.

   d. Consideration must be given to the coin's composition. It should not contain any material that may damage the environment during its mining, refining, processing, or recycling.

SECTION C SUMMARY

 Section C Supplement

Reviewing the Concepts

1. Matter can be neither created nor destroyed, only changed in form.

2. A generalization about the behavior of nature based on repeated observations

3. Atoms of elements are not used up during chemical reactions—they are rearranged. It is impossible to throw anything "away" because Earth is self-contained; materials do not escape into space.

4. a.

Reactants	Products
1 tin atom	1 tin atom
1 hydrogen atom	2 hydrogen atoms
1 fluorine atom	2 fluorine atoms
Not balanced	

b.

Reactants	Products
1 silicon atom	1 silicon atom
1 carbon atom	1 carbon atom
2 oxygen atoms	1 oxygen atom
Not balanced	

c.

Reactants	Products
1 aluminum atom	1 aluminum atom
6 hydrogen atoms	6 hydrogen atoms
3 oxygen atoms	3 oxygen atoms
3 chlorine atoms	3 chlorine atoms
Balanced	

5. a. 3, b. 2, c. 1

6. a.

$$\underline{1}\ WO_3(s) + \underline{3}\ H_2(g) \rightarrow \underline{1}\ W(s) + \underline{3}\ H_2O(l)$$

b.

$$\underline{2}\ PbS(s) + \underline{3}\ O_2(g) \rightarrow \underline{2}\ PbO(s) + \underline{2}\ SO_2(g)$$

c.

$$\underline{4}\ Fe(s) + \underline{3}\ O_2(g) \rightarrow \underline{2}\ Fe_2O_3(s)$$

7. a. $\underline{1}\ Ca_3(PO_4)_2(s) + \underline{3}\ H_2SO_4(aq) \rightarrow \underline{2}\ H_3PO_4(aq) + \underline{3}\ CaSO_4(aq)$

b. $\underline{2}\ C_8H_{18}(g) + \underline{25}\ O_2(g) \rightarrow \underline{16}\ CO_2(g) + \underline{18}\ H_2O(g)$

8. a.

Reactants	Products
2 sodium atoms	2 sodium atoms
1 sulfur atom	1 sulfur atom
4 oxygen atoms	4 oxygen atoms
2 potassium atoms	2 potassium atoms
1 chlorine atom	1 chlorine atom
Atoms are conserved.	

SECTION C SUMMARY
Reviewing the Concepts

> The atoms that compose matter are neither created nor destroyed in chemical reactions.

1. State the law of conservation of matter.

2. What is a scientific law?

3. Why are expressions such as "using up" and "throwing away" misleading, if the law of conservation of matter is taken into account?

4. Complete atom inventories to decide if each of these chemical expressions is balanced.

   a. the preparation of tin(II) fluoride, a component of some toothpastes (called *stannous fluoride* in some ingredient lists):

   $$Sn(s) + HF(aq) \longrightarrow SnF_2(aq) + H_2(g)$$

   Tin metal   Hydrofluoric acid   Tin(II) fluoride   Hydrogen gas

   b. the synthesis of carborundum for sandpaper:

   $$SiO_2(s) + C(s) \longrightarrow SiC(s) + CO(g)$$

   Silicon dioxide (sand)   Carbon   Silicon carbide (carborundum)   Carbon monoxide

   c. the reaction of an antacid with stomach acid (hydrochloric acid):

   $$Al(OH)_3(s) + 3\ HCl(aq) \longrightarrow AlCl_3(aq) + 3\ H_2O(l)$$

   Aluminum hydroxide   Hydrochloric acid   Aluminum chloride   Water

> Coefficients in a chemical equation indicate the relative number of units of each reactant and product involved. Subscripts in a substance's formula may not be changed to balance an equation.

5. Consider this equation:

   $$N_2(g) + 3\ H_2(g) \longrightarrow 2\ NH_3(g)$$

   a. What is the coefficient for hydrogen gas?
   b. What is the coefficient for NH_3 gas?
   c. What is the coefficient for nitrogen gas?

6. For each of the following processes, draw a representation of the chemical statement, balance the representation, and verify your answer.

   a. preparing tungsten from one of its minerals:

   $$\_\_WO_3 + \_\_H_2 \longrightarrow \_\_W + \_\_H_2O$$

   b. heating lead(II) sulfide in air:

   $$\_\_PbS + \_\_O_2 \longrightarrow \_\_PbO + \_\_SO_2$$

   c. rusting (oxidation) of iron metal:

   $$\_\_Fe + \_\_O_2 \longrightarrow \_\_Fe_2O_3$$

7. Balance each of these chemical expressions.

   a. preparing phosphoric acid (used in making soft drinks, detergents, and other products) from calcium phosphate and sulfuric acid:

   $$\_\_Ca_3(PO_4)_2 + \_\_H_2SO_4 \longrightarrow \_\_H_3PO_4 + \_\_CaSO_4$$

   b. completely burning gasoline:

   $$\_\_C_8H_{18} + \_\_O_2 \longrightarrow \_\_CO_2 + \_\_H_2O$$

8. A student is asked to balance this chemical expression:

   $$Na_2SO_4 + KCl \longrightarrow NaCl + K_2SO_4$$

   The student decides to balance it this way:

   $$Na_2SO_4 + K_2Cl \longrightarrow Na_2Cl + K_2SO_4$$

   a. Complete an atom inventory of the student's answer. Are the atoms conserved?
   b. Did the student create a properly balanced chemical equation? Explain.
   c. If your answer to Question 8b is *no,* write a correctly balanced equation.

One mole of substance contains 6.02×10^{23} particles. The molar mass of a substance can be calculated from the atomic weights of its component elements.

9. If you could spend a billion dollars (1×10^9 dollars) per second, how many years would it take to spend one mole of dollars?

10. Find the molar mass of each of the following substances:
   a. oxygen gas, O_2
   b. ozone, O_3
   c. limestone, $CaCO_3$
   d. a typical antacid, $Mg(OH)_2$
   e. aspirin, $C_9H_8O_4$

11. How can samples of 63.6 g copper metal and 23.0 g sodium metal, with different masses, volumes, and densities, both correctly represent 1.00 mol of substance?

12. A major advantage of the mole concept is that it enables a chemist to "count by weighing." If one mole of potassium metal has a mass of 39.1 g,
   a. how many atoms are in 39.1 g potassium?
   b. how many atoms are in 19.55 g potassium?
   c. how many atoms are in 3.91 g potassium?
   d. how many atoms are in 1.0 g potassium?

The coefficients in a balanced chemical equation indicate the molar relationships among all reactants and products.

13. For the equation

   $3\,PbO(s) + 2\,NH_3(g) \longrightarrow 3\,Pb(s) + N_2(g) + 3\,H_2O(l)$,

   a. how many moles NH_3 are needed to react with 9 mol PbO?
   b. how many moles N_2 are produced by the reaction of 10 mol NH_3?
   c. how many moles Pb are produced from 5 mol PbO?

14. For the equation in Question 13,
   a. how many moles (maximum) N_2 can be produced from 34.0 g NH_3?
   b. what mass Pb can be produced from the complete reaction of 3.0 mol PbO?
   c. what maximum mass N_2 can be produced from 34.0 g NH_3?
   d. what mass PbO, which fully reacts, will produce 415 g Pb?

The percent composition of a substance can be calculated from the relative number of atoms of each element in the substance's formula.

15. In carbon dioxide, two-thirds of the atoms are oxygen atoms; however, the percent oxygen by mass is not 67%. Explain.

16. Find the percent metal (by mass) in each of the following compounds:
   a. Ag_2S
   b. Al_2O_3
   c. $CaCO_3$

17. A 50.0-g sample of ore contains 5.00 g lead(II) sulfate, $PbSO_4$:
   a. What is the percent lead (Pb) in $PbSO_4$?
   b. What is the percent $PbSO_4$ in the ore sample?
   c. What is the percent Pb in the total ore sample?
   d. Use a diagram to represent the proportions of lead and lead(II) sulfate in the ore.

Section Summary   181

---

b. No. The student changed subscripts, inventing formulas for substances that do not exist. In balancing an equation, only *coefficients* are manipulated.
   c. $Na_2SO_4 + 2\,KCl \rightarrow 2\,NaCl + K_2SO_4$
9. 1 mol dollars $\times$
$$\frac{6.02 \times 10^{23} \text{ dollars}}{1 \text{ mol dollars}} \times$$
$$\frac{1s}{1 \times 10^9 \text{ dollars}} \times \frac{1 \text{ min}}{60 \text{ s}} \times$$
$$\frac{1 \text{ h}}{60 \text{ min}} \times \frac{1 \text{ d}}{24 \text{ h}} \times \frac{1 \text{ y}}{365.25 \text{ d}} =$$
$$1.91 \times 10^7 \text{ y} = 19.1 \text{ million y}$$
10. a. 32.00 g/mol   d. 58.33 g/mol
    b. 48.00 g/mol   e. 180.15 g/mol
    c. 100.09 g/mol

11. Both contain Avogadro's number, 6.02×10^{23}, of particles.

12. a. 6.02×10^{23} atoms
    b. 19.55 g K $\times$
    $$\frac{6.02 \times 10^{23} \text{ atoms}}{39.1 \text{ g K}} = 3.01 \times$$
    10^{23} atoms
    c. 6.02×10^{22} atoms
    d. 1.54×10^{22} atoms

13. a. 9 mol PbO $\times 2$ mol NH_3/3 mol PbO = 6 mol NH_3
    b. 10 mol $NH_3 \times 1$ mol N_2/2 mol NH_3 = 5 mol N_2
    c. 5 mol PbO $\times$ 3 mol Pb/3 mol PbO = 5 mol Pb

14. a. 34.0 g $NH_3 \times \dfrac{1 \text{ mol } NH_3}{17.0 \text{ g } NH_3} \times$
    $$\frac{1 \text{ mol } N_2}{2 \text{ mol } NH_3} = 1.00 \text{ mol } N_2$$
    b. 3 mol PbO $\times \dfrac{3 \text{ mol Pb}}{3 \text{ mol PbO}} \times$
    $$\frac{207.2 \text{ g Pb}}{1 \text{ mol Pb}} = 621.6 \text{ g Pb}$$
    c. 1 mol N_2 = 28.0 g N_2
    d. 415 g Pb $\times \dfrac{1 \text{ mol Pb}}{207.2 \text{ g Pb}} \times$
    $$\frac{3 \text{ mol PbO}}{3 \text{ mol Pb}} \times \frac{223.2 \text{ g PbO}}{1 \text{ mol PbO}} =$$
    447.1 g PbO

15. Carbon and oxygen atoms do not have the same mass. The molar mass of carbon dioxide is 44.0 g, of which 32.0 g, or 73% (by mass), is oxygen.

16. a. Molar mass Ag_2S = (2 $\times$ 107.9 g) + 32.06 g = 247.9 g
    % Ag = (2 $\times$ 107.7 g)/(247.9 g) $\times$ 100% = 86.9%
    b. Molar mass Al_2O_3 = (2 $\times$ 26.98 g) + (3 $\times$ 16.00 g) = 101.96 g; % Al = (2 $\times$ 26.98 g)/(101.96 g) $\times$ 100% = 52.9%
    c. Molar mass $CaCO_3$ = 40.08 g + 12.01 g + (3 $\times$ 16.00 g) = 100.09 g
    % Ca = (40.08 g)/(100.09 g) $\times$ 100% = 40.0%

17. a. Molar mass $PbSO_4$ = 207.2 g + 32.06 g + (4 × 16.00 g) = 303.3 g
% Pb = (207.2 g)/(303.26 g) × 100% = 68.3%

b. % $PbSO_4$ = (5.00 g)/(50.0 g) × 100% = 10.0%

c. % Pb = 68.3% × 10.0% = 6.83%

d.

18. a. When a material is reused, it is used again in its original form. In recycling, an item is reprocessed to allow resources in it to be used again in another form.

b. Reusing: Answers will vary. Possibilities include using plastic grocery bags to carry lunch, using the back sides of waste office paper as scratch paper, washing and reusing plastic cutlery, and using plastic food containers as planters. Recycling: reprocessing old fabric and clothing to make fiber for paper, reprocessing rubber tires into material for flooring or construction material, recycling aluminum soda cans, newspapers, and plastics.

19. a. Biomass; plant and animal products like wood, paper, and food; ethanol; water; and soil

b. Metals; natural diamonds and other precious stones; building stones such as marble and granite; and petroleum

20. Reusing: a, c Recycling: b

21. Answers should consider materials needed for light bulbs (glass, metals) and newspapers (paper, ink); how energy is used in processing and using each item; and ultimate disposal options for each.

Resources are either renewable or nonrenewable. Resources can be conserved by recycling, controlling the rate of use, or replacing them with substitute resources.

18. a. What is the difference between *reusing* and *recycling*?

b. Give two examples of each, other than those presented in the textbook.

19. In addition to those found in the textbook, list four examples of

a. renewable resources.

b. nonrenewable resources.

20. Classify each use as either *recycling* or *reusing*:

a. storing water in used juice bottles for an emergency.

b. converting plastic milk containers into fibers used to weave clothing fabric.

c. packing breakable items with shredded newspapers.

21. How would the life cycle of a light bulb compare to that of a newspaper? Consider material sources and disposal and recycling.

Connecting the Concepts

22. How is a scientific law, such as the law of conservation of matter, different from a law created by the government?

23. What additional information would you need to be able to count 1000 nails by weighing them?

24. In Investigating Matter B.3 and C.11, you converted and retrieved copper through a series of chemical reactions:

a. Compare the physical properties of (i) copper metal, (ii) copper(II) oxide, and (iii) copper(II) chloride.

b. Describe a chemical process that produced one of the substances listed in Question 24a.

c. Student results often show less than 100% recovery of the initial copper sample. Does this suggest that the law of conservation of matter is not always true? Explain.

25. The Earth has been compared to a space station.

a. In what ways is this analogy useful?

b. In what ways is it misleading?

26. Chromium minerals are found at three different mine sites in these forms:

a. site 1: chromite, $FeCr_2O_4$

b. site 2: crocoite, $PbCrO_4$

c. site 3: chrome ochre, Cr_2O_3

Based only on percent composition of these minerals, at which site would chromium mining be most feasible?

27. Describe at least two benefits of discarding less waste material and recycling more of it.

28. One method to produce chromium metal includes, as a final step, the reaction of chromium(III) oxide with silicon at high temperature:

$$2\ Cr_2O_3(s) + 3\ Si(s) \longrightarrow 4\ Cr(s) + 3\ SiO_2(s)$$

a. How many moles of each reactant and product are shown in this chemical equation?

b. What mass (in grams) of each reactant and product is indicated by this equation?

c. Show how this equation illustrates the law of conservation of matter.

Connecting the Concepts

22. Scientific laws describe observed relationships among natural phenomena, while laws created by the government regulate behavior and specify penalties for misconduct.

23. The average mass of one nail (or any known number of nails, from which to calculate the average mass of one nail)

24. a. Copper is a shiny, reddish metal that melts at 1083 °C. Copper(II) oxide is a black powder that melts at 1326 °C and is relatively insoluble in water.

Extending the Concepts

29. Why is aluminum metal more easily produced from recycled aluminum cans than from aluminum contained in clay, bauxite, or aluminum oxide ore?

30. Atoms that presently make up your body once may have been part of the body of a Tyrannosaurus rex, or even Alexander the Great or Cleopatra. Explain how this is possible.

31. Investigate the amount and composition of wastes in your community. Construct a pie chart like those shown in Figure 2.38 (page 175).

  a. How does your community compare to the nation?

  b. What steps could be taken to reduce the quantity of discards in your community?

32. In your laboratory experiences, you may encounter some compounds called *hydrates.* Examples of hydrates include
    (i) $Na_2S_2O_3 \cdot 5H_2O$,
    (ii) $CaSO_4 \cdot 2H_2O$,
    (iii) $Na_2CO_3 \cdot 10H_2O$:

  a. Why are these compounds called hydrates?

  b. Calculate the molar mass of each listed hydrate.

  c. Calculate the percent composition of water in each hydrate.

  d. Although hydrates contain significant amounts of water, they are found as solid substances at room temperature. How is this possible?

Section Summary   **183**

Copper(II) chloride is a bluish green solid that melts at 620 °C and dissolves readily in water and alcohol.
b. Copper(II) oxide is produced by heating copper in the presence of oxygen. Copper(II) chloride is produced by

allowing copper(II) oxide to react with hydrochloric acid.
  c. Results are due to loss to the surroundings in some lab procedures. For instance, copper or copper(II) oxide can remain in the crucible after heating,

copper can remain in the beaker when being transferred for drying, copper(II) chloride may remain in solution even after the solution appears to have completed reacting, and recovered copper can adhere to zinc pieces and not be transferred for weighing.

25. a. Earth and its atmosphere essentially represent a closed system. The quantity of resources is limited because matter can be neither lost nor gained. The analogy is useful in understanding that there is a finite supply of resources and that all wastes remain "aboard."
b. Earth continually gains useful radiant energy from the sun, while a space station more closely resembles a closed system. A truly closed system exchanges neither mass nor energy with its surroundings.

26. a. Molar mass $FeCr_2O_4 =$ 55.85 g + (2 × 52.00 g) + (4 × 16.00 g) = 223.85 g
% Cr = (2 × 52.00 g)/(223.85 g) × 100% = 46.46%
b. Molar mass $PbCrO_4 =$ 207.2 g + 52.00 g + (4 × 16.00 g) = 323.2 g
% Cr = (52.00 g)/(323.2 g) × 100% = 16.09%
c. Molar mass $Cr_2O_3 =$ (2 × 52.00 g) + (3 × 16.00 g) = 152.00 g
% Cr = (2 × 52.00 g)/(152.00 g) × 100% = 68.42%
Site 3 has the highest percentage of chromium and would be most feasible.

27. It decreases the waste-storage problem and may lower demand for resources, resulting in a lower price. Other proven benefits include pollution reduction, energy savings, and creation of new jobs.

28. a. Reactants: 2 mol Cr_2O_3 and 3 mol Si
Products: 4 mol Cr and 3 mol O_2
b. Reactants: 2 mol Cr_2O_3 = 2 × [(2 × 52.00 g) + (3 × 16.00 g)] = 304.00 g; 3 mol Si = 3 × 28.09 g = 84.27 g
Products: 4 mol Cr = 4 × 52.00 g = 208.00 g; 3 mol SiO_2 = 3 × [28.09 g + (2 × 16.00 g)] = 180.27 g
c. Total mass of reactants = 304.00 g + 84.27 g = 388.27 g
Total mass of products = 208.00 g + 180.27 g = 388.27 g
The mass of products and reactants are identical, illustrating the law.

Extending the Concepts

29. Energy is used to separate bauxite from unwanted minerals and dirt. A large quantity of electrical energy is needed to break the bonds in Al_2O_3 and reduce Al^{3+} ions to aluminum metal. The cost of electrical energy per mole of aluminum produced is very high.

Recycling aluminum cans requires minimal energy (for melting and recasting) compared to the energy needed to process aluminum from its ores. It is estimated that recycling an aluminum can costs approximately one-twentieth as much as making a new can from ores.

30. Atoms are never destroyed under ordinary chemical conditions. Atoms in living organisms are recycled when the organisms die and decay.

31. Answers will vary.

32. a. Because they incorporate water molecules into their crystal structures
b. $Na_2S_2O_3 \cdot 5 H_2O$ =
(2 × 22.99 g) + (2 × 32.06 g) + (3 × 16.00 g) + (5 × (16.00 g + 2.016 g)) = 248.18 g/mol;
$CaSO_4 \cdot 2 H_2O$ = 40.08 g + 32.06 g + (4 × 16.00 g) + (2 × 18.016 g) = 172.17 g/mol;
$Na_2CO_3 \cdot 10 H_2O$ = (2 × 22.99 g) + 12.01 g + (3 × 16.00 g) + (10 × 18.016 g) = 286.15 g/mol
c. $Na_2S_2O_3 \cdot 5 H_2O$ = (5 × 18.016 g)/(248.18 g) × 100% = 36.296%;
$CaSO_4 \cdot 2 H_2O$ = (2 × 18.016 g)/(172.17 g) × 100% = 20.928%;
$Na_2CO_3 \cdot 10 H_2O$ = (10 × 18.016 g)/(286.15 g) × 100% = 62.910%
d. They retain a stable crystalline structure with the attached water molecules.

Materials: Designing for Desired Properties

Ideal alternatives to chemical resources would be plentiful, inexpensive, and equal to or better than the original material. However, most real alternatives do not fully satisfy these requirements. That is why people consider the pros and cons— or benefits and burdens—of alternatives. This section identifies some materials and treatments and invites students to consider them as alternatives to traditional coin materials and processing techniques.

Activate and encourage the coin-design teams to complete their work during their study of Section D. You may decide to allow class time for teams to work. Students may also need some class time to conduct guided research of their chosen material. Help students identify sources of their raw materials and generate production-cost analyses. As teams work on their coin-design proposals, you may provide an evaluation rubric (a rubric is provided in the TRB and on the TRCD) to create awareness of project expectations. Establish a tentative date for the coin-design presentations required in the Putting It All Together activity.

Materials: Designing for Desired Properties

As Earth's chemical resources continue to be extracted and used, issues of scarcity, cost, and environmental, economic, or political factors sometimes motivate people to consider alternatives. Three related options are to find, modify, or create new materials to serve as substitutes. An ideal substitute satisfies three requirements: It is plentiful, inexpensive, and, of course, its useful properties match or exceed those of the original material. Alternative materials seldom meet all these conditions completely. As a result, we must weigh the benefits and burdens involved in each option. This is true whether the design challenge involves a new coin, a better microwave oven, or a new computer memory device.

D.1 STRUCTURE AND PROPERTIES: ALLOTROPES

Structures and Properties: Allotropes

You have learned in your study of chemistry that elements are the fundamental building blocks of matter. You also know that each element— identified by a name, symbol, and particular numbers of electrons and protons in its atoms—displays characteristic properties. Elements can be classified as metals, nonmetals, and metalloids by such properties. You are aware that some elements, such as magnesium, are reactive and others, such as krypton, are virtually inert. Given all of that, try solving the following puzzle.

ChemQuandary 2

A CASE OF ELUSIVE IDENTITY

Imagine that you receive samples of three solids and are told that each is a pure element.

You examine the first sample. It is a black solid that feels soft and a bit "greasy" to the touch. The sample leaves black marks when you rub it on paper. It is a useful lubricant and a fairly good conductor of electricity. A gram of the material sells for less than a penny.

You then inspect the second sample. It is a colorless, glasslike solid. The sample leaves deep scratch marks when rubbed on the table; in fact, it is among the hardest substances known. It is useful as an abrasive and as a coating for saw blades. The sample is an electrical insulator, which means that it does not conduct electricity. Depending on the quality of the solid sample, it can cost $50 per gram or more than $20 000 per gram.

(continued)

(continued from page 184)

Finally, you consider the third sample. It is a fine, powdery solid made up, it is claimed, of the roundest-shaped molecules known. Although it has been found in prehistoric layers of Earth's crust, the substance was only discovered in 1985. The cost of this substance is dropping; however, in pure form, it currently costs between $170 and $3000 per gram, depending on the chemical supplier and the amount purchased at one time. That price—gram-for-gram—is currently higher than the cost of gold.

These are, indeed, three distinctly different substances. Yet, you are told that all three samples are exactly the *same* element.

How can atoms of one element make up such different materials? What additional information do you need to explain this? Which element is being described?

Before you attempt to answer these questions, it will be helpful for you to know that chemists recognize the three samples just described as allotropes of the same element. **Allotropes** are different forms of an element that each have distinctly different physical or chemical properties.

To be considered allotropes, the forms of the element must be in the same state. Solid iron (Fe) and molten iron have distinctly different properties; however, because they are in different states, they are not allotropes. Oxygen exists as two allotropes, O_2 and O_3. O_2, commonly referred to as *oxygen gas,* is the more common form, making up 20% of the air you breathe. O_3, called *ozone,* is a gaseous substance found in the upper layers of our planet's atmosphere, as well as in some of the air pollution associated with cities.

It is possible that some information in ChemQuandary 2 provided enough clues for you to identify the element involved. If you guessed carbon (C), you are correct. The identities of each of the three carbon allotropes can now be revealed. Look at Figure 2.41 (page 186).

The first sample, a soft, black solid, is the carbon allotrope known as *graphite.* You encounter graphite either directly or indirectly nearly every day. It is a major component of pencil lead. Due in part to its conductive properties, it is also found in many batteries.

The second sample is carbon in the form of *diamond.* Its melting point is among the highest of all elements. Both natural and synthetic diamonds exist. The cost of a diamond depends in part on its quality and optical characteristics. When carefully selected and cut, natural diamonds have high decorative value, even though their chemical formula, C(s), is the same as the formula for the graphite in common pencil lead.

The third sample is one of the many recently identified allotropes of carbon, a group of ball-like structures, and even tube-like structures, known as *fullerenes.* The particular fullerene described here is *buckminsterfullerene,* a 60-carbon hollow sphere (C_{60}), which resembles a soccer ball. Other fullerene molecules have formulas such as C_{70}, C_{240}, and C_{540}. Structures composed of a "rolled-up" layer

Because graphite and diamond are both pure carbon, they can burn in oxygen to produce carbon dioxide gas and thermal energy. Despite that, diamonds (and even graphite) are not recommended as a heat source. The estimated bill would obviously be astronomically high!

SECTION D

D.1 Structure and Properties: Allotropes

This material focuses on the allotropes of carbon. Review the definition of an element and the properties of some elements before allowing students to attempt solving the ChemQuandary. Other common elements that include allotropes are sulfur (S_2 and S_8), oxygen (O_2 and O_3), and phosphorus (P_4 and P_2).

Some additional references include **http://georgiagulfsulfur.com/properties.htm**, **http://education.jlab.org/itselemental/ele015.html**, and **http://en.wikipedia.org/wiki/Allotrope**.

ChemQuandary 2

A Case of Elusive Identity

Emphasize that an element's allotropes are made up of the same atoms but have different structures and properties. (Allotropes must be in the same physical state; different physical states of the same element are not allotropes.)

Using the Figures

Figures 2.41 and 2.42: Encourage students to examine the photographs and molecular structures of the carbon allotropes in Figure 2.41. *Developing Skills D.2* asks students to devise connections between selected macroscopic properties of each allotrope and its molecular structure. After answering the questions in D.2, students may be able to think of other, similar macroscopic-particulate connections. You could also challenge them to brainstorm types of macroscopic properties carbon nanotubes could exhibit, based on the representation in Figure 2.42. A reference for this example is **http://en.wikipedia.org/wiki/ Carbon_nanotubes**.

Figure 2.41 *Allotropic forms of carbon—their appearance and structures. From left to right, graphite, diamond, and buckminsterfullerene. The three-dimensional diamond and graphite structures continue in all directions.*

Carbon nanotubes

Figure 2.42 *Representation of a nanotube—another form of carbon. Nanotubes are very strong. They also have conductive properties that may prove useful in nanoelectronic devices.*

of carbon atoms that form hollow tubes are called *nanotubes*, which are represented in Figure 2.42.

How do chemists account for the different properties of allotropes? The explanation lies in how the atoms of the element are linked and organized—that is, in the structure of the substances. Although the three allotropes of carbon are all composed only of carbon atoms, they have distinctly different atomic arrangements. The three allotrope models in Figure 2.41 illustrate this fact. Figure 2.43 shows another example of one of these allotropes, that of a diamond formed through synthetic rather than natural processes.

Figure 2.43 *Using high temperature and pressure, it is possible to convert graphite to diamonds.*

D.2 LINKING PROPERTIES TO STRUCTURE

Based on the structural models shown in Figure 2.41, answer the following questions about some properties of carbon allotropes. The following example has been answered for you.

Sample Problem: *What feature of diamond's structure may account for its property as a hard, rigid substance, one that can scratch most other materials?*

Notice that every carbon atom in the interior of the diamond model is linked to four other carbon atoms by chemical bonds. These bonds have the effect of holding each carbon atom in place in a rigid, three-dimensional structure. Each carbon–carbon linkage in diamond is a covalent bond involving a shared pair of electrons. Thus, bending or denting a diamond crystal would be extremely difficult because it would involve breaking a network of strong chemical bonds that locks each carbon atom in a fixed position. This accounts for diamond's rigidity and hardness.

1. How might the actual structure of diamond help explain why it is sometimes found in the form of large, single crystals?
2. What feature of graphite's structure might account for its usefulness as a lubricant?
3. Why are fullerenes powdery as solids rather than composed of large-scale chunks?
4. A molecule of buckminsterfullerene (C_{60}) can be regarded as a hollow sphere. Chemists have demonstrated that it is possible to place an atom of another element inside the sphere. Can you think of any practical applications for carrying atoms of another element inside fullerene molecules?

D.3 ENGINEERED MATERIALS

Ceramics

Throughout history—first by chance and more recently guided by science and technology—humans have greatly extended the array of materials available for their use. Chemists and materials scientists have learned to modify the properties of matter by physically blending or chemically combining two or more substances. Sometimes they desire only slight changes in a material's properties. At other times, chemists create new materials with properties different from those of starting substances.

The black "lead" in a pencil is mainly graphite, a natural form of the element carbon. You have just learned that pure carbon can display very different properties depending on how the atoms are bonded together in three-dimensional space. Thus, carbon in the form of graphite has properties different from those of carbon in diamonds or fullerenes.

When first discovered, graphite was mistakenly identified as a form of lead, and the name stuck.

D.2 Linking Properties to Structure

This activity helps students link macroscopic properties to particulate structures. Students should practice articulating the relationship between structure and properties of substances.

Answers

1. The simple and regular structure provides a pattern that can be extended indefinitely as long as conditions permit and carbon atoms are available. This can result in large crystals.
2. Planar sheets of graphite atoms can slip by one another easily.
3. Fullerenes are essentially small spheres of self-contained carbon atoms; the spheres are not inter-linked, so they behave as a powder.
4. Fullerenes could serve as protective cages to transport medicines within the body.

D.3 Engineered Materials

Scientists and engineers constantly work to find new and better materials for common and unique applications. Materials engineering encompasses altering properties of existing materials—by adding other substances or by varying manufacturing methods and conditions—and creating new materials for novel or present applications. The text gives a variety of examples of how engineers may modify and change the properties of materials to meet specific needs and uses.

People often try to substitute new materials for materials that are expensive or made from scarce resources. You can put this into context by asking students to describe changes in the materials used to make sports equipment (vaulting poles, golf clubs), medical equipment (heart valves, replacement joints, artificial skin), and automobiles (ceramic engines, plastic bumpers). Remind students that substitutions have benefits and burdens and discuss pros and cons of some material substitutions.

Ceramics For an overview of ceramics, see **http://www.ceramics. org/acers/aboutceramics.asp?id= outreach**. Engineered ceramics are sometimes referred to as *advanced ceramics*. You may challenge students to identify everyday objects made of ceramics.

Plastics The text briefly discusses uses and structures of plastics, a topic that will be revisited in Unit 3. Emphasize the customizability of plastics and their wide range of properties.

Hard pencil lead (such as No. 4) produces very light lines on paper. Why is that so different from the properties of soft pencil lead (such as No. 1), which makes very broad, easily smudged lines? The properties of pencil lead are controlled by the amount of clay mixed with the graphite. Increasing the quantity of clay produces harder pencil lead, which means that less graphite can be rubbed off onto paper.

Examples abound of other materials designed or modified to meet specific needs. Clay, one of the most plentiful materials on this planet, is composed mainly of the mineral kaolinite ($Al_2O_3 \cdot 2SiO_2 \cdot 2H_2O$), along with magnesium, sodium, and potassium ions. Early humans found that they could mix clay with water and then mold and heat the mixture to create useful products, such as pottery and bricks.

In more recent times, researchers have used newly developed techniques and materials to produce *engineered ceramics*. Figures 2.44a and 2.44b compare the sources, processing, and products of conventional ceramics with newer, stronger engineered ceramics.

Figure 2.44a *Conventional ceramic products, such as bricks and pottery, are made from clay. For example, kaolinite clay (top left) can be formed by hand or machine and fired in a kiln.*

What properties of conventional ceramics made them useful in pottery and bricks? Characteristics such as hardness, rigidity, low chemical reactivity, and resistance to wear were certainly desirable. This durability has made ceramics an attractive option for medical applications, such as ceramic hip replacements. The main attractions of ceramics for future use, however, are their high melting points and their strength at high temperatures. Indeed, such ceramics have become attractive substitutes for steel in some applications. For example, diesel or turbine engines made of ceramics can operate at higher temperatures than can metal engines. Such high-temperature engines run with increased efficiency, thus reducing fuel use.

The major problem for researchers to solve is that ceramics are brittle. They can fracture if exposed to rapid temperature changes, such as during hot engine cool down. To avoid cracks in ceramic engine components (and resulting engine failure), scientists and engineers have developed low-thermal-expansion materials and precise manufacturing methods that carefully control the microstructure of the materials. As these manufacturing practices become more economical, ceramics are likely to be more widely used in high-temperature applications.

Plastics

These synthetic substances are composed of carbon-atom chains and rings with hydrogen and other atoms attached. Plastics generally are less dense than metals and can be designed to be "springy" or resilient in situations where metals might become dented. They have already replaced metals for many uses, such as plastic automobile bumpers and even automobile bodies.

The properties of certain plastics can be customized. For example, polyethylene can be tailored to display relatively soft and pliable properties (as in a squeeze bottle for water) or crafted to be hard and brittle, almost glasslike in its behavior. Unfortunately, most plastics are made from petroleum, a nonrenewable resource already in great demand as a fuel.

Optical fibers developed by chemists, physicists, and engineers are well on their way to replacing conventional copper wires in phone- and

Figure 2.44b *Engineered ceramics, many of which are designed to be higher melting, stronger, or less brittle than conventional ceramics, are used in computer circuit board resistors and in huge jet-engine turbines, both shown here.*

Using the Figures

Figure 2.44: This figure depicts conventional ceramic items as well as slightly less ubiquitous items crafted from engineered ceramics. Engineered ceramics have the advantage of being higher melting, stronger, and less brittle than conventional ceramics. Why haven't conventional ceramics been replaced by engineered ceramics in all applications? The primary reason is that conventional ceramics are much less expensive to produce than engineered ceramics. The properties of such conventional ceramics are adequate for their applications.

Making Decisions

D.4 Alternatives to Metals

Answers

1. Answers will vary. Examples of uses (a) and alternatives (b) are:

    Household wiring, motors, generators, power distribution—aluminum

    Communication equipment, satellite transmissions—fiber optics

    Plumbing—plastic pipes

    Roofing—aluminum, fiberglass, plastics

    Coins—other alloys, ceramics, paper money

    Jewelry—silver, gold, chromium-plated nickel

    Pots and pans—stainless steel, aluminum, ceramics

    Shell casings—zinc

    Food preparation machinery—stainless steel

    Auto radiators—aluminum, plastics, ceramics

2. a. Examples include car bumpers, automobile engines, plumbing materials, sports gear, and aircraft parts.

    b. Answers will follow those to Question 2a. Ceramic replacements can withstand higher temperatures but tend to be brittle. Plastic may be more flexible (or less), but may not last as long in many applications.

3. In wiring, silver would be more electrically conductive than copper. Silver might also replace copper in coins, since it is less reactive.

---

data-transmission lines. See Figure 2.45. Voice or electronic messages are sent through these thin, specially designed glass tubes of very pure silicon dioxide (SiO_2) as pulses of laser light. As many as 50 000 phone conversations or data transmissions can take place simultaneously in one glass fiber the thickness of a human hair. A typical 72-strand optical fiber ribbon can carry over a million messages. The fiber's larger carrying capacity and noise-free characteristics outweigh its higher initial cost.

Chemists, chemical engineers, and materials scientists continue to find new and better alternatives to traditional materials for a variety of applications. Such custom tailoring at the molecular level is possible because of chemical knowledge—knowledge of how the atomic composition of materials affects their observable properties and behavior.

Now it's your turn to consider possible uses of some alternative materials.

Figure 2.45 *Fiber optic material transmits considerably more information using light than copper wires can transmit using electrical signals.*

Making Decisions

D.4 ALTERNATIVES TO METALS

1. a. Select four uses of copper from the list contained in Figure 2.18 (page 138).

    b. For each use, suggest an alternative material that could serve the same purpose. Consider both conventional materials and possible new materials.

2. a. Suggest some common metallic items that might be replaced by ceramic or plastic versions.

    b. i. In what ways would the ceramic or plastic versions be preferable?

    ii. In what ways might the original metallic versions be preferable?

3. Suppose silver became as common and inexpensive as copper. In what uses would silver most likely replace copper? Explain.

D.5 STRIKING IT RICH

Introduction

Seeing is believing—or so it is said. In this investigation, you will change the appearance of some pennies through chemical and heat treatment.

 Lab Video: Striking it Rich

Before starting, read the procedure to learn what you will need to do, note safety precautions, and plan necessary data collecting and observations. You will record observations at several points in the investigation.

Procedure

1. Construct a data table appropriate for recording the data you will collect in this investigation.

2. Obtain three pennies. Use steel wool to clean each penny until it is shiny. Record the appearance of the pennies.

3. Set aside one of the cleaned pennies to serve as a *control;* that is, as an untreated sample that can be compared later to the other two treated coins.

4. Weigh a 2.0-g to 2.2-g sample of granulated zinc (Zn) or zinc foil. Place it in a 250-mL beaker.

5. Use a graduated cylinder to measure 25 mL of 1 M zinc chloride ($ZnCl_2$) solution. Add the solution to the beaker that contains the zinc metal. (***Caution:*** *1 M zinc chloride solution can damage skin. If any accidentally spills on you, ask a classmate to notify your teacher immediately; wash the affected area with tap water immediately.*)

6. Cover the beaker with a watch glass and place it on a hot plate. Gently heat the solution until it just begins to bubble, then lower the temperature just to sustain gentle bubbling. Do not allow the solution to boil vigorously or become heated to dryness. (***Caution:*** *Note the warning in Step 5 about the zinc chloride solution.*)

7. Using forceps or tongs, carefully lower two clean pennies into the solution in the beaker. To avoid causing a splash, do not drop the coins into the solution. Put the watch glass on the beaker and keep the solution boiling gently for two to three minutes. You should notice a change in the appearance of the pennies during this time.

8. Using forceps or tongs, remove the two coins from the beaker. Rinse them under running tap water, then gently dry them with a paper towel. Set one treated coin aside for later comparisons and use the other treated coin in Step 9.

D.5 Striking It Rich

 D.5 Striking It Rich Student Worksheet and Data Table

This investigation should generate student interest in metallic resources and the chemistry involved in their transformation into useful materials. Students produce two types of brass, an alloy of zinc and copper. The final brass color may remind students of "gold," and an intermediate brass type suggests the appearance of a "silver" coating

on the penny. Do not disclose these anticipated results—allow students to make their own observations and enjoy discovering changes in the pennies.

Time

30 min

Materials

(For a class of 24 working in pairs)

24 250-mL beakers

12 25-mL graduated cylinders

12 crucible tongs

12 watch glasses

12 hot plates

36 pennies

36 g granulated zinc (Zn) or zinc foil

350 mL 1 M $ZnCl_2$ (136 g $ZnCl_2$/1 L solution)

2 L distilled water

100 g steel wool

Safety

Students must wear protective goggles and aprons throughout the investigation.

Advance Preparation/Lab Tips

• Success in this investigation depends, in part, on the type and condition of pennies you use. Clean them before use either with steel wool or by soaking them in a solution of vinegar and salt (5 g NaCl per 250 mL vinegar). You can use pre- or post-1982 pennies; post-1982 pennies contain a much higher percent zinc than pre-1982 pennies (97.6% vs. 5%), so they are more likely to warp if overheated (melting point of copper = 1083 °C vs. zinc: 420 °C). Post-1982 pennies give good results, especially if you use a hot plate for temperature control.

• When drying their coins, students should very *gently* rub (or lightly dab) the coin surfaces with a paper towel. Aggressive drying may loosen the brass surface layer.

• Granulated zinc works best in this investigation. You may prepare the zinc/zinc chloride mixtures in advance. You can use the same mixtures for several classes by replenishing the solution as it evaporates and, less frequently, the zinc as it is depleted. This also streamlines the lab for students.

Answers

1. a. Untreated—copper; heated in Zn and $ZnCl_2$ solution—shiny "silver"; heated in Zn and $ZnCl_2$ solution and by hot plate—"gold"
    b. They resemble silver and gold.

2. Compare the physical and chemical properties of the treated coins with known properties of the precious metals such as density (Zn = 7.1, Cu = 9.0, Ag = 10.5, Au = 19.3 g/mL), melting point (Zn = 420 °C, Cu = 1083 °C, Ag = 962 °C, Au = 1064 °C), and chemical reactivity (zinc, copper, and silver all react, for example, with nitric acid, while gold does not).

3. Producing inexpensive substitutes for silver or gold jewelry and changing the heat-conducting properties of cookware

4. a. The surface atoms of Cu dissolved in Zn, producing a solid solution of brass. No Cu was deposited, and no blue color (copper ions) was detected, suggesting that Cu atoms are still in the penny.
    b. Yes; allowing Zn to react with an acid such as HCl would remove Zn and leave the Cu layer untouched. (You may elect to demonstrate this for students.)

Post-Lab Discussion

Focus the discussion on changes in properties that occur in the investigation. Such changes can be useful in the manufacture of new or improved products.

9. Set a hot plate to medium-high heat. Using the tongs, place the second treated penny directly on the hot plate surface and count to five. Use the tongs to flip the coin and count to five again. Repeat until you observe a color change. See Figure 2.46.

Figure 2.46 *Heating the treated penny on a hot plate.*

10. Pick up the coin from the hot plate surface with the tongs, rinse the heated coin under running tap water, and gently dry it with a paper towel. Record your observations.

11. Observe and compare the appearances of the three pennies. Record your observations.

12. When finished, discard the used zinc chloride solution and the used zinc as directed by your teacher.

13. Wash your hands thoroughly before leaving the laboratory.

Questions

1. a. Compare the color of the three coins—untreated (the control), heated in the zinc chloride solution only, and heated in the zinc chloride solution and then on a hot plate.
    b. Do the treated coins appear to be composed of metals other than copper? If so, explain.

2. If someone claimed that a precious metal was produced in this investigation, how would you decide whether the claim was correct?

3. Identify at least two practical uses for metallic changes similar to those you observed in this investigation.

4. a. What happened to the copper atoms originally present in the treated pennies? Provide evidence to support your conclusion.

b. Do you think the treated pennies could be converted back to ordinary coins? If so, what procedures would you use to accomplish this? (**Caution:** *No laboratory work should be performed without your teacher's approval and direct supervision.*)

D.6 COMBINING ATOMS: ALLOYS & SEMICONDUCTORS

The investigation you just completed demonstrated how metallic properties can be modified by creating an **alloy,** a solid combination of atoms of two or more metals. The immersion of a penny in hot zinc chloride solution produced a silvery alloy of zinc and copper called *brass*. When you heated the penny on the hot plate, the zinc and copper atoms mixed more. The overall mixing of zinc and copper atoms to form brass is depicted in Figure 2.47. The resulting solid solution has a different proportion of zinc and copper atoms and is another form of brass. Most brass materials have a golden color, unlike either copper or zinc. Brass is also harder than copper metal. Some other common alloys with familiar names are listed in Table 2.7 (page 194).

It is clear that one way to modify the properties of a particular metal is to form it into an alloy, just as you did when you produced a gold-colored penny. Often the results of alloying metals are unexpected, as you are about to discover.

Combinations of Elements: Alloys

(a)

(b)

(c)

Figure 2.47 *Forming a brass outer layer onto a penny (a–c). Brass samples contain mostly copper and anywhere between 10% to 40% zinc (by mass).*

ChemQuandary 3

FIVE CENTS' WORTH
A U.S. nickel is composed of an alloy of nickel and copper. Based on your familiarity with the appearance of that common five-cent coin, you might be surprised to learn it is composed of more copper than nickel! Specifically, each U.S. five-cent coin contains only 25% nickel and 75% copper.

In terms of its composition, what would be a more accurate name for a nickel?

What does this suggest about the difference between an alloy (in this case, a "solid solution" of copper and nickel atoms) and a simple mixture of powdered copper and powdered nickel?

Emphasize that the goal in making an alloy is to change the physical and/or chemical properties of a metal. Despite such change in properties, the formation of the alloy is not a chemical change; it is a physical change.

Using the Figures

Figure 2.47: This figure provides particulate-level representations of the atom "mixing" students just completed in *Investigating Matter D.5.* Ask students to identify the steps of the investigation that match each of the three representations (a–c). Illustrations a and b could be matched with the second penny generated (in Step 8), while illustration c represents the third penny (completed in Step 10).

ChemQuandary 3

Five Cents' Worth

Prompt students to imagine a powdered mixture of copper and nickel. What color would it be? Students should realize it would probably be a primarily coppery color. (Demonstrate if materials are available.) Solid solutions such as alloys, however, often possess characteristics quite distinct from those of their components or of a mixture. Though counterintuitive, it is not unusual that the five-cent coin does not look as though it contains 75% copper.

D.6 Combining Atoms: Alloys & Semiconductors

 D.6 Content Reading Guide

As a follow-up to the penny investigation, students encounter the concept of an alloy. The properties of an alloy—a solid solution of two or more metals—are different from those of the pure metals and can be difficult to predict. **Table 2.7** (page 194) gives names, compositions, properties, and uses of some common alloys. You may ask students to think of alloys used in everyday applications before discussing the alloys in the table.

Certain alloys (and other specialized materials) display superconductivity. This means that at low temperatures (and, for some, at higher temperatures) the material displays no electrical resistance. The free flow of electricity through a superconductor has led to advances in digital circuitry, electric power transmission, particle accelerators, and magnetic resonance imaging. For an overview and links, see **http://en.wikipedia.org/wiki/Superconductor** or **http://science.howstuffworks.com/question610.htm**.

Students read that most semiconductors are made from metalloids to which impurities are added—a process called *doping*. This allows for the controlled movement of electrons and has contributed to development of computers and other electronic devices. For more information on semiconductors and computer chips, see **http://electronics.howstuffworks.com/diode.htm** or **http://www-306.ibm.com/chips/technology/makechip/**.

COMMON ALLOY COMPOSITIONS AND USES

Alloy and Composition	Examples (composition in mass percent)	Comments
Brass Copper and zinc	Red brass 90% Cu, 10% Zn Yellow brass 67% Cu, 33% Zn Naval brass 60% Cu, 39% Zn, 1% Sn	Properties of brass vary with the proportion of copper and zinc used and with the addition of small amounts of other elements. Brass is used in plumbing and lighting fixtures, rivets, screws, and ships.
Bronze Primarily copper, with tin, zinc, and other elements	Coinage bronze 95% Cu, 4% Sn, 1% Zn Aluminum bronze 90% Cu, 10% Al Hardware bronze 89% Cu, 9% Zn, 2% Pb	Bronze is harder than brass. Its properties depend on the proportions of its components. Bronze is used in bearings, machine parts, telegraph wires, gunmetal, coins, medals, artwork, and bells.
Steel Primarily iron, with carbon and small amounts of other elements	Steel 99% Fe, 1% C Nickel steel 96.5% Fe, 3.5% Ni Stainless steel 90–92% Fe, 0.4% Mn, <0.12% C, Cr (trace)	Properties of steel are often determined by carbon content. High-carbon steel is hard and brittle; low- or medium-carbon steel can be welded and shaped. Steel is used in automobile and airplane parts, kitchen utensils, plumbing fixtures, and architectural decoration.
Other common alloys	Pewter 85% Sn, 6.8% Cu, 6% Bi, 1.7% Sb	Pewter is often used in figurines and other decorative objects.
	Mercury amalgams 50% Hg, 20% Ag, 16% Sn, 12% Cu, 2% Zn	Mercury amalgams have often been used for dental fillings.
	14-carat gold 58% Au, 14–28% Cu, 4–28% Ag	14-carat gold is popular in jewelry.
	White gold 90% Au, 10% Pd	White gold is also principally used in jewelry.

| Table 2.7

In addition to alloys composed of "solid solutions" of two or more metals, such as steel, other useful alloys include some well-defined compounds; that is, they have a constant, definite ratio of metallic atoms. One example is Ni_3Al, a low-density, strong metallic alloy of nickel and aluminum used as a component of jet aircraft engines. A very hard chromium–platinum alloy, Cr_3Pt, forms the basis of some commercial razor blade edges. And a special group of alloys, including the niobium–tin compound Nb_3Sn, displays **superconductivity**—the ability to conduct an electric current without any electrical resistance—if cooled to a sufficiently low temperature.

Thus, one strategy for modifying the properties of metals is to produce alloys, which have properties that differ from those of the component elements. In fact, dramatic changes in the properties of a substance are possible when an extremely small amount of an element—as small as one atom per million atoms—is intermingled within a solid substance.

The metalloid silicon belongs in a class of materials called **semiconductors.** What does this term mean? You should recall that some elements (metals) are good conductors of electricity, whereas other elements (nonmetals) are not. Semiconductors, as the name implies, lie somewhere in between. In addition to silicon (Si), elements and compounds with semiconducting properties include germanium (Ge), gallium arsenide (GaAs), and cadmium sulfide (CdS). Locate the elements identified as semiconductors on the periodic table (page 124).

In the crystal structure of pure silicon, each atom is bonded to four other atoms. As a result, silicon's electrons are incapable of moving through the crystal. In other words, crystals of pure silicon display poor electrical conductivity at normal temperatures.

Although it sounds strange, adding certain impurities to pure silicon dramatically enhances its semiconducting properties. The impurities are atoms of other elements such as phosphorus, arsenic, aluminum, or gallium. This process, called **doping,** creates a situation in the solid silicon that allows charge carriers—either electrons or tiny regions of positive charge—to become mobilized within the crystal. This greatly improves silicon's semiconductor characteristics.

Most semiconductor devices, such as transistors and integrated circuits used in computers and other electronics, are based on solid crystals of silicon that contain intentionally added impurities. See Figure 2.48. Those added atoms are responsible for our present silicon-based technological era.

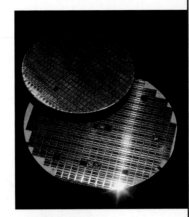

Figure 2.48 *Semiconductor devices like these allow computers to process digital information.*

Silicon Valley in California got its name from the element that is vital to many computer-related companies located there.

D.7 MODIFYING SURFACES

In Section A, you learned that high copper prices in the early 1980s forced the United States to use zinc as the primary metal in pennies. Copper covers the coin's surface. This copper exterior not only preserves the traditional appearance of the coin, it also protects it from corrosion. Using one material to protect the surface of another, less durable material is by no means new or unusual. A layer of protective material can enhance the performance or appearance of a manufactured

D.7 Modifying Surfaces

D.7 Content Reading Guide

The performance of materials can sometimes be improved by coating or electroplating the surface or by applying a thin film. Most processes by which surfaces are modified protect, strengthen, and/or make the surface attractive. Some processes convey special properties such as thermal resistance or electrical conductivity.

This text development is conducive to a "jigsaw" strategy in cooperative learning. Begin by creating expert groups of several students each. Have each group take a different subtopic (coatings, electroplating, or thin films) and become well acquainted with the material. Some instructors craft questions to guide expert groups.

After the expert groups complete their work, disband them. Form new groups that contain representative experts from each expert group. Members of these "jigsawed groups" can then complete a graphic organizer that requires the combined expertise and contributions of all.

Coatings

Coatings include paints, varnishes, lacquers, and other finishes. They are generally not chemically bonded to the surface that they coat and protect. For some interesting facts on paint and coatings, see **http://www.paint.org/con_info/facts.cfm** or **http://www.pcimag.com/**.

Electroplating

Plating, or electroplating, is a method of applying a layer of metal atoms to a metal surface. It usually requires an electrical power source to provide electrons for the redox reaction. Students may be confused by seeing the terms *anode* and *cathode* in relation to this process. The anode is usually a piece of the metal that will be applied as a plating/coating. It is separated from the object to which the plating is to be applied, but both are immersed in (usually) an aqueous solution of a salt of the metal to be plated or (sometimes) a molten salt. As metal ions are reduced at the cathode (the object to be plated), metal atoms at the anode (with the plating material) are oxidized and enter the solution as ions. Plated metals attach to surfaces they coat through metallic bonding. For further information on electroplating, see **http://www.finishing.com/faqs/howworks.html**, **http://electrochem.cwru.edu/ed/encycl/art-e01-electroplat.htm**, or **http://www.deutsches-museum.de/ausstell/dauer/chemie/e_chemi3.htm**.

product, while allowing a less expensive or more available material to be used for most of the item. As you continue reading, you will learn about several types of surface treatments, both new and old, and how they can enhance materials and products.

Coatings

The surface treatment that is probably most familiar to you is a **coating.** Coatings include paints, varnishes, and shellacs that are commonly applied to homes, cars, and many other products. These materials are generally applied late in the manufacturing or construction process and are physically attached to the surface to be protected. Although coatings sink into pores of the base material, no chemical bonding between the coating and the base takes place.

Paint, a typical coating, contains a *pigment* and a *solvent,* and may also contain a resin or other components, depending on intended uses. The paint pigment provides color, the solvent allows application of the paint in liquid form, and the resin provides the desirable protective properties. Although paints have existed for centuries, growing concerns about the solvents released in their application and the heavy metals in their pigments have spurred development of new formulations and methods of application.

Of particular interest is the technique of *powder coating,* which eliminates the need for a solvent. See Figure 2.49. In this method, all coating components are blended and ground to an extremely fine powder. The product to be coated is then cleaned to ensure good adhesion. The powder is mixed with compressed air, pumped into spray guns, and given an electrical charge. The product is electrically grounded, allowing it to be coated by the charged powder. After coating, the product is heated to "cure" the powder into a tough shell. Many products, including bicycle and auto parts, are powder coated to create long-lasting, attractive surfaces.

Figure 2.49 *This motor scooter's metal parts were powder coated to resist corrosion.*

Electroplating

The process used to cover one metal with another involves using direct-current (DC) electricity, which causes redox reactions to occur between the metal and a metal-ion solution. This general process is known as **electroplating.** As you have already learned, cations of most metallic elements can be reduced. This fact is exploited in electroplating. For example, metal bumpers on trucks are often made of steel. In wet or snowy climates, the exposed steel would quickly corrode or rust. Manufacturers protect the steel by coating it with chromium and nickel. See Figure 2.50. Coins, too, have been plated with nickel to resist corrosion.

Figure 2.50 *Chrome plating can protect exposed steel surfaces.*

Writing **half-reaction** equations, which separately represent the reduction and oxidation parts of a redox process, can be helpful in understanding the plating process. The reduction half-reaction for plating nickel metal on steel is written this way:

$$Ni^{2+}(aq) + 2\ e^- \longrightarrow Ni(s)$$

Where do the electrons in this equation come from? Electroplating requires a power source, usually a battery or power supply when the reaction is conducted in the laboratory. The power source transports electrons to the **cathode** (where reduction occurs). The ultimate source of electrons in any electrochemical process is the **anode.** In electroplating, the anode is usually made of the metal to be plated. As metal cations are reduced (removed from the solution) and deposited on the object attached to the cathode, metal atoms at the anode are oxidized and dissolve into the plating solution. Figure 2.51 illustrates this process.

Thus, the other half-reaction for the plating system is an oxidation reaction, the reverse of the half-reaction shown above. Based on what you know about metal reactivities, would you expect this system of reactions to proceed on its own without any external power source? Although systems that can plate metals without applying electric current have been developed, they must include a chemical reducing agent, which is sometimes more expensive than electric current.

Figure 2.51 *Electroplating is the result of an oxidation–reduction process. The new coating is a layer of metal atoms deposited by reducing metal ions from the electroplating solution.*

Using the Figures

Figure 2.51: As students study this figure, you might ask them to predict what macroscopic changes they would expect to observe during electroplating. Elicit or make the observation that over time, a particular metal appears to "magically" move from one location to another. For instance, during electroplating the metal constituting the anode slowly becomes depleted, while new layers of that same metal deposit on the object at the cathode. You could also ask students to discuss particulate-level behavior that underlies these macroscopic changes. This type of discussion leads into *Investigating Matter D.8.*

CHEMISTRY at Work

All That's Gold Doesn't Glitter . . . Or Does It?

Did you ever wonder where the gold metal that makes up a high-school ring comes from? Or who is responsible for locating and recovering the material? John Langhans may have helped. He's a metallurgist with Barrick Goldstrike Mines Inc., a large mining company in Elko, Nevada, that finds and recovers gold.

John's job is not an easy one. The normal concentration of gold in Earth's crust is only about 15 parts per billion (ppb). During the 1800s and early 1900s, miners looked for areas where gold was concentrated in the form of nuggets. More refined mining techniques enabled miners to locate deposits of finely divided gold. Such deposits account for most of today's gold mines.

Gold is often associated with certain types of rocks; quartz is an example. It is relatively easy to recover gold from these rock deposits. In the past decade, however, many of these deposits have been mined out, and the remaining gold is much harder to process.

John supervises laboratory personnel whose job it is to research and develop new methods for recovering gold. . .

When associated with sulfide minerals, gold is known as *refractory ore*. More sophisticated equipment and techniques must be employed to recover this gold. By using knowledge of chemistry and highly efficient recovery methods, John and his coworkers can extract gold from this material.

One method John's company uses is "autoclaving." In this process, the sulfide minerals are cooked under fairly high temperatures and pressures to dissolve the sulfides and expose the gold. The autoclaves work in a manner similar to that of a pressure cooker. You may be familiar with this piece of cookware if it is used to prepare meals in your home. Once the gold is exposed, a dilute basic solution containing cyanide ions (CN^-) is added to the ore to dissolve the gold. A gold cyanide complex $[Au(CN)_2]^-$ forms when gold atoms come in contact with the solution:

$$4\,Au + 8\,CN^- + 2\,H_2O + O_2 \longrightarrow 4\,[Au(CN)_2]^- + 4\,OH^-$$

Later, the gold is recovered through a process called *electrowinning*. Electrowinning uses an electrical current to transfer the gold onto steel wool. Finally, technicians heat the gold-plated steel wool to liquefy the gold, and pour the liquid gold into bar molds.

John supervises laboratory personnel whose job it is to research and develop new methods for recovering gold that are both safe and economical. He and his team also monitor the processing operations of mines to ensure that the environment is not degraded as a result of those operations.

Some Questions to Ponder . . .

Class rings are not 100% pure gold. Because pure gold is very soft, it is mixed with other metals (copper, silver, nickel, or zinc) to increase hardness and durability. The greater the amount of added metal, the lower the karat value. Pure gold is 24 karat. Most gold-containing rings are probably 12 karat, or about 50% gold.

Because of the specialized processes that Barrick Goldstrike uses, the company is able to profitably recover gold from refractory ore, even at grades as low as 5 grams gold per metric ton ore.

1. If a 12-karat-gold class ring has a mass of 11.2 g, how many metric tons of ore were processed in order to produce the gold to make the ring?

2. What is the value of the gold in the class ring if the market value of gold is about $10.50/g? (You may want to use the current actual price of gold, which is available in the business section of many newspapers or on the World Wide Web.)

3. During the 1800s, gold miners looked for gold in the form of nuggets. What property of gold allows it to be found in this form?

Thin Films

Thin films are applied in incredibly thin layers. They are of scientific interest because the first few layers of atoms or molecules behave differently from the bulk substance. Thin films have been used to protect currency.

Highlight interactions between science and society here. Use the variety of concrete examples in the text to discuss how people modify materials for specific needs and uses.

Unlike coatings, platings are usually bonded to the surface of the bulk material. This is desirable because it keeps the metal finish firmly attached to the object. After several layers of atoms have been deposited, the plating has the properties of the plating metal; therefore, it can impart the properties for which it was selected. What about the first few layers of atoms? Metallurgists have known for years that these layers tend to have properties distinct from both the plating and the base materials. This knowledge helped lead to the development of another type of surface modification—thin films.

Thin Films

Films are materials distinguished by the incredibly small thickness of their deposition on a surface. Modern *thin films* may be only one or two atoms or molecules thick! Films made of metal compounds, such as carbides and oxides, were originally developed to harden the edges of cutting tools. They are also used to decorate or protect many metal products. Alternating layers of these materials can enhance certain desired properties of the metal.

Thin metal films find many applications in the optics and electronics industries. For example, tungsten films connect circuits on microelectronic devices. Gold films can be deposited on glass or other surfaces to produce high-quality mirrors. Semiconductors also include thin films in their design.

Scientists are investigating a model provided by nature to develop new thin-film approaches. For example, seashells are gradually formed through the deposition of layers of inorganic and organic substances. Similar approaches are being used to create layers of engineered ceramics on surfaces.

The most common organic thin films are made of polymers, a subject you will explore in more detail in Unit 3. For now, you should know about the existence of polymer films because they are used to protect currency and documents from counterfeiting and could be similarly used to protect coins. Polymers coat many products you use daily. Some common examples are automobile glass and the UV-protective and antiglare films on sunglasses.

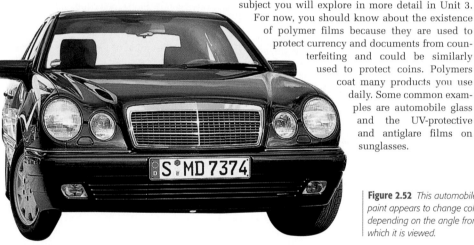

Figure 2.52 *This automobile paint appears to change color depending on the angle from which it is viewed.*

Scientific American Working Knowledge Illustration

Figure 2.53 *Color-changing paint. This diagram shows a cross-section of a transparent mica-based pigment in color-changing paint. Mica (brown layer) is thinly coated on both sides with titanium dioxide (TiO_2, light-blue layers). The pigment is then covered with a clear lacquer coating (top and bottom layers).* **Left:** *White light travels through the lacquer coating. As it encounters each TiO_2-mica interface, blue light waves reflect and reinforce each other (called constructive interference). Viewed at this angle, the paint appears blue.* **Right:** *Changing the angle at which white light contacts the pigment affects the distance that it travels through each layer. This causes a different wavelength of light (shown as green) to reflect and constructively interfere at the two TiO_2-mica interfaces, while other colors of light destructively interfere. At this viewing angle, the paint appears green. The mica and TiO_2 coating thicknesses can be altered to produce different color variations.*

A novel use of polymer thin films is in color-changing paint. Scientists have observed that the colors of butterflies result from the interference patterns of light caused by tiny fibers in their wings. Seeking to duplicate this effect, researchers have used spun polyester, liquid-crystal polymers, and mica-based films to develop car paint that appears to change color depending upon the angle from which it is viewed. Figure 2.52 illustrates this feature, and Figure 2.53 shows how the color-changing paint works.

The development of thin films is a good example of productive interaction of science and technology. As new discoveries are made, new applications result. Demands for better methods and more desirable properties lead to additional basic research and subsequent applications.

Scientific American Working Knowledge Illustration

To help students understand color-changing paints, ask them what they observe when they look at a water puddle with some oil on its surface, at the back side of a CD, or at soap bubbles. These phenomena have one thing in common—thin films of material that cause particular wavelengths of light to be enhanced when viewed at some angles but not others. Give students a minute to look at the figure and then draw attention to the difference in the angles of the incident rays of light. As light reflects off of the surface, the angle at which we view the reflected light determines how extensively we see that light interacting with the surface. The extent of interaction determines the color of light that would be enhanced and—just as importantly—the colors of light that would be cancelled out. (The terms *enhance* and *cancel* tie to *constructive interference* and *destructive interference* in the figure caption.) Scientists use this effect in some analytical techniques that shine selected wavelengths of light through samples for analysis (spectrophotometry).

Websites that show examples of color-changing paint include **http://www.gmhightechperformance. com/features/htp_0401_extreme/**.

Investigating Matter

D.8 Copper Plating

D.8 Copper Plating Student Worksheet and Data Table

This investigation allows students to explore electroplating, which can modify the surface of materials and may also help reduce metal from ores. Emphasize that this process is endothermic, which contributes to the higher cost of producing some metals.

Time

30 min

Materials

(For 24 students working in pairs)

12 U-tubes

12 beakers or other containers to hold U-tubes

100 mL 0.75 M $CuSO_4$ (18.75 g $CuSO_4 \cdot 5 \ H_2O$/100 mL solution) and 0.75 M H_2SO_4 (4.2 mL 18 M H_2SO_4/100 mL solution)

12 iron or zinc nails or other metallic objects to be coated

24 wire leads with alligator clips

12 1.5-V or 9-V batteries or low-voltage power supplies

12 copper metal strips

12 voltmeters or CBLs (optional)

Safety

Students should wear protective goggles and aprons throughout the investigation. Always be careful when working with electricity, especially with high-voltage power supplies.

Caution: Do not allow any student activity (such as plating unauthorized objects) without prior teacher approval.

D.8 COPPER PLATING

Introduction

 Lab Video: Copper Plating

As you just learned, plating a metal requires applying direct current, the presence of metal ions, and a suitable anode, usually made of the metal to be plated. In this investigation, you will plate copper onto a metal object. You will need the following materials:

► beaker, U-tube or transparent plastic (Tygon) tubing
► copper-plating solution (***Caution:*** *Copper-plating solutions are hazardous and corrosive.*)
► object to be electroplated (an iron nail, a nickel or quarter, a steel key, pencil lead)
► copper strips
► a 1.5-V or 9-V battery or other low-voltage power supply (***Caution:*** *Always be careful when working with electricity.*)
► wire leads with alligator clips
► voltmeter or CBL kit (optional)

Before starting, read the procedure to learn what you will need to do, note safety precautions, and plan necessary data collecting and observations.

Procedure

Set up a system to deposit copper onto a metallic object. Keep in mind which metal should act as the *anode* and which metal should act as the *cathode*. Think about how electrons will flow—from which terminal will the electrons come and to which terminal will the electrons go? Test your setup, taking care not to immerse the alligator clips in the plating solution, and record your results. If nothing happens, have your teacher check your setup. When you finish the investigation, be sure to follow your teacher's instructions for disposing of wastes. Wash your hands thoroughly before leaving the laboratory.

Questions

1. What was the anode in this oxidation–reduction process? Explain how you came to this conclusion, based on observational evidence from the investigation.
2. Write an equation for the reaction that occurred at the anode.
3. What was the cathode?
4. Write an equation for the reaction that occurred at the cathode.

Advance Preparation/Lab Tips

• Students can use this procedure to plate keys, steel spoons, coins, and other objects, at your discretion.

• You can purchase U-tubes or bend 25-cm lengths of clear plastic tubing to use as reaction vessels. You can buy the batteries, connectors, and small alligator clips from local electronics supply stores.

• Fresh batteries give the best results. Rechargeable batteries can be economical if you have time to recharge them between uses.

Extension: If balances with sufficient precision are available, students can determine the mass of an object before and after electroplating to find the mass (and calculate moles) of copper plate.

5. Would the metal used as the cathode affect the result of electroplating? Explain.

6. Do you think this method would be useful for large-scale copper plating? Why or why not?

D.9 MORE COIN DESIGN CONSIDERATIONS

In D.6 and D.7 (pages 193–201), you learned about using alloys and surface modification to create various products. Would you consider using either option for your coin design?

Perhaps you have thought about using one of the alloys described in Table 2.7 (page 194). You might be considering using a surface modification technique that has been described.

1. What properties of alloys make them an attractive option in coin design?

2. Why might simply modifying the coin's surface be preferable?

3. List the benefits and the drawbacks of using alloys versus using surface modification. Consider factors such as chemical reactivity, durability, and cost.

Pre-Lab Discussion

Stress the connection between this investigation and previous experiences, the metal-activity table (Table 2.5, page 145), and concepts of oxidation and reduction. Review the terms *anode* and *cathode* and ask students to predict the direction of electron flow from the battery based on the terminal labels.

Answers

1. The anode is the strip of copper metal. The strip decreased in size, and copper formed on the electroplated object. Copper atoms must have been oxidized (resulting in ion formation), so the copper strip must be the anode.

2. $Cu(s) \rightarrow Cu^{2+} + 2\ e^-$

3. The cathode is the object to be plated.

4. $Cu^{2+} + 2\ e^- \rightarrow Cu(s)$

5. Metal of cathode does not matter unless an external source of electricity is not applied or the metal reacts with water.

6. Large-scale copper plating would require longer-lasting sources of electricity and ions.

Post-Lab Discussion

Review oxidation–reduction terminology and address any student problems with the questions. A memory device is *Red Cat* (reduction occurs at the cathode). Remind students of the energy cost of electrolysis. Point out that the more active elements of Groups I and II on the periodic table, as well as aluminum, are commercially produced by electrolysis. Students should be able to explain that reversing the leads reverses the anode and cathode, resulting in deposition on the copper strip rather than the object to be plated.

D.9 More Coin Design Considerations

This activity asks students to consider applying alloy or surface-modification technology to their coin design. You may challenge students to identify benefits and burdens of various technologies before directing them to answer the questions individually or in their design teams.

Answers

1. Beneficial properties of alloys include resistance to corrosion and oxidation, durability, and color.

2. It might be less expensive.

3. Students may list benefits from Answers 1 and 2 and burdens that include cost, lack of durability, and availability.

SECTION D SUMMARY

 Section D Supplement

Reviewing the Concepts

1. Allotropes are forms of the same element that have different physical and chemical properties.

2. Phosphorus, sulfur, oxygen.

3. a. Diamonds are one of the hardest known substances and do not conduct electricity. Graphite is black, slippery, and conducts electricity. Coal, an impure form of carbon, is a nonconductor.
   b. The properties differ due to bonding arrangement. Diamond atoms have rigid tetrahedral bonding, graphite atoms are arranged in sheets, and coal contains a mixture of C–C structures.
   c. Their abundance makes coal and graphite less expensive than diamonds.

4. They have been modified through physical blending or chemically combining substances to alter properties.

5. Advantages: high melting points, strength at high temperatures. Disadvantages: brittleness, sensitivity to temperature change.

6. They may become more flexible (resilient), soft and pliable, or hard and brittle.

7. A solid solution of two or more different metals

8. Stainless steel, brass, bronze, mercury amalgams, 12-karat gold.

9. Carbon

10. Examples are Ni_3Al, a strong, low-density alloy used in aircraft engines, and Cr_3Pt, a very hard alloy used in razor blades.

11. In and near the metalloids section

12. Phosphorus, arsenic, aluminum, gallium.

SECTION D SUMMARY
Reviewing the Concepts

> Allotropes of an element have distinctly different physical or chemical properties. These variations are explained by differences in the arrangement and bonding of the element's atoms.

1. What is an allotrope?

2. Name two elements other than carbon that form allotropes.

3. A diamond, a chunk of coal, and your pencil lead contain the same substance:
   a. How are their properties different?
   b. Why are their properties different?
   c. What accounts for the differences in the cost of these items?

> The properties of matter may be modified by physically blending or chemically combining two or more substances.

4. How do engineered materials differ from natural materials?

5. List two advantages and two disadvantages of using engineered ceramics in high-temperature applications.

6. Describe two examples of properties that can be modified in plastics to make them useful for new applications.

> An alloy possesses properties that differ, sometimes significantly, from the properties of its constituent elements.

7. What is an alloy?

8. Give examples of two alloys you use regularly. (*Hint:* See Table 2.7, page 194.)

9. What nonmetal is a component of both steel and stainless steel? (*Hint:* See Table 2.7, page 194.)

10. Give the formula, use, and an important physical property of an alloy that is also a well-defined compound.

> A poorly conductive material can sometimes be transformed into a semiconductor by adding a small amount of a particular impurity.

11. Describe the periodic table location of elements that behave as semiconductors.

12. List three elements commonly used for doping semiconductors.

13. What is the primary use of the products of semiconductor technology?

---

13. In computers and other electronics

14. Paint, wax, varnish, shellac

15. Protection, color, water resistance, luster

16. Steel bumpers on cars are electroplated with chromium and nickel to prevent rusting. Coins are plated with nickel for corrosion protection. Silver and gold are electroplated on less expensive metals in producing silver plate and "gold" jewelry.

17. Hardening the edges of cutting tools, decoration, circuitry on microelectronic components, mirroring, currency protection, UV filtering, color-changing paint

> The surface properties of a material can be modified through application of coatings, thin films, or electro-plated metals.

14. Give three examples of coatings.

15. What desirable properties do coatings provide?

16. Describe two ways that electroplating is used in industry.

17. List two applications of thin-film technology.

Connecting the Concepts

18. Classify each major method of coating a surface—coating, plating, and thin films—as either a chemical change or a physical change. Explain your answers.

19. In Investigating Matter D.8 (page 202), electricity was used to convert Cu^{2+} ions to $Cu(s)$.

  a. Was this chemical change an oxidation or a reduction?

  b. Rather than obtaining electrons from electricity, you could use another metal to provide electrons. Based on the metal activity series (Table 2.5, page 145), name two metals that could be used for this purpose.

20. Can a rusty car bumper be protected from further rusting by electroplating? Explain.

21. New materials can successfully substitute for metals in some products. Explain why each of the following replacements can be made:

  a. Ceramics replace steel in turbine engines.

  b. Plastics replace steel in automobile bumpers.

  c. Optical fibers replace copper in phone wires.

Extending the Concepts

22. Obtain information about various allotropic forms of the element sulfur.

  a. Draw models depicting the major sulfur allotropes.

  b. Compare the properties of these allotropes.

23. Research and report on new applications of carbon allotropes known as *fullerenes*.

24. Research how *doping* works, and, specifically, how it allows electrons to move more easily within semiconductors.

25. Investigate recent advances and potential applications in the field of superconductivity.

c. Optical fibers can carry more messages with less noise.

Extending the Concepts

22. a.

S_8 Amorphous

Orthorhombic and monoclinic S_8 allotropes appear as shown first. Amorphous sulfur allotropes would appear as clumped sulfur atoms.

b. The amorphous allotrope is not crystalline. Orthorhombic crystals form when sulfur cools below 95.5 °C, and monoclinic, needlelike crystals form when molten sulfur cools below 119 °C. The orthorhombic variety is yellow and slightly soluble in alcohol and ether. The monoclinic allotrope is elongated and transparent with similar properties to the orthorhombic. The amorphous form is transparent, sticky, and elastic. See **http://pubs.acs. org/cen/80th/sulfur.html** or **http:// georgiagulfsulfur.com/properties. htm** for more information.

23. Helpful sites include **http://www.nano-c.com/ fullerene_applications.asp**, and **http://www.chemistry.wustl.edu/ ~edudev/Fullerene/**.

24. Helpful sites include **http:// en.wikipedia.org/wiki/ Semiconductor**, and **http:// science.howstuffworks.com/ diode2.htm**.

25. Helpful sites include **http:// superconductors.org/**, **http:// www.howstuffworks.com/ question610.htm**, **http://en. wikipedia.org/wiki/ Superconductivity**, and **http:// www.eere.energy.gov/EE/power_ superconductivity.html**.

Connecting the Concepts

18. Coating is a physical change; no chemical bonds are formed between the base and coating. Electroplating is a chemical change; metal ions are reduced on the object, and metallic bonds form between the plating material and the base. Thin films can be either physical or chemical, depending on how the film is applied.

19. a. Reduction

b. Lead, iron, chromium, zinc, manganese, aluminum, magnesium.

20. Oxide substances (like rust) do not readily conduct electrons, so a metallic bond between plating material and a rusty bumper is unlikely.

21. a. Ceramics can withstand high temperatures.

b. Plastics resist denting, don't corrode, and are inexpensive.

PUTTING IT ALL TOGETHER: MAKING MONEY

 Putting It All Together: Selecting the Best Coin Rubric

This culminating material continues to develop the relationship between properties of metals and their uses.

Selecting the Best Coin Design

Using concepts developed in this unit, each student group designs a coin and shares the design with the class. Posters are an easy way for teams to present their proposals to the class. Depending on available technology, students can use Power-Point to present their proposals.

Proposals should include a coin model, material specifications, material sources, life-cycle analysis, and cost analysis. Additionally, encourage students to use the terminology and science learned in the unit. Proposals should reflect comprehension of concepts such as physical properties, chemical properties, reactivity, conservation, and percent composition.

A rubric provided in the TRB and on the TRCD may be distributed to students as they complete the project and used to assess group performance. You can use the rubric as provided or modify it to meet your own expectations.

PUTTING IT ALL TOGETHER

MAKING MONEY

SELECTING THE BEST COIN DESIGN

When a new product is created, the design process often includes proposals from several individuals or teams. A panel of experts or consumers then chooses the best proposal. Because each school can submit only one design for the new coin, you will follow a similar process in selecting the best proposal. Each team will present its coin design and findings to the class, which will serve as the selection committee. The following information summarizes the essential features expected of your coin design proposal:

Coin Model

Include a model or a detailed drawing of the proposed coin. If you create a model, it does not have to be made of the specified material, but it should resemble the desired material. Ensure that all models and designs are at least five times the actual coin size. In addition, specify the actual size, thickness, and mass of the proposed coin.

Material Specifications

Describe the material or materials selected for the coin. Present your rationale for choosing those materials. Include an analysis of the necessary and desirable properties of the selected material or materials, as well as strategies that will discourage counterfeiting.

Material Sources

Provide details on the source or sources of the raw materials needed to produce the new coin.

Life-Cycle Analysis

Present an analysis of the life cycle of the proposed coin. How long do you expect the coin to last in general circulation? Will the material or materials that make up the coin be recycled or reused? If so, how?

Cost Analysis

Present an analysis of estimated production costs for the new coin.

Looking Back and Looking Ahead

In this unit, students encountered chemical language (symbols, formulas, and equations), laboratory techniques, and basic chemical concepts that relate to societal problems and decisions associated with resource use. Chemical insight can help citizens identify and rationally address many complex problems.

This unit has extended beyond water in Unit 1 to consider the issues associated with general use of chemical resources. In contrast to water, which is plainly a renewable resource, metallic resources can be used up or scattered so widely that it is economically impractical to retrieve them. In the next unit, students will examine another nonrenewable resource (petroleum) in detail, exploring problems involved in its wide use—now and in the future. Since it is impossible to recycle petroleum after it has burned, students will explore alternatives to petroleum, consistent with approaches developed in this unit.

LOOKING BACK AND LOOKING AHEAD

As you come to the end of this unit, pause and reflect on what you have learned so far. You have learned some working language of chemistry, such as symbols, formulas, and equations; laboratory techniques; and major ideas in chemistry, such as periodicity, the law of conservation of matter, and atomic theory.

This knowledge can help you better understand some societal issues. Central among these concerns are the use and management of Earth's chemical resources, which include water, metals, petroleum, food, and air.

You also have explored other issues that enter into policy decisions about emerging technological challenges. Chemistry often plays a crucial role in helping people recognize and resolve such issues, as you have learned.

However, many problems are far too complex for a simple technological fix. Issues of policy are not usually "either/or situations," but they often involve weighing many considerations. As a voting citizen, you will deal with issues that require some scientific understanding. Tough decisions may be needed. The remaining chemistry units that you study will continue to prepare you for those responsibilities.

Unit 3 deals with petroleum, a nonrenewable chemical resource.

SECTION	CLASS TIME	STUDENT EDITION FEATURES	PROGRAM RESOURCES	MEDIA AND TECHNOLOGY
Section A. **Petroleum: What Is It?** **Objectives:** • Describe the chemical makeup of petroleum and how it is refined. • Describe and give examples of two primary uses for petroleum (energy source and raw material for synthesizing new substances). • Describe the use of distillation as a separation technique. • Describe fractional distillation and its application to petroleum refining. • Describe electron arrangements between covalently bonded atoms. • Represent covalent bonding in selected hydrocarbons with electron-dot, structural, and molecular formulas. • Identify and write formulas for alkanes. • Define *isomer* and draw structural formulas for possible isomers of a particular hydrocarbon. • Predict and explain relative boiling points of hydrocarbons in terms of their intermolecular forces.	**6 Class Periods**	**Developing Skills** A.5 Hydrocarbon Boiling Points A.8 Trends in Alkane Boiling Points A.10 Boiling Points of Alkane Isomers **Investigating Matter** A.2 Separation by Distillation A.7 Modeling Alkanes A.9 Alkanes Revisited **Making Decisions** A.11 Fuels and Climate	**TRB** **Investigating Matter** A.2 Separation by Distillation Student Worksheet and Data Table A.7 Modeling Alkanes Student Worksheet and Data Table A.9 Alkanes Revisited Student Worksheet and Data Table **Content Reading Guides** A.1 through A.3 Content Reading Guide **Supplements and Practice** A.1 Supplement: It's a Petroleum World A.1 Supplement: Who Has the Oil and Who Uses It? A.4 Supplement: Viscosity A.9 Supplement: IUPAC Rules A.9 Supplement: Naming Branched Alkanes Section A Supplement **Black line Masters** Petroleum Distribtion Worldwide Annual U.S. Energy Consumption	**TRCD** **All TRB and Test Bank Materials for Unit 3, Section A** **Videos** Separation by Distillation **Exercises** Modeling Alkanes **Animations** Chemical Bonding Modeling Alkanes Intermolecular Forces and Boiling Point

SECTION	CLASS TIME	STUDENT EDITION FEATURES	PROGRAM RESOURCES	MEDIA AND TECHNOLOGY
Section B. Petroleum: An Energy Source **Objectives:** • Distinguish between *kinetic* and *potential* energy. • Identify and give examples of kinetic energy and potential energy. • Explain *endothermic* and *exothermic* reactions in terms of total energy involved in bond breaking and bond making. • Draw and interpret potential energy diagrams representing endothermic and exothermic reactions. • State, explain, and give examples of the law of conservation of energy. • Describe energy conversion and energy-conversion efficiency using examples. • Explain *heat of combustion* and *specific heat capacity*. • Use specific heat capacity values and experimental data to calculate molar heats of combustion. • Write balanced equations for combustion of specified hydrocarbons, including energy involved. • Define *catalyst*. • Describe a catalyst's role in cracking large hydrocarbon molecules. • Describe *octane rating* and identify methods used to increase a fuel's octane rating.	6 Class Periods	**Developing Skills** B.3 Automobile Energy Conversions B.4 Energy Efficiency B.8 Heats of Combustion **Investigating Matter** B.6 Combustion **Making Decisions** B.10 Fuel for Transportation **ChemQuandary 1** Energy Tracing **ChemQuandary 2** A Burning Problem: Part I **ChemQuandary 3** A Burning Problem: Part II	**TRB** **Investigating Matter** B.6 Combustion Student Worksheet and Data Table **Content Reading Guides** B.1 Content Reading Guide B.9 Content Reading Guide Chemistry At Work Content Reading Guide **Supplements and Practice** B.7 Supplement: Heats of Combustion and Energy Efficiency Section B Supplement	**TRCD** **All TRB and Test Bank Materials for Unit 3, Section B** **Videos** Combustion **Exercises** Energy from Combustion **Animations** Energy and Fossil Fuels

SECTION	CLASS TIME	STUDENT EDITION FEATURES	PROGRAM RESOURCES	MEDIA AND TECHNOLOGY
Section C. **Petroleum: A Building-Material Source** **Objectives:** • Define and distinguish *monomer* and *polymer*. • Explain how molecular structure affects physical properties of a polymer. • Compare saturated and unsaturated hydrocarbons in terms of structure and properties. • Identify the functional groups in alcohols, ethers, carboxylic acids, and esters. • Give examples of how functional groups impart characteristic properties to organic compounds. • Identify and describe two major classes of ring compounds. • Identify and describe the roles of addition and condensation reactions in polymerization.	5 Class Periods	**Investigating Matter** C.4 The Builders C.8 Condensation **Making Decisions** C.9 Builder Molecules in Transportation **Modeling Matter** C.2 Polymer Structure and Properties	**TRB** **Investigating Matter** C.4 The Builders Student Worksheet and Data Table C.8 Condensation Student Worksheet and Data Table **Modeling Matter** C.2 Polymer Structure and Properties Student Worksheet **Content Reading Guides** C.1 and C.7 Content Reading Guide Section C Content Reading Guide **Supplements and Practice** C.6 Supplement: Builders C.6 Supplement: Functional Groups Section C Supplement	**TRCD** All TRB and Test Bank Materials for Unit 3, Section C **Videos** Condensation **Exercises** Polymers–3D Structure and Properties Rubber Formation and Chemical Structure Nylon Formation and Chemical Structure **Animations** Polymers–3D Structure and Properties Rubber Formation and Chemical Structure Nylon Formation and Chemical Structure

SECTION	CLASS TIME	STUDENT EDITION FEATURES	PROGRAM RESOURCES	MEDIA AND TECHNOLOGY
Section D. Energy Alternatives to Petroleum **Objectives:** • Describe major sources of energy used throughout history. • Describe and evaluate potential alternative sources of fuels and builder molecules. • Evaluate biodiesel as an alternative to petroleum-based diesel fuel. • Describe alternative-fuel vehicles in use or in development.	**3 Class Periods**	**Developing Skills** D.2 Fuel Sources over the Years **Investigating Matter** D.4 Biodiesel Fuel **Making Decisions** D.5 Biodiesel as a Petroleum Substitute D.7 Evaluating Alternate-Fuel Options	**TRB** **Investigating Matter** D.4 Biodiesel Fuel Student Worksheet and Data Table **Content Reading Guides** D.3 Content Reading Guide D.6 Content Reading Guide **Supplements and Practice** Section D Supplement	**TRCD** **All TRB and Test Bank Materials for Unit 3, Section D** **Exercises** Fuel Cells **Animations** Fuel Cells
Putting It All Together: Getting Mobile	**2 Class Periods**	**Putting It All Together** • Getting Mobile	**TRB** **Putting It All Together** Putting It All Together: Petroleum as Source of Energy and Building Blocks Rubric	**TRCD** All TRB Materials for Unit 3, Putting It All Together

SUPPLY LIST

Equipment, Expendable Items, and Unusual Materials (per 24 Students Working in Pairs)

Sorted by Item

QUANTITY	ITEM	SECTION USED
50 mL	acetic acid	C.8
6	balances	B.6, D.4
24	beakers, 100-mL	A.2, C.8, D.4
12	beakers, 250-mL	D.4
24	boiling chips	A.2, C.8
12	candles, paraffin	B.6
24	clamps	A.2
12	condensers	A.2
600 mL	distillation solution	A.2
120 mL	distilled water	D.4
48	dropping bottles for organic reactants	C.8
12	empty soft-drink cans with pull tabs, 12-oz	B.6, D.4
12	Florence flasks, 125-mL	A.2
12	graduated cylinders, 100-mL	A.2, B.6, D.4
12	graduated cylinders, 10-mL	C.8, D.4
12	hot plates	A.2, C.8
5 lb	ice	B.6, D.4
1 g	iodine (I_2)	A.2
12	matchbooks	B.6, D.4
12	metal sample cups (empty tea-candle holders)	D.4
225 mL	methyl alcohol	C.8, D.4

Sorted by Item (continued)

QUANTITY	ITEM	SECTION USED
50 mL	octyl alcohol	C.8
50 mL	pentyl alcohol	C.8
12	Beral pipets	D.4
12	pencils	B.6, D.4
25 mL	potassium hydroxide (KOH), 9 M	D.4
1	reagent bottle for dispensing 18 M H_2SO_4	C.8
24	ring stands	A.2, B.6, D.4
12	rings	B.6, D.4
12	rubber stoppers, two holes	A.2
18 m	rubber tubing	A.2
6 g	salicylic acid	C.8
12	space-filling or ball-and-stick model sets	A.7, A.9, C.4
100 g	steel wool	D.4
12	stirring rods, glass	B.6, D.4
12	stopwatches or timers	A.2
50 mL	sulfuric acid, concentrated (18 M H_2SO_4)	C.8
12	test tube holders	C.8
36	test tubes (15 × 125 mm)	C.8
12	thermometers, alcohol, −10 to 110 °C	A.2, B.6, D.4
1.5 L	vegetable oil	D.4
12	wooden splints	A.2

Equipment, Expendable Items, and Unusual Materials (per 24 Students Working in Pairs)

Sorted by Section

QUANTITY	ITEM	SECTION USED
24	beakers, 100-mL	A.2
12	graduated cylinders, 100-mL	A.2
12	Florence flasks, 125-mL	A.2
12	thermometers, alcohol, −10 to 110 °C	A.2
12	hot plates	A.2
24	ring stands	A.2
24	clamps	A.2
12	rubber stoppers, two holes	A.2
12	condensers	A.2
12	wooden splints	A.2
600 mL	distillation solution	A.2
24	boiling chips	A.2
18 m	rubber tubing	A.2
1 g	iodine (I_2)	A.2
12	stopwatches or timers	A.2
12	space-filling or ball-and-stick model sets	A.7

Sorted by Section (continued)

QUANTITY	ITEM	SECTION USED
12	space-filling or ball-and-stick model sets	A.9
12	empty soft-drink cans with pull tabs, 12-oz	B.6
12	graduated cylinders, 100-mL	B.6
12	ring stands	B.6
12	rings	B.6
12	thermometers, alcohol, −10 to 110 °C	B.6
12	stirring rods, glass	B.6
6	balances	B.6
12	candles, paraffin	B.6
5 lb	ice	B.6
12	pencils	B.6
12	matchbooks	B.6
12	space-filling or ball-and-stick model sets	C.4
12	beakers, 100-mL	C.8
12	hot plates	C.8
36	test tubes (15 × 125 mm)	C.8

Sorted by Section (continued)

QUANTITY	ITEM	SECTION USED
12	graduated cylinders, 10-mL	C.8
12	test tube holders	C.8
48	dropping bottles for organic reactants	C.8
1	reagent bottle for dispensing 18 M H_2SO_4	C.8
25 mL	methyl alcohol	C.8
6 g	salicylic acid	C.8
50 mL	pentyl alcohol	C.8
50 mL	acetic acid	C.8
50 mL	octyl alcohol	C.8
24	boiling chips	C.8
50 mL	sulfuric acid, concentrated (18 M H_2SO_4)	C.8
12	graduated cylinders, 100-mL	D.4
12	beakers, 250-mL	D.4
200 mL	methyl alcohol	D.4
25 mL	potassium hydroxide (KOH), 9 M	D.4
12	stirring rods, glass	D.4

Sorted by Section (continued)

QUANTITY	ITEM	SECTION USED
120 mL	distilled water	D.4
12	Beral pipets	D.4
100 g	steel wool	D.4
12	empty soft-drink cans with pull tabs, 12-oz	D.4
12	ring stands	D.4
12	rings	D.4
12	thermometers, alcohol, −10 to 110 °C	D.4
6	balances	D.4
5 lb	ice	D.4
12	beakers, 100-mL	D.4
12	graduated cylinders, 10-mL	D.4
12	matchbooks	D.4
1.5 L	vegetable oil	D.4
12	pencils	D.4
12	metal sample cups (empty tea-candle holders)	D.4

UNIT 3
PETROLEUM: BREAKING AND MAKING BONDS

Introduction to the Unit

This unit explores petroleum use throughout the world and especially in the United States. It also probes some social and technological issues resulting from society's heavy reliance on petroleum products. Students investigate fractional distillation, energy, organic chemistry, and alternative fuels as they develop an advertisement for an alternative-energy powered vehicle.

The chemistry "theme" of Unit 3 is bond breaking and making—the role of energy in chemical reactions. Emphasize from the beginning that much of petroleum's usefulness is related to the energy used and produced in its reactions. You may also focus on two main uses of petroleum—building and burning—to organize the material in this unit (Section B addresses burning, while Section C focuses on building, and Section D deals with alternatives for both but primarily for burning).

UNIT 3
Petroleum: Breaking and Making Bonds

WHAT are important chemical and physical properties of hydrocarbons?

WHY are hydrocarbons commonly used as fuels?

WHY are carbon-based molecules so versatile as chemical building blocks?

WHAT properties are important to consider in finding substitutes for petroleum?

? Interest is growing in alternative-energy-powered transportation. Why? What advantages and disadvantages do petroleum alternatives offer? How can the global supply of petroleum best be used? Turn the page to learn more about this energy-rich resource.

Using the Unit Project

Unit 3 opens with a script for a hybrid-car commercial. Several claims are made about the product, only some of which may be valid. As students learn about molecules that make up petroleum and their uses as both fuels and product building blocks, they will be able to analyze and evaluate the information in this advertisement. At the end of the unit, student teams will design and present their own advertisements featuring an imaginary (but plausible) vehicle that uses a particular type of fuel (biodiesel, CNG, hybrid gasoline-electric, or hydrogen–oxygen fuel cell).

Several activities contribute to students' completion of the final project. In *Making Decisions B.10,* students revisit the television ad to analyze ways that manufacturing and operating the *Hybris* use petroleum for fuel. In *Making Decisions C.9,* students analyze the role of petroleum in making materials that equip the *Hybris.* Section D focuses on alternative energy sources, and students evaluate alternative-fuel options in *Making Decisions D.7* before moving on to the *Putting It All Together* culminating activity. You may decide to ask students to complete the Making Decisions activities in the same groups they will be in for the final project. This will help cultivate productive group dynamics.

Demonstration Idea

Display common products made from petroleum and also samples of crude oil. Use these to discuss the nature of crude oil and products derived from it. Simple examples are food containers, such as milk jugs, plastic wrap, and plastic grocery bags. Consider discussing such sports equipment as roller blades and nylon jerseys as well. Use questions embedded in the student text as discussion openers.

HYBRIS HYBRID VEHICLE TV COMMERCIAL: WORKING SCRIPT

Text/Script	Image/Sound
Clean . . . *Comfortable . . .* *Convenient . . .*	(Video image of driver and three passengers riding in a *Hybris.*) (The words "clean," "comfortable," and "convenient" appear, in turn, as the announcer speaks them. "Clean" appears at the top of the screen; "Comfortable" appears in the middle; "Convenient" appears at the bottom. The "C" moves from the top to the bottom as the words appear.)
Those three words describe *Hybris,* the new breakthrough in personal vehicles. *Clean . . .* Unlike older petroleum-fueled vehicles, the *Hybris* hybrid-powered automobile is virtually emission free. In fact, it is considered an Ultra Low-Emissions Vehicle by the EPA. Why? Because the *Hybris's* gasoline engine is combined with an energetic electric motor to deliver maximum power and efficiency. Excess energy generated by the gasoline engine is stored in rechargeable batteries to later power the electric motor. You can drive knowing that you're helping, not hurting, the environment.	(Show the *Hybris* traveling on a road.) (*"Clean"* appears on the screen and moves from left to right.) (Show the *Hybris* decelerating at a stoplight and then, after sitting at a stoplight, accelerating next to nonhybrid vehicles.)
Comfortable . . . You and three others can easily ride in the *Hybris.* And—thanks to the electric motor that takes over in city driving—the ride can be so quiet that driving the *Hybris* seems more like a walk in the park.	 (*"Comfortable"* appears on the screen and moves from the top left corner to the bottom right corner.)

Text/Script	Image/Sound
Convenient . . .	("*Convenient*" appears on the screen and moves from top center to bottom center.)
Imagine not having to stop as often at gas stations.	(The *Hybris* drives past a gasoline station.)
The *Hybris* uses nearly all the energy in each drop of gasoline. In fact, every time you step on the brake pedal, you store energy that will save you big money.	
With an EPA-rated mileage ranging from 50 to 56 miles per gallon, driving your *Hybris* hybrid-powered automobile is easy on your pocketbook—as little as five cents per mile to operate. Compare that to more than eleven cents per mile for conventional gasoline-burning vehicles.	(*Hybris* shown in a variety of settings—beach, mountains, recreation areas.) (Image of a piggy bank being shaken with coins, mostly pennies, falling onto a table.)
Help conserve petroleum resources! Visit your *Hybris* dealer today.	(View of a *Hybris* at a dealer showroom with several people examining it. The *Hybris* logo then appears below the vehicle.)

Additional Introduction Activities—Personal Petroleum Use

1. Use "It's a Petroleum World" from the TRB or TRCD.
2. Alternatively, ask students to answer the following questions (this may be difficult for students, as they may not be aware of many uses of petroleum):
   a. List 10 personally important items made from petroleum.
   b. Suppose there were a severe petroleum shortage.
      i. Which five products on your list would you be most willing to do without?
      ii. Which five would you be least willing to give up?
   c. List items in the classroom that are *not* made from any petroleum.

   After completing either activity, discuss with students whether they were surprised by all the items that are made from petroleum. Petroleum is so ubiquitous in modern life that its role tends to go unnoticed. Emphasize that petroleum is a non-renewable resource and the world is rapidly using up its limited supply. Have students consider whether petroleum supplies can meet demands throughout their lifetimes.

SECTION A

Petroleum: What Is It?

This section focuses on the composition, separation, and uses of major components of petroleum. The section explores characteristics of some compounds in petroleum through a series of activities that emphasize structure and properties. Bonding in hydrocarbons is used to explain covalent bonding and introduce students to electron shells and electron-dot structures. The text uses molecular models to explore names and structures of alkanes and introduce the idea of structural isomers.

A.1 What Is Petroleum?

In its natural state, crude oil is a complex mixture of hydrocarbons and other substances such as water, sulfides, basic amines, metals, and salts. Petroleum is a mixture that must be refined before it can be used for building or burning. A large fraction of refined petroleum (~84%) is burned as fuel.

Petroleum, like other natural resources, is distributed unequally among regions and countries of the world. Much commercial trade among nations results from this unequal distribution. Because petroleum is such a vital resource in modern society, petroleum reserves and consumption play a major role in world politics.

Petroleum: What Is It?

You live in a world of newly developed products and materials. Whether on billboards, on radio, on television, or in magazines, each advertisement attempts to sell a product by educating its audience about the product's unique features. The product may be faster, lighter, easier to use, newer, or great tasting—to sample a few of many common product claims. The advertisement for the *Hybris* is no exception; it highlights several energy- and fuel-related features of the new vehicle that will (or so it is claimed) "help conserve petroleum resources."

The word *petroleum* is quite familiar to you. But do you know what petroleum *is* or what it is *made of*? See Figure 3.1. Can you explain what properties make petroleum useful for both burning and building? In this section, you will explore characteristics of some key compounds found in petroleum. Specifically, you will focus on their physical properties, their molecular structures, and how atoms bond to form these compounds.

Figure 3.1 *Much time and energy will be expended to refine this mixture of petroleum before it is viable as a fuel or as a source of "builder molecules." What about petroleum makes it such an attractive resource?*

A.1 WHAT IS PETROLEUM?

Petroleum is a vital chemical world resource. Petroleum pumped from underground is called **crude oil.** This liquid varies from colorless to greenish-brown to black, and can be as fluid as water or as resistant to flow as soft tar.

We cannot use crude oil commercially in its natural state. Instead, we transport it by pipeline, ocean tanker, train, or barge to oil refineries, where it is separated into simpler mixtures. See Figure 3.2. Some

> Crude oil was used as lamp oil in ancient times.

Figure 3.2 *The largest oil tanker in the world can carry up to 4.1 million barrels (over 150 billion gallons) of crude oil. Such ships are so big, onboard crew members often need bicycles to travel from one point to another.*

 A.1 Supplement: It's A Petroleum World

mixtures are ready to use, while others require further refinement. Refined petroleum is chiefly a mixture of various **hydrocarbons,** which are molecular compounds that only contain atoms of hydrogen and carbon. You can readily see how this class of compounds got its name.

Burning petroleum provides nearly half of the total annual U.S. energy needs. Most petroleum is used as a fuel. Converted to gasoline, petroleum powers millions of U.S. automobiles, each traveling an average of 14 000 miles annually. Other petroleum-based fuels provide heat to homes and to office buildings, deliver energy to generate electricity, and power diesel engines and jet aircraft.

Petroleum's other major use is as a raw material from which a stunning array of familiar and useful products is manufactured—from CDs, sports equipment, clothing, automobile parts, plastic charge cards, and carpeting to prescription drugs and artificial limbs. Figure 3.3 shows some petroleum-based products.

Based on your experiences with petroleum fuels and products, what percent of petroleum would you estimate is used for burning? What percent of petroleum would you estimate is used for producing other useful substances? Can you identify other uses of petroleum? The answers in the next paragraph may surprise you.

What did you predict for the percent of petroleum used for burning? Did you predict 50%? Was your prediction 60%? Astonishingly, 89% of all petroleum is burned as fuel. Only about 7% is used for producing new substances, such as medications and plastics. The remaining 4% is used as lubricants, road-paving materials, and an assortment of miscellaneous products. In fact, for every gallon of petroleum used to produce useful products, more than five gallons are burned for energy.

What happens to molecules contained in petroleum when they are burned or used in manufacturing? As in all chemical reactions, the atoms become rearranged to form new molecules.

When hydrocarbons burn, they react with oxygen gas to form carbon dioxide (CO_2) gas and water vapor. (See equations below representing the burning of two typical hydrocarbons.) These gases then disperse in the air. The hydrocarbon fuel is used up; it will take millions of years for natural processes to replace it. Thus, petroleum is a *nonrenewable resource,* as were the minerals you studied in Unit 2.

$$CH_4 + 2 O_2 \longrightarrow CO_2 + 2 H_2O + energy$$

$$2 C_2H_6 + 7 O_2 \longrightarrow 4 CO_2 + 6 H_2O + energy$$

> The word *petroleum* comes from the Latin words *petr-* ("rock") and *oleum* ("oil").

Figure 3.3 *It is likely you use petroleum-based products in almost every area of your life. How many can you identify?*

 A.1 Supplement: Who Has the Oil and Who Uses It?

Additional Activities

1. Who Has the Oil and Who Uses It? (See TRB or TRCD)

   Figure 3.4 (page 214) indicates where the world's known supplies of petroleum are, along with regional distribution of the world's population. **Figure 3.4** also shows the regional distribution of world petroleum consumption. Use the figure to answer the associated questions.

2. Invite students to discuss how the following might affect long-term regional petroleum availability, use, and trade relationships:
   • Industrialization/modernization of second- and third-world nations
   • Political unrest in the Middle East
   • Population growth in China and India
   • Depletion of Alaskan oil reserves (or consequences of drilling in the Arctic National Wildlife Refuge)

A.2 Separation by Distillation

 A.2 Separation by Distillation
Student Worksheet and Data
Table

Pre-Lab Discussion

This investigation models techniques used in petroleum refineries to separate the many components of crude oil. Remind students that this is a "simple" distillation in which only two components are separated.

The distillation mixture is flammable.

Discuss the role of the iodine, used only to distinguish the products. Only one or two crystals are used in each distillate.

Students need to create a data table appropriate for recording time and temperature data. Remind them to include proper units for both time and temperature. You may choose to review data tables before the investigation to ensure proper data collection. At least one member of each group will need a timepiece (watch, stopwatch) if a classroom clock is not available.

Review graphing expectations and procedures. (You may invite students to make their graphs with a computer.)

Time

50 min

Materials

(For 12 student pairs)

Many of these items may vary, depending on your distillation equipment.

24 100-mL beakers

12 100-mL graduated cylinders

12 125-mL Florence (or round-bottom) flasks

12 thermometers, alcohol, (−10 to 110 °C)

12 hot plates (do not substitute a burner)

12 stopwatches or timers

24 ring stands

24 clamps

12 rubber stoppers with 2 holes to fit tops of the flasks

12 condensers with appropriate connection to the distillation flask (exact tubing and stopper configuration for connection to flask depends on style of condenser available)

12 wooden splints for adding iodine to distillates

600 mL distillation solution prepared by mixing 420 mL water and 180 mL 2-propanol (isopropyl alcohol)

Boiling chips

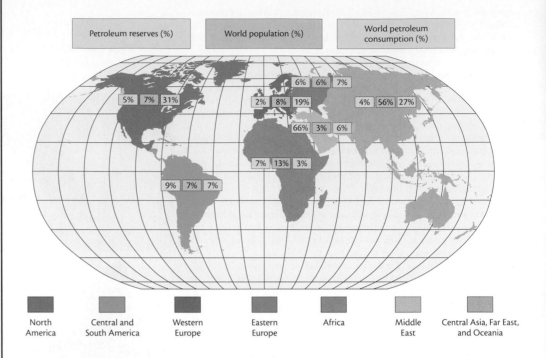

| | Petroleum reserves (%) | World population (%) | World petroleum consumption (%) |

6% 6% 7%
5% 7% 31%   2% 8% 19%   4% 56% 27%
66% 3% 6%
7% 13% 3%
9% 7% 7%

North America | Central and South America | Western Europe | Eastern Europe | Africa | Middle East | Central Asia, Far East, and Oceania

	Petroleum Reserves		Population		Petroleum Consumption	
	10^9 Barrels	Percent	Millions	Percent	10^3 Barrels per day	Percent
North America	54	5.3	421	6.7	23 843	30.5
Central and South America	96	9.3	434	6.9	5238	6.7
Western Europe	17	1.7	485	7.8	14 698	18.8
Eastern Europe	58	5.7	386	6.2	5257	6.7
Africa	77	7.4	831	13.3	2675	3.4
Middle East	686	66.4	178	2.9	5043	6.5
Central Asia, Far East, and Oceania	44	4.2	3508	56.2	21 452	27.4
Totals	1032	100.0	6243	100.0	78 206	100.0

Figure 3.4 *Distribution of world's petroleum reserves, population, and consumption of petroleum.*

Like other resources, petroleum is not uniformly distributed around the world. The worldwide distributions are summarized in Figure 3.4. The North American petroleum reserves are only about 5% of the world's known supply. Central Asia, the Far East, and Oceania account for 56% of the world's population, but this region has only about 4% of the world's petroleum reserves. In contrast, approximately 66% of the world's known crude oil reserves are located in Middle Eastern nations (see Figure 3.5).

You have just learned what petroleum is, how we use it, and where we find it. Petroleum is a complex mixture of hydrocarbons that must be refined or separated into simpler mixtures to become useful. In the following investigation, you will learn about this basic separation process as you study a simple mixture of two liquids.

Figure 3.5 *Two employees of the Kuwait Oil Company work on a crude oil flowline at Maqwa Oil Field, 50 kilometers south of Kuwait City.*

Recall that you used several separation techniques to clean up the foul-water mixture in Unit 1.

A.2 SEPARATION BY DISTILLATION

Investigating Matter

Introduction

You know that you can often separate substances by taking advantage of their different physical properties. One physical property commonly used to separate liquids is their density. However, density differences will work only if substances are insoluble in each other, which is not the case with petroleum; its components are soluble in each other. Another physical property chemists often use is *boiling point.* The separation of liquid substances according to their differing boiling points is called **distillation.**

As you heat a liquid mixture containing two components, the component with the lower boiling point will vaporize first and leave the distillation flask. That component will then condense back to a liquid as it passes through a condenser—all before the second component begins to boil. See Figure 3.6. Each condensed liquid component, called the **distillate,** can thus be collected separately.

Lab Video: Separation by Distillation

Thermometer
Glass tubing
Water out
Rubber stopper
Condenser
125-mL Florence flask
Cork stopper
Mixture to be distilled
Distillate
Hot plate
Beaker
Water in

| **Figure 3.6** *A simple distillation apparatus.*

Use non-mercury thermometers. Demonstrate how to insert the thermometer and glass tube into the stopper, using glycerin or other lubricant and hand protection. Be sure to grasp the thermometer close to the stopper. You may pre-assemble the pieces to minimize risk of accident.

Advance Preparation

Use only a mixture of water and 2-propanol in the distillation mixture (see Materials). This system poses the least hazard and provides good results. Do not reveal the composition of the mixture to students.

If you do not have adequate equipment for all students to complete the distillation, consider doing this investigation as a teacher demonstration, so that students can see distillation being performed before they discuss fractional distillation. Even if it is done as a demonstration, students can collect and analyze data. Consider having a student volunteer record time and temperature data on the chalkboard during the distillation. On completion of the separation, the entire class can create a single graph of the data. Alternatively, have students use the class data to complete the analysis individually. Question 3 can be omitted if you do a demonstration.

Construct and display a distillation setup (see **Figure 3.6**).

Approximately 18 m rubber tubing to connect condensers to the water source and sink/drain
1 g iodine crystals

Safety

Students should wear protective goggles and aprons.

The unknown liquid is flammable. No flames should be allowed in the laboratory.

Point out the hazards of heating unknown liquids that might be flammable.

Never heat the flask to dryness, because of the risk of explosion.

Remind students that iodine must be treated with special care. Skin contact with iodine crystals can cause lesions, and iodine vapor is intensely irritating to skin and lung tissue.

Lab Tips

• Table 3.1 lists four possible substances for students to consider as components of their original mixture. Use only a distillation solution that contains the 2-propanol–water mixture. Do not reveal the composition of the mixture. Let students use their observations to identify the mixture's components.

• Check all connections and hose routing in each distillation apparatus before allowing students to begin work. Remind them to keep water pressure low to prevent the rubber tubing from separating from the condenser. Students should connect the incoming water to the *lower* connection of the condenser and outgoing water to the *upper* connection to completely fill the condenser and avoid putting too much pressure on the lower hose.

• To monitor the use of iodine, provide a central location, such as the fume hood, where students add iodine crystals directly into the two distillate samples.

Expected Results

The time will vary, but the boiling liquid should pass through or reach two temperature plateaus. The first plateau, representing the boiling point of 2-propanol, will be about 82 °C; the second will be at about 100 °C, the boiling point of water. At higher altitudes, boiling-point plateaus will be at lower temperatures. Iodine is more soluble in the first distillate (2-propanol) than in the second (water). Use this opportunity to remind students of the "like dissolves like" rule introduced in Unit 1.

| Table 3.1

POSSIBLE COMPONENTS OF DISTILLATION MIXTURE			
Substance	**Formula**	**Boiling Point (°C)**	**Appearance with I_2**
2-Propanol (rubbing alcohol)	C_3H_8O	82.4	Bright yellow
Acetone	C_3H_6O	56.5	Yellow to brown
Water	H_2O	100.0	Colorless to light yellow
Cyclohexane	C_6H_{12}	80.7	Magenta

The boiling points listed in Table 3.1 are based on normal sea-level atmospheric pressure.

In this investigation, you will use distillation to separate a mixture of two liquids. Then you will identify the two substances in the mixture by comparing the observed distillation temperatures with the boiling points of several possible compounds listed in Table 3.1.

The following procedure provides guidance about when you should collect and record data (consider Step 8). Create a data table with columns to record time and temperature data. Remember to include proper units for each data column. Before you begin, carefully read the procedure to learn what is involved, note safety precautions, and plan for your data collecting and observations.

Procedure

Figure 3.7 *This distillation apparatus is used to separate a mixture of two liquids. The component with the lowest boiling point vaporizes first, converts back to a liquid in the condenser, and collects (here) in a beaker.*

(**Caution:** *This distillation should only be completed with a hot plate or other electric heating source. The presence of open flames near the distillation apparatus represents a fire hazard.*)

1. Construct data tables to record your observations and measurements.

2. Assemble an apparatus similar to that shown in Figure 3.6. Label two beakers *Distillate 1* and *Distillate 2*.

3. Using a clean, dry, graduated cylinder, measure a 50-mL sample of the distillation mixture. Pour the mixture into the distillation flask and add a boiling chip.

4. Record your observations of the starting mixture.

5. Connect the flask to a condenser, shown in Figure 3.6 (page 215). Ensure that the hoses are attached to the condenser and to the water supply as shown. Position the Distillate 1 beaker at the outlet of the condenser so that it will catch the distillate, as shown in Figure 3.7.

6. Ensure that all connections are tight and will not leak.

7. Turn on the water to the condenser, and then turn on the hot plate to start gently heating the flask. (**Caution:** *The substances, other than water, are volatile and highly flammable. Be sure that no flames or sparks are in the area.*)

8. Record the temperature every minute until the first drop of distillate falls into the beaker. Then continue to record the

temperature every 30 seconds. Continue to heat the flask and collect the distillate until the temperature begins to rise again. At this point, replace the Distillate 1 beaker with the Distillate 2 beaker.

9. Continue heating and recording the temperature every 30 seconds until the second substance just begins to distill. Record the temperature at which the first drop of the second distillate falls into the beaker. Collect 1 to 2 mL of the second distillate. (**Caution:** *Do not allow all of the liquid to boil from the flask.*)

10. Turn off the hot plate and allow the distillation apparatus to cool. While the apparatus is cooling, test the relative solubility of solid iodine (I_2) in Distillate 1 and Distillate 2 by adding a few crystals of iodine to each beaker and stirring. Record your observations. (**Caution:** *Iodine is corrosive on contact. It will stain skin or clothing.*)

11. Disassemble and clean the distillation apparatus, and dispose of your distillates as directed by your teacher.

12. Wash your hands thoroughly before leaving the laboratory.

Data Analysis

Plot your data on a graph of time (*x*-axis) versus temperature (*y*-axis). As you observed, heating the liquid mixture raised its temperature. However, once the first component began to boil and vaporize from the mixture, the temperature of the liquid remained steady until that component completely distilled. Continued heating then caused the temperature to rise again, this time until the second component began to boil and distill. Because the liquid temperature does not change appreciably during distillation of a particular component, those graph-line portions should appear flat (horizontal).

> Features of a correctly drawn graph are given on pages 80–81.

Questions

1. a. Using your graph, identify the temperatures at which Distillate 1 and Distillate 2 were collected.
   b. How well do the horizontal plateaus in your graph match the temperatures at which you collected the first drops of each distillate?

2. Use data in Table 3.1 to identify each distillate sample.

3. Combine your data with the data of students who distilled the same mixture:
   a. Examine the combined data, and find the average temperature (*mean*) and the most frequently observed temperature (*mode*) for each of the two plateaus you observed.
   b. All laboratory teams investigating the same mixture did not observe the same distillation temperatures. Describe some factors that may contribute to this inconsistency.

> As you learned in Unit 1 (pages 13–14), the mean and median are useful values for describing "middle" characteristics for a set of related data.

Data Analysis

Student graphs will vary somewhat but should show a temperature increase, followed by a plateau, another temperature increase, and another plateau. Time should be on the independent (*x*) axis, and temperature should be on the dependent (*y*) axis. Graphs should be labeled so that someone who was not in class, but had a basic understanding of the concepts, could interpret them.

Answers

1. a. Temperatures should correspond to the plateaus at 82 and 100 °C, or lower at higher altitudes.
   b. The first drops will be collected slightly before the normal boiling point is reached, so plateaus will be slightly higher than the collection temperature.

2. The first is 2-propanol; the second is water.

3. a. Data will vary, but should approximate the boiling point for your altitude.
   b. Possible sources of difference (error) include heating the mixture too rapidly and having poorly calibrated or improperly placed thermometers.

4. Iodine is more soluble in 2-propanol (the first distillate). Evidence for this is that the 2-propanol is more uniformly yellow, indicating that the iodine dissolved.

5. Several approaches could be used to answer this question:
Distill again the liquid left in the flask. If two plateaus occur, it is not a pure substance.
Compare the liquid's boiling point to that of the substances in Table 3.1.
Calculate the liquid's density and compare it with the known densities (which would have to be looked up) of the substances.

6. 2-propanol and cyclohexane, because their boiling points are similar.

a. It would show an increase in temperature with time, with four plateaus, one for each liquid at its boiling point.

b. Graphs should be similar to the graph drawn for Data Analysis, but should have four plateaus at appropriate temperatures (56.6, 80.7, 82.4, and 100 °C).

Post-Lab Discussion

Ask students to compare their conclusions about the components of the mixture. The discussion may focus on the contrasting physical and chemical properties of water and 2-propanol. Discuss the properties used to separate the mixture, namely volatility and boiling points.

Compare the results of the investigation with petroleum distillation. In both, a mixture is separated by differences in boiling point. The laboratory sample involved two components, but crude oil contains countless compounds, many with similar boiling points. Use this fact to introduce the next material on fractional distillation.

4. In which of the distillates was solid iodine more soluble? What observational evidence leads you to that conclusion?

5. What laboratory tests could you complete to decide whether the liquid left behind in the flask is a mixture or a pure substance?

6. Of the substances listed in Table 3.1 (page 216), which two would be most difficult to separate by distillation? Why?

a. How would a graph of time vs. temperature look for the distillation of a mixture of all *four* substances listed in Table 3.1 (page 216)?

b. Sketch the predicted graph and describe its features.

A.3 PETROLEUM REFINING

Although the names given to various fractions and their boiling ranges may vary somewhat, crude oil refining always has the same general features.

Unlike the simple laboratory mixture you separated in the preceding investigation, crude oil is a mixture of many compounds. Separating such a complex mixture requires applying distillation techniques in large-scale oil refining. The refining process does not separate each compound in crude oil. Rather, it produces several distinctive mixtures, called **fractions.** This process is known as **fractional distillation.** See Figure 3.8. Compounds in each fraction have a particular range of boiling points and specific uses.

Figure 3.9 illustrates fractional distillation (fractionation) of crude oil. First, the crude oil is heated to about 400 °C in a furnace and then pumped into the base of a distilling column (fractionating tower), which is usually more than 30 m (100 ft) tall. Many components of the heated crude oil vaporize. The temperature of the distilling column is highest at the bottom, and it decreases toward the top. Trays arranged at appropriate heights inside the column collect the various condensed fractions.

During distillation, the vaporized molecules move upward in the distilling column. The smaller, lighter molecules have the lowest boiling points and either condense high in the column or are drawn off the top of the tower as gases. Fractions with larger molecules have higher boiling points and are more difficult to separate from one another; therefore, they require more thermal energy (heat energy) to vaporize. These larger molecules condense back to liquid in trays lower in the column. Substances with the highest boiling points never do vaporize. These thick (*viscous*) liquids—called *bottoms*—drain from the column's base. Each arrow in Figure 3.9 indicates the name of a particular fraction and its boiling-point range.

Figure 3.8 *These fractionating towers contain many different levels of condensers to cool the oil vapor as it rises. Temperatures range from about 400 °C (at the base) to 40 °C (at the top).*

A.3 Petroleum Refining

Figure 3.9 clarifies several aspects of fractional distillation. Fractional distillation works by heating petroleum in a furnace and allowing vaporized particles to rise up a fractioning tower. As molecules move up the tower, they lose kinetic energy: Their temperature (related to average kinetic

energy) decreases. When temperature falls to the boiling/condensing point of the substance, the molecules condense and are collected in trays. In contrast to simple distillation, the trays collect a variety of substances that have similar boiling points—a *petroleum fraction*.

Heating oil

Less than 40 °C
Gases
1 to 4 carbon atoms
- Heating and cooking fuel
- Petrochemicals
- Starting material for plastics and gasoline additives

40 °C–200 °C
Gasoline
5 to 12 carbon atoms
- Heating fuel
- Natural gasoline useful as a motor fuel and in industrial solvents
- Liquified petroleum gas
- Carbon black
- Petrochemicals

Kerosene

200 °C–300 °C
Light distillates
12 to 16 carbon atoms
- Aviation gasoline and motor gasoline
- Naphthas and solvents
- Petrochemicals
- Kerosene
- Refined oils

250 °C–350 °C
Intermediate distillates
15 to 18 carbon atoms
- Gas oil
- Petrochemicals
- Heavy furnace oil
- Diesel fuel oil

300 °C–370 °C
Heavy distillates
16 to 20 carbon atoms
- Lubricating oil and grease
- Heavy oils and wax
- Cracking stock
- Petrochemicals

Wax

Greater than 370 °C
Residues
More than 20 carbon atoms
- Lubricating oil and fuel oil
- Petroleum jelly
- Road oils and asphalt
- Petroleum coke

Decreasing temperature

Crude oil   Furnace   Fractionating tower

Asphalt

As you learn more about characteristics of the fractions obtained from petroleum, think about how people use petroleum-based products in both traditional and hybrid vehicles.

Figure 3.9 *Fractional distillation (fractionation) of crude oil.*

A.4 EXAMINING PETROLEUM'S MOLECULES

Petroleum's gaseous fraction contains compounds with low boiling points (less than 40 °C). These small hydrocarbon molecules, which contain from one to four carbon atoms, have low boiling points because they are only slightly attracted to each other or to other molecules in petroleum. Forces of attraction between molecules are called **intermolecular forces.** As a result of their weak intermolecular forces, these small hydrocarbon molecules readily separate from each other and rise through the distillation column as gases.

Petroleum's liquid fractions—including gasoline, kerosene, and heavier oils—consist of molecules that have from five to about twenty carbon atoms. Molecules with even more carbon atoms are found in the greasy

> Just as "interstate highway" refers to a road that runs *between* states, intermolecular forces act *between* molecules.

Using the Figures

Figures 3.8 and 3.9: Show students the transparency of a fractionating tower and point out the fate of each type of molecule in the tower. Ask students to compare a fractionating tower to their simple distillation apparatus.

A.4 Examining Petroleum's Molecules

A.4 Supplement: Viscosity

This material relates the properties of petroleum fractions, obtained through fractional distillation, to their molecular structures. Specifically, it relates a fraction's boiling point and uses to the average number of carbon atoms—and thus the average intermolecular forces—of the fraction's components. Prompt students to think about other instances where molecular size is a good predictor of properties.

Additional Activity

Another property that depends on average number of carbon atoms is *viscosity*. This is a property that students can easily understand and observe. To investigate viscosity in the laboratory, use the *Alternate Investigation "Viscosity"* on the TRB and TRCD.

Two exceptions exist to the general behavior of molecules in the fractioning tower: (1) Substances that do not vaporize at the temperature of the furnace due to their strong intermolecular forces are collected as liquids and semisolids from the base of the tower and are known as *bottoms* or *residues;* (2) at the other extreme, some substances have such weak intermolecular attractions that they never lose enough energy to condense and be collected. These gases are collected from the top of the fractioning tower.

For additional information, see the overview at **http://science.howstuffworks.com/oil-refining.htm**.

Developing Skills

A.5 Hydrocarbon Boiling Points

Chemists investigate substances' physical and chemical properties and identify useful patterns among data, often stimulating efforts to explain such regularities.

Organic nomenclature will be introduced in *Investigating Matter A.7*. That scheme will relate to total carbon atoms, reinforcing ideas presented here.

Answers

1. a. Alphabetically
   b. Only in a very limited context, such as in a handbook or chart for locating a hydrocarbon
2. a. Arranged by boiling-point values or total carbons (or hydrogens)
   b. With lowest boiling point first, the order is methane, ethane, propane, butane, pentane, hexane, heptane, octane, nonane, decane.
3. Methane, ethane, propane, butane
4. It must be less than 22 °C.
5. Pentane
6. Decane's boiling point is higher, suggesting that decane's intermolecular forces are greater than those among butane molecules.

Additional ChemQuandaries

1. Why would butane be a poor substitute for propane under some conditions in the tanks of portable camp stoves?

   Discussion: Butane's boiling point (0.5 °C) is higher than propane's (−42.1 °C). At winter temperatures (or higher pressures), butane might liquefy. Since camp stoves are designed for pressurized gas, this is a poor fuel choice. A better

---

fraction—the bottoms—that does not vaporize. These viscous compounds have the strongest intermolecular forces among all substances found in petroleum. It is not surprising that they are solids at room temperature.

Now complete the following activity to learn more about a key physical property of hydrocarbons—their boiling points.

Developing Skills

A.5 HYDROCARBON BOILING POINTS

Chemists often gather and analyze data about the physical and chemical properties of substances. These data can be organized in many ways, but the most useful techniques are those that uncover trends or patterns among the data. The development of the periodic table is an example of this approach.

You can examine patterns among boiling points of some hydrocarbons to make useful predictions.

| Table 3.2

BOILING POINTS OF SELECTED HYDROCARBONS		
Hydrocarbon	**Boiling Point (°C)**	**Molecular Formula**
Butane	−0.5	C_4H_{10}
Decane	174.0	$C_{10}H_{22}$
Ethane	−88.6	C_2H_6
Heptane	98.4	C_7H_{16}
Hexane	68.7	C_6H_{14}
Methane	−161.7	CH_4
Nonane	150.8	C_9H_{20}
Octane	125.7	C_8H_{18}
Pentane	36.1	C_5H_{12}
Propane	−42.1	C_3H_8

"Infer" means to reach a conclusion based on evidence and reasoning.

Use the data found in Table 3.2 to answer the following questions:

1. a. In what pattern or order are the data in Table 3.2 organized?
   b. Is this a useful way to present the information? Explain.
2. Suppose that you were searching for a trend or a pattern among these boiling points.
   a. Propose a more useful way to arrange these data that might suggest how the molecules of each hydrocarbon interact.
   b. Reorganize the data table based on your idea.

Now use your reorganized data table to answer the following questions:

3. Which substance or substances are gases at room temperature (22 °C)?
4. If a substance is a gas at 22 °C, what can you infer about the boiling point of that substance?
5. Which substance or substances boil between 22 °C (room temperature) and 37 °C (body temperature)?
6. What can you infer about intermolecular forces among decane molecules compared to those forces among butane molecules?

A.6 CHEMICAL BONDING

Hydrocarbons and their derivatives are the focus of a branch of chemistry known as **organic chemistry.** These substances are called *organic compounds* because early chemists thought that living systems—plants or animals—were needed to produce them. However, chemists have

---

substitute might be ethane or methane, since their boiling points are lower than that of propane.

2. A transparent butane lighter reveals that at least some butane is in the liquid state. Explain why this is possible if the lighter is at room temperature.

Discussion: A liquid's boiling point also depends on pressure. Apparently, butane is under pressure above 1 atm (where it boils at 0.5 °C); its boiling point at this pressure is greater than room temperature. Therefore, some is liquid.

known for more than 150 years how to make most organic compounds without any assistance from living systems. In fact, reactants other than petroleum can be used to produce organic compounds. You will learn about some of these important reactants in Section C.

In hydrocarbon molecules, carbon atoms are joined to form a backbone called a **carbon chain.** Hydrogen atoms are attached to the carbon backbone. Carbon's versatility in forming bonds helps explain the abundance of different hydrocarbon compounds, as you will soon learn. Hydrocarbons can be regarded as the starting point of an even larger number of compounds that contain atoms of other elements attached to a carbon chain.

> The carbon chain forms a framework to which a wide variety of other atoms can be attached.

Electron Shells

How are atoms of carbon or other elements held together in compounds? The answer is closely related to the arrangement of electrons in atoms. You know that atoms are made up of neutrons, protons, and electrons. In addition, you know that neutrons and protons are located in the small, dense, central region of the atom, the *nucleus.* Electrons reside in separate energy levels in space surrounding the nucleus. Similar energy levels are grouped into **shells,** each of which can hold only a certain maximum number of electrons. For example, the first shell surrounding the nucleus of an atom has a capacity of two electrons. The second shell can hold a maximum of eight electrons.

Consider an atom of helium (He), the first member of the noble gas family. See Figure 3.10 (left). A helium atom has two protons (and two neutrons) in its nucleus, and two electrons occupying the first, or innermost, shell. Because two is the maximum this shell can hold, the shell is completely filled.

The next noble gas, neon (Ne), has atomic number 10. See Figure 3.10 (right). Each electrically neutral neon atom contains 10 protons and 10 electrons. Two electrons occupy and completely fill the first shell. The remaining eight electrons fill the second shell. In neon, each filled shell has reached its electron capacity.

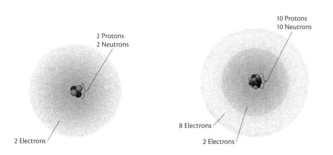

2 Protons
2 Neutrons

10 Protons
10 Neutrons

2 Electrons

8 Electrons

2 Electrons

Figure 3.10 *Atomic structure of helium (left). Note that the nucleus is composed of two protons and two neutrons. Two electrons are located within—and fill—the first electron shell, depicted here by an electron cloud.*
Atomic structure of neon (right). Note that the nucleus is composed of ten protons and ten neutrons. Two electrons are located—and fill— the first electron shell, and eight electrons are located within—and fill—the second electron shell.

Section A   Petroleum: What Is It?   **221**

---

warm. Ask, "What's actually burning in the candle?" Students often say, "The wick."

Ignite a string to show it burns quickly; this helps students realize something else must burn— *the candle wax.* The wick helps wax melt and vaporize under the hot flame. Thus, wax's intermolecular forces are stronger than similar forces among alkanes considered so far. Most wax molecules are long-chain esters; similar alkane principles apply—more carbons, stronger intermolecular forces. If the wick cools, intermolecular forces prevent wax from vaporizing; its fumes are not available to ignite the wick.

A.6 Chemical Bonding

 A.6 Supplement: Chemical Bonding

Carbon's versatility in bonding with hydrogen, itself, and other elements accounts for the abundance of organic compounds. Carbon forms primarily covalent bonds. Covalently bonded carbon atoms provide support *(backbones)* for organic molecules.

Using the Figures

Figure 3.10: Ask students to examine He and Ne atom models—He has one filled electron shell, which is larger than the first (inner) shell of Ne. Why? (A Ne nucleus has 10 protons, exerting stronger pull on electrons than can two He protons.) Ne is also the larger atom. Why? Moving down a group, atoms' sizes increase due to more electron shells and shielding effects (inner-shell electrons "shield" outer-shell electrons from full nuclear attraction).

Demonstration Ideas

1. Add a *small* volume of liquid butane from a lighter-refueling canister to a zipseal bag and quickly seal it. The liquid butane vaporizes and fills the bag. *Caution:* Move bag into a fume hood before reopening it.

2. Light a candle and let it burn for about a minute. Have a lit match ready. Blow out the candle and immediately relight it by bringing the lit match into "smoke" just above wick. With practice, you can relight the candle several centimeters above the wick—as long as the wick is

A.6 Chemical Bonding (Continued)

Carbon's bonding versatility is tied to its four valence-shell electrons. Since this shell can hold eight electrons maximum—and attains stability (lowest energy) when it is filled—each of the four electrons can (and probably will) pair with an electron from another atom in covalent bonding. *Electron sharing* means that both bonding electrons are simultaneously attracted to nuclei of both atoms. Both electrons "belong" to both nuclei; atoms participating in covalent bonding gain filled valence shells.

Electron-dot formulas, also called Lewis structures after G. N. Lewis, are a convenient way to represent the outer-shell electrons in a molecule. Each dot represents one electron. A *bonding pair* of electrons is situated between the atoms it bonds. A bonding pair (also known as a *shared pair*) can be replaced by a dash between the atoms, which also represents a bonded pair of electrons. Remind students that the dash is used only as symbol of a single covalent bond. Covalent bonds are *not* physical, tangible structures like sticks or rods; rather, they arise from attractions between and among atoms resulting from the shared pair(s) of electrons.

Be sure to emphasize the electron-dot arrangements of carbon and hydrogen as described in the text. This will be very helpful to students when they construct structural formulas of hydrocarbons in upcoming investigations. Point out that the number of outer-shell electrons is significant in chemical reactivity and note that only the outermost electrons can easily form bonds with other atoms.

Figure 3.11 *One product of the reaction between sodium (Na) and water is hydrogen gas. So much heat is produced in this violent reaction that the hydrogen gas often undergoes combustion accompanied by flames.*

Chemical Bonding

Helium (He, atomic number 2) and neon (Ne, atomic number 10) are not chemically reactive; their atoms do not combine with each other or with atoms of other elements to form compounds. By contrast, sodium (Na) atoms—with atomic number 11 and one more electron than neon atoms—are extremely reactive (Figure 3.11). Chemists explain sodium's reactivity as due to its tendency to lose that one electron from its third, unfilled shell. Doing so leaves 10 electrons, giving the atom the same electron occupancy as a neon atom. Fluorine (F) atoms each have nine electrons—one fewer than neon atoms—and are also extremely reactive. Their reactivity is due to their tendency to gain an additional electron, thus achieving a filled outer shell of electrons.

Noble-gas elements are essentially unreactive because their separate atoms have filled electron shells. All but helium have eight electrons in their outer shell; helium needs only two electrons to attain its first-shell maximum. A useful key to understanding the chemical behavior of many elements is to recognize that atoms with *filled electron shells* are particularly stable; that is, they tend to be chemically unreactive.

Covalent Bonds

In most substances composed of nonmetals, atoms achieve filled electron shells by *sharing* electrons. Typically, only **valence electrons,** which are the electrons within an atom's unfilled, outer shell, participate in bonding. As you will see, the sharing of two or more valence electrons between two atoms—called a **covalent bond**—allows both atoms to fill their outer shells completely.

A hydrogen molecule (H_2) provides a simple example of electron sharing. Each hydrogen atom contains only one electron, so one more electron is needed to fill the first shell. Two hydrogen atoms can accomplish this if they each share their single electron. If an electron is represented by a dot ($\cdot$), then the formation of a hydrogen molecule can be depicted as shown below.

$$\bigcirc + \bigcirc \longrightarrow \bigcirc\!\bigcirc$$
$$H\cdot \; + \; \cdot H \; \longrightarrow \; H\!:\!H$$

The chemical bond formed between two atoms that share a pair of electrons is called a **single covalent bond** (see Figure 3.12). Through such sharing, both atoms achieve the stability associated with completely filled electron shells. A carbon atom, atomic number 6, has six electrons—two in its first shell and four more in the second shell. To fill the second shell to its capacity of eight, four more electrons are needed. These electrons can be obtained through covalent bonding.

The number of valence electrons in an atom—and thus its bonding behavior—is related to the element's position on the periodic table. This idea, introduced in Unit 2, can be developed in more detail here. Elements in the first column/group of the periodic table (alkali metals) each have one valence electron. Elements in the second column (alkaline earth metals) each have two valence electrons. Transition metals behave differently due to their delocalized electrons. Elements in the 13th column of the periodic table (formerly called Group 3A) have three valence electrons. This pattern continues through the noble gases (column 18), which have 8 valence electrons.

Scientific American Conceptual Illustration

Figure 3.12 *Model of a hydrogen (H₂) molecule.* *A hydrogen molecule is held together by a single covalent bond. Each hydrogen atom in the molecule shares two electrons, thereby filling each atom's outer electron shell. Electrical attractions between shared electrons and each atom's positively charged nucleus (depicted by the high cloud density between the two nuclei) hold the H₂ molecule together.*

Consider the simplest hydrocarbon molecule, methane (CH_4). In this molecule, each hydrogen atom shares its single electron with a valence electron of the carbon atom. A representation of this arrangement is:

$$4\,H\cdot\ +\ \cdot\overset{\cdot}{\underset{\cdot}{C}}\cdot\ \longrightarrow\ H\!:\!\overset{\displaystyle H}{\underset{\displaystyle H}{C}}\!:\!H$$

Scientific American Conceptual Illustration

Compare this figure to **Figure 2.11,** page 121, **Figure 3.10,** page 221, and the particulate-level representation of $2H \rightarrow H_2$ on page 222. First, ask students how they know Figure 3.12 represents a hydrogen molecule (and not an oxygen or carbon dioxide molecule, for instance). They should recognize that hydrogen atoms have only one proton and that these atoms have only one proton each. Other atoms would have more protons and neutrons in the nucleus. Also, this is a two-atom molecule.

Then focus on the electron cloud. Refer to Figures 2.11 and 3.10, which show electron clouds of isolated atoms. These models indicate areas of higher and lower electron density, not exact locations of individual electrons. Within isolated atoms, the electron density is higher near the nucleus and is symmetric with respect to the nucleus (electron density is consistent within any given radius of the nucleus). Contrast this with the H_2 molecule in this figure: Electron density is higher *between* the nuclei and lower toward the "ends" of the molecule. The shared electrons (negatively charged) are attracted to both nuclei (positively charged); this area of higher electron density between the nuclei constitutes the covalent bond. It may be useful to discuss limitations of this model (for instance, the protons occupy much less volume than shown) and compare it to the model of $2H \rightarrow H_2$ on the facing page (in which individual electrons *are* represented).

Emphasize that bonds do not form due to any so-called "desire" of an element to possess a filled electron shell (this is misleading anthropomorphism) but rather because bonding produces a lower-energy condition compared to the unbonded state. The lower-energy condition is favorable; it indicates greater stability.

One way to show Lewis structures is to use disk magnets on white boards (most can be used with magnets). Use small disks to represent electrons and large disks (or alphabet magnets) to represent atoms or ions. Colored transparency film on the overhead projector will give the same effect. (A one-hole punch works well to make the smaller disks.)

Investigating Matter

A.7 Modeling Alkanes

**A.7 Modeling Alkanes
Worksheet and Data Table**

Students will build three-dimensional models of methane, ethane, and propane. The general formula for alkanes is derived from these three-dimensional models. Students will practice writing electron-dot representations. Constructing models and diagrams enables them to learn differences among the three types of formulas.

Time

50 min

Materials

(For 12 student pairs)

12 sets of space-filling or ball-and-stick models

Pre-Lab Discussion

Show students how to draw a three-dimensional structure on a two-dimensional surface. The convention generally accepted by chemists is that any bond represented by the traditional solid line is in the plane of the paper. Any bond represented using a solid wedge is coming out toward the viewer; any bond represented using a dashed line is receding behind the plane of the paper. Owing to carbon's tetrahedral geometry when engaged in four single bonds, the most common representation is to

> The American chemist G. N. Lewis is credited with laying the foundation for our current understanding of bond formation.

As in the formula for a hydrogen molecule, dots surrounding each element's symbol represent the valence electrons for that atom. Structures such as those on page 223 are **electron-dot formulas,** also known as **Lewis dot structures** or, simply, **Lewis structures.** The two electrons in each covalent bond "belong" to both bonded atoms. Dots placed between the symbols of two atoms represent electrons that are shared by those atoms.

When determining the electrons associated with each atom, each shared electron in a covalent bond is "counted" twice, once for each element. For example, count the dots surrounding each atom in methane (see below). Note that each hydrogen atom has a filled outer electron shell with two electrons. The carbon atom also has a filled outer electron shell with eight electrons. Each hydrogen atom is associated with one pair of electrons; the carbon atom has four pairs of electrons, or eight electrons.

For convenience, each pair of electrons in a covalent bond can be represented by a line drawn between the symbols of each atom. This yields another common representation of a covalently bonded molecule, called a **structural formula.**

$$
\begin{array}{cc}
\text{H} & \text{H} \\
\text{H:C:H} & \text{H—C—H} \\
\text{H} & \text{H}
\end{array}
$$

Electron-dot formula of methane, CH₄	Structural formula of methane, CH₄

Although you can draw flat, two-dimensional pictures of molecules on paper, assembling three-dimensional models gives a far more accurate representation. Such models help predict a molecule's physical and chemical behavior. The following investigation provides an opportunity for you to assemble and use molecular models.

Investigating Matter

Modeling Alkanes

A.7 MODELING ALKANES

Introduction

In this investigation, you will assemble models of several simple hydrocarbon molecules. See Figure 3.13. Your goal is to associate the three-dimensiona shapes of these molecules with the names, formulas, and pictures used to represent them on paper.

There are several useful ways to construct models of molecules; each model has its own advantages and disadvantages (Figure 3.14). Two common types of molecular models are shown in Figure 3.15. Most likely, you will use *ball-and-stick models*. Each ball represents an atom, and each stick represents a single covalent bond (one shared electron pair) connecting two atoms.

Of course, molecules are not composed of ball-like atoms located at the ends of stick-like bonds. Experimental evidence shows that atoms are in contact with each other, much like that depicted in *space-filling*

> See Figure 3.12 (page 223) for a more realistic molecular model of a covalently bonded molecule.

Figure 3.13 *Due to the extremely small size of atoms and molecules, people often use model kits to visualize the three-dimensional geometry of hydrocarbons and other molecular structures.*

models. However, ball-and-stick models are still useful because they can clearly represent the bonding and geometry of molecules.

Look again at the Lewis dot structure and the structural formula for methane (CH_4) on page 224. Methane, the simplest hydrocarbon, is the first member of a series of hydrocarbons known as **alkanes.** Each carbon atom in an alkane forms *single* covalent bonds with four other atoms. You will explore alkanes in this investigation.

Before you begin, carefully read the procedure to learn what is involved and to plan for your data collecting and observations.

Procedure

1. Assemble a three-dimensional model of a methane (CH_4) molecule. Compare your model to the Lewis dot formula and the structural formula on page 224. Note that the angles defined by bonds between atoms are not 90°, as you might have expected by looking at the structural formula. If you were to build a close-fitting box to surround a CH_4 molecule, the box would be shaped like a pyramid with a triangle as its base. This three-dimensional shape is called a **tetrahedron.**

Figure 3.14 *Scientists use many types of physical and mental models to better understand concepts related to atoms and molecules.*

depict two of the four bonds in the plane of the paper, and one bond coming toward the viewer and one bond receding from the viewer. As students make their initial attempts at these representations, it can help for them to hold the models in front of them in the same orientation that they are trying to depict.

Remind students that they can use models to assist with writing molecular formulas and drawing structural formulas for compounds. Depending on students' abilities, you may elect to work through an example.

Answers

1. No question—students assemble models.

Figure 3.15 *Three-dimensional CH_4 models: ball-and-stick (left); and space-filling (right).*

Section A   Petroleum: What Is It?   **225**

2.

3. a. 6

b. 8

c.

d.
$$H:C:C:H$$

ethane

$$H-C-C-H$$

ethane

$$H:C:C:C:H$$

$$H-C-C-C-H$$

propane

4. C_3H_8

C_4H_{10}

5. No question—students disassemble models.

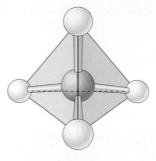

The tetrahedral geometry that you observe results from the fact that similar electrical charges repel. The four pairs of electrons in the bonds surrounding the carbon atom repel each other and arrange themselves to be as far away from one another as possible. In this spatial arrangement, they point to the corners of a tetrahedron, as shown in Figure 3.16. The angle formed between the C—H bonds is 109.5°, a value that has been verified experimentally.

2. Convert your three-dimensional model into a two-dimensional drawing, similar to the one shown in Figure 3.16, that conveys the tetrahedral structure of methane. Shade the carbon atom to distinguish it from the hydrogen atoms.

Figure 3.16 *The tetrahedral shape of a methane molecule.*

3. Assemble models of a two-carbon alkane molecule and a three-carbon alkane molecule. Recall that each carbon atom in an alkane is bonded to four other atoms.

   a. How many hydrogen atoms are in a two-carbon alkane molecule?

   b. How many hydrogen atoms are in a three-carbon alkane molecule?

   c. Draw a ball-and-stick model, similar to the one shown in Figure 3.15 (page 225), of the three-carbon alkane. Shade the carbon atoms to distinguish them from the hydrogen atoms.

   d. Draw Lewis dot structures and structural formulas for the two- and three-carbon alkanes.

Table 3.3

			Alkane Formulas	
Name	**Total Carbon Atoms**	**Boiling Point (°C)**	**Molecular Formula**	**Condensed Formula**
Methane	1	−161.7	CH_4	CH_4
Ethane	2	−88.6	C_2H_6	CH_3CH_3
Propane	3	−42.1	C_3H_8	$CH_3CH_2CH_3$
Butane	4	−0.5	C_4H_{10}	$CH_3CH_2CH_2CH_3$
Pentane	5	36.1	C_5H_{12}	$CH_3CH_2CH_2CH_2CH_3$
Hexane	6	68.7	C_6H_{14}	$CH_3CH_2CH_2CH_2CH_2CH_3$
Heptane	7	98.4	C_7H_{16}	$CH_3CH_2CH_2CH_2CH_2CH_2CH_3$
Octane	8	125.7	C_8H_{18}	$CH_3CH_2CH_2CH_2CH_2CH_2CH_2CH_3$
Nonane	9	150.8	C_9H_{20}	$CH_3CH_2CH_2CH_2CH_2CH_2CH_2CH_2CH_3$
Decane	10	174.0	$C_{10}H_{22}$	$CH_3CH_2CH_2CH_2CH_2CH_2CH_2CH_2CH_2CH_3$

SOME MEMBERS OF THE ALKANE SERIES

Figure 3.17 *Propane often serves as an emergency energy source during power outages. Here, workers weigh filled tanks to determine how much propane they contain.*

4. **Molecular formulas** specify the number of each atom type within a molecule. The molecular formulas of the first two alkanes are CH_4 and C_2H_6. Identify the molecular formula for the third alkane.

Examine your three-carbon alkane model and the structural formula you drew for it. Note that the middle carbon atom is attached to *two* hydrogen atoms, but the carbon atom at each end is attached to *three* hydrogen atoms. This molecule can be represented as CH_3—CH_2—CH_3, or $CH_3CH_2CH_3$. Formulas such as these provide convenient information about how atoms are arranged in molecules. For many purposes, such **condensed formulas** are more useful than molecular formulas, such as C_3H_8.

Consider the molecular formulas of the first few alkanes: CH_4, C_2H_6, and C_3H_8. Given the pattern represented by that series, try to predict the formula of the four-carbon alkane. The general molecular formula of all open-chain alkane molecules can be written as C_nH_{2n+2}, where n is the number of carbon atoms in the molecule. Therefore, even without assembling a model, you can predict the formula of a five-carbon alkane: If $n = 5$, then $2n + 2 = 12$, and the resulting formula thus is C_5H_{12}.

The names of the first ten alkanes are given in Table 3.3 and some examples of uses of these compounds are shown in Figure 3.17 and Figure 3.18. As you can see, each name is composed of a prefix, followed by *-ane* (designating an alk*ane*). The prefix indicates the number of carbon atoms in the backbone carbon chain. *Meth-* means one carbon atom, *eth-* means two, *prop-* means three, and *but-* means four. For alkanes with five to ten carbon atoms, the prefixes are derived from Greek—*pent-* for five, *hex-* for six, and so on.

5. Disassemble your molecular models and replace all parts in their container.

> *n* can be any positive integer.

Figure 3.18 *Butane is a liquid commonly used as fuel in lighters.*

Section A   Petroleum: What Is It?   **227**

6.

butane

pentane

7. a. (i) heptane   (ii) nonane
   b. (i) C_7H_{16} (ii) C_9H_{20}
8. a. $C_{25}H_{52}$
   b. The molecular formula. This shorter version takes much less time and space.
9. $5(12) + 12(1) = 72$ g/mol
10. a. ethane (C_2H_6: $2(12) + 6(1) = 30$ g/mol)
    b. butane (C_4H_{10}: $4(12) + 10(1) = 58$ g/mol)
    c. octane (C_8H_{18}: $8(12) + 18(1) = 114$ g/mol)

Post-Lab Discussion

The enormous number and variety of hydrocarbons require an orderly, rational system of nomenclature. Learning prefixes of the first 10 alkanes allows students to name many compounds. Encourage students to draw on prior knowledge of prefixes as they name and draw organic compounds.

Stress the general formula for alkanes and alternate ways of writing formulas, as shown in **Table 3.3** (page 226). Molecular formulas give information about the number and type of atoms in the molecule. Condensed formulas give information on the arrangement of the atoms in a molecule. Structural formulas provide information about both the arrangement and the orientation of atoms in a molecule. Each type of formula has advantages and appropriate uses.

Questions

6. Write structural formulas for butane and pentane.
7. a. Name the alkanes with the following condensed formulas:
      i. $CH_3CH_2CH_2CH_2CH_2CH_2CH_3$
      ii. $CH_3CH_2CH_2CH_2CH_2CH_2CH_2CH_2CH_3$
   b. Write molecular formulas for the two alkanes in Question 7a.
8. a. Write the formula of an alkane containing 25 carbon atoms.
   b. Did you decide to write the molecular formula or the condensed formula for this compound? Why?
9. Find the molar mass of pentane. (*Hint:* Remember to take subscripts into account, as you first learned to do in Unit 2, page 163.)
10. Name the alkane molecule that has a molar mass of
    a. 30 g/mol.   b. 58 g/mol.   c. 114 g/mol.

Developing Skills

A.8 TRENDS IN ALKANE BOILING POINTS

In Investigating Matter A.2, you used the technique known as *distillation* that separates liquid mixtures according to the boiling points of the components. You also know that the fractions of petroleum are separated based on their boiling points. Why do fractions with the largest molecules have the highest boiling points? Why are the smallest molecules found in fractions with the lowest boiling points? In this activity, you will explore this trend in alkane boiling points.

Using data for the alkanes found in Table 3.3 (page 226), prepare a graph of boiling points. The x-axis scale should range from 1 to 13 carbon atoms (even though you will initially plot data for 1 to 10 carbon atoms). The y-axis scale should extend from -200 °C to $+250$ °C.

1. Label the axes appropriately and plot the data. Draw a best-fit line through your data points according to the following guidelines:
   ▶ The line should follow the trend of your data points.
   ▶ The data points should be roughly equally distributed above and below the line.
   ▶ The line should not extend past your data points.
   Figure 3.19 shows an example of a best-fit line.
2. Estimate the average change in boiling point (in °C) when one carbon atom and two hydrogen atoms ($-CH_2-$) are added to a particular alkane chain.
   The pattern of boiling points among the first ten alkanes allows you to predict the boiling points for other alkanes.
   a. Using your graph, estimate the boiling points of undecane ($C_{11}H_{24}$), dodecane ($C_{12}H_{26}$), and tridecane ($C_{13}H_{28}$). To do this, follow the trend of your graph line by extending a dashed line from the graph line you drew for the first ten alkanes. This procedure is called *extrapolation*. Then read your predicted boiling points for C_{11}, C_{12}, and C_{13} alkanes on the y-axis.

228   **Unit 3**   Petroleum: Breaking and Making Bonds

Developing Skills

A.8 Trends in Alkane Boiling Points

This activity examines trends in alkane boiling points with respect to molecular size. Students plot the boiling-point values of the straight-chain alkanes from methane to decane (1- through 10-carbon straight-chain alkanes) and then predict boiling points of the next three straight-chain alkanes in the series.

Discuss the chemical explanation for differences in alkane boiling points, based

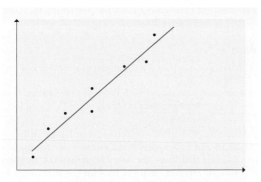

Figure 3.19 *An example of a best-fit line drawn through several data points.*

b. Compare your predicted boiling points to actual values provided by your teacher.

3. You learned that a substance's boiling point depends in part on its *intermolecular forces,* which are the attractions among its molecules. For the alkanes you have studied, what is the relationship between the strength of these attractions and the number of carbon atoms in each molecule?

A.9 ALKANES REVISITED

Introduction

The alkane molecules you have considered so far are **straight-chain alkanes,** where each carbon atom is only linked to one or two other carbon atoms.

In alkanes with four or more carbon atoms, other arrangements of carbon atoms are possible. In **branched-chain alkanes,** one carbon atom can be linked to three or four other carbon atoms. An alkane composed of four or more carbon atoms can have either a straight-chain structure or a branched-chain structure. In this activity, you will use ball-and-stick molecular models (see Figure 3.20) to investigate such variations in alkane structures—variations that can lead to different properties.

Investigating Matter

A straight-chain structure:

C—C—C—C—C

A branched-chain structure:

C—C—C—C
       |
       C

A ring structure:

Figure 3.20 *Students working together to construct molecular models.*

Section A   Petroleum: What Is It?   **229**

on intermolecular forces. The primary intermolecular forces in hydrocarbons are weak van der Waals forces that require relatively little energy to overcome. As the straight-chain alkanes increase in size, they have more points of contact with other molecules, and greater intermolecular attractions arise. A variation on this phenomenon will be

investigated later in *Developing Skills A.10.*

Prediction accuracy decreases as the number of carbons increases. Ask students whether a linear model—the simplest mathematical model—seems to be the best choice in this case. It does not. Close examination of the graphed data should reveal some curvature in the relationship.

You may remind students of expected procedures and specifications for graphing.

Answers

1. Graphs should show a direct relationship.
2. Approximately 30 °C. (The ΔT as one —CH_2— is added is represented by the slope of the line.) a and b.
   $C_{11}H_{24}$: 204 °C (actual: 196 °C);
   $C_{12}H_{26}$: 234 °C (actual: 216 °C);
   $C_{13}H_{28}$: 264 °C (actual: 235 °C)
3. Attractive forces increase in strength as the number of carbons in each alkane molecule increases.

Investigating Matter

A.9 Alkanes Revisited

A.9 Alkanes Revisited Worksheet and Data Table

Students build C_4H_{10} and C_6H_{14} models. They find several possible atom arrangements for each formula (two and five, respectively), introducing the idea of isomers. *Isomers* are compounds with the same molecular formula but different structural formulas. Point out that isomers have differing physical properties due to their different atomic arrangements.

Students may confuse *isomers* with *isotopes,* introduced in Unit 2. Isotopes are the same element with different atomic masses (different total neutrons), while isomers are molecules with identical numbers and types of atoms in different arrangements.

Time

50 min

SECTION A

Materials

(For 12 student pairs)

12 space-filling or ball-and-stick
model kits

Lab Tips

• Each team (with one kit) may need
to share kits with another team so
they can build all hexane isomers.

• Students may have difficulty
deciding if structures are identical,
rather than isomers. Remind students that rotation occurs around
single bonds. Practice rotating structures and viewing them from different angles to distinguish "isomers"
from similar substances. Bonds need
to be broken and reformed for two
isomers to become the same.

 A.9 Supplement: IUPAC Rules

 **A.9 Supplement: Naming
Branched Alkanes**

Answers

1. Two isomers are possible.

2. a.

H H H H
H : C : C : C : C : H
H H H H

H   H   H
H : C : C : C : H
H   H
   H : C : H
       H

b.

H   H   H   H
H—C—C—C—C—H
H   H   H   H
butane

H   CH₃ H
H—C—C—C—H
H   H   H
2-methylpropane

3. Students build isomers of pentane (see **Table 3.4**).

Before starting, read the following procedure to learn what is
involved and plan for your data collecting and observations.

Procedure

1. a. Assemble a ball-and-stick model of a molecule with the
formula C_4H_{10}.

b. Compare your model with those built by others. How many
different arrangements of atoms in the C_4H_{10} molecule did
your class construct?

Molecules that have identical molecular formulas but different arrangements of atoms are called **structural isomers.** By comparing models,
convince yourself that there are only two structural isomers of C_4H_{10}.
The formation of isomers helps to explain the very large number of
compounds composed of carbon in chains or rings.

2. a. Draw a Lewis dot structure for each C_4H_{10} isomer.

b. Write a structural formula for each C_4H_{10} isomer.

3. As you might expect, alkanes containing larger numbers of
carbon atoms also have larger numbers of structural isomers. In
fact, the number of different isomers increases rapidly as the
number of carbon atoms increases. For example, chemists have
identified three pentane (C_5H_{12}) isomers, as shown in Table 3.4.
Try building these structural isomers.

4. Now consider possible structural isomers of C_6H_{14}, hexane.

a. Working with a partner, draw structural formulas for as many
different C_6H_{14} isomers as possible. Compare your structures
with those drawn by other groups.

b. How many different C_6H_{14} isomers were found by your class?

5. Build models of one or more C_6H_{14} isomers, as assigned by your
teacher.

a. Compare the three-dimensional models built by your class
with corresponding structures drawn on paper.

b. Based on your careful examination of the three-dimensional
models, how many different C_6H_{14} isomers are possible?

PENTANE ISOMERS AND THEIR BOILING POINTS	
Structural Formula	**Boiling Point (°C)**
$CH_3-CH_2-CH_2-CH_2-CH_3$	36.1
$CH_3-CH-CH_2-CH_3$ $\quad\quad CH_3$	27.8
CH_3 CH_3-C-CH_3 CH_3	9.5

| **Table 3.4**

---

4. a. Students draw several hexane isomers:

H H H H H H
H—C—C—C—C—C—C—H
H H H H H H
hexane

2-methylpentane

2,2-dimethylbutane

A.10 BOILING POINTS OF ALKANE ISOMERS

You have already observed that boiling points of straight-chain alkanes are related to the number of carbon atoms in their molecules. Increased intermolecular forces are associated with the greater molecule-to-molecule contact possible for larger alkanes.

Intermolecular
Forces &
Boiling Point

1. Boiling points for several isomers of pentane and octane are listed in Table 3.4 and Table 3.5. For each set of isomers, how does the boiling point change as the extent of carbon-chain branching increases? Based on your conclusions, assign each of these boiling points to one of the following C_7H_{16} isomers: 98.4 °C, 92.0 °C, 79.2 °C.

   a. $CH_3-CH_2-CH_2-CH_2-CH_2-CH_2-CH_3$
   b. $CH_3-CH_2-CH-CH_2-CH_2-CH_3$
      $\quad\quad\quad\quad\quad | $
      $\quad\quad\quad\quad CH_3$

   c. $CH_3-CH_2-CH_2-\overset{\displaystyle CH_3}{\underset{\displaystyle CH_3}{\overset{\displaystyle |}{\underset{\displaystyle |}{C}}}}-CH_3$

2. Here is the structural formula of a C_8H_{18} isomer:

   $CH_3-CH_2-CH_2-\overset{\displaystyle CH_3}{\underset{\displaystyle CH_3}{\overset{\displaystyle |}{\underset{\displaystyle |}{C}}}}-CH_2-CH_3$

   a. Compare this isomer to each C_8H_{18} isomer listed in Table 3.5. Predict whether this isomer has a higher or lower boiling point than each of the other listed C_8H_{18} isomers.
   b. Would the C_8H_{18} isomer shown here have a higher or lower boiling point than each of the three C_5H_{12} isomers depicted in Table 3.4? Why?

3. How do you explain the boiling point trends that you investigated in this activity?

SOME OCTANE ISOMERS AND THEIR BOILING POINTS	
Structural Formula	**Boiling Point (°C)**
$CH_3-CH_2-CH_2-CH_2-CH_2-CH_2-CH_3$	125.7
$CH_3-CH_2-CH_2-CH_2-CH_2-CH-CH_3$ with CH_3 below	117.7
$CH_3-CH-CH_2-C-CH_3$ with two CH_3 groups above and two CH_3 groups below	99.2

| Table 3.5

2,3-dimethylbutane

3-methylpentane

Developing Skills

A.10 Boiling Points of Alkane Isomers

This activity further explores links between alkane structures and boiling points and the effect of molecular branching. Increased branching leads to molecules that are more spherical. This shape minimizes surface-area contacts between molecules, leading to lower intermolecular attractions and decreased boiling points.

Students are not asked to name isomers, but each isomer must have correct total carbon and hydrogen atoms.

Answers

1. Boiling points decrease as the extent of branching increases.
   a. 98.4 °C (*n*-heptane)
   b. 92.0 °C (3-methylhexane)
   c. 79.2 °C (2,2-dimethylpentane)
2. a. Students should predict its BP between 99.2 °C and 117.7 °C. Its actual BP is 112 °C, lower than the two isomers with less branching and higher than the isomer with more branching.
   b. One would expect it to have a higher BP than all C_5H_{12} isomers, due to larger size. Its BP is 112 °C, compared to 36.1 °C for pentane. Molecular weight also influences BP in many cases more strongly than degree of branching.
3. Boiling point decreases as carbon side-chain total increases for isomers of a given alkane. The more compact shape affords fewer intermolecular contacts, which allows these molecules to separate more easily from one another.

b. Students often "find" over five isomers due to drawings of duplicate structures, not isomers.

5. a. Models will vary; some may miss similar isomers due to twists and bends in their drawings.
   b. 5

Making Decisions

A.11 Fuels and Climate

Students reflect on gasoline's composition, which prepares them for Section B. Use questions to review how people modify mixture properties to meet particular needs.

Gasoline composition varies across the United States based on variations in temperature and altitude. Also, the composition of gasoline mixtures within one geographic region can differ from season to season. Summer-blend gasoline, formulated to reduce smog, has fewer volatile hydrocarbons and is often more costly, due to additional processing. Federal and local guidelines specify criteria for these gasoline blends.

Answers

1. Volatility affects performance under varying temperature and pressure (that is, altitude) conditions. In winter, fuel with more volatile components enables cold starts, while in summer, fuel with fewer volatile components prevents vapor lock, wherein fuel vaporizes, blocks the fuel line, and cannot be pumped into the engine. Warmer climates require a fuel that does not easily vaporize, while colder climates require a mixture that does not solidify or become too viscous to pump.

2. Boiling point or volatility; viscosity

3. Maine's winter fuel should have smaller-chain and/or more-branched hydrocarbon components than Arizona's summer fuel.

Making Decisions

A.11 FUELS AND CLIMATE

Different parts of the nation experience very different climates. Automobile fuel used in Maine during its cold winter months differs from fuel used in Arizona during hot summer months (Figure 3.21).

1. Why do differing climates require different automobile fuels? What practical reasons are there (in terms of transport, storage, and transfer of fuel) for tailoring fuel to a specific climate?

2. Suggest a physical property that petroleum engineers should consider when supplying gasoline for two such disparate climates.

3. Based on your answer to Question 2, what aspects of the components of fuel used in a Maine winter would differ from the components of fuel used during a summer in Arizona? (*Hint:* Think in terms of molecular structures.)

Chemists and chemical engineers use information about molecular structures and boiling points to separate the complex mixture known as petroleum into a variety of useful substances, many of which you are quite familiar with. In Section B, you will learn how bonding helps explain the use of petroleum as a fuel.

Figure 3.21 *How would the properties of the gasoline being pumped in these two situations vary?*

SECTION A SUMMARY
Reviewing the Concepts

Petroleum (crude oil), a nonrenewable resource that must be refined prior to use, consists of a complex mixture of hydrocarbon molecules.

1. What is a hydrocarbon?
2. What does it mean to *refine* a natural resource?
3. What characteristics of petroleum make it a valuable resource?

4. What is the likelihood of discovering a pure form of petroleum that can be used directly as it is pumped from the ground? Explain your answer.
5. What is meant by saying that oil is *crude*?

Petroleum is a source of fuels that provide thermal energy. It is also a source of raw materials for the manufacture of many familiar and useful products.

6. On average, the United States uses about 20 million barrels of petroleum daily:
   a. What is the average number of barrels of petroleum used daily in the United States for building (nonfuel) purposes?
   b. How many barrels of petroleum, on average, are burned as fuel daily in the United States?
7. Name several fuels obtained from crude petroleum.

8. a. List four household items made from petroleum.
   b. What materials could be substituted for each of these four household items if petroleum were not available to make them?
9. List several products that might not be widely and easily available if petroleum supplies were to dwindle.

The distribution of crude oil reserves does not necessarily correspond to areas of high petroleum use.

The following two questions refer to Figure 3.4, page 214.

10. a. Which world region has the most petroleum reserves relative to its population?
    b. Which region has the least petroleum reserves relative to its population?

11. a. Which regions consume a greater proportion of the world's supply of petroleum than they possess?
    b. Which regions consume a smaller proportion of the world's supply of petroleum than they possess?

SECTION A SUMMARY

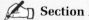 **Section A Supplement**

Reviewing the Concepts

1. A molecular compound made of hydrogen and carbon

2. To remove impurities from the raw material and/or separate the raw material into useful components

3. It can provide large quantities of energy when burned and can be used to synthesize many items.

4. In chemistry, *pure* implies a single substance of uniform composition. Petroleum is a complex mixture of many

hydrocarbons with a wide range of boiling points, so it can never be pure. To be useful, petroleum must be separated into fractions. It would be highly unlikely to find crude oil that could be used directly.

5. It contains many impurities and components; it must be refined to become useful.

6. a. 16% or 3 million barrels
   b. 84% or 16 million barrels

7. Natural gas, gasoline, kerosene, fuel oil, diesel fuel

8. a. Answers will vary. Examples: plastic containers, fibers (clothing), medicines, detergents, adhesives, cosmetics
   b. Answers will vary. Examples: *Plastic food containers*—glass or cardboard; *plastic film*—wax paper; *PVC pipe*—copper pipe; *plastic furniture*—wood; *plastic housing for computers, radios, TVs, stereos*—wood; *latex or acrylic paints*—vegetable-oil-based paint; *synthetic fibers*—natural fibers such as wool, cotton, linen; *medicines*—vegetable or herbal remedies; *detergents*—soap; *adhesives*—natural adhesives such as pitch; *laminated plastic countertops*—granite, marble, wood; *cosmetics*—plants and minerals

9. Answers may include fuels, such as gasoline, fuel oil, kerosene, diesel fuel; and products, such as plastics, medicines, cosmetics, adhesives.

10. a. The Middle East
    b. Asia (Central Asia, Far East, Oceania)

11. a. North America, Asia, and Eastern and Western Europe
    b. Central and South America, Africa, and the Middle East

12. If they are immiscible—that is, if they do not form a solution when they are mixed.

13. Water and acetone, because their boiling points are most different from each other.

14. Sketches should include a distillation flask, a heat source, a thermometer, a condenser, and a container for distillate.

15. Graphs should show a distillation curve (temperature vs. time) with two plateaus, at approximately 56.5 and 100 °C.

16. Simple distillation is a batch process that separates mixtures into individual components. Fractional distillation is a continuous process that separates mixtures into fractions.

17. *Light:* gasoline, gasoline additives, solvents; *intermediate:* kerosene, jet fuel, solvents, alcohols, dyes; *heavy:* fuel oil, diesel oil, lubricants, heavy oil; *residues:* asphalt, paraffin, petroleum jelly, greases.

18. At the bottom. This fraction requires the most energy to vaporize and to travel upward.

19. By another distillation

20. CH_4, C_5H_{12}, C_6H_{14}, C_8H_{18}
    Forces of attraction increase with increasing mass/charge and surface area, so longer straight-chain hydrocarbons have higher BPs than shorter ones.

21. A bond formed by *sharing* of a pair of electrons between two atoms

22. There are no energetic advantages to sharing electrons for such atoms.

23. Electrons are attracted to (tugged by) the nuclei of both atoms; they "belong" to neither nucleus but share their time between them.

24. A valence-shell electron

25. It is simpler to draw.

Liquid substances can often be separated according to their differing boiling points in a process called distillation.

12. Under what conditions could density be used to separate two different liquids?

13. Referring to Table 3.1 (page 216), a mixture of which two of the substances listed would be the easiest to separate from each other by distillation? Explain your reasoning.

14. Sketch the basic setup for a laboratory distillation. Label the key features of your sketch.

15. Referring to Table 3.1 (page 216), sketch a graph of the distillation of a mixture of acetone and water. Label its key features.

Fractional distillation of crude oil produces several distinctive and usable mixtures (fractions). Each fraction contains molecules of similar sizes, boiling points, and intermolecular forces.

16. How does fractional distillation differ from simple distillation?

17. Petroleum fractions include light, intermediate, and heavy distillates and residues. List three useful products derived from each of these three fractions.

18. Where in a distillation tower—top, middle, or bottom—would you expect the fraction with the *highest* boiling point range to be removed? Why?

19. After fractional distillation, each fraction is still a mixture. Suggest a way to further separate the components of each fraction.

20. Rank the following straight-chain hydrocarbons from their lowest boiling point to their highest: hexane (C_6H_{14}), methane (CH_4), pentane (C_5H_{12}), and octane (C_8H_{18}). Explain your rankings in terms of intermolecular forces.

The atoms in hydrocarbons and in other molecules are held together by covalent bonds.

21. What is a covalent bond?

22. Why do atoms with filled outer electron shells not form covalent bonds?

23. It has been suggested that a covalent bond linking two atoms is like two dogs tugging on the same sock. Explain how this analogy describes the way that shared electrons hold together atoms in a covalent bond.

Molecules can be represented by Lewis dot structures, structural formulas, or molecular formulas.

24. What does each dot in a Lewis dot structure represent?

25. What is the advantage of using a dash instead a pair of electron dots to represent a covalent bond?

26. a. What information does a structural formula convey that a molecular formula does not?
    b. In what ways is a structural formula an inadequate representation of an actual molecule?

27. Choose a branched six-carbon hydrocarbon molecule
    a. Draw a Lewis dot structure to represent its structure.
    b. Draw a structural formula for the same molecule.

28. Each carbon atom has six total electrons. Why, then, does the electron-dot representation of a carbon atom show only *four* dots?

---

26. a. The arrangement of atoms within the molecule
    b. It shows the molecule in two dimensions; molecules are three-dimensional and less rigid than structural formulas suggest.

27. a. Refer to structural formulas in b. Each line should be replaced by 2 dots.
    b.

Alkane molecules, hydrocarbons with single covalent bonds, are represented by the general molecular formula C_nH_{2n+2}.

29. Use the general molecular formula to write the molecular formula for an alkane containing

a. 9 carbons.   c. 10 carbons.

b. 16 carbons.   d. 18 carbons.

30. Calculate the molar mass of each alkane listed in Question 29.

31. Name and give the molecular formula for the alkane with a molar mass of

a. 44 g/mol.

b. 72 g/mol.

32. What does -*ane* imply about the carbon–carbon bonding in hexane?

Isomers are molecules with identical molecular formulas, but different arrangements of atoms. Each isomer is a distinct substance with its own characteristic properties.

33. Are the following three molecules isomers of one another? Explain your answer.

$$CH_3 \quad CH_3 \quad CH_3$$
$$| \qquad | \qquad |$$
$$CH_2-CH_2-CH_2 \quad CH_2$$
$$\qquad\qquad\qquad CH_2-CH_2-CH_3$$

$$CH_3-CH_2-CH_2-CH_2-CH_3$$

34. Draw structural formulas for at least three structural isomers of C_9H_{20}.

35. What is the shortest-chain alkane that can demonstrate isomerism?

36. An unbranched hydrocarbon molecule can be represented as a linear chain or as a zig-zag chain. Explain in what way both representations are correct.

The structures of hydrocarbons affect their intermolecular attractions and, thus, their boiling points.

37. a. Draw two hexane structural isomers, one a straight-chain molecule and the other a branched-chain molecule.

b. Which of the two isomers you drew would have the lower boiling point? Explain your choice.

38. Which of each pair of the following hydrocarbon molecules would have the lower boiling point? In each case, describe your reasoning.

a. a short, straight chain or a long, straight chain

b. a short, branched chain or a long, branched chain

c. a short, branched chain or a long, straight chain

Section Summary   **235**

---

28. Only valence electrons are represented. Carbon has two inner-shell electrons that are not represented.

29. a. C_9H_{20}, b. $C_{16}H_{34}$
c. $C_{10}H_{22}$, d. $C_{18}H_{38}$

30. a. $9(12) + 20(1) = 128$ g/mol
b. $16(12) + 34(1) = 226$ g/mol
c. $10(12) + 22(1) = 142$ g/mol
d. $18(12) + 38(1) = 254$ g/mol

31. a. propane, C_3H_8
b. pentane, C_5H_{12}

32. That all carbon atoms are linked in single covalent bonds

33. No, these are representations of the same molecule. Each could be redrawn as a straight chain.

34.

35. Butane, C_4H_{10}

36. A linear chain correctly communicates the connectivity of all carbon atoms. A zig-zag arrangement shows tetrahedral bonding angles.

37. a. See Answer 27b for structures. Drawings should include the straight-chain isomer.
b. The branched-chain isomer, because it has less surface area for intermolecular attractions, so the molecules separate and vaporize more readily.

38. a. A short, straight chain.
b. A short, branched chain.
c. A short, branched chain; in each case, the hydrocarbon molecules with least surface area will have the lower BP.

Connecting the Concepts

39. The total inventory of available petroleum is decreasing, and is not able to be replenished on a human time scale.

40. Students should draw a two-circle Venn diagram. The fractional distillation circle contains such entries as *continuous*, *separates more complex mixtures*, and *more complex*. The simple distillation circle contains such entries as *easy to set up*, *smaller scales* and *batch*. The intersection of the two circles indicates that both *separate mixtures using differences in boiling points*.

41. Some molecules of the higher-boiling component may vaporize before the other component has been completely condensed at its boiling point.

42. Hydrocarbons with boiling points above 300 °C would not undergo vaporization and condensation. They would all be aggregated in the bottom residue.

43. Water has stronger forces of attraction between its molecules.

44. 10 000 mi × 1 gal gasoline/ 27 mi × 1 barrel/21 gal gasoline = 18 barrels

45. Pentane (36 °C) and straight-chain octane (126 °C), because they have a greater difference in boiling points (BP of isooctane is 116 °C).

46. Thermal energy must be applied to the mixture to vaporize the lower-boiling component. The vapor must then be cooled (via a condenser or in trays) so that thermal energy can be removed.

Connecting the Concepts

39. Why is petroleum considered a nonrenewable resource?

40. Using a Venn diagram, distinguish fractional distillation from simple distillation.

41. Simple distillation is never sufficient to separate two liquids completely. Explain.

42. In a fractionating tower, petroleum is generally heated to 400 °C. What would happen if it were heated only to 300 °C?

43. The molar masses of methane (16 g/mol) and water (18 g/mol) are similar. At room temperature, methane is a gas and water is a liquid. Explain this difference in terms of their intermolecular forces.

44. The traditional unit of volume for petroleum is the barrel, which contains 42 gallons. Assume that those 42 gallons of petroleum provide 21 gallons of gasoline. How many barrels of petroleum does it take to operate an automobile for one year, assuming the vehicle travels 10 000 miles and gets 27 miles per gallon of gasoline?

45. Which mixture would be easier to separate by distillation—a mixture of pentane and straight-chain octane or a mixture of pentane and a branched-chain octane isomer? Explain the reasoning behind your choice.

46. Explain why thermal energy is added at one point and removed at another point in the process of distillation.

Extending the Concepts

47. Is it likely that the composition of crude oil found in Texas is the same as that of crude oil found in Kuwait? Explain your answer.

48. Gasoline's composition is varied by oil companies for use in different parts of the nation and for use in different seasons. What factors help determine the composition of gasoline blended for different seasons?

49. What kind of petroleum trade relationship would be expected between North America and the Middle East? If other world regions become more industrialized and if global petroleum supplies decrease, how might the North America–Middle East trade relationship change?

50. How would the hydrocarbon boiling points listed in Table 3.2 (page 220) change if they were measured under increased atmospheric pressure? (*Hint:* Although butane is stored as a liquid inside of a butane lighter, it escapes through the lighter's nozzle as a gas.)

51. The two isomers of butane have different physical properties, as illustrated by their different boiling points. They also have different chemical properties. Explain how isomerism may contribute to their differences in chemical behavior.

52. What properties of petroleum make it an effective lubricant?

53. One problem with diesel fuel is that it solidifies at cold temperatures. How can its formulation be altered to prevent this problem?

Extending the Concepts

47. The compositions would differ greatly, depending on the makeup of the original living matter transformed into the crude oil as well as conditions under which the types of crude oil formed.

48. The factors are *viscosity* and *volatility*. In cold, more highly volatile hydrocarbon molecules are added to promote proper fuel vaporization in the engine. Under warmer conditions, the blend contains more low-volatility hydrocarbon fractions, to avoid the premature or too-rapid vaporization that may increase levels of smog.

49. A good trade relationship is needed between North America and parts of the Middle East. As other nations increase their use of Middle-Eastern oil, the North America–Middle East trade relationship will depend on price increases. If it becomes too expensive to import oil from the Middle East, North America may turn to locally available resources or search for petroleum substitutes. Developing technology in other world regions might lead other nations to become oil exporters.

50. They would increase with increased pressure. Butane, normally a gas at room temperature, is a liquid when held under pressure in a closed volume. The increased pressure means that greater energy is needed for butane molecules to overcome intermolecular forces to vaporize. This corresponds to an increase in butane's boiling point. When the valve is opened to the lower pressure of the atmosphere, the boiling point of butane becomes lower than room temperature; the liquid vaporizes.

51. In each isomer, the arrangement of atoms in space affects how it interacts with other molecules in chemical reactions. For example, the different arrangement of bonds and atoms in each isomer leads to unique interactions with oxygen molecules in combustion; branched alkanes burn more evenly than straight-chained alkanes.

52. It is a very slippery, viscous liquid at room temperature, insoluble in water, and relatively inert.

53. Add other hydrocarbons with lower melting points (while maintaining the original chemical and physical properties that make diesel fuel useful).

Petroleum: An Energy Source

SECTION
B

For almost 5000 years, humans have used petroleum in small amounts. Only in the last 150 years, roughly since the first U.S. oil well was drilled in 1859, has society become much more dependent on this nonrenewable resource. See Figure 3.22. In the following activity, you will begin to understand just how much everyday life is influenced by petroleum's role as an energy source—not just in powering automobiles and other vehicles, but in energizing modern society itself.

Figure 3.22 *In 1859, Edwin Drake struck oil at the world's first successful oil well, in Titusville, PA. Oil was already refined and used for many purposes at that time. Drake developed an efficient way to retrieve petroleum, leading to an oil boom in that region.*

ChemQuandary 1

ENERGY TRACING

Examine a paper clip. It is composed of a metallic alloy that could have a "materials history" written about it— a story revealing the origins of the paper clip's material, similar to those materials you studied in Unit 2.

What is less obvious, perhaps, is that this same paper clip can also be analyzed in terms of its energy history. Complete an "energy trace" for a paper clip by following these steps. (a) Decide what general events must have occurred to produce the paper clip and to deliver it to your school. (b) From where did the energy for each event come? In other words, what was the source of the needed energy? (c) In your view, is the total cost of a box of paper clips related more to the materials used (the metals in the alloy) or to the energy required? Explain your reasoning.

After completing an "energy trace" for a paper clip, consider how much more complicated and energy-consuming it is to produce the *Hybris* or any other automobile.

ChemQuandary 1

Energy Tracing

The table below summarizes energy transformations that may have taken place to produce a paper clip.

EVENT (A)	SOURCE (B)
Mine iron ore	Petroleum, ammonium nitrate/ nitroglycerin
Process iron ore	Coal
Form steel	Coke (from coal), limestone, oxygen
Draw into wires	Coal or petroleum
Cut wire	Coal or petroleum
Bend clips	Coal or petroleum
Produce packaging	Wood, sulfate, petroleum, or coal
Transport to warehouse or retailer	Petroleum
Transport to school	Petroleum

c. The total cost of a box of paper clips is more related to the energy required. The materials used to produce a paper clip are readily available, so their cost should be relatively low. However, many production steps are energetically costly. For example, mining and processing the metal, forming the metal into appropriate shapes, packaging, and transportation are steps that require significant energy.

Petroleum: An Energy Source

In Section B, students learn about petroleum as a source of energy—its "burning" role. Energy released from burning petroleum is analyzed in terms of bond breaking and bond making. Students measure the energy released by burning a hydrocarbon in a simple calorimeter investigation and also consider the concept of energy efficiency.

B.1 Energy and Fossil Fuels

B.1 Content Reading Guide

This material identifies the sun as the primary source of energy on earth and introduces the chemistry of energy storage and energy release from petroleum molecules. Chemical reactions are discussed in terms of endothermic and exothermic processes.

Energy classifications may confuse some students. A helpful web resource is NEED, National Energy Education Development, which offers several short topic papers at **http://www.need.org/needpdf/ infobook_activities/SecInfo/IntroS. pdf**. Another excellent site is Energy Quest, **http://www.energyquest.ca. gov/index.html**.

Remind students that energy is either kinetic or potential, but that both categories include several more forms of energy, as shown in the table below.

Using the Figures

Figure 3.23: Emphasize that this illustration is based on evidence for types of plants and animals that probably existed in the Paleozoic Era. Ask students to compare the forest depicted to forests with which they are familiar. This scene depicts a coal forest, including horsetails and lycopods (prehistoric spore-bearing plants that grew as large trees), and insects, most notably the giant winged dragonfly *(Meganeura)*. The figure helps illustrate that coal originated from plants and animals, which ultimately required energy from the sun to grow.

Energy and Fossil Fuels

Energy is a measure of the ability of a system to do work.

Figure 3.23 *Fossil fuels are thought to have originated from living matter; this illustration depicts a forest in the Upper Carboniferous or Pennsylvanian division of the Paleozoic Era.*

A rock poised at the top of a hill has more potential energy—energy of position—than the same rock resting at the bottom of the hill.

B.1 ENERGY AND FOSSIL FUELS

Fossil fuels are believed to originate from biomolecules of prehistoric plants and animals. See Figure 3.23. The energy released by burning these fuels represents energy originally captured from sunlight by prehistoric green plants during photosynthesis. Thus, **fossil fuels**—petroleum, natural gas, and coal—can be thought of as forms of buried sunshine.

Most evidence indicates that fossil fuels originated from living matter in ancient seas some 500 million years ago. These species died and eventually became covered with sediments. Pressure, heat, and microbes converted what was once living matter into petroleum, which became trapped in porous rocks. It is likely that some petroleum is still being formed from sediments of dead matter. However, such a process is far too slow to consider petroleum a renewable resource.

Fossil-fuel energy is comparable in some ways to the energy stored in a wind-up toy race car. The "winding-up" energy that was originally supplied tightened a spring in the toy. Most of that energy, stored within the coiled spring, is a form of **potential energy,** which is energy of position (or condition). As the car moves, the spring

FORMS OF KINETIC ENERGY	FORMS OF POTENTIAL ENERGY
Motion	Gravitational
Heat (thermal)	Chemical
Sound	Stored mechanical (as in springs)
Radiation	Nuclear
Electrical	

unwinds, providing energy to the moving parts. Energy related to motion is called **kinetic energy.** Thus, the movement of the car is based on converting potential energy into kinetic energy. Eventually, the toy "winds down" to a lower-energy, more stable state and stops.

In a similar manner, **chemical energy,** which is another form of potential energy, is stored within bonds in chemical compounds. When an energy-releasing chemical reaction takes place (such as when fuel burns), bonds break and reactant atoms reorganize to form new bonds. The process yields products with different and more stable bonding arrangements of their atoms. That is, the products have less potential energy (chemical energy) than did the original reactants. Some of the energy stored in the reactants has been released in the form of heat and light.

The combustion, or burning, of methane (CH_4) gas illustrates such an energy-releasing reaction. It can be summarized this way:

$$CH_4 + 2\ O_2 \longrightarrow CO_2 + 2\ H_2O + Energy$$

Methane   Oxygen   Carbon   Water
gas   gas   dioxide gas

The reaction releases considerable **thermal energy** (heat). In fact, laboratory burner flames are based primarily on that reaction—conducted, of course, under very controlled conditions. To gain a better understanding of the energy involved, just imagine that the reaction takes place in two simple steps: One step involves bond breaking and one step involves bond making.

In the first step, suppose that all the chemical bonds in one CH_4 molecule and two O_2 molecules are broken. The result of this bond-breaking step is that separated atoms of carbon, hydrogen, and oxygen are produced. All such bond-breaking steps are energy-requiring processes, or **endothermic** changes. In an endothermic change, energy must be added to "pull apart" the atoms in each molecule. Thus, energy appears as a *reactant* in Step 1, as shown in the following chemical equation:

Step 1

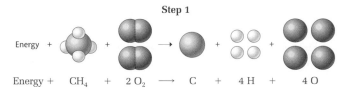

$$Energy + CH_4 + 2\ O_2 \longrightarrow C + 4\ H + 4\ O$$

Energy from Combustion

Methane is a major component of natural gas.

This simplification allows us to more easily analyze the energy involved. The actual reaction is more complicated.

An endothermic reaction can proceed only if energy is continuously supplied.

This discussion uses the combustion of methane, which is exothermic, to illustrate that the energy needed to break bonds is less than the energy released when making bonds. If a reaction is exothermic, then the reverse reaction is endothermic. If in one direction the bond-making energy exceeds the bond-breaking energy (exothermic reaction), in the opposite direction— breaking the bonds that were made and making the bonds that were broken—bond-breaking energy must exceed bond-making energy and the reaction will be endothermic.

Encourage students to include the energy of reaction on the product or reactant side of an equation to represent, respectively, an exothermic or endothermic reaction.

Activation energy is not explored here; it is developed in Unit 5. If you decide to introduce this term now, explain it as "starting energy" for a reaction. **Figure 3.24** (page 240) is also helpful in explaining activation energy—since the separated atoms have more potential energy than the bonded atoms (in either reactant or product state), energy must be added to pull atoms apart that will later be released when they bond. Although in most cases the atoms never become fully separated, but rather form a higher-energy "activated complex," the notion of atom separation may help students to see why energy must be added even though the reactant state is energetically favorable.

Emphasize that the exact sequence of events involved in a reaction is often quite complex at the atomic/molecular level. Reactions proceed through a series of steps represented in the *reaction mechanism.* Overall chemical equations simply summarize the initial and final states of the system. Likewise, only the *net* energy difference between initial and final states of the system determines whether the overall reaction is *endothermic* or *exothermic.*

Using the Figures

Figure 3.24: This diagram illustrates the energy absorbed and released as bonds are broken and formed in a reaction. It does *not* depict how the reaction takes place (the mechanism). The middle portion shows methane and water molecules broken into individual atoms; this is not what *actually* occurs. (In reality, several intermediate structures form.)

Demonstration Ideas

1. The electrolysis of water, producing H_2 and O_2, demonstrates that the decomposition of water is endothermic. To demonstrate the reverse reaction, collect small quantities of hydrogen gas and oxygen gas in a test tube and ignite with a glowing splint. This dramatizes that the combination of hydrogen and oxygen is exothermic. A small quantity of energy (from the glowing splint) is needed to initiate the reaction, but much more energy is produced once the reaction proceeds (the explosion and flame). (See *Chemical Demonstrations, A Sourcebook for Teachers,* vol. 1, Summerlin and Ealy, 1988, ACS Publications, for appropriate procedures and safety information.)

2. An endothermic reaction is used in cold packs. Add 100 mL water to a large beaker and record the temperature. Quickly add 10–15 g ammonium nitrate crystals. Note the temperature change as the solid dissolves. The dissolving of ammonium nitrate is clearly endothermic; the temperature should decrease 6 to 9 °C. In this reaction, 140–210 J are absorbed per 100 mL water. You may obtain a more accurate reading by using an insulated or Styrofoam cup with a lid.

To complete the methane-burning reaction, suppose that the separated atoms now join to form the new bonds needed to make the product molecules: one CO_2 molecule and two H_2O molecules. The formation of chemical bonds is an energy-releasing process, or an **exothermic** change. Because energy is given off, it appears as a *product* in Step 2, as shown in the following chemical equation:

Step 2

$$C \quad + \quad 4\,H \quad + \quad 4\,O \quad \longrightarrow \quad CO_2 \quad + \quad 2\,H_2O + Energy$$

When methane burns, the energy released in forming carbon–oxygen bonds in CO_2 and hydrogen–oxygen bonds in H_2O is greater than the energy used to break the carbon–hydrogen bonds in CH_4 and the oxygen–oxygen bond in O_2. That is why this overall chemical change is exothermic. The complete energy "accounting summary" for burning methane is shown in Figure 3.24.

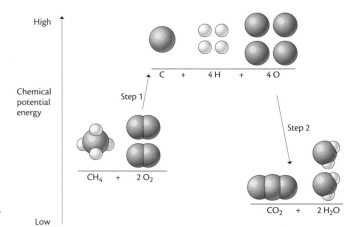

Figure 3.24 *A potential energy diagram for the formation of carbon dioxide and water from methane and oxygen gases. In Step 1, bonds break. This is an endothermic process. Step 2, bond making, releases energy, so it is an exothermic process. Because more energy is released in Step 2 than is required in Step 1, the overall reaction is exothermic.*

Whether an overall chemical reaction is exothermic or endothermic depends on how much energy is added (endothermic process) in bond breaking and how much energy is given off (exothermic process) in bond making. If more energy is given off than is added, the overall change is exothermic. However, if more energy is added than is given off, the overall change is endothermic.

Once an exothermic reaction begins, it releases energy until the reaction stops.

Equation: Heat + $NH_4NO_3(s)$ + $H_2O(l) \rightarrow NH_4^+(aq) + NO_3^-(aq)$

Figure 3.25 *Bicycling is an example of continuous conversions between potential and kinetic energy.*

In general, if a process converts potential energy into kinetic energy, then the reverse process converts kinetic energy back to potential energy. For example if you wind the spring of a model race car, you are converting your energy of motion (winding) into energy stored in the spring. A biker or a skateboarder uses the transformation of potential energy into kinetic energy to complete jumps and other tricks (Figure 3.25).

Likewise, if a particular chemical reaction is exothermic (releasing thermal energy), then the reverse reaction is endothermic (converting thermal energy into potential energy). For example, burning hydrogen gas—involving the formation of water—is exothermic. The energy released by the formation of H—O bonds in water is greater than that required to break H_2 and O_2 bonds:

$$2 H_2 + O_2 \longrightarrow 2 H_2O + Energy$$

Therefore, the separation of water into its elements—the reverse reaction—must be endothermic, equal in energy used to that released when water is formed from gaseous H_2 and O_2. Electrical energy is expended and is converted into potential energy that is stored, again, in chemical bonds. See Figure 3.26.

$$Energy + 2 H_2O \longrightarrow 2 H_2 + O_2$$

If a rock rolling downhill is an exothermic process, then pushing the same rock back uphill must be an endothermic process.

Figure 3.26 *An electric current provides energy to decompose water, producing hydrogen (right test tube) and oxygen (left test tube) gas. This process is referred to as the "electrolysis" of water. As follows from the formula of water (H_2O), hydrogen and oxygen gas are produced in a 2 to 1 ratio.*

Section B   Petroleum: An Energy Source   **241**

3. Another exothermic reaction: Add 100 mL water to a large beaker and record the temperature. Quickly add 10–15 g calcium chloride. Note the temperature change as the solid dissolves. The temperature should increase about 12 °C. The heat of solution for calcium chloride is about 490 J per 100 mL water. You may obtain a more accurate reading by using an insulated or Styrofoam cup. Discard the cup after the demonstration.
   Equation: $CaCl_2(s) + H_2O(l) \rightarrow Ca^{2+}(aq) + 2 Cl^-(aq) + Heat$

4. Demonstrate exothermic reactions using a commercially available hot pack and endothermic reactions with a commercially available cold pack. Pass the packs around the room for students to observe. Emphasize that in the hot pack, energy is flowing *from* the pack into their hands—an exothermic reaction—while in a cold pack, energy flows from their hands *into* the pack, creating the sensation of "cold"—an endothermic reaction.

   Many hot packs contain a supersaturated solution of sodium acetate trihydrate and a metal disk. A seed crystal is created as this disk is flexed and crystallization proceeds. Crystallization is exothermic, so the pack liberates thermal energy. Other heat packs rely on iron filings, oxygen, and the exothermic rusting process for thermal energy release. Many cold packs consist of a sealed tube of ammonium nitrate inside a packet of liquid water. The cold pack is activated by breaking open the tube; ammonium nitrate dissolves in the water. The dissolving process is endothermic, so the pack absorbs heat and feels cold.

B.2 Energy Conversion

Energy may go through several conversions before we actually use it to do work. Energy is not "used up" in any conversion; it is simply changed from one form to another. Like matter, the total energy is conserved.

An exception to both the law of conservation of energy and the law of conservation of matter occurs when matter and energy are inter-converted in nuclear processes. You might decide to mention this as an exception here. (Students will learn more about it in Unit 6.)

Demonstration Idea

You can make a simple steam engine from a 12-oz aluminum beverage can. Punch a hole in the middle of the side of an *unopened* carbonated beverage can using a thumbtack. Do this over a sink and continually shake the can, using the pressure generated by carbonation to force the beverage out through the hole. When the can is empty, punch a second hole on the side opposite the first. Rinse the can with a wash bottle, squirting water into one of the two holes. Once you have emptied and rinsed the can, use the wash bottle to add about 10 mL water (or enough so you hear it sloshing around inside the can). Use the thumbtack to bend each of the two holes in the same direction, tangential to the can's surface.

Tie a string to the can's unopened pull tab and secure the can to a ring stand at a height that allows a Bunsen burner or hot plate to warm it. When the can is heated, water vapor exits both holes, resulting in a net force to set the can spinning. Discuss with students

B.2 ENERGY CONVERSION

Scientists and engineers have increased the usefulness of energy released from burning fuels through devices that convert thermal energy into other forms of energy. In fact, much of the energy you use daily goes through several conversions before it reaches you.

Consider the energy-conversion steps involved in the operation of a hair dryer, illustrated in Figure 3.27. What detailed, step-by-step "energy story" can you devise using these illustrations?

You probably noted that in the first step, stored chemical energy (potential energy) in a fossil fuel, Figure 3.27(a), is released in a power-plant furnace, producing thermal (heat) energy, as shown in Figure 3.27(b). The thermal energy then converts water in the boiler to steam that spins the turbines (mechanical energy), generating electrical energy as shown in Figure 3.27(c). Thus, the power plant converts thermal energy produced in the furnace to mechanical energy, which is a form of kinetic energy, in the turbines. It is then converted

(a)

(b)

(c)

(d)

(e)

Figure 3.27 *Many steps are involved in the processes by which the chemical energy stored in the bonds of hydrocarbon molecules is eventually converted to the thermal energy a hair dryer produces.*

energy transformations, from chemical energy of the fuel (or the fuel that produced the electricity powering the hot plate) to kinetic energy of the rotating can, to the potential energy of twisted string, and so on. Challenge students to explain why the can behaves as it does—as long as the water is heated gently, the steam is not visible as it exits the can—"magically" spinning by its own volition.

to electrical energy, as shown in Figure 3.27(d). When electricity reaches the hair dryer, it is converted back to thermal energy to dry your hair, and it is also converted to mechanical energy, Figure 3.27(e), as a small fan blade spins to blow the hot air. Some sound energy is also produced, as any hair-dryer user knows!

Despite all the changes involved, no energy is consumed or "used up" in any of these steps. The form of energy just changes from *chemical* to *thermal* to *mechanical* to *electrical*. This concept is summarized by the **Law of Conservation of Energy,** which states that energy is neither created nor destroyed in any mechanical, physical, or chemical processes.

B.3 AUTOMOBILE ENERGY CONVERSIONS

In one sense, an automobile—whether powered by electricity, gasoline, or even solar energy—can be considered a collection of energy-converting and energy-powered devices. Imagine that you are an "energy detective," and follow some typical energy conversions in an automobile. Use Figure 3.28 to answer the following questions:

Figure 3.28 *What energy conversions are necessary to propel a car? Trace the energy conversions, starting with the gas tank and ending with movement of the wheels.*

1. Name the type of energy involved in each step required to cause the wheels to propel a conventional automobile forward.
2. Do you think that all the energy originally stored in gasoline can be traced to the rotating wheels? Explain.

Developing Skills

B.3 Automobile Energy Conversions

In this activity, students apply their knowledge of energy conversions to a familiar system.

Answers

Based on **Figure 3.28:**

1. Step One: chemical (potential) energy

   Step Two: Chemical energy is converted to thermal and mechanical energy.

   Step Three: *Pistons* convert translational (up and down) mechanical energy into rotational mechanical energy (spinning the crankshaft).

   Steps Four and Five: Rotational mechanical energy is converted to mechanical energy for rotating the *wheels*.

2. No. Much of the energy stored in gasoline is lost to the environment as heat (thermal energy).

SECTION B

Developing Skills

B.4 Energy Efficiency

Remind students that no device is 100% efficient. Every system involves energy conversions, and no single conversion is 100% efficient. Less-efficient conversions and multiple conversions decrease overall efficiency of a system.

Emphasize that the automobile is a system of a series of interconnected and coordinated energy conversion devices. During conversion from energy stored in fuel to motion (operation of car and accessories), about 75% of the energy is lost to the environment (wasted), generally as heat.

Using the Figures

Figure 3.29: This drawing illustrates the fate of energy from gasoline as it is burned in an automobile. About one-third of fuel energy is lost with exhaust gases, including thermal energy of the gases and chemical energy of both unburned fuel and combustion by-products. Additional energy is lost when gases burn in the cylinders and the gases and surrounding cylinders are heated incidentally to piston movement. This thermal energy is removed by engine coolant (cylinder cooling in the figure) and (in cold weather) used to heat the vehicle's interior, but is not useful to provide motion or operate accessories. Another portion of initial energy is used to draw air into the cylinders for combustion. (This is similar to the energy needed to draw a fluid into a syringe.) Friction among moving parts in the engine and the resulting thermal energy

transferred to the engine account for additional energy loss. The percent of potential energy input that is actually converted into mechanical kinetic energy is a measure of efficiency. This internal combustion engine is only about 25% efficient.

244

Developing Skills

B.4 ENERGY EFFICIENCY

Petroleum is neither limitless nor inexpensive. One way to maximize the benefits from available supplies of petroleum-based fuels is to reduce the total number of energy conversions the fuel undergoes. We can also seek ways to increase the efficiency of energy-conversion devices.

Unfortunately, devices that convert chemical energy to thermal energy and then to mechanical energy are typically less than 50% efficient. Solar cells, which convert solar energy to electrical energy, and fuel cells, which convert chemical energy to electrical energy, hold long-term promise for either replacing petroleum or increasing the efficiency of its use.

Although energy-converting devices definitely have increased the usefulness of petroleum and other fuels, some of these devices have problems associated with their use. For example, they may sometimes generate potentially harmful by-products. (You will learn more about this issue later in the unit.) More fundamentally, some useful energy is always "lost" whenever energy is converted from one form to another. That is, no energy conversion is totally efficient; some energy, usually liberated as heat energy, always becomes unavailable to do useful work.

Consider an automobile with 100 units of chemical energy stored in the mixture of molecules that make up gasoline in its fuel tank. See Figure 3.29. Even a well-tuned automobile converts only about 25% of that chemical energy (potential energy) to useful mechanical energy (kinetic energy). The remaining 75% of gasoline's chemical energy is lost to the surroundings as heat (thermal energy). The following activity will allow you to realize what this means in terms of gasoline consumption and expense.

You will learn more about fuel cells later in this unit on pages 290–291.

Figure 3.29 *Energy use in a moving automobile. Note that only about 25% of the potential energy in the gasoline is used to power the vehicle.*

B.5 ENERGY CONVERSION EFFICIENCY

How much gasoline in a car's gas tank is actually used by the engine? How much is wasted—and at what cost?

Sample Problem: *Assume that your family drives 225 miles each week and that the car can travel 23.0 miles on one gallon of gasoline. How much gasoline does the car use in one year?*

This question can be answered by attaching the units to all values, then multiplying and dividing them as though they were arithmetic expressions.

For example, the relevent information can be expressed as:

$$\frac{225 \text{ mi}}{1 \text{ wk}} \quad and \quad \frac{23.0 \text{ mi}}{1 \text{ gal}}$$

or, if needed, as inverted expressions:

$$\frac{1 \text{ wk}}{225 \text{ mi}} \quad and \quad \frac{1 \text{ gal}}{23.0 \text{ mi}}$$

Calculating the desired answer also involves using information you already know—there are 52 weeks, for example, in one year. You also know that the desired answer must have units of "gallons per year" (gal/yr). When care is taken to ensure that units are multiplied and divided to produce gal/yr, the following expression is formed:

$$\frac{225 \text{ mi}}{1 \text{ wk}} \times \frac{1 \text{ gal}}{23.0 \text{ mi}} \times \frac{52 \text{ wk}}{1 \text{ yr}} = 509 \text{ gal/yr}$$

Now answer the following questions:

1. Assume that a conventional automobile averages 23.0 miles per gallon of gasoline and travels 11 000 miles annually:
   a. How much fuel will be burned in one year?
   b. If gasoline is $3.00 per gallon, what would be spent in one year?

2. Assume that a *Hybris* hybrid-powered automobile averages 50.0 miles per gallon of gasoline and travels 11 000 miles annually.
   a. How much gasoline will the *Hybris* burn in one year?
   b. If gasoline is $3.00 per gallon, what would be spent on fuel annually?

3. Assume the automobile in Question 1 uses only 25.0% of the energy released by burning gasoline.
   a. How many gallons of gasoline are wasted each year due to energy conversion inefficiency?
   b. How much does this wasted gasoline cost at $3.00 per gallon?

4. Suppose a new car travels 70.0 miles on one gallon of gasoline with a 40.0% efficient engine:
   a. How much fuel is saved annually compared to cars in Questions 1 and 3?
   b. How much fuel is wasted annually due to energy inefficiency?

B.5 Energy Conversion Efficiency

In this activity, students use realistic estimates for automobile use and efficiency to calculate the costs of energy loss associated with various energy conversions. Work through the sample problem (and other examples) with students. Students may also benefit from doing the calculations in groups.

Answers

1. a. 11 000 mi/yr × 1 gal/23.0 mi = 478 gal/yr
   b. 478 gal/yr × $3.00/gal = $1434/yr

2. a. 11 000 mi/yr × 1 gal/50 mi = 220 gal/yr
   b. 220 gal/yr × $3.00/gal = $660/yr

3. a. 478 gal/yr × 0.75 = 359 gal/yr wasted
   b. 359 gal/yr × $3.00/gal = $1077/yr

4. a. 11 000 mi/yr × 1 gal/70 mi = 157 gal/yr

   Gasoline saved: 321 gal compared with car 1, 63 gal compared with car 2
   b. 157 gal/yr × 0.60 = 94 gal/yr wasted ($283 at $3.00/gal)

People have tried to increase the efficiency of processes involving energy conversions, but technology is still quite far from achieving full, 100% efficiency. One interesting folly in the history of technology involves repeated attempts by different experimenters to devise a perpetual motion machine. Invention of such a machine is inherently impossible due to the fact that no manner of energy transfer from one form to another is 100% efficient.

CHEMISTRY at Work

Oil's Well That Ends Well: The Work of a Petroleum Geologist

Susan Landon is an independent petroleum geologist. Using her knowledge of chemistry, geology, geography, biology, and mathematics, she analyzes rocks and other geologic and geographic features for indications of likely oil and natural-gas reserves.

Susan searches for the folded or faulted terrain of Earth that often contains petroleum. Hydrocarbons (oil or natural gas) may be trapped in reservoirs in these areas. Using data about a given geographic area—such as satellite images, aerial photographs, topographic maps, and information about the rocks—Susan predicts the quantity of oil or natural gas that may have been generated from organic matter in the rocks, and where it might occur.

> A geologist can examine the chips . . . and identify the presence of oil.

If signs are good for a substantial petroleum deposit, Susan and her team work to find investors to fund further exploration. Such exploration often includes more detailed research, analysis, and drilling. During drilling, Susan and her colleagues examine rock samples and analyze data regarding electrical and other physical properties of the rocks encountered. Based on the findings, the group recommends either completing the well or plugging it.

In Susan's opinion, a good liberal arts background with a major in geology or a related science is excellent preparation for advanced studies in geology.

Wells? Now There's a Deep Subject!

Although there are many techniques for predicting the presence of underground oil or natural gas, the only way to know for sure is to drill a well.

The process of drilling a well begins with a drilling rig consisting of a derrick—a large, vertical structure made of metal that holds and supports a drilling pipe. Rotated by a motor, the drilling pipe ends in a bit that digs and scrapes down through soil and rock. Drilling fluid (usually a special mixture of water and other materials that is called "mud") is pumped down through the pipe to cool the bit and carry chips of rock back to the surface.

A geologist can examine the chips and other material brought to the surface to determine the rock type and identify the presence of oil.

Although oil or natural gas sometimes flows to the surface spontaneously as a result of underground pressure, the more common procedure is to install a pump. Pumped from the well, the oil or natural gas is transported by truck or pipeline to a refinery. At the refinery, the oil or natural gas is processed and delivered to commercial and private consumers, who convert it into everything from polypropylene socks to carpeting to household heat.

Section B Petroleum: An Energy Source **247**

SECTION B

B.6 Combustion

 B.6 Combustion Student Worksheet and Data Table

Students explore *combustion*, including balancing equations representing energy release. Knowing how to measure the energy from different fuels can help students choose among fuels.

Introduce and define **calorimetry,** the measure of thermal energy emitted, required, or transferred in a process. Here students trap thermal energy from a burning tea candle in a soda-can calorimeter and calculate the heat of combustion.

Time

50 min

Materials

(For 12 student pairs)

12 12-oz, empty soft-drink cans (with pull tabs)

12 ring stands

12 rings

12 thermometers, alcohol, −10 to 110 °C

12 stirring rods, glass

12 pencils, wood

12 paraffin ($C_{25}H_{52}$) tea candles

12 graduated cylinders, 100-mL

5 lb ice

Balances

Matches

Safety

Students should wear protective goggles and aprons. Caution them to stir water with a stirring rod, *not* a thermometer, to avoid thermometer breakage.

Caution students not to inhale carbon soot. If carbon soot (a possible irritant) gets on skin, wash it off immediately.

B.6 COMBUSTION

Lab Video "Combustion"

Figure 3.30 *As with all combustion reactions, thermal energy is released when candles burn. What other form(s) of energy result from this process?*

Introduction

You strike a match and a hot, yellow flame appears. If you bring the flame close to a candlewick, the candle ignites and burns (Figure 3.30). These events are so commonplace that you probably do not think about the complex chemical reactions at work.

Candle burning involves chemical reactions of the wax, which is composed of long-chain alkanes, with oxygen gas at elevated temperatures. Although many chemical reactions are involved in burning (or *combustion*), chemists simplify the process by usually focusing on the overall changes. For example, the complete burning of one component of candle wax, $C_{25}H_{52}$, can be summarized this way:

$$C_{25}H_{52}(s) \ + \ 38 \ O_2(g) \longrightarrow 25 \ CO_2(g) \ + \ 26 \ H_2O(g) \ + \ Energy$$

Paraffin wax (alkane)   Oxygen gas   Carbon dioxide gas   Water vapor

As you already know, a burning candle gives off energy—the reaction is exothermic. Thus, less energy must be stored in the product molecules (in the carbon-to-oxygen bonds of carbon dioxide gas and the hydrogen-to-oxygen bonds of water vapor) than was originally stored in the reactant molecules (in the carbon-to-hydrogen bonds of wax and the oxygen-to-oxygen bonds of oxygen gas).

Fuels provide thermal energy as they burn. But how much energy is released? How can we measure the quantity of released energy? In this investigation, you will measure the *heat of combustion* of a candle (paraffin wax) and compare this quantity with known values for other hydrocarbons.

Before you begin, carefully read the procedure to learn what is involved, note safety precautions, and plan for your data collecting and observations. In this laboratory investigation, you will record data before and after the candle is burned. The first (left) column of your data table can be used to record each data item collected. The two middle columns can be used for values recorded before and after burning the candle. A fourth (right) column can be used to report the difference between the *before* and *after* values that you noted.

Procedure

1. Determine the mass of the tea candle. Record its value.
2. Carefully measure (to the nearest milliliter) about 100 mL of chilled water. (The chilled water, provided by your teacher, should be 10 to 15 °C colder than room temperature.) Pour the 100-mL sample of chilled water into an empty soft-drink can.

Advance Preparation

A day or two ahead of time, ask each student to bring in at least one clean, empty aluminum soft-drink can with pull tab still attached. Flip up the can tabs so pencils or stirring rods can pass through (see **Figure 3.31**). Stirring may be slightly challenging, but this nearly closed soda can minimizes

thermal loss. Have extra aluminum cans on hand in case tabs break off some cans. Some students, with your permission, may repeat the procedure and will need a second (unused) can.

Each class uses chilled water. If tap water is not cool enough, add ice until the temperature is about 10 °C cooler than room temperature. Starting at the same number of

3. Set up the apparatus as shown in Figure 3.31, but do not light the candle yet! Adjust the can so that the top of the candlewick is about 2 cm from the bottom of the can.

4. Measure both the room temperature and the water temperature to the nearest 0.1 °C. Record these values.

⚠ 5. Place the candle under the can of water. Light the candle. As the water heats, stir it gently. (*Caution: Do not stir with the thermometer—use a stirring rod.*)

⚠ 6. As the candle burns and becomes shorter, you may need to lower the can so that the flame remains just below the bottom of the can. (*Caution: Lower the can with great care.*)

7. Continue heating the water until its temperature rises as far above room temperature as it was below room temperature at the start. (For example, if the water temperature were 15 °C before heating and room temperature is 25 °C, you would heat the water to 35 °C, 10 °C higher than room temperature.)

8. When the desired temperature is reached, extinguish the candle flame.

9. Continue stirring the water until its temperature stops rising. Record the highest temperature reached by the warmed water.

10. Determine and record the mass of the cooled candle, including all wax drippings.

11. Wash your hands thoroughly before leaving the laboratory.

Figure 3.31 *Apparatus for determining heat of combustion.*

Data Analysis

A characteristic property of a material is the quantity of heat needed to raise the temperature of one gram of the material by one degree Celsius. This value is called the **specific heat capacity** of the material. The specific heat capacity of liquid water is about 4.2 J/(g·°C) (joules per gram per °C). This means that each 4.2 J of energy absorbed by one gram of water will increase its temperature by one degree Celsius.

Sample Problem: *Suppose a 10.0-g water sample is heated from 25.0 °C to 30.0 °C, an increase of 5.0 °C. How much thermal energy must have been added to the water?*

The answer can be reasoned this way: It takes 4.2 J to raise the temperature of 1 g water by 1 °C. In this example, however, there is 10.0 times more water and a temperature increase that is 5.0 times greater. Thus, 10.0 × 5.0, or 50 times more thermal energy is needed. Therefore, the specific heat must be multiplied by 50 to obtain the answer: 50 × 4.2 J = 210 J. It takes 210 J to increase the temperature of 10.0 g water by 5.0 °C.

> Specific heat capacity is sometimes shortened to the term specific heat.

> The precise specific heat capacity of water is 4.184 J/g. However, a rounded-off value of 4.2 J/g is adequate.

Pre-Lab Discussion

Referring to **Figure 3.30**, identify energy types released during combustion. Students will point to thermal energy but may overlook light and (sometimes) sound energy. Here students use calorimetry to measure thermal energy released as a candle burns. Ask students to think how the term *calorimetry* possibly originated or what alternative terms they associate with calorimetry. They should identify the term *calorie.* The calorie and Calorie, non-SI units of energy, are still sometimes used in the United States.

Introduce or review the SI energy unit, the joule (J). A joule can also be expressed as a "N·m" or $\frac{\text{kg m}^2}{\text{s}^2}$ or even "W·s." Remind students that the kinetic-energy equation is $E = 1/2\ mv^2$, where m = mass (in kg) and v = velocity (in m/s). To link these units with familiar experiences: One joule is enough energy to lift a person a mere 1 to 3 mm upward, or the energy contained in sunlight falling for one second on a 10 cm × 10 cm area. Students should also realize that 4.2 J (1 cal) is required to raise the temperature of 1 g water by 1 °C.

Lab Tips

• Most student-quality thermometers are reliable only to the nearest 0.5 °C. Remind students to report all data to correct significant figures.

• As time and resources permit, students may repeat the procedure. Ideally, they need a new aluminum can (soot will accumulate on the first can, introducing a new source of experimental error).

degrees *below* room temperature and ending at the same number of degrees *above* room temperature crudely counterbalances two experimental errors—*heat gain from surroundings* versus *heat loss to surroundings.* Students can ignore these offsetting effects and assume that all burning-candle heat is captured. Tell students to remove unmelted ice from the water before heating it.

Give students a place (whiteboard, chalkboard, poster board, or overhead transparency) to record group values for calculated candle-wax heat of combustion in kJ/g and kJ/mol. These data will be useful for analysis of pooled class results.

Data Analysis Answers

1. The calculation is:
   Water volume (mL) × 1.00 g/mL = Water mass (g).
2. Final temperature − Initial temperature = Temperature change
3. Thermal energy = Mass × Specific heat capacity of material × Temperature change
4. Mass burned = (Mass of candle + card before heating) − (Mass of candle + card after heating)
5. Student values may vary widely. Example:
   Total thermal energy = 98.6 g water × (4.2 J/g °C) × 21.2 °C = 8800 J
   Mass candle burned = 0.25 g
   Heat of combustion, J/g = 8800 J/0.25 g = 35 000 J/g
   Heat of combustion, kJ/g = 35 000 J/g × 1 kJ/1000 J = 35 kJ/g
6. Heat of combustion, kJ/mol = 35 kJ/g × 352 g/mol = 12 000 kJ/mol

Answers

1. Propane's heat of combustion (50.0 kJ/g) is higher than paraffin's (42.0 kJ/g). Despite the relatively crude calorimeter used here, class-averaged results are often quite satisfactory. Students' experimental values will often be lower than theoretical values because of heat loss to surrounding air and to the can.
2. Paraffin's molar heat of combustion (about 14 800 kJ/mol) is greater than propane's (2200 kJ/mol).
3. Burning 1 g propane releases more energy than burning 1 g paraffin, but 1 mol paraffin has a larger mass than 1 mol propane. Answers to Questions 1 and 2 are not contradictory. Each average wax "molecule" has 24 C—C bonds, while a propane molecule has two C—C bonds. Burning each

—CH$_2$— unit produces one molecule each of CO$_2$ and H$_2$O and additional thermal energy, so burning 1 mol paraffin releases more energy than burning 1 mol propane.
4. Gram for gram, propane is slightly better, but mole for mole (or molecule for molecule), paraffin is better.
5. a. No. Some thermal energy is lost to the surroundings from the flame, through

can walls, and from the water surface. This energy is unaccounted for in calculations, so heat-of-combustion values are lower than the true value.
   b. The burning wick's small energy contribution to total heat released (its heat of combustion is probably lower than that of wax) and incomplete wax combustion may lower measured thermal energy.

| Table 3.6

HEATS OF COMBUSTION FOR SELECTED HYDROCARBONS

Hydrocarbon	Formula	Heat of Combustion (kJ/g)	Molar Heat of Combustion (kJ/mol)
Methane	CH$_4$	55.6	890
Ethane	C$_2$H$_6$	52.0	1560
Propane	C$_3$H$_8$	50.0	2200
Butane	C$_4$H$_{10}$	49.3	2859
Pentane	C$_5$H$_{12}$	48.8	3510
Hexane	C$_6$H$_{14}$	48.2	4141
Heptane	C$_7$H$_{16}$	48.2	4817
Octane	C$_8$H$_{18}$	47.8	5450

The quantity of thermal energy given off when a certain amount of a substance burns is called the **heat of combustion**. See Table 3.6. The heat of combustion can be expressed as the thermal energy released when either one gram or one mole of substance burns. If the amount of substance burned is one mole, the quantity of thermal energy involved is called the **molar heat of combustion**.

Using your laboratory data, you can calculate the heat of combustion of paraffin wax:

1. Calculate the mass of water heated. (*Hint:* The density of liquid water is 1.0 g/mL. Thus, each milliliter of water has a mass of 1.0 g.)
2. Calculate the total rise in the temperature of the water.
3. Calculate how much thermal energy was used to heat the water sample. Use values from the two preceding steps to reason out the answer, as illustrated in the earlier sample problem.
4. Calculate the total mass of paraffin wax burned.
5. Calculate the heat of combustion of paraffin, expressed in units of
   a. joules per gram (J/g) of paraffin.
   b. kJ/g of paraffin.
   (*Hint:* Assume that all the energy released by the burning paraffin wax is absorbed by the water.)
6. Calculate the molar heat of combustion of paraffin, expressed in units of kJ/mol. (*Hint:* First calculate the thermal energy released when one mole of paraffin burns. Because one mole of paraffin (C$_{25}$H$_{52}$) has a mass of 352 g, the *molar* heat of combustion will be 352 times greater than the heat of combustion expressed in units of kJ/g.)

1 kJ = 1000 J

Questions

Your teacher will collect your heat of combustion data, expressed in units of kilojoules per gram (kJ/g) of paraffin. Use the combined results of your class to determine the *best estimate* for this value. Will you decide to use the average value of the class results or the median value? Why? Use your selected value to answer the following questions:

1. How does your experimental heat of combustion (in kJ/g) for paraffin wax, $C_{25}H_{52}$, compare to the accepted heat of combustion for propane, C_3H_8? See Table 3.6.

2. How do the molar heats of combustion (in kJ/mol) for paraffin and propane compare?

3. Explain the differences in your answers to Questions 1 and 2 for paraffin and propane. (*Hint:* Keep in mind the calculation you completed in Step 6.)

4. In your view, which hydrocarbon—paraffin or propane—is the better fuel? Explain your answer, citing evidence from your observations and data.

5. In calculating the heat of combustion of paraffin, you assumed that all thermal energy from the burning wax went to heating the water:
   a. Was this a good assumption? Explain.
   b. What other laboratory conditions or assumptions might cause errors in your calculated values?

B.7 USING HEATS OF COMBUSTION

With abundant oxygen gas and complete combustion, the burning of a hydrocarbon can be described by the equation

Hydrocarbon + Oxygen gas $\longrightarrow$ Carbon dioxide + Water + Thermal energy

"Thermal energy" is written as a product of the reaction because energy is released when a hydrocarbon burns (Figure 3.32). The combustion of a hydrocarbon is a highly exothermic reaction.

The equation for burning ethane (C_2H_6) is

$$2\,C_2H_6 + 7\,O_2 \longrightarrow 4\,CO_2 + 6\,H_2O + ?\ \text{kJ thermal energy}$$

To complete this equation, the correct quantity of thermal energy involved must be included. Table 3.6 indicates that ethane's molar heat of combustion is 1560 kJ/mol. That is, burning one mole of ethane releases 1560 kilojoules of energy. According to the chemical equation above, two moles of ethane (2 C_2H_6) are burned. Of course, the total thermal energy must correspond to the amounts of all other reactants and products involved. Thus, the total thermal energy released will be *twice* that quantity released when 1 mole of ethane burns. Therefore, the complete combustion equation for ethane is:

$$2\,C_2H_6 + 7\,O_2 \longrightarrow 4\,CO_2 + 6\,H_2O + 3120\ \text{kJ}$$

Figure 3.32 *Natural gas (often used as a fuel to heat homes and for cooking) is a mixture of hydrocarbons. Its primary component is methane, the smallest of the hydrocarbon molecules, consisting of only one carbon and four hydrogen atoms.*

Post-Lab Discussion

Focus on team results. Some results may differ substantially. Ask students to check calculations carefully and identify experimental errors. Students can consider their experimental setup; heat-loss sources, such as heat absorbed by the can and by any soot already collected on it; and heat radiated directly to surrounding air.

Link these results to the idea of energy storage in substances. Ask students where the thermal energy originated. They should realize that this energy arose from bond making in CO_2 and H_2O during paraffin combustion. By contrast, energy is required to break bonds within paraffin molecules, but this bond-breaking energy is much lower than bond-making energy.

Additional Activities

1. Students can list advantages and disadvantages of using propane versus paraffin to heat their homes. You could discuss packaging, transport, system design, and cost.

2. Seek student suggestions for designing a more accurate calorimeter. Then, if you borrow a laboratory or commercial calorimeter, demonstrate its design and function. Consider using **http://www.chem.yale. edu/~chem125/125/history99/ 2Pre1800/Lavoisier/Instruments/ calorimeter.html** to generate a design discussion. This site describes a calorimeter designed by Lavoisier that measured the ice melted to find heat released by burning oil.

B.7 Using Heats of Combustion

Students are introduced here to incorporating reaction energy in an equation. The heat of reaction, typically in J or kJ, is often included.

Students may have difficulty distinguishing *heat of combustion* from *molar heat of combustion*. ChemQuandary 2 helps address this confusion. You may also decide to show the conversion from heat of combustion to molar heat of combustion for one of the hydrocarbons listed in **Table 3.6** (page 250). Using methane as an example,

molar heat of combustion =

$$\frac{55.6\ \text{kJ}}{\text{g}} \times \frac{16.0\ \text{g}}{\text{mol}} = 890\ \frac{\text{kJ}}{\text{mol}}, \text{where}$$

55.6 kJ/g is the heat of combustion of methane and 16.0 g/mol is its molar mass.

Emphasize to students that they must consider coefficients when using molar heats of combustion to determine the energy released by a given reaction. For instance, the equation for the combustion of hexane is

$2 C_6H_{14} + 19 O_2 \rightarrow 12 CO_2 + 14 H_2O + energy$

The molar heat of combustion of hexane is 4141 kJ/mol. However, *two* moles of hexane undergo combustion in the equation, so this value must be doubled:

$$\frac{4141 \text{ kJ}}{\text{mol}} \times 2 \text{ mol} = 8282 \text{ kJ}$$

and the final equation is $2 C_6H_{14} + 19 O_2 \rightarrow 12 CO_2 + 14 H_2O + 8282$ kJ.

 B.7 Supplement: Hearts of Combustion and Energy Effiency

ChemQuandary 2

A Burning Problem: Part I

The heats of combustion for hydrocarbons expressed as kJ/g decrease slightly as the size of the hydrocarbon (number of carbons) increases. The heat of combustion for hydrocarbons expressed as kJ/mol increases linearly as the number of carbons increases.

For alkanes and other saturated hydrocarbons, the mass of a mole of substance increases by about 14 g for every carbon added to the chain. Consequently, the molar heat of combustion increases about 660 kJ per carbon atom in a hydrocarbon. Using this pattern and data in Table 3.6, the molar heat of combustion of decane should be: 5450 kJ/mol + 2 × (660 kJ/mol) = 6770 kJ/mol, since it has two more carbon atoms per molecule than octane.

The heat of combustion per gram of decane should be slightly

As you found in Investigating Matter B.6, and as suggested in Table 3.6 (page 250), heats of combustion can also be expressed as the energy involved when one gram of hydrocarbon burns (kJ/g). That information is useful in finding out how much energy is released when a certain mass of fuel is burned.

Sample Problem: *How much thermal energy would be produced by burning 12.0 g octane, C_8H_{18}?*

Table 3.6 indicates that burning 1.00 g octane releases 47.8 kJ. Burning 12.0 times *more* octane produces 12.0 times *more* thermal energy, or

$$12.0 \times 47.8 \text{ kJ} = 574 \text{ kJ}$$

The calculation can also be written this way:

$$12.0 \text{ g octane} \times \frac{47.8 \text{ kJ}}{1 \text{ g octane}} = 574 \text{ kJ}$$

ChemQuandary 2

A BURNING PROBLEM: PART I

Examine the heat of combustion and the molar heat of combustion data summarized in Table 3.6 (page 250). What do you notice about the trend in the heat of combustion for hydrocarbons expressed as kilojoules per gram (kJ/g) compared with the trend expressed as kilojoules per mole (kJ/mol)? The units *grams* and *moles* both specify the *quantity* of a substance. What difference in these two quantities would explain the trends you observed in Table 3.6?

Assuming these trends apply to larger hydrocarbon molecules, predict the heat of combustion for decane, $C_{10}H_{22}$, expressed as kilojoules per gram (kJ/g) decane and kilojoules per mole (kJ/mol) decane. Which prediction was easier to make, and why might this be so?

Moles express amount; grams express mass.

Developing Skills

B.8 HEATS OF COMBUSTION

This activity will give you a better understanding of the energy involved in burning hydrocarbon fuels. Use Table 3.6 (page 250) to answer these questions.

Sample Problem: *How much energy (in kilojoules) is released by completely burning 25.0 mol hexane, C_6H_{14}?*

less than 47.8 kJ/g. Because the pattern of decrease is not linear, the exact value cannot be predicted. Students should note that the differences decrease as the carbon chain size increases, so their answers should be in the range of 47.4 to 47.7 kJ/g.

The molar heat of combustion (kJ/mol) is easier to predict, because it varies linearly with carbon chain size.

Developing Skills

B.8 Heats of Combustion

The major use of petroleum is as a fuel. Thermal energy produced per gram is a primary factor in choosing types of hydrocarbons for burning. Model the sample problem before assigning this material to students.

According to Table 3.6, the molar heat of combustion of hexane is 4141 kJ. This means that 4141 kJ of energy is released as 1.00 mol hexane burns. Therefore, burning 25.0 times more hexane will liberate 25.0 times more energy:

$$25.0 \text{ mol } C_6H_{14} \times \frac{4141 \text{ kJ}}{1 \text{ mol } C_6H_{14}} = 104\ 000 \text{ kJ}$$

Burning 25.0 mol hexane would thus release 104 000 kJ of thermal energy.

1. Write a chemical equation that includes thermal energy for the complete combustion of the following alkanes:

   a. propane   c. octane
   b. butane   d. decane

2. a. How much thermal energy is produced by burning two moles of octane?
   b. How much thermal energy is produced by burning one gallon of octane? (A gallon of octane occupies a volume of about 3.8 L. The density of octane is 0.70 g/mL.)
   c. Suppose a car operates so inefficiently that only 16% of the thermal energy from burning fuel is converted to useful "wheel-turning" (mechanical) energy. How many kilojoules of useful energy would be stored in a 20.0-gallon tank of gasoline? (Assume that octane burning and gasoline burning produce the same results.)

3. The molar heat of combustion of carbon contained in coal is 394 kJ/mol C.

   a. Write a chemical equation for burning the carbon contained in coal. Include the thermal energy produced.
   b. Gram for gram, which is the better fuel—carbon or octane? Explain your answer using calculations.
   c. In what applications might coal replace petroleum-based fuel?
   d. Describe one application in which coal would be a poor substitute for petroleum-based fuel.

B.9 ALTERING FUELS

As automobile use grows throughout the world, the demand for gasoline continues to increase rapidly. Because the gasoline fraction in a barrel of crude oil normally represents only about 18% of the total, researchers have been anxious to find a way to increase this yield. One promising method has been based on the discovery that it is possible to alter the structures of some of petroleum's hydrocarbon molecules so that 47% of a barrel of crude oil can be converted to gasoline. This chemical technique deserves further attention.

Chemists and chemical engineers are adept at modifying or altering available chemical resources to meet new needs. Such alterations might also involve converting less-useful materials to more-useful products, or converting a low-demand material into high-demand materials.

c. $20 \text{ gal } C_8H_{18} \times \frac{1.3 \times 10^5 \text{ kJ}}{1 \text{ gal } C_8H_{18}} \times$
$\frac{16 \text{ useful kJ}}{100 \text{ kJ}} = 4.1 \times 10^5 \text{ useful kJ}$

3. a. $C(s) + O2(g) \text{ B } CO2 (g) + 394 \text{ kJ}$
   b. Burning octane releases 47.8 kJ/g.

   Burning coal releases $\frac{394 \text{ kJ}}{1 \text{ mol C}} \times$
   $\frac{1 \text{ mol C}}{12.01 \text{ g C}} = 32.8 \text{ kJ/g}$

   Octane is the better fuel on a mass basis.
   c. Applications that do not require gas-phase fuels, such as charcoal briquettes for barbecues
   d. An automobile engine, which requires fuel to be finely dispersed for rapid combustion

B.9 Altering Fuels

> **B.9 Content Reading Guide**

Chemists have altered hydrocarbon molecules or mixtures to fulfill particular needs, such as cracking large hydrocarbons into smaller molecules, isomerizing fuel fractions to produce branched-chained hydrocarbons, and making additives that affect burning characteristics of gasoline, such as tetraethyl lead, methanol, and methyl-t-butyl ether (MTBE).
Helpful Web sites include **http://chemcases.com/fuels**, **http://www.epa.gov/history/topics/perspect/lead.htm**, **http://science.howstuffworks.com/gasoline.htm**, and **http://science.howstuffworks.com/oil-refining5.htm**.

Answers

1. a. $C_3H_8(g) + 5\ O_2(g) \rightarrow 3\ CO_2(g) + 4\ H_2O(g) + 2200 \text{ kJ}$
   b. $2\ C_4H_{10}(g) + 13\ O_2(g) \rightarrow 8\ CO_2(g) + 10\ H_2O(g) + 5718 \text{ kJ}$
   c. $2\ C_8H_{18} + 25\ O_2 \rightarrow 16\ CO_2 + 18\ H_2O + 10\ 900 \text{ kJ}$
   d. $2\ C_{10}H_{22} + 31\ O_2 \rightarrow 20\ CO_2 + 22\ H_2O + 13\ 540 \text{ kJ}$ (based on decane's predicted molar heat of combustion from ChemQuandary 2)

2. a. $2 \text{ mol } C_8H_{18} \times 5450 \text{ kJ/mol} = 10\ 900 \text{ kJ}$
   b. $1 \text{ gal } C_8H_{18} \times \frac{3.8 \text{ L } C_8H_{18}}{1 \text{ gal } C_8H_{18}} \times$
   $\frac{1000 \text{ mL } C_8H_{18}}{1 \text{ L } C_8H_{18}} \times \frac{0.70 \text{ g } C_8H_{18}}{1 \text{ mL } C_8H_{18}} \times$
   $\frac{47.8 \text{ kJ}}{1 \text{ g } C_8H_{18}} = 1.3 \times 10^5 \text{ kJ}$

Cracking The cracking processes developed in the early 20th century used heat and pressure to break larger hydrocarbon molecules into hydrocarbons with 5 to 12 carbons per molecule that are useful as automobile fuel. By the 1930s, catalytic processes were developed that lowered the energy required to complete cracking. A catalyst allows for formation of an intermediate that is not as high in energy as the intermediate formed in the absence of a catalyst. Isomerization also uses catalysts—typically platinum dispersed on silica or alumina—to improve efficiency.

Octane Rating Octane numbers depend on characteristics of a complex mixture of hydrocarbons and additives. As such, they are determined experimentally instead of predicted. Sometimes a gasoline pump says that octane ratings were obtained by the "(R+M)/2 method." That means the rating is an average of two test values: (1) the research octane number (RON) for a test engine run under conditions simulating city driving and (2) the motor octane number (MON) for the engine run under highway conditions. If RON = 93 and MON = 91, then the octane rating = 92.

Oxygenated Fuels Oxygenated fuels (originally developed and tested in the 1920s) can improve octane ratings. The Clean Air Act of 1992 accelerated use of oxygenates in gasoline by requiring 41 populated U.S. metropolitan areas to use gasoline with 2.7% oxygen (by mass) during winter. Oxygenated fuel burns cleaner than standard gasoline; increased oxygen favors production of carbon dioxide (complete burning) rather than carbon

> Recall that the gasoline fraction obtained from crude oil refining includes hydrocarbons with 5 to 12 carbons per molecule. (See Figure 3.9, page 219.)

> Modern, well-tuned engines rarely knock under normal conditions.

Cracking

By 1913, chemists had devised a process for converting larger molecules in kerosene into smaller, gasoline-sized molecules by heating the kerosene to 600 to 700 °C. The process of converting large hydrocarbon molecules into smaller ones through the application of thermal energy (heat) and a catalyst is known as **cracking.** Today, more than a third of all crude oil undergoes cracking. The process has been improved by adding catalysts. A **catalyst** increases the speed of a chemical reaction by participating in it; however, the catalyst is not used up. Catalytic cracking is more energy efficient because it occurs at a lower temperature, 500 °C rather than 700 °C, which is made possible by the catalyst's lowering the energy requirements of reacting molecules.

Through cracking, a 16-carbon molecule, for example, might be changed into two 8-carbon molecules:

$$C_{16}H_{34} \longrightarrow C_8H_{18} + C_8H_{16}$$

In practice, molecules with up to about 14 carbon atoms can be produced through cracking. Molecules with 5 to 12 carbon atoms are particularly useful in gasoline, which remains the most important commercial product of refining. Some C_1, C_2, C_3, and C_4 molecules produced in cracking are immediately burned, keeping the temperature high enough for more cracking to occur.

Octane Rating

Gasoline is composed mainly of straight-chain alkanes, such as hexane (C_6H_{14}), heptane (C_7H_{16}), and octane (C_8H_{18}). In most automobiles, the gasoline–air mixture is compressed in cylinders just prior to being ignited by spark plugs. This compression can be enough to heat the alkanes to the point where they burn before the spark plug ignites them. The premature burning causes engine "pinging," or "knocking," as the piston bangs backwards against the crankshaft at the wrong time and may contribute to engine problems. Branched-chain alkanes burn more satisfactorily, being less likely to undergo combustion due to compression in engine cylinders; they do not ping as much. The structural isomer of octane shown here has excellent combustion properties in automobile engines. This octane isomer is known chemically as 2,2,4-trimethylpentane. Can you see how the name of the molecule relates to its structure? For convenience, this substance is frequently referred to by its common name, *isooctane:*

$$CH_3-\underset{\underset{CH_3}{|}}{\overset{\overset{CH_3}{|}}{C}}-CH_2-\underset{\underset{CH_3}{|}}{CH}-CH_3$$

Isooctane, C_8H_{18}

monoxide (incomplete burning). That is particularly important in winter, when fuel is blended with lower-boiling components to provide volatility needed for combustion at low temperatures. Thus, oxygenated fuels improve gasoline's octane rating while reducing air pollutants. Unfortunately, gasoline containing oxygen delivers less energy per gallon than regular gasoline. However, EPA studies show this energy decrease accounts for only a 2–3% loss in fuel economy (miles per gallon).

As you probably know, gasoline is sold in a variety of grades—and at corresponding prices. A common reference standard for gasoline quality is the *octane scale*. On this scale, isooctane, the branched-chain hydrocarbon you just learned about, is assigned an octane number of 100. Straight-chain heptane (C_7H_{16}), a fuel with very poor engine performance, is assigned an octane number of zero. Gasoline samples can be rated in comparison with isooctane and heptane.

The **octane rating** for a particular fuel is determined by testing the fuel's burning efficiency under two conditions: in a free-running engine and in an engine under load, as in towing or passing conditions (Figure 3.33). The results of these two tests are then averaged to obtain the octane rating. The higher the octane rating of a gasoline becomes, the better its antiknock characteristics. Octane ratings in the high 80s and low 90s (87, 89, 92) are quite common, as a survey of nearby gasoline pumps, like those pictured in Figure 3.34, will reveal.

From the 1920s until the 1970s, the octane rating of gasoline was increased at low cost by adding a substance such as tetraethyl lead, (C_2H_4)$_4$Pb, to the fuel. This additive enhanced the burning efficiency of straight-chain gasoline molecules and added about three points to "leaded" fuel's octane rating. Unfortunately, lead from the treated gasoline was discharged into the atmosphere along with other vehicle exhaust products. Lead is harmful to the environment; therefore, lead-based gasoline additives are no longer used in the United States.

Figure 3.34 *Octane ratings posted on gasoline pumps.*

Figure 3.33 *Researchers use test engines to determine the octane rating of fuel.*

Assigning an octane number of 100 to isooctane is arbitrary and does not imply that it has the highest possible octane number. In fact, several fuels burn more efficiently in engines than isooctane does; they are assigned octane numbers higher than 100.

Oxygenated Fuels

The phaseout of lead-based gasoline additives in the United States meant that alternative octane-boosting supplements were required. A group of additives called **oxygenated fuels** now are blended with gasoline to enhance its octane rating. The molecules of these additives contain oxygen in addition to carbon and hydrogen.

Although oxygenated fuels actually deliver less energy per gallon than regular gasoline hydrocarbons do, their economic appeal stems from their ability to increase the octane number of gasoline while reducing exhaust-gas pollutants. In most conditions, oxygenated fuels encourage more complete combustion, producing lower emissions of air pollutants, such as carbon monoxide (CO).

A common oxygenated fuel is *methanol* (methyl alcohol, CH_3OH), which is added to gasoline at distribution locations. In addition to its octane-boosting properties, methanol can be made from natural gas, coal, corn, or wood—a contribution toward conserving nonrenewable

Lead-Based Additives To introduce this subject, ask students why gasoline is referred to as *unleaded,* when "leaded" gasoline is not sold. In the 1920s, before cracking and isomerization were well developed, an additive was sought to improve gasoline quality. Tetraethyl lead (TEL), though toxic, could be inexpensively produced; small amounts helped prevent engine knock—premature combustion of the air/fuel mixture inside engine cylinders, causing pistons to slap against the cylinder walls. Higher-octane fuels prevent engine knock, particularly in high-performance engines, which have high compression ratios (volume ratio of the fully expanded cylinder to the cylinder just before sparking). Low octane rating, high compression, or a combination can cause the air/fuel mixture to ignite on its own. This phenomenon also causes engine "dieseling," where the engine continues to run even after the ignition is turned off.

Although TEL increased gasoline octane ratings, its use emitted lead compounds into the atmosphere. As a result, in the early 1970s, the U.S. Environmental Protection Agency banned TEL. The TEL phase-out met some opposition but was essentially completed over 20 years ago. One factor influencing phase-out of "leaded" gasoline was development of the catalytic converter to meet new air-quality standards (more about this in Unit 4). Catalytic converters are fouled and rendered useless by lead in "leaded" gasoline.

MTBE (page 256), one oxygenating additive, mixes well with gasoline at all concentrations and has desirable octane-increasing and emissions-decreasing properties. However, MTBE use is being reevaluated due to an unpleasant taste and odor it gives to groundwater, even in minute concentrations. No promising alternatives have been identified. Most states that avoid MTBE employ ethanol as an easy-to-blend, oxygenated additive.

ChemQuandary 3

A Burning Problem: Part II

The quantity of energy liberated by combustion of a hydrocarbon fuel is ultimately determined by breaking C—C and C—H bonds and forming C—O and H—O bonds. Because the energy released in forming O-containing bonds is much greater than the energy required for breaking C—H and C—C bonds, the overall process is highly exothermic.

Oxygenated fuels already contain some C—O and/or H—O bonds. In combustion, these bonds must be broken and re-formed, for a net energy effect of zero. Thus, gram for gram, these oxygenated fuels do not deliver as much energy as hydrocarbons that contain only C—H and C—C bonds. Oxygenated additives are used despite their lower heats of combustion because they promote complete combustion (by adding oxygen to the combustion mixture) and lead to fewer harmful emissions.

petroleum resources. A blend of 10% ethanol (ethyl alcohol, CH_3CH_2OH) and 90% gasoline, sometimes called *gasohol*, can be used as an oxygenated fuel in nearly all modern automobiles without engine adjustments or problems.

> ### ChemQuandary 3
>
> #### A BURNING PROBLEM: PART II
> Methanol (CH_3OH) and ethanol (CH_3CH_2OH), sometimes produced from corn, are used as gasoline additives or substitutes. The heat of combustion values for methanol and ethanol are 23 kJ/g and 30 kJ/g, respectively. Consider the chemical formulas of methanol and ethanol. Gram for gram, why are the heats of combustion of methanol and ethanol considerably lower than those of any hydrocarbons considered so far? See Table 3.6 (page 250).

Methyl tertiary-butyl ether (MTBE), with an octane rating of 116, was initially introduced in the late 1970s as an octane-boosting fuel additive. In the 1990s, MTBE became the most common oxygenated fuel additive in gasoline. At its peak, annual U.S. production of MTBE increased to more than 4 billion gallons (about 16 gallons per person), making it a top-ten industrial chemical substance.

By the late 1990s, however, evidence began to mount of contamination of groundwater and drinking water supplies due to MTBE seeping from defective underground gasoline storage systems. MTBE dissolves readily in water and is difficult to remove in water-treatment processes. The unpleasant taste and odor that MTBE imparts to water, even at concentrations below those regarded as a public health concern, triggered consumer complaints. The EPA credited MTBE with substantial reductions in emissions of air pollutants from gasoline-powered vehicles in the 1990s. However, in light of these more recent concerns, policies to reduce or to ban the use of MTBE as an oxygenated fuel are under active consideration.

Other octane-boosting strategies involve altering the structures of hydrocarbon molecules in petroleum. This works because branched-chain hydrocarbons burn more satisfactorily than do straight-chain hydrocarbons. (Recall isooctane's octane number compared with that of straight-chain heptane.) Straight-chain hydrocarbons are converted to branched-chain hydrocarbons by a process called **isomerization**. During isomerization, hydrocarbon vapor is heated with a catalyst:

$$CH_3-CH_2-CH_2-CH_2-CH_2-CH_3 \xrightarrow[\text{Catalyst}]{\text{Heat}} CH_3-\overset{\displaystyle CH_3}{\underset{\displaystyle CH_3}{\overset{|}{C}H}}-CH-CH_3$$

$C_6H_{14}(g)$
Straight-chain
isomer

$C_6H_{14}(g)$
Branched-chain
isomer

The branched-chain alkanes produced by isomerization are blended with C_5 to C_{12} molecules obtained from cracking and distillation, producing a high-quality gasoline. Although cracked and isomerized molecules improve how gasoline burns, they also increase its cost. One reason for this increase is the extra fuel needed to produce such gasoline.

B.10 FUEL FOR TRANSPORTATION

Making Decisions

Now that you have examined the importance of petroleum as a fuel, particularly for transportation (Figure 3.35), it is time to revisit the television ad for the *Hybris* that opened this unit. Later, you will have the opportunity to critically review and design an advertisement for an alternate-powered vehicle.

Use what you have learned about petroleum to answer the following questions:

1. In what ways does the manufacture of a *Hybris* hybrid-powered car use petroleum as a fuel?

2. What alternatives to petroleum can you suggest for each petroleum use that you listed in Question 1?

3. How do the alternatives that you suggested in Question 2 compare to petroleum in terms of energy efficiency?

4. What direct, nonfuel uses of petroleum or its fractions are involved in the daily operation of a *Hybris*?

5. What alternatives to petroleum can you suggest for each direct, nonfuel use that you listed in answering Question 4?

6. Write one or two paragraphs that evaluate other assertions made in the *Hybris* advertisement.

Section C will enrich your knowledge of the "building" role of petroleum, focusing on petroleum as a source of an impressive array of useful compounds and products. This information will help you further decide about the accuracy of the claims in the *Hybris* TV advertisement and will also guide your design of an advertisement for an alternative-fuel vehicle.

Figure 3.35 *Petroleum, precursor to the fuels used by these vehicles, is a nonrenewable resource. What alternative fuels can be devised to power vehicles such as these?*

SECTION B

Making Decisions

B.10 Fuel for Transportation

Answers

1. In processing raw materials, manufacturing and transporting parts, and assembling vehicles

2. Answers will vary. Examples: *processing*—coal, natural gas (methane), wood, or other biomass; *manufacture*—coal or natural gas, or electricity from solar energy wind power, hydropower, or nuclear reactors; *transport*—natural gas or electricity (ultimately from coal-burning power plants); *assembly*—electricity from coal, natural gas, solar energy, wind power, hydropower, or nuclear reactors.

3. In general, the alternatives are less efficient or require costly infrastructure and safety measures (dams, wind farms, solar cells, or nuclear containment systems).

4. Engine lubricant, tar-removal solvent, and lubricants for door hinges and other moving parts

5. Synthetic or biomass-derived lubricants

6. Students might evaluate assertions such as *"Hybris* makes use of nearly all the energy in each drop of gasoline," "Three cents per mile to operate," "Conserves petroleum resources," and "Uses a significantly greater portion of gasoline's energy than conventional engines."

SECTION B SUMMARY

✎ **Section B Supplement**

Reviewing the Concepts

1. Millions of years ago, green plants captured energy from the sun, then decomposed over time, forming petroleum. The energy stored in petroleum hydrocarbons is the solar energy (sunshine) once stored in—and buried with—plants.

2. a. Energy of position or condition, as in a coiled spring, a ball at the top of a hill, or a molecule of fuel
   b. Energy of motion, as of a rolling ball, a swinging pendulum, a moving molecule

3. Bonds of reactants are broken. Then new bonds are formed, creating products. Energy is required to break bonds and released when bonds are formed.

4. Butane, because it has more C—C and C—H bonds

5. Kinetic: c, e; potential: a, b, d

6. Strong attractive forces between electrons in one atom and the nucleus of the other atom must be overcome.

7. a. Exothermic; more energy is released in making bonds than is required to break bonds.
   b. Endothermic; more energy is required to break bonds than is released in bond making.
   c. Exothermic; more energy is released by formation of products than is required to break bonded reactant atoms (otherwise food would not provide energy).

8. The total energy required to break the bonds in reactants is less than the total energy given off by formation of product bonds.

SECTION B SUMMARY
Reviewing the Concepts

> Chemical energy, a form of potential energy, is stored within the bonds in chemical compounds.

1. From a chemical viewpoint, why is petroleum sometimes considered "buried sunshine"?

2. Define and give one example of
   a. potential energy.   b. kinetic energy.

3. In terms of chemical bonds, what happens during a chemical reaction?

4. Based on its structural formula, which has more potential energy, a molecule of methane or a molecule of butane? Explain your answer.

5. Classify each of the following as primarily a demonstration of kinetic energy or potential energy:
   a. a skateboard positioned at the top of a hill
   b. a charged battery in a flashlight that's turned off
   c. a rolling soccer ball
   d. gasoline in a parked car
   e. water flowing over a waterfall

> The energy change in a chemical reaction equals the difference between the energy required to break reactant bonds and the energy released in forming product bonds. Reactions are classified as either exothermic or endothermic.

6. Why is energy required to break chemical bonds?

7. For each of the following events, determine whether the reaction is exothermic or endothermic. Explain your answers in terms of bond breaking and bond making:
   a. burning wood in a campfire
   b. cracking large hydrocarbon molecules
   c. digesting a candy bar

8. Burning a candle is an exothermic reaction. Explain this fact in terms of the quantity of energy stored in the bonds of the reactants compared with the quantity of energy stored in the bonds of the products.

9. Using Figure 3.24 on page 240 as a model, draw a potential energy diagram that illustrates the energy change when hydrogen gas reacts with oxygen gas to produce water and thermal energy.

> Thermal energy can be converted into other forms of energy. Although energy can neither be created nor destroyed, useful energy is lost each time energy is converted from one form to another.

10. State the law of conservation of energy.

11. Match the following events (a–d) with the energy conversions (i–iii) that are involved:
    a. riding a bike
    b. illuminating a lightbulb
    c. producing electricity in a wind-powered generator
    d. running a gasoline-powered lawn mower
       i.   mechanical to electrical energy
       ii. chemical to mechanical energy
       iii. electrical to light energy

12. In powering an automobile, 25% of the energy is said to be useful. What happens to the other 75% of the energy?

13. Explain what energy conversion efficiency means.

14. One gallon of gasoline produces about 132 000 kJ of energy when burned. Assume that an automobile is 25% efficient in converting this energy into useful work:
    a. How much energy (in kJ) is "wasted" when a gallon of gasoline burns in an automobile?
    b. What happens to this wasted energy?

9.

10. Energy can neither be created nor destroyed. The total energy in a closed system is constant.

11. a. ii, b. iii, c. i, d. ii

12. It is lost to the surroundings as heat.

13. The percent of initial energy input converted into useful work

14. a. 132 000 kJ × 0.75 = 99 000 kJ
    b. It is released to the surroundings, primarily as heat.

When a hydrocarbon burns completely, it reacts with oxygen gas from the air to liberate thermal energy and produce carbon dioxide gas and water vapor.

15. Write a balanced chemical equation, including the quantity of thermal energy (refer to Table 3.6, page 250), for the complete combustion of

a. pentane. b. propane. c. hexane.

16. The combustion of acetylene, C_2H_2 (used in a welder's torch), can be represented as

$$2\ C_2H_2 + 5\ O_2 \longrightarrow 4\ CO_2 + 2\ H_2O + 2512\ kJ$$

a. What is the molar heat of combustion of acetylene in kilojoules per mole?
b. If 12 mol acetylene burns fully, how much thermal energy will be produced?

17. a. List two factors that would help you decide which hydrocarbon fuel to use in a particular application.
b. Explain how you would use each factor in making your decision.

18. When candle wax (a mixture of hydrocarbons) burns, it seems to disappear. What actually happens to the wax?

19. Water gas (a 50–50 mixture of CO and H_2) is made by the reaction of coal with steam. Because the United States has substantial coal reserves, water gas might serve as a substitute fuel for natural gas (composed mainly of methane, CH_4). Water gas burns according to this equation:

$$CO + H_2 + O_2 \longrightarrow CO_2 + H_2O + 525\ kJ$$

a. How does water gas compare to methane in terms of the thermal energy produced when fully burned?
b. If a water gas mixture containing 10.0 mol CO and 10.0 mol H_2 were completely burned in O_2, how much thermal energy would be produced?

The thermal energy (measured in joules) required to raise the temperature of one gram of a material by one degree Celsius is its specific heat capacity.

20. In a laboratory activity, a student team measures the heat released by burning heptane (C_7H_{16}). Using the following data, calculate the molar heat of combustion of heptane in kJ/mol:

- mass of water   179.2 g
- initial water temperature   11.6 °C
- final water temperature   46.1 °C
- mass of heptane burned   0.585 g

21. How much energy is released when a 5600-g sample of water cools from 99 °C to 28 °C? The specific heat capacity of water is 4.18 J/(g·°C).

Larger molecules in petroleum's kerosene fraction (C_{12} to C_{16}) can be converted to smaller molecules useful in the gasoline fraction (C_5 to C_{12}). The speed of the process, called cracking, is increased by using a catalyst.

22. What is a catalyst?

23. Write one possible balanced equation showing how each of the following molecules could be cracked into molecules for the gasoline fraction:

a. $C_{17}H_{36}$ b. $C_{18}H_{38}$

24. In terms of energy efficiency, why are catalysts used during the cracking process?

25. Explain why only small amounts of catalysts are needed to crack large amounts of petroleum.

Section Summary   **259**

---

19. a. The energy released by water gas (525 kJ/mol) is about 60% of the energy (891 kJ/mol) released by methane.
b. 10 mol × 525 kJ/mol = −5250 kJ

20. Energy absorbed by water =

$$mC\Delta T = 179.2\ g \times \frac{4.18\ J}{g \cdot °C} \times$$

$$(46.1\ °C - 11.6\ °C) \times \frac{1\ kJ}{1000\ J} =$$

25.8 kJ

One mole heptane = 7 × 12.01 + 16 × 1.008 = 100.2 g/mol
Molar heat of combustion =

$$\frac{-25.8\ kJ}{0.585\ g} \times \frac{100.2\ g}{1\ mol} =$$

$$-4430 \frac{kJ}{mol}$$

21. Energy = $mC\Delta T$ = 5600 g ×

$$\frac{4.18\ J}{g \cdot °C} \times (28\ °C - 99\ °C) \times$$

$$\frac{1\ kJ}{1000\ J} = -1662\ kJ = -1700\ kJ$$

22. A material used to lower the activation energy of a reaction, increasing the reaction rate without itself being changed

23. Samples:
a. $C_{17}H_{36} \rightarrow C_9H_{18} + C_8H_{18}$
b. $C_{18}H_{38} \rightarrow C_9H_{20} + C_9H_{18}$

24. Catalysts allow cracking to take place at much lower temperatures. Energy efficiency is improved, because less energy is required for cracking.

25. The catalyst is not consumed or changed, thus a small amount of catalyst can be used repeatedly.

---

15. a. $C_5H_{12} + 8\ O_2 \rightarrow 5\ CO_2 + 6\ H_2O + 3510\ kJ$
b. $C_3H_8 + 5\ O_2 \rightarrow 3\ CO_2 + 4\ H_2O + 2200\ kJ$
c. $2\ C_6H_{14} + 19\ O_2 \rightarrow 12\ CO_2 + 14\ H_2O + 8282\ kJ$

16. a. 2512 kJ ÷ 2 mol C_2H_2 = 1256 kJ/mol C_2H_2
b. 1256 kJ/mol C_2H_2 × 12 mol C_2H_2 = 15 070 kJ

17. a. Boiling point and heat of combustion
b. Boiling point identifies the fuel's state during the application and thus the type of container and precautions required. Heat of combustion specifies the energy provided by each fuel.

18. The atoms in wax are rearranged, and new products form, including H_2O and CO_2, which are released into the surroundings as gases.

26. The lead in tetraethyl lead was emitted into the atmosphere, presenting a health hazard.

27. Isooctane is a branched-chain hydrocarbon. Octane is a straight-chain hydrocarbon.

28. They increase a fuel's octane rating because they are less likely than hydrocarbons to ignite on compression.

29. Increase the percent of branched-chain alkanes or add oxygenated fuels.

Connecting the Concepts

30. a. Energy released = 4.2 g ethanol × (1 mol ethanol/46.1 g ethanol) × (1366 kJ/1 mol ethanol) = 120 kJ

b. Energy absorbed = $mC\Delta T$ =

468 g water × $\dfrac{4.18\ J}{g\ water\cdot{}^\circ C}$ ×

$(89\ ^\circ C - 21\ ^\circ C) \times \dfrac{1\ kJ}{1000\ J}$ = 130 kJ

c. More energy was absorbed by the calorimeter than was produced by burning ethanol. Extra heat must have gone into the system from some other source; perhaps the room was quite warm. Temperature measurements could also have been in error.

31. Answers should address the need to contain the fuel and measure the quantity of fuel used. Students may also mention safety considerations.

32. Examples: Using petroleum is cheaper than obtaining and using solar energy. Petroleum can be readily transformed into desired forms of energy. Petroleum is readily available in a usable form. Petroleum is a more concentrated and dependable source of energy; solar energy is diffuse and erratic.

The octane rating is an expression of a fuel's burning performance in an engine. Additives may enhance gasoline's burning performance.

26. Why do we no longer use tetraethyl lead as a gasoline additive?

27. Compare the molecular structures of octane and isooctane.

28. How does the addition of oxygenating compounds affect a fuel's octane rating?

29. List two ways to increase a fuel's octane rating.

Connecting the Concepts

30. In a laboratory activity, a student completely burns 4.2 g ethanol (C_2H_5OH). The molar heat of combustion of ethanol is 1366 kJ/mol.

a. How much thermal energy is released?

b. The thermal energy from this reaction is used to warm a 468-g sample of water in a calorimeter. The water temperature changes from 21 °C to 89 °C. How much thermal energy is absorbed by the water? The specific heat capacity of water is 4.18 J/(g·°C).

c. Compare the quantity of heat released by this reaction to the quantity of heat absorbed by the calorimeter. What accounts for the difference?

31. What modifications would have to be made to the laboratory procedure in Section B.6 (pages 248–251) if a liquid or gaseous fuel were used?

32. Why is the energy stored in petroleum more useful than solar energy for most applications? Give at least three reasons in your explanation.

Extending the Concepts

33. MTBE was once widely used as an oxygen source for automobile fuels. Investigate the chemical properties of this additive and the controversy surrounding its use. Report on its current status.

34. Referring to Figure 3.29 (page 244), suggest specific engine-design modifications that might increase the proportion of energy available to propel the car.

35. Write a word equation for photosynthesis. Include energy in your equation.

36. Using Figure 3.24 on page 240 as a model, draw a potential energy diagram for photosynthesis.

37. Compare the equation for burning hydrocarbons to the equation for photosynthesis. How are these two reactions related?

Extending the Concepts

33. MTBE is an anti-knock additive that promotes complete combustion of hydrocarbons. It is a potential human carcinogen.

34. Answers will vary.

35. Carbon dioxide and water, with added energy, react to form glucose and oxygen.

36. See Figure 3.24, page 240

37. They are opposite reactions.

SECTION C

Petroleum: A Building-Material Source

J ust as an architect uses knowledge of available construction materials in designing a building, a chemist—a "molecular architect"—uses knowledge of available molecules in designing new molecules (Figure 3.36). Architects must know about the structures and properties of common building materials. Likewise, chemists must understand the structures and properties of their raw materials. The "builder molecules"—that small portion of petroleum not used for energy, lubricants, and road tar—are available for building by molecular architects. In this section, you will explore the structures of common hydrocarbon builder molecules and some materials made from them.

Figure 3.36 *When designing a new molecule, chemists often use computer modeling programs to make predictions about its structure and properties. This is particularly helpful when considering how a new biomolecule will interact with other substances inside the human body.*

Petroleum: A Building-Material Source

Section C focuses on petroleum's use as a starting material—its "building" role. Students explore the myriad useful compounds and materials produced directly or indirectly from petroleum, collectively called *petrochemicals*. The section introduces the concept of functional group and the idea of multiple bonds, such as those in alkenes, alkynes, and aromatic compounds. Students use molecular models to visualize all these types of "builder" molecules. Polymerization processes are explored with models and through using a condensation reaction to prepare an ester.

The Macrogalleria Web site (**http://www.pslc.ws/macrog/index.htm**) is an excellent source of information about polymer structure, properties, and uses.

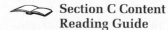 **Section C Content Reading Guide**

C.1 Creating New Options: Petrochemicals

✎ **C.1 and C.7 Content Reading Guide**

Begin by pointing out the variety of petrochemicals highlighted in the text and ask students to think about the impact of these materials on their lives. You can also relate this variety of products to the pervasive role of the chemical industry.

Using the Figures

Figure 3.37: Encourage students to examine these two photographs and to note similarities and differences in use of materials. Both markets use wood to display fruits and vegetables. However, wood is much more prominent in the earlier photo; even the wagon has wooden wheels. Plastic (shopping bag, tail lights) and synthetic fibers are visible in the modern photo and absent in the earlier photo. In the context of the photographs, discuss advantages and disadvantages of widespread use of plastics and other petrochemicals as replacements for wood products and natural fibers.

C.1 CREATING NEW OPTIONS: PETROCHEMICALS

Until the early 1800s, all objects and materials used by humans were either created directly from wood or stone or crafted from metals, glass, and clays. Available fibers included cotton, wool, linen, and silk. All medicines and food additives came from natural sources. Celluloid (from wood) and shellac (from animal materials) were the only sources for commercially produced **polymers,** which are large molecules typically composed of 500 to 20 000 or more repeating units of simpler molecules known as **monomers.**

Today, many common objects and materials created by the chemical industry are unlike anything seen or used by citizens of the 1800s or even the mid-1900s. See Figure 3.37. Many of these differences are due to the use of compounds produced from oil or natural gas, called **petrochemicals.** Some petrochemicals, such as detergents, pesticides, pharmaceuticals, and cosmetics, are used directly. Most petrochemicals, however, serve as raw materials in producing other synthetic substances, particularly a wide range of polymers.

Synthetic polymers include paint components, fabrics, rubber, insulating materials, foams, adhesives, molding, and structural materials. Worldwide production of petroleum-based polymers is more than four times that of aluminum products.

The astonishing fact is that it takes relatively few *builder molecules* (small-molecule compounds) to make thousands of new substances, including many polymers. One builder molecule is *ethene*, C_2H_4, a hydrocarbon compound commonly called *ethylene*. The structural formula for ethene is shown in the following equation. The two carbon atoms in an ethene molecule share *two* pairs of electrons. This produces an arrangement of electrons called a **double covalent bond.** Because of the high reactivity of its double bond, ethene is readily transformed into many useful products. A simple example—the formation of ethanol (ethyl alcohol) from water and ethene—illustrates how ethene reacts:

Figure 3.37 *Two street scenes—one from the early 1900s (top) and one from the early 2000s (bottom). What similarities and differences do you notice in the use of materials?*

Double bonds will be discussed in more detail on page 266.

$$\underset{\text{Ethene}}{\overset{H}{\underset{H}{>}}C=C\overset{H}{\underset{H}{<}}} + \underset{\text{Water}}{H-OH} \xrightarrow[\text{Catalyst}]{\text{Acid}} \underset{\text{Ethanol}}{H-\overset{H}{\underset{H}{C}}-\overset{H}{\underset{OH}{C}}-H}$$

In this reaction, the water molecule (HOH) "adds" to the double-bonded carbon atoms by adding an H to one carbon atom and an OH group to the other carbon atom. This type of chemical change is called an **addition reaction.**

Ethene can also undergo an addition reaction with itself. Because the added ethene molecule also contains a double bond, another ethene molecule can be added, and so on. This creates a long-chain substance called *polyethene,* commonly known as *polyethylene,* a polymer consisting of 500 to 20 000 or more repeating units of ethene (ethylene) monomer. The chemical reaction that produces polyethene can be represented this way:

Ethene
(ethylene)

The growing polymer
chain

Polyethene
(polyethylene)

Polymers formed by reactions such as this are called—sensibly enough—**addition polymers.** Polyethene is commonly used in grocery bags and packaging. The United States produces millions of kilograms of polyethene annually.

We can make a great variety of addition polymers from monomers that closely resemble ethene. The most common variation is to replace one or more hydrogen atoms in ethene with an atom or atoms of another element. In the following examples, note the replacements for hydrogen atoms in each monomer and polymer:

Vinyl chloride

Polyvinyl chloride (PVC)

Acrylonitrile

Polyacrylonitrile (PAN)

Styrene

Polystyrene

Perhaps you wonder why two names are shown for the same substance—ethene/ethylene and polyethene/polyethylene. Chemists have developed a system for naming substances that makes it easy to communicate clearly with each other. However, some substances were given names long before this system was universally accepted. Some "common names" of substances, such as ethylene and polyethylene, continue in wide use.

The hexagon-shaped ring depicted in styrene and polystyrene represents benzene, a substance discussed later on page 271.

Ethene (C_2H_4), or ethylene, is introduced as a representative builder molecule. It is also an *unsaturated*—not fully bonded with hydrogen—hydrocarbon molecule, an idea addressed in *Modeling Matter C.2.* Emphasize that alkenes are much more reactive than alkanes. Thus, alkenes are good starting materials for making many new molecules. One way to form new molecules from alkenes (and other unsaturated hydrocarbons) is through *addition reactions.* In these reactions, the second bond between the carbons is broken (requiring energy), and new bonds are formed between the carbon atoms and added atoms (releasing energy). Addition reactions can only take place at a multiple bond. This enables formation of new bonds without cleaving the original molecule.

Alkenes (and other builder molecules) can often polymerize into macromolecules through a series of self-addition reactions. When an ethene molecule—the monomer—links to another ethene molecule, a dimer forms. As this process continues (without loss of any atoms), an addition polymer forms. These polymers may grow into chains containing 10 000 or more monomer units.

At this introductory point, emphasize the variety and usefulness of substances that can be created from petrochemicals, rather than focusing on names, formulas, or characteristic reactions. These will arise later.

Demonstration Ideas

1. Students are often fascinated by the following demonstration, which illustrates some physical and chemical characteristics of polystyrene. The demonstration is based on the breakdown of polystyrene in acetone. Fill a transparent container, such as a large beaker or graduated cylinder, one-third full of acetone (*Caution:* Highly flammable acetone should be handled only by the instructor, preferably working in a fume hood.) Add Styrofoam pellets to the acetone. The Styrofoam will break down, appearing to "melt," and release bubbles of air. A remarkably large quantity of Styrofoam can be broken down in this manner because the pellets are mostly air. The acetone destroys polymer cross-linking (*cross-linking* is addressed in *Modeling Matter C.2*) and allows air to escape, leaving the polystyrene behind. You may wish to do this demonstration *after* the *Modeling Matter* activity so students can readily interpret it.

2. Fill a gallon-sized zip-seal bag with water. Seal it tightly, then insert a sharpened pencil through both sides. The water does not leak out because of the elastic nature of the polymer in the bag (generally low-density polyethylene). You can poke many pencils into the bag at the same time, as long as they have smooth shafts. Do not try to use mechanical pencils or pens.

Figure 3.38 *Products commonly made from (a) polyvinyl chloride, (b) polypropylene, and (c) polystyrene.*

The atoms that compose the monomers determine the properties of the resulting polymer. Thus, polyethene and polyvinyl chloride are fundamentally different materials. However, as with many modern materials, the properties of a polymer are often altered to meet a variety of needs and to produce many products. See Figure 3.38.

C.2 POLYMER STRUCTURE AND PROPERTIES

 Modeling Matter

Polymers— 3D Structures & Properties

Unmodified, the arrangement of covalent bonds in long, stringlike polymer molecules causes the molecules to coil loosely. A collection of polymer molecules (such as those in a sample of molten polymer) can intertwine, much like strands of cooked spaghetti. In this form, the polymer is flexible and soft.

1. Using a pencil line on paper to represent a linear polymer, draw a collection of loosely coiled polymer molecules.

Ductility refers to the ability of a material to be drawn out, as into thin strands. For most polymers like the ones you just drew, flexibility and ductility depend on temperature. When the material is warm, the polymer chains can slide past one another easily. The polymer becomes more rigid when it cools. We use such polymers, classified as *thermoplastics,* in many everyday products, such as soft drink bottles, milk bottles, and plastic bags.

The flexibility of a polymer can also be enhanced by adding molecules that act as internal lubricants among the polymer chains. For example, untreated polyvinyl chloride (PVC) is used in rigid pipes and house siding. With added lubricant molecules, polyvinyl chloride becomes flexible enough for use in such consumer goods as raincoats and inflatable pool toys.

The reactions that form polymer chains can also take place perpendicular to the main chain, forming *side chains.* These polymers are called **branched polymers.** The branched form of polyethylene is shown in the following illustration. The extent of branching can be controlled by adjusting reaction conditions.

Branch

Branch

2. Draw at least two different models of branched-chain polymers. Try to vary your representations—the forms of branched polymers can differ greatly.

Modeling Matter

C.2 Polymer Structure and Properties

 C.2 Polymer Structure and Properties Student Worksheet

Emphasize to students that their drawings in this activity can be very simple. The idea is to focus on macrostructures, not discrete atoms.

1.

2.

3.

4.

5.

6.

C.3 Beyond Alkanes

Alkenes, unsaturated hydrocarbons, contain at least one carbon-to-carbon double covalent bond. As noted in C.1, this makes alkenes (and other unsaturated hydrocarbons) much more reactive than alkanes.

This material also introduces substituted hydrocarbons, compounds that include elements other than hydrogen and carbon. Emphasize that adding atoms such as nitrogen, oxygen, sulfur, or chlorine, as well as arrangement of atoms within a molecule, has a significant impact on the chemical reactivity (and physical properties) of a compound.

Branching changes the properties of a polymer by affecting the ability of chains to slide past one another and by altering intermolecular forces.

Another way to alter the properties of polymers is through **cross-linking.** Polymer rigidity can be increased if the polymer chains are cross-linked so that they can no longer move or slide readily. You can see this for yourself if you compare the flexibility of a plastic soda bottle with that of its screw-on cap. Polymer cross-linking is much greater in the cap. The following illustration shows a cross-linked form of polyethene.

Crosslink

Rubber-Formation &
Chemical Structure

3. Draw several linear polymer chains that have been cross-linked.

4. Draw several cross-linked, branched polymers. Then describe how cross-linked *branched* polymers compare to cross-linked *linear* polymers.

Chemists can control polymer strength and toughness. To do this, the polymer chains are arranged so that they lie in the same general direction. The aligned chains are stretched until they uncoil. Polymers that remain uncoiled after this treatment make strong, tough films and fibers. Such materials include polyethene, which is used in everything from garbage bags to artificial ice rinks, and polypropylene, which is used in bottles and some carpeting.

5. Draw several aligned linear polymer chains.

6. Draw several aligned and cross-linked linear polymer chains.

C.3 BEYOND ALKANES

Carbon atoms are versatile building blocks. Carbon can form bonds with other atoms in several different ways. As you learned in Section A, each carbon atom in an alkane molecule is bonded to four other atoms. Compounds such as alkanes are called **saturated hydrocarbons** because each carbon atom forms as many single covalent bonds as it can.

In some hydrocarbon molecules, carbon atoms bond to three other atoms, not four. Members of this series of hydrocarbons are called **alkenes.** The simplest alkene was briefly introduced to you (see page 262)— ethene, C_2H_4.

The carbon–carbon bonding that characterizes alkenes is a double covalent bond. In a double bond, four electrons (two electron pairs) are shared between the bonding partners. Alkenes, which contain carbon–

At this point, students should be comfortable with names, suffixes, and identifying characteristics of alkanes (-*ane*, all single bonds, saturated), alkenes (-*ene*, one or more

double bonds), and alkynes (-*yne*, one or more triple bonds). Students will review these structures through building molecular models in *Investigating Matter C.4.*

carbon double bonds, are described as **unsaturated hydrocarbons.** Not all carbon atoms are bonded to their full capacity with four other atoms. Because of their double bonds, alkenes are more chemically reactive—and therefore better builder molecules—than are alkanes.

The **substituted alkenes** make up another class of builder molecules. In addition to carbon and hydrogen, these molecules contain one or more other atoms, such as oxygen, nitrogen, chlorine, or sulfur. Adding atoms of other elements to hydrocarbon structures significantly changes their chemical reactivity.

Even molecules composed of the same elements can have quite different properties. For example, ethanol and dimethyl ether both contain carbon, hydrogen, and oxygen atoms. In fact, they share the same molecular formula, C_2H_6O. However, ethanol, also called grain alcohol, is liquid at room temperature, while dimethyl ether—often used as a refrigerant—is a gas. The dramatic differences in their properties and uses result from particular arrangements of atoms in these two molecules, as shown by the following structures.

> Dimethyl ether is a propellant in many aerosol spray cans and recently has been successfully used as a diesel-fuel substitute.

$$
\begin{array}{cc}
\overset{\displaystyle H}{\underset{\displaystyle H}{H-\overset{|}{\underset{|}{C}}-\overset{\displaystyle H}{\underset{\displaystyle H}{\overset{|}{\underset{|}{C}}}}-OH} & \overset{\displaystyle H}{\underset{\displaystyle H}{H-\overset{|}{\underset{|}{C}}-O-\overset{\displaystyle H}{\underset{\displaystyle H}{\overset{|}{\underset{|}{C}}}}-H}
\end{array}
$$

Ethanol　　　　　　Dimethyl ether

As you know, the strength of intermolecular forces is related to molecular structure. In this case, attractions among ethanol molecules, in which oxygen is bonded to hydrogen, are stronger than attractions among dimethyl ether molecules. This helps to explain why ethanol is liquid and dimethyl ether is gaseous at room temperature.

> **Investigating Matter**

C.4 THE BUILDERS

Introduction

This investigation, in which you will use models to represent various arrangements of atoms, will help you become more familiar with alkenes and their polymers. Be prepared to record your observations and answers to questions in your laboratory notebook.

Procedure

Part I: Alkenes

1. Examine the following Lewis-dot formula and structural formula for ethene, C_2H_4. Confirm that each atom has attained its filled outer shell of electrons:

$$
\begin{array}{ccc}
\overset{\displaystyle H\ \ H}{H:\overset{..}{C}::\overset{..}{C}:H} & \overset{\displaystyle H\ \ H}{H-\overset{|}{C}=\overset{|}{C}-H} & CH_2CH_2 \text{ or } C_2H_4 \\
\text{Lewis dot} & \text{Structural} & \text{Molecular formula} \\
\text{formula} & \text{formula} &
\end{array}
$$

> **Investigating Matter**

C.4 The Builders

C.4 The Builders Student Worksheet and Data Table

Students work with models to explore bonding and characteristics of alkenes, alkynes, oxygen-substituted hydrocarbons, and alkene-based polymers. The molecular model kits for this activity must be able to represent double bonds (often with springs or longer, flexible plastic "bonds")—if they cannot, consider substituting gumdrops or clay spheres (atoms) and toothpicks or thin straws (bonds).

As students construct alkene molecules, call attention to the fact that the molecule cannot rotate around the double bond. When students construct polymers, help them to link their models to ideas and drawings from *Modeling Matter C.2*. Although several compound names are mentioned, do not focus on nomenclature in this activity.

Time

60 to 90 min

Materials

(For 12 student pairs)

12 sets of space-filling or ball-and-stick models (that can represent double bonds that do not allow rotation)

Part I: Alkenes

Electron-dot structures, structural formulas, condensed formulas, and systematic nomenclature are used to describe hydrocarbon molecules with multiple bonds.

Answers

1. Students should confirm that each C atom shares 8 electrons, and each H atom shares 2 electrons.

2. C_nH_{2n}

3. a. The ethene molecule is impossible to rotate around the "stiff" double bond.

   b. No

   c. Alkene molecules resist rotation about the double bond.

4. a. Three arrangements are possible, as illustrated in **Figure 3.40.** Other possible C_4H_8 isomers are cyclobutane and methylcyclopropane, which are not alkenes.

   b. Results will vary, but many students will build 1-butene and 2-butene. Methylpropene is less easily recognized as a butene isomer.

5. Each pair alone represents the same substance (not isomers). Some students may correctly point out, however, that the substance represented by the first pair (1-butene) is an isomer of the substance represented by the second pair (2-methylpropene).

6. Only one structure is possible for propene.

7. Isomers; these structures have the same formula (C_5H_{10}) but different arrangements of atoms. The left is cyclopentane, and the right structure is methylcyclobutane.

8. a. $H-C{\equiv}C-H$

   b. $CH_3-C{\equiv}C-CH_3$

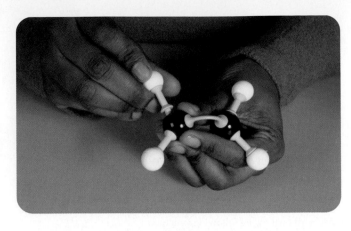

Figure 3.39 *You can use the flexible connector pieces to model the double bonds in molecules such as ethene.*

1-Butene, or simply butene

2-Butene

Methylpropene

Figure 3.40 *Three isomers of butene, C_4H_8.*

The names of alkenes follow a pattern much like that of the alkanes. The first three alkenes are *ethene, propene,* and *butene.* The same prefixes that you learned for alkanes are used to indicate the number of carbon atoms in the molecule's longest carbon chain. However, each alkene name ends in *-ene* instead of *-ane.*

2. Recall that the alkane general formula is C_nH_{2n+2}. Examine the molecular formulas of ethene (C_2H_4) and butene (C_4H_8). What general formula for alkenes do these molecular formulas suggest?

3. Assemble models of an ethene (C_2H_4) molecule and an ethane (C_2H_6) molecule. See Figure 3.39. Compare the arrangements of atoms in the two models. Rotate the two carbon atoms in ethane about their single C—C bond. Then try a similar rotation with ethene.

   a. What do you observe?

   b. Can you build a molecule in which you can complete a rotation about a C=C double bond?

   c. Write a general rule to summarize your findings.

4. Build a model of butene (C_4H_8). Remember that alkenes must contain a double bond. Compare your model to those made by others.

   a. How many different arrangements of atoms in a C_4H_8 molecule appear possible? Each arrangement represents a different substance—another example of isomers.

   b. Which structural formulas in Figure 3.40 correspond to models built by you and your classmates?

As with alkanes, we name alkenes according to their longest carbon chain. The carbon atoms are numbered, beginning at the end of the chain closest to the double bond. The name of each isomer starts with the number assigned to the first double-bonded carbon atom. Look again at the butene isomer structures in Figure 3.40 and confirm these naming rules with 1-butene and 2-butene.

5. Do each of the following pairs represent isomers of the same substance, or do they both represent the same substance?

   a. $CH_2=CH-CH_2-CH_3$ and $CH_3-CH_2-CH=CH_2$

   b. $CH_2=C-CH_3$ and CH_3-C-CH_3
      $\quad\quad\;|\quad\quad\quad\quad\quad\;\|$
      $\quad\quad CH_3\quad\quad\quad\quad\; CH_2$

6. How many isomers of propene (C_3H_6) are there? Support your answer with appropriate structures.

7. Do the following two structures represent isomers or the same substance? Explain.

$$CH_2-CH_2 \quad\quad CH_3-CH-CH_2$$
$$\;|\quad\quad\;| \quad\quad\quad\quad\quad|\quad\quad\;|$$
$$CH_2\;\;\;CH_2 \quad\quad\quad\quad CH_2-CH_2$$
$$\quad\;\;CH_2$$

8. Assemble a model of a hydrocarbon molecule containing a *triple* covalent bond. Base this on your knowledge of hydrocarbon molecules with either single or double bonds between carbon atoms. Your completed model represents a member of the hydrocarbon series known as **alkynes.** Given your understanding of the naming of alkanes and alkenes, write structural formulas for

   a. ethyne, commonly called *acetylene* (Figure 3.41).
   b. 2-butyne.

9. Are alkynes saturated or unsaturated hydrocarbons? Explain.

Part II: Compounds of Carbon, Hydrogen, and Singly Bonded Oxygen

10. Assemble as many different molecular models as possible, using all nine of the following atoms:

    ▶ 2 carbon atoms (each forming four single bonds)
    ▶ 6 hydrogen atoms (each forming a single bond)
    ▶ 1 oxygen atom (forming two single bonds)

Figure 3.41 *Ethyne (commonly called acetylene) is the primary fuel in blowtorches. When burned, it generates the high temperatures needed to weld and to cut through metal.*

9. Unsaturated; they do not contain as many hydrogen atoms or carbon–hydrogen bonds as possible.

Part II: Compounds of Carbon, Hydrogen, and Singly Bonded Oxygen

Students should readily construct the two isomers of C_2H_6O. They should recognize that the molecule with the $-OH$ group (ethanol) would be more soluble in H_2O, since the $-OH$ group is similar to water. Also remind students that they have already tested the solubility of ethanol in water in Unit 1 (*Investigating Matter C.11: Solvents*). Ethanol has a higher boiling point (80 °C) than dimethyl ether (-24 °C). This difference is explained by the greater degree of intermolecular attraction (hydrogen bonding) among ethanol molecules, also due to the $-OH$ functional group.

10. If you use commercial model kits, the number of holes in each atom will limit possible arrangements of atoms. For instance, H atoms have only one hole, while O atoms have two and C atoms have four. If you are using gumdrops or another type of noncommercial model, you may need to remind students of these limitations. Also emphasize, as the instructions indicate, that they should use only single bonds.

11. a. Two are possible—
$CH_3—CH_2—O—H$ (ethanol) and
$CH_3—O—CH_3$ (dimethyl ether).
b. Yes. They share the same formula, but their atoms are arranged differently.

12. a. Ethanol. Students should recognize that the —OH functional group in ethanol is similar to the structure of water.
b. Ethanol, because it has stronger intermolecular forces due to its —OH functional group.

Part III: Alkene-Based Polymers

13. Students should build two identical models, $H_2C=CH_2$.

14. It is necessary to break the double bond in one ethene molecule. The resulting model has the structure
$H_3C—CH_2—CH=CH_2$.

15. Students should repeat the process from Question 14 with other groups to form a polyethylene chain.

Polyethylene
grows by chains of 2 carbons
as each group connects.

16. Students should build the structures shown for monomers and polymers involving vinyl chloride and propene. Structures for styrene and polystyrene parallel these, except that a benzyl ring is the side-chain extending from the C=C double bond instead of either —Cl (in vinyl chloride) or —CH₃ (in propene). Students may have difficulty physically constructing styrene and may need to make a substitution for the benzyl ring.

270

---

11. On paper, draw a structural formula for each compound you assembled in Step 10, indicating how the nine atoms are connected. Compare your structures with those built by other classmates. Be sure that you are satisfied that all possible structures have been produced, then answer these questions:
  a. How many distinct structures did you identify?
  b. Are all of these structures isomers? Explain.

12. Each structure you have identified possesses distinctly different properties.
  a. Recalling that "like dissolves like," which molecule should be most soluble in water?
  b. Which molecule should have the highest boiling point? Why?

> Remember that boiling points are related to strengths of intermolecular forces.

Part III: Alkene-Based Polymers

In this part of the investigation, you and your classmates will use models to simulate the formation of several addition polymers.

13. Build models of two ethene molecules.

14. Using the information on page 263 as a guide, combine your two models into a **dimer,** a two-monomer structure. How did you have to modify the monomer structure to accomplish this?

15. Combine your dimer with that of another lab team. Continue this process until your class has created one long-chain structure. Although your resulting molecular chain is not yet long enough to be regarded as a model of a polymer, you have simulated the processes involved in creating a typical addition polymer.

16. Repeat Steps 13 and 14, first by replacing ethene with vinyl chloride and then by replacing ethene with propene. Then find out whether you can follow the same steps for styrene. (See page 263 for the molecular structures of these substances.)

17. Assume the structures you built in Steps 15 and 16 became significantly larger. Give the name of each resulting polymer.

18. Are the chains you built *linear* or *branched*? How would this affect the properties of the polymer?

19. Build a polyethene chain that includes some cross-linking.
  a. How does cross-linking change the behavior of the model, if at all?
  b. How would this cross-linking change the observed properties of the polymer?

C.5 MORE BUILDER MOLECULES

So far, you have examined only a small part of the inventory of builder molecules available to chemical architects. Now you will explore two classes of compounds in which carbon atoms are joined in *rings* rather than in chain structures.

vinyl chloride

polyvinyl chloride

propene

polypropylene

As a first step to doing this, picture a straight-chain hexane molecule:

$$CH_3-CH_2-CH_2-CH_2-CH_2-CH_3$$

Next, remove one hydrogen atom from the carbon atom at each end. Then imagine those two carbon atoms bonding to each other. The result is the molecule known as *cyclohexane:*

Hexane   Cyclohexane

Cyclohexane, obtained by petroleum refining, is a starting reactant for making nylon, a familiar petrochemical polymer. Cyclohexane is representative of the **cycloalkanes,** which are saturated hydrocarbons made up of carbon atoms joined in rings.

Another class of hydrocarbon builder molecules is **aromatic compounds.** Aromatic compounds have chemical properties distinctly different from those of the cycloalkanes and their derivatives. The structural formula of benzene (C_6H_6), which is the simplest aromatic compound, is shown in the following illustration. In the representation on the right, each "corner" of the six-carbon (hexagonal) ring represents a carbon atom with its hydrogen atom:

Although chemists who first investigated benzene proposed these structures, the chemical properties of the compound did not support their models. Recall that carbon–carbon double bonds (C=C) are usually very reactive. But, in terms of its reactivity, benzene behaves as though it does not contain any such double bonds. A deeper understanding of chemical bonding was needed to explain benzene's puzzling structure.

Substantial experimental evidence indicates that all carbon–carbon bonds in benzene are identical. Thus, its structure is not well represented by alternating single and double bonds. Instead, chemists often represent a benzene molecule in the following way:

The inner circle represents equal sharing of bonding electrons among all six carbon atoms. The hexagonal ring represents the bonding of six carbon atoms to each other. "Each corner" in the hexagon ring is the location of one carbon atom and hydrogen atom, thus accounting for benzene's formula, C_6H_6.

Nylon-Formation & Chemical Structure

> The pleasant odor of the first aromatic compounds that were discovered prompted their descriptive name.

Benzene, C_6H_6

SECTION C

C.5 More Builder Molecules

Students are introduced to two classes of organic compounds in which carbon atoms are joined in rings—cycloalkanes and aromatic compounds. Cycloalkanes are similar to linear alkanes in terms of their relative reactivity. Aromatic compounds are more reactive than linear alkanes but not as reactive as alkenes. Although they are unsaturated, aromatic compounds do not have double bonds like alkenes. Instead, electrons are shared equally among all six-carbon atoms in the benzene ring, giving each bond strength and length intermediate to that of single and double bonds. This accounts for their moderate reactivity, as well as their usefulness as builder molecules. Aromatic compounds tend to undergo substitution rather than addition reactions. Benzene also has a lower heat of combustion than would be expected from a comparable alkene. Because of their properties, aromatic compounds are commercially important builders, particularly in the dye, drug, and fragrance/flavor industries.

---

17. Step 15: polyethylene. Step 16: Polyvinyl chloride, polypropylene, and polystyrene.
18. Linear. Branched-chain polymers tend to be less flexible than straight-chain polymers.
19. a. The cross-linked models are more rigid.

    b. Cross-linked polymers are typically more rigid and heat resistant than straight-chain polymers. Cross-linked chains are not softened by heat; they simply char if exposed to flame. Cross-linked polymers usually cannot be remolded once they have been shaped.

Using the Figures

Figure 3.42: Note the array of vibrant dye colors. Such dyes are composed of aromatic compounds, which tend to absorb and reflect visible light.

C.6 Builder Molecules Containing Oxygen

This material formally introduces organic compounds containing oxygen as well as carbon and hydrogen. It describes the functional groups that characterize alcohols, acids, and esters. The functional group(s) in an organic compound determine its physical and chemical properties. Remind students that, with the exception of combustion, unsubstituted alkanes are fairly unreactive. Molecules that contain the same functional group(s) share similar properties.

Remind students that they built structures incorporating oxygen in *Investigating Matter C.4.* They should be able to identify one of those structures as an alcohol. The other is an ether, a structure in which the H in an alcohol's —OH functional group is replaced by a hydrocarbon group. Similarly, a carboxylic acid has a double-bonded oxygen and an —OH functional group, while an ester replaces the H (in the —OH group) with a hydrocarbon group.

Figure 3.42 *Aromatic compounds are the primary builder molecules for dyes such as these.*

The —OH alcohol functional group should not be confused with the hydroxide anion, OH⁻, found in ionic compounds such as sodium hydroxide, NaOH.

Although only small amounts of aromatic compounds are found in petroleum, fractionation and cracking produce large amounts of these aromatic compounds. Gasoline contains benzene and other aromatic compounds as octane-number enhancers, but they are used primarily as builder molecules. Entire chemical industries (dye and drug manufacturing, in particular) are based on the unique chemistry of aromatic compounds (Figure 3.42).

C.6 BUILDER MOLECULES CONTAINING OXYGEN

In assembling molecular models with C, H, and O atoms, you probably discovered one of the following compounds:

$$CH_3—OH \qquad CH_3—CH_2—OH$$
Methanol   Ethanol
(methyl alcohol)   (ethyl alcohol)

As you can see, each molecule has an —OH group attached to a carbon atom. This general structure is characteristic of a class of compounds known as **alcohols.** The —OH group is recognized by chemists as one type of **functional group**—an atom or group of atoms that imparts characteristic properties to organic compounds. If the letter R is used to represent all the rest of the molecule other than the functional group, then the general formula of an alcohol can be written as

$$R—OH$$
Any alcohol

In this formula, the line indicates a covalent bond linking the oxygen of the —OH group with the adjacent carbon atom in the molecule. In methanol (CH_3OH), the letter R would represent CH_3—; in ethanol (CH_3CH_2OH), R would represent CH_3CH_2—.

The formulas and structures of two common alcohols follow. What would R represent in each compound?

$$CH_3CH_2CH_2OH$$

1-Propanol   Cyclohexanol

Two other classes of oxygen-containing organic compounds, **carboxylic acids** and **esters,** are versatile builder molecules. The functional group in each of these classes of compounds contains two oxygen atoms, as shown at the top of the next page:

✍ **C.6 Supplement: The Builders**

$$R-\overset{\overset{\displaystyle O}{\parallel}}{C}-OH \qquad R-\overset{\overset{\displaystyle O}{\parallel}}{C}-OR$$

Carboxylic acid   Ester

Note that both classes of compounds have one oxygen atom double-bonded to a carbon atom and a second oxygen atom single-bonded to the same carbon atom. *Ethanoic acid* (a carboxylic acid that is better known as *acetic acid*) and *methyl ethanoate* (an ester more commonly called *methyl acetate*) are examples of these two classes of compounds:

$$H-\overset{\overset{\displaystyle H}{\mid}}{\underset{\underset{\displaystyle H}{\mid}}{C}}-\overset{\overset{\displaystyle O}{\parallel}}{C}-OH \qquad H-\overset{\overset{\displaystyle H}{\mid}}{\underset{\underset{\displaystyle H}{\mid}}{C}}-\overset{\overset{\displaystyle O}{\parallel}}{C}-OCH_3$$

Ethanoic acid   Methyl ethanoate

Some familiar examples that include or involve the use of alcohols, carboxylic acids, and esters are shown in Figure 3.43. These builder molecules can be modified by adding other functional groups that include nitrogen, sulfur, or chlorine atoms. The rich variety of functional groups greatly expands the types of molecules that chemists can ultimately build.

Figure 3.43 *Examples that include or involve (a) carboxylic acids and (b) esters and alcohols.*

(a) carboxylic acids   (b) esters and alcohols

Using the Figures

Figure 3.43: Items containing carboxylic acids are ants (formic acid, HCOOH) and vinegar (acetic acid, CH_3COOH). Items containing alcohols are antifreeze (ethylene glycol, $HOCH_2CH_2OH$), windshield-washing fluid (methanol, CH_3OH), rubbing alcohol (isopropyl alcohol, $CH_3CHOHCH_3$), cough medicine, hair spray, and aftershave lotion. Items containing esters are flowers and bananas.

C.6 Supplement: Functional Groups

SECTION C

C.7 Condensation Polymers

✏ C.1 and C.7 Content Reading Guide

Condensation polymers arise as two or more monomers react to form a larger molecule and a small "by-product." By contrast, addition polymerization does not produce any other products.

Some natural and synthetic polymers are condensation polymers. To continue building a chain, each reacting monomer must have at least two functional groups.

Condensation-polymer examples include polyurethane foam, epoxy glue, nylon, Dacron, peptides, and proteins. *Investigating Matter C.8 involves a condensation reaction to form a small molecule.*

Demonstration Idea

Nylon synthesis (aka "nylon-rope trick"): *Nylon* molecules are synthetic polyamides. Nylon made from diamines and dibasic acids or diacid chlorides are designated by two numbers (for example, "nylon-66"). The first indicates the diamine's total carbon atoms, and the second indicates total dibasic acid carbon atoms.

Caution: *The diamine, dichloride, and sodium hydroxide are all irritating to skin, eyes, and the respiratory system; use a fume hood. Wear protective gloves and goggles. Do not directly touch the polymer product until it is washed with ethanol or water. Some laboratory suppliers provide pre-assembled kits for a similar "nylon" demonstration.*

C.7 CONDENSATION POLYMERS

Earlier in this section, you learned that many polymers can be formed from alkene-based monomers through addition reactions. Not all polymers are formed in this way, however. Natural polymers, such as proteins, starch, cellulose (in wood and paper), and synthetic polymers, including familiar nylon and polyester, are also formed from monomers. However, unlike addition polymers, these polymers form with the loss of simple molecules, such as water, when monomer units join. The term **condensation reaction** applies to this second type of polymer-making process, and the resulting product is called a **condensation polymer.** Here is a simple representation of this process:

$$-R_1-O-H \ + \ H-O-R_2- \ \longrightarrow \ -R_1-O-R_2- \ + \ H-OH$$

Monomer 1   Monomer 2   Condensation polymer   Water

One common condensation polymer is polyethylene terephthalate (PET). This polymer is often used in large soft-drink containers. It has many other applications—as thin film for videotape and as Dacron for clothing, surgical tubing, and fiberfill. More than two million kilograms of PET are produced each year in the United States. Some examples of products made from PET are shown in Figure 3.44.

> Recall that R stands for the "rest" of the molecule, or everything other than the functional group.

| **Figure 3.44** *Common uses of PET.*

Solution 1: Open and gradually warm a reagent bottle of 1,6-diaminohexane (also called hexamethylenediamine, melting point = 42 °C) in a water bath until the solid begins to melt. Decant 2.9 g directly into a 100-mL beaker and dilute to 50 mL with 0.5 M NaOH (2 g NaOH per 100 mL).
Solution 2: Prepare a 0.25 M diacid chloride solution by diluting 2.3 g adipoyl dichloride to 50 mL with hexane.

The reaction does not depend on exact amounts of reactants, but these concentrations lead to optimal results. The aqueous diamine solution may be stored, but acid chloride solutions are unstable due to hydrolysis (prepare only enough for that day).

While some PET may be recycled, material containing high quantities of additives, such as dyes or other polymers, is either disposed of in a landfill or is incinerated. Another option is a DuPont process that breaks down PET into its monomers, which are then repolymerized into high-quality PET products. This technology decreases the need for new petroleum-based builder molecules as well as decreases the quantity of PET discarded in landfills.

Condensation reactions can be used to make small molecules as well as polymers. In the next investigation, you will use condensation reactions to produce several esters. These reactions illustrate how you can chemically combine organic compounds to create new, useful substances.

The structure of the PET polymer

C.8 CONDENSATION

Investigating Matter

Introduction

In this investigation, you will produce several products through the condensation reaction of an organic acid (an acid derived from a hydrocarbon) with an alcohol. The esters you will produce have familiar, pleasing fragrances. Many perfumes contain esters; the characteristic aromas of many herbs and fruits arise from esters in the plants.

One example of the formation of an ester is the production of methyl acetate from ethanoic acid (acetic acid) and methanol in the presence of sulfuric acid as a catalyst:

$$CH_3-\overset{\overset{\displaystyle O}{\|}}{C}-OH \ + \ H-O-CH_3 \ \xrightarrow{H_2SO_4} \ CH_3-\overset{\overset{\displaystyle O}{\|}}{C}-O-CH_3 \ + \ H-OH$$

Ethanoic acid   Methanol   Methyl acetate   Water

To emphasize the roles of functional groups in the formation of an ester, a general equation can be written using *R* notation:

$$R-\overset{\overset{\displaystyle O}{\|}}{C}-OH \ + \ H-O-R \ \xrightarrow{H_2SO_4} \ R-\overset{\overset{\displaystyle O}{\|}}{C}-O-R \ + \ H-OH$$

Carboxylic acid   Alcohol   Ester   Water

Note how the functional groups of the acid and alcohol combine to form a water molecule, while the remaining atoms join to form an ester molecule.

Using a chemical process similar to the one in the preceding reaction, you will now produce the ester known as *methyl salicylate*.

Before starting, read the procedure to learn what you will need to do, note safety precautions, and plan necessary data collecting and observations. Because this investigation involves the reactions of various alcohols and carboxylic acids, your data table should clearly communicate which substances you combined and the observed properties of the resulting esters.

Lab Video: Condensation

Organic acids are also called *carboxylic acids*. See page 273.

Investigating Matter

C.8 Condensation

C.8 Condensation Student Worksheet and Data Table

Students synthesize esters from carboxylic acids and alcohols. Review the synthesis described in the text (methyl acetate from methanol and ethanoic acid) so students understand relationships among functional groups. This investigation produces several esters with distinctive odors.

Time

30 min

Materials

(For 12 student pairs)

36 test tubes (15 × 125 mm)

12 10-mL graduated cylinders

12 100-mL beakers

12 test tube holders

12 test tube brushes

12 hot plates

Dropping bottles to dispense alcohols

50 mL concentrated sulfuric acid (18 M H_2SO_4)

1 reagent bottle for dispensing 18 M H_2SO_4

24 mL methyl alcohol (methanol)

6 g salicylic acid

24 boiling chips

For additional esters:

50 mL glacial (concentrated) acetic acid

50 mL iso-amyl alcohol (3-methyl-1-butanol) or *n*-pentyl alcohol (*n*-pentanol)

50 mL octyl alcohol (octanol)

Use equal volumes of Solutions 1 and 2 (just 5 mL each is enough). Pour Solution 1 into a small beaker; then slowly pour Solution 2 down the same beaker's inside wall, gently layering it above Solution 1. Minimize agitation between layers.

Using forceps or a bent paper clip, hook the polymer film formed at the interface of the layers and slowly pull it up from the middle of the beaker. Continue pulling nylon "thread" until the solutions are depleted. A continuous 3- to 4-m thread is possible. If it breaks, hook a new thread.

Add any excess solutions to a solvent-waste container or simply stir them. Wash the resulting solid and discard it in a solid-waste container.

Safety

Do not use burners; many reactants are flammable. Methanol, particularly, is a serious fire hazard; its flame is almost invisible.

Students should wear protective goggles, aprons, and gloves.

Demonstrate how to smell vapors cautiously (see **Figure 3.46**).

Students should treat 18 M sulfuric acid with extreme caution. It is caustic and corrosive. You may decide to dispense concentrated acids rather than allowing students to handle them.

Pre-Lab Discussion

Discuss the general reaction that yields esters. Flavor and perfume makers depend on chemically synthesized esters. Many esters have fruity odors and tastes.

Lab Tips

• Caution students not to overheat test tubes.
• Adding a few water drops to the test tube after reaction may help enhance the odor.
• *Caution students not to ingest any products, regardless of their familiarity with the odor.*
• *Remind students to avoid direct inhalation of any fumes.*

Boiling chips minimize erratic boiling, which may "bump" liquid from test tubes. The hot-water bath should *not* boil vigorously; its temperature should be just above methanol's boiling point (56 °C).

Many reactant combinations are possible, given reagents and class time (see SourceBook, Vol. 3, *Organic Chemistry*, pp. 5–10, ChemSource, Inc., 1994).

Answers

1. Methanol, CH_3OH
   Salicylic acid (or 2-hydroxy-benzoic acid), $C_7H_6O_3$
2. $CH_3OH + C_7H_6O_3 \rightarrow C_8H_8O_3 + H_2O$

Figure 3.45 *Proper setup for heating substances with a water bath.*

Figure 3.46 *To avoid burning or irritating your nasal passages, gently "waft" vapors toward your nose with your hand.*

Procedure

1. Prepare a hot-water bath by adding about 50 mL tap water to a 100-mL beaker. Place the beaker on a hot plate, and heat the water until it is near boiling. Be sure that no flames or sparks are in the area. (*Note:* Use a hot plate, *not* a Bunsen burner, to heat the water bath.)

2. Obtain a small, clean test tube. Place 10 drops of methanol into the tube. Next add 0.1 g salicylic acid. Then add 2 drops of concentrated sulfuric acid to the tube. (*Caution: Concentrated sulfuric acid will cause burns to skin or fabric. Add the acid slowly and very carefully. Other than water and sulfuric acid, the substances used in this investigation are volatile and flammable.*)

3. As you dispense these reagents, note their odors. (*Caution: Do not directly sniff any reagent fumes—some may irritate or burn nasal passages.*) Record any odors you happen to note.

4. Place the test tube in the hot-water bath you prepared in Step 1, as shown in Figure 3.45.

5. Keep the tube in the hot water, and do not spill the contents. Note any color changes. Continue heating for five minutes.

6. If you have not noticed an odor from the test tube after five minutes, remove the test tube from the water bath, hold the test tube away from you with the tongs, and wave your hand across the top of the test tube to waft any vapors toward your nose. See Figure 3.46. Record your observations about the odor of the product. Compare your observations with those of other class members.

7. Repeat Steps 1 through 6 using 20 drops of pentyl alcohol (not methanol), 20 drops of glacial (concentrated) acetic acid (not salicylic acid), and 2 drops of concentrated sulfuric acid. (*Caution: Avoid inhaling any glacial acetic acid fumes.*)

8. Now repeat Steps 1 through 6, this time using 20 drops of octyl alcohol, 20 drops of glacial (concentrated) acetic acid, and 2 drops of concentrated sulfuric acid.

9. Dispose of your products as directed by your teacher.

10. Wash your hands thoroughly before leaving the laboratory.

Questions

1. Write the molecular formulas of the acid and alcohol from which you produced methyl salicylate. (*Hint:* You may need to consult a chemistry reference book.)

2. Write a chemical equation for the formation of methyl salicylate.

3. Pentanol, $C_5H_{11}OH$
   Acetic acid, CH_3COOH
   $C_5H_{11}OH + CH_3COOH \rightarrow CH_3COOC_5H_{11} + H_2O$
   Octanol, $C_8H_{17}OH$
   Acetic acid, CH_3COOH
   $C_8H_{17}OH + CH_3COOH \rightarrow CH_3COOC_8H_{17} + H_2O$

4. Students should describe wintergreen, banana, and orange.

5. a. Alcohol b. Ester
   c. Carboxylic acid
   d. Carboxylic acid

Post-Lab Discussion

Focus on reactions of organic-acid and alcohol functional groups to produce esters. Emphasize that small differences in molecular structure can make significant property differences; note contrasting odors of reactants and products.

3. Repeat Questions 1 and 2 for the second and third esters you produced.

4. Describe the odors of the three esters produced in this laboratory investigation.

5. Classify each of the following substances as a carboxylic acid, an alcohol, or an ester:

a. $CH_3—CH_2—CH_2—CH_2—OH$

c. $CH_3—CH—CH_2—CH_3$ with $CH_2—\overset{\overset{\displaystyle O}{\|}}{C}—OH$ below

b. $CH_3—\overset{\overset{\displaystyle O}{\|}}{C}—O—CH_2—CH_3$

d. $CH_3—\overset{\overset{\displaystyle O}{\|}}{C}—OH$

Making Decisions

C.9 BUILDER MOLECULES IN TRANSPORTATION

You have surveyed how some petroleum components are used as building blocks for countless everyday objects. You can easily find examples of products built from petroleum-based materials in your surroundings, products that were unknown even a few decades ago. See Figure 3.47. Synthetic polymers have many advantages over traditional materials, including favorable strength-to-weight ratios and recyclability.

In the TV ad that opened this unit (see page 210), a new automobile was described as helping to conserve petroleum resources. Is this possible? Is it plausible? In this activity, you will consider this claim and evaluate how builder molecules are used in automobile construction.

Figure 3.47 *How many petroleum-based components do you see?*

1. List several automobile components commonly made of polymers.

2. The TV advertisement claimed that driving the *Hybris* will "help conserve petroleum resources."

   a. Does that claim refer to petroleum-based builder molecules used in the manufacture of the *Hybris*?

   b. Would the components on your list from Question 1 possibly differ between a *Hybris* and a traditional automobile? Why?

3. Try to think of a replacement material (not another polymer or petrochemical) for each component on your list.

ANTICIPATED RESULTS		
ACID	**ALCOHOL**	**RESULTING ODOR**
0.1 g salicylic acid	10 drops methanol	wintergreen
20 drops acetic acid	20 drops pentanol	banana
20 drops acetic acid	20 drops octanol	orange

Distinguish organic acids (RCOOH) from common inorganic acids (HCl, HNO_3). Organic acids are usually weak acids originally isolated from plants or animals—formic acid (HCOOH, methanoic acid) was first obtained by destructive distillation of ants; acetic acid (CH_3COOH, ethanoic acid) was obtained by aerobic fermentation of cider and honey. Commercial organic acids are typically synthesized from petroleum or coal tar, as are alcohols with which they are combined to form esters.

Making Decisions

C.9 Builder Molecules in Transportation

Students consider claims that *Hybris* will "help conserve petroleum resources." They may work more successfully in small groups.

1. Examples: instrument panel, grille, interior trim, handles, dials, seats, C-V and U-joints, exterior panels, upholstery, fuel tanks

2. One view is that the claim refers only to fuel for the *Hybris*. Another is that the claim addresses *both* fuel and builder molecules. The list of petroleum-based components could differ under those scenarios. If the sole objective were fuel conservation, one might list *more* polymer components; they have lower density and contribute to fuel efficiency. If the goal is also to conserve builder molecules, one could elect to make components from materials *other* than petroleum.

3. See the answer to Question 4 on page 278.

4. The dashboard could be replaced with metal; disadvantages include that it is nonrenewable, expensive, and potentially less safe. The radio/CD player could be replaced with metal; it is nonrenewable and more expensive. Seat covers could be replaced with leather, which is more expensive. Tires could be made with natural rubber, which is scarce.

5. Making vehicle components represents a one-time use of petroleum resources. Fuel consumption is an ongoing use of petroleum resources. Optimizing energy efficiency (including using low-mass polymer components) decreases long-term, more significant uses of petroleum.

SECTION C SUMMARY

✍ **Section C Supplement**

Reviewing the Concepts

1. a. one b. two c. three d. many

2.

It increases polymer rigidity.

3. Natural polymers include: starch, wool, silk, linen, cellulose, and cotton. Synthetic polymers include: fabrics, such as Dacron, polyester, and nylon; and plastics, such as polyethylene, Teflon, and PET.

4. The primary feature is the nature of the monomer unit. Other features include extent of branching and cross-linking.

4. Decide whether any disadvantages are associated with each replacement material you have suggested. List the two biggest disadvantages for each component, or write "none" if the replacement material provides similar properties at a comparable cost. A table such as the one shown here will help you organize your ideas and answers.

Summary For Question 4			
Automobile Component	**Petroleum Based? (yes or no)**	**Potential Replacement Material**	**Disadvantages of Replacement Material**

5. Advocates of petroleum conservation typically emphasize increasing an automobile's energy efficiency, rather than replacing auto components made from petroleum's polymer-based builder molecules. Why might that be?

5. (1) Adding molecules that act as internal lubricants for polymer chains makes the polymer more flexible. Untreated polyvinyl chloride (PVC) is used in rigid pipes and house siding. With added lubricant, polyvinyl chloride becomes flexible enough to use in raincoats and shoes. (2) Arranging polymer chains so that they lie generally in the same direction can control strength and toughness. Strong films like polyethylene (used in plastic bags) or polyacrylonitrile (in fabrics) are examples.

6. They have fewer than the maximum number of hydrogen atoms bonded to the carbon atoms in their molecular structures.

SECTION C SUMMARY
Reviewing the Concepts

The chemical combination of small, repeating molecular units (monomers) forms large molecules (polymers). Polymers can be designed or altered to produce materials with desired flexibility, strength, and durability.

1. How many repeating units are found in each of these structures?
   a. a monomer   c. a trimer
   b. a dimer   d. a polymer
2. Draw pictures of polymers with and without cross-links. How does cross-linking alter the properties of a polymer?

3. List four examples of natural polymers and four examples of synthetic polymers.
4. What structural features make the properties of one polymer different from those of another?
5. List and explain two methods for altering the characteristics of a polymer.

Unsaturated hydrocarbons that contain one or more double bonds are called alkenes. Unsaturated hydro-carbons that contain a triple bond are called alkynes.

6. Why is the term *unsaturated* used to describe the structures of alkenes and alkynes?
7. Rank the following in order of decreasing chemical reactivity: alkyne, alkane, and alkene. Explain your answer.
8. Why is an unsaturated hydrocarbon likely to be more reactive than a saturated hydrocarbon?
9. Write the molecular formula for a compound named
   a. octane.
   b. pentyne.
   c. decene.

10. How does the presence of a double or triple bond affect the ability of a hydrocarbon molecule to rotate about its carbon chain?
11. Draw a Lewis dot structure and a structural formula for each of the following molecules:
   a. propane
   b. propene
   c. propyne
12. Why is it impossible to have a sample of *methene*, a one-carbon alkene?

Addition reactions involve the chemical combination of monomers to form a polymer.

13. Use structural formulas to illustrate how propylene (propene), shown below, can polymerize to form polypropylene:

14. Explain why alkanes cannot be used to make polymers.
15. What change occurs in the monomer structure during polymerization?

---

12. By definition, an alkene is a double bond between *two* carbon atoms.

13.

14. Alkanes are saturated hydrocarbons; they do not contain reactive double bonds with electrons that can bond to added atoms.
15. The double bond breaks.

---

7. Alkyne, alkene, alkane: The bonds in alkynes and alkenes are much more reactive than single bonds in alkanes. Triple bonds are more reactive than double bonds.
8. Because they can achieve greater stability by bonding with other atoms in an addition reaction.
9. a. C_8H_{18} b. C_5H_8 c. $C_{10}H_{20}$

10. The molecule cannot rotate about those bonds.
11.

16. Cycloalkanes are saturated hydrocarbons, with singly-bonded carbon atoms joined in a ring. Aromatic compounds have carbon atoms joined in a ring, but have fewer than 2 hydrogen atoms per carbon atom and have delocalized electrons.

17. C_5H_{10},

18. Several have intense odors.

19. Experimental evidence shows that bonding electrons in benzene are distributed uniformly around the ring, not in alternating double bonds. All bonds are equal in length, and intermediate in reactivity between single and double bonds.

20. A carbon atom and its associated (bonded) hydrogen atom

21. a. i. Two possible structures:

$$CH_3—CH_2—CH_2—OH$$

ii.

iii.

b. Students should circle the OH, COOH, and COO in the respective formulas.

c. Propanol or isopropanol, propanoic acid, methyl ethanoate

22. a. The "rest" of the molecule

b. An alcohol

23. The ester (R—COO—R) group

24. See table below.

25. Water (or condensation) forms in the reaction.

26. Nylon, polyester, PET, polyurethane foam, epoxy glue, Dacron, peptides, proteins.

| Ring compounds include cycloalkanes and aromatic compounds.

16. In what ways are cycloalkanes different from aromatic compounds?

17. Draw a structural formula and write the molecular formula for cyclopentane.

18. How did the term *aromatic compounds* originate?

19. Why is the circle-within-a-hexagon representation of a benzene molecule a better model than a hexagon with alternating double bonds?

20. What do the six "corners" in the hexagon-shaped benzene representation signify?

| Functional groups—such as alcohols, carboxylic acids, and esters—impart characteristic properties to organic compounds.

21. a. Write the structural formula for a molecule containing three carbon atoms that represents
   i. an alcohol.
   ii. an organic acid.
   iii. an ester.

b. Circle the functional group within each structural formula.

c. Name each compound.

22. a. What does the R stand for in ROH?
b. What type of compound would this be?

23. What functional group is responsible for the pleasing odors of many herbs, fruits, and perfumes?

| Condensation reactions involve the chemical combination of two larger molecules with the loss of a small molecule.

24. Acetic acid, CH_3COOH, and butyric acid, $CH_3(CH_2)_2COOH$, are common reactants in condensation reactions. Their structural

formulas are

and

. Predict the products of a condensation reaction between each of these two acids and each of the alcohols in the following list. Provide the name and structural formula for the product. For example, the product of a condensation reaction between acetic acid and ethanol is *ethyl acetate*. (*Hint:* To organize your response, construct a table with two columns—one for each acid—and three rows—one for each alcohol.)

a. methanol (CH_3OH)
b. ethanol (C_2H_5OH)
c. propanol (C_3H_7OH)

25. Why is the word *condensation* used to describe the reaction that forms esters?

26. Name three examples of polymers formed by condensation reactions.

CONDENSATION PRODUCTS OF ALCOHOLS WITH CARBOXYLIC ACIDS		
CONDENSATION REACTANTS	ACETIC ACID CH_3COOH (ETHANOIC ACID)	BUTYRIC ACID $CH_3(CH_2)_2COOH$ (BUTANOIC ACID)
a. CH_3OH (methanol)	Methyl acetate, CH_3COOCH_3	Methyl butyrate, $C_3H_7COOCH_3$
b. C_2H_5OH (ethanol)	Ethyl acetate, $CH_3COOC_2H_5$	Ethyl butyrate, $C_3H_7COOC_2H_5$
c. C_3H_7OH (propanol)	Propyl acetate, $CH_3COOC_3H_7$	Propyl butyrate, $C_3H_7COOC_3H_7$

Connecting the Concepts

27. Identify the missing molecule (represented by a question mark) in each of the following equations. (*Hint:* If you are uncertain about an answer, start by completing an atom inventory. Remember that the final equation must be balanced.)

    a. $CH_2=CH_2 + ? \longrightarrow CH_3-CH_2Br$

    b.
    $$CH_3-\overset{\overset{\displaystyle H}{|}}{C}=CH_2 + ? \longrightarrow CH_3-\underset{\underset{\displaystyle OH}{|}}{CH}-CH_3$$

    c.
    $$C_6H_{13}-\overset{\overset{\displaystyle O}{\|}}{C}-OH + ? \longrightarrow$$
    $$C_6H_{13}-\overset{\overset{\displaystyle O}{\|}}{C}-O^-Na^+ + HOH$$

28. Assemble models of benzene and cyclohexane. Describe differences between the two molecular structures.

29. Architects have a saying, "form follows function." Does this saying apply to chemistry or is the opposite—"function follows form"— more correct? Explain your answer.

30. List five products manufactured from cyclic compounds.

31. How does adding a double or a triple bond change the shape of the carbon backbone in a hydrocarbon?

32. Draw structural formulas for both a saturated form of C_4H_8 and an unsaturated form of C_4H_8.

Extending the Concepts

33. Considering that petroleum is a natural resource, why aren't all petroleum-based polymers classified as natural?

34. Research and write about one example in which substituting a different functional group in the drug's molecular structure has had a dramatic effect on its medicinal properties.

35. Organic molecules that contain alcohol or carboxylic acid functional groups are often more soluble in water than are similarly sized hydrocarbon molecules. Explain.

36. Investigate several different polyesters. How are they formed? What explains their differences in properties? Give two structural formulas for polyesters. List five everyday products made of polyester.

37. C_2H_6O is the formula for two isomers; one has a boiling point of 78 °C and the other has a boiling point of −22 °C:

    a. Draw the structural formula for each isomer.
    b. Which of the two isomers has the higher boiling point? Explain your choice.

32. Saturated C_4H_8 is cyclobutane:

$$\begin{array}{c} H_2C-CH_2 \\ |\qquad| \\ H_2C-CH_2 \end{array}$$

Unsaturated forms include:

$$H_3C-CH=CH-CH_3$$

Extending the Concepts

33. They are not found in nature in the form in which they are used.

34. Students should cite sources and identify the drug and substituted functional group.

35. These functional groups allow formation of intermolecular forces between the organic molecules and water.

36. Everyday products include plastic bottles, Mylar balloons, clothing, carpet, and hoses.

Polyethylene terephthalate (PET)

Polybutylene terephthalate (PBT)

See **http://www.pslc.ws/macrog/ pet.htm** for further information.

37. a.
$$H-\overset{\overset{\displaystyle H}{|}}{\underset{\underset{\displaystyle H}{|}}{C}}-\overset{\overset{\displaystyle H}{|}}{\underset{\underset{\displaystyle H}{|}}{C}}-OH$$
ethanol

$$H-\overset{\overset{\displaystyle H}{|}}{\underset{\underset{\displaystyle H}{|}}{C}}-O-\overset{\overset{\displaystyle H}{|}}{\underset{\underset{\displaystyle H}{|}}{C}}-H$$
dimethyl ether

b. Ethanol would have a higher boiling point, because its polarity leads to stronger intermolecular forces.

Connecting the Concepts

27. a. HBr b. H_2O c. NaOH
28. Cyclohexane has all single bonds, and benzene shares bonding electrons throughout the ring. Benzene's carbon atoms are planar while cyclohexane's carbon atoms are arranged in a zigzag pattern.

29. Properties and uses of an organic molecule depend on its structure and on functional groups. The opposite may also be true—a molecule can be designed for desired properties.

30. Polystyrene, TNT, nylon, Kevlar, Dacron, Mylar, aspartame.

31. The double or triple bond constrains rotation about the bond and disrupts the zigzag of an alkane chain.

Energy Alternatives to Petroleum

Section D explores various substitutes for petroleum. The text examines renewable and nonrenewable options, including coal, oil shale, and biodiesel, and considers alternative sources of fuel for commercial and personal vehicles. One goal of this section is to understand how and why reliance on petroleum-based products and dependence on petroleum as a major source of energy lead to a need for research on replacing petroleum as a primary fuel source. You may discuss the complementary roles of conservation and continued research in chemical technologies that can produce economically and environmentally suitable alternatives to petroleum. Insights gained in this section lead to the unit's culminating activity—designing an advertisement for an alternative-fuel vehicle.

If you haven't already stated your expectations for the culminating activity, communicate the assignment for the alternative-vehicle advertisement at the beginning of this section, so that students will have time for researching, designing, and producing their advertisement.

D.1 Energy: Past and Present

This material explores Earth's key energy sources, with the sun as the ultimate source of most available energy. This is a good time to revisit energy transformations, focusing on conversion of solar energy into chemical potential energy and of

---

Energy Alternatives to Petroleum

Petroleum is a nonrenewable resource; its total available inventory on Earth is finite. Thus, people must eventually find other energy sources to meet needs of modern society. In this section, you will explore alternatives to petroleum and also learn about other emerging ways to power personal and commercial vehicles.

D.1 ENERGY: PAST AND PRESENT

The Sun is our planet's primary energy source. Through photosynthesis, radiant energy from the Sun is stored as chemical potential energy. That is, green plants use the Sun's radiant energy to convert carbon dioxide and water (molecules involving chemical bonds with low potential energy) into carbohydrates and oxygen gas (molecules involving chemical bonds that have high potential energy). Thus, green plants convert solar energy into chemical potential energy, which is stored in the bonds of carbohydrate and oxygen molecules (Figure 3.48). When animals ingest and digest the plants and combine the carbohydrates with oxygen in a complex stepwise process, this chemical energy is released and used by the animals to form other organic molecules. Organic molecules found in plants and animals are called **biomolecules.**

> The energy used in one week in the United States is approximately 2×10^{18} J. That is equivalent to the energy released by a hydrogen-bomb explosion, a severe earthquake, or by burning 2×10^{10} gallons of gasoline. By contrast, the radiant energy received by Earth daily from the Sun is approximately 1×10^{26} J; which is nearly 100 million times more.

> Even though energy is required in digestion to break the chemical bonds in carbohydrates and oxygen, the digestion of plants is, overall, exothermic. More energy is released by forming products with low-energy bonds than is required to break higher-energy bonds in the reactants. These ideas were introduced in Section B.1 (introduced on pages 238–241).

Figure 3.48 *Through photosynthesis, solar energy is converted into chemical energy stored in biomolecules of these plants. The challenge is to find the cleanest, most efficient approach to harnessing this chemical potential energy.*

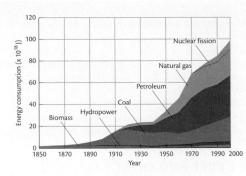

Figure 3.49 *Annual U.S. consumption of energy from various sources (1850–2000).*

Solar energy and energy stored in biomolecules are key energy sources for life on Earth. Since the discovery of fire, human use of stored solar energy held in the chemical bonds that make up wood, coal, and petroleum has had a major influence on civilization's development. In fact, the forms, availability, and cost of energy greatly influence how—and even where—people live.

In the past, abundant supplies of inexpensive energy were available. Until about 1850, wood, water, wind, and animal power satisfied the United States' slowly growing energy needs. Wood, then the predominant energy source, was readily available to most people for heating, cooking, and lighting. People used water, wind, and animal power, all forms of energy whose primary source was the Sun, for transportation and to power machinery and industrial processes. With industrialization and population growth, the demand for energy increased and the primary fuel sources changed.

Figure 3.49 illustrates how U.S. energy sources have changed since 1850. In the next activity, you will explore how energy supplies and fuel use have shifted in the United States during the past 150 years.

> In 1850, the population of the United States was 23 million. By 2005, the U.S. population had increased to nearly 300 million.

Developing Skills

D.2 FUEL SOURCES OVER THE YEARS

As you can see from Figure 3.49, there has been a definite shift away from biomass (mainly wood, but also ethanol and waste) toward fossil fuels—coal, petroleum, and natural gas. Use Figure 3.49 to answer the following questions:

1. a. Find the dates of the period during which biomass (mainly wood) was used to meet at least half of the nation's total energy needs.
   b. What were the chief modes of travel during that period?
   c. What factors might explain the declining use of biomass after that period?
   d. What main energy source did people use to replace biomass?
2. Compared with other energy sources, only a small quantity of petroleum was used as fuel before the 1920s. What do you think petroleum's main uses might have been before that time?

Section D   Energy Alternatives to Petroleum   **283**

chemical potential energy into thermal energy and work. Students should be able to explain the connection between the sun and biomolecules after studying this section. Another idea for group discussion is to compare and contrast human and geologic time, and to relate this to the formation and use of petroleum and the concept of renewable and nonrenewable resources. Specifically, petroleum is believed to have formed over millions of years, while it has been used on a large scale for less than 200 years. Thus, petroleum is considered nonrenewable, even though it is replenished "over time."

Developing Skills

D.2 Fuel Sources Over the Years

In this activity, based on **Figure 3.49**, students trace the growth of energy use and trends in types of energy used and explore relationships among trends and socioeconomic factors. They practice and apply graph-reading and interpreting skills.

Answers

1. a. Up to about 1910
   b. Trains were the main long-distance transportation means; horses were used for short distances.
   c. The decline in local supplies of wood and development of the internal-combustion engine
   d. Coal
2. Oil burned in lamps

3. a. Oil became an important energy source in the 1920s; coal began to decline in 1925.

b. The number of automobiles increased.

c. Coal, petroleum, and nuclear energy

d. To generate electrical power (coal, nuclear energy) and power vehicles (petroleum)

4. a. Petroleum use has continued to increase, although the rate of increase is less pronounced than between 1950 and 1975. Coal use has also increased, at a rate that has been fairly steady since 1950.

b. Slower increases in petroleum use may be due to conservation efforts, including laws aimed at increasing fuel efficiency of motor vehicles, spurred by the oil embargo of the 1970s. The increase in coal use reflects population increases, but is probably offset by the use of other energy sources and increases in efficiency.

D.3 Alternate Fuel and Energy Sources

D.3 Content Reading Guide

This material explores options for supplementing or replacing petroleum as an energy source through extraction of petroleum from shale, liquefaction of coal, and production of hydrocarbons from plants.

Divide students into groups representing either advantages or disadvantages of a petroleum replacement. Allow students time to read the text and collect more information (particularly if Internet access is available), and invite each group to

3. Petroleum use increased and coal use began to decline at about the same time.

a. When did this occur?

b. What could explain the growing use of petroleum after this date?

c. Which energy sources have been used comparatively more since 1975?

d. What are major uses of these energy sources?

4. a. Describe the trends in petroleum and coal use since 1975.

b. What factors could account for these trends?

D.3 ALTERNATE FUEL AND ENERGY SOURCES

Everyday life in the United States requires considerable quantities of energy. As you just learned, the energy sources used in this country have changed over time. As energy demands have accelerated, the nation increasingly has relied on nonrenewable fossil fuels—coal, petroleum, and natural gas. What is the future for fossil fuels, particularly petroleum?

The United States is a mobile society. Some 70% of the petroleum consumed in the United States is used for transportation. Although efforts to revitalize and improve public transportation systems merit attention, most experts predict our nation's citizens will continue to rely on personal vehicles well into the foreseeable future. And remember, even energy-conserving mass-transit systems must have a fuel source. What options, then, does chemistry offer to extend, supplement, or even replace petroleum as a primary energy source?

Oil Shale

Petroleum from tar sands and oil shale rock is an option with some promise. See Figure 3.50. Major deposits of **oil shale** are located west of the Rocky Mountains. These rocks contain *kerogen*, which is partially formed oil. When the rocks are heated, *kerogen* decomposes into a material quite similar to crude oil.

> One metric ton of oil shale typically contains the equivalent of 80 to 330 L of oil.

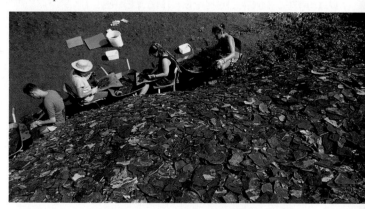

Figure 3.50 *The people in this photo are searching for fossils within a pile of oil shale. When heated, oil shale will decompose into a liquid similar to crude oil. However, it takes several steps to remove impurities present in the oil shale.*

284   **Unit 3**   Petroleum: Breaking and Making Bonds

present a summary. As a class, discuss advantages and disadvantages of alternatives, future implications, and need for conservation.

Additional alternative-fuel information appears at **http://www.eere.energy.gov/afdc/** and **http://www.eia.doe.gov/fuelrenewable. html**.

Unfortunately, vast quantities of sand and rock must be processed to recover this fuel. Moreover, current extraction methods use the equivalent of half a barrel of petroleum to produce every barrel of shale oil. Enormous volumes of water are also needed for processing, which poses a problem where water is scarce.

Coal Liquefaction

Because known coal (see Figure 3.51) reserves in the United States are much larger than known reserves of petroleum, another possible alternative to petroleum is a liquid fuel produced from coal. The technology to convert coal to liquid fuel (and also to convert coal to builder molecules) has been available for decades, having been used in Germany since the mid-1900s. Current coal-to-liquid-fuel technology is quite well developed here in the United States. However, the present cost of mining and converting coal to liquid fuel (commonly known as *coal liquefaction*) is considerably greater than that of producing the same quantity of fuel from petroleum. But if petroleum costs increase sufficiently, obtaining liquid fuel from coal—itself a nonrenewable resource—may become a more attractive option.

Renewable Petroleum Replacements

Petroleum replacement candidates are not limited to other fossil fuels; currently there is rising interest in transitioning to renewable fuel sources. Certain plants, including some 2000 varieties of the genus *Euphorbia,* capture and store solar energy as hydrocarbon compounds, rather than as carbohydrates. These compounds may prove to be extractable and usable as a petroleum substitute.

Another such petroleum substitute under consideration is **biodiesel,** a fuel that can be burned in diesel engines. One major benefit of biodiesel is that any source of plant or animal fat can be converted into biodiesel. Although biodiesel must be refined for use in automobiles, it would offer a "green" strategy for producing a renewable petroleum substitute. Currently, biodiesel is sold blended with petroleum-based diesel and is seldom used as a pure fuel on its own. In the coming Investigating Matter D.4, you will have the opportunity to synthesize crude biodiesel from common vegetable cooking oil.

Other Energy Strategies

To meet some U.S. energy requirements, it is possible to move away from petroleum-based technology altogether. Alternative energy sources currently in use or under investigation include hydropower (water power), *nuclear fission* and *fusion, solar energy, wind energy* (Figure 3.52), burning *biomass,* and *geothermal energy.* Alternate approaches include

Figure 3.51 *Trains often transport coal, an important source of energy.*

One disadvantage of coal as an energy source is the air pollution generated when it burns. You will learn more about this in Unit 4.

Figure 3.52 *Wind moves these turbines—generating electricity without burning fossil fuels.*

Section D   Energy Alternatives to Petroleum   **285**

down the chemical structure of coal to increase the hydrogen-to-carbon ratio.

During World War II, when Germany was unable to import oil, the Nazis used coal-derived gasoline to fuel aircraft and tanks. South Africa's Sasol I plant has been producing oil and pipeline gas from coal for over 40 years.

Shale Oil   Oil shale is a type of sedimentary rock containing kerogen, an oil-like substance. Retorting—heating at 500 °C in the absence of air—converts kerogen in oil shale to oil. Of the estimated 1.8 trillion barrels of shale oil in Colorado, Wyoming, and Utah, about 600 billion barrels are considered recoverable. Unfortunately, there are several problems with extraction of shale oil: (1) A great deal of energy is required to extract the kerogen; (2) one to four barrels of water are needed to produce one barrel of oil; and (3) considerable waste is generated (1.5 tons of waste shale are generated per barrel of oil produced). Thus, at present, shale oil is regarded as both economically and environmentally expensive.

Alcohols   As partially oxidized hydrocarbons, alcohols have a lower energy content than comparable volumes of gasoline. The chief advantages of using alcohols are that they come from renewable resources and also can be mixed with regular gasoline, up to concentrations of 10 to 15%, without requiring engine redesign. Methanol is made from wood, and, given methanol's high affinity for water, is commonly used as a fuel-drying additive. Ethanol is made from grain (wheat or corn) and is less toxic and corrosive than methanol.

Additional Resources

Coal-Derived Fuels (Synfuels)   Ordinary coal is composed primarily of carbon, with only about 1 hydrogen atom for every 16 carbons. Because liquid and gaseous hydrocarbon fuels contain a much higher percent hydrogen (methane, 4 H/1 C; octane, 2.25 H/1 C; heavy fuel oil, 1 H/6 C), temperature and pressure are used to break

Investigating Matter

D.4 Biodiesel Fuel

D.4 Biodiesel Fuel Student Worksheet and Data Table

This investigation was adapted from *Introduction to Green Chemistry,* American Chemical Society, 2002. Copies are available from the ACS Office of Society Services at 1-800-227-5558 or **http://chemistry.org**.

Students synthesize biodiesel from cooking oil, using methanol and a potassium hydroxide catalyst. The cooking oil is a triglyceride, consisting of a glycerol and three fatty acids, as shown below (also see Unit 7, page 588). R in the molecules below represents a long-chain hydrocarbon.

$$
\begin{array}{c}
\quad\quad\quad\quad O \\
\quad\quad\quad\quad \| \\
CH_2 \!-\! O \!-\! C \!-\! R \\
\quad\quad\quad\quad O \\
\quad\quad\quad\quad \| \\
HC \!-\! O \!-\! C \!-\! R \\
\quad\quad\quad\quad O \\
\quad\quad\quad\quad \| \\
CH_2 \!-\! O \!-\! C \!-\! R
\end{array}
$$

Vegetable oil

Biodiesel synthesis breaks the bonds between the glycerol and fatty acids and adds a methyl group to the end of the fatty acid, giving the molecule below.

$$
\begin{array}{c}
H \quad\quad O \\
| \quad\quad \| \\
H \!-\! C \!-\! O \!-\! C \!-\! R \\
| \\
H
\end{array}
$$

Biodiesel

The other reaction product is glycerol. Potassium hydroxide catalyst also remains.

constructing more energy-efficient buildings, vehicles, and machines, as well as using alternative fuels. In addition, reducing energy use—through such actions as carpooling, using public transportation, and turning off unneeded appliances—helps to conserve fossil fuels and to reduce energy needs overall. All of these steps are intended to further reduce our need to burn petroleum.

Investigating Matter

D.4 BIODIESEL FUEL

Introduction

Biodiesel is a mixture of methyl esters of fatty acids. It is made from any source of fat or oil. In this investigation, you will use ordinary vegetable cooking oil. As you will see, enough fuel can be produced by this procedure to be burned, although it is not pure enough to be used as a fuel in a car or truck. See Figure 3.53.

This laboratory synthesis is based on a chemical reaction that produces biodiesel and glycerol. Cooking oil is initially mixed with methanol; potassium hydroxide is added as a catalyst. The products separate into two layers, with biodiesel on top. The biodiesel is separated, washed, and then is ready for further testing.

Before starting, read the following procedure to learn what you will need to do, note safety precautions, and plan all necessary data collecting and observations. In setting up your data table, note that Step 17 calls for completing a second trial.

Figure 3.53 *This person makes fuel for the biodiesel-powered 1974 automobile from used cooking oil donated by a local restaurant.*

Procedure

1. After reading the procedure and the questions that follow, construct a data table appropriate for recording the data you will collect in this investigation.

2. Using a graduated cylinder, measure 100 mL of vegetable oil and pour it into a 250-mL beaker.

3. Carefully add 15 mL of methanol to the liquid in the beaker. (***Caution:*** *Methanol is flammable and toxic.*)

4. Slowly add 1 mL of 9 M potassium hydroxide (KOH) to the liquid in the beaker. (***Caution:*** *Potassium hydroxide is corrosive.*)

5. Taking turns with your partner, stir the mixture for 10 minutes. As you take turns stirring, set up the apparatus described in Step 13.

Time

50 min

Materials

(For 12 student pairs)

12 100-mL graduated cylinders
12 10-mL graduated cylinders

12 250-mL beakers
12 Beral pipets
100 g Steel wool
12 Metal sample cups (such as empty tea-candle containers)
25 mL 9 M potassium hydroxide (KOH) (13 g KOH in 25 mL solution)

6. Allow the mixture to sit for two minutes so that it separates into two layers.

7. Using a Beral pipet, carefully remove the top layer (biodiesel) and place it into a clean 100-mL beaker.

8. Wash the biodiesel fluid by adding 10 mL of distilled water to it. Stir vigorously for several seconds.

9. Allow the mixture to sit for two minutes so that it separates into two layers.

10. Using the same Beral pipet as before, carefully remove the top layer (biodiesel) and place it into a clean, previously weighed 100-mL graduated cylinder.

11. Measure and record the mass and volume of biodiesel that you collected.

12. Carefully pour 5 mL of biodiesel onto a wad of steel wool (about the diameter of a quarter coin) in a metallic sample cup, as shown in Figure 3.54. Measure and record the total mass of the cup and its contents.

Figure 3.54 *Biodiesel being poured onto steel wool in a metallic sample cup.*

13. Set the metal sample cup underneath a soft-drink can, similar to the calorimeter setup shown in Figure 3.31, page 249. Measure 100.0 mL of chilled water provided by your teacher and pour the water into the soft-drink can.

14. Measure and record both the room temperature and the water temperature to the nearest 0.1 °C.

15. Ignite the biodiesel. Allow it to warm the water to the same number of degrees Celsius *above* room temperature as the number of degrees Celsius it started *below* room temperature.

16. Extinguish the flame by blowing on it. Allow the cup to cool; record the cup's total mass.

17. Repeat Steps 12 through 16.

1.5 L vegetable oil
200 mL methyl alcohol (methanol)
12 12-oz, empty soft-drink cans (with pull tabs)
12 ring stands
12 rings
12 thermometers, alcohol, −10 to 110 °C

12 stirring rods
12 pencils
5 lb ice
12 matchbooks
6 balances

Safety

Burners must *not* be used, since many reagents are flammable. Methanol particularly poses a serious fire hazard; its flame is almost invisible.

Students should wear protective goggles and aprons throughout the investigation.

Remind students to exercise extreme caution with 9 M KOH. It is caustic and corrosive. You may decide to dispense the concentrated base rather than allowing students to handle it.

Pre-Lab Discussion

Demonstrate how to swirl the mixture and how to remove the top layer with a Beral pipet. Review procedures for calorimetry and prompt students to explain the purpose of those procedures. They should realize that calorimetry, in this case, supplies data about the fuel's energy value.

Lab Tips

• Caution students about the corrosive nature of KOH.
• Encourage students to exercise care when handling steel wool. Small pieces of steel wool can break from a larger sample and irritate hands.
• Remind students to find the mass of the sample both before and after they burn it.
• The two minutes suggested for separation in Steps 6 and 9 may be insufficient. It is suggested that students work on Making Decisions D.5 after completing the stirring in Step 5. At the end of the first laboratory session, students could complete Step 8 and allow the biodiesel to sit until the next session when the calorimeter portion of the investigation could be completed.

Answers

1. Students should calculate density using data from Step 11 (mass and volume). Expected results are 0.8–0.9 g/mL.
2. The starting materials are generally colorless and odorless, while the biodiesel exhibits slight color and odor. Students may also note differences in volatility or viscosity.
3. Washing removes the potassium hydroxide catalyst, which is soluble in water.
4. Answers will vary. The example is approximately a 90% yield.
5. Results may differ due to variations in technique, such as how carefully students separated the layers.
6. Answers will vary. A sample calculation follows:
   Data:
   Mass of biodiesel burned: 3.4 g (difference between fuel, container, and steel wool before and after burning)
   Mass of water: 100 g
   Initial water temperature: 5°C
   Final water temperature: 67°C
   $E = mC\Delta T = 100 \text{ g} \times 4.18 \text{ J/g°C} \times 62 \text{ °C} = 26\,000 \text{ J}$
   Thermal energy produced (per gram) = 26 kJ/3.4 g = 7.6 kJ/g
7. Gram for gram, biodiesel produces less energy.

Post-Lab Discussion

Discuss biodiesel's viability as a replacement fuel, based on students' laboratory experiences. Consider energy produced, resources required, the process, starting materials, and potential applications. This discussion will prepare students for the next activity about the practicality of biodiesel as a fuel.

Questions

1. What is the density of the biodiesel that you produced?
2. In producing the biodiesel sample, what changes did you observe in the characteristics of the starting materials compared to those of the final products?
3. What was the purpose of washing the biodiesel fluid in Step 8?
4. Compare the mass of biodiesel obtained (the yield) in your laboratory production of fuel with that of other laboratory teams.
5. All students followed the same laboratory procedure in producing biodiesel. What can account for the differences in biodiesel yield noted in Question 4 among teams?
6. Calculate the heat of combustion for your sample of biodiesel.
7. Gasoline produces 48 kJ/g of thermal energy when burned. How does your biodiesel compare to gasoline?

Making Decisions

D.5 BIODIESEL AS A PETROLEUM SUBSTITUTE

Consider these data, and then answer the following questions.

▶ 41 pounds of soybeans are required to make one gallon of biodiesel
▶ 1 bushel of soybeans weighs 60 pounds
▶ 38.1 bushels of soybeans, on average, are produced per acre (Figure 3.55)
▶ U.S. agriculture uses nearly 990 million acres (47.3% for crops, 52.6% for livestock) and has 74 million surplus acres
▶ biodiesel releases 123 540 kJ per gallon
▶ gasoline releases 120 560 kJ per gallon
▶ the production of one gallon of biodiesel or gasoline requires about 24 900 kJ

Figure 3.55 *Soybeans are one possible source of biodiesel. What benefits of biodiesel can you identify?*

Questions

1. Approximately 30 billion gallons of diesel fuel are used in the United States each year.
   a. How many pounds of soybeans would be required to produce enough biodiesel to meet this need?
   b. How many bushels of soybeans is this?
   c. How many acres would be required to grow the quantity of soybeans needed to produce enough biodiesel to meet all U.S. diesel needs?
2. Could the United States grow enough soybeans to replace all fossil diesel fuel with soybean-based biodiesel? Explain.
3. Create a list of pros and cons of using biodiesel as a petroleum replacement.

Making Decisions

D.5 Biodiesel as a Petroleum Substitute

This activity revisits "scaling up," a concern in industrial chemistry. Emphasize that cited data are approximate but adequate for answering general questions—and that such estimating is widely practiced in science, business, and industry.

Answers

1. a. 30 billion gallons × $\dfrac{41 \text{ pounds soybeans}}{1 \text{ gallon}} = 1200$ billion (or 1.2 trillion) pounds of soybeans

D.6 ALTERNATE-FUEL VEHICLES

As you now know, personal vehicles consume a significant portion—about 50%—of petroleum burned for fuel in the U.S. Because there is a limited supply of petroleum as a resource and emissions are produced by petroleum-burning engines, alternate-fuel vehicles are being developed, tested, and used. What are some of these fuels, and how are they used to power the vehicles? What are advantages and disadvantages of various alternative fuels? The overview that follows will help you prepare your own automobile advertisement.

Compressed Natural Gas

Most passenger vehicles and buses can be converted to dual-fuel vehicles that run on either natural gas or gasoline. Natural gas, mainly methane (CH_4), is produced either from gas wells or during petroleum processing. Compressed and stored in high-pressure tanks, this product is commonly known as **compressed natural gas (CNG)**. A refillable CNG tank, capable of powering an automobile up to 300 miles, can be comfortably installed in a car's trunk. Many CNG-powered vehicles are operating worldwide, particularly in government and mass transit fleets. See Figure 3.56.

Among the advantages of CNG are wide availability and an 80% decrease (compared to gasoline) in carbon monoxide (CO) and nitrogen oxide (NO_x) emissions. However, refueling systems require a compressor, which increases the vehicle cost by $2000 to $4000. Also, there is a higher fire risk resulting from a collision of a CNG-powered vehicle.

Some homes are heated with compressed natural gas.

Figure 3.56 *Natural gas–powered buses line up in front of Freeborn Hall at the University of California, Davis. The buses replaced the 1960-era diesel buses on campus; one will run on a mixture of natural gas and hydrogen—the first of its kind in the nation.*

SECTION D

D.6 Alternate-Fuel Vehicles

D.6 Content Reading Guide

Students explore three types of alternative-fuel vehicles here that are in use or under development.

You may invite students to evaluate (in small groups or individually) each alternative fuel in a chart similar to the one on page 290. This may require students to do some additional research on the Internet or with library resources.

You may also present this using a jigsaw cooperative-learning strategy. Assign students to expert groups corresponding to CNG, electric cars, fuel cells, and hybrid gasoline–electric cars. Each expert group, using the Internet, library resources, and the textbook, researches missing information prompted by the table on page 290. On completion of their research, reassign students to mixed groups that include an "expert" on each alternative-vehicle type. Then let students teach each other based on their separate areas of expertise.

The text will help students prepare their alternative-fuel vehicle advertisements. You need not limit the choices of alternative-fuel vehicles to those presented in the text. Some Web links and additional information appear below. In addition, new information on alternative-fuel vehicles is emerging all the time, so Web searches may be productive.

b. $1230 \text{ billion pounds} \times \dfrac{1 \text{ bushel}}{60 \text{ pounds}} =$ 20 billion bushels of soybeans

c. $20 \text{ billion bushels} \times \dfrac{1 \text{ acre}}{38.1 \text{ bushels}} =$ 0.54 billion (or 540 million) acres of soybeans

2. The United States could potentially grow enough if more than half of available agricultural land were devoted to producing soybeans for biodiesel.

3. Answers should consider impact on agriculture, biodiversity, land use, similar emissions, availability of source material, energy supplied, and ability to use the replaced diesel in other applications.

Fuel Cells

Fuel-Cell Power

One developing option for generating electricity to power vehicles is the **fuel cell.** It did not become a practical energy source until the 1960s, when fuel cells were designed and used in the U.S. Space Program. Any fuel containing hydrogen (such as methanol or natural gas) can be used in a fuel cell.

As shown in Figure 3.57, one common form of fuel cell converts oxygen gas and hydrogen fuel into electrical energy and water, which is its only emission. From a chemical viewpoint, such an operating fuel cell represents another way to release and harness the chemical potential energy stored in the chemical bonds that hold hydrogen and oxygen molecules together:

$$2\,H_2 + O_2 \longrightarrow 2\,H_2O + \text{Electrical energy (and some thermal energy)}$$

The fuel cell involves platinum electrodes that catalyze the removal of electrons from hydrogen atoms. In one common type of fuel cell called a *proton exchange membrane* (PEM) fuel cell (see Figure 3.58), electrodes are in contact with a polymer that allows hydrogen ions to pass through, but not hydrogen molecules. The electrons flow from the fuel cell through an external circuit (where they do useful work), returning to the fuel cell at the other electrode. See Figure 3.58. That second electrode catalyzes the reaction of oxygen gas (the oxidant) with hydrogen ions and electrons to produce water molecules, thus completing the electrical circuit. In the PEM hydrogen–oxygen fuel cell, the net products are water molecules and electrical energy.

Fuel cells require no electrical recharging and eliminate or substantially reduce release of air pollutants. They are more efficient than are internal-combustion engines; they can obtain more useful power from a given quantity of fuel than can be obtained by burning it. However, challenges remain in developing fuel handling and processing options, and reducing fuel-cell manufacturing costs and operating costs.

ALKALINE FUEL CELL

Figure 3.57 *The reaction 2 H$_2$ + O$_2$ ⟶ 2 H$_2$O + electrical energy takes place inside this fuel cell.*

ALTERNATIVE VEHICLE	FUEL TYPE	AVAILABILITY	EASE OF REFUELING	FUEL EFFICIENCY	ENVIRONMENTAL IMPACT (EMISSIONS)	SAFETY	RENEWABILITY
COMPRESSED NATURAL GAS (CNG)							
ELECTRIC CARS							
FUEL CELL							
HYBRID GASOLINE–ELECTRIC							

THE OPERATION OF A HYDROGEN FUEL CELL

Electron flow

Electric motor

Excess hydrogen fuel out $H_2(g)$

Proton flow

$O_2(g)$ Oxygen in

Electrolyte

Hydrogen fuel in $H_2(g)$

Water $H_2O(g)$ product out

Anode — Electrodes — Cathode

Figure 3.58 *Schematic diagram of a proton exchange membrane (PEM) fuel cell. Hydrogen ions form when electrons are removed from H_2 at the anode. The electrons flow through the circuit to the cathode, doing useful work along the way (note the electric motor in the circuit). The H^+ ions (protons) flow through polymer to the cathode, where they combine with oxygen gas and electrons to produce water.*

The expense (in terms of high energy costs) required to obtain high-purity hydrogen (H_2) for the type of fuel cell just described represents a major challenge. Currently, there is no commercial-scale energy-efficient way known to produce and distribute hydrogen gas in large enough quantities to make large-scale fuel cell use commercially viable. All current sources of hydrogen gas require petroleum-based hydrocarbons as a source of both the hydrogen gas and the energy required to produce it.

Hybrid Gasoline–Electric Power

Some car designers believe that a *gasoline–electric vehicle* will best meet consumer needs while reducing emissions and fuel costs. See Figure 3.59. *Hybrid gasoline–electric vehicles,* or **hybrid vehicles,** like the fictitious *Hybris* featured in this unit, come equipped with a gasoline-burning engine as well as a battery-powered electric motor. The batteries are recharged while driving, partially through conversion of the car's kinetic energy into stored chemical potential energy whenever the vehicle's brakes are applied.

As you learned in Section B, traditional gasoline-powered automobiles are unable to convert all the chemical energy stored in the bonds of gasoline and oxygen gas into useful mechanical energy. Figure 3.29 (page 244) documented that only 25% of the original chemical energy is converted into usable horsepower, while the other 75% is lost to the surroundings as thermal energy.

Figure 3.59 *In the past few years several commercial hybrid vehicles have entered the U.S. automobile market.*

SECTION D

Hybrid Gasoline–Electric Vehicle Links

http://www.ott.doe.gov/hev/

http://auto.howstuffworks.com/hybrid-car.htm

http://www.motortrend.com/roadtests/alternative/

http://www.intellichoice.com/carBuying101/AlternativeGuide.cfm

Biofuels Links

http://www.eya.ca/biodiesel/

http://www.biodiesel.org/

http://www.worldenergy.net/

Electric Car Links

http://www.howstuffworks.com/electric-car.htm

http://inventors.about.com/library/weekly/aacarselectrica.htm

http://avt.inel.gov/index.shtml

Scientific American Working Knowledge Illustration

Various hybrid gasoline–electric vehicles are now being sold, and the number of available models will probably increase in the next several years. As the caption suggests, some hybrid vehicles can run solely on electric power at low speeds. Other models are always powered by the gasoline engine, which the electric motor "assists" during acceleration. Most models shut off the gasoline engine when at a complete stop, so they do not idle. Other features that can vary include type of transmission and whether accessories such as the air conditioning and heater are powered by the gasoline engine or the electric motor.

Some models include a display similar to this figure that indicates the flow of energy within the vehicle at any given time. This illustration shows two possible modes: the vehicle being powered by both the gasoline engine and electric motor and the battery recharging while braking or coasting. Both modes contribute to overall increase in gas mileage. Other possibilities include using "excess" power from the gasoline engine to recharge the batteries and "electric-only" mode. In some vehicles, it is also possible to lightly tap the accelerator so that energy is not flowing in any direction; the car is essentially coasting in neutral.

Point out that decreased fuel consumption is not the only benefit of most hybrid vehicles. Reducing air-polluting emissions is equally— if not more—beneficial, and some models are engineered so that emissions are reduced by 80% compared to traditional vehicles.

A hybrid vehicle, however, is able to store some of the energy that would otherwise be "lost" and save it for later use. (See Figure 3.60.) In essence, chemical potential energy—originally stored in gasoline and oxygen—is converted into kinetic energy as the car accelerates. When the car possesses more kinetic energy than is required—for example, as it goes downhill or when brakes are applied—excess kinetic energy is converted back into chemical potential energy stored in the car's battery. (By comparison, when brakes are applied in traditional gasoline-

Scientific American Working Knowledge Illustration

Figure 3.60 *Hybrid car* *Hybrid gasoline-electric vehicles represent alternatives to traditional gasoline-powered vehicles. Left: As the hybrid car accelerates (green arrows), it draws power from both the gasoline engine and electric storage battery. In some models, the electric battery provides all the needed power at low speeds, which also lowers gasoline consumption. Right: When brakes are applied (red arrows), some kinetic energy is transformed into chemical potential energy stored in the car's electric battery. This energy is used when the car again accelerates; in traditional gasoline-powered vehicles, all of this energy would be lost as heat through friction by the brakes.*

Ask your students about their experiences with hybrid gasoline–electric vehicles or encourage them to research and compare various models currently available.

powered vehicles, the car's kinetic energy is converted into wasted thermal energy through friction as the brakes pads slow the car.) Additionally, hybrid cars are engineered to switch over from the gasoline engine to the electric motor whenever possible, such as when idling at a red light. This increases the car's overall energy efficiency; nearly 40% of the gasoline's chemical energy is converted into useful kinetic energy.

Hybrid vehicles typically achieve over 40 miles per gallon and can travel more than 650 miles between fueling stops. Although these vehicles produce the same kinds of emissions as fossil-fuel-burning vehicles, the quantity produced over a given distance is smaller.

D.7 EVALUATING ALTERNATE-FUEL OPTIONS

Making Decisions

Based on what you have just learned about alternate-fuel vehicles, create a table that will easily enable you to compare the three power options in terms of *fuel type, availability, efficiency, cost, environmental impact, renewability*, and *ease of refueling*. Work as a group to enter appropriate information in the table. Refer to the information in your completed table to answer the following questions:

1. While driving each of the three types of alternative-fuel vehicles, under what circumstances do they still rely on petroleum as a fuel? Explain.

2. Which of the three alternative-fuel vehicle options involve completely renewable fuel sources? Explain.

3. Which of the three options has the greatest potential for a completely renewable fuel source in the future? For each option you name, propose an approach that might support the transition from nonrenewable fuel to renewable fuel.

4. The *Hybris* advertised at the start of this unit is a hybrid vehicle. Why is this type of alternative-fuel vehicle currently the best-selling vehicle of the three alternate-fuel vehicle types?

5. Which of the three options do you consider the most promising overall for future use? Be prepared to list and explain the factors upon which you based your decision.

> The three power options are fuel cells, compressed natural gas (CNG), and hybrid gasoline-electric.

Making Decisions

D.7 Evaluating Alternate-Fuel Options

In this activity, students apply information that they have just organized in preparation for the culminating unit activity.

Answers

1. CNG and fuel-cell vehicles require petroleum as a fuel to process CNG or hydrogen. Hybrid gasoline–electric vehicles use petroleum directly.

2. All three vehicle options are potentially renewable. CNG could be completely renewable if derived from biomass. Fuel cells could be renewable if the hydrogen is produced from electrolysis of water using renewable energy. Hybrid gasoline–electric vehicles could be renewable if they used biodiesel.

3. Hybrid diesels running on biodiesel are likely in the immediate future. The cost of fuel cells and issues associated with renewable hydrogen production and distribution make renewable fuel cells unlikely. Renewable sources of methane, for CNG vehicles, are also unlikely in the immediate future.

4. It uses fuel that is readily and (relatively) inexpensively available. From an owner's perspective, there is little operational difference between a hybrid and more familiar vehicles. The increased gasoline mileage provided by a hybrid gasoline–electric vehicle is also appealing.

5. Answers should reflect an understanding of material developed throughout Unit 3. Any option is acceptable, if supported with appropriate evidence.

SECTION D SUMMARY

 Section D Supplement

Reviewing the Concepts

1. A molecular substance that occurs naturally in living organisms

2. a. Biomass (wood) b. Coal c. Petroleum

3. Petroleum, wood, coal, biomass.

4. It originated in the sun. Plants convert solar energy into carbohydrates, which are converted to biomolecules by living organisms.

5. Answers may include invention or mass production of automobiles, development of trucks for transporting goods, and conversion of home-heating systems from coal to oil.

6. a. Advantage: major deposits in the United States; disadvantages: requires large quantities of energy and water to process, creates pollution
b. Advantages: large, known U.S. reserves; disadvantages: high cost to convert to liquid fuel, nonrenewable
c. Advantages: readily available, renewable, lower sulfur content than in petroleum, no increase in greenhouse gases produced; disadvantages: similar pollution/greenhouse effects as for petroleum, cost of processing, need for land

7. Hydropower, nuclear fission and fusion, solar energy, wind energy, and geothermal energy.

8. More than 60%

9. An ester group

10. KOH serves as a catalyst.

11. It is readily available, it is made from renewable sources, it has lower sulfur content than petroleum, and it creates no net increase in greenhouse gases.

SECTION D SUMMARY
Reviewing the Concepts

Throughout human history, society has relied on a variety of biomolecules as energy sources.

1. What is a *biomolecule*?

2. Refer to Figure 3.49 (page 283). Identify the primary source of energy in the United States
   a. in 1900.   b. in 1940.   c. since 1975.

3. List three fuels that contain biomolecules used for energy.

4. What is the source of the energy stored in biomolecules?

5. Although petroleum has been used for thousands of years, only in relatively recent history has it become a major energy source. List three technological factors that can explain this.

Since petroleum is a nonrenewable resource, it will be eventually necessary to develop alternative energy sources.

6. List one advantage and one disadvantage of using each of the following alternate fuel sources:
   a. oil shale
   b. coal
   c. biodiesel

7. List three alternative energy sources that do not involve biomolecules.

8. What percent of petroleum consumed in the United States is used for transportation?

Diesel-fuel substitutes can be produced from renewable resources.

9. What is the primary functional group in biodiesel molecules?

10. Why was potassium hydroxide used in making biodiesel in Investigating Matter D.4 (Step 4, page 286)?

11. What are three advantages of biodiesel over petroleum-based diesel fuel?

Several types of alternative-fuel vehicles are being developed, tested, and used.

12. List an advantage and a disadvantage of each of the following alternative power sources for vehicles:
   a. compressed natural gas
   b. hydrogen fuel cell
   c. hybrid gasoline–electric

13. What are the emission products of fuel-cell powered vehicles?

14. What is the most common source of the hydrogen gas used in fuel cells?

15. Name the energy transformation that occurs in a hybrid vehicle when
   a. the vehicle is accelerated.
   b. the vehicle's brakes are applied.

---

12. a. Advantages: wide availability, decrease in CO and NO_x emissions; disadvantages: refueling requires a compression system, nonrenewable
b. Advantages: nearly zero emissions, no recharging required, more efficient than internal combustion; disadvantages: expensive fuel, manufacturing costs, refueling infrastructure needed
c. Advantages: reduced emissions, no recharging required, refueling infrastructure already in place; disadvantages: continues to burn fossil fuels and produce some emissions

13. Water

14. Methane (natural gas)

15. a. Chemical potential energy in storage batteries and gasoline is converted to the vehicle's kinetic energy.

Connecting the Concepts

16. Some energy authorities recommend exploring ways to use more renewable energy sources such as hydroelectric, solar, and wind power as replacements for nonrenewable fossil fuels.

    a. Why might this be a useful policy?

    b. Which of these renewable sources are least likely to replace fossil fuels at this time? Why?

17. If there is a dramatic increase in petroleum prices on the world market, explain which alternative source of energy you would expect to serve as the most practical substitute

    a. immediately.

    b. in ten years.

18. Suggest three ways individuals could reduce their total consumption of petroleum products.

19. We often consider alternative energy sources to be pollution free. Choose two alternative energy sources and evaluate them in terms of their possible impact on the environment.

20. Using Figure 3.49 on page 283 as a guide, make a pie chart showing the percent of all fuel sources used in

    a. 1900.   b. 2000.

21. Some people who do not own a car believe that they do not consume any fossil fuel. Evaluate their claim.

22. When biodiesel burns, it emits CO_2, like any other hydrocarbon-based fuel. Explain why it is not considered as a *net* contributor to atmospheric CO_2.

Extending the Concepts

23. Predict how your community would respond to a proposal for installing wind- or solar-power devices on a large scale to provide electrical power. Consider both advantages and disadvantages that might be considered in a town meeting.

24. Analyze how the relatively low cost and abundant availability of petroleum have affected the search for and development of alternative energy sources.

25. Identify and evaluate some state or federal programs that encourage development or use of alternative energy sources.

26. Experts disagree about how long fossil-fuel supplies will last. Research and evaluate some of their current opinions.

Section Summary   295

---

b. Kinetic energy of the moving vehicle is converted to chemical potential energy within the vehicle's storage batteries.

Connecting the Concepts

16. a. It improves air quality, extends time that fossil fuels will be available, and helps ensure that substitutes will be in place when petroleum is no longer readily available.

    b. Hydroelectric, solar, and wind power are least likely because they cannot be used directly as fuel for transportation.

17. a. Answers should be supported by evidence and valid reasoning. Immediate substitutes might include natural gas and liquid fuels from coal, since those technologies are well developed.

    b. Answers should be supported by evidence and valid reasoning. Longer-term substitutes might include oil from oil shale and tar sands, petroleum from plants, and biomass.

18. Answers may include: Increase the fuel efficiency of an automobile by keeping its engine tuned up and maintaining proper tire pressure. Turn the thermostat to 68 °F (or lower) in the winter to decrease fuel consumption and ensure the furnace is properly maintained. Turn off unnecessary lights. Purchase a hybrid or other "greener" automobile. Walk or take public transportation. Combine errands into a single trip. Buy goods made from recycled plastic.

19. Possible answers include: *Oil shale*—processing requires substantial energy, water, and destructive and unsightly mining practices. *Biomass*—processing requires energy, emissions are produced similar to burning petroleum. *Solar*—manufacturing of cells uses some toxic substances; large areas of land are required, affecting habitats; toxic spills are possible. *Nuclear*—produces radioactive waste, requires mining enrichment of uranium (which create pollutants), and poses operating risks. *Wind*—can cause erosion, kills birds in turbine collisions, requires large areas of land.

20.

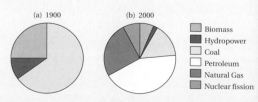

(a) 1900   (b) 2000

- Biomass
- Hydropower
- Coal
- Petroleum
- Natural Gas
- Nuclear fission

21. Everyone who uses electricity originating from an oil- or coal-burning power plant consumes fossil fuels. One must generally use fossil fuels for heating or public transportation. Most consumer products, including food items, require fossil fuels for production, packaging, and transportation to markets. Fossil fuels serve as building materials for plastics, fabrics, dyes, medications, and numerous other products.

22. Although CO_2 is emitted, it is initially taken up by growing plants that serve as biodiesel's source materials. Therefore, the net contribution of CO_2 is zero.

Extending the Concepts

23. Answers should consider advantages and disadvantages cited in answering Answer 16 and address beliefs and attitudes within the community.

24. Students should probably conclude that these factors have slowed support for research and development of alternative-energy resources, because they have contributed to a sense of low priority in the government and among consumers. Students should support their analysis with reliable references.

25. Through the Partnership for a New Generation of Vehicles, several U.S. government agencies worked with automakers to develop "green car" technologies. FreedomCar is one partnership between the U.S. Department of Energy and automobile manufacturers. (See **http://www.eere.energy.gov/vehiclesandfuels/**.) Encourage students to investigate programs within your state or region as well as new federal initiatives.

26. Students should examine reference materials and opinion pieces and evaluate claims made by each, based on what they have learned. Some references to help students start their search include:
    Scientific American theme issue, March 1998
    http://sepwww.stanford.edu/sep/jon/world-oil.dir/lynch/worldoil.html
    (partially a response to articles in *Scientific American*)
    http://www.peakoil.net/
    http://www.oil.com/
    http://economics.about.com/od/theoilsupply/

PUTTING IT ALL TOGETHER

Getting Mobile

 Getting Mobile Rubric

• This culminating activity engages students in designing, presenting, and evaluating mock television advertisements for an alternative-fuel vehicle.

• Students may require as much as two class days to design presentations. Depending on school procedures, you may decide to reserve appropriate reference materials or an area in the school library and/or computer lab to support students' research. Remind students to use their results and research from the unit's Making Decisions activities (A.11, B.10, C.9, and D.7). Encourage students to use technology (computers, video, camcorders, etc.) to support their presentations.

• Advertisements should reflect what students know about petroleum, energy, and fuels (both fossil and alternative). Students will choose a power option—biodiesel, CNG, hybrid gasoline–electric or hydrogen–oxygen fuel cell—for their imaginary vehicle. Remind them that their message must include accurate scientific claims and information about emissions, fuel efficiency, and use of petroleum compared to a standard gasoline-based vehicle.

• Advertisements should be designed for one minute of "air time." Students will need careful planning to promote their vehicle within the time allowed. You may provide stopwatches or timers to help students monitor their practice presentations. Allow some time after each presentation for questions and answers.

 Putting It All Together

GETTING MOBILE

If you are an average U.S. high school student, you have already viewed about a half-million television commercials, many of them for automobiles. As alternative-fuel vehicles become more available, advertisements similar to the one that opened this unit will become more common.

To make informed, intelligent consumer decisions, you should analyze information conveyed in such advertisements. You can further develop your analytical skills by devising and defending your own product claims.

You will now draft and produce your own automobile advertising message. After presenting your commercial message, you will answer questions posed by other students.

DESIGNING AND EVALUATING VEHICLE ADS

Each student team will create and present an advertisement featuring an imaginary but plausible vehicle that uses a particular type of fuel. You can choose from these power options: biodiesel, CNG, hybrid gasoline-electric, or hydrogen–oxygen fuel cell. You will present the commercial message to the class for analysis and comment, based on ideas introduced and discussed in your chemistry class.

Each advertising message must meet certain specifications. Use these specifications to guide the development of your advertisement, as well as to evaluate the presentations of your classmates.

Timing

Your message should take no more than one minute of "air time."

Scientific Claims

All scientific claims must be accurate. Because the type of fuel (energy source) represents the unique feature of your vehicle, you should highlight and explain it briefly. If appropriate, compare your vehicle to those that depend solely on petroleum for fuel. Include implications of emissions released by your vehicle, fuel efficiency, and how, other than in its possible use as a fuel, petroleum is related to your vehicle. (*Hint:* Review your earlier responses to Making Decisions D.7 (page 293).)

Presentation

In addition to presenting a commercial message with accurate claims, your goal is to present an organized, visually stimulating, and motivating advertisement. Remember that any commercial message should interest a potential buyer in the product.

LOOKING BACK AND LOOKING AHEAD

This unit has illustrated once again that chemical knowledge can help inform personal and community decisions related to resource use and possible replacement options. Thus far in your *ChemCom* studies, you have focused on three types of resources: water, minerals, and petroleum. The next unit explores another kind of resource—the atmosphere—the thin, virtually invisible envelope of gases that surrounds Earth's surface. As you will learn, human interactions with the atmosphere have provoked important questions and concerns.

Putting It All Together   **297**

• Remind students that, to be effective, an advertisement must be organized, attention-getting, and appealing. In days preceding the design and presentation of their advertisement, encourage students to critically view actual television and print automobile advertisements. Some style elements run through many automobile advertisements that might be useful for students as they plan their own ads. For example, many automobile ads use a catchphrase or slogan to distinguish one car from the competition.

A rubric for evaluating this activity is contained in the TRB an on the TRCD. You may share this rubric (or one of your own devising) with students ahead of time to help them plan their presentations.

LOOKING BACK AND LOOKING AHEAD

A primary objective of *ChemCom* is to enable students to make wise personal and community decisions. This brief transitional passage reflects on how knowledge of the three types of natural resources studied thus far—water, minerals, and petroleum—may inform their decisions. Each unit topic relates to the survival or well-being of humans on Earth. So does the next unit, "Air: Chemistry and the Atmosphere."

SECTION	CLASS TIME	STUDENT EDITION FEATURES	PROGRAM RESOURCES	MEDIA AND TECHNOLOGY
Section A: **Gases in the Atmosphere** **Objectives** • Identify the major components of the troposphere. • Describe how properties of the atmosphere change with increasing altitude. • Define and apply the concept of pressure, using various units. • Describe and apply the relationship between pressure and volume of a gas sample at constant temperature. • Describe and apply the relationship between kelvin temperature and volume of a gas sample at constant pressure. • Describe and apply the relationship between pressure and kelvin temperature of a gas sample at constant volume. • State and explain postulates of the kinetic molecular theory. • State and explain Avogadro's law for gases. • Apply Avogadro's law in calculations, including stoichiometric problems. • Describe the behavior of an ideal gas. • Use the ideal gas law in problems involving gases.	10–12 Class Periods	**Developing Skills** A.2 Graphing Atmospheric Data A.5 Applications of Pressure A.9 Predicting Gas Behavior: Pressure–Volume A.12 Predicting Gas Behavior: Temperature–Volume A.14 Using Gas Relationships A.18 Molar Volume and Reactions of Gases A.20 Using the Ideal Gas Law **Investigating Matter** A.3 Properties of Gases A.10 Exploring Temperature–Volume Relationships **Modeling Matter** A.16 Understanding Kinetic Molecular Theory **Making Decisions** A.21 Preparing to Explore Bus-Idling Policy	**TRB** **Investigating Matter** A.3 Properties of Gases Student Worksheet and Data Table A.10 Exploring Temperature–Volume Relationships Student Worksheet and Data Table **Modeling Matter** A.16 Understanding Kinetic Molecular Theory Student Worksheet **Content Reading Guides** A.8 and A.11 Content Reading Guide **Supplements and Practice** A.8 Supplement: Boyles Law A.11 Supplement: Charles' Law A.13 Pressure–Temperature Relationships A.18 Supplement: Molar Volume A.19 Supplement: The Ideal Gas Law Section A Supplement **Skill Building Supplements** Skill Building Supplement Topic 6: Understanding and Interpreting Graphs and Tables	**TRCD** **All TRB and Test Bank Materials for Unit 4, Section A** **Exercises** Structure of the Atmosphere Properties of Gases Gas Laws **Videos** Exploring Properties of Gas Temperature–Volume Relationships **Animations** Structure of the Atmosphere Properties of Gases Gas Laws

SECTION	CLASS TIME	STUDENT EDITION FEATURES	PROGRAM RESOURCES	MEDIA AND TECHNOLOGY
Section B: **Radiation and Climate** **Objectives** • Identify major types of electromagnetic radiation. • Describe the relation between electromagnetic radiation's energy, frequency, and wavelength. • Describe how Earth's atmosphere interacts with solar radiation. • Calculate thermal energy transferred between materials based upon their relative specific heat capacities. • Explain how the greenhouse effect works, including typical gases involved and their main sources. • Discuss the carbon cycle and how natural or human factors can affect it.	**5 Class Periods**	**Developing Skills** B.3 Solar Radiation B.5 Thermal Properties of Materials B.12 Trends in Atmospheric CO_2 Levels **ChemQuandary 1** Always Harmful? **Investigating Matter** B.6 Specific Heat Capacity B.9 Carbon Dioxide Levels **Modeling Matter** B.10 Incomplete Combustion **Making Decisions** B.8 Considering the Global Carbon Cycle B.13 Considering Greenhouse Gases	**TRB** **Investigating Matter** B.6 Specific Heat Capacity Student Worksheet and Data Table B.9 Carbon Dioxide Levels Student Worksheet and Data Table **Content Reading Guide** B.1 Content Reading Guide **Supplements and Practice** B.10 Supplement: Limiting Reactants Section B Supplement **Skill Building Supplements** Skill Building Topic 10: Understanding Mass Relationships in Chemical Reactions	**TRCD** **All TRB and Test Bank Materials for Unit 4, Section B** **Exercises** Solar Energy Earth's Energy Balance **Videos** Specific Heat Capacity Carbon Dioxide Levels **Animations** Earth's Energy Balance

SECTION	CLASS TIME	STUDENT EDITION FEATURES	PROGRAM RESOURCES	MEDIA AND TECHNOLOGY
Section C: **Acids in the Atmosphere** **Objectives** • Explain why precipitation is naturally acidic and can become more acidic due to atmospheric contaminants. • Describe how certain gases can contribute to acid rain. • Define and describe characteristics of acids and bases. • Distinguish among strong and weak acids and bases. • Calculate and compare concentrations of hydronium and hydroxide ions in acidic, basic, and neutral aqueous solutions. • Describe, calculate, and compare pH values of acidic, basic, and neutral solutions. • Describe effects of acidic precipitation (acid rain) and pH changes on natural systems. • Describe the composition and chemical behavior of a buffer.	**5 Class Periods**	**Developing Skills** C.5 Acids and Bases C.7 Interpreting the pH Scale **ChemQuandary 2** The Rain in Maine . . . **Investigating Matter** C.2 Making Acid Rain C.11 Buffers **Modeling Matter** C.9 Strong Versus Concentrated **Making Decisions** C.3 Preventing Acid Rain C.12 Considering Acid Rain	**TRB** **Investigating Matter** C.2 Making Acid Rain Student Worksheet and Data Table C.11 Buffers Student Worksheet and Data Table **Modeling Matter** C.9 Strong Versus Concentrated Student Worksheet and Data Table **Content Reading Guide** C.1 Content Reading Guide **Supplements and Practice** C.5 Supplement: Acids and Bases Section C Supplement	**TRCD** **All TRB and Test Bank Materials for Unit 4, Section C** **Exercises** Acid Concentration and Strength **Videos** Buffers Making Acid Rain **Animations** What is Acidic Pollution? What is pH? Buffer Action

SECTION	CLASS TIME	STUDENT EDITION FEATURES	PROGRAM RESOURCES	MEDIA AND TECHNOLOGY
Section D: **Air Pollution: Sources, Effects, and Solutions** **Objectives** • Identify primary and secondary air pollutants and their sources. • Identify factors and contaminants that contribute to photochemical smog. • Describe personal and global strategies that may help reduce air pollution. • Describe the role of CFCs in stratospheric ozone depletion.	**5 Class Periods**	**Developing Skills** D.2 Identifying Major Air Contaminants **ChemQuandary 3** Limiting Reactants and Scrubbers **ChemQuandary 4** Controlling Air Pollution **Investigating Matter** D.6 Cleansing Air **Making Decisions** D.4 Vehicles and Smog	**TRB** **Investigating Matter** D.6 Cleansing Air Student Worksheet and Data Table **Content Reading Guide** D.8 Content Reading Guide **Supplements and Practice** Section D Supplement	**TRCD** **All TRB and Test Bank Materials for Unit 4, Section D** **Videos** Cleansing Air **Animations** Ozone Formation Ozone Depletion
Putting It All Together: Bus-Idling Policy and Air Quality	**2 Class Periods**	**Putting It All Together** • Bus-Idling Policy and Air Quality	**TRB** **Putting It All Together:** Bus-Idling Policy and Air Quality Rubric	**TRCD** **All TRB Putting It All Together Materials**

Equipment, Expendable Items, and Unusual Materials (per 12 Student Pairs)

Sorted by Item

QUANTITY	ITEM	SECTION USED
12	aluminum soft-drink can, empty	A.3
10 mL	ammonia (NH_3), concentrated, 14.8 M	D.6
2	apples, red	C.2
12	aspirator adaptors	B.9, D.6 (1)
12	bags, zip-seal, pint-sized	C.2
1	balance	A.3
12	balances	B.6
48	balloons, medium to large	A.3
1	beaker, 600-mL	A.10
12	beakers, 400-mL	B.6
36	Beral pipets	C.2
12	Beral pipets containing 0.1 M HCl (hydrochloric acid)	C.11
12	Beral pipets containing 0.1 M NaOH (sodium hydroxide)	C.11
12	Beral pipets containing buffer solution	C.11
12	Beral pipets containing distilled water	C.11
12	Beral pipets containing universal indicator	C.11
1	bottle, plastic, clear, 1- or 2-L	A.3
1	bottle, plastic, clear, 1- or 2-L, with 0.5 cm hole in side	A.3
200 mL	bromothymol blue solution, 0.04% (m/v)	B.9
3	buckets, plastic, clear, 2-L or larger	A.3
12	candles, tea light or similar	B.9

Sorted by Item (continued)

QUANTITY	ITEM	SECTION USED
12	capillary melting-point tubes	A.10
12	cardboard squares, 8 cm × 8 cm	B.6
1	cardboard, heavy, 1 cm² piece, smoke source	D.6
12	clamps, flask	B.9
1 m	copper wire, bare, approx. 18 gauge	D.6
300 mL	corn oil	A.10
12	cups, Styrofoam	B.6
100 mL	distilled water	C.11
250 mL	distilled water	C.2
1	drinking glass, plastic, clear	A.3
12	filter flasks, 250-mL	B.9
1	filter flasks, 500-mL	D.6
2	flasks, Erlenmeyer, 500-mL	D.6
12	flasks, Erlenmeyer, 250-mL	B.9
12	funnels, glass, 70-mm diameter	B.9
1	graduated cylinder, 100-mL	D.6
12	graduated cylinders, 100-mL	B.6
1	hot plate	A.3
12	hot plates	B.6
1 pkg	Hydrion (pH) paper, wide-range	C.2, D.6
25 mL	hydrochloric acid (HCl), 6.0 M	C.2
10 mL	hydrochloric acid (HCl), concentrated, 12.0 M	D.6

Sorted by Item (continued)

QUANTITY	ITEM	SECTION USED
5 lb	ice	A.3
1 pkg	litmus paper, blue	C.2
1 pkg	litmus paper, red	C.2
12 cm	magnesium ribbon	C.2
24	marble chips (calcium carbonate, $CaCO_3$)	C.2
12	metal samples	B.6
12 sheets	paper towels	A.10, C.2
1	peeler or paring knife	C.2
1	plastic sheet, stiff, 3 × 3 cm	A.3
6	plastic wrap, 3 × 3 cm pieces	A.3
12	ring stands	B.9
250 g	rock salt	A.3
24	rubber bands, orthodontic, small	A.10
12	rulers, cm	A.10
1	stopper, rubber, 1-hole, to fit graduated cylinder	D.6
200 mL	sodium hydroxide (NaOH), 0.1 M	B.9
12 g	sodium sulfite (Na_2SO_3)	C.2
12	stirring sticks, coffee	C.11
1	stopper, 1-hole	D.6
12	stoppers, 1-hole	B.9
2	stoppers, 2-hole	D.6

Sorted by Item (continued)

QUANTITY	ITEM	SECTION USED
12	straws, drinking	B.9
1	syringe, large (>30 mL), Luer-tip, with cap	A.3
1 roll	tape, transparent	D.6
1	Tesla coil	D.6
36	test tubes (18 × 150 mm)	A.3, C.2, B.9
12	thermometers, alcohol –10 to 110 °C	B.6
12	thermometers, non-mercury (readable to 150 °C)	A.10
2	tongs	A.3
12	tongs	B.6
1	tube, thistle	D.6
12	tubing, glass, bent	B.9
12	tubing, glass, straight	B.9
4 pieces	tubing, glass, straight	D.6
24	tubing, rubber, 30-cm lengths	B.9
3	tubing, heavy-wall rubber, 30-cm lengths	D.6
12	universal indicator color charts	C.11
5 mL	universal indicator solution	D.6
12	well plates, 24-well	C.11
1 pair	wire cutters	D.6

Equipment, Expendable Items, and Unusual Materials (per 12 Student Pairs)

Sorted by Section

QUANTITY	ITEM	SECTION USED
48	balloons, medium to large	A.3
1	bottle, plastic, clear, 1- or 2-L	A.3
1	syringe, large (>30 mL), Leur-tip with cap	A.3
5 lb	ice	A.3
250 g	rock salt	A.3
2	tongs	A.3
3	buckets, plastic, clear, 2-L or larger	A.3
1	balance	A.3
12	aluminum soft-drink can, empty	A.3
1	bottle, plastic, clear, 1- or 2-L with 0.5 cm hole in side	A.3
2	test tubes (18 × 150 mm)	A.3
1	drinking glass, plastic, clear	A.3
1	plastic sheet, stiff, 3 × 3 cm	A.3
6	plastic wrap, 3 × 3 cm pieces	A.3
1	hot plate	A.3
1	beaker, 600-mL	A.10
300 mL	corn oil	A.10
24	rubber bands, orthodontic, small	A.10
12	capillary melting-point tubes	A.10
12	thermometers, non-mercury (readable to 150 °C)	A.10
12	rulers, cm	A.10
12	paper towels	A.10

Sorted by Section (continued)

QUANTITY	ITEM	SECTION USED
12	beakers, 400-mL	B.6
12	metal samples	B.6
12	balances	B.6
12	cups, Styrofoam	B.6
12	graduated cylinders, 100-mL	B.6
12	thermometers, alcohol –10 to 110 °C	B.6
12	hot plates	B.6
12	tongs	B.6
12	cardboard squares, 8 cm × 8 cm	B.6
12	funnels, glass, 70-mm diameter	B.9
12	filter flasks, 250-mL	B.9
12	stoppers, 1-hole	B.9
12	aspirator adaptors	B.9
24	tubing, rubber, 30-cm lengths	B.9
12	tubing, glass, straight	B.9
12	tubing, glass, bent	B.9
12	ring stands	B.9
12	clamps, flask	B.9
36	test tubes (18 × 150 mm)	B.9
12	candles, tea light or similar	B.9
12	straws, drinking	B.9
200 mL	bromothymol blue solution, 0.04% (m/v)	B.9
12	flasks, Erlenmeyer, 250-mL	B.9

SUPPLY LIST

Sorted by Section (continued)

QUANTITY	ITEM	SECTION USED
200 mL	sodium hydroxide (NaOH), 0.1 M	B.9
2	apples, red	C.2
12 g	sodium sulfite (Na$_2$SO$_3$)	C.2
12 cm	magnesium ribbon	C.2
12	bags, zip-seal, pint-sized	C.2
1	peeler or paring knife	C.2
12	test tubes (18 × 150 mm)	C.2
24	marble chips [calcium carbonate (CaCO$_3$)]	C.2
36	Beral pipets	C.2
25 mL	hydrochloric acid (HCl), 6.0 M	C.2
1 pkg	Hydrion (pH) paper, wide-range	C.2
1 pkg	litmus paper, red	C.2
1 pkg	litmus paper, blue	C.2
12 sheets	paper towels	C.2
250 mL	distilled water	C.2
12	well plates, 24-well	C.11
12	Beral pipets containing distilled water	C.11
12	Beral pipets containing 0.1 M NaOH (sodium hydroxide)	C.11
12	Beral pipets containing 0.1 M HCl (hydrochloric acid)	C.11
12	Beral pipets containing buffer solution	C.11
12	Beral pipets containing universal indicator	C.11
12	stirring sticks, coffee	C.11

Sorted by Section (continued)

QUANTITY	ITEM	SECTION USED
12	universal indicator color charts	C.11
100 mL	distilled water	C.11
1	graduated cylinder, 100-mL, glass	D.6
1 m	copper wire, bare, approx. 18 gauge	D.6
1	rubber stopper, 1 hole, to fit graduated cylinder	D.6
1 pair	wire cutters	D.6
1 roll	tape, transparent	D.6
1	Tesla coil	D.6
1	cardboard, heavy, 1 cm^2 piece, smoke source	D.6
1 pkg	Hydrion (pH) paper, wide-range	D.6
5 mL	universal indicator solution	D.6
10 mL	hydrochloric acid (HCl), concentrated, 12.0 M	D.6
10 mL	ammonia (NH_3), concentrated, 14.8 M	D.6
2	flasks, Erlenmeyer, 500-mL	D.6
1	filter flasks, 500-mL	D.6
2	stoppers, 2-hole	D.6
1	stopper, 1-hole	D.6
1	tube, thistle	D.6
4 pieces	tubing, glass, straight	D.6
3 pieces	tubing, rubber, 30-cm lengths	D.6
1	aspirator adaptor	D.6

UNIT 4
AIR: CHEMISTRY AND THE ATMOSPHERE

Introduction to the Unit

This unit introduces students to gases, particularly those in our atmosphere, as well as to properties that gases exhibit. Students will consider gas behavior on the macroscopic level by exploring changes and relationships among volume, pressure, and temperature. They will then have opportunities to build connections between their macroscopic observations and the particulate descriptions of gases provided by the kinetic molecular theory (KMT). Ideal and nonideal gas behaviors are considered.

UNIT 4

Air: Chemistry and the Atmosphere

The principal of Riverwood High School has just announced a new school bus-idling policy. You will investigate this decision for an article in the *Riverwood High Gazette.* What are the benefits and drawbacks of this policy? Turn the page to learn more about your reporting assignment.

After learning about gases that make up Earth's atmosphere in Section A, students study the chemistry of these gases within specific contexts. In Section B, they learn how atmospheric gases interact with solar radiation (energy) to influence Earth's climate. Section C addresses acid–base chemistry, as students investigate causes and the impact of acid rain. Finally, Section D focuses on the chemistry of several different human-generated pollutants and their effects on air quality.

The organizing issue for this unit is a new school bus-idling policy at Riverwood High School. In the culminating activity, students write a feature that presents the background on the bus-idling policy and its advantages and disadvantages.

Using the Unit Project

The Riverwood High School no-idling school bus policy serves as the organizing issue for Unit 4. Make students aware of their reporting assignment at the beginning of the unit and set tentative dates for first-draft and final-draft completion to allow time to conduct background research. Some students may require assistance in writing these feature articles. You may also ask students to complete prewriting activities, such as creating outlines or using graphic organizers, to establish the structure and main components of their feature articles.

• Length and other formatting requirements for these student-created features are intentionally not specified to allow for individual instructor preferences. For your later ease in evaluating the features, be clear about such requirements from the very beginning of the unit. Help students by giving them written guidelines and/or examples of what is acceptable or unacceptable. You might also provide students a rubric to guide their work on the culminating activity. A rubric is provided in the TRB and on the TRCD.

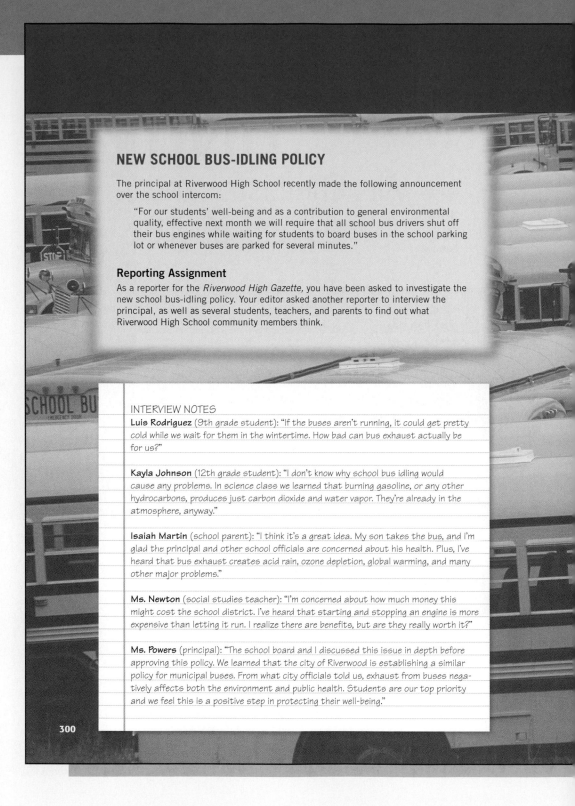

NEW SCHOOL BUS-IDLING POLICY

The principal at Riverwood High School recently made the following announcement over the school intercom:

"For our students' well-being and as a contribution to general environmental quality, effective next month we will require that all school bus drivers shut off their bus engines while waiting for students to board buses in the school parking lot or whenever buses are parked for several minutes."

Reporting Assignment

As a reporter for the *Riverwood High Gazette,* you have been asked to investigate the new school bus-idling policy. Your editor asked another reporter to interview the principal, as well as several students, teachers, and parents to find out what Riverwood High School community members think.

INTERVIEW NOTES

Luis Rodriguez (9th grade student): "If the buses aren't running, it could get pretty cold while we wait for them in the wintertime. How bad can bus exhaust actually be for us?"

Kayla Johnson (12th grade student): "I don't know why school bus idling would cause any problems. In science class we learned that burning gasoline, or any other hydrocarbons, produces just carbon dioxide and water vapor. They're already in the atmosphere, anyway."

Isaiah Martin (school parent): "I think it's a great idea. My son takes the bus, and I'm glad the principal and other school officials are concerned about his health. Plus, I've heard that bus exhaust creates acid rain, ozone depletion, global warming, and many other major problems."

Ms. Newton (social studies teacher): "I'm concerned about how much money this might cost the school district. I've heard that starting and stopping an engine is more expensive than letting it run. I realize there are benefits, but are they really worth it?"

Ms. Powers (principal): "The school board and I discussed this issue in depth before approving this policy. We learned that the city of Riverwood is establishing a similar policy for municipal buses. From what city officials told us, exhaust from buses negatively affects both the environment and public health. Students are our top priority and we feel this is a positive step in protecting their well-being."

300

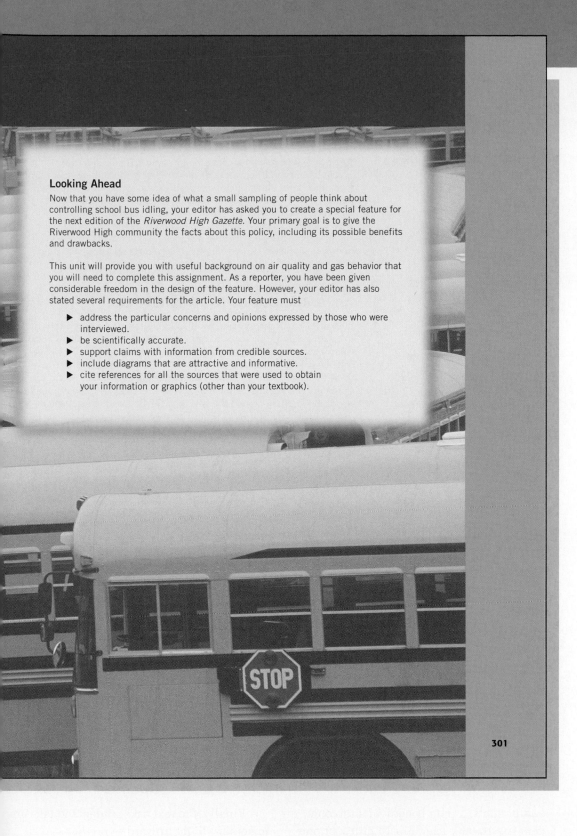

Looking Ahead

Now that you have some idea of what a small sampling of people think about controlling school bus idling, your editor has asked you to create a special feature for the next edition of the *Riverwood High Gazette*. Your primary goal is to give the Riverwood High community the facts about this policy, including its possible benefits and drawbacks.

This unit will provide you with useful background on air quality and gas behavior that you will need to complete this assignment. As a reporter, you have been given considerable freedom in the design of the feature. However, your editor has also stated several requirements for the article. Your feature must

▶ address the particular concerns and opinions expressed by those who were interviewed.
▶ be scientifically accurate.
▶ support claims with information from credible sources.
▶ include diagrams that are attractive and informative.
▶ cite references for all the sources that were used to obtain your information or graphics (other than your textbook).

301

• Two graphics, such as diagrams or illustrations, are required in each student's feature. Be clear about your requirements for these graphics. Decide what you consider as acceptable resources: Should students obtain graphics from properly referenced sources outside the text? Or will you require them to create both graphics? Consider setting an early due date for submission of these items so you can give students feedback on their quality and appropriateness.

• Once students have created first drafts, use one class period as an "editing day" where they trade papers with at least two classmates for proofing. Editing is just as challenging as writing, and without proper guidance, it can be conducted in a negative and/or superficial manner. Consider developing a feedback form that prompts students to evaluate specific aspects of their peers' air-quality features and, thus, provides useful, constructive comments. The text's list of proofreading criteria is a good resource in creating such a form. You may wish to include additional criteria.

Gases in the Atmosphere

Common atmospheric gases are introduced, and students create graphs of atmospheric temperature and pressure versus altitude using data provided. This section explores gas behavior through several activities that encourage students to investigate relationships among pressure, volume, and temperature. Mathematical manipulation of gas laws addressing these same relationships is also included, as are the concepts of pressure, the units of pressure, absolute zero, standard temperature, and the kelvin temperature scale. Students learn about kinetic molecular theory (KMT) and the conditions under which nonideal gases deviate from the postulates of KMT. The section introduces Avogadro's law of gaseous molar volume and application of this law to reaction stoichiometry and, finally, presents concepts and mathematical manipulations pertaining to all previous gas laws within the ideal gas law. Students then conduct a preliminary analysis of the statements included in the interview notes on page 300.

A.1 Structure of the Atmosphere

Students examine the composition of the first 10 to 15 km of Earth's atmosphere. The composition of the troposphere has remained constant over time. Gaseous components are discussed in terms of their percent abundances and, in some cases, parts per million (ppm).

A brief review of *ppm* and *ppb* may help students visualize the minute concentrations of some air

---

SECTION A

Gases in the Atmosphere

You have been asked to inform the Riverwood High community about the benefits and drawbacks of the new school bus-idling policy. In their interviews, Kayla Johnson, Isaiah Martin, and Principal Powers implied that bus exhaust changes the composition of the atmosphere. Is this true? To address this question, you will need some information. To start, you will find out what gases are naturally present in the atmosphere and how those gases behave under various conditions. The activities and information provided in Section A will help you learn more about atmospheric gases.

Structure of the Atmosphere

The word *troposphere* is based on the Greek words *tropos*, which means turn, and *sphaira*, which means sphere.

A.1 STRUCTURE OF THE ATMOSPHERE

Most of the atmosphere's mass and all of its weather are located within 10 to 15 km of Earth's surface (see Figure 4.1). This is a very small distance compared to the size of Earth; if Earth were roughly the size of a basketball, the portion of the atmosphere called the **troposphere** would be relatively thinner than the basketball's pebbled texture that covers its surface. Gases mix continuously in the troposphere; therefore, its composition is reasonably uniform around the world. Table 4.1 lists the main components of the troposphere. Chemical analysis reveals that ancient air trapped in glacial ice has about the same chemical makeup as does our current atmosphere (Figure 4.2). This finding suggests that there has been

Figure 4.1 *Just how thin is the atmosphere that surrounds us? Looking up from Earth, the skies can seem endless. This view highlights the narrow strip of atmosphere that separates Earth from space.*

Figure 4.2 *Analysis of gases trapped in glacial ice shows that the composition of the atmosphere has not changed much since ancient times.*

---

components. 1 ppm is equivalent to one cent in $10 000, 1 inch in 16 miles, or one minute in 2 years. 1 ppb is equivalent to one cent in 10 million dollars, 1 inch in 16 000 miles, or one second in 32 years.

Finally, the text asks students to take an imaginary flight upward to predict atmospheric conditions at various altitudes. This leads to the Developing Skills activity that follows.

COMPONENTS OF DRY TROPOSPHERIC AIR		
Substance	**Formula**	**Percent of All Gas Molecules**
Major components		
Nitrogen	N_2	78.08
Oxygen	O_2	20.95
Minor components		
Argon	Ar	0.93
Carbon dioxide	CO_2	0.033
Trace components		
Neon	Ne	0.0018
Ammonia	NH_3	0.0010
Helium	He	0.0005
Methane	CH_4	0.0002
Krypton	Kr	0.0001

Table 4.1 *This chart identifies gases normally present in the tropospheric air closest to Earth's surface. The pie chart (right) illustrates the relative amounts of each gaseous substance contained in this air.*

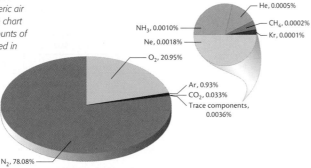

He, 0.0005%
CH_4, 0.0002%
Kr, 0.0001%
NH_3, 0.0010%
Ne, 0.0018%
O_2, 20.95%
Ar, 0.93%
CO_2, 0.033%
Trace components, 0.0036%
N_2, 78.08%

little change, except for carbon dioxide concentrations, in tropospheric air over a very long time.

Air is a mixture of gases. Nitrogen is the most abundant gas, followed by oxygen and substantially lower amounts of argon and carbon dioxide. In addition to the gases listed in Table 4.1, air samples can contain up to 5% water vapor, although in most locations the water vapor range is from 1 to 3%. Other gases naturally present in air at concentrations below 0.0001% (1 ppm) include hydrogen gas (H_2), xenon (Xe), ozone (O_3), nitrogen oxides (NO and NO_2), carbon monoxide (CO), and sulfur dioxide (SO_2). Human activity and natural phenomena, such as volcanic eruptions, can alter the concentrations of some trace gases and add other substances to air. This may lead to decreased air quality, as you will learn later in this unit.

The amount of water vapor in the air determines its humidity.

Section A   Gases in the Atmosphere   303

Figure 4.2: Researchers use ice cores, cylinders of ice drilled out of polar ice sheets or glaciers, to investigate the history of Earth's climate. When snow falls, it carries substances that are in the air at the time, and (in places where temperatures are rarely above freezing, such as in polar regions or at high altitude) the snow from one year piles onto previous years' snowfall. As each year's snowfall is buried by successive years' snowfall, the substances it carried are buried with it. By drilling down from the surface of an ice sheet and analyzing snow from greater and greater depths, scientists obtain a history of the substances in the air.

Further, deeper snow traps small pockets of air as it turns into ice from the pressure of snow above it. Thus, ice sheets trap air itself. Analyzing this trapped air provides information about the composition of the atmosphere at the time the ice formed. Typically, analysis involves isotopic dating techniques, calculating the ratio of O-18 to O-16. This isotopic ratio provides information about ancient climates because it is influenced by atmospheric temperature fluctuations. Ice cores also provide information about historical CO_2 levels in the environment.

The National Ice Core Laboratory in Lakewood, Colorado, is dedicated to examining, sampling, and analyzing ice cores. For more information about ice cores and the NICL, visit **http://nicl.usgs.gov/who.htm.**

Using the Figures

Figure 4.1: Estimating the thickness of Earth's atmosphere is trickier than one might think. The notion of "the higher the elevation, the less dense the atmosphere, but it never quite goes to zero" is an example of *asymptotic* behavior (similar to the concept of half-life). If you visualize a boundary containing 99% of the atmosphere, it would be located 31 km above Earth's surface. Invite students to compare that distance with Earth's diameter, 12 742 km.

Developing Skills

A.2 Graphing Atmospheric Data

By graphing atmospheric data, students can identify the effect of increasing altitude on temperature and air pressure. Encourage students to use their best techniques to construct their graphs and to draw their best-fit lines. (Graphs may also be computer generated.) Advise students that the data in Table 4.2 do not reflect a warming trend from 83 km, the start of the thermosphere, to 700 km.

Answers

1. Predictions will vary, but should indicate that with increasing altitude, air temperature will first decrease, then increase, then decrease again (a) and air pressure will decrease (b).

2. a., b. Graphs should be similar to those below.
   c. The best fit line for (a) is made of three straight lines through plotted data. An exponential curve is the best line for (b).
   d. Answers will vary, depending on students' predictions in Answer 1. Responses should address inconsistencies between those predictions and the graphs.

> The only components of the atmosphere visible from space are condensed water vapor in the form of clouds and, at times, traces of colored nitrogen oxide (NO$_x$) pollutants near urban areas.

Developing Skills

> The unit mmHg, millimeters of mercury, is a common unit of gas pressure (see page 312).

Suppose it were possible for you to fly from Earth's surface up into the farthest regions of the atmosphere. What do you think you would encounter as you traveled 5, 10, or 50 km away from Earth? Would the air temperature change? Would you be surrounded by the same mixture of gas molecules as your altitude increased? Although you cannot take a trip such as this right now, you can find answers to these and other questions about the atmosphere. Technology allows scientists to measure a range of air characteristics at different altitudes. In the following activity, you will analyze this type of data.

A.2 GRAPHING ATMOSPHERIC DATA

Table 4.2 summarizes atmospheric data gathered at various altitudes. Use the information provided to answer the questions that follow:

ATMOSPHERIC DATA				
Altitude (km)	Air Temperature (°C)	Air Pressure (mmHg)	Mass (g) of 1-L Air Sample	Molecules in 1-L Air Sample
0	20	760	1.20	250×10^{20}
5	−12	407	0.73	150×10^{20}
10	−45	218	0.41	90×10^{20}
12	−60	170	0.37	77×10^{20}
20	−53	62	0.13	27×10^{20}
30	−38	18	0.035	7×10^{20}
40	−18	5.1	0.009	2×10^{20}
50	2	1.5	0.003	0.5×10^{20}
60	−26	0.42	0.0007	0.2×10^{20}
80	−87	0.03	0.00007	0.02×10^{20}

| **Table 4.2**

1. Predict the shape of the graph line for a y versus x plot of
   a. air temperature versus altitude.
   b. air pressure versus altitude.

2. Prepare graphs according to the following instructions. Your teacher will indicate whether you can use graphing software or graphing calculators for these tasks:
   a. Plot air temperature versus altitude data.
   b. Plot air pressure versus altitude data.
   c. Draw a best-fit line through the plotted points for each graph. (*Note:* The graph line may be straight or curved.)
   d. Does the shape of either graph differ from your prediction in Question 1? If so, how?

304   **Unit 4**   Air: Chemistry and the Atmosphere

---

a.

b.
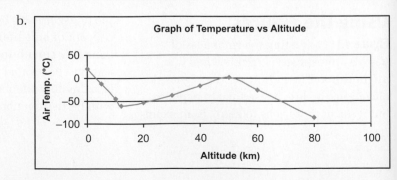

3. Compare ways that air temperature and air pressure change with increasing altitude.
   a. Which follows a more regular pattern?
   b. Explain this behavior.

4. Based on the data, would you expect air pressure to rise or fall if you traveled from sea level (0 km) to
   a. Pike's Peak (4301 m above sea level)?
   b. Death Valley (86 m below sea level)?

5. a. Suppose you gathered 1-L samples of air at several altitudes. How would the following values change with altitude?
   i. mass of the air sample
   ii. total molecules in the air sample
   b. If you were to plot the air-sample mass versus the number of molecules contained in the sample, what would the graph look like?
   c. Why?

6. Scientists often characterize the atmosphere as composed of four general layers. In order, they are the *troposphere* (nearest Earth's surface), the *stratosphere,* the *mesosphere,* and the *thermosphere* (outermost layer).
   a. Mark both graphs from Question 2 with lines at appropriate altitudes to indicate where you think the general transitions between the atmospheric regions might be.
   b. How confident are you in marking the mesosphere–thermosphere transition on your graph? Explain.

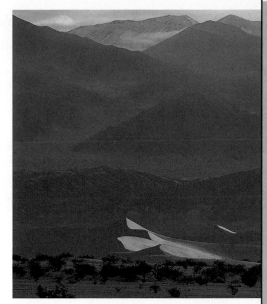
Death Valley

A.3 PROPERTIES OF GASES

Investigating Matter

Introduction

Kayla Johnson said in her interview (see page 300), quite correctly, that gases such as carbon dioxide and water vapor are naturally present in the atmosphere. Because atmospheric gases are generally colorless, odorless, and tasteless, you might doubt that they are forms of matter; they seem to be "nothing." However, gases do have definite physical and chemical properties, just as the materials in the other two states of matter—solids and liquids—do. In this laboratory investigation, you will complete activities that illustrate some properties of air.

Before starting this investigation, read the procedure carefully. Predict what you think will happen in each of the nine activities; write down your predictions. Also, note safety precautions and plan necessary data collecting and observations.

 Properties of Gases

Section A   Gases in the Atmosphere   **305**

---

3. a. Pressure.
   b. The number of gas molecules changes fairly regularly with altitude, and thus pressure changes regularly.

4. a. Fall. Increased altitude means fewer gas molecules, which reduces pressure.
   b. Rise. Decreased altitude means more gas molecules, which increases pressure.

5. a. i. Mass would decrease with increasing altitude.
      ii. The number of molecules would decrease with increasing altitude.
   b. A straight line.
   c. As long as relative composition is consistent, air-sample mass depends only on the number of gas molecules, so they are directly related.

6. a. Students should identify layers with about these thicknesses: troposphere 0–12 km, stratosphere 12–50 km, mesosphere 50–83 km, and thermosphere 83–700 km.
   b. Answers will vary, but students should express low confidence in marking this transition, since they did not graph data for the thermosphere.

Investigating Matter

A.3 Properties of Gases

These activities explore and build understanding of properties of gases. Since atmospheric gases are colorless, odorless, and tasteless, students tend to think of them as "nothing." After completing this investigation, they should conclude that gases, like solids and liquids, have definite physical and chemical properties.

 A.3 Properties of Gases Student Worksheet and Data Table

Students should write their predictions before the investigation. This helps identify their preconceptions.

Encourage students to visualize and write what may happen at the particulate level.

Some students may have difficulty explaining gas behavior from a particulate perspective at this point in the course.

Students may record their observations in a table similar to this one.

Activity Number	Prediction	Observation

Time

50 min

Materials

(for 12 student pairs)

syringe, large (> 30 mL), Luer-tip with cap

2 tongs

ice

salt

48 balloons, medium to large

balance (accurate to 0.01 g)

pin

bottle, plastic, clear 1- to 2-L

2 test tubes (18 × 150 mm)

stiff plastic (such as a CD jewel case or a coffee-can lid)

hot plate

drinking glass, plastic, clear

6 pieces plastic wrap, 3 × 3 cm

empty aluminum soft-drink can

3 buckets, plastic, clear, 2-L or larger

bottle, plastic, clear, 1- or 2-L with 0.5 cm hole in side

 Lab Video: Exploring Properties of Gases

Procedure

Five stations, A through E, have been set up around the laboratory. At each station you will complete the activities indicated for that station. These activities can be done in any order; that is, work at Station D can be completed before Station B activities, and so on. Follow these general instructions:

▶ Reread the procedure.

▶ Review your prediction.

▶ Complete the activity.

▶ Record your observations.

▶ Restore the station to its original condition.

When you have completed your work at all five stations, answer the questions that follow.

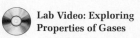

Figure 4.3 *Manipulating a sealed syringe (Activity 1).*

Station A

Activity 1

1. Draw some air into a syringe.
2. Seal the tip by placing the cap on the *open* end.
3. Holding the cap in place, gently push the plunger down with your thumb, as shown in Figure 4.3.
4. Release the plunger.
5. Record your observations.

Activity 2

1. Inflate and tie off two new balloons so that they are approximately the same size; about the size of a grapefruit.
2. Use tongs to submerge one inflated balloon in an ice–salt water bath.
3. Use tongs to submerge the second inflated balloon in a container of hot tap water.
4. Record your observations.

Station B

Activity 3

1. Inflate a balloon to approximately the size of a grapefruit and tie off the end.
2. Place the inflated balloon on a balance, using a piece of tape to hold it in place.
3. Record the mass of the balloon (and attached tape).

Pre-Lab Discussion

Before students start, ensure that they have written predictions about the outcomes. Urge them to observe carefully and to identify the particular gas property involved.

Safety

Students should wear protective goggles and aprons throughout the investigation. Remind them to exercise care when using hot plates.

Caution: Students with latex allergies should not do Activities 2, 3, and 4 with latex balloons. Depending on allergy severity, all students may refrain from using latex balloons. Alternatives include:

Activity 2: Use small Mylar balloons or use the first follow-up demonstration.

Activity 3: Use small Mylar balloons or small plastic bags secured by a rubber band.

Activity 4: Omit for latex-allergic students.

4. Remove the balloon from the balance. Use a pin to gently puncture the balloon near its neck, and release most of the gas contained within the balloon.

5. Place the deflated balloon on the balance, with the tape still attached, and record its mass.

6. Record your observations.

Activity 4

1. As shown in Figure 4.4, insert the rounded end of a new, uninflated balloon part way into an empty soft-drink bottle, stretching the balloon's neck over the mouth of the bottle.

2. Try to blow up the balloon so that it fills the bottle.

3. Remove and discard the used balloon.

4. Record your observations.

Station C
Activity 5

1. Lower an empty drinking glass, with its open end facing downward, into a larger container of water.

2. With the open end still under water, slowly tilt the drinking glass.

3. Record your observations.

Activity 6

1. Fill a test tube to the rim with water.

2. Cover the test tube opening with a piece of stiff plastic.

3. Press down the plastic to make a tight seal with the mouth of the test tube.

4. While continuing to press the plastic to the test tube, invert the test tube above a sink or a pan.

5. Without causing any jarring, gently remove your hand from the piece of plastic.

6. Repeat the process with the test tube half-full of water.

7. Record your observations.

Figure 4.4 *Placement of a balloon in a bottle (Activity 4).*

Observations

• **Activity 1 (Station A):** P *and* V *are inversely related.* There's resistance to pushing the plunger, thus demonstrating Boyle's law and gas compressibility.

• **Activity 2 (Station A):** T *and* V *are directly related.* The balloon submerged in ice–salt water bath shrinks, while the one submerged in hot tap water expands, thus demonstrating Charles' law.

• **Activity 3 (Station B):** *Air has weight.* The balance reveals a difference of about 0.2 g between filled and empty balloons, demonstrating that "invisible" gases possess weight, like other forms of matter. (This procedure doesn't allow for buoyant effect of surrounding air.)

• **Activity 4 (Station B):** *Air occupies space and exerts pressure.* P *and* V *are inversely related.* The balloon can be slightly inflated inside the bottle; it becomes more difficult to blow up as it enlarges—air initially in the bottle is trapped by the expanding balloon. As the balloon inflates, air in the bottle has less volume, and thus exerts more pressure on the balloon. Eventually, pressure exerted by blowing into the balloon is unable to exceed pressure exerted by trapped air.

• **Activity 5 (Station C):** *Air occupies space.* Water does not initially enter the glass; air occupies that space. With the glass tilted, water should enter the glass as air is allowed to escape. The rising bubbles also suggest that air is less dense than water.

• **Activity 6 (Station C):** *Air exerts pressure in all directions.* The plastic cover stays on the inverted test tube, suggesting that air exerts pressure in all directions (upward against the cover) and supports water's weight. As a demonstration, repeat without filling the test tube completely. Ask students to account for observed differences.

Lab Tips

• Station A–E designations keep similar materials together. You can regroup activities to work for your lab setting.

• You may decide to limit student time; 4 to 5 min per station should be sufficient. Ask students to rotate among stations based on allotted time.

• Pairing students typically works best for this investigation; when groups are larger, some students may not be engaged. With more groups, setting up duplicate stations facilitates student movement.

• Activity 2: Use ice–salt water bath for lowest temperature.

• Activity 9: You can do this as a demonstration if time and/or supplies are limited.

307

- **Activity 7 (Station D):** *Air (and water) exerts pressure in all directions.* Water level in the test tube does not change. First part: Water in test tube is pushed up by a force equal to the gravitational pull down. Second part: Air in the test tube above the water must push down on the water, since water below it exerts an upward force (first part).
- **Activity 8 (Station D):** *Air exerts pressure in all directions.* No water escapes the bottle hole until its cap is removed. Then water in the bottle experiences atmospheric pressure from above, which overcomes atmospheric pressure from the side, allowing water to escape.
- **Activity 9 (Station E):** *Air exerts pressure in all directions.* **Caution students—the can is hot; don't boil its contents to dryness.** The inverted can is crushed in cold water. Water vapor generated by boiling displaces most air in the can. Upon cooling, water vapor condenses, producing a partial vacuum in the can. External pressure crushes it.

Answers

1. Activities 3, 4, and 5. The balloon inflated weighed more than did it deflated (Activity 3), showing that air has mass (and thus matter). Activities 4 and 5 showed that air occupies volume. Otherwise, we could blow up the balloon inside the bottle. Tilting the glass (Activity 5) allowed water to displace trapped air.

2. Answers are based on what students expected and observed.

3. Refer to "Observations." Answers will vary based on student choices. Particle models should depict gas particles farther apart than solid or liquid particles. The motion of particles in each activity should account for gas P, V, and T.

Station D
Activity 7

1. Fill a test tube to the rim with water.
2. Cover the test tube mouth with a piece of plastic wrap.
3. While continuing to press the plastic wrap to the mouth of the test tube, invert the test tube and partially immerse it in a container of water.
4. Remove the piece of plastic wrap.
5. Move the test tube up and down, keeping its lower (open) end under water.
6. Repeat the process with the test tube half-full of water.
7. Record your observations.

Activity 8

1. Locate the plastic bottle with a small hole in its side.
2. Cover the hole in the side of the bottle with your finger.
3. Fill the bottle with water.
4. Replace the cap tightly.
5. Holding the bottle over a sink, remove your finger from the hole.
6. Still holding the bottle over the sink, remove the cap.
7. Record your observations.

Station E
Activity 9

1. Place about 10 mL of water in a clean, empty aluminum soft-drink can.
2. Place the can on a hot plate and bring the water to a rapid boil.
3. Using tongs to handle the soft-drink can, quickly remove the can from the heat and immediately invert it into a container of ice water, as shown in Figure 4.5.
4. Record your observations.

Figure 4.5 *Use tongs to quickly invert a can containing boiling water into a container of ice water (Activity 9).*

Questions

1. Which of the previous activities suggest that air is composed of matter? Explain, using observational evidence to support your answer.

2. For each activity, briefly describe how well your predictions corresponded with the actual results you observed, and propose explanations for any differences between your predictions and the observed results of the activities.

4. Answers will vary. Possibilities include (a) breath is fogging in the cold; air is attracted by gravity (Earth's atmosphere) and (b) leaning into the wind; headwinds or crosswinds experienced in moving vehicles; ears "popping" on airplanes or subway trains.

5. a. Liquid rises in a single straw. No liquids move in two straws (unless the tongue closes the end of one straw).
   b. When one draws on a single straw, pressure is decreased within the straw. Atmospheric pressure on the fluid surface is then greater than the pressure inside the straw;

3. For any three activities in this investigation,
   a. describe your observations in detail.
   b. explain the role of air in the activity.
   c. draw particle models that show the interactions between the gas particles and the other particles of matter.

4. Describe another investigation or experience that suggests that
   a. air is matter.
   b. air exerts pressure.

5. Complete this investigation at home or in the school lunchroom: Put one end of a straw in a glass of water. Hold another straw outside the glass. Place the ends of both straws in your mouth and try to drink the water through the straw in the glass. See Figure 4.6.

   Describe what you observed when you tried this investigation. Based on your observations, what makes it possible to drink liquid through a straw?

Figure 4.6 *What will happen when you try to drink water through the straw inside the glass?*

A.4 PRESSURE

In everyday language, the word *pressure* can have many meanings. Perhaps you use it to mean that you feel too busy or that you feel forced to behave in certain ways. The greater the pressure, the more "boxed in" you feel. To scientists, pressure also refers to force and space, but in quite different ways.

In science, **pressure** refers to the force applied divided by the surface area upon which the force is applied:

$$\text{Pressure} = \frac{\text{Force}}{\text{Area}}$$

You can see from the equation that pressure is *directly* proportional to the force applied, and it is *inversely* proportional to the area upon which the force acts.

Think back to a common experience: Someone steps on your foot. The pressure (or maybe even pain) that you feel depends on the two variables involved in the previous equation—*force* and *area*. You surely can feel the difference between a light-weight person or a heavy person stepping on your foot, assuming that both people have the same size foot and wear similar shoes. The larger the force, in this case the weight, the more pressure that is exerted. If applied weight (force) is the same, then different shoe types (area) will affect the pressure (Figure 4.7).

Figure 4.7 *If someone were to accidentally step on your foot, which "shoes" would you prefer that the person wore? Explain your choice in terms of the concept of pressure.*

Section A   Gases in the Atmosphere   **309**

liquid is pushed (not drawn) up through the straw. With two straws where one not immersed in liquid, pressure cannot be decreased inside the straws; air is continually drawn in. With no pressure difference between the atmospheric pressure and the inside of the straw, fluid cannot rise.

Students are not now expected to construct correct molecular models for their observations. After learning KMT and gas laws, they will better understand intermolecular interactions. For now, they can evaluate their previous ideas and reflect on gas properties.

Follow-Up Demonstrations

Challenge students to link each demonstration to the activity (1–9) that demonstrates the same principle.

• Attach enough weight (using paper clips or staples) to a string tied to a partially filled Mylar helium balloon so it is neutrally buoyant. Heat the balloon gently with a hair dryer. As its volume increases, its density decreases, and it rises until it cools down and descends. This corresponds to Activity 2. You can use the balloon for several days; change the weights as necessary to make it neutrally buoyant.

• Add 20 mL water to a 1-L Florence flask; heat the water to boiling on a hot plate. Remove the flask from the hot plate and quickly seal its top with a balloon. ***Caution:*** The flask and water are hot. Larger balloons with more elastic openings facilitate securing the balloon. Hold the flask with ring stand and clamp if needed. Water vapor inside the flask cools and condenses; fewer total gas particles collide with the inside of the balloon than with the outside of the balloon; the balloon is *pushed* (not *sucked*) into the flask.

This illustrates two points: (1) *Gas P and T are directly related* (Activity 9). The pressure exerted by water vapor decreases rapidly as it condenses, resulting in its container (either can or balloon) being crushed by external pressure. (2) *Water vapor is a nonideal gas.* Its condensation is due to particle "stickiness." Repeat the demonstration without water in the flask: Only a small balloon depression is noted; air does not condense to liquid at room temperature.

A.4 Pressure

The scientific meaning of *pressure* is developed with several common examples. The relationship among pressure, force, and area is expressed mathematically. Ensure that students understand the difference between *direct* and *inverse* relationships.

Using the Figures

Figure 4.7 (page 309): Ask students to consider which shoes they'd prefer their friend to wear when stepping on their foot—the scuba fins or inline skates. How does their choice relate to pressure (force/area)?

A brief discussion of base units and derived units in the modernized metric system (SI) may benefit students. The authoritative references on SI are **http://www1.bipm.org/en/si/** (internationally) and **http://ts.nist.gov/ts/htdocs/200/202/mpo_home.htm** (in the United States).

The Teacher Resource Binder has supplementary information and practice problems using SI units.

This material introduces the SI units of force and pressure. Pressure is expressed in both English and SI units, but students should use pascals or kilopascals in their calculations.

1 atm = 760 mmHg = 29.92 in Hg = 101.3 kPa

Scientists have established standards upon which all measurements are based. These include units of temperature, length, time, and mass. For example, the standard for length (the meter) is currently based on the distance traveled by light in a vacuum during 1/299 792 458 of a second.

The abbreviation SI is based on *Système International de Unités*, its official French name.

Another volume unit with which you are familiar, the milliliter (mL), is equal to 1 cm^3.

In the same way that someone exerts pressure on your foot, gas molecules exert pressure on the walls of their container. You observed this in several recent laboratory investigations (see pages 306–308). For instance, in Activity 6 (page 307), you may have possibly concluded that air pressure holds the piece of plastic against the water in an inverted test tube. How much pressure did the air exert on the piece of plastic, and how could you measure this pressure?

You probably are familiar with several units used to report pressure. For example, U.S. weather forecasters report barometric air pressure in *inches of mercury*. When you check air pressure in car or bicycle tires, most likely your tire gauge reads *pounds per square inch*, or psi. Other pressure units you may have already heard of are *millimeters of mercury* (mmHg), and *atmospheres* (atm). With so many different units available for measuring and reporting pressure, how do scientists communicate with one another?

Scientists have agreed to use certain units when communicating results. This system of units, called the **International System of Units (SI)**, allows scientists from around the world to communicate clearly with each other. Table 4.3 lists some SI units. Note that some units, such as *length* and *mass*, are **base units;** they express the fundamental

SI UNITS FOR SELECTED PHYSICAL QUANTITIES

The Seven Base Units of SI		
Physical Quantity	**Name**	**Symbol**
Length	meter	m
Mass	kilogram	kg
Time	second	s
Electric current	ampere	A
Thermodynamic temperature	kelvin	K
Amount of substance	mole	mol
Luminous intensity	candela	cd
Some Derived Units		
Area	square meter	m^2
	square centimeter	cm^2
Volume	cubic meter	m^3
	cubic centimeter	cm^3
Force	newton	N (equal to $kg \cdot m/s^2$)
Pressure	pascal	Pa (equal to N/m^2)

| **Table 4.3**

physical quantities of the modernized metric system. Others, such as *area, force, volume,* and *pressure,* are **derived units;** they are formed by mathematically combining two or more base units.

Recall that pressure can be expressed as *force per area.* It is useful to understand the SI units of force and area before learning about the SI derived unit for pressure. The SI derived unit for force is the **newton (N).** To visualize one newton of force, imagine holding a personal-sized bar of soap (with a mass slightly greater than 100 g) in your open hand. That bar of soap "pushes" downward on your open hand with a force of about one newton (1 N).

The **force** (or weight) of any object depends on its mass and gravitational attraction. **Area** refers to the total surface of an object. For a square or a rectangular surface, area is calculated by multiplying the lengths of its two adjacent sides. The SI base unit of length is the **meter** (m); thus, area is expressed as a derived unit—m × m, or square meters (m²).

When a one-newton (1-N) force is exerted upon an area of one square meter (1 m²), the pressure equals one *pascal* (1 Pa). The **pascal** (Pa) is the SI derived unit of pressure. One pascal (1 Pa) is a relatively small pressure; it is roughly the pressure exerted downward on a slice of bread by a thin layer of soft butter spread on its top surface. Because a pascal is so small, the *kilopascal* (kPa), a unit 1000 times larger than the pascal, is commonly used to express many pressures.

> *Pascal* is pronounced so it rhymes with *rascal.* Some automobile tires specify inflation pressure in kilopascals (kPa), as well as pounds per square inch (psi).

Developing Skills

A.5 APPLICATIONS OF PRESSURE

Using what you have learned about pressure, answer the following questions:

1. Figure 4.8 shows two bricks of the same mass lying on the ground.
   a. Is each brick exerting the same total *force* upon the ground? Explain.
   b. Is each brick exerting the same *pressure* upon the ground? Explain.

2. Calculate the pressure, expressed in pascals, that the brick on the right side of the photo exerts upon the ground. It is exerting a force of 18 N, and the dimensions of the brick surface touching the ground are 9.3 cm × 5.5 cm. (Remember, there are 100 cm in 1 m.)

3. You need to chop some wood to build a fire. You quite obviously reach for an ax rather than a hammer to complete this task. Explain your choice in terms of the concept of pressure.

Figure 4.8 *Two similar bricks lie on the ground. Are they exerting the same pressure upon the ground?*

Developing Skills

A.5 Applications of Pressure

In this activity students analyze and calculate pressure in realistic situations.

Answers

1. a. The force is the same in both cases because both bricks weigh the same.

   b. The area over which the force is applied is different. The brick on its end exerts more pressure because it has less surface area in contact with the ground.

2. Pressure = force/area =
   18 N/(0.093 m × 0.055 m) =
   18 N/0.0051 m² = 3500 Pa

3. The cutting edge of an ax has a much smaller surface area. Pressure equals force/area, so the smaller the area, the greater the pressure when the same force is applied.

A.6 Atmospheric Pressure

If a barometer is installed in your classroom or laboratory, you may point it out to students when you explain atmospheric pressure and its measurement. However, do *not* construct a mercury barometer—it is both hazardous and prohibited in many cities and states. For several days you could regularly post daily atmospheric pressures (displayed in several units) from the National Weather Service. Keep in mind that those values are altitude corrected and may not match the absolute atmospheric pressure in your area. Also, point out that the atmospheric pressure reported by TV meteorologists is often expressed in *inches of mercury*. Some students may be interested in comparing pressure expressed in inches of mercury to pressure expressed in mmHg or kPa (units they will use in this course). You may decide to perform a sample pressure conversion.

Consider mentioning historical issues surrounding the removal of water from mines. Until the 1700s, this was an ongoing problem for mines that were more than 10.3 m deep: Water could not be removed with a simple surface pump because atmospheric pressure could not push water up that high. This led to development of the steam engine. Early steam engines used condensation of steam (similar to Activity 9 in *Investigating Matter A.3*) to create a low-pressure area beneath a piston. Atmospheric pressure then pushed the piston down and the piston moved a beam that drove a water pump. A good summary and diagrams are available at **http://www.egr.msu.edu/~lira/supp/steam.**

Figure 4.9 *Tornados are powerful reminders of atmospheric pressure.*

Height of column proportional to external pressure

Pressure of atmosphere

Mercury

A.6 ATMOSPHERIC PRESSURE

You have just learned what pressure means to a scientist and how it can be expressed in quantitative units. Perhaps you are wondering how pressure relates to the gases in the atmosphere that are of concern at Riverwood High School. As you discovered in Investigating Matter A.3, the atmosphere exerts a force on every object within the atmosphere. (Figure 4.9). On a typical day at sea level, air exerts a force of about 100 000 N on each square meter of your body, resulting in air pressure of about 100 kPa. This pressure is also roughly equal to one *atmosphere* (1 atm), which is another unit commonly used by scientists and one with which you will become familiar. One atmosphere is equal to 101.3 kPa.

Pressure can also be expressed in units of *mmHg*, or *inches of mercury*. Such units suggest that air pressure can be measured as the height of a column of mercury. How is this possible? Recall that in part of a laboratory investigation that you completed (Activity 7, page 308), you covered a test tube filled with water and inverted it into a container of water. You then uncovered the test tube. What did you observe? What force supported the weight of the column of water in the test tube?

Now imagine repeating that laboratory investigation with a taller test tube and once again with an even taller test tube. If the test tube were tall enough, at a certain height water would no longer fill the tube entirely when it was inverted in a container of water. This puzzling effect was first observed in the mid-1600s. Scientists discovered that 1 atm of air pressure could support a column of water only as tall as about 10.3 m (33.9 ft). If the investigation was tried with even taller inverted test tubes, the water column still would reach only the 10.3-m level.

A *barometer* (a device that measures atmospheric pressure) based on a tube filled with water would be much too tall to be useful. Therefore, scientists replaced the water with mercury, a liquid 13.6 times denser than water. The resulting mercury column, illustrated by the barometer depicted in Figure 4.10, is shorter than the water column by a factor of 13.6. Thus, at 1 atm pressure, the mercury column has a height of 760 mm; 1 atm = 760 mmHg.

Figure 4.10 *A mercury barometer. On a typical day at sea level, the atmosphere will support a column of mercury 760 mm high. The pressure unit of atmospheres is related to pressure in millimeters of mercury: 1 atm = 760 mmHg.*

Demonstration Idea

Place an expendable meter stick on a table so that approximately one-third of the meter stick extends over the table edge. Then place 2 or 3 sheets of unfolded newspaper on the table, covering the stick. Smooth the newspaper sheets as flat and as close to the table (and meter stick) as possible. The newspaper sheets may overlap (depending on the table size). Ask students to predict what would happen if you hit the protruding end of the meter stick as hard as possible. Then hit the hanging end of the stick with a fast, downward chop. If done correctly, the paper will not move. In fact, when hit hard and fast enough, the stick

A.7 ATOMS AND MOLECULES IN MOTION

As you get up on a cold winter morning, you look out the window to see clouds of exhaust coming from cars, trucks, and buses driving past your home. Your hand recoils from the hot spray coming from the shower head; it is too uncomfortable for you to enjoy your morning shower. Turning on too much cold water, however, leads to a chilling experience.

Your experiences with gases, liquids, and solids are all at a sensory level; that is, you observe matter and its changes through your senses of sight, smell, touch, taste, and hearing. In so doing, you arrive at some generalizations about the world around you. Making observations is the first step in "doing science." A more difficult task is crafting a theory that explains all observations and that also predicts the outcomes of investigations yet to be completed.

One such theory concerns the motion of atoms and molecules within all states of matter. What do you already know about the three states of matter from observing them? You know that a *solid* has a definite shape and that its structure is rigid. Experience also tells you that a *liquid* flows and, unlike a solid, depends on a container to define its shape. A sample of *gas*, likewise, does not have a definite shape. If you have blown up a balloon and then let go of it without tying it off, you also know that air rapidly leaves the balloon and the balloon changes shape.

The atoms, molecules, or ions that make up solids are held closely to one another. Although the particles in solids vibrate about a position, they are tightly packed and cannot move past one another. The molecules and ions within liquids are more mobile, they can move past each other; however, intermolecular attractive forces prevent them from moving too far apart. The arrangement of particles in solids and liquids are depicted in Figure 4.11.

> Scientific laws describe the behavior of events in nature, but they do not provide explanations for the observed behavior. Scientific theories and models attempt to offer how-type explanations of phenomena in the natural world.

> As you learned in Unit 3 (page 219), intermolecular forces are attractive forces between molecules.

Figure 4.11 *You can observe the properties of solids (zinc, left) and liquids (mercury, right) using your senses. Models help explain how atoms interact with each other and their surroundings.*

will break and the paper will remain relatively undisturbed. This effect is a consequence of atmospheric pressure on the newspaper. This demonstration both reinforces the concept of atmospheric pressure and demonstrates the amount of pressure the atmosphere exerts.

Using the Figures

Figure 4.9: A tornado represents a spinning column (vortex) of rapidly rising air (a miniature low-pressure system). Ask students to visualize this phenomenon, and invite them to predict how a tornado affects the pressure of air beneath it. They should

indicate that the tornado creates an area of low pressure beneath it, since air rises into the spinning low-pressure system.

A.7 Atoms and Molecules in Motion

The differences among relative motions of molecules in solid, liquid, and gaseous states are discussed, with emphasis on the average kinetic energy of gas molecules. The kinetic molecular theory (KMT) is introduced and developed.

KMT is a model that explains gas behavior, developed from observations. (This a good opportunity to review processes of science and the goal of generalizing results into a theory or model.) KMT postulates were very successful in accounting for empirical gas laws that describe gas behavior under varying conditions of temperature, pressure, and volume, which students will soon study. You may emphasize here or later in the unit that any model is by its very nature an approximation and encourage students to keep this in mind in their exploration of gas phenomena. In A.15 and A.16, they will explore some limitations of this particular model.

Using the Figures

Figures 4.11 and 4.12 (page 314): Challenge students to build connections between their experiences with macroscopic properties of solids, liquids, and gases and these molecular-level depictions (models). For example, what do these models imply about compressibility (squeezing a rock compared to squeezing liquid water or a balloon)?

Scientific American Conceptual Illustration

As students become familiar with postulates associated with KMT (see student page 315), they can identify features of this illustration corresponding with each postulate. While doing so, they can assess how well this illustration models the postulates. For instance, the first KMT postulate deals with the size of gas particles relative to the great distances that separate them. Although more "distance" is correctly depicted among gas particles in **Figure 4.12** than among liquid or solid particles in **Figure 4.11,** the gas particles in this figure are, for artistic convenience, depicted as too close together. Ask students to identify features in the illustration that represent gas molecules in constant, random, straight-line motion; elastic collisions; and a range of kinetic energies.

The kinetic molecular theory, or, in simpler language, "the theory of moving particles" (Rudolph Clausius, 1857), admirably meets key expectations of any productive scientific model—(a) it must be simple enough to be solvable and (b) it must be understandable and useful.

The KMT postulates (page 315) may prompt some student questions—a common one is *Why don't gas molecules eventually stop moving?* The key to this quandary is the postulate of *elastic collisions* (third postulate, page 315)—all collisions are "non-sticky" with no loss in total kinetic energy due to interactions with each other or with the container walls. A thought experiment might help: Imagine placing a gas sample in a totally insulated con-

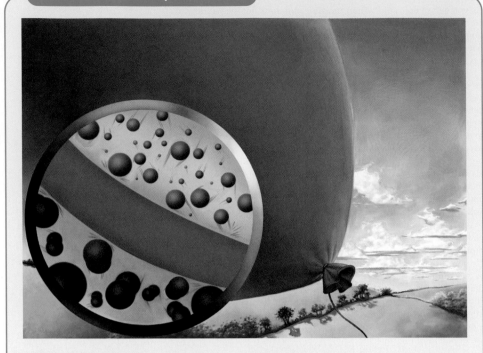

Figure 4.12 *Particulate-level model of gases. A helium-filled balloon soars above the landscape. In magnification, helium atoms are depicted within the balloon, He(g). Nitrogen molecules (N$_2$, blue) and oxygen molecules (O$_2$, red), representing 98% of air, are shown outside the balloon. What does this model suggest about spacing and movement of gas particles compared to those in liquids and solids?*

Most molecules in the gaseous state are not as strongly attracted to each other. In contrast to particles in solids and liquids, particles in gases are very far apart. In fact, their size is negligible compared to the great distances that separate them. Gas molecules move in straight-line paths at very high speeds and change direction only when they collide with each other or with another object. Collisions of gaseous molecules with the container walls produce gas pressure. Figure 4.12 illustrates the motion of particles in a gas sample. Compare this model of gases to the models of solids and liquids in Figure 4.11 (page 313).

Gas molecules move at average speeds that depend on how much kinetic energy they possess. Recall from Unit 3 (page 239) that kinetic energy, which sometimes is called *energy of motion,* is the energy associated with any moving object. Its value depends on both the mass of

tainer. Observations would reveal that this gas sample doesn't spontaneously "wear out" or cool down to absolute zero (0 K), suggesting that the gas particles maintain their average kinetic energy even

though they are continually colliding.

Some data may help students build a useful mental model based on KMT: The average velocity of O$_2$ molecules at 25 °C and 1 atm pressure is about 480 m/s; that's

Figure 4.13 *A technician in Wheat Ridge, CO, repairs a hail-damaged trunk panel. Was this damage more likely caused by pea-sized hail or golf ball-sized hail?*

the moving object and its velocity. Traveling at the same velocity, a more massive object has greater kinetic energy than does a less massive object (see Figure 4.13). Thus, a baseball has much greater kinetic energy than a ping-pong ball when both are traveling at the same speed. If two moving objects have equal mass, the object moving faster has greater kinetic energy. This helps to explain the difference in damage to a car bumper when it taps the wall of a parking garage at 10 km/h compared to a collision with a parked car at 30 km/h.

The behavior of moving gas molecules can be explained by the idea of kinetic energy. This explanation is based on several postulates, some of which you have just considered. The following list summarizes these postulates:

> 10 km/h = 6.3 mph

> A *postulate* is a statement accepted as the basis for further reasoning and study.

- ▶ Gases consist of tiny particles (molecules) whose size is negligible compared with the great distances that separate the molecules from each other. On average, the separation between gaseous molecules at 1 atm pressure and 0 °C is about 11 times greater than the diameter (size) of the molecules.

- ▶ Gas molecules are in constant, random motion. They collide with each other and with the walls of their container or surrounding objects. Gas pressure is caused by molecular collisions with the container walls.

- ▶ Molecular collisions are *elastic*. This means that although individual molecules in a gas sample may gain or lose kinetic energy, there is no gain or loss in total kinetic energy from all of these collisions.

- ▶ At a given temperature, gas molecules have a range of kinetic energies. However, the *average* kinetic energy of the molecules is constant and depends only on the temperature of the gas sample. Therefore, molecules of different gases at the same temperature have equal average kinetic energies. As gas temperature increases, the average velocity and kinetic energy of the gas molecules also increase.

These postulates serve as the basis of the **kinetic molecular theory (KMT)** of gases, which can be used to explain various observations of gas behavior. The postulates can also be used to make predictions. For example, the theory can predict what will happen to the pressure of a gas sample if its volume is doubled, assuming no change in temperature. Read on to see how.

Section A   Gases in the Atmosphere   **315**

about 1726 km/h, or nearly 1080 mph. That implies, as some alert students may realize, that gas molecules travel on average *faster than the speed of sound*—quite correct! To understand why this must be so, invite stu-

dents to think about how sound "travels" through air. Physics textbooks customarily speak of the motion of sound waves. Applying KMT postulates, however, suggests that sound is actually propagated by a rapid

SECTION A

series of molecular interactions (collisions). If gas molecules move *randomly* (second postulate, page 315), sound impulses necessarily follow a zigzag pathway from their source to the ear. These willy-nilly motions must be faster than the speed of sound itself.

Another consequence of this phenomenon is observed in the very slow movement (diffusion) of an odiferous gas such as ammonia across a room—one might think that the average velocity of gas molecules would imply that the odor would speed across the room. The answer, once again, is that gas molecules do not travel very far in any one direction—their straight-line motion is impeded by molecular collisions. In fact, the average distance an O_2 molecule at 25 °C and 1 atm travels before colliding with another O_2 molecule (its *mean free path*) is 67 nm—in other words, it travels, on average, only about 180 molecular diameters before encountering another O_2 molecule. An O_2 molecule collides with another one, on average every 0.13 ns, or an unimaginable 10 billion (10^{10}) collisions per O_2 molecule per second.

The fourth postulate stresses that the *average* kinetic energy of gas molecules is directly proportional *only* to the sample's kelvin temperature—not to the mass or size of the gas particles. A consequence of this is that at a fixed temperature, more massive gas molecules must move more slowly, on average, than low-mass gas molecules; for example, at 25 °C, the average N_2 velocity (28.0 g/mol) is 515 m/s, compared to 482 m/s for O_2 (32.0 g/mol).

A.8 Pressure–Volume Behavior of Gases

When the volume of a gas sample is reduced while its temperature is held constant, the gas pressure will increase. This occurs because the reduced volume means that gas particles (still moving at the same average rate since their temperature is unchanged) will collide with the container walls more frequently and thus produce a greater force on each unit of container-wall area. Conversely, if gas volume increases at constant temperature, fewer wall collisions will occur and pressure will thus decrease.

If pressure increases on the outer walls of a flexible container of gas, the volume of that container (at constant temperature) will decrease. Similarly, a decrease of pressure on a flexible container results in increased gas volume.

Thus, gas pressure and volume at constant temperature are inversely related—if one increases, the other decreases and their product is a constant. The formal statement of this relationship is Boyle's law, which can be written $P \times V = k$ or $P = k/V$ or $P_1V_1 = P_2V_2$.

Students may experience difficulties with inverse relationships. Invite them to reason through a problem and predict whether the answer should be larger or smaller—*before* they set up a ratio or start their calculations. For instance, if the problem asks what the pressure inside a syringe will be if its volume is reduced from 6.0 mL to 5.0 mL and the initial pressure is 2.0 atm, students should first consider whether the final pressure would be greater or less than 2.0 atm. They should reason that the gas pressure

You observed that gas trapped in a syringe could be compressed in Activity 1 page 306.

Gas Laws

A.8 PRESSURE–VOLUME BEHAVIOR OF GASES

Earlier, when you pushed down on a sealed syringe filled with gas, you observed that a gas sample can easily be compressed. A gas sample can be compressed much more easily than can a liquid or solid sample. In other words, the volume of a gas sample is easily changed when an external pressure is applied to it.

Consider your experience with the syringe. The more pressure you applied to the plunger, the smaller the volume of gas held inside the syringe became. Consequently, the pressure of the gas sample trapped below the plunger increased. Think of it this way: As the syringe volume within which the gas particles are confined continues to become smaller, the particles collide with each other and with the syringe walls more frequently. The net force exerted by all of those collisions upon the interior walls of the syringe, or pressure, increases.

Assume that the pressure of gas inside the syringe was 1 atm before you started pushing in on the plunger (at this point, the atmosphere was exerting the only pressure on the plunger). If, by pushing on the plunger, the volume of gas in the syringe were then lowered to *one-half* of its original volume, the pressure of the gas sample would be *doubled*. If the gas volume in the syringe were reduced to *one-fourth* of its original value, the gas pressure would become *four times larger*. In each case, the gas pressure inside the syringe increases as the gas volume decreases (see Figure 4.14). Figure 4.15 illustrates this relationship between gas pressure and its volume.

Figure 4.14 *A student pushes a plunger into a closed syringe. What's keeping him from pushing it in all the way?*

Figure 4.15 *As pressure increases, the volume of gas trapped in the syringe decreases proportionally.*

increases as the volume *decreases*. They then select the ratio by which they will multiply 2.0 atm. The options are 6.0/5.0 and 5.0/6.0. Since the final value should be *greater*, students should choose to multiply

2.0 atm by 6.0/5.0 to obtain a final gas pressure of 2.4 atm.

You may also use the sample problem in the text to help students understand the nature of this inverse relationship.

The Pressure–Volume Relationship

How can kinetic molecular theory help explain the gas behavior just described? Gas molecules are in constant, random motion; gas pressure is caused by molecules colliding with the walls of their container.

The relationship between the volume and the pressure of a gas sample at constant temperature can be described in several ways. The changes in volume and pressure predicted by KMT for a particular gas sample at constant temperature can be described with words or pictures, such as those shown in Figures 4.15 and 4.16. These changes can also be described graphically, as shown in Figure 4.17. Note the shape of the curve; this indicates an *inverse relationship* between gas pressure and volume.

This relationship is useful for predicting the new gas pressure or volume resulting from a change in one of these two variables. Again, consider the syringe shown in Figure 4.15.

Sample Problem: *You know that initially the gas sample occupies a volume of 8.0 mL and exerts a pressure of 1.0 atm. How would the pressure of the gas sample change if its volume were increased to 10.0 mL?*

Take a few moments to think about this question, using your own experiences with the syringe and the illustrations in Figure 4.15 to guide your thinking. If you increase the volume of the syringe by pulling out on the plunger, what will happen to the gas pressure within the syringe? Will the new pressure be less than or greater than the initial pressure? Did you reason that the new pressure would be *lower* than 1.0 atm? By now, you probably have gained an understanding of the relationship between gas volume and pressure that can guide you in predicting general results of such changes. Now you are ready to learn how to make *quantitative* predictions about this type of gas behavior.

Figure 4.16 *As the volume of a sample of gas is reduced, the number of molecular collisions with the container wall—and thus the gas pressure—increases proportionally. The gas molecules in each syringe have been greatly magnified to depict the relative distances among them, and thus to account for the more frequent collisions with the container wall (and, thus, higher gas pressure) in the syringe on the right.*

Figure 4.17 *The volume (V) of a gas sample, maintained at constant temperature and amount, is inversely proportional to its pressure (P). Therefore P × V is constant. A plot of pressure versus volume for any gas sample at constant temperature and amount will be similar to this one.*

Section A   Gases in the Atmosphere   **317**

 A.8 Supplement: Boyles Law

 A.8 and A.11 Content Reading Guide

Using the Figures

Figure 4.15: Students can use data in this figure to confirm $P_1V_1 = P_2V_2$, since (1 atm)(8 mL) = (2 atm)(4 mL) = (4 atm)(2 mL). Challenge students to draw a syringe that shows the predicted volume when 1.5 atm is applied to the plunger.

Figure 4.17: When asked to predict the shape of a *P* vs. *V* graph, many students draw a straight line with negative slope. Students may be surprised by the shape of this graph. Have students find points that represent doubling or tripling of volume and confirm that those points correspond to pressures that are half or one-third the original values. For instance, two such data pairs are: (0.020 mL, 200 mmHg) and (0.040 mL, 100 mmHg).

Demonstration Ideas

• Review *Investigating Matter A.3* Activity 1: Use a plastic syringe to illustrate the relationship between gas pressure and volume.

• Connect a eudiometer tube (or stoppered buret) partly filled with water to a leveling bulb (or large funnel) via plastic tubing. When the leveling bulb is raised or lowered, the volume of trapped gas in the tube changes: The gas volume in the tube decreases as the bulb is raised (increased pressure) and increases when the bulb is lowered (decreased pressure).

• Many physics departments have a vacuum pump and a bell jar. See if you can borrow these, obtain operating instructions, and then demonstrate gradually evacuating the bell jar with a marshmallow or marshmallow Peeps® shape held inside—a dramatic *P–V* demonstration!

Developing Skills

A.9 Predicting Gas Behavior: Pressure–Volume

In this activity, students apply Boyle's law to household and laboratory situations.

Answers

1. a. When air pressure outside one's body decreases, gases in the lungs, stomach, and sinuses and those dissolved in blood expand, which can cause discomfort.

   b. New tennis balls have an internal pressure that is slightly greater than atmospheric pressure. The cans/tubes in which they are sold are pressurized to the same pressure as the gas in the tennis balls, so gas does not leak into or out of the tennis balls. If tennis balls lose pressure through gas leakage, they will also lose some of their "bounce."

   Tennis balls bounce because most of the energy of their collision with ground or racquet goes into compressing the air inside. The compressed air "responds" with more collisions against the inside of the ball. The ball then bounces back. As the ball loses its internal pressure, more of the impact energy goes into deforming the ball and fewer gas particles are left to collide with the inside of the ball, so its "bounce" decreases.

   c. At the mountaintop, gas pressures inside and outside the bottle were equalized. As you descended, the pressure outside the bottle increased as the altitude decreased. The pressure inside the bottle does not change. Since the applied (atmospheric) pressure on the bottle has increased, its volume decreased. You can also explain this in terms of KMT as an increase in the relative numbers of collisions on the outside of the bottle compared to the inside.

Boyle's Law

Robert Boyle, an English scientist who studied gases, was the first to propose a quantitative law based upon the volume–pressure relationship for gases. He found that, for a sample of gas at constant temperature, the product of its measured pressure (P) and volume (V) remains the same, or $P \times V = k$. This relationship is known as **Boyle's law.**

Even when either the pressure or volume of that same sample of gas is changed, the product of pressure multiplied by volume will still be equal to that same value (k) if the temperature and amount of gas are kept constant:

$$P_2 \times V_2 = k$$

An inverse relationship is a mathematical relationship, where an *increase* in one variable results in a *decrease* of another variable. However, the product of the two variables remains the same.

Boyle's law expresses an inverse relationship. In fact, when changes in volume and pressure are made to a gas sample at constant temperature, a relationship can be expressed between the initial and final conditions of the gas sample. If P_1 and V_1 represent the initial pressure and volume of a sample of gas and P_2 and V_2 represent its final values, then this equation can be written as

$$P_1 \times V_1 = P_2 \times V_2$$

or

$$P_1V_1 = P_2V_2$$

This equation, which is an expanded expression of Boyle's law, will help you to decide whether your prediction from page 317 was, in fact, correct.

$$P_1 = 1.0 \text{ atm} \longrightarrow P_2 = ? \text{ atm}$$
$$V_1 = 8.0 \text{ mL} \longrightarrow V_2 = 10.0 \text{ mL}$$
$$P_1V_1 = P_2V_2$$
$$1.0 \text{ atm} \times 8.0 \text{ mL} = P_2 \times 10.0 \text{ mL}$$
$$P_2 = \frac{(1.0 \text{ atm})(8.0 \text{ mL})}{10.0 \text{ mL}} = 0.80 \text{ atm}$$

The final gas pressure (0.80 atm) is less than the initial gas pressure: As gas volume in the syringe in Figure 4.15 (page 316) *increases,* the gas pressure *decreases.* Does this match your original reasoning?

In the following activity, you will explain several common observations based on what you know about the relationship between gas pressure and volume. You will also have the opportunity to apply Boyle's law to solve several pressure–volume gas problems.

318   **Unit 4**   Air: Chemistry and the Atmosphere

A.9 PREDICTING GAS BEHAVIOR: PRESSURE–VOLUME

1. Explain each of the following observations:

   a. Even if they have ample supplies of oxygen gas, airplane passengers experience discomfort when the cabin undergoes a drop in air pressure.

   b. New tennis balls are sold in pressurized containers.

   c. After descending from a high mountain, the capped, half-filled plastic water bottle from which you drank while standing at the summit now appears dented or slightly crushed.

2. You buy helium gas in small pressurized cans to inflate party balloons. The can label indicates that the container delivers 7100 mL of helium gas at 100.0 kPa pressure. The volume of the gas container is 492 mL:

   a. Do you think that the initial pressure of helium gas inside the can is greater or less than 100.0 kPa? Explain.

   b. Calculate the initial pressure of helium gas inside the container.

   c. Was your prediction in Question 2a correct?

3. Two glass bulbs are separated by a closed valve (see Figure 4.18). The 0.50-L bulb on the left contains a gas sample at a pressure of 6.0 atm. The 1.7-L bulb on the right is evacuated; it contains no gas:

   a. Draw a model of gas molecules in the two glass bulbs before and after the middle valve is opened.

   b. Explain your model in terms of kinetic molecular theory.

   c. Predict, in general, what will happen to the total volume of the gas sample if you open the middle valve. Explain.

   d. Predict, in general, what will happen to the total pressure of the gas sample if you open the middle valve. Explain.

   e. Calculate the actual pressure of the gas sample after the middle valve is opened.

Filled with gas

Empty

Figure 4.18 *Two glass bulbs are separated by a closed valve. The bulb on the left is filled with gas; the bulb on the right is empty. What would happen to the gas pressure if the middle valve were opened?*

2. a. Since 7100 mL gas is compressed into a 492-mL can, pressure on the inside of the can must be greater than 100.0 kPa.

   b. $P_1V_1 = P_2V_2$
   7100 mL × 100 kPa = 492 mL × P_2
   P_2 = 1440 kPa

   c. Students should indicate whether their answers to Questions 2a and 2b were consistent.

3. a. Sketches should show molecules in only one bulb before the valve is opened and the molecules distributed proportionally (by bulb size) in the two bulbs after the valve is opened.

   b. When the valve is opened, the gas molecules continue their straight-line movements until they experience collisions. Since there are initially no gas molecules and then fewer gas molecules in the bulb on the right, gas molecules will tend to travel there without "bouncing back" due to collisions until pressure is equalized in the two bulbs.

   c. The gas will expand to occupy the total volume of both bulbs. See Answer 2b.

   d. The total pressure will decrease. The same number of gas molecules now has a much larger surface area with which to collide, so the number of collisions per unit area (pressure) will decrease.

   e. 0.50 L × 6.0 atm = 2.2 L × P_2
   P_2 = 1.4 atm

A.10 Exploring Temperature–Volume Relationships

 A.10 Exploring Temperature–Volume Relationships Student Worksheet and Data Table

This section introduces students to the T–V relationship for a gas sample at constant P. Students observe the volume of a trapped air column at different temperatures. After constructing a graph of their T–V data, students predict the temperature corresponding to zero gas volume. Results are used to introduce students to kelvin temperatures. (You may wish to specify that *273 K* is pronounced *273 kelvins*.)

Time

50 min

Materials

(for 12 student pairs)

Beaker, 600-mL, and a hot plate *or* a small deep-fry appliance
300 mL yellow corn oil (to fill heating container deep enough for capillary tube immersion
24 rubber bands, orthodontic, small, *or* rings cut from rubber tubing
12 capillary melting-point tubes
12 thermometers, non-mercury (readable to 150 °C)
Paper towels
12 rulers, cm

Advance Preparation

Yellow corn oil has produced consistently satisfactory results. Results have been less satisfactory, for example, with mineral oil. If you use some other oil, be sure to test it before students do the investigation.

 Lab Video: Temperature–Volume Relationships

Introduction

Most matter is observed to expand when heated and contract when cooled. As you know, gas samples expand and shrink to a much greater extent than either solids or liquids. In this investigation, you will study how temperature changes influence the volume of a gas sample, assuming that pressure and the amount of gas remain unchanged. To do this, you will heat a thin glass tube containing a trapped air sample and record the changes in volume as the air sample cools.

Before starting, read the procedure to learn what you will need to do, note safety precautions, and plan necessary data collecting and observations.

Procedure

1. Using two small rubber bands, fasten a capillary tube to the lower end of a thermometer. (See Figure 4.19.) Place the open end of the tube close to the thermometer bulb; about 5 to 7 mm above the bulb's tip.

2. Immerse the tube and thermometer in a hot oil bath that has been prepared by your teacher. Be sure the entire capillary tube is immersed in oil. Wait for your tube and thermometer to reach the temperature of the oil (approximately 100 °C). Record the temperature of the bath.

3. After your tube and thermometer have reached a steady temperature, lift them up until only about one-quarter of the capillary tube is still in the oil bath. Pause for about three seconds to allow some oil to rise into the tube. Then quickly place the tube and thermometer on a paper towel (to avoid dripping) and carry them back to your desk. *(**Caution:** Be careful not to touch the hot end of the thermometer or drips of hot oil.)*

4. Lay the tube and thermometer on a clean piece of paper towel on the desk. Make a reference line on the paper at the sealed end of the capillary tube. Also mark the upper end of the oil plug, as shown in Figure 4.19. Alongside this mark, write the temperature at which the mark was made, corresponding to that air-column length.

5. As the temperature of the gas sample drops, make at least six marks to represent the length of the air column trapped above the oil plug at various temperatures. Write the corresponding temperature next to each mark. Allow enough time so that the temperature drops by 50 to 60 °C.

Figure 4.19 *Apparatus for studying how gas volume changes with temperature.*

Labels in figure:
Reference line marked on paper for top of air sample
Trapped air
Oil plug
85 °C
95 °C
Lengths and corresponding temperatures marked on paper as tube cools

Safety

Students should wear protective goggles and aprons throughout the investigation. Be especially careful with hot oil, as it can cause serious burns. Do not heat the oil with a Bunsen burner; a hot plate is the safest method. Maintain oil temperature below 130 °C.

Pre-Lab Discussion

In this investigation of gas V and T at constant P, the gas is trapped by an oil droplet inside a capillary tube. Point out that measuring the *length* of trapped air is valid; tube length is proportional to gas volume.

Students construct their own data tables. Point out that the first data point is at the hot-oil temperature at the full length of the capillary tube; students will measure the distance from the closed end of the tube

6. When the thermometer shows a steady temperature (near room temperature), make a final observation of length and temperature. Discard the tube and the rubber bands according to your teacher's instructions. Wipe the thermometer clean.

7. Measure the length (in millimeters) from each marked line to the mark for the sealed end of the tube. Record each length of the gas sample. Have your teacher check your data before you discard your paper towel. Your teacher may ask you to submit your paper towel along with your report, so be sure to get specific instructions before disposing of the towel.

8. Wash your hands thoroughly before leaving the laboratory.

Data Analysis

1. Plot the length–temperature data for your air sample, with length on the vertical axis and temperature on the horizontal axis. The y-axis (length) should range from 0 to 10 cm; the x-axis (temperature) should include values from −350 to 150 °C. Label your axes, and arrange the scales so that the graph nearly fills the space available.

2. Draw the best straight line through your plotted points with a ruler. Using a dashed line, extend this straight graph line so that it intersects the x-axis. Use your completed graph to help you answer the following questions.

Questions

1. At what temperature does your extended graph line intersect the x-axis?

2. a. What would be the volume of your gas sample at that temperature?
   b. Why is that predicted volume only a theoretical value?

3. Renumber the temperature scale on your graph, assigning the value "zero" to the temperature at which your plotted graph line intersects the x-axis. The new scale now expresses temperature in *kelvins* (K), the **kelvin temperature scale.** One kelvin is the same size as one degree Celsius. However, unlike zero degrees Celsius, zero kelvins is the lowest temperature theoretically possible. It is called **absolute zero.**

4. Based on your graph,
   a. what temperature in kelvins (K) would correspond to 0 °C, the freezing point of water?
   b. what kelvin temperature would correspond to 100 °C, the normal boiling point of water?

Expected Results

Temperature–length data will yield reasonably linear graphs. Laboratory data have led to a median extrapolated temperature of −280 °C at zero volume, compared to an "expected" value of −273 °C.

Data Analysis

1. Students should make an x-y scatter plot with axes properly incremented and labeled.

2. Students should draw a visual trend line that extends beyond plotted data to intercept the x-axis.

Answers

1. Answers will vary, but will be close to −273 °C.

2. a. Zero milliliters (0 mL).
   b. The answer was obtained by extrapolation. We assume that the gas behaves consistently as temperature decreases. Real gases condense to liquids before reaching absolute zero.

3. Students should re-label their graphs showing temperature in kelvins (no answer required).

4. a. 273 K.
   b. 373 K. Answers may vary based on student graphs, but will be close to these values.

Post-Lab Discussion

Focus on student results. Use lab data to discuss the kelvin temperature scale. Students may have heard of *absolute zero*. Explore the meaning of absolute zero in terms of molecular motion and the volume of a sample of ideal gas at that temperature.

This may be a good time to introduce percent error calculations. Percent error = [|experimental value − actual value|/actual value] × 100. Generally, students are within 10% of −273 °C or can account for data-gathering errors. You may decide to pool class data to illustrate "improving" results by averaging several trials.

to the oil plug. Check student data tables before the investigation.

Lab Tips

• Heat corn oil to 130 °C (not higher) in a small deep-fry appliance or in a beaker on a hot plate. Only use a deep-fry appliance dedicated to non-food laboratory settings. Since hot oil can be hazardous, use one oil bath (under your personal control) for the entire class. Maintain oil temperature as close to

130 °C as possible. Remind students to read and follow the investigation's procedure and cautions carefully to avoid burns from hot oil.
• Capillary tubes should be fully immersed in oil for optimal results.
• If they follow procedure, students will record temperature–length data over at least a 90 °C to 100 °C range. This is necessary to provide good data points for extrapolation to zero volume.

A.11 Temperature–Volume Behavior of Gases

Students' previous data help establish the relationship between gas volume and kelvin temperature at constant pressure. When the absolute (kelvin) temperature of a gas sample increases, its volume will increase by the same proportion, if pressure is constant. This relationship is Charles' law, $V/T = k$ or $V_1/T_1 = V_2/T_2$, where gas temperatures are expressed in kelvins.

Take time to review and compare graphs of Charles' law (direct relationship) and Boyle's law (inverse relationship).

A.11 Supplement: Charles' Law

Using the Figures

Figure 4.20: Ask students to explain why a hot-air balloon rises. The caption suggests that *T* and *V* both play roles. One less-obvious aspect of hot-air balloons is that they are *not* closed systems. The total gas molecules inside a balloon vary over its flight. As air is heated, the balloon volume expands (as mentioned in the caption); some gas molecules exit the balloon. The gas density inside the balloon thus becomes lower than air density outside the balloon, and the balloon rises.

Once students understand why balloons rise, ask them to explain what happens when gas inside the balloon is allowed to cool. Further discussion could link hot-air balloon behavior to KMT. Specifically, consider how or why pressures inside and outside of a hot-air balloon remain equalized, while temperatures change and molecules are lost and gained within the balloon.

Figure 4.20 *The gas held in hot-air balloons expands when heated.*

Figure 4.21
Temperature–volume measurements of various gas samples at 1.0 atm pressure. Extrapolation has been made for temperatures below liquefaction.

Volume (L) vs. Temperature (°C); $T = -273\,°C$; lines labeled 10.0 g N$_2$, 10.0 g O$_2$, 5.0 g N$_2$, 5.0 g O$_2$.

A.11 TEMPERATURE–VOLUME BEHAVIOR OF GASES

Your plotted data from the preceding laboratory investigation should indicate the relationship between volume and temperature for a sample of gas at constant pressure. The volume–temperature relationship for gases was also demonstrated in Activity 2 (page 306), when you placed the two balloons of equal size into water baths of differing temperatures. As you observed, increasing or decreasing the temperature of a gas sample produces changes in its volume (Figure 4.20).

In the 1780s, French chemists (and hot-air balloonists) Jacques Charles and Joseph Gay-Lussac studied the changes in gas volume caused by temperature changes at constant pressure. Data for oxygen gas and nitrogen gas are shown in Figure 4.21. The plots for different gases and different sample sizes have different appearances. However, if all the graph lines are smoothly extended down to the *x*-axis (an extrapolation), the lines meet at the same low temperature. Lord Kelvin (an English scientist) used the work of Charles and Gay-Lussac to establish a simple mathematical temperature–volume relationship for gases, known as *Charles' law*. Lord Kelvin based his own new temperature scale on this relationship.

Doubling the kelvin temperature of a gas sample doubles its volume at constant pressure and amount of gas. Lowering the kelvin temperature in half causes the gas sample to decrease to one-half of its original volume, and so on. These relationships are summarized in **Charles' law.** At constant pressure and amount of gas, the volume (*V*) of a gas sample divided by its temperature in kelvins (*T*) is always a constant value:

$$\frac{V}{T} = k$$

where *k* is a constant. This is true even when the temperature and volume of that same sample of gas are changed, as long as pressure and amount of gas are kept constant:

$$\frac{V_2}{T_2} = k$$

Additional Information

Jacques Charles, after whom Charles' law is named, was a French chemist and also an avid hot-air balloonist. Charles invented and launched the first hydrogen balloon in 1783. Peasants attacked one of Charles' balloons as it landed because they did not know what it was.

Demonstration Ideas

• A way to provide additional data to verify the *T*–*V* relationship for gases is to measure the circumference (and calculate the volume, if desired) of an inflated balloon at hot, cold, and room temperatures.
• The April 2002 *ChemMatters* provides directions for building a hot-air balloon from

Because both expressions are equal to the same value (k), a temperature–volume relationship can be expressed between the initial and final state of the gas sample:

$$\frac{V_1}{T_1} = \frac{V_2}{T_2}$$

This expression of Charles' law is useful in predicting changes in gas volume and temperature at constant pressure and amount of gas.

A.12 PREDICTING GAS BEHAVIOR: TEMPERATURE–VOLUME

Apply Charles' law to answer the following questions. For some questions, it may be necessary to convert temperatures to kelvins.

$$K = °C + 273$$

1. What would happen to a balloon's volume, originally at 20 °C, if you took the balloon outdoors in a temperature of 40 °C? Assume that pressure is constant and the balloon does not allow any gas to escape.

2. In planning to administer a gaseous anesthetic to a patient,

   a. why must the anesthesiologist take into account the fact that during surgery the gaseous anesthetic is used both at room temperature (18 °C) and at the patient's body temperature (37 °C)?

   b. what problems might arise if the anesthesiologist did not allow for the patient's higher body temperature?

3. An air bubble trapped in bread dough at room temperature (291 K) has a volume of 1.0 mL. The bread bakes in the oven at 623 K (350 °C):

   a. Predict whether the air-bubble volume will increase or decrease as the bread bakes. Explain your prediction, using kinetic molecular theory.

   b. Calculate the new volume of the air bubble, using Charles' law. (*Hint:* Remember that Charles' law only applies to temperatures expressed in kelvins.)

4. You buy a 3.0-L helium balloon in a mall and place it in a car sitting in hot summer sunlight. The temperature in the air-conditioned mall was 22 °C, and the temperature inside the closed car is 45 °C:

   a. What will you observe happening to the balloon as it sits in the warm car?

   b. What will be the new volume of the balloon?

   c. Sketch two illustrations that depict the helium atoms in the balloon, one when the balloon was in the mall and one when it is in the car.

   d. Explain your illustrations, using kinetic molecular theory.

tissue paper. Allowing students to build their own is time consuming; you can build one for demonstration in several hours and use it for years with minor maintenance. Alternatively, you may invite students to build hot-air balloons as a project outside of class and conduct a launch during class. *Caution:* Only launch balloons outdoors in calm conditions and tether them securely with string.

A.12 Predicting Gas Behavior: Temperature–Volume

Remind students to use kelvin temperatures in their calculations. You may discuss implications of using very low (negative)

Celsius temperatures in these calculations ("negative" volumes can arise). Remind them that all exercises assume constant pressure. You may work through a few examples before assigning questions to students or student groups.

Answers

1. Gas V, and thus balloon V, will increase by 313 K/293 K, indicating a direct relationship.

2. a. Due to the direct relationship of gas V and T, the anesthetic gas volume would be greater inside the patient's body at the higher temperature. When the gas enters the body, its volume will increase by 310 K/291K.

   b. This could change the rate of anesthesia flow into the lungs and could result in an incorrect patient dose.

3. a. The volume will increase. An increase in T raises the average kinetic energy of the gas particles. The particles move more quickly and collide more frequently with the inside surface of the bubble, which increases the volume.

   b. $V_2 = 1.0$ mL $\times$ 623 K/291 K = 2.1 mL

4. a. The volume of the balloon increases; the air temperature in the car is greater than the air temperature in the mall. The balloon may burst.

   b. $V_1/V_2 = T_1/T_2$
   $V_2 = V_1 \times T_2/T_1 = 3.0$ L $\times$ 318 K/295 K = 3.2 L

   c. Sketches should show the same total gas molecules in both balloons. The molecules in the mall balloon should move more slowly and be closer together, while molecules in the car balloon move faster and are farther apart. Students may show motion in various ways, including with arrows or lines. The car balloon should be noticeably larger than the mall balloon.

d. As gas temperature increases, the average molecular speed increases, causing more collisions with the balloon walls and increasing the balloon's volume.

A.13 Temperature–Pressure Behavior of Gases

Students are challenged to use their knowledge of Boyle's law and Charles' law to predict the relationship between gas temperature and pressure. Ask students to consider the balloon examples and previous exercises and then imagine that the balloon's volume was constrained by a rigid container. Ask what the effect would be of increased gas temperature in this situation. Students should reason that since the volume could not increase in response to the faster molecules and increased collisions, the gas pressure within the balloon or container would increase.

Since the average kinetic energies of gas molecules increase with an increase in temperature, gas pressure will increase with increasing temperature. Thus, if volume is held constant, the pressure of a gas sample is directly proportional to its kelvin temperature. This relationship is called Gay-Lussac's law and can be expressed as $P/T = k$ or $P_1/T_1 = P_2/T_2$.

Encourage students to reason through the exercises qualitatively before they apply gas-law formulas.

 A.13 Pressure–Temperature Relationships

Using the Figures

Figure 4.22: Students can answer the question in the caption based on their understanding of the relationship between gas temperature and pressure. Encourage them to think beyond this basic relationship and incorporate KMT in their answers.

Figure 4.22 *Scuba divers in the Arctic ocean (top) and in the tropics (bottom). Assuming the cylinders are of equal volume and contain the same amount of gas, which of the cylinder pressure-gauge readings will be higher?*

A.13 TEMPERATURE–PRESSURE BEHAVIOR OF GASES

Picture a closed cylinder of gas, such as a deep-sea scuba tank where volume is constant. See Figure 4.22. What would happen to the average kinetic energy of gas molecules in the cylinder if you were to heat the tank? How would this affect the gas pressure?

If you concluded that raising the kelvin temperature of the gas at constant volume should cause an increase in gas pressure, you are correct. Increasing temperature increases the average kinetic energy (and thus average velocity) of gas molecules. Because the molecules, on average, are traveling faster, the number of molecular collisions with the container walls increases, and the energy involved in each collision also increases. These effects cause a corresponding increase in gas pressure. The mathematical expression for this relationship is

$$\frac{P}{T} = k$$

where k is a constant. Particular changes in gas pressure and temperature at constant volume can be found, using this equation:

$$\frac{P_1}{T_1} = \frac{P_2}{T_2}$$

You can also reason out an answer using your understanding of the temperature–pressure relationship. For calculations, remember that all gas temperatures must be expressed in kelvins.

Developing Skills

A.14 USING GAS RELATIONSHIPS

Solve the following problems, using appropriate gas relationships:

1. a. If the kelvin temperature of a gas sample held in a steel tank increases to three times its original value, predict what will happen to the pressure of the gas. Will it increase or decrease? By what factor do you expect the gas pressure to change?
   b. Draw two molecular models that represent the movement of gas molecules inside the tank at the two temperatures.
   c. Explain your models, using kinetic molecular theory.

2. A gas sample at a constant pressure shrinks to one-fourth its initial volume. What must have happened to its temperature? Did it increase or decrease? By what factor did the kelvin temperature of the gas change?

3. Explain why automobile owners in severe northern climates often add air to their tires in the wintertime and release some air from the same tires in the summertime.

Developing Skills

A.14 Using Gas Relationships

In this activity students apply the gas laws studied so far to the behavior of gases.

Answers

1. a. Increase by a factor of three.

b. Models should show equal numbers of particles in motion; the motion in the higher-temperature condition should be three times that in the cooler tank.

c. As temperature increases, the average molecular motion of the molecules increases. This increases both the number of gas-molecule collisions and the force of those collisions, resulting in increased gas pressure.

4. Use kinetic molecular theory and gas laws to explain why a weather balloon expands in size as it rises from Earth's surface.

5. Why does the label on an aerosol container caution you not to dispose of the container in a fire?

A.15 NONIDEAL GAS BEHAVIOR

All gas relationships considered up to now have related to *ideal gases.* That is, a gas sample that behaves under all conditions as the kinetic molecular theory predicts is called an **ideal gas.** Most gas behavior approximates that of an ideal gas. Thus, such gas behavior is satisfactorily explained by the kinetic molecular theory. However, at very high gas pressures or at very low gas temperatures, real gases do not behave ideally. That is, the gas laws you have considered do not accurately describe gas behavior under such extreme conditions.

On average, gas molecules move slowly at very low temperatures. As their average kinetic energy decreases, the weak intermolecular attractive forces among molecules may become such a significant factor (when compared to their relative motions) that the gas condenses to a liquid, such as when air is liquefied. At very high gas pressures, if the temperature is not too high, gas molecules become so close together that these same weak forces of attraction may also cause the gas to condense to a liquid. These extreme temperature and pressure conditions are well beyond normal values for atmospheric gases.

A.16 UNDERSTANDING KINETIC MOLECULAR THEORY

Modeling Matter

Previously, you modeled the structure of matter and changes in matter using pictures and symbols. Another way that matter can be modeled is through the use of *analogies.* An analogy can help you relate certain features of an abstract idea or theory to a situation that is familiar to you. Read the analogy provided in the next paragraph and answer the questions that follow concerning the kinetic molecular theory of gases.

Imagine that you cause several highly elastic, small "super-bounce balls" to bounce around inside a box that you steadily shake; this serves as an analogy for gas molecules randomly bouncing around inside a sealed container. The balls bounce randomly around inside the box. See Figure 4.23.

Figure 4.23 *Super-bounce balls moving about randomly inside a box.*

1. Decide which of these four gas variables—*volume, temperature, pressure,* or *number of molecules*—best matches each of the following factors, and explain each choice:

  a. the number of super-bounce balls inside the box
  b. the size of the box
  c. the vigor with which you shake the box
  d. the number and force of collisions with the box walls of the randomly moving super-bounce balls

2. The absolute temperature (in kelvins) must decrease by a factor of four to cause a fourfold decrease in volume; the absolute temperature will be one-fourth its original value.

3. Car owners add air to their tires in winter because lower temperatures decrease the pressure of the enclosed air. More air molecules are needed to ensure proper tire pressure. Tire air is released when summer arrives because the pressure from the enclosed air increases as the temperature increases. Both underinflation and overinflation cause improper tire wear and contribute to decreased fuel efficiency.

4. When the balloon rises, the external pressure decreases, which causes the volume to increase. Temperature also decreases, which should cause the volume to decrease. Data in Table 4.2 (page 304) show that the pressure changes are larger than the temperature changes. Therefore, pressure changes (Boyle's law) predominate, and the balloon's volume will increase.

5. As the gas temperature in the can increases, the gas pressure will also increase, possibly causing the can to explode. (There is more to the story: At higher temperatures, more liquid propellant in the can vaporizes, causing major buildup of vapor pressure inside the can, well beyond what gas-law calculations would predict.)

A.15 Nonideal Gas Behavior

This section introduces the term *ideal gas* and describes conditions under which gases fail to behave ideally (high pressure and/or low temperature). The text analyzes reasons for nonideal gas behavior. Emphasize that real gases are never ideal, but their behavior under most normal conditions approximates ideal behavior—thus we can confidently apply the ideal gas law and KMT.

Modeling Matter

A.16 Understanding Kinetic Molecular Theory

Students answer questions comparing a box of "super-bounce balls" to gas molecules.

   A.16 Understanding Kinetic Molecular Student Worksheet

Answers

1. a. Number of molecules
   b. Volume
   c. Temperature
   d. Pressure

SECTION A

2. a. This is similar to Boyle's law—at constant temperature (speed of shaking) and number of particles (super-bounce balls) if the volume (box size) decreases, the pressure (total ball collisions) increases.

b. This situation illustrates Gay-Lussac's law (pressure and temperature are directly related). If the volume (box size) and the number of particles (super-bounce balls) remain constant, while the temperature (speed of shaking) increases, pressure (ball collisions) increases.

c. If volume (box size) and temperature (speed of shaking) are constant, but the number of molecules (super-bounce balls) increases, the pressure (ball collisions) increases.

3. Answers will vary. Example: The size of the box (volume) and the number of super-bounce balls (number of particles) remain the same, but the speed of shaking (temperature) decreases. (Many other answers are possible.)

4. Answers will vary. Example: The extremely small size of gas molecules relative to the total volume of the gas sample and the *relative* sizes of molecules and the space between them.

5. Analogies and answers will vary. Other analogies may include people dancing on a dance floor (dancers = gas molecules, beat of music = temperature, collisions of dancers = pressure, size of dance floor = volume).

A.17 Ideal Gases and Molar Volume

This material explores the effect of sample size (number of molecules) on gas behavior and introduces Avogadro's law. Avogadro concluded, based on experimental evidence,

326

---

2. How does each of the following changes relate to what you have learned about gases and the kinetic molecular theory?
 a. The vigor of shaking and the number of super-bounce balls remain the same, but the size of the box is decreased.
 b. The size of the box and the number of super-bounce balls remain the same, but the shaking becomes more vigorous.
 c. The size of the container and the vigor of shaking are kept the same, but the number of super-bounce balls is increased.

3. Suggest another situation similar to those in Question 2 that can serve as an analogy for the behavior of gases. Explain.

4. All analogies have limitations. For example, the super-bounce ball analogy fails to represent certain characteristics of gases. Gas molecules travel at *very* high velocities (on the order of 6000 km/h), while the super-bounce balls move much more slowly (on the order of 1 km/h). Suggest two other characteristics of actual gases that are not properly represented by this super-bounce ball analogy.

5. Describe your own analogy that might be useful for modeling gas behavior.
 a. Identify features of your analogy that relate to features of the kinetic molecular theory and T–V–P relationships for gases.
 b. Point out some key limitations of your analogy.

A.17 IDEAL GASES AND MOLAR VOLUME

Thus far, you have considered gas behavior under differing conditions of volume, pressure, and temperature. One variable that you have not yet fully considered is the actual *amount* of the gas sample; that is, the number of gas molecules contained in a particular sample. If you have the same volumes of oxygen gas, nitrogen gas, and carbon dioxide gas in three different balloons at the same temperature and pressure, how do the numbers of gas molecules compare? See Figure 4.24.

That same question was investigated in the early 1800s by the Italian lawyer and mathematical physics professor Amedeo Avogadro. By making careful observations of gas samples

6000 km/h nearly equals 10 000 mph; 1 km/h is about 2 mph.

Figure 4.24 *These three equally sized balloons contain three different gases at the same temperature and pressure. Are the total gas molecules in each balloon the same or different?*

like those you have worked with, he proposed: *Equal volumes of all gases at the same temperature and pressure contain the same number of molecules.* This important statement is commonly known as **Avogadro's law.**

One useful consequence of Avogadro's law is that *all* gases have equal molar volumes if they are measured at the same temperature and pressure. The **molar volume** is the volume occupied by one mole of a substance. At conditions of 0 °C and 1 atm, the molar volume of *any* gas sample is 22.4 L. (See Figure 4.25.) There is no similar simple relationship between moles of various solids or liquids and their corresponding volumes.

> Avogadro's complete name was Lorenzo Romano Amedeo Carlo Avogadro, conte di Quaregna e di Cerreto.

> The conditions of 0 °C and 1 atm are known as standard temperature and pressure (STP).

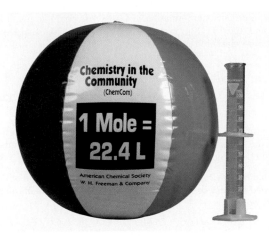

Figure 4.25 *This beach ball contains one mole of gas.*

The realization that all gases have the same molar volume under the same conditions greatly simplifies our thinking about chemical reactions involving gases. For example, consider the following chemical equations that involve gaseous reactions:

$$N_2(g) + O_2(g) \longrightarrow 2\ NO(g)$$

$$2\ H_2(g) + O_2(g) \longrightarrow 2\ H_2O(g)$$

You have learned that coefficients in chemical equations indicate the relative numbers of molecules or moles of reactants and products. Based on Avogadro's law, similar calculations can also involve *volumes* of gaseous reactants and products.

Hence, the first equation above can now be interpreted: 1 volume of $N_2(g)$ and 1 volume of $O_2(g)$ combine to form 2 volumes of $NO(g)$, assuming all gases were measured at the same conditions of temperature and pressure. Based on this information, consider the sample problem at the top of the next page.

Section A   Gases in the Atmosphere   **327**

that equal volumes of gases at the same temperature and pressure contain the same number of molecules. This law permits direct calculation of gas stoichiometry using gas volumes. Since any gas will have the same number of molecules in a given volume, liters or other volume measurements can be substituted for the stoichiometric coefficients in a chemical equation. So, given that $2\ H_2(g) + O_2(g) \rightarrow 2\ H_2O(g)$, possible interpretations include:

2 molecules H_2 and 1 molecule O_2 react to form 2 molecules H_2O.

2 moles H_2 and 1 mole O_2 react to form 2 moles H_2O.

2 L H_2 and 1 L O_2 react to form 2 L H_2O (all measured at the same *T* and *P*).

2 mL H_2 and 1 mL O_2 react to form 2 mL H_2O (all measured at the same *T* and *P*).

Students read that the molar volume of a gas at STP, 22.4 L, is the volume of one mole of *any* gas at 0 °C and 1 atm. These conditions are referred to as standard temperature and pressure (STP). You might stress that 22.4 L is the molar volume for helium, chlorine, methane, propane, argon, and *any other gas* at STP, regardless of its formula. A natural useful extension of this concept is to calculate gas density at STP using the following formula:

Density (any gas at STP) = molar mass of gas/22.4 L

Using the Figures

Figure 4.25: If you own a *ChemCom* molar beach ball, or a similarly sized beach ball, have students verify its volume with the equation for a volume of a sphere: $4/3\pi r^3$.

Some generalizations about gas behavior:

- The physical properties of all gases are nearly the same, provided gas temperature is not too low and pressure is not too high.
- Avogadro's law and molar volume simplify monitoring gaseous reactions by measuring the volumes of gases involved. This simplification is based on the fact that (at constant T and P) gas volume is directly proportional to the amount of gas (in moles).
- Volumes of gaseous reactants and products can be used in place of moles in problems, if T and P remain constant.
- An ideal gas is one whose molecules occupy no volume and where there is no attraction among molecules. Real gases at STP can behave nearly ideally because their molecules are relatively far apart. When gases are under high pressure and/or low temperature, their molecules approach each other and no longer act ideally.

Hint: 22.4 L of gas is about the volume of three basketballs—a standard NBA basketball, radius = 11.9 cm, has a volume of just over 7 L.

Demonstration Idea

Construct a box 28.2 cm × 28.2 cm × 28.2 cm, or purchase a beach ball (or other ball with a radius of 17.5 cm), and label it "1 mole of any gas at STP = 22.4 L," or display a *ChemCom* molar beach ball (see **Figure 4.25,** page 327). As a project, you could ask students to design, create, and decorate their own "molar volume" gas containers.

Sample Problem 1: *What volume (in liters) of NO(g) is produced as 3 L N_2(g) and 3 L O_2(g) react? See equation, page 327.*

Because the amounts of both the reactants have tripled, the amount of product will also be tripled: 6 L NO(g) will be produced.

Similar relationships hold for the volumes of all gaseous reactants and products. Using Avogadro's law, you can interpret the coefficients in terms of gas volumes:

$$1 \text{ volume } N_2(g) + 1 \text{ volume } O_2(g) \longrightarrow 2 \text{ volumes } NO(g)$$

$$2 \text{ volumes } H_2(g) + 1 \text{ volume } O_2(g) \longrightarrow 2 \text{ volumes } H_2O(g)$$

The measured volumes could be expressed in any convenient units, such as liters (L) or cubic centimeters (cm^3). In the second equation, which represents the formation of water, you could combine 200.0 L H_2(g) and 100.0 L O_2(g) and expect to produce 200.0 L H_2O(g), if all gases were measured at the same conditions. Note that, unlike mass,

Figure 4.26 *Two volumes H_2(g) combine with one volume O_2(g) to form two volumes H_2O(g).*

gas volumes are *not* necessarily conserved in a chemical reaction. Using the second equation, note that 200 L + 100 L of reactants generates 200 L of product, and *not* 300 L. See Figure 4.26.

Sample Problem 2: *In the following equation, what volume of C_2H_6(g) is needed to produce 12 L CO_2(g)? All measurements are at the same temperature.*

$$2 \, C_2H_6(g) + 7 \, O_2(g) \longrightarrow 4 \, CO_2(g) + 6 \, H_2O(g)$$

From the chemical equation, we know that 2 L C_2H_6(g) will produce 4 L CO_2(g). If we want to produce 12 L of CO_2(g), which is three times more than is represented in the equation, then we must start with *three times* as much C_2H_6(g); that is, 6 L C_2H_6(g).

Sample Problem 3: *Using this same scenario, how many liters of O_2(g) would be needed to produce 12 L CO_2(g)? Think through this question and make a prediction.*

Problems such as this can also be solved using ratios made from coefficients from the balanced equation. If we know from the previous equation that

$$7 \text{ L } O_2(g) \longrightarrow 4 \text{ L } CO_2(g)$$

and we want to know how many liters O_2(g) are needed to produce 12 L CO_2, we can set up a conversion factor to solve for the answer:

$$? \text{ L } O_2 = 12 \text{ L } \cancel{CO_2} \times \frac{7 \text{ L } O_2}{4 \text{ L } \cancel{CO_2}} = 21 \text{ L } O_2$$

According to this calculation, 21 L O_2(g) are needed to produce 12 L CO_2(g). Was your prediction correct?

These volume relationships allow chemists to monitor gaseous reactions by measuring the gas volumes involved. In the activity that follows, you have an opportunity to check your understanding of this concept.

A.18 MOLAR VOLUME AND REACTIONS OF GASES

Developing Skills

1. What volume would be occupied by 3 mol $CO_2(g)$ at 0 °C and 1 atm?

2. In a certain gaseous reaction, 2 mol NO react with 1 mol O_2:

$$2 NO(g) + O_2(g) \longrightarrow 2 NO_2(g)$$

22.4 L = 1 mol of any gas at 0 °C and 1 atm (see Figure 4.25, page 327).

   a. Given the same conditions of temperature and pressure, what volume of $O_2(g)$ would react with 4 L NO gas?
   b. How might chemists use their knowledge of molar volumes to monitor the progress of this reaction?

3. Toxic carbon monoxide (CO) gas is produced when fossil fuels, such as gasoline, burn without sufficient oxygen gas. The CO can eventually be converted to CO_2 in the atmosphere. Automobile catalytic converters are designed to speed up this conversion:

   Carbon monoxide gas + Oxygen gas $\longrightarrow$ Carbon dioxide gas

   a. Write the balanced equation for this conversion.
   b. How many moles of oxygen gas would be needed to convert 50.0 mol carbon monoxide to carbon dioxide?
   c. What volume of oxygen gas would be needed to react with 968 L CO? (Assume both gases are at the same temperature and pressure.)

A.19 THE IDEAL GAS LAW

Starting on page 316, you learned about the relationship between the pressure and volume of an ideal gas sample when its temperature is held constant (Boyle's law). Similarly, you are now familiar with the relationship between the temperature and volume of an ideal gas sample (Charles' law) and the relationship between the amount of gas (in moles) and the volume of the gas sample (Avogadro's law).

In 1834, a more general relationship—the **ideal gas law**—was derived from these experimentally based laws of researchers such as Boyle and Charles. All of the variables represented in the laws of Boyle, Charles, and Avogadro are included in the ideal gas law:

$$P \times V = n \times R \times T \quad \text{or} \quad PV = nRT$$

where P = pressure, V = volume, n = moles (amount) of gas, R = a constant, and T = temperature.

✍ A.18 Supplement: Molar Volume

Developing Skills

A.18 Molar Volume and Reactions of Gases

This activity helps reinforce a practical consequence of Avogadro's law: If all gases (at the same T and P) have the same molar volume, then in a chemical reaction involving gases, the coefficients indicate the relative volumes of reactants and products as well as the relative number of moles.

Answers

1. 3.0 mol $CO_2 \times$ 22.4 L/1 mol $CO_2 =$ 67 L CO_2

2. a. The ratio of moles NO to moles O_2 is 2:1; therefore, the ratio of liters NO to liters O_2 is also 2:1. 2 L O_2 would react with 4 L NO.

$$\text{vol } O_2 = 4 \text{ L NO} \times \frac{1 \text{ L } O_2}{2 \text{ L NO}} = 2 \text{ L } O_2$$

   b. In the given system, there are 2 mol total products for every 3 mol total reactants. Thus, for every 3 L reactants, 2 L products result. As the reaction progresses, the volume of the system should decrease according to this relationship.

3. a. $2 CO(g) + O_2(g) \rightarrow 2 CO_2(g)$
   b. 50 mol CO $\times$ 1 mol O_2/2 mol CO = 25 mol O_2
   c. 968 L CO $\times$ 1 L O_2/2 L CO = 484 L O_2

A.19 The Ideal Gas Law

Here we consider combining all gas laws introduced in Section A—Boyle's, Charles', Gay-Lussac's, and Avogadro's—to derive the ideal gas law, the familiar $PV = nRT$. This encourages students to consider the role of amount (moles) of gas in predictions and calculations of ideal gas behavior. The value of the gas constant, R, is calculated from standard conditions as 0.0821 atm $\times$ L/(mol $\times$ K). R is also equal to 8.314 J/(mol $\times$ K).

Using the Figures

Figure 4.27: The question posed in this caption is a good exercise in synthesizing everything students have learned within this section. Among other variables they may identify, ask them if the *type* (identity) of the gas is important for solving this quantitative question (remind them of what they learned in A.18).

Figure 4.28: It is likely that students will correctly predict that the gas pressure inside the light bulb increases after it is turned on. Ask them how this phenomenon may influence the engineering of light bulbs. Section A Summary Question 11 challenges students with a related calculation.

Developing Skills

A.20 Using the Ideal Gas Law

This activity gives students practice using the ideal gas law. Remind students to use temperatures in kelvins.

Answers

1. $V = 0.50$ L, $P = 10.0$ atm,
   $T = 298$ K
   $n = PV/RT =$

   $$\frac{10.0 \text{ atm } \times 0.50 \text{ L}}{0.0821 \text{ L atm/mol K} \times 298 \text{ K}} =$$

   0.20 mol

2. $V = nRT/P =$

   $$\frac{2.0 \text{ mol} \times 0.0821 \dfrac{\text{L atm}}{\text{mol}} \text{K} \times 313 \text{ K}}{0.50 \text{ atm}} =$$

   100 L

3. a. The volume of gas in a flexible container changes with pressure and temperature.

   b. Liquids and solids are essentially incompressible and do not expand/contract very much on heating/cooling, so temperature and pressure do not have much effect on their volume.

330

Figure 4.27 *What would you need to know to estimate the number of molecules of gas inside this blimp?*

Figure 4.28 *Incandescent light bulbs are filled with inert (unreactive) gas. When the light is turned on, what will happen to the gas pressure inside the bulb? Why?*

As you probably noticed, the ideal gas law contains a constant (R). Before using this equation on page 329, we must find the value of the constant. Recall (see page 327) that the volume of one mole of any ideal gas at 1.00 atm and 0 °C is equal to 22.4 L. Substituting this information into the ideal gas law will allow us to find the value of R:

$$1.00 \text{ atm} \times 22.4 \text{ L} = 1.00 \text{ mol} \times R \times 273 \text{ K}$$

$$R = 1.00 \text{ atm} \times \frac{22.4 \text{ L}}{1.00 \text{ mol}} \times \left(\frac{1}{273 \text{ K}}\right)$$

$$R = 0.0821 \frac{\text{atm} \times \text{L}}{\text{mol} \times \text{K}}$$

The value of the constant, R, depends on the units in which pressure, volume, temperature, and amount of gas are expressed. The value of R given in the previous calculations is used when pressure is expressed in atmospheres, volume is measured in liters, temperature is expressed in kelvins, and amount of gas is expressed in moles.

Under particular circumstances, the ideal gas law can be reduced to each of the gas laws upon which it is based. Boyle discovered that for a gas sample at constant temperature, the product of its measured pressure (P) and volume (V) remains the same, or

$$P \times V = k$$

In this case, a relationship between pressure and volume is apparent if both the temperature and the amount of gas are kept constant. Consider these variables as you reexamine the ideal gas law:

$$P \times V = n \times R \times T$$

If n and T are both held constant, then the product $n \times R \times T$ must also be equal to a constant value. In other words, the equation could be rewritten as

$$P \times V = k$$

330   **Unit 4**   Air: Chemistry and the Atmosphere

✍ **A.19 Supplement: Ideal Gas Law**

The ideal gas law can be similarly simplified to Charles' law (when P and n are held constant), and to Avogadro's law (when P and T are held constant). However, holding certain variables constant is not always possible when working in the laboratory with gas samples. The ideal gas law is useful if you know the values of any three of the gas variables (P, V, n, or T) and seek to find the fourth value. See Figures 4.27 and 4.28.

A.20 USING THE IDEAL GAS LAW

Developing Skills

Solve the following problems, using the ideal gas law equation.

1. A 0.50-L canister of hazardous sarin gas was discovered at an old, abandoned military installation. To properly dispose of this gas, technicians must know how much gas is held in the canister. The gas pressure is measured as 10.0 atm at room temperature (25 °C). How many moles of sarin are held inside the canister?

2. What volume will 2.0 mol $H_2(g)$ occupy at 40.0 °C and 0.50 atm pressure?

3. When the volume of a gas sample is measured, its pressure and temperature must also be specified.
   a. Why?
   b. That practice is normally not necessary in measuring the volumes of liquids or solids. Why?

> Sarin is considered a very toxic substance. It prevents chemical signals from being properly transmitted between nerve cells.

A.21 PREPARING TO EXPLORE BUS-IDLING POLICY

Making Decisions

At the start of this unit, you learned about the new school bus-idling policy at Riverwood High School (see Figure 4.29, page 332). You have been assigned to write an article detailing facts, benefits, and drawbacks of this school policy. Thus far, you have learned how gas behavior is influenced by various conditions related to gas temperature and pressure. Now you are prepared to investigate the school bus-idling policy and the concerns and opinions voiced by those quoted at the opening of this unit (see page 300).

In the following sections, you will learn about air pollutants and air-quality concerns. In preparing to write your article, it will be helpful to decide what aspects of this policy you intend to investigate and what questions you have *prior* to obtaining further information on the policy.

1. In your group, revisit the opening of this unit, and reread the statements of Principal Powers and others about the school bus-idling policy. Generate a table of *tentative* benefits and drawbacks of the new policy as claimed by these statements. Keep in mind that the information included in those statements has not yet been verified.

Making Decisions

A.21 Preparing to Explore Bus-Idling Policy

Ask each student group to generate lists of benefits and drawbacks to the new policy, as well as questions related to any factual statements made on pages 300–301. Remind students that those statements remain to be verified; they should not accept them at face value. Encourage students to think of themselves as critical reporters with the job of authenticating what they have "been told" in these interviews. Students should use this activity to share ideas, within their groups, about how to develop their features.

Answers

1. Possible answers include:

   Benefits
   Improved student health
   Improved environmental quality
   Lowered acid rain, ozone depletion, global warming

   Drawbacks
   Expensive to stop and start a vehicle
   Buses will be cold

2. Questions might include
How does bus exhaust affect health?
How does bus exhaust affect the environment?
Will shutting off the buses really make a difference?
Does it cost more money to stop and start a vehicle than to just keep it running?

3. Categories may include health, environment, cost, and personal comfort.

SECTION A SUMMARY

 Section A Supplement

Reviewing the Concepts

1. N_2, 78.08%; O_2, 20.95%; Ar, 0.93%; CO_2, 0.033%

2. Solution, because it is homogeneous. (Students may also state that this mixture does not show the Tyndall effect.)

3. Sketches should show the troposphere, stratosphere, mesosphere, and thermosphere in order from Earth's surface.

4. a. No.
b. The chemical composition of Earth's atmosphere is about the same today as in ancient air trapped in glacial ice. Many types of preserved samples indicate that air composition has not changed significantly.

5. Answers may include: Temperature decreases, increases, and then decreases again. Pressure decreases. The mass of a 1-L sample decreases. The number of molecules in a 1-L sample decreases. (Composition generally remains constant. Students should not indicate a change in composition.)

Figure 4.29 *What are some benefits and drawbacks of the new school bus-idling policy?*

2. Review the benefits and drawbacks summarized in your group's table, and identify questions you have about this table and the statements upon which it is based. As a group, list at least five factual questions you plan to explore to verify interview statements. Some typical questions might be: *What emissions are typically found in bus exhaust? How, if at all, does bus exhaust affect human health?*

3. Once you have completed Steps 1 and 2, select one group representative to share your list of questions with the class. Listen carefully to the questions generated by the other groups, and see if you detect similarities among them. Guided by your teacher, identify major categories and topics within which questions fall.

Later in this unit, you will learn about many of the topics and questions you have identified in this activity. It is likely that you will also consult sources other than this textbook as you seek answers to questions you have posed in preparing to write your article.

In the next section, you will learn how radiation from the Sun interacts with gases in the atmosphere to maintain a habitable climate on Earth. Learning about the natural processes involved in maintaining Earth's climate will provide you with further insight into benefits or drawbacks of the school bus-idling policy at Riverwood High School. It will also enable you to better evaluate the concerns and opinions expressed by individuals interviewed at the opening of this unit.

SECTION A SUMMARY
Reviewing the Concepts

Earth's atmosphere is composed of a mixture of gases.

1. List the percent values of the four most plentiful gases found in the atmosphere.

2. Is the mixture of gases in the atmosphere considered a solution, a suspension, or a colloid? (*Hint:* See Figure 1.24, page 30.) Explain your answer.

3. Sketch and label four layers of the atmosphere.

4. a. Has the atmosphere's composition changed significantly throughout human history?
   b. What evidence can you cite to support your answer?

5. List three changes in the atmosphere as altitude increases from sea level upward.

Pressure involves a force applied over a particular area. Air pressure is often expressed in units of atmospheres (atm), kilopascals (kPa), or millimeters of mercury (mmHg).

6. It is much easier to slice a piece of pie with the edge of a sharp knife than with the edge of a pencil. Explain this observation in terms of applied pressure.

7. U.S. weather reports generally express air pressure in units of inches of mercury. During a severe storm, the barometric pressure can drop to as low as 27.2 inches of mercury. Convert this air-pressure value to
   a. millimeters of mercury (mmHg).
      (*Hint:* 1 inch = 25.4 mm)
   b. atmospheres (atm).
   c. kilopascals (kPa).

8. Heavy vehicles that must move easily over loose sand are often equipped with special tires.
   a. Would you expect these tires to be wide or narrow?
   b. Explain your answer using the concept of pressure.

9. Which is more likely to cause damage to a wooden floor: A 1068-N (240-lb) basketball player in athletic shoes (floor-contact area = 420 cm^2) or a 534-N (120-lb) sports reporter standing in high heels (floor-contact area = 24 cm^2). Support your answer with suitable pressure calculations.

The volume of a sample of gas in a flexible, impermeable container will increase if external pressure is reduced and decrease if external pressure is increased.

10. Explain why a sealed bag of potato chips "puffs out" (increases in volume) when it is carried from sea level up to a high mountain pass.

11. A small quantity of the inert gas argon (Ar) is added to incandescent light bulbs to reduce vaporization of tungsten (W) atoms from the solid filament. What volume of argon gas measured at 760 mmHg is needed to fill a 0.21-L light bulb to a pressure of 1.30 mmHg? Assume the argon gas temperature remains constant.

12. If the same bag of potato chips (see Question 10) were carried under water by a scuba diver, what would happen to its volume as the sealed bag descended into deep water?

13. A party-supply store sells a helium-gas cylinder with a volume of 1.55×10^{-2} m^3. If the cylinder provides 1.81 m^3 of helium for balloon inflation (at STP), what must be the pressure inside the cylinder?

Section Summary   333

6. The applied force is exerted over a smaller area when using the knife, so pressure on the pie is greater with the sharp knife. Pressure = force/area.

7. a. 27.2 in Hg $\times \dfrac{25.4 \text{ mmHg}}{1 \text{ in Hg}} =$ 691 mmHg

   b. 691 mmHg $\times \dfrac{1 \text{ atm}}{760 \text{ mmHg}} =$ 0.910 atm

   c. 0.910 atm $\times \dfrac{101.325 \text{ kPa}}{1 \text{ atm}} =$ 92.1 kPa

8. a. Wide
   b. For a given force (the weight of the vehicle), a larger area will result in a smaller applied pressure. (The low pressure prevents the vehicle's wide tires from sinking into the sand.)

9. Pressure = Force/Area. For basketball player, Pressure = 1068 N/420 cm^2 = 2.54 N/cm^2. For sports reporter, Pressure = 534 N/24 cm^2 = 22 N/cm^2. The sports reporter in high heels will cause more damage.

10. The bag inflates while it moves upward from sea level because the pressure on the inside of the bag remains constant, while atmospheric pressure on the outside decreases.

11. $V_2 = 0.21$ L, $P_2 = 1.30$ mmHg, $P_1 = 760$ mmHg
    $V_1 = (P_2 V_2)/P_1 = (1.30 \text{ mmHg} \times 0.21 \text{ L})/760 \text{ mmHg} = 0.00036 \text{ L} = 0.36 \text{ mL}$

12. The bag would collapse (assuming T is constant).

13. $V_1 = 1.55 \times 10^{-2}$ m^3, $V_2 = 1.81$ m^3, $P_1 = $??, $P_2 = 1.00$ atm
    $P_1 = (P_2 V_2)/V_1 = (1.00 \text{ atm} \times 1.81 \text{ m}^3)/1.55 \times 10^{-2} \text{ m}^3 = 117 \text{ atm}$

14. $V_1 = 2.50$ L, $T_1 = 25 + 273 =$ 298 K, $T_2 = -5 + 273 = 268$ K $V_2 = V_1 T_2 / T_1 = (2.50$ L $\times$ 268 K$)/$ 298 K $= 2.25$ L

15. At a temperature close to absolute zero, the volume of gas approaches zero. A marshmallow, therefore, would look shrunken and wrinkled.

16. After driving for several hours, the temperature of air in the tire would increase from tire friction and flexing, resulting in an increase in pressure.

17. On cold days, the pressure of the air inside the ball would be less than it would be on warm days, if ball volume remains constant.

18. $T_1 = 299$ K, $P_1 = 1.92$ atm, $P_2 = 7.34$ atm $T_2 = 299$ K $\times$ 7.34 atm$/$ 1.92 atm $= 1140$ K

19. The change in volume would be by the factor 303 K/288 K, or about 1.05 times the original volume. Students may make the mistake of saying that the Celsius temperature doubles and, therefore, the pressure should also double.

20. a. Decreasing the volume means there is less space within which gas molecules can move. This means molecules will hit the walls more frequently per unit time, increasing gas pressure. b. At higher temperatures, the average kinetic energy of the molecules is greater because of their higher average velocities. This increased kinetic energy causes more energetic and frequent collisions with the walls and thus higher gas pressure.

The volume of a sample of gas in a flexible, impermeable container at constant pressure will increase if its temperature is increased and decrease if its temperature is decreased.

14. A 2.50-L balloon at 25 °C is inflated with helium. At constant pressure, the temperature of the balloon is then lowered to −5 °C. What will be the balloon's volume at this new temperature?

15. What do you think a marshmallow, composed mainly of small pockets of air, would look like at temperatures close to absolute zero? Explain your answer.

The pressure exerted by a sample of gas in a rigid, impermeable container will increase if its temperature is increased and decrease if its temperature is decreased.

16. Experts recommend measuring automobile tire pressure when the tires are cold rather than just after driving for several hours. Why?

17. Soccer players often notice that kicking the ball feels different on cold days compared to warm days. Explain why this might be so.

18. A steel tank at 299 K contains 0.285 L of nitrogen gas at 1.92 atm pressure. The tank will burst if its internal pressure exceeds 7.34 atm. At what temperature should the tank burst?

19. An oxygen gas sample in a rigid container is heated from 15 °C to 30 °C. By what factor will the oxygen gas pressure increase?

The kinetic molecular theory states that gases are composed of particles of negligible size that are in constant random motion and undergo elastic collisions. The average kinetic energy of a gas sample is directly related to its kelvin temperature.

20. Use the kinetic molecular theory to explain each of the following observations:
a. Decreasing the volume of a gas sample at constant temperature causes the gas pressure to increase.
b. At constant volume and constant amount of gas, the pressure of a gas sample changes if its temperature is changed.

21. Sketch the gas particles inside an inflated balloon submerged in
a. hot water.   b. ice water.

22. Think of a pool-table set up as a model (analogy) for gas behavior:
a. How would you use pool balls to demonstrate the effect of an increase in the temperature of a gas sample?
b. How would you use this model to demonstrate the effect of adding more gas molecules to the sample?
c. In what ways is the pool-table model unsuccessful and misleading in modeling gas behavior?

21.

Hot water   Ice water

22. Each pool ball represents a molecule of gas; the volume (area) of the pool table remains constant.
a. The pool balls would move faster.
b. By increasing the number of pool balls on the table.
c. Limitations include relatively inelastic collisions, large particles, particles stationary unless external force is applied, no random motion, particles

Equal numbers of gas molecules at the same temperature and pressure occupy the same total volume. One mole of a gas sample at 0.0 °C and 1.0 atm occupies a volume of 22.4 L.

23. What volume would 8.0 g helium (He) gas occupy at 0.0 °C and 1.0 atm?

24. How many moles of gas molecules would you expect to find in a 2.0-L bottle of air at 0.0 °C and 1.0 atm?

25. What would be the mass of gas inside a 3.0-L balloon at 0 °C and 1.0 atm filled with
a. He(g)? b. CO_2(g)? c. CH_4(g)?

26. a. How many moles of oxygen gas would be present in a 1.0-mL gas sample at 0.0 °C and 1.0 atm?

b. How many *molecules* of oxygen gas does your answer to Question 26a represent?

The coefficients in a balanced chemical equation that involves gases indicate the relative volumes of gaseous reactants or products.

27. The following equation represents the production of ammonia (NH_3) by the reaction of nitrogen gas with hydrogen gas

$$N_2(g) + 3 H_2(g) \rightleftharpoons 2 NH_3(g)$$

a. If 1 mol N_2(g) reacts with 3 mol H_2(g) in a flexible container at constant temperature and pressure, would you expect the total gas volume to increase or decrease? Why?
b. How many moles of NH_3 would form if 2.0 mol N_2 react completely with hydrogen gas?
c. How many grams of hydrogen gas would be needed to react completely with 2.0 mol N_2?

28. In a chemical reaction, 1 L hydrogen gas (H_2) reacts with 1 L chlorine gas (Cl_2) to produce 2 L hydrogen chloride gas (HCl). All volumes are measured at the same temperature and pressure. Create a depiction of this chemical reaction, using

a. a sketch involving molecular models.
b. a balanced chemical equation.

For a given gas sample, the ideal gas law expresses the relationship among its volume, pressure, temperature, and amount of gas molecules present.

29. Determine the pressure exerted by 0.122 mol oxygen gas in a 1.50-L container at room temperature (25 °C).

30. At what temperature will 2.5 mol nitrogen gas exert a pressure of 10.0 atm in a 2.0-L container?

c. $3.0 \text{ L CH}_4 \times \dfrac{1 \text{ mol CH}_4}{22.4 \text{ L CH}_4} \times$

$\dfrac{16.042 \text{ g CH}_4}{1 \text{ mol CH}_4} = 2.1 \text{ g CH}_4$

26. a. Total mol O_2 = 1.0 mL $\times$ 1 L/1000 mL $\times$ 1 mol/22.4 L = 4.5×10^{-5} mol O_2

b. Total O_2 molecules = 4.5×10^{-5} mol $\times 6.02 \times 10^{23}$ molecules/1 mol = 2.7×10^{19} O_2 molecules

27. a. Decrease. This can be inferred from the sum of the reactant coefficients (4) compared to the product coefficient (2).
b. According to the equation, 4 mol NH_3(g) would be produced when 2 mol N_2(g) reacts completely with H_2(g).
c. 2 mol N_2(g) requires 6 mol H_2(g) to react completely.

$6 \text{ mol H}_2 \times \dfrac{2.0 \text{ g H}_2}{1 \text{ mol H}_2} = 12 \text{ g H}_2.$

28. a.

H_2 + Cl_2 $\longrightarrow$ 2 HCl

b. H_2(g) + Cl_2(g) → 2 HCl(g)

29. n = 0.122 mol, V = 1.50 L, T = 25 + 273 = 298 K

$$P = \dfrac{nRT}{V} =$$

$$\dfrac{0.122 \text{ mol} \times 0.0821 \dfrac{\text{L} \times \text{atm}}{\text{mol} \times \text{K}} \times 298 \text{K}}{1.50 \text{ L}} =$$

1.99 atm

30. n = 2.5 mol, V = 2.0 L, P = 10.0 atm

$$T = \dfrac{PV}{nR} =$$

$$\dfrac{10.0 \text{ atm} \times 2.0 \text{ L}}{2.5 \text{ mol} \times 0.0821 \dfrac{\text{L} \times \text{atm}}{\text{mol} \times \text{K}}} =$$

97 K = −180 °C

---

move in only two dimensions, relative "molecular" size compared to between-molecule spacing is unrealistic.

23. What volume would 8.0 g helium (He) gas occupy at 0.0 °C and 1.0 atm?

$8.0 \text{ g He} \times \dfrac{1 \text{ mol He}}{4.0 \text{ g He}} \times$

$\dfrac{22.4 \text{ L He}}{1 \text{ mol He}} = 45 \text{ L He}$

24. 2.0 L ÷ (22.4 L/mol) = 0.089 mol gas molecules

25. a. $3.0 \text{ L He} \times \dfrac{1 \text{ mol He}}{22.4 \text{ L He}} \times$

$\dfrac{4.003 \text{ g He}}{1 \text{ mol He}} = 0.54 \text{ g He}$

b. $3.0 \text{ L CO}_2 \times \dfrac{1 \text{ mol CO}_2}{22.4 \text{ L CO}_2} \times$

$\dfrac{44.01 \text{ g CO}_2}{1 \text{ mol CO}_2} = 5.9 \text{ g CO}_2$

Connecting the Concepts

31. According to Boyle's law, gas pressure and volume are inversely proportional, so pressure should increase as volume decreases. According to Charles' law, gas pressure and temperature are directly proportional, so pressure should increase as temperature increases. Since both effects are the same, the gas pressure will increase.

32. According to Charles' law, gas temperature and volume are inversely proportional as long as pressure remains constant. To keep volume constant under conditions of changing temperature, either (a) allow pressure to change or (b) (more relevant to the operation of hot-air balloons) allow gas to escape as the temperature increases.

33. Density = mass/volume. As temperature increases, volume will also increase. Mass will remain constant. Therefore, the density will decrease.

34. a. 1.28 g/L $\times$ 2.00 $\times$ 10^5 L = 2.56 $\times$ 10^5 g
b. i. Mass will remain constant.
ii. If the room is not sealed, the increased average molecular motion would cause some air molecules to spread into adjacent rooms, so mass would decrease in the original room.

Extending the Concepts

35. a. There are different environments at different heights. Pressure and temperature change with depth and height. They are both solutions. Composition remains relatively constant over time.

Connecting the Concepts

31. If the temperature of one mole of gas increases while its volume decreases, would you expect the gas pressure to increase, decrease, or remain the same? Explain your reasoning in terms of the gas laws.

32. The volume of a hot-air balloon remains constant while the temperature of the gas in the balloon changes. How is this possible?

33. Based on your knowledge of gas properties, predict what will happen to the density of a 100.0-g helium gas sample if you heat it from room temperature to 62 °C at constant pressure.

34. If air at 25 °C has a density of 1.28 g/L and your classroom has a volume of 2.0 $\times$ 10^5 L,
a. what mass of air is contained in your classroom?
b. assume that the room temperature is increased. How would this affect the total mass of air contained in the room if the room were
i. tightly sealed?
ii. not sealed?

Extending the Concepts

35. a. In what ways is an analogy involving an "ocean of gases" useful in thinking about the atmosphere?
b. In what ways does that analogy *not* apply to the atmosphere's observed behavior?

36. Some people suggest that they could dive to the bottom of a swimming pool and stay there, breathing through an empty garden hose that extends above the water surface. ⚠ *(Caution: Do not try this!)* How would you argue against this plan?

37. The gas behavior described by Boyle's law is a matter of life and death to scuba divers. On the water's surface, the diver's lungs, tank, and body are at atmospheric pressure. However, under water, a diver's body experiences the combined pressures of the atmosphere and the water:
a. Why do scuba divers need to use pressurized tanks?
b. What would happen to the tank volume if it were not strong enough to withstand the pressure of the outside water?
c. How do the problems of a diver compare with those of a pilot climbing to a higher altitude in an unpressurized airplane?

38. Consider the behavior of an ideal gas, as described by the postulates of the kinetic molecular theory (see page 315). For each postulate, predict how gas behavior might change if the postulate did not hold.

39. Oxygen gas is essential to life as we know it. Earth's atmosphere contains approximately 21% oxygen gas. Would a higher concentration of atmospheric oxygen gas be desirable? Explain.

40. The kelvin temperature scale is used extensively in theoretical and applied chemistry work.
a. Find out how closely scientists have approached a temperature of zero kelvins (0 K) in a laboratory setting.
b. Results from research in cryogenics have suggested intriguing applications of low-temperature chemistry and physics concepts. Report on activities in this field.

---

b. In some ways the atmosphere is more complex than the ocean: (1) Pressure changes exponentially, not linearly; (2) the temperature profile creates fairly permanent strata; and (3) its chemical composition varies with height and depth.

36. The mass of water pressing on the diver's lungs becomes so great, even in shallow water, that it quickly becomes impossible for the diver to draw air into the hose. The pressure exerted by the water is greater than the force human lungs can develop to draw in the air.

37. a. To withstand the increased external pressure without being crushed, to enable sufficient air to be transported in a reasonable volume, and to deliver air at the higher pressures required by the water depth.
b. The volume would decrease (the tank would be crushed).
c. Divers experience increased pressures during the descent and, like pilots, experience reduced pressures during the ascent.

38. *Gases consist of tiny particles (molecules) whose size is negligible compared with the great distances that separate them.*

    If the postulate did not hold, forces among particles would be more important, so the identity of the gas would affect gas-behavior calculations. Gases could be much more dense and pressure could increase accordingly.

    Gas molecules are in constant, random motion. They collide with each other and with the walls of their container or surrounding objects. Gas pressure is caused by molecular collisions with container walls.

    If the postulate did not hold, gas might not exert pressure, gas molecules could remain stationary or accumulate on the bottom or walls of a container, and gases would not diffuse.

    Molecular collisions are elastic. This means that although individual molecules in a gas sample may gain or lose kinetic energy, there is no gain or loss in total kinetic energy from all of these collisions.

    If the postulate did not hold, gas particles could stick together when they collided or get hotter when some of the collision energy was transformed into heat. Also, particles might stick to the sides of containers rather than increasing pressure.

    At a given temperature, gas molecules have a range of kinetic energies. However, the average *kinetic energy of the molecules is constant and depends only on the temperature of the gas sample. Therefore, molecules of different gases at the same temperature have equal average kinetic energies. As gas temperature increases, the average velocity and kinetic energy of the gas molecules also increase.*

    If the postulate did not hold, the velocity and kinetic energy (and pressure) of a gas would be unpredictable. Pressure would depend on the identity of the gas. Kinetic energy might be affected by pressure.

39. A higher atmospheric concentration of O_2 would cause more rapid corrosion (oxidation) of metals. Fires would be more common and difficult to control.

40. a. Students will learn that physicists have approached absolute zero (zero kelvins) to within a tiny fraction of one kelvin. For example, in 2000, scientists in the Low Temperature Lab, Helsinki University of Technology, cooled a piece of rhodium metal down to 0.000 000 000 1 K (100 picokelvins).
b. Cryogenic temperatures are customarily regarded as below −150 °C (123 K). Cryogenic applications include superconducting electromagnets, food preservation, cryogenic fuels, cryosurgery, metal tempering, and liquefied gases.

Radiation and Climate

Without Earth's atmosphere, the midday sunshine would heat a rock hot enough to fry an egg, and the Sun's ultraviolet rays would burn exposed skin quickly; nights would be so cold that carbon dioxide gas would freeze to a solid. Because Earth's moon lacks an atmosphere, these extreme conditions are not science fiction; they exist there now (Figure 4.30).

The Sun's radiant energy and the gases that make up Earth's atmosphere combine to maintain a hospitable climate for life on this planet. Along with its vital role as an abundant reservoir for both oxygen gas and carbon dioxide gas, Earth's atmosphere provides protection from some of the Sun's ultraviolet radiation. Additionally, the atmosphere helps moderate Earth's temperature by controlling how much solar radiation is trapped close to Earth's surface.

In this section, you will learn about the nature of solar radiation, how it affects humans directly, and how it interacts with gases in the atmosphere.

B.1 THE ELECTROMAGNETIC SPECTRUM AND SOLAR RADIATION

The enormous quantity of energy produced by the Sun, which is Earth's main external source of energy, is a result of the fusion of hydrogen nuclei to form helium. *Nuclear fusion* is the combining of two nuclei to form a new, heavier nucleus, with the accompanying release of energy. Nuclear fusion occurs at high temperature and pressure, powering the Sun and other stars (Figure 4.31).

Figure 4.30 *Since the Moon lacks an atmosphere, it has very different temperatures on its "Sun-facing" side than it does on its other side.*

Solid carbon dioxide, $CO_2(s)$, is often called, somewhat misleadingly, *dry ice.*

You can learn more about nuclear fusion in Unit 6.

Figure 4.31 *The Sun is powered by nuclear fusion—a process that releases huge quantities of energy. This energy is used by growing plants, drives the hydrologic cycle, and warms the atmosphere on Earth.*

Using the Figures

Figure 4.30: Students may enjoy researching the atmospheric composition and climates of other planets and moons in the solar system. For example, Triton (a moon of Neptune) has very little atmosphere, is the coldest measured object in the solar system, and has geysers that shoot plumes of liquid nitrogen up to 8000 m above the surface.

B.1 The Electromagnetic Spectrum and Solar Radiation

B.1 Content Reading Guide

This material focuses on the nature of solar radiation and the fate of various types of electromagnetic radiation in earth's atmosphere. The energy liberated by solar fusion is transferred to earth as electromagnetic radiation. All electromagnetic radiation

• travels at the speed of light (3.0×10^8 m/s).

• does not require a medium through which to travel.

• moves through space as bundles of energy (photons).

• has effects on living things related to the energy of the radiation.

Radiation and Climate

Section B focuses on interaction of radiation and matter in the atmosphere and the resulting effects on climate. It begins with a discussion of the electromagnetic spectrum and the nature of energy input from the sun to earth. It explores the thermal properties of materials, including specific heat capacity. It introduces the carbon cycle, reasons for the greenhouse effect, global warming, and the role of CO_2 in these processes. Students learn about the relative quantities of CO_2 produced in respiration and combustion and propose changes that might lower atmospheric CO_2 levels.

If students have not recently studied light and radiation in physics or physical science, you may spend time reviewing relationships among frequency, wavelength, and energy. This will help students understand why ultraviolet radiation is more damaging than infrared or visible radiation, for instance. The energy of electromagnetic radiation is related to its frequency by the equation: $E = h\nu$, where ν is frequency and h is Planck's constant = 6.6×10^{-34} J·s. Thus, energy is directly proportional to frequency, and (as mentioned in the text) high-frequency radiation is high-energy radiation.

Frequency and wavelength are related by the expression: Speed (c) = $\nu\lambda$, where ν = frequency, λ = wavelength, and speed = c (the speed of light) = 3.0×10^8 m/s. Frequency and wavelength are inversely proportional. Combing the equations above, $\nu = c/\lambda$, so

$$E = \frac{hc}{\lambda}.$$

Therefore, energy and wavelength are also inversely proportional—long-wavelength radiation is low-energy radiation.

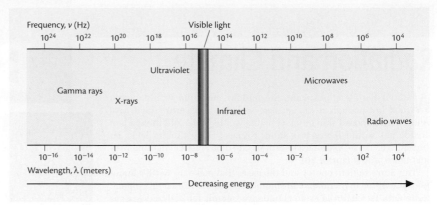

Figure 4.32
The electromagnetic spectrum.

Figure 4.33 *Satellite dishes atop roofs in a French village receive electromagnetic signals from a satellite above Earth.*

Wavelength and frequency are inversely proportional.

Electromagnetic Radiation

Some energy liberated through nuclear fusion in the Sun is transmitted to Earth as **electromagnetic radiation,** which consists of a broad range of energetic emissions. It is useful to identify particular types of electromagnetic radiation, with each type representing a particular energy range, that together make up the **electromagnetic spectrum.** Figure 4.32 shows major types of electromagnetic radiation. Radio waves and microwaves are at the low-energy end of the spectrum; X-rays and gamma rays are at the high-energy end of the spectrum.

Between these extremes are infrared and ultraviolet radiation and the familiar visible spectrum, which is the only type of electromagnetic radiation that is visible to the unaided human eye.

Electromagnetic radiation is composed of **photons,** or bundles of energy. Photons travel as waves and, as you might expect, move at the speed of light. Unlike sound waves or ocean waves, electromagnetic waves do not require a medium, or substance, to support their movement. Electromagnetic radiation can move through a vacuum as well as through air and other media (Figure 4.33).

Photons of electromagnetic radiation have energy ranges characteristic of the type of radiation involved (such as visible, ultraviolet, and gamma radiation). All waves, including photon waves of electromagnetic radiation, involve oscillation. The rate of oscillation, or the number of waves that pass by a given reference point per second, is called **frequency.** The frequency of a wave is directly proportional to its energy; high-frequency radiation is also high-energy radiation.

Another characteristic of waves is *wavelength,* shown in Figure 4.34. The distance between the tops (or any corresponding part) of successive waves equals the **wavelength.** The wavelength and energy of a photon are inversely proportional; radiation with longer wavelengths is less energetic than is radiation with shorter wavelengths.

Photons can transfer their energy as they collide and interact with matter. The photon's energy, and thus either its wavelength or frequency, largely determines its effect on living things and other types of matter.

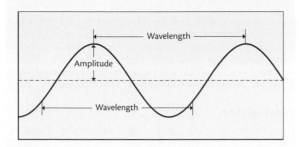

| **Figure 4.34** *Parts of a wave.*

Solar Radiation

The complete *solar spectrum* is shown in Figure 4.35. Most of the radiant energy emitted by the Sun is spread over a large portion of the electromagnetic spectrum: About 45% is in the infrared (IR) region, 46% is in the visible region, and 9% of this radiation is in the ultraviolet (UV) region. In the following paragraphs, you will be introduced to these three regions of the solar spectrum in more detail. Less than 1% of solar radiation falls outside of these three regions.

 Solar Radiation

Infrared Radiation

Electromagnetic radiation with frequencies slightly lower than that of red light is called **infrared (IR)** radiation. Infrared radiation causes certain bonded atoms to vibrate more energetically, which is observed as an increase in the material's temperature; infrared radiation is "heat" radiation. Most of the infrared radiation from the Sun cannot reach Earth's

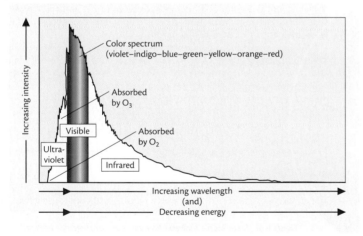

Figure 4.35 *The solar spectrum. Intensity, plotted on the y-axis, is an expression of the quantity of radiation at a given wavelength.*

Section B Radiation and Climate **339**

SECTION B

Using the Figures

Figure 4.32: Encourage students to spend time examining the relationships among frequency, wavelength, and energy. Prompt them to consider their experiences with different types of electromagnetic radiation and how those experiences relate to the relative energies of the radiation. For instance, when receiving dental X-rays, people wear lead aprons, which protect tissues and organs from high-energy X-rays. Sunburn is due to overexposure to ultraviolet light, which is energetic enough to break covalent bonds in skin. Radio waves that carry FM stations have long wavelengths and are low in energy. Also point out that visible light—our most apparent and continual encounter with electromagnetic radiation—makes up just a small slice of the spectrum.

ChemQuandary 1

Always Harmful?

"All radiation" includes the entire electromagnetic spectrum. It includes visible light, which allows human vision and is not considered harmful. Avoiding *all* radiation would mean isolation from radio waves, microwave equipment, all lighting sources, and infrared heaters, which is neither practical nor possible. This statement is obviously wrong-headed.

In the 1860s, John Tyndall demonstrated the ability of CO_2 and gaseous H_2O to absorb radiant energy.

Photon–electron interactions also occur in the double bonds of certain molecules within your eyes, making it possible for you to see.

Specially designed light bulbs are available that produce particular UV radiation suitable for specific applications, including use in tanning booths and sterilizing cabinets.

surface because it is absorbed by CO_2 and gaseous H_2O molecules in the atmosphere. However, some of the shorter wavelength (higher energy) solar radiation absorbed by Earth is transformed and reradiated as infrared energy. This reradiated energy is reflected back and retained by the atmosphere, a fact that will come into play later when we consider the role of CO_2 and certain other gases in the atmosphere.

Visible Radiation

On a clear day, more than 90% of the visible region of solar radiation directed toward Earth travels down to Earth's surface. The scattering of this portion of the Sun's radiation by water, air, and dust is the cause of red sunsets and blue skies, such as those depicted in Figure 4.36.

Visible radiation can energize electrons in some chemical bonds. An example of this is the interaction of visible light with electrons in chlorophyll molecules, which provides the energy needed for photosynthesis reactions.

Ultraviolet Radiation

There are three subcategories of **ultraviolet** (**UV**) radiation, all of which possess greater energy than does visible light. Of the three, *UV-A radiation* has the longest wavelengths and, thus, the lowest energy. *UV-B radiation* has more energy; it can cause sunburn; and, with long-term exposure, it is linked to skin cancer. *UV-C radiation*, the most energetic form of ultraviolet radiation, is useful for sterilizing materials because it can kill bacteria and destroy viruses. This is due to the fact that UV-C photons have enough energy to break covalent bonds. As a result,

Figure 4.36 *Some visible radiation from the Sun is scattered by Earth's atmosphere. This scattering creates the colors we see in the sky.*

chemical changes can occur in materials exposed to some ultraviolet radiation, including damage to tissues of living organisms. UV-C consists of ultraviolet radiation with wavelengths shorter than 280 nm, UV-B wavelengths range from 280 to 320 nm, and UV-A radiation has wavelengths longer than 320 nm.

UV-C radiation is absorbed in the stratosphere before reaching Earth's surface. Most UV-B radiation, and much UV-A radiation, does not reach Earth's surface; it is absorbed by the stratospheric ozone layer, which you will learn more about later in this unit.

If all the UV radiation reaching the atmosphere actually reached the Earth's surface, it is likely that most life on Earth would be destroyed. Ultraviolet radiation, however, is not all bad. Humans and animals must have some exposure to it because vitamin D is produced when the skin receives moderate doses of ultraviolet radiation included in sunlight.

> Approximate Wavelengths
> Infrared: 10^3–10^4 nm
> Visible: 380–780 nm
> Ultraviolet: 180–380 nm
> (1 nm = 10^{-9} m)

> Vitamin D is discussed further in Unit 7.

B.2 Earth's Energy Balance

This material explains earth's relatively stable temperature as a balance between solar radiation entering earth's atmosphere and the outward flow of energy from earth into space. The re-radiation of visible light at lower-energy infrared frequencies not only warms the atmosphere but also drives the hydrologic system.

ChemQuandary 1

ALWAYS HARMFUL?

How accurate is the following statement: "All radiation is harmful and should be avoided"?

B.2 EARTH'S ENERGY BALANCE

The mild average temperature (15 °C, or 59 °F) at Earth's surface is determined partly by a balance between the inward flow to Earth of the Sun's energy and the outward flow into space of solar energy following its interaction with the Earth and its atmosphere. Certain properties of Earth's surface and atmosphere help determine how much thermal energy our planet can hold near its surface—where, of course, terrestrial life resides—and how much energy Earth radiates back into space. The combination of these two factors helps establish a balanced energy flow, leading to a hospitable climate here on Earth.

 Earth's Energy Balance

Section B   Radiation and Climate   **341**

Be sure to distinguish the greenhouse effect from global warming. The greenhouse effect is a natural process. Molecules in the atmosphere, primarily water, carbon dioxide, and methane, absorb infrared radiation. They then emit radiation in all directions. (Although the text calls this process *re-radiation* for simplicity, the emitted radiation is not the same radiation that was absorbed.) Because these molecules prevent some radiation from leaving the atmosphere and return radiation to earth's surface, the effect is likened to a greenhouse trapping thermal energy on a sunny day. The greenhouse effect is necessary for life on Earth as we know it. The text uses the average surface temperatures of Mars and Venus to illustrate this idea.

By contrast, global warming is an increase in the magnitude of the greenhouse effect, leading to higher temperatures at earth's surface. Human-caused emissions of greenhouse gases may contribute to global warming.

Earth's climate and weather are influenced by (a) the interaction of solar radiation with the atmosphere, (b) the rotation of Earth on its axis, (c) the revolution of Earth around the Sun, (d) the tilt of Earth on its axis, and (e) the differing thermal properties of materials on earth's surface.

Figure 4.37 *One-third of the solar energy that reaches Earth powers the hydrologic cycle. Imagine how much thermal energy was generated as water vapor condensed in this developing thunderhead.*

Chlorofluorocarbons are discussed in more detail later in this unit.

About 30% of incoming solar radiation never reaches Earth's surface, but is reflected directly back into space by clouds and atmospheric particles. Solar radiation is also reflected when it strikes materials, such as snow, sand, or concrete on Earth's surface. In fact, visible light reflected in this way allows Earth's illuminated surface to be seen from space.

Of the remaining 70% of incoming solar radiation that actually reaches Earth's surface, about two-thirds is absorbed, warming the atmosphere, oceans, and continents. The other one-third of this energy powers the hydrologic cycle, which is the continuous cycling of water into and out of the atmosphere by evaporation and condensation. Solar energy causes water to evaporate from the oceans and land masses. The water condenses to form clouds, which then release water back to Earth as precipitation (see Figure 4.37).

Greenhouse Gases

All objects with temperatures above zero kelvins (0 K) radiate energy. The quantity of this radiated energy is directly related to an object's kelvin temperature. Specifically, Earth's surface reradiates most absorbed solar radiation, but usually at longer wavelengths (lower energy) than that of the original incoming radiation. This reradiated energy plays a major role in Earth's energy balance. Certain types of molecules in the air do not absorb the Sun's UV and visible radiation, allowing it to reach the surface of Earth, but absorb any infrared radiation that is reradiated from Earth's surface, thus holding warmth in the atmosphere.

Carbon dioxide and water readily absorb infrared radiation, as do methane (CH_4), nitrous oxide (N_2O), and halogenated hydrocarbons such as CF_3Cl and other chlorofluorocarbons (CFCs). Because clouds are composed of droplets of water or ice, they absorb infrared radiation. Energy absorbed by these molecules in the atmosphere is reradiated in all directions. Thus, energy can pass back and forth between Earth's surface and molecules in the atmosphere many times before it finally escapes to outer space.

This trapping and returning of infrared radiation by carbon dioxide, water, and other atmospheric molecules is known as the **greenhouse effect** because this process resembles, to some extent, the way thermal energy is held in a greenhouse (or in a closed car) on a sunny day. (See Figure 4.38.) Atmospheric gas molecules that effectively absorb infrared radiation are classified as **greenhouse gases.**

Without water and carbon dioxide molecules in the atmosphere to absorb and reradiate thermal energy back to Earth, scientists estimate that our planet would have an average temperature of a frigid −18 °C (0 °F). At the other thermal extreme is the planet Venus, demonstrating a runaway greenhouse effect. The Venusian atmosphere is composed of 96% carbon dioxide (and clouds made of sulfuric acid), which prevents the escape of most infrared radiation. As a result, the average surface temperature on Venus (450 °C) is much higher than that on Earth (15 °C).

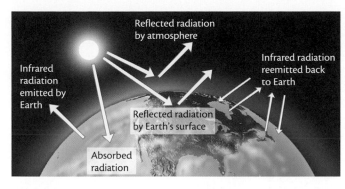

Reflected radiation by atmosphere

Infrared radiation emitted by Earth

Infrared radiation reemitted back to Earth

Reflected radiation by Earth's surface

Absorbed radiation

Figure 4.38 *When solar energy strikes Earth, clouds reflect about 30% back into space, and 70% moves through the atmosphere to reach Earth's surface. Energy that reaches the surface can be reflected or absorbed. Objects that absorb the Sun's UV and visible light reradiate it at lower-energy wavelengths such as infrared (IR) radiation, which is absorbed by atmospheric gases such as water, carbon dioxide, and methane (CH_4). IR radiation can be absorbed and reradiated by atmospheric gases and Earth's surface several times before escaping into space. This "greenhouse effect" helps maintain warm temperatures on Earth.*

Although some of this difference is due to their planetary positions relative to the Sun, Venus (the second planet from the Sun) is actually hotter than Mercury (the planet nearest to the Sun).

Climate Connections

In addition to maintaining a habitable average temperature on Earth, the interaction of solar radiation with Earth's atmosphere is a major factor in determining climates and weather. Radiant energy from the Sun warms Earth's land and water surfaces. Earth's warm surfaces, in turn, warm the air above them. As warmer air expands, its density decreases. This warmer air becomes displaced by colder, denser air, causing the warmer air to rise. These movements of warm and cold air masses help create continuous air currents that drive the world's weather (see Figure 4.39).

The differing thermal properties of materials on Earth's surface are another factor that influences climate. You will learn more about thermal properties, such as reflectivity and specific heat capacity, on pages 344–345.

Figure 4.39 *This hang glider depends on strong air currents as it is launched near San Francisco.*

Using the Figures

Figure 4.37: Students often have difficulty grasping the concept that energy is *released* in freezing or condensation. Encourage them to think about their own experiences with melting ice or boiling water (where energy needs to be put into the system), and remind them that the opposite processes, therefore, involve release of energy.

Figure 4.39: Ask students to predict how pressure gradients create winds (which are really just the movement of atmospheric gases). Winds occur when a pressure gradient exists. They move from areas of higher pressure to areas of lower pressure. Differences in temperature also affect wind formation, since warmer air is less dense (contains fewer molecules per liter than colder air) and therefore exerts less pressure than cooler air. For an overview of these concepts, visit **http://ww2010. atmos.uiuc.edu/(Gh)/guides/mtr/fw/ home.rxml**.

Developing Skills

B.3 Solar Radiation

These questions focus attention on radiation from the sun and factors that determine the temperature of the atmosphere.

Answers

1. Ultraviolet radiation has shorter wavelengths than infrared radiation. Short-wavelength radiation has more energy than long-wavelength radiation. Ultraviolet radiation has enough energy to break chemical bonds and harm living systems.

2. Visible light activates photoreceptors in eyes, making sight possible, and provides energy for photosynthetic reactions.

3. Water molecules in the air continue to trap and re-radiate infrared radiation even at night, so temperature fluctuations between day and night in humid areas would be less drastic than in a dry climate. Very few water molecules trap the infrared radiation in dry climates, so the night time lack of incoming solar radiation would have a more drastic effect.

4. a. They would be higher, because there would be fewer molecules to absorb incoming radiation.
   b. They would be lower, because there would be fewer molecules to radiate infrared energy that was trapped during the day.

B.4 Thermal Properties at Earth's Surface

This material addresses two properties that affect how a material interacts with thermal and light energy. *Reflectivity,* based largely on color, describes the proportion of incom-

---

The average or prevailing weather conditions in a region, commonly referred to as *climate,* are influenced by other factors. One factor is Earth's rotation, which causes day and night and also influences wind patterns. Other significant factors are Earth's yearly revolution around the Sun and Earth's tilt on its axis. The combination of these factors causes uneven distribution of solar radiation, which results in four distinct seasons in Earth's midlatitudes, a climatic pattern.

Developing Skills

B.3 SOLAR RADIATION

Check your understanding of the interaction of radiation with matter and of radiation's role in controlling Earth's surface temperature by answering the following questions:

1. Why is human exposure to ultraviolet radiation potentially more harmful than exposure to infrared radiation?
2. Describe two essential roles played by visible solar radiation.
3. Explain why dry, arid regions in the United States, such as New Mexico and Arizona, experience wider air-temperature fluctuations from night to day than do states with more humid conditions, such as Florida.
4. Suppose Earth had a less dense atmosphere (fewer gas molecules) than it does now:
   a. How would average daytime temperatures be affected? Why?
   b. How would average nighttime temperatures be affected? Why?

B.4 THERMAL PROPERTIES AT EARTH'S SURFACE

If you live in the South or Southwest, or if you have visited these areas, you may have noticed that many cars are light colored, both inside and out. Do you know why? A particular property of materials helps keep these vehicles cooler in sunlight than those with darker surfaces.

Reflectivity

When solar radiation strikes a surface, some photons are absorbed, which increases the surface temperature, and other photons are reflected. The proportion of radiation that is reflected, expressed as the material's *reflectivity,* does not raise the object's temperature. Light-colored surfaces reflect more radiation, and therefore remain cooler, than dark-colored surfaces. For example, clean snow reflects almost 95% of solar radiation, whereas forests reflect very little. Variations in the reflectivity of materials at Earth's surface help determine local surface temperatures. See Figures 4.40 and 4.41. On a sunny, hot day, it is more comfortable to walk barefoot across a concrete sidewalk than across an asphalt parking lot. Walking across a lawn feels even more comfortable. The lawn reflects 15 to 30% of the Sun's rays, whereas black asphalt reflects almost no solar radiation. Instead, asphalt absorbs the radiation, which causes it to become hotter.

If you had to walk barefoot across an asphalt parking lot on a hot, sunny day, you would probably find that carefully walking on the white, painted stripes is more comfortable than walking on the dark asphalt. Why?

Figure 4.40 *Asphalt absorbs almost all solar radiation that strikes it, which causes asphalt roads to become quite hot and radiate heat.*

Figure 4.41 Clean snow (left) has high reflectivity, but trees (right), by contrast, possess relatively low reflectivity—when they're not snow-covered as depicted here.

Specific Heat Capacity

Every material has a characteristic reflectivity and heat capacity, which together determine how much and how fast the material warms. As you already learned (refer to page 249), *specific heat capacity* is the quantity of thermal energy (heat) needed to raise the temperature of one gram of a particular material by one degree Celsius.

In effect, a specific heat capacity value for a material can be considered as its "storage capacity" for thermal energy. The lower a material's specific heat capacity, the higher its temperature will rise if a certain quantity of thermal energy is added. The higher the specific heat capacity of the material, the less its temperature will rise for a given quantity of added thermal energy.

Thus, materials with higher specific heat capacities can store more thermal energy. For instance, copper metal, with a specific heat capacity of 0.387 J/(g·°C), will have a larger temperature change in response to the same quantity of thermal energy added than will water, with a specific heat capacity of 4.18 J/(g·°C). In particular, 10.0 J of thermal energy will raise the temperature of 1.00 g of copper by 25.8 °C; however, it will increase the temperature of an equal mass of water by only 2.4 °C, which is less than 10% of copper's temperature increase. Table 4.4 summarizes the specific heat capacities of some common materials.

Water's unique properties make it influential in the world's climates. As you can see in Table 4.4, water's specific heat capacity is higher than that of most other common materials. Because of this, bodies of liquid water can store large quantities of thermal energy and are thus slow to heat up or cool down. By contrast, land surfaces have much lower specific heat capacities; they heat up and cool down much more readily.

SPECIFIC HEAT CAPACITIES FOR COMMON MATERIALS AT 20 °C

Material	Specific Heat Capacity, J/(g·°C)
air	1.00
aluminum	0.895
asphalt	0.92
brass	0.380
carbon dioxide	0.832
copper	0.387
ethyl alcohol	2.45
gold	0.129
granite	0.803
iron	0.448
lead	0.128
sand	0.29
silver	0.233
stainless steel	0.51
water (liquid)	4.18
zinc	0.386

| Table 4.4

ing radiation reflected by a material's surface. *Specific heat capacity* is a measure of how readily a material changes temperature with added thermal energy. A material that becomes hot or cold readily (gram for gram) has a lower specific heat capacity than one that does so less readily (one that requires more thermal energy for a given temperature change to occur). Water has a particularly high heat capacity on a "per unit mass" basis. This enables water to moderate the temperature of land areas near oceans (and lakes). The moderating effect occurs because ocean temperatures do not vary widely from season to season. In winter, the ocean is warmer than the air; winds bring released thermal energy from the ocean to nearby lands. In summer, the ocean is cooler than the air, thus cooling the air above it, which then cools the land through breezes. The release of energy from the Gulf Stream (a warm-water current in the Atlantic Ocean) when it is near the European coast is responsible for relatively moderate climate there compared to other regions at similar latitudes (such as parts of Canada).

Using the Figures

Figures 4.40 and 4.41: Based on the ability to absorb and reflect solar radiation, ask students to predict which might be more likely to result in sunburn—walking on asphalt or on snow. Some students may have personal experiences to share related to this "thought experiment." Since snow reflects most solar radiation while asphalt tends to absorb solar radiation, sunburn is more likely when walking on snow than when walking on asphalt (based solely on reflectivity).

B.5 Thermal Properties of Materials

Students apply specific heat capacity and reflectivity concepts to common experiences.

Answers

1. a. The fenders reflect more radiant energy than dark seats, which readily absorb radiant energy.
   b. Concrete is nearly white; it reflects more light than dark-colored asphalt. (Their specific heat capacities are similar.)
2. A given mass of water can store more thermal energy and can release it over a longer time than can the same mass of alcohol, due to water's higher specific heat capacity
3. Sand is light-colored and reflects considerable light energy; sand's specific heat capacity allows it to get hotter than the grass.
4. a. A city far from a large body of water will be hotter.
   b. Water temperatures change more slowly than the temperatures of air, soil, or asphalt. Temperature differences between land and water lead to daytime sea breezes, and, at night, a land breeze.

B.6 Specific Heat Capacity

B.6 Specific Heat Capacity Student Worksheet and Data Table

Students heat a sample of metal to a known temperature and place it in a calorimeter with a known quantity of water at a known temperature. Coming to thermal equilibrium, hot metal loses thermal energy; water gains thermal energy; the final temperature is the same for both. Due to the law of conservation of energy, heat gained by water must equal heat lost by the metal. $E = mC\Delta T$ applies to both thermal changes. Equating the two allows students to find the metal's specific heat capacity. Students then identify the sample using a table of specific heat capacity values.

B.5 THERMAL PROPERTIES OF MATERIALS

1. Explain each of the following observations made on a hot, sunny day:
   a. The chrome fender of a white convertible car with its top down is cooler to the touch than are its dark red plastic seats.
   b. An asphalt sidewalk is warmer to the touch on a sunny day than is a concrete sidewalk.
2. Use data in Table 4.4 (page 345) to explain why water is a better liquid to use in a hot pack than is ethyl alcohol.
3. a. The surface of beach sand feels hotter than does grass on a hot, sunny day. Which property is likely to be more responsible for this observation, *specific heat capacity* or *reflectivity*?
   b. Explain your choice.
4. a. On average, which would you expect to be hotter in the summer, a city far away from any large body of water or a similar city located near a large body of water?
   b. Explain your choice.

B.6 SPECIFIC HEAT CAPACITY

Lab Video: Specific Heat Capacity

Introduction

As you have learned, each material has a characteristic specific heat capacity. In Unit 3, Investigating Matter B.6, you used the specific heat capacity of water to determine the heat of combustion of candle wax. In this investigation, you will use this property to identify an unknown metal sample. To accomplish this, you will investigate the transfer of thermal energy from the hot metal sample to cool water. The quantity of thermal energy gained by the water is described by this formula:

Thermal energy gained (E) =

Mass of water (m) × Specific heat capacity of water (C) × Change in water temperature (ΔT)

or

$$E_{H_2O} = (m_{H_2O})(C_{H_2O})(\Delta T_{H_2O})$$

$$\Delta T = T_{final} - T_{initial}$$

The thermal energy gained by the water must equal the thermal energy lost by the metal. To indicate the loss of thermal energy, a negative sign is used:

$$E_{gained\ by\ water} = -E_{lost\ by\ metal}$$

or

$$(m_{H_2O})(C_{H_2O})(\Delta T_{H_2O}) = -(m_{metal})(C_{metal})(\Delta T_{metal})$$

Remember that you are trying to find the specific heat capacity of the metal, C_{metal}. All other values in the expression can be measured or calculated or they can be found in your textbook.

Time

50 min

Materials

(For 12 student pairs)

12 beakers, 400-mL
12 metal samples (see Advance Preparation)
6 balances
24 cups, Styrofoam

After reading the following procedure, construct a data table appropriate for recording the data you will collect in this investigation.

Procedure

1. Half-fill a 250- or 400-mL beaker with water. Place the beaker on a hot plate and start heating it to boiling.

2. Obtain a metal sample and record a description of its appearance.

3. Determine and record the mass of the metal sample.

4. Carefully place the metal sample into the water that is heating in the beaker. *(**Caution:** Do not drop the metal sample into the beaker.)* Allow the water to come to a boil, and keep boiling it for several minutes.

5. While the water is heating, obtain or assemble a *calorimeter*. A simple version of a calorimeter is shown in Figure 4.42.

6. Accurately measure a room-temperature water sample with a volume of about 60 to 80% of the capacity of the calorimeter. Record the exact volume of water you will add to the calorimeter. Carefully pour the water into the calorimeter.

7. Measure and record the temperature of the water in the calorimeter.

8. Measure and record the temperature of the water boiling in the beaker on the hot plate.

9. After the water has boiled for 2 to 3 min, use tongs to remove the metal sample from the water, and quickly lower the metal sample into the calorimeter. *(**Caution:** Do not drop the metal sample into the calorimeter.)*

10. Gently stir the water in the calorimeter, and record its temperature every 30 s until it reaches a maximum value and starts to drop.

11. Repeat Steps 3 through 10 using the same metal sample and average the recorded masses and temperature changes for the two trials.

12. Wash your hands thoroughly before leaving the laboratory.

Data Analysis

1. Find the quantity of thermal energy absorbed by the water in the calorimeter.

2. Assume that the thermal energy absorbed by the water equals the thermal energy released by the metal sample. In addition, assume that the metal sample was initially at the temperature of the boiling water. Calculate the specific heat capacity of the metal.

Questions

1. Using your calculated specific heat capacity value, as well as the data provided in Table 4.4 (page 345), identify your metal sample.

Figure 4.42 *A Styrofoam-cup calorimeter consisting of two nested cups, a cardboard lid, and a thermometer.*

Section B   Radiation and Climate   **347**

Pre-Lab Discussion

Remind students to move metal samples *quickly* from boiling water to the calorimeter to minimize heat loss and experimental error. Also, students must read temperatures *immediately* on adding metal to the calorimeter. High-specific-heat metals involve small ΔTs; these may be missed if students are too slow.

Lab Tips

• If you have a lab oven, heat metal samples to a known temperature before students arrive. Either handle hot metal samples yourself with heat-resistant gloves and/or tongs, or instruct students to handle hot metals safely.

• Ensure that students remove excess water from metal samples before placing them into water in the Styrofoam cup. Any water held by the metal could alter their calculations.

Data Analysis

1. $E = m_{water} \times C_{water} \times \Delta T_{water}$.
   Example:
   E = 200.0 g $\times$ 4.18 J/(g °C) $\times$ (22.0 °C $-$ 20.0 °C) = 1700 J
   Significant figures in ΔT_{water} limit calculated energy precision— read temperatures to the nearest 0.1 °C.

2. $m_{water} \times C_{water} \times \Delta T_{water} = -m_{metal} \times C_{metal} \times \Delta T_{metal}$
   $$C_{metal} = \frac{m_{water} \times C_{water} \times \Delta T_{water}}{m_{metal} \times \Delta T_{metal}}$$

Answers

1. Students identify their samples. Typical student specific heat capacity values are within 15% of accepted values.

---

12 graduated cylinders, 100-mL
12 thermometers, alcohol, −10 to 110 °C
12 hot plates
12 tongs
12 cardboard squares, 8 cm × 8 cm

Safety

Students should wear protective goggles and aprons throughout the investigation. Tell them to be cautious handling hot water.

Advance Preparation

Select metal samples from these: Pb, Al, Sn, Cu, and Zn. Al and Zn produce larger ΔTs. Scientific-supply vendors sell metal samples in density or specific-heat kits. You can find other specific heat capacity values in a chemistry handbook. To save time, prepare or start to boil water before students arrive.

2. Sources of error may include heat absorbed by the thermometer, heat lost from the calorimeter, water transferred with the metal, and initial metal temperature being less than boiling-water or oven temperature.

3. a. Assumptions: The boiling temperature of the water (or oven temperature) is the same as the temperature of the metal; all heat lost by the metal was gained by the water in the calorimeter; no heat was exchanged between the calorimeter and the surroundings.
   b. If the initial metal temperature is lower than actually assumed, the change in metal temperature will be inflated, and the calculated specific heat capacity will be too small. If some heat lost by the metal is not gained by the water, the change in water temperature will be too small, and the calculated heat capacity will be too small. If some heat is exchanged between the calorimeter and surroundings, the most likely result is that the change in temperature of the water will be too small, leading to a lower-than-actual calculated specific heat capacity.

4. a. Each metal would have to be heated to a known temperature, then the quantity of heat released by the metal to water measured. This is not a reasonable plan.
   b. Students may propose using physical and chemical properties such as magnetism, reactivity with acids, density, or appearance as the basis for separating the metals. They may also propose a coding/labeling system, similar to the system currently used for recyclable plastics.

2. The level of certainty you have about the actual identity of your metal sample depends in part on sources of error in the laboratory procedure. List and explain several potential sources of error in the procedure that you followed. Remember to distinguish between human error and experimental error.

3. Closely related to sources of error are any simplifying assumptions you made to complete your laboratory task and calculations.
   a. List some assumptions that you made in completing this investigation and its calculations.
   b. Evaluate each assumption in terms of how it could adversely affect your calculated result.

4. A recycling company decides to separate the various metals it receives by using the different specific heat capacities of the metals.
   a. Do you think that this is a reasonable plan? Explain.
   b. Propose an alternative method for separating the metals.

B.7 THE CARBON CYCLE

More than a century ago, it was suggested that a significant increase in burning fossil fuels might release enough carbon dioxide into the atmosphere to affect Earth's surface temperature. This suggestion was based on the idea that human activity can affect processes in natural ecosystems, producing changes that might not always be beneficial. In particular, burning fossil fuels might perturb the natural movement of carbon within Earth's systems—the global **carbon cycle.**

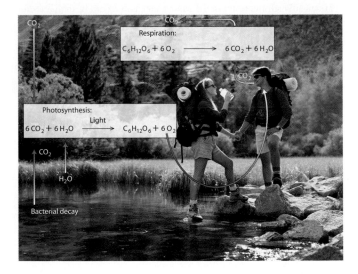

Figure 4.43 The carbon cycle—major pathways within the biosphere.

In the carbon cycle, which is illustrated in Figures 4.43 and 4.44, the different forms and compounds in which carbon atoms are found can be considered as "chemical reservoirs" of carbon atoms. These reservoirs include atmospheric CO_2 gas, solid calcium carbonate ($CaCO_3$) in limestone, natural gas (methane, CH_4), and organic molecules.

Each movement within the carbon cycle, and thus among these reservoirs, either requires energy or releases energy. For instance, plants use CO_2 and solar energy to form carbohydrates through photosynthesis. The carbohydrates are consumed by other organisms (or by the plant itself) and are eventually broken down or oxidized, releasing energy for use by organisms that consumed them.

The carbon atoms used and circulated in photosynthesis represent only a tiny portion of available global carbon. Gaseous CO_2 continually moves between the atmosphere and the oceans. In fact, 71% of Earth's carbon atoms, in the form of CO_2, are dissolved in the oceans. Another 22% are trapped in fossil fuels and in carbonate rocks formed when dissolved CO_2 reacted with water, which first produced carbonates, then sediments, then rocks. Dead organisms and terrestrial ecosystems (such as trees, crops, and other living matter) account for the remaining global carbon-atom inventory.

Without the influence of human activities, the distribution of carbon within various reservoirs would remain relatively unchanged over time. Atmospheric CO_2 levels, however, have increased by about 30% since 1800. This increase is the result of several processes. See Figure 4.45 (right). For example, clearing forests removes vegetation that would ordinarily consume CO_2 through photosynthesis; see Figure 4.45 (left). As cuttings and scrap timber are burned, they release CO_2 into the atmosphere. Most significantly, burning fossil fuel releases CO_2 into the air, as the following equations illustrate:

Burning coal: $C(s) + O_2(g) \longrightarrow CO_2(g)$

Burning natural gas: $CH_4(g) + 2\,O_2(g) \longrightarrow CO_2(g) + 2\,H_2O(g)$

Burning gasoline: $2\,C_8H_{18}(g) + 25\,O_2(g) \longrightarrow 16\,CO_2(g) + 18\,H_2O(g)$

As you continue to learn about the role of CO_2 in the atmosphere, recall the concerns raised at the start of this unit by individuals such as Principal Powers and Isaiah Martin about Riverwood High School's new school bus-idling policy.

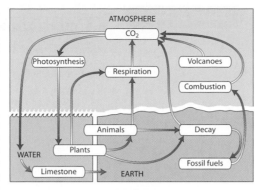

Figure 4.44 *The carbon cycle—relationships among major carbon reservoirs.*

Figure 4.45 *How does each of these scenes affect atmospheric carbon dioxide (CO_2) levels?*

B.7 The Carbon Cycle

Although the total carbon atoms on earth are fixed, carbon is constantly being exchanged among various chemical reservoirs. The reservoirs include atmospheric CO_2 and CO_2 dissolved in lakes and oceans, limestone ($CaCO_3$), and organic molecules. Any exchange of carbon among reservoirs requires or releases energy. The increase in the percent CO_2 in earth's atmosphere is due, in part, to steady decreases in forested areas and an increase in the combustion of natural gas, gasoline, coal, and other carbon-based fuels. *The Periodic Table* by Primo Levi contains several stories featuring chemical elements. Levi brilliantly depicts the carbon cycle; you may invite students to read "Carbon."

Using the Figures

Figure 4.43: Have students use this photo to identify as many steps of the carbon cycle as they can. Encourage them to look beyond the few highlighted processes. For instance, glucose ($C_6H_{12}O_6$) is included as a *reactant* in respiration and a *product* of photosynthesis. What connections can students draw (via glucose) between those two processes?

Figure 4.45: These photos focus on CO_2 output and uptake. Ask students to consider what effect increasing or decreasing each activity would have on the balance within the carbon cycle.

Making Decisions

B.8 Considering the Global Carbon Cycle

1. $\dfrac{0.25 \text{ kg CO}_2}{10 \text{ min}} \times 40 \text{ min} \times$

   $10 \text{ buses} = 10.0 \text{ kg CO}_2$

2. $\dfrac{0.10 \text{ L fuel}}{10 \text{ min}} \times 40 \text{ min} \times$

   $10 \text{ buses} = 4 \text{ L fuel}$

3. $10.0 \text{ kg CO}_2/\text{day} \times 180 \text{ days}$

   $= 1800 \text{ kg CO}_2$

   $4 \text{ L fuel/day} \times 180 \text{ days}$

   $= 720 \text{ L fuel}$

4. Unless you specify a certain value, students may devise different estimates of the volume of a school-bus fuel tank. Students should agree that the *creation* of the fuel occurred over a much longer time scale than *combustion* of the fuel. Starting in the 1800s, petroleum combustion increased significantly, contributing to atmospheric CO_2 increases since then.

5. Students will probably state that the policy at Riverwood High School will not significantly affect annual worldwide conversion of petroleum-based fuel to CO_2, because Riverwood's total CO_2 contribution is small compared to millions of operating vehicles worldwide.

6. Other considerations, such as the health of students and bus drivers, may be among their reasons. Also, though one school might not make much of a difference, a movement among all schools to eliminate bus idling could make a significant difference in worldwide CO_2 levels.

Making Decisions

B.8 CONSIDERING THE GLOBAL CARBON CYCLE

Idling a vehicle for 10 min typically consumes about 0.10 L of fuel and produces about 0.25 kg of carbon dioxide. On average, the ten Riverwood High School bus engines each idle 40 minutes daily.

1. What mass of carbon dioxide is produced daily by all 10 Riverwood High School buses?

2. How many liters of fuel are consumed daily by buses idling at Riverwood High School?

3. In a 180-day school year, what mass of carbon dioxide would be released into the atmosphere by these buses while idling? How many liters of fuel would be consumed?

4. Compare how long it takes for a Riverwood High School bus to convert a tank of fossil fuel to atmospheric carbon dioxide with the time required for that same quantity of fossil fuel to become originally formed by nature. Explain why atmospheric CO_2 levels have increased by about 30% since 1800 from the perspective of these two contrasting rates.

5. The values that you calculated in Questions 1 through 3 were for ten school buses over one school year. Do you think the school bus-idling policy at Riverwood High School will significantly affect the annual worldwide supply of fossil fuel that is converted to carbon dioxide gas? Explain.

6. In light of your answer to Question 5, why would Isaiah Martin, Principal Powers, and others believe that the school bus-idling policy is necessary?

Investigating Matter

B.9 CARBON DIOXIDE LEVELS

Introduction

Lab Video: Carbon Dioxide Levels

Air usually contains very low concentrations of CO_2. However, the CO_2 concentration in a small, enclosed airspace can be increased by burning coal or petroleum, by allowing organic matter to decompose, or by gathering a crowd of people or animals.

In this investigation, you will estimate and compare the amounts of CO_2 contained in several air samples. To accomplish this, air will bubble through water that contains an acid–base indicator, bromthymol blue. Carbon dioxide reacts with water to form carbonic acid, H_2CO_3(aq):

$$CO_2(g) + H_2O(l) \longrightarrow H_2CO_3(aq)$$

As the concentration of carbonic acid in the bromthymol blue solution increases (thus increasing acidity), the indicator color changes from blue to green and finally to yellow.

Investigating Matter

B.9 Carbon Dioxide Levels

B.9 Carbon Dioxide Levels Student Worksheet and Data Table

Students estimate the amount of CO_2 in normal, combustion, and exhaled air by monitoring the change in acidity caused by CO_2 absorption in a solution. The indicator used is bromthymol blue.

Time

50 min

Before starting, read the procedure to learn what you will need to do, note safety precautions, and plan necessary data collecting and observations.

Procedure

Part I: CO₂ in Normal Air

1. Pour 400 mL of distilled water into a 500-mL flask and add 1 mL bromthymol blue indicator solution. The solution color should appear blue. If it does not, add one drop of 0.1 M NaOH, and gently swirl the flask. Save this solution for later steps. ⚠ (*Caution: Sodium hydroxide solution is corrosive. If any splashes on your skin, wash it immediately with water and inform your teacher.*)

2. Pour 10 mL of the solution prepared in Step 1 into a test tube labeled "Control." Stopper the test tube. Set this control aside for later comparisons. Add 125 mL of the solution you prepared in Step 1 to a 250-mL filter flask.

3. Assemble the apparatus illustrated in Figure 4.46.

4. Record the starting time. Then gradually turn on the water tap until the aspirator pulls air through the flask. Mark or note the position of the faucet handle so that you can run the aspirator at the same flow rate later in the investigation.

5. Allow the aspirator to run until the indicator solution turns yellow. Record the total time needed to reach the yellow color. Detach the aspirator hose from the flask, then turn off the water. Remove the stopper from the flask.

6. Pour 10 mL of the used indicator solution from the flask into a second test tube labeled "Normal air" and stopper the tube. Compare this sample's color with the color of the control. Record your observations. Save the "Normal air" and "Control" test tubes.

Part II: CO₂ from Hydrocarbon Combustion

7. Empty the filter flask and rinse it thoroughly with distilled water.

8. Pour 125 mL of indicator solution, prepared in Step 1, into the filter flask. Reassemble the apparatus as in Figure 4.46.

9. Light a candle. Hold the glass funnel above the flame so that the flame tip reaches just inside the base of the funnel.

To aspirator

Clamped filter flask

Glass funnel

| **Figure 4.46** *Apparatus for collecting air.*

12 Erlenmeyer flasks, 250-mL
0.1 M NaOH (0.8 g NaOH in 200 mL solution, placed in each of six 15–20 mL dropper bottles)

Safety

Students should wear protective goggles and aprons throughout this investigation. Insert the glass tubes into the rubber stoppers yourself to prevent student injury. If you decide to allow students to do this, emphasize the proper technique: using glycerin, protective towels, a close grip on the tube, and a twisting motion.

Advance Preparation

You can purchase bromthymol blue as either a 0.04% solution or a solid that can be used to prepare a solution.

Pre-Lab Discussion

Draw students' attention to **Figure 4.46,** which shows the proper setup.

For health reasons, only *one* student from each group should use the straw for testing exhaled air.

Lab Tips

• This investigation can be completed as an interactive teacher demonstration if time, aspirators, or drainage for water aspiration (or water-use concerns) limit aspirator use by the entire class.

• Heavy-walled rubber tubing works best with aspirators. Thin-walled tubing usually collapses and fails to draw air through the system.

Materials

(For 12 student pairs)

12 small glass (not plastic) funnels (7-cm diameter)

12 filter flasks, 250-mL, wrapped with clear tape

12 stoppers, 1-hole, to fit filter flasks

12 aspirator adapters for faucets

12 straight glass tubes

12 glass bends

12 ring stands and clamps

24 small (30-cm) lengths of rubber tubing

36 test tubes (18 × 150 mm)

12 candles, tea light or similar

12 straws, drinking

200 mL bromthymol blue solution, 0.04% (m/v)

Answers

1. The bromthymol blue changes to yellow fastest when exposed to the burning-candle gas sample. Exhaled air causes a color change at a moderate rate, while normal air takes the longest time. The burning candle produced the most CO_2.

2. It only gives a rough approximation. Not all combustion air is captured. The flow rates are also not precisely controlled.

3. The burning candle: The indicator changed color more quickly. Students might note that the rate of reaction for combustion gas is much greater than for exhaled air.

4. a. Green plants use CO_2—time should increase.
   b. People generate CO_2—time should decrease.
   c. Better ventilation reduces the concentration of exhaled CO_2—time should increase.
   d. Combustion produces CO_2—time should decrease.

Post-Lab Discussion

Combustion has fascinated humans throughout history and probably earlier. Antoine Lavoisier first linked *combustion* with *respiration*. In 1860, Michael Faraday presented popular lectures on the chemistry of candle combustion. His lectures are contained in *The Chemical History of a Candle*. Present-day research on combustion focuses on ways to extract more energy while generating less pollution from burning fossil fuels.

One focus of a post-laboratory discussion can be on the inevitable production of CO_2 when fuels, including foods, combine with O_2. Ask students how CO_2 can be mini-

10. Record the starting time. Then turn on the water tap to the same position you established in Step 4. Run the aspirator until the indicator solution color turns yellow. Record the total time needed to reach the yellow color. Detach the aspirator hose from the flask, then turn off the water.

11. Pour 10 mL of the solution into a clean test tube labeled "Combustion CO_2" and stopper the tube. Compare its color with that of the "Normal air" and the "Control" solutions. Record your observations.

Part III: CO_2 in Exhaled Air

12. Place 125 mL of indicator solution, prepared in Step 1, in a 250-mL Erlenmeyer flask.

13. Record the starting time. Then blow your breath through a clean straw into the solution until the indicator color changes to yellow. (*Caution: Do not draw any solution into your mouth.*) Record the total time it takes for the indicator color to change.

14. Pour 10 mL of the solution into a clean test tube labeled "Breath CO_2." Stopper the tube. Compare its color with those of the other three solutions. Record your observations.

15. Dispose of the waste solutions as directed by your teacher. Wash your hands thoroughly before leaving the laboratory.

Questions

1. Compare how long it took for the indicator solution to turn yellow in each test. Explain any differences you noted.

2. How accurate do you think this laboratory technique is for measuring the amount or concentration of CO_2 in gas samples? Explain.

3. Which sample contained a higher concentration of CO_2, the air surrounding the burning candle or exhaled air? Explain your answer.

4. If left exposed in a closed room indefinitely, the indicator solution would absorb CO_2 from the surroundings and could change color. Discuss the effect of each of the following conditions on the time required for the indicator color to change to green or yellow, or explain why you think the indicator color would not change.
   a. Many plants are growing in the room.
   b. Fifty people enter and remain in the room.
   c. Better ventilation is achieved in the room.
   d. Several people are using Bunsen burners in the room.

mized. Answers may include using nuclear and solar energy and reducing energy use.

Discuss analytical techniques used in the investigation. Chemists routinely make quantitative analyses, using sensitive instrumental techniques, detecting concentrations as low as ppm, ppb and even ppt. Challenge motivated students to design an investigation that would allow quantitative measurements of CO_2 levels. One possibility is based on the reaction of CO_2 with limewater and the subsequent increase in limewater mass.

B.10 INCOMPLETE COMBUSTION

Modeling Matter

The products of hydrocarbon burning were shown as CO_2 and H_2O in the chemical equations summarized on page 349. As you probably know, however, these are not the only possible products of combustion. When hydrocarbons undergo *incomplete combustion*, carbon monoxide (CO) and soot (C) also form.

Why might incomplete combustion occur? One possible reason is that there is not enough oxygen gas available for complete combustion; that is, there is not enough oxygen for all carbon atoms to form molecules of CO_2; CO forms instead. In such cases, oxygen would become the **limiting reactant** in the combustion process; it *limits* the amount of hydrocarbon that can be completely burned.

This is somewhat analogous to a situation you might encounter if you bought one package of hot-dog buns and one package of hot dogs for a picnic. Hot dogs are normally sold in packages of ten, but hot-dog buns are sold in packages of eight. Thus, hot-dog buns would become the *limiting reactant* if you had just one package of each. They limit the number of hot-dog sandwiches to eight sandwiches with two excess hot dogs.

> CO is an air pollutant you will study further later in this unit.

1. Consider the combustion of propane, C_3H_8:
   a. Draw a molecular model of one propane molecule.
   b. Imagine taking that one propane molecule and allowing it to react with as much oxygen gas (O_2) as needed to get all the carbon atoms to form CO_2 and all the hydrogen atoms to form H_2O. Draw all the CO_2 and H_2O molecules formed by complete combustion of one propane molecule.
   c. How many oxygen molecules (O_2) are needed for the complete combustion of one molecule of propane?

2. Now consider the combustion of butane, C_4H_{10}:
   a. Draw models of one C_4H_{10} molecule and four O_2 molecules.
   b. Form as many molecules of CO_2 and H_2O as possible from the models you drew in answering Question 2a.
   c. Do four O_2 molecules provide sufficient oxygen atoms to support complete combustion of one C_4H_{10} molecule?
   d. Which is the limiting reactant, C_4H_{10} or O_2?

3. Assume that 1.0 mol C_4H_{10} is completely burned in excess oxygen gas to form carbon dioxide and water:
   a. How many moles of CO_2 would be produced?
   b. How many moles of H_2O would be produced?
   c. What is the minimum moles of O_2 required in that reaction?
   d. If it were possible to form CO instead of CO_2, how many moles of oxygen gas would be required?
   e. Consider your answers to Questions 3c and 3d. Under what conditions would CO formation be favored over CO_2 formation? Why?

Modeling Matter

B.10 Incomplete Combustion

 B.10 Incomplete Combustion Student Worksheet

Answers

1. a.

   b.

   c. 5

2. a.

   b. Several answers are possible, including: $2\ CO_2 + 3\ H_2O$; $4\ CO_2$; $1\ CO_2 + 5\ H_2O$.
   c. No
   d. O_2

3. a. 4 mol CO_2
   b. 5 mol H_2O
   c. 7 mol O_2
   d. 4.5 mol O_2 ($C_4H_{10} + 9/2\ O_2 \longrightarrow 4\ CO + 5\ H_2O$)
   e. With a shortage of available O_2

Additional Information and Extensions

• CO is sometimes produced in homes by poorly functioning furnaces, fuel-burning heaters, or appliances. Discuss why this can happen and ways to avoid it. CO binds to hemoglobin, a protein in red blood cells, and inhibits oxygen transport to heart, lungs, brain, and tissues. CO cannot be detected by human senses; inexpensive detectors are available.

• CO is produced if insufficient oxygen is present to complete the reaction. Thus, O_2 becomes the limiting reactant.

• To identify a limiting reactant, the appropriate equation must be balanced.

• Analogies to cooking and recipes may help explain the limiting-reactant idea. For example, decide how much food you can prepare based on supplies on hand.

 B.10 Supplement: Limiting Reactants

B.11 Greenhouse Gases and Global Change

This material introduces the "spiraling up" of CO_2 concentrations and temperatures increasing atmospheric greenhouse gas concentrations could produce. This is sometimes called a *runaway greenhouse effect.* Processes that create and contribute other greenhouse gases, including N_2O and CH_4, are mentioned.

Many climate scientists believe that global temperature increases are likely without changes in emissions and control of CO_2 and other greenhouse gases. See **http://yosemite.epa. gov/oar/globalwarming.nsf/content/ Climate.html** for more detailed information.

The text states the possible impact of temperature increases, including increased flooding, health effects that accompany it, and regional climate changes that could significantly shift agricultural patterns. Finally, it outlines world response to the issue of greenhouse gases—see **http://unfccc.int/resource/kpstats.pdf** for more information.

Greenhouse gases were first discussed on page 342.

B.11 GREENHOUSE GASES AND GLOBAL CHANGE

As long as concentrations of carbon dioxide and other greenhouse gases in the atmosphere remain relatively constant, the greenhouse effect will comfortably maintain Earth's average temperature. The hydrologic cycle (page 87) and the carbon cycle (pages 348–349) maintain stable concentrations of water and carbon dioxide in their respective reservoirs, including the atmosphere. However, as you already realize, the effect of human activity must be considered.

"Spiraling-Up"

If more CO_2 is added to the atmosphere than can be removed by natural processes, its concentration will increase. Eventually, if sufficient CO_2 were added, the atmosphere could retain enough additional infrared radiation from the Sun to increase Earth's average surface temperature. With an increased surface temperature, CO_2 stored in ice, water, and the frozen floors of northern forests could also be released. A "spiraling-up" effect could occur, where warmer temperatures produce more carbon dioxide, which produces warmer temperatures, and so on.

The hydrologic cycle must also be considered. The atmosphere contains about 12 trillion metric tons of water vapor, a quantity so large that it might seem impossible that human activity could significantly affect it. However, if global temperatures increase, oceans and other bodies of water will also become warmer.

The amount of water vapor released increases as temperature increases, so more of this slightly warmer water will evaporate, increasing the atmospheric concentration of water vapor. As a greenhouse gas, increased water vapor may cause an even greater increase in global temperatures due to absorption and the release of infrared radiation, which causes another "upward spiral."

This spiraling-up effect is also commonly known as a *runaway greenhouse effect.* However, by contrast, increased water vapor concentration would also lead to increased cloud cover, which would reflect more solar radiation, thus counteracting some of the predicted temperature increase.

Two other naturally occurring greenhouse gases are also produced by human activity: nitrous oxide (N_2O) and methane (CH_4). Many agricultural and industrial activities, as well as the burning of solid waste and fossil fuels, contribute to the concentration buildup of N_2O in the atmosphere. CH_4 occurs naturally as a decomposition product of plant and animal wastes, but it also is produced from refining fossil fuels and raising livestock. See Figure 4.47. Finally, some gases that do not occur naturally can also contribute to the greenhouse effect. Of particular significance are fluorocarbons used in refrigeration and air conditioning. As you can see in Table 4.5, some of these gases are much more effective than CO_2 is in retaining heat at Earth's surface.

| Table 4.5

GREENHOUSE GAS EFFECTIVENESS

Greenhouse Gas	Relative Effectiveness	Percent Abundance in Troposphere
Carbon dioxide (CO_2)	1 (assigned value)	3.3×10^{-2}
Methane (CH_4)	30	1.7×10^{-4}
Nitrous oxide (N_2O)	160	3×10^{-4}
Water vapor (H_2O)	0.1	1
Ozone (O_3)	2 000	4×10^{-6}
Trichlorofluoromethane (CCl_3F)	21 000	2.8×10^{-8}
Dichlorodifluoromethane (CCl_2F_2)	25 000	4.8×10^{-8}

Figure 4.47 *In addition to carbon dioxide, atmospheric gases such as methane (CH_4) and nitrous oxide (N_2O) are considered greenhouse gases. Raising cattle (top) increases methane concentrations, while burning solid waste (right) adds nitrous oxide to the atmosphere.*

Using the Figures

Figure 4.47: These photos show sources of methane and nitrous oxide, which both act as greenhouse gases. **Table 4.5** compares effectiveness of these gases in trapping and returning infrared radiation. Invite students to discuss the relative merits of controlling CO_2, CH_4, or N_2O emissions. For another discussion of greenhouse gases, see *ChemMatters,* Vol. 21, No. 3, October 2003, **acswebcont.acs.org/education**.

Using the Figures

Figure 4.48: Consider asking the following questions to help students understand the graph.

1. Ask students to look at the y-axis title and scale on this graph. Why might the graph be designed this way?

2. By how much has the global annual mean temperature increased in the last century? What features of the graph make this question difficult to answer?

3. Is the trend represented by this graph significant? Explain.

Answers

1. While students may answer that it is easier to interpret the data displayed this way, mean surface air temperatures are also difficult to define, and anomalies, such as those graphed here, are more commonly used. See **http://data.giss.nasa.gov/gistemp/abs_temp.html** for more information.

2. Approximately 0.6 °C. The fluctuations in this graph make a definitive answer difficult.

3. Answers will vary, but students should compare the change to historical variation or relate it to personal experience in their explanation.

Temperature Increases

What are implications of increased atmospheric concentrations of greenhouse gases? Has any effect on Earth's climate been noted thus far? Examine Figure 4.48. The 20th century's 10 warmest years all occurred within the last 15 years of that century. Of these, 1998 was the warmest year on record.

Figure 4.48 *Global annual mean surface air temperature trends since 1880. The 1951–1980 mean surface air temperature has been used as the zero-point base for comparison.*

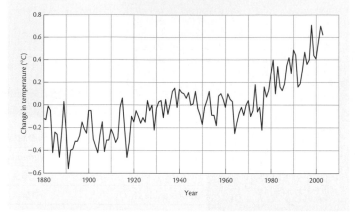

These observed and predicted increases in average global surface temperatures are often referred to as *global warming*, which was a concern mentioned by Isaiah Martin at the beginning of this unit.

An international panel of climate scientists has predicted that under a business-as-usual scenario, in which no steps are taken to control the release of human-generated CO_2 and other greenhouse gases, the average global surface temperature could rise 0.8 °C to 2.9 °C (1.4 °F to 5.8 °F) in the next 50 years and 1.4 °C to 5.8 °C (2.2 °F to 10 °F) in the next 100 years, with significant regional variation. This prediction can be compared to evidence that Earth has warmed only 3 °C to 5 °C since the depths of the last Ice Age, some 20 000 years ago.

The 2001 report of the United Nations Intergovernmental Panel on Climate Change reported that Earth's average global surface air temperature increased by 0.4 °C to 0.8 °C over the past 100 years. The 2000-page report was prepared by 500 climate scientists and reviewed by another 500 climate experts.

Although most climate specialists agree that Earth's average temperature will increase, there is still some disagreement about causes of this predicted warming. New data indicate that the lower atmosphere may not be warming at the same rate as Earth's surface, which suggests that additional factors contribute to the buildup of greenhouse gases and to the warming trend. Among these additional factors is the circulation of ocean water. Ocean currents, such as El Niño and La Niña, transport thermal energy within the oceans and can affect climates when this energy is transferred to land and to the atmosphere.

Possible Impact

What are the projected effects of global warming? Based on the assumption that the average temperature increases 0.5 °C per decade, the oceans are predicted to rise about 5 cm each decade over this century. This is due to the major effect of melting polar ice caps and also to a very small contribution of expansion of ocean water with increasing temperature. Such changes could produce an approximately 15-cm increase in ocean levels by 2030, a situation that could cause flooding in coastal cities, such as Miami and New York. Possible regional climate changes, including reduced summer precipitation and soil moisture in North America, might be expected (see Figure 4.49). For example, northern regions might benefit from lengthened growing seasons, while growers in southern regions would probably shift to crops that can benefit from warmer winters.

What Can Be Done?

Scientists today understand the influence of CO_2 and other greenhouse gases on world climate better than they did even a decade ago. Sophisticated computer modeling has enhanced their research efforts. This new understanding supports the idea of a surface global warming trend. In 1992, representatives of more than 150 nations developed the Framework Convention on Climate Change, where they agreed to develop policies and procedures to reduce greenhouse gas emissions. In 1997, the third meeting of parties to this agreement, held in Kyoto, Japan, resulted in a protocol to address climate change. By late 2004, 126 nations had signed the protocol; thus, this international agreement entered into force in 2005, since, according to the protocol's stipulations, it had been ratified by nations producing at least 55% of 1990 emissions of six gases, including CO_2.

The *Kyoto Protocol* sets ambitious goals for reducing greenhouse gas emissions. For industrialized nations, this involves developing energy-efficient technologies, relying more heavily on renewable energy, and applying alternative processes that do not release greenhouse gases into the atmosphere. For instance, an alternative process has been developed for producing the polystyrene foam used to make such items as plastic egg cartons and meat trays. This process uses CO_2 that would normally be released during production of ammonia. The captured CO_2 replaces chlorofluorocarbons (CFCs) that had been used in this foam-producing process, thus reducing greenhouse gases in two ways. First, CO_2 that would normally be released by another industry is used. Second, CO_2 replaces CFCs, which have a global-warming potential much greater than that of CO_2. In an application of Green Chemistry principles, Hangers Cleaners, a chain of dry-cleaning stores, also uses liquid carbon dioxide (formed by compressing the gas under high pressure) and special detergents to replace potentially harmful dry-cleaning solvents.

Figure 4.49 *The glacier on Mt. Kilimanjaro as photographed in February 1993 (top) and in February 2000 (bottom).*

As of 2005, some industrialized nations, including the United States and Australia, had not ratified the Kyoto Protocol.

This topic presents a good opportunity to explore the ideas of *cycles*. Both the global carbon cycle and the global water cycle are important in understanding global change related to greenhouse gas buildup. Both cycles operate to keep levels fairly constant within the various reservoirs (atmosphere, lithosphere, biosphere, hydrosphere), but levels will shift in response to stress on the system.

Another topic that ties into this material well is Green Chemistry. Green Chemistry seeks (among other goals) to eliminate pollution at its source by changing methods and starting materials. Students first encountered the Green Chemistry principles in Unit 3. You may decide to revisit principles of Green Chemistry and ask students how they might apply those principles to the problem of air pollution. The use of waste CO_2 to produce polystyrene, described on page 357, is an excellent example of Green Chemistry principles in action.

Using the Figures

Figure 4.49: These photos and their potential role as indicators of global warming can be good springboards for considering the processes of scientific investigation. Are these photos *direct* proof of global warming? The majority of the scientific community agrees that global warming is a concern, but considerable confusion and uncertainty remain. Encourage discussion of this issue, focusing on how scientists gather evidence and use it to clarify and support their conclusions.

Developing Skills

B.12 Trends in Atmospheric CO$_2$ Levels

Students use trends to predict near-future situations. They plot known atmospheric CO$_2$ concentrations by year and extrapolate to predict CO$_2$ concentrations in 2050. To facilitate extrapolation, tell students to create a y-axis that includes 600 ppm.

Preparing a transparency of the graph may be useful in helping students extrapolate the results. During the discussion be sure to emphasize limitations of extrapolation and underlying assumptions that support its use.

Mauna Loa Observatory (on the Big Island of Hawaii) continually monitors and collects data relating to atmospheric change. The key areas of investigation include carbon-cycle gases (such as CO$_2$), ozone, water vapor, and halocompounds, as well as intensity of solar radiation. The observatory also does some meteorological work. The Web address for its CO$_2$ data is **http://cdiac.esd.ornl. gov/ftp/maunaloa-co2/maunaloa.co2**, and the general Web address for the Mauna Loa Observatory is **http://www.mlo.noaa.gov/**.

Answers

Mauna Loa CO$_2$ concentrations

1. See graph
2. CO$_2$ levels increased slowly until about 1970 and more rapidly into the early 2000s.
3. a. ~375–380 ppm
   b. ~420 ppm
   c. ~460–500 ppm

4. a. The prediction for next year
   b. The rate of CO$_2$ buildup in the atmosphere may change from previous rates. The further into the future we extrapolate, the more uncertain our prediction becomes.

Developing Skills

| Table 4.6

B.12 TRENDS IN ATMOSPHERIC CO$_2$ LEVELS

The CO$_2$-level data reported in Table 4.6 summarize average measurements of trapped gas bubbles in Antarctic ice or, more recently, of air at the Mauna Loa Observatory in Hawaii. These data are also available on the Internet. If possible, locate the most recent annual data before you start this activity. Graph the data summarized in Table 4.6. Prepare the x-axis scale to include the years 1800 to 2050 and the y-axis to represent CO$_2$ levels from 280 ppm to 600 ppm. Plot the data and draw a smooth curve to indicate the trend among plotted points.

APPROXIMATE CARBON DIOXIDE LEVELS IN THE ATMOSPHERE, 1800–2003

Year	Approximate CO$_2$ Level (ppm by volume)
1800	283
1820	284
1840	285
1860	286
1880	291
1900	297
1920	303
1940	309
1960	317
1965	320
1970	326
1975	331
1980	339
1985	346
1990	354
1995	361
2000	369
2001	371
2002	373
2003	376

Note: Data before 1960 are based on air bubbles trapped in ice-core samples, Law Dome, East Antarctica. Data since 1960 are based on air samples collected at Mauna Loa Observatory, Hawaii.

1. Assuming the trend in your smooth curve will continue, extrapolate your curve with a dashed line from the last year for which you have data to the year 2050. You can now make and evaluate some predictions, using the graph you have just completed.

2. What does your graph indicate about the general change in CO$_2$ levels since 1800?

3. Based on your extrapolation, predict CO$_2$ levels for
   a. next year.
   b. the year 2020.
   c. the year 2050.

4. a. Which of your predictions from Question 3 is likely to be the most accurate?
   b. Why?

5. a. Does your graph predict a doubling of the 1900 CO$_2$ level?
   b. If yes, in what year will this doubling presumably occur?

6. a. What assumptions must you make when extrapolating from known data trends?
   b. How do these assumptions affect the accuracy of your predictions?

7. Why might present CO$_2$ data for air samples collected at Mauna Loa Observatory be different from data collected at other locations around the planet?

8. At the beginning of this unit, Kayla Johnson was quoted as claiming that the carbon dioxide added to the atmosphere by bus exhaust should not be problematic because it is already a natural component of the atmosphere. Based on your graph and what you have learned about greenhouse gases, such as carbon dioxide, how would you respond to Kayla's assertion?

B.13 CONSIDERING GREENHOUSE GASES

Making Decisions

Later in this unit, you will design and write a special newspaper feature on the school bus-idling policy that recently was approved at Riverwood High School. Consider the following questions as you prepare to inform *Riverwood High Gazette* readers about this new policy.

1. Do idling school buses generate any greenhouse gases? If yes, list the typical gases produced.

2. If the school bus-idling policy were implemented, would the policy resolve the issue of school buses and greenhouse gases? Why?

3. Assume that Riverwood High School buses were hybrid vehicles, as shown in Figure 4.50. How would this fact alter the benefits or drawbacks of the school bus-idling policy?

> See Unit 3, pages 291 to 293, for background on hybrid vehicles.

4. List three other forms of transportation that students could use to get to and from school. For each transportation mode listed, discuss its potential for emitting greenhouse gases, such as CO_2. Consider whether strategies, such as the school bus-idling policy, could reduce CO_2 emissions from these transportation sources. Describe such strategies, if they are applicable.

As you learned in Unit 1, water is naturally cleansed through processes within the hydrologic system. Similar cleansing of air takes place in the atmosphere; impurities are converted to more polar, water-soluble forms (hydrocarbons are converted to CO_2 and H_2O, for instance). These substances are then removed from the atmosphere through precipitation, which also is called a *raining-out process*. The consequences and effects of these natural processes, as well as the possible effects of human influences on these processes, are considered in Section C.

| **Figure 4.50** *A hybrid electric bus.*

---

7. CO_2 levels depend on the location, the type of industry, and the climate of the location. Mauna Loa is on a tropical island with low industrial development but near volcanic activity.

8. Students may say that the CO_2 contributed by idling buses is in addition to natural CO_2 in the atmosphere.

Making Decisions

B.13 Considering Greenhouse Gases

Answers

1. Yes. They produce CO_2, water vapor, and unreacted hydrocarbons.

2. No. School buses will still produce CO_2, but not until they are moving.

3. Hybrid vehicles do not produce emissions when they are idling (see Unit 3), so there would be no need for the "no idling" policy. See **http://www.ieahev.org/ hybrid.html** for background information.

4. Possible answers: *Personal cars*— emit CO_2, car pool; *parent drop off/pick up*—emit CO_2, no idling while waiting, car pool; *city bus*— emits CO_2, no idling if stopped more than 30 seconds; *walking*— CO_2 only from respiration; *bike or skateboard*—CO_2 only from respiration; *subway/train*—CO_2 from electric power plant, increased efficiency

---

5. a. Yes
   b. Within the next 50 to 60 years
6. a. That there will be no drastic change in the processes that have produced the known data and that the data are reliable and consistent

   b. If the data are not reliable or consistent, the prediction will be unreliable. The extrapolation will not be valid if the processes that resulted in the original data change.

SECTION B SUMMARY

 Section B Supplement

Reviewing the Concepts

1. The frequency of radiation is directly proportional to its energy. $E = h\nu$

2. It implies a range. Each type of electromagnetic radiation covers a specific range of wavelengths.

3. Only visible light interacts with chlorophyll molecules in plants.

4. a. Infrared, visible, ultraviolet
   b. Infrared radiation heats the atmosphere, visible radiation provides energy for photosynthesis, and ultraviolet radiation is essential to vitamin D production.

5. Photons in UV-C have sufficient energy to break bonds, which kills bacteria and viruses.

6. Most infrared, UV-C, UV-B, and much UV-A radiation are absorbed in the atmosphere, while more than 90% of visible radiation reaches earth's surface.

7. Warming the planet and energizing the water cycle and photosynthesis reactions

8. a. Asphalt heats up quickly, while water heats up slowly.
   b. Specific heat capacity and reflectivity

9. White reflects all frequencies of visible light; colored materials absorb some frequencies. Absorbed energy is converted to thermal energy, so wearing white helps one keep cooler.

10. The pan material should have a relatively low specific heat capacity so that it will heat up and cool down quickly. The handle material should have a much higher heat capacity. (Low conductivity is also important.)

11. Iron. The specific heat capacity of aluminum is much higher than that of iron.

SECTION B SUMMARY
Reviewing the Concepts

Electromagnetic radiation includes X-rays; gamma rays; ultraviolet (UV), visible, and infrared (IR) radiation; radio waves; and microwaves. The energy transmitted by electromagnetic radiation varies according to its wavelength; the shorter the wavelength, the higher the energy.

---

1. Write an equation or a sentence that describes the relationship between the frequency of electromagnetic radiation and its energy.

2. Why is the word *spectrum* a good descriptor of the types of energy found in electromagnetic radiation?

3. Why is visible light useful in plant photosynthesis, while other forms of electromagnetic radiation are not?

4. a. List the main types of electromagnetic radiation in order of increasing energy.
   b. Describe how each type of radiation listed in your answer to Question 4a affects living things.

5. Ultraviolet light is often used to sterilize chemistry laboratory protective goggles. Why is ultraviolet light effective for this use, while visible light is not effective?

Earth's atmosphere protects living organisms by absorbing and distributing solar radiation.

---

6. Compare infrared, visible, and ultraviolet radiation in terms of how well they are absorbed by the atmosphere.

7. Describe two main effects of the solar radiation that reaches Earth's surface.

Electromagnetic radiation can interact with matter to transfer energy. The change in temperature of a material when thermal energy is absorbed depends on its specific heat capacity.

---

8. a. Compare lake water and asphalt in terms of how readily each warms up when exposed to sunlight.
   b. What properties of these two materials account for differences in their behavior?

9. From a scientific viewpoint, why do many desert dwellers elect to wear white or light-colored garments?

10. Given their respective functions, compare the specific heat capacities of the material from which the *handle* of a frying pan is made and the material from which the frying pan itself is made.

11. Given the same energy input, which would you expect to have the greater temperature increase, equal masses of aluminum or iron? Refer to Table 4.4 on page 345. Explain your answer in terms of the concept of specific heat capacity.

12. Lake Erie has a water volume of about 484 km³. How much energy would be required to raise its temperature 1 °C? Show your calculations.

13. Normal human body temperature is about 37 °C. Room temperature is usually about 25 °C:
    a. How much energy is required to raise the temperature of 1.0 L of air (density = 0.0012 g/mL) from room temperature to body temperature?
    b. How much energy is required to raise the temperature of 1.0 L of liquid water (density = 1.0 g/mL) from room temperature to body temperature?
    c. Using your answers to Questions 13a and 13b, explain why cold water, or even room-temperature water, feels colder on the skin than does air at the same temperature.

12. $E = mC\Delta T = 484 \text{ km}^3 \times$
$$\left(\frac{1000 \text{ m}}{1 \text{ km}}\right)^3 \times \left(\frac{100 \text{ cm}}{1 \text{ m}}\right)^3 \times \frac{1 \text{ g}}{1 \text{ cm}^3} \times$$
$$4.18 \frac{\text{J}}{\text{g} \times °\text{C}} \times 1 \text{ °C} = 2.02 \times 10^{18} \text{ J}$$

13. a. $E = mC\Delta T = 1.0 \text{ L} \times \dfrac{1000 \text{ mL}}{1 \text{ L}} \times$
$$\frac{0.0012 \text{ g}}{1 \text{ mL}} \times 1.00 \frac{\text{J}}{\text{g} \times °\text{C}} \times$$
$$(37 \text{ °C} - 25 \text{ °C}) = 14 \text{ J}$$

b. $E = mC\Delta T = 1.0 \text{ L} \times \dfrac{1000 \text{ mL}}{1 \text{ L}} \times$
$$\frac{1.0 \text{ g}}{1 \text{ mL}} \times 4.18 \frac{\text{J}}{\text{g} \times °\text{C}} \times (37 \text{ °C} - 25 \text{ °C})$$
$$= 5.0 \times 10^4 \text{ J or 50. kJ}$$

c. Water readily absorbs energy from the body without much change in water temperature, while air close to one's body warms quickly without much energy transfer from the body.

Some atmospheric gases, such as carbon dioxide, methane, and water vapor, absorb infrared radiation.

14. Describe how atmospheric CO_2 and water vapor help maintain moderate temperatures at Earth's surface.

15. List two natural processes and two human activities that can increase the amount of
    a. CO_2 in the atmosphere.
    b. CH_4 in the atmosphere.

16. What changes in the composition of the atmosphere would cause the average surface temperature of the Earth to
    a. increase?   b. decrease?

17. Explain why, on a sunny winter day, a greenhouse with transparent glass walls is much warmer than is a structure with opaque wooden walls.

18. Draw sketches to show how
    a. a greenhouse works.
    b. the global greenhouse effect works.

Cycles, such as the carbon cycle, play important roles within the workings of the atmosphere.

19. List three chemical reservoirs of carbon atoms.

20. Explain how, over time, a particular carbon atom can be part of the atmosphere, biosphere, lithosphere, and hydrosphere.

21. Write a chemical equation that depicts the transfer of a carbon atom between any two "spheres" listed in Question 20.

Connecting the Concepts

22. Many inexpensive sunglasses block visible light, but they do not block ultraviolet radiation. Explain the hazards of wearing such sunglasses at the beach or on a ski slope during a bright, sunny day.

23. If the air–fuel mixture is incorrect when using a Bunsen burner, the yellow flame will deposit black carbon on the bottom of a heating beaker of water. Explain why, in terms of limiting reactants.

24. Consider the following equation, which is part of a series of chemical changes used to recover sulfur from hydrogen sulfide (H_2S) produced during crude-oil processing and natural-gas processing:

    $$2\ H_2S + SO_2 \longrightarrow 3\ S + 2\ H_2O + Heat$$

    a. If 4.0 mol H_2S and 3.0 mol SO_2 are the reactants, which is the limiting reactant?
    b. If 7.5 mol H_2S and 2.8 mol SO_2 are the reactants, which is the limiting reactant?

25. Consider the equation shown in Question 24:
    a. What mass of H_2S would be required to react completely with 205 g SO_2?
    b. If 45.4 kg SO_2 and 67.3 kg H_2S were present in the reaction chamber, which would become the limiting reactant?

26. If you see considerable black exhaust emitted by a bus, what might that indicate about the combustion processes in the engine?

27. a. What would be the effect on the average global temperature if significant atmospheric increases occurred in
    i. carbon dioxide?
    ii. methane?
    iii. water vapor?
    b. How would such global temperature changes, in turn, affect Earth's atmosphere? Explain.

---

19. Atmospheric CO_2, $CaCO_3$ in limestone, natural gas (CH_4), and organic compounds

20. Example: A C atom contained in a molecule of CO_2 in the atmosphere is taken up by a tree (biosphere) for photosynthesis. The C atom then becomes part of a fossil fuel (lithosphere), which is burned to emit the C atom back into the atmosphere (as CO_2). The CO_2 then dissolves in the ocean, becoming part of the hydrosphere.

21. Examples include:
    $$6\ CO_2 + 6\ H_2O \longrightarrow C_6H_{12}O_6 + 6\ O_2$$
    $$CH_4 + 2\ O_2 \longrightarrow CO_2 + 2\ H_2O$$

Connecting the Concepts

22. The dark lenses cause the iris to open wide, allowing harmful UV light to enter.

23. If the limiting reactant in combustion is oxygen, other products, such as CO and C, will form instead of CO_2.

24. a. H_2S
    b. SO_2

25. a. $? \text{ g } H_2S = 205 \text{ g } SO_2 \times$
    $\dfrac{1 \text{ mol } SO_2}{64.07 \text{ g } SO_2} \times \dfrac{2 \text{ mol } H_2S}{1 \text{ mol } SO_2} \times$
    $\dfrac{34.09 \text{ g } H_2S}{1 \text{ mol } H_2S} = 218 \text{ g } H_2S$
    b. Given 45.4 kg SO_2:
    $? \text{ g } H_2S = 45\ 400 \text{ g } SO_2 \times$
    $\dfrac{1 \text{ mol } SO_2}{64.07 \text{ g } SO_2} \times \dfrac{2 \text{ mol } H_2S}{1 \text{ mol } SO_2} \times$
    $\dfrac{34.09 \text{ g } H_2S}{1 \text{ mol } H_2S} = 48.3 \text{ kg } H_2S$
    SO_2 is the limiting reactant.

26. Incomplete fuel combustion is taking place.

27. a. i, ii, iii. An increase in surface temperature
    b. CO_2 gas stored in ice, water, and northern forests would be released, increasing its concentration in the atmosphere as well as earth's surface temperature.

---

14. CO_2 and H_2O trap IR that is re-emitted by earth. This maintains earth's temperature at a moderate level.

15. a. Natural processes: respiration, bacterial decay, volcanic eruptions. Human activities: burning fuels, removing green plants.
    b. Natural processes: decomposition, termite emissions. Human activities: refining fossil fuels, raising livestock, growing rice.

16. a. Increased CO_2 and H_2O
    b. Decreased CO_2 and H_2O

17. The greenhouse allows light to enter and traps resulting IR inside. The walls of the opaque structure block most incoming radiation.

18. Sketches should show the glass in a greenhouse allowing light to enter, but IR not passing back out. In the global system, the upper atmosphere takes the role of the greenhouse glass.

Extending the Concepts

28. One type of goggles transforms infrared radiation into an image and is sensitive to a broad spectrum of light from visible light to IR. Other night-vision devices use an image-intensifier tube to amplify amounts of IR and visible radiation not usually visible to the human eye.

29. Example: Bees are sensitive to ultraviolet radiation, which may help them locate flowers.

30. As they absorb energy, their energy increases. Depending on the type of radiation absorbed and the type of molecule doing the absorbing, (1) the molecule's bonds may stretch and contract more vigorously, (2) the molecules might spin more rapidly, or (3) the molecules might move (translationally) faster.

31. Most interactions between matter and radiation depend on interactions between radiation and electrons. Depending on how electrons are arranged, different absorptions are possible. For example, certain arrangements of double bonds allow for absorption of UV or visible light, while other arrangements make a particular chemical bond vibrationally sensitive to IR radiation.

32. Look for explanations that reflect the fact that C cycles constantly between living and nonliving systems (see Figures 4.43 and 4.44). Great amounts are stored in oceans as dissolved CO_2, in forest floors, and in rainforest trees. Students may use other carbon sinks as their examples but should defend and explain their choices.

Extending the Concepts

28. Investigate and describe how night-vision goggles allow objects to become visible in low-light conditions.

29. Some animals "see" a portion of the electromagnetic spectrum different from the wavelengths to which human eyes respond. Investigate some examples and speculate on the benefit of these abilities to the animals you research.

30. In terms of the kinetic molecular theory, describe changes in the behavior of gas molecules as they absorb electromagnetic radiation.

31. Investigate and describe the characteristics of molecules that allow them to absorb various types of radiation.

32. The presence of carbon dioxide in the atmosphere is only one aspect of the global carbon cycle. Assess current scientific knowledge of the global carbon cycle and evaluate the roles of one or more major carbon sinks (carbon reservoirs).

33. Scientists analyze deep-ice samples from the Antarctic to estimate the atmospheric carbon dioxide concentrations many thousands of years ago (see Figure 4.2, page 302). Research and prepare a report on how such ice samples are analyzed to obtain this information.

33. Tiny bubbles of ancient atmospheric gas are locked in the samples. Look for students to discuss analysis techniques. The U.S. National Ice Core Laboratory is a useful source of information on this topic: **http://nicl.usgs.gov/**.

Acids in the Atmosphere

As you learned in Section B, the burning of fossil fuels has world-wide implications. Scientists predict that every region on Earth will be affected, in some way, by increasing concentrations of carbon dioxide in the atmosphere. Unfortunately, this is not the only wide-ranging concern associated with fuel burning. The effects of fuel combustion can be experienced hundreds of kilometers away from the original source, when by-products of combustion (along with other air pollutants) combine with water to produce *acid rain*.

C.1 ACID RAIN

What is acid rain? To answer that question, it is worth noting that "acid rain" does not have to be rain; it can be any form of atmospheric precipitation. **Acid rain** is defined as fog, sleet, snow, or rain with a pH lower than about 5.6, which is the average pH of natural precipitation in the absence of air pollution. You probably recall that pure water is neutral, with a pH of 7. (See Figure 1.44, page 70.) Why, then, does natural precipitation have a pH less than 7?

In Unit 1, you learned that water samples, although they may be clean and healthful, are rarely pure. Even water that evaporates from Earth's surface condenses and dissolves atmospheric gases, such as nitrogen, oxygen, and carbon dioxide. The pH of rainwater is normally slightly acidic, about 5.6, mainly due to the reaction of carbon dioxide with water, forming carbonic acid, H_2CO_3:

$$CO_2(g) + H_2O(l) \rightleftharpoons H_2CO_3(aq)$$

This dilute solution of carbonic acid then falls to Earth as rain, snow, or sleet.

Other natural events can contribute to the acidity of precipitation. Volcanic eruptions, forest fires, and lightning bolts produce sulfur dioxide (SO_2), sulfur trioxide (SO_3), and nitrogen dioxide (NO_2). These gases can then react with atmospheric water in much the same way that carbon dioxide does:

$$SO_2(g) + H_2O(l) \rightleftharpoons H_2SO_3(aq)$$
$$\text{Sulfurous acid}$$

$$SO_3(g) + H_2O(l) \rightleftharpoons H_2SO_4(aq)$$
$$\text{Sulfuric acid}$$

$$2\,NO_2(g) + H_2O(l) \rightleftharpoons HNO_3(aq) + HNO_2(aq)$$
$$\text{Nitric acid} \quad \text{Nitrous acid}$$

The result, as the previous equations suggest, is the formation of acidic precipitation. If rain customarily is acidic, why does acid rain

> The expression *acidic precipitation* is sometimes used instead of acid rain to indicate that any form of precipitation—fog, sleet, snow, or rain—can be acidic.

> Double arrows indicate that both forward and reverse reactions occur simultaneously. You will learn more about reversible reactions on page 375.

> The actual processes that generate acid rain are more complex than depicted here.

Acids in the Atmosphere

Section C explores the issue of acidic precipitation. Students consider sources of acid rain precursors, mechanisms of acid rain formation, and deleterious effects of acidic precipitation. The text introduces Arrhenius definitions of acid and bases, along with equations representing ion formation in each. It compares strong and weak acids and bases in terms of the extent of ionization (or dissociation) and pH. Distinctions are made between *strengths* of acids (and bases) and their *concentrations*. Finally, students explore and test the composition and behavior of buffers in an investigation.

C.1 Acid Rain

C.1 Content Reading Guide

Rainfall is naturally acidic (pH ~ 5.6) because atmospheric CO_2 dissolves in water to form carbonic acid (H_2CO_3). Oxides of nitrogen and sulfur, including NO_2 and SO_2, also contribute to acid rain. When these gases are dissolved by water droplets in the atmosphere, acids form, and the resulting precipitation is more acidic than that found naturally.

The term *acid rain* describes any type of precipitation that includes products of reactions between water and nonmetallic oxides. These oxides are emitted from power plants, industries, vehicles, and other sources that burn fossil fuels or produce nonmetal oxides.

Acid rain can damage natural ecosystems, particularly lakes and trees and flora and fauna living in and around them. Buildings and structures made of metals, marble, and limestone are also damaged by acidic precipitation through reactions with acid rain.

Problems related to acid rain are difficult to manage because pollutants produced in one part of the world may, through natural air circulation, affect structures and ecosystems in another region or political jurisdiction. The U.S. Environmental Protection Agency (EPA) has regulated the nitrogen and sulfur oxides that contribute to acid rain largely through procedures for issuing permits to fossil-fuel-burning power plants. In the 1990s, a system was instituted that allowed utility companies emissions quotas. Companies that reduced their emissions could sell or trade their "emissions credits." You might discuss with students benefits and drawbacks of an emissions trading scheme such as this. Consider, for instance, whether the system will reduce emissions, how it could affect new construction, how power plants can reduce emissions, how each method affects costs, and who the "winners" and "losers" are in this scheme. For instance, power plants using high-sulfur coal when the scheme was instituted may have easily reduced emissions by switching to low-sulfur coal, resulting in job loss for miners and mine owners in high-sulfur coal areas.

The EPA website provides much information related to emissions and emissions trading at **http://www.epa.gov/ebtpages/airairquaemissionstrading.html**.

pose a problem? The fact that this precipitation is *more* acidic than normal leads to the problems associated with acid rain.

Impact of Acid Rain

Why would Principal Powers and others at Riverwood High School be concerned about acid rain? The reality is that sulfur oxides and nitrogen oxides emitted from power plants, various industries, and fossil-fuel-burning vehicles react with water vapor to form acids that lower the pH of rainwater—at times to 4.5 or lower in the northeastern United States. See Figure 4.51.

Figure 4.51 *pH of precipitation throughout the continental United States (National Atmospheric Deposition Program).*

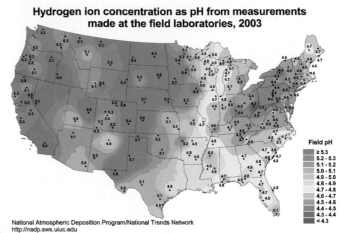

Hydrogen ion concentration as pH from measurements made at the field laboratories, 2003

Field pH
≥ 5.3
5.2 - 5.3
5.1 - 5.2
5.0 - 5.1
4.9 - 5.0
4.8 - 4.9
4.7 - 4.8
4.6 - 4.7
4.5 - 4.6
4.4 - 4.5
4.3 - 4.4
< 4.3

National Atmospheric Deposition Program/National Trends Network
http://nadp.sws.uiuc.edu

Figure 4.52 *This forest in the Czech Republic has been badly damaged by acid rain.*

Similar changes in pH have been observed for precipitation in Scandinavia, Central Europe, and other areas downwind from large industrial centers and power plants. Excessively acidic rain can lower the pH of lakes and streams enough to kill fish eggs and other aquatic life. Acid rain also damages plants by leaching needed minerals from the soil. See Figure 4.52.

Problems caused by acid rain are not limited to effects on natural ecosystems. Most buildings and other structures contain metal, limestone, or concrete, which are all materials susceptible to damage by acids. Statues and monuments (such as the Parthenon in Greece) that have stood for centuries show signs of significant surface damage, due, in part, to acid rain. Acid attacks calcium carbonate in limestone, marble, and cement according to this equation:

$$H_2SO_4(aq) + CaCO_3(s) \longrightarrow CaSO_4(s) + H_2O(l) + CO_2(g)$$

| Sulfuric acid (in acid rain) | Calcium carbonate | Calcium sulfate | Water | Carbon dioxide |

Calcium sulfate is much more soluble in water than is calcium carbonate. Thus, as calcium sulfate forms, it washes away, uncovering fresh solid calcium carbonate that reacts further with acid rain. See Figure 4.53.

Addressing Acid Rain

Control of acid rain is difficult because air pollutants do not respect political boundaries. Carried by air currents, acid rain often shows up hundreds of kilometers from the original sources of air contamination. For example, much of the acid rain that falls in Scandinavia has its origins in the industrial regions of Germany and the United Kingdom. Acid rain falling on New England and southern Canada originates largely from the industrial Ohio Valley in the United States.

The Clean Air Act Amendments of 1990 were enacted, in part, to address issues of acid rain. The compliance plan created by these amendments imposed emissions restrictions on fossil-fueled power plants. Figure 4.54 (page 366) shows that fuel combustion is the largest contributor to SO_2 emissions. To achieve SO_2 reductions, the U.S. Environmental Protection Agency (EPA) issued permits to electric utility plants, particularly coal-burning power plants that have consistently been the largest sulfur dioxide emitters. The permits specify the maximum amount of SO_2 each plant can release annually. As a bonus for reducing emissions, plants with low emissions are allowed to auction or sell their excess permits to plants that produce more emissions. National SO_2 emissions have decreased steadily since the early 1980s.

Reductions in SO_2 emissions were accomplished primarily by using more expensive lower-sulfur coal. From 1988 to 1997, the percent of low- and medium-sulfur coal shipped by rail increased from 82% (221 million short tons) to 92% (337 million short tons), while the percent of high-sulfur coal fell from 18% (49 million short tons) to 8% (29 million short tons). Some power plants have installed scrubbers to remove SO_2 from smokestack emissions, but the cost of this option is currently higher than that associated with using low-sulfur coal.

Unlike SO_2 emissions, which are produced by burning fuels containing sulfur, nitrogen oxide (NO_x) emissions are formed by the reaction of atmospheric nitrogen gas with oxygen gas at the high temperatures associated with most forms of combustion—including internal combustion engines.

Figure 4.53 *Acid rain has disfigured these limestone gargoyles on the Cathedral of Notre Dame in Paris, France.*

Scrubbers are described in Section D.

Using the Figures

Figure 4.51: You can refer to this figure several times in Section C. First, ask students to identify the pH of precipitation in your home region. They can compare this value to "normal" pH of precipitation (5.6). Ask them to describe any apparent patterns in the data (for example, average precipitation along the U.S. East Coast is highly acidic, while average midwestern and West Coast precipitation is closer to normal acidity). Once students have studied chemical reactions and sources that contribute to acid rain, they can formulate explanations for such trends. (**Figures 4.54** and **4.55,** page 366, provide some relevant information.) Once students have studied the pH scale in greater detail, they may *quantitatively* compare the acidity of precipitation in U.S. regions.

Figures 4.52 and 4.53: These two figures depict damage inflicted by acid rain involving nature (a conifer forest) and human-made objects (decorative architecture). Now or at the end of the section, ask students to discuss ramifications of both types of damage, whether one type is of more concern than the other, and which type might be easier to prevent.

ChemQuandary 2

The Rain in Maine . . .

Prevailing winds bring airborne pollutants from power plants and industrial facilities (and large cities) in the central United States and the Great Lakes area to Maine. These pollutants combine with water and fall as acidic precipitation in Maine.

Investigating Matter

C.2 Making Acid Rain

 C.2 Making Acid Rain Student Worksheet and Data Table

The purpose of this investigation is to make "acid rain," then to observe its effects on plant material, an active metal, and marble.

Time

50 min

Materials

(For 12 student pairs)

Pieces of fresh cut red apple peel

12 cm magnesium ribbon, cut into
1-cm segments

12 test tubes (18 × 150 mm)

12 pint-sized zip-seal plastic bags

36 Beral pipets

24 marble chips (calcium carbonate
[CaCO₃])

12 g sodium sulfite (Na_2SO_3)

25 mL 6.0 M HCl (hydrochloric
acid), (50 mL 12 M HCl/100 mL
solution)

1 pkg. Hydrion (pH) paper

1 pkg. red litmus paper

1 pkg. blue litmus paper

paper towels

250 mL distilled water

1 peeler or paring knife

| **Figure 4.54** SO_2 emissions by source, 2002. EPA data.

Industrial processes 9%
Transportation 5%
Miscellaneous <1%
Stationary fuel burning (power plants, heating, etc.) 86%

| **Figure 4.55** NO_x emissions by source, 2002. EPA data.

Transportation 56%
Miscellaneous 2%
Stationary fuel burning (power plants, heating, etc.) 37%
Industrial processes 5%

Nitrogen monoxide (NO), which is also called nitric oxide, and nitrogen dioxide (NO_2) are sometimes referred to collectively as NO_x (pronounced "nocks").

Figure 4.55 indicates that fuel combustion by power plants is joined by transportation as major sources of nitrogen oxide emissions. Although the 2002 national SO_2 emissions were 39% lower than in 1993, total national NO_x emissions were only 12% lower. The EPA estimates that reducing NO_x emissions from fixed-location sources, such as power plants, is a cost-effective strategy. But the issue of NO_x emissions from mobile sources, such as automobiles and other modes of transportation, has yet to be addressed.

ChemQuandary 2

THE RAIN IN MAINE . . .

The state of Maine has no coal-fired power plants and relatively few residents. (The average population density of Maine is approximately 41 people per square mile; Maine's largest city, Portland, has about 64 000 residents). However, Figure 4.51 (page 364) indicates that the average pH of precipitation in the state is lower than that of rainfall free of air contaminants (pH ~ 5.6). Why might this be?

Investigating Matter

C.2 MAKING ACID RAIN

Introduction

 Lab Video: Making Acid Rain

Have you seen any evidence of the effects of acid rain near where you live? In this investigation, you will generate some laboratory-scale "acid rain." You then will observe the effects this acidic solution has on

Safety

Students should wear protective goggles and aprons throughout the investigation. Use caution when handling 6 M HCl. Acetone is highly flammable. Use only with proper ventilation. The sulfur dioxide gas generated during the investigation is an irritant. Caution students to avoid inhaling this gas.

Advance Preparation

The red apple skins should be wiped with acetone to dissolve any protective wax, then rinsed with water and dried.

plant material (an apple skin), on a chemically reactive metal (magnesium, Mg), and on marble (calcium carbonate, $CaCO_3$). You will use acid–base indicators to estimate the acidity of the solution. After reading the following procedure, construct a data table appropriate for recording the data you will collect in this investigation.

Procedure

1. Place a 1-g sample of sodium sulfite (Na_2SO_3) in a test tube. Place the test tube inside a one-pint reclosable zip-seal bag, holding it upright from outside the bag.

2. Carefully fill a Beral pipet with 6 M hydrochloric acid (HCl). *(Caution: 6 M hydrochloric acid is corrosive. If you spill it on yourself or others, wash it off thoroughly and inform your teacher. Avoid breathing any HCl fumes.)* Using a wash bottle, carefully rinse off any acid left on the outside of the pipet.

3. Without squeezing the Beral pipet bulb, place the filled pipet inside the test tube containing sodium sulfite. Then carefully add 10 mL of distilled water to the inside of the bag. Make sure that the distilled water does not come in contact with the hydrochloric acid or sodium sulfite. Carefully smooth the bag to force out most of the air. Close the bag with the zip-seal strip. See Figure 4.56.

4. Slowly squeeze the Beral pipet bulb through the outside of the bag so that hydrochloric acid drips onto the solid sodium sulfite. Keep the test tube upright, so its contents do not spill out. Keep the bag sealed.

5. Allow the reaction in the test tube to proceed for 1 to 2 min, gently tapping the test tube every few seconds. After the reaction in the test tube has stopped, gently swirl the water in the bottom of the bag for another 1 to 2 min. Do not swirl the water so vigorously that it mixes with the contents of the test tube.

6. *(Caution: Avoid inhaling the gas released when you open the bag.)* Carefully open a top corner of the bag and, using a clean, dry Beral pipet, transfer three pipets of water from the bottom of the bag to a clean, dry test tube. Reseal the bag. Label the test tube "A."

6 M HCl

Na_2SO_3

H_2O

Figure 4.56 *Seal the Beral pipet and test tube inside the bag with the water sample as shown.*

- Caution students to ensure that the plastic bag is sealed *quickly* after adding materials. It often works well for one student to dispense reactants into the plastic bag and for another student to hold the bag and then quickly seal it. The 6 M HCl is corrosive.

- If marble chips give poor results, substitute small pieces of chalk.

- If an operating fume hood is available, students should only open the bag in the hood after adding the acid.

- Tell students not to sniff the generated gas.

Alternative Procedure

In place of a zip-seal bag, obtain 12 plastic petri dishes and covers. Before the investigation, drill or melt a 0.5-cm diameter hole in each petri cover, 2–3 cm from the edge. Students place 0.5 g sodium sulfite and 5 mL distilled water in separate locations (both of which can be accessed through the cover's hole) in the petri dish and seal the hole in the lid with tape. When students are ready, they secure the lid, lift the tape, add 5 drops of 6 M HCl to the sodium sulfite through the hole, and quickly replace the tape. In a fume hood, rotate the lid so that the hole is directly over the 5-mL sample of water. The tape can be removed and water withdrawn for testing. Dispose of the material in the petri dish in accord with local regulations; clean and dry the petri dishes for later use.

Lab Tips

- Peel the apples just before or during each session to avoid giving students paring knives.

- You may substitute fresh orange peel for apple peel.

- Ensure that students do not pour the test-tube solution into the plastic bag. The *gas* generated in the test tube should acidify the water, *not* the solution itself.

Answers

1. 2 $HCl(aq)$ + $Na_2SO_3(aq) \longrightarrow$
$SO_2(g)$ + $H_2O(l)$ + $2NaCl(aq)$

2. The dissolved gas increased the water's acidity. SO_2 reacts with water to form sulfurous acid and sulfuric acid. The solution turns blue litmus paper red, indicating an acid is present. Hydrion paper changes to red-orange, also indicating an acidic solution.

3. SO_2 + $H_2O \longrightarrow H_2SO_3$

4. The SO_2 produced in this chemical reaction is identical to the SO_2 released by combustion. It dissolves in water to form an acid.

5. Students' reports of pH will vary but probably will be lower than 5.6.

6. Because marble and iron react with acid, the statue and bridge would gradually deteriorate.

7. a. $H_2SO_3(aq)$ + $CaCO_3(s) \longrightarrow$
$CaSO_3(aq)$ + $H_2O(l)$ + $CO_2(g)$

   b. The $CaSO_3$ is soluble and will wash away. This is why marble structures are damaged.

Post-Lab Discussion

Each part of the investigation is designed to model the behavior of acid rain and its precursors in the environment. Discuss experimental results and how they "scale up" to acid-rain effects within the environment. Discuss limitations of this simulation.

7. Peel two pieces of fresh apple skin, approximately 2 cm long, and place them on a paper towel. Add 4 to 5 drops of liquid from test tube A to the outside of one piece of apple skin. Add 4 to 5 drops of distilled water to the second piece of apple skin. (The second apple-skin sample serves as a control. Why?) After 3 min, observe the two apple-skin samples; record your observations.

8. Place one drop of distilled water each on fresh strips of red litmus paper, blue litmus paper, and pH paper. Record your observations.

9. Repeat Step 8, except use solution from test tube A in place of the distilled water. Record your observations.

10. Place a 1-cm length of magnesium ribbon in a separate clean, dry test tube. Add one pipet of solution from test tube A. Observe the reaction for 3 min. Record your observations.

11. Add two small marble chips (calcium carbonate, $CaCO_3$) to the solution remaining in test tube A. Observe the marble chips for 3 min; record your observations.

12. Dispose of all remaining solutions as directed by your teacher.

13. Wash your hands thoroughly before leaving the laboratory.

> Recall from Unit 1 (page 68) that the vegetable dye litmus turns blue in a basic solution and red in an acidic solution.

Questions

1. The gas formed in the test tube by the reaction of hydrochloric acid with sodium sulfite was sulfur dioxide, SO_2. The other products were water and $NaCl(aq)$. Write a balanced equation for the reaction that produced SO_2 gas.

2. What effect did this gas have on the acidity of the distilled water placed inside the plastic bag? Support your answer by referring to specific observations and test results.

3. Write a chemical equation that shows how "acid rain" (H_2SO_3) was produced from SO_2 gas and water inside the zip-seal bag.

4. Explain how this laboratory investigation models the production of acid rain.

5. As you know, precipitation with a pH less than 5.6 is defined as acid rain. How does the pH of your solution compare to this value?

6. If a liquid similar to the solution in the plastic bag moistened a marble statue or steel girders, what effect might it have?

7. a. Write an equation for the reaction between your "acid rain" (H_2SO_3) and marble chips ($CaCO_3$). (*Hint:* Carbon dioxide gas and calcium sulfite solution were two of the three products formed.)

   b. Explain how your equation in Question 7a relates to acid rain's effects on marble statues and building materials.

CHEMISTRY at Work

Using Chemistry to Bring Criminals to Justice

For a moment, no one in the courtroom moved. Aware that everyone was staring at her, Susan could hear the sound of her own heart beating.

Then the prosecutor continued. "Ms. Ragudo, please tell this court," he said, holding up the small plastic bag of white powder, "the results of your analysis of the substance labeled Exhibit A."

For many people, the thought of testifying in a criminal court case is enough to make them break out in a sweat. But for Susan Ragudo, it's just another part of her job as a forensic scientist employed by the Commonwealth of Virginia. *Forensic science*—the use of science in criminal investigations—can describe many types of inquiry. Susan's specialized area involves analyzing crime scene material for evidence of illegal substances.

To identify the unknown white material, for instance, Susan begins by adding the material to a test reagent. Depending on the resulting color change, Susan knows what the substance most probably is. For example, the drug heroin will turn purple, cocaine will turn blue, and so on. Next, Susan uses thin-layer chromatography (TLC) to compare the substance to a known sample of the suspected drug. This narrows Susan's choices even more and also tells her whether one or more substances are present. Finally Susan tests her conclusion by using gas chromatography/mass spectroscopy. Then she returns the material—and her analysis data—to law enforcement officers.

Susan explains that in her field it is essential to know one's way around a laboratory. It's also important to have an analytical mind—to "zero in on" an unknown material logically, by conducting and interpreting tests. Susan adds that she must also be comfortable speaking in public, because she sometimes testifies in court about her findings.

Calling All Sleuths

Susan Ragudo uses chemistry to help determine whether materials are illegal drugs. In what other types of criminal investigation could chemistry be helpful? What types of tests could be used? Write a story about a crime in which everyone overlooks a small chemical clue—everyone but you, that is. Don't be bashful—make yourself the hero, and explain how you used a basic understanding of chemistry to unravel the crime and convict the criminal!

Truth vs. Evidence

1. Some chemical tests can conclusively prove what a substance is *not*; it is often much harder to establish what it *is*. Explain why one type of proof is more difficult than the other.

2. Most tests are quite reliable but still may only be 95% or 99% accurate. Given that no test is likely to be 100% accurate, how sure must evidence be for you to accept it as "the truth"? Explain your answer.

3. Juries sit in judgment regarding the facts in a criminal case. Who serves as the jury in deciding which scientific research results are regarded as true?

Section C   Acids in the Atmosphere   369

Demonstration ideas

1. Place a drop of paramecium (or mixed) culture on a microscope slide. Pond water, if available, provides an interesting alternative. Allow student groups to examine the drop under the microscope and record observations—or use a video microscope to display the slide on a video monitor. Add three drops of the acid rain solution prepared in the zip-seal plastic bag and observe the effects.

2. Fit a deflagration spoon with a one-hole stopper that allows it to be secured inside a 500-mL flask with the spoon positioned about 4 cm from the flask bottom. Remove the deflagration spoon and place about 100 mL of bromothymol blue indicator solution in the flask. Add 1 drop of 0.1 M NaOH. Fill the deflagration spoon with powdered sulfur, ignite it with a Bunsen burner, and secure the spoon in the flask with the stopper. Very gently swirl the flask. The burning sulfur produces sulfur oxides, which react with water, increasing the acidity of the solution. The indicator should turn from blue to green to yellow. Open the flask in a fume hood and dispose of the solution according to local regulations.

Making Decisions

C.3 Preventing Acid Rain

To encourage discussion and exchange of ideas, students should complete this activity in groups of three to five.

Answers

1. SO$_2$ and SO$_3$ form from burning coal and other fossil fuels, often in power plants. Nitrogen oxides generally come from operating automobile engines.

   a. Sulfur oxides are easier to control because there are fewer power plants than automobiles, and it is easy to regulate and monitor power plant emissions. It is harder to monitor nitrogen oxide emissions from millions of moving vehicles across the country.

   b. Regulating power plants may lead to higher energy costs for consumers. It can be difficult to implement anti-pollution measures that may raise costs for consumers.

2. a. Answers will vary, but could include incentives for trying new technologies and tax breaks for companies that reduce emissions significantly.

   b. Answers will vary. Emissions that clearly result from technologies that could be avoided or updated, or from inappropriate conduct, are probably best regulated through penalties.

3. You would need to compare the total emissions released by each vehicle over the same time or distance, including emissions related to production of required electrical energy.

4. Answers will vary. Some possibilities include walking to school or work (no vehicle emissions), turning off lights and computers (decreases need for fossil-fuel-generated power), and buying local products (decreases need for transportation).

Making Decisions

C.3 PREVENTING ACID RAIN

You have learned about the roles of sulfur oxides and nitrogen oxides in forming acid rain, as well as current efforts to control these emissions. Use this information to answer the following questions:

1. a. In what ways is the large-scale generation of sulfur oxides easier to control than the generation of nitrogen oxides?

   b. In what ways is it more difficult?

2. a. Describe incentives that you think could be offered by the government to encourage decreasing SO$_x$ and NO$_x$ emissions.

   b. Which emissions might be reduced more effectively through the use of penalties?

3. In terms of decreasing the total release of sulfur oxides and nitrogen oxides into the atmosphere, how could you decide whether an electric vehicle that uses electricity from a fossil-fuel-burning power plant is preferable to a gasoline-powered vehicle?

4. If students at Riverwood High School decided to reduce their personal contributions to acid rain, what changes could they make in their daily activities? List three reduction strategies they might employ, explaining how each would lead to reduced amounts of acid-rain-causing emissions. It may be helpful to refer to the source categories of acid rain in Figures 4.54 and 4.55 (page 366) and to think about your own daily activities.

C.4 STRUCTURE DETERMINES PROPERTIES

What Is an Acidic Solution?

Arrhenius also proposed that increases in atmospheric carbon dioxide may increase global temperatures.

Swedish chemist Svante Arrhenius, in 1887, defined an acid as any substance that generates hydrogen ions (H$^+$) when dissolved in water. He defined a base as a substance that generates hydroxide ions (OH$^-$) in water. In aqueous solutions, the hydrogen ion released by the acid is bonded to water. Such a combination can be represented as H$^+$(aq), H(H$_2$O)$^+$, or more commonly as H$_3$O$^+$(aq), the *hydronium* ion:

$$H^+(aq) + H_2O(l) \rightleftharpoons H_3O^+(aq)$$

Consider the earlier example of carbon dioxide dissolving in water to produce carbonic acid, H$_2$CO$_3$(aq):

$$H_2O(l) + CO_2(g) \rightleftharpoons H_2CO_3(aq)$$

The transfer of a hydrogen ion, H$^+$, from carbonic acid to a water molecule produces a hydrogen carbonate (bicarbonate) ion and a hydronium ion (H$_3$O$^+$), which is responsible for the solution's acidity:

$$H_2O(l) + H_2CO_3(aq) \rightleftharpoons H_3O^+(aq) + HCO_3{}^-(aq)$$

Water   Carbonic   Hydronium   Bicarbonate
         acid   ion   ion

Most common acids are substances containing one or more hydrogen atoms that can be released as $H^+(aq)$ in water. The remainder of the original acid molecule, with hydrogen's single electron still attached to it, becomes an anion. As shown in the following equations for two common acids, the dissolved acid produces hydronium ion and an anion.

Nitric acid: $H_2O(l) + HNO_3(aq) \longrightarrow H_3O^+(aq) + NO_3{}^-(aq)$

Sulfuric acid: $H_2O(l) + H_2SO_4(aq) \longrightarrow H_3O^+(aq) + HSO_4{}^-(aq)$

Bases are generally composed of a cation and the hydroxide anion OH^-. When such bases dissolve in water, the cations and hydroxide ions separate and disperse uniformly throughout the solution. The hydroxide ions (OH^-) give basic solutions, which also are referred to as *alkaline* solutions, their characteristic properties:

Potassium hydroxide: $KOH(s) + H_2O(l) \longrightarrow K^+(aq) + OH^-(aq)$

Barium hydroxide: $Ba(OH)_2(s) + H_2O(l) \longrightarrow Ba^{2+}(aq) + 2\,OH^-(aq)$

Acidic solutions have more $H_3O^+(aq)$ than $OH^-(aq)$, while alkaline solutions have more $OH^-(aq)$ than $H_3O^+(aq)$. Pure water is a neutral substance (pH = 7.0 at 25 °C); it contains equal amounts of $H_3O^+(aq)$ and $OH^-(aq)$, as is true of all neutral solutions.

Mixing equal amounts of $H_3O^+(aq)$ and $OH^-(aq)$ produces a **neutralization** reaction. When these two ions react, water is the only product formed:

$$H_3O^+(aq) + OH^-(aq) \rightleftharpoons 2\,H_2O(l)$$

Both acidic and basic characteristics are destroyed in this neutralization reaction; pure (neutral) water is produced, which contains small, equal amounts of $H_3O^+(aq)$ and $OH^-(aq)$.

Consider the neutralization of hydrochloric acid with sodium hydroxide, according to this equation:

$$HCl(aq) + NaOH(aq) \longrightarrow H_2O(l) + NaCl(aq)$$

As is true for all neutralization reactions between compounds, this reaction produces water and a salt (an ionic compound).

C.4 Structure Determines Properties

The text defines acids and bases in terms of the ions generated when they dissolve in water: hydronium ion (H_3O^+) for acids and hydroxide ion (OH^-) for bases. It gives equations for formation of acids and bases in water.

Neutralization reactions occur between an acid and a base and result in formation of an ionic compound (a salt) and water. When the added amount of hydronium ion (from the acid) and hydroxide ion (from the base) are equivalent, the resulting solution (of water and an ionic substance) is neutral.

This development is based on the Arrhenius definition of acids, bases, and neutralization. The text does not develop other acid–base concepts, such as the Lewis and Brønsted definitions; this explanation does not require alternate approaches.

C.5 Acids and Bases

Students practice writing ionization and dissociation equations.

Answers

1. a. $HCl(aq) + H_2O(l) \longrightarrow$ $H_3O^+(aq) + Cl^-(aq)$

b. Hydrochloric acid + water $\longrightarrow$ hydronium ion + chloride ion

2. For nitric acid:

a. $HNO_3(aq) + H_2O(l) \longrightarrow$ $H_3O^+(aq) + NO_3^-(aq)$

b. Nitric acid + water $\longrightarrow$ hydronium ion + nitrate ion

c.

$$H_2O \quad + \quad HNO_3 \quad \longleftrightarrow \quad H_3O^+ \quad + \quad NO_3^-$$

For sulfuric acid:

a. $H_2SO_4(aq) + H_2O(l) \longrightarrow$ $H_3O^+(aq) + HSO_4^-(aq)$

b. Sulfuric acid + water $\longrightarrow$ hydronium ion + hydrogen sulfate (bisulfate) ion

c. Sketches should resemble the sketch for nitric acid, with each H connected directly to an O.

3. a. Magnesium hydroxide $Mg(OH)_2(s) \longrightarrow Mg^{2+}(aq) +$ $2\,OH^-(aq)$

b. Aluminum hydroxide $Al(OH)_3(s) \longrightarrow Al^{3+}(aq) +$ $3\,OH^-(aq)$

c. Sodium hydroxide $NaOH(s) \longrightarrow Na^+(aq) + OH^-(aq)$

4. a. $2\,HCl(aq) + Mg(OH)_2(aq) \longrightarrow$ $2\,H_2O(l) + MgCl_2(aq)$

b. Water and magnesium chloride

C.5 ACIDS AND BASES

1. Hydrochloric acid (HCl) is an acid found in gastric juice (stomach fluid):

   a. Write an equation for the formation of ions as HCl dissolves in water.

   b. Name each ion formed.

2. Separate equations for carbonic acid, nitric acid, and sulfuric acid reacting with water are shown on page 371. Note that the expression for carbonic acid's reaction also includes names and molecular models for each reactant and product. Complete the following steps for both nitric acid and sulfuric acid:

   a. Write the equation for the acid's reaction with water.

   b. Write the name of each reactant and product.

   c. Draw molecular models for each reactant and product. (*Hint:* Just as in carbonic acid, each hydrogen atom in nitric acid and sulfuric acid is connected directly to an oxygen atom.)

3. Each base in the following list has commercial and industrial uses. Name each base and write an equation showing the ions that are liberated when the base dissolves in water:

   a. $Mg(OH)_2$, the active ingredient in milk of magnesia, an antacid

   b. $Al(OH)_3$, a compound used to bind dyes to fabrics

   c. NaOH, a compound often found in drain and oven cleaners

4. A person consumes some antacid containing magnesium hydroxide, $Mg(OH)_2$, to relieve discomfort from excess stomach acid, HCl(aq):

   a. Write the overall equation for the neutralization of HCl(aq) with $Mg(OH)_2(aq)$.

   b. Name each product shown in the equation you wrote in answer to Question 4a.

C.6 ACIDITY, MOLAR CONCENTRATION, AND pH

Water and its solutions contain both hydronium ions (H_3O^+) and hydroxide ions (OH^-).

▶ In pure water and in a **neutral solution,** the concentrations of these ions are equal, but very small.

▶ In an **acidic solution,** the hydronium-ion concentration is larger than the hydroxide-ion concentration. In *very* acidic solutions, the hydronium-ion concentration is much larger than the hydroxide-ion concentration.

C.6 Acidity, Molar Concentration, and pH

This material characterizes acidic and basic solutions in terms of their concentrations of hydronium and hydroxide ions. It defines *molar concentration* (molarity), the amount of solute (in moles) per liter of solution. In addition to using mathematical examples, it might be helpful to prepare one or more solutions in front of students to demonstrate molarity as a unit of concentration. Some possible simple solutions are 29 g NaCl dissolved in 500 mL solution to make a 1.0 M

▶ In a **basic solution,** the hydroxide-ion concentration is larger than the hydronium-ion concentration. In *very* basic solutions, the hydroxide-ion concentration is much larger than the hydronium-ion concentration.

Molar Concentration

Chemists often express a solution's concentration as the amount of solute dissolved in a particular volume of solution. When the amount of solute (in moles) is divided by the volume of solution (in liters), the resulting value is called the **molar concentration,** or **molarity (M).** Figure 4.57 illustrates how a solution of a particular molar concentration (molarity) can be prepared in the laboratory.

Expressed in symbolic terms,

$$M = \frac{\text{mol solute}}{\text{L solution}}$$

Thus, if 2.0 mol sodium chloride (NaCl) were dissolved in 1.0 L of total solution, the molar concentration of the NaCl solution would be

$$\frac{2.0 \text{ mol NaCl}}{1.0 \text{ L solution}} = 2.0 \text{ M NaCl}$$

A solution containing 1.0 mol NaCl in 0.50 L of solution is *also* a 2.0-M NaCl solution. Does this make sense? Take a moment to think about why these two solutions would have identical molar concentrations.

Sample Problem: *If 0.16 mol NaCl were completely dissolved in 2.0 L of solution, what would be the solution's molar concentration of NaCl?*

Applying the definition of molar concentration, the answer is

$$\frac{0.16 \text{ mol NaCl}}{2.0 \text{ L solution}} = 0.080 \text{ M NaCl}$$

Figure 4.57 *Preparing a 0.1000-M solution of sodium chromate, Na_2CrO_4. The molar mass of Na_2CrO_4 is 162.0 g/mol. A 0.1000-mol sample of that solute (16.20 g) is dissolved in enough water to produce 1.000 L of final solution. A line etched into the neck of the volumetric flask shown in the photo precisely indicates that final volume measurement.*

The pH Scale

The pH value of an aqueous solution is related to its hydronium-ion concentration (H_3O^+). The symbol *pH* stands for "power of hydronium ion," where "power" refers to the mathematical power (exponent) of 10 that expresses the hydronium's ion's molar concentration.

 What Is pH?

SECTION C

Emphasize that a change of one power of ten in the concentration of hydronium ion (H_3O^+) is equivalent to a one-unit change in pH. The pH scale is an example of a *logarithmic* scale—one unit change in pH represents a tenfold change in acidity and alkalinity, two units of pH change represent a hundredfold change in acidity or alkalinity, and so on. After such a discussion, you may revisit **Figure 4.51** (page 364) with students. Although it is not specifically discussed in the text, depending on the mathematical background of your students you may decide to use the relationship $pH = -log[H^+]$ in your quantitative explanation of pH.

A solution with pH = 0 is *very* acidic; in fact, the solution would have a H^+ (H_3O^+) concentration of 1 M: $pH = -log[H^+] = log(1) = 0$. It *is* possible to have negative pH values. Solutions with H_3O^+ concentrations greater than 1.0 M will necessarily have pH values of less than zero.

C.5 & C.6 Supplement: Acids and Bases

A Note on pOH   pOH is analogous to pH for OH^- concentrations. Generally, $p(X) = -log[X]$. The relationship between pH and pOH at room temperature stems from the self-ionization of water: $H_2O + H_2O \Leftrightarrow H_3O^+ + OH^-$. The equilibrium constant for this process at room temperature is $K_w = 1 \times 10^{-14}$. Thus, $[H_3O^+][OH^-] = 1 \times 10^{-14}$. Taking the negative logarithm of both sides of this equation:
$-log[H_3O^+] + -log[OH^-] = pK_w = -(-14)$
or, pH + pOH = 14.

NaCl solution or 10.1 g KNO_3 dissolved in 100 mL solution to yield a 1.0 M KNO_3 solution. You might also vary the amount of solute and challenge students to calculate the resulting molarity of the solution.

The pH concept, introduced in Unit 1, is explored more thoroughly here. Students should recognize that smaller pH values indicate more acidic solutions. As pH decreases, the concentration of H^+ (H_3O^+) increases. As pH increases, the concentration of OH^- also increases. At room temperature, pH + pOH = 14.0.

C.7 Interpreting the pH Scale

In this activity, students use Figure 4.58 and their knowledge of pH to classify and calculate relative acidities of substances.

Answers

1. a. As the concentration of H_3O^+ decreases, the pH increases.
   b. As concentration of H_3O^+ decreases, the OH^- concentration increases.

   Students may also indicate that the pH value is the opposite of the power of 10 and the product of the concentrations of H^+ and OH^- is a constant.

2. See the table below.

3. 1000 (10^3) times more acidic

4. The Clingmans Dome clouds were 3200 ($10^{3.5}$) times more acidic than normal. Students should give an estimate of between 1000 and 10 000. A pH of 2.0 represents a 0.01-M H_3O^+ concentration, and a pH of 5.5 represents a H_3O^+ concentration between 0.000 000 1 M and 0.000 001 M (actually, 0.000 003 2 M). The ratio is then ~ 3200—$10^{-2.0}/10^{-5.5} = 1/10^{-3.5} = 10^{3.5} = 3200$ (to two significant figures).

5. a. mol NaOH = 10.0 g NaOH $\times$ $\dfrac{1 \text{ mol NaOH}}{40.0 \text{ g NaOH}}$ = 0.25 mol NaOH

   b. $\dfrac{0.25 \text{ mol NaOH}}{2.5 \text{ L solution}} =$ 0.10 mol NaOH

   c. Since the concentration of OH^- is 0.1 (10^{-1}), **Figure 4.58** indicates that pOH = 1 and pH = 13 for this solution.

Figure 4.58 *The relationships among pH, molar concentration of H_3O^+, and molar concentration of OH^- at 25 °C.*

For example, a solution containing 0.001 mol H_3O^+ (1×10^{-3} mol H_3O^+) per liter has an H_3O^+ concentration of 0.001 M (10^{-3} M), and, thus, a pH value of 3. The pH value can be interpreted as the exponent on the power of 10 with its sign changed. Thus, a solution with 0.000 000 01 mol H_3O^+ (1×10^{-8} mol H_3O^+) per liter (0.000 000 01 M) would have a pH of 8. Figure 4.58 shows how the pH of an aqueous solution is related to the molar concentration of H^+ (H_3O^+) and OH^-.

As you have just learned, the pH scale expresses acidity and alkalinity based on powers of 10. Thus, lemon juice, with pH 2.0, is *10 times* more acidic than is a soft drink at pH 3.0, which is *10 000 times* more acidic than is pure water, at pH 7.0 (four steps farther up the pH scale). Similarly, a solution with pH 11.0 is *100 times* more basic than is a solution with pH 9.0.

> Using similar reasoning, a solution with a pOH of 2 would contain 1×10^{-2} mol OH^- (0.01 mol OH^-) per liter.

C.7 INTERPRETING THE pH SCALE

1. Using the values shown in Figure 4.58, describe the mathematical relationship for aqueous solutions at 25 °C

   a. between pH values and H_3O^+ (H^+) concentrations.
   b. between H_3O^+ and OH^- concentrations.

2. Some common aqueous solutions and their typical pH values appear in the following list. Classify each solution as *acidic, basic,* or *neutral* and estimate the hydronium-ion and hydroxide-ion concentrations found in each:

   a. milk, pH = 6.0
   b. stomach fluid, pH = 1.0
   c. a solution of drain cleaner, pH = 13.0
   d. a cola drink, pH = 3.0
   e. sugar dissolved in pure water, pH = 7.0
   f. a solution of household ammonia, pH = 11.0

3. How many times more acidic is a cola drink than milk? (See the information provided in Question 2.)

4. Clouds over Clingmans Dome, a peak in Great Smoky Mountains National Park, have had pH levels as low as 2.0. Compared to rainfall at pH 5.5, estimate how many times more acidic the moisture has been in these clouds.

374   **Unit 4   Air: Chemistry and the Atmosphere**

	HYDRONIUM ION	**HYDROXIDE ION (OH^-)**
a. Acidic	1×10^{-6} M	1×10^{-8} M
b. Acidic	1×10^{-1} M	1×10^{-13} M
c. Basic	1×10^{-13} M	1×10^{-1} M
d. Acidic	1×10^{-3} M	1×10^{-11} M
e. Neutral	1×10^{-7} M	1×10^{-7} M
f. Basic	1×10^{-11} M	1×10^{-3} M

5. Products used to remove clogs in drains contain strong bases, such as sodium hydroxide (NaOH). If drain cleaner containing 10.0 g NaOH(s) is added to a clogged drain pipe filled with 2.5 L water,

  a. how many moles of NaOH were added?

  b. what is the molar concentration of NaOH in the resulting solution? (*Hint:* This is also equal to the molar concentration of OH^- in the solution.)

  c. use Figure 4.58 to find the pH of this drain-cleaner solution.

C.8 STRENGTHS OF ACIDS AND BASES

In everyday discussions of solutions, *strong* tends to be associated with the idea of "concentrated," while *weak* usually means "diluted." (See Figure 4.59.)

However, to a chemist, *strong* and *weak*—in relation to acid and base solutions—have very different meanings. Acids and bases are classified as strong or weak according to the extent to which they **ionize,** or form ions in solution. An acid is considered a **strong acid** if it ionizes completely, meaning that every dissolved acid molecule or unit reacts to produce a hydronium ion and an anion. A base is considered a **strong base** if every dissolved molecule or unit produces an hydroxide ion and a cation. The total number of dissolved molecules or ions does not matter. *Strong* signifies *complete* ionization, while *weak* implies only *partial* ionization.

When a strong acid dissolves in water, none of the original acid molecules remain. Nitric acid (HNO_3), which is found in acid rain, is a strong acid. The complete reaction within a nitric acid solution is represented this way:

$$H_2O(l) + HNO_3(aq) \longrightarrow H_3O^+(aq) + NO_3^-(aq)$$

All of the original HNO_3 molecules have reacted with water, forming hydronium ions and nitrate ions.

In a **weak acid,** by contrast, only a relatively few dissolved acid molecules ionize to form hydronium ions and anions. That is, weak acids are only slightly ionized. Nitrous acid (HNO_2), sometimes also found in acid rain, is a typical weak acid. The partial ionization within aqueous nitrous acid solution is represented this way:

$$H_2O(l) + HNO_2(aq) \Longleftrightarrow H_3O^+(aq) + NO_2^-(aq)$$

Note that a double arrow is written in the equation. It is used to indicate that it is a **reversible reaction;** that is, it proceeds at equal rates in each direction, both to the right and to the left.

An analogy is useful to illustrate this idea of reversible reactions: At a basketball game, if the number of people walking out of the arena to buy snack foods and drinks equals the number of people returning to their seats after buying their snacks and drinks, the system is described as being in **dynamic equilibrium;** two offsetting processes occur at equal rates, producing a state of balance where no net change is observed.

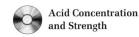
Acid Concentration and Strength

Strong acids are strongly ionized.

Weak acids are only weakly ionized.

Figure 4.59 *What terms would you use to express the relative concentrations of these two tea beverages?*

SECTION C

C.8 Strengths of Acids and Bases

The text defines the strength of an acid or a base by the extent to which it ionizes in aqueous solution. Strong acids and bases ionize essentially completely in solution to form hydronium or hydroxide ions, whereas weak acids and bases ionize only slightly in solution. A common misconception is to confuse *strong* and *weak* with *concentrated* and *dilute*. Emphasize that *concentrated* and *dilute* depend on how much acid or base is dissolved in solution, while *strong* and *weak* depend on the behavior (ionization) of the dissolved acid or base. For example, hydrochloric acid is regarded as a strong acid; in aqueous solutions it ionizes almost completely to produce H^+ and Cl^- ions. Acetic acid is considered a weak acid because only about 1% of its molecules usually ionize in solution.

This presents an opportunity to address equilibria. Weak acids and bases represent equilibrium systems—some molecules ionize while ions recombine. When the rates of ionization and recombination are equal, the system is in dynamic equilibrium. Reversible reactions and equilibrium will be further addressed in Unit 5. The proportion ionized to molecular species at any instant is defined by the equilibrium constant K_a (for acids) or K_b (for bases).

Using the Figures

Figure 4.59: Invite students to consider the caption question before studying the material in C.8. Often, students have an intuitive understanding of concentration based upon everyday experiences. Encourage them to think of the tea solutions in terms of how they might taste or smell.

SECTION C

Modeling Matter

C.9 Strong Versus Concentrated

 C.9 Strong Versus Concentrated Student Worksheet

In this activity, students use two generic acids—one strong (HSt) and one weak (HWe)—to model the behavior of strong and weak acids in water solution.

Students often confuse the terms *strong* and *concentrated*. *Concentration* refers to the amount of solute in a specified amount of solution. *Strength* refers to the proportion of molecules that ionize, forming H⁺ and OH⁻ ions in solution.

Hints

Rather than having students draw on paper, you may ask them to draw models on the board. An alternative is to obtain 1 ft × 1 ft squares of white shower board (usually available at home-improvement stores) and have student groups draw on the boards with dry-erase markers. Students can then use the boards to explain their models.

Answers

1. a. A weak acid or base is one in which there are relatively few ionized particles compared to the number of unionized molecules. A dilute acid or base is one with a low concentration—relatively few solute molecules compared to solvent molecules.

   b. A strong acid or base is highly ionized in water solutions. A concentrated solution contains many solute particles, which may or may not be ionized.

It is important to realize that the forward and reverse *rates*—not the *amounts* of products and reactants—are *equal* in a system at equilibrium. In the basketball-arena analogy, it is clear at any particular time that many more people remain seated watching the game than are moving to and from the snack counters. Likewise, at equilibrium, the concentration of HNO_2 is much larger than are the concentrations of H_3O^+ and NO_2^-. However, a state of balance (dynamic equilibrium) is attained in both cases.

In addition to nitrous acid, acid rain may contain other weak acids, commonly sulfurous acid (H_2SO_3) and carbonic acid (H_2CO_3). Strong acids, such as sulfuric acid (H_2SO_4), may also be present.

Sodium hydroxide (NaOH) and potassium hydroxide (KOH) are two strong bases. Their aqueous solutions completely consist of sodium or potassium cations and OH^- ions. Even though the OH^- concentration may be limited by the solubility of a particular solid base in water, such a substance is regarded as a strong base. Magnesium hydroxide, $Mg(OH)_2$, a commercial antacid ingredient, is an example of a strong (but sparingly soluble) base.

A weak base commonly found in the environment is the carbonate anion (CO_3^{2-}), which is a component of limestone and marble. This poses an apparent contradiction: Why are carbonate anions considered basic, even though they have no hydroxide ions (OH^-) in their formula? The answer is shown by the following equation, where water reacts with carbonate anions to *produce* basic OH^- ions in an aqueous solution:

$$H_2O(l) + CO_3^{2-}(aq) \rightleftharpoons OH^-(aq) + HCO_3^-(aq)$$

Other anions that are basic, such as phosphate (PO_4^{3-}) and sulfite (SO_3^{2-}), also produce OH^- ions in water.

> Only 0.01 g $Mg(OH)_2$(s) can dissolve in 1 L of water at room temperature, but magnesium hydroxide is still regarded as a strong base.

Modeling Matter

C.9 STRONG VERSUS CONCENTRATED

In this activity, you will depict concentrated and dilute solutions of two imaginary acids—one strong (HSt) and the other weak (HWe).

In referring to an acidic solution, as you recall, *strong* indicates that all (or nearly all) acid molecules have reacted with the water to produce hydronium ions and anions. By contrast, *concentrated* indicates that there are a very large number of particles—molecules or ions—dissolved in a particular volume of solution.

Figure 4.60 depicts possible models for strong and weak acids. In this activity, you will illustrate the ideas you have just learned about.

Draw four equally sized rectangular boxes. Each box represents 1.0 L of solution. Use H⁺ to represent hydrogen ions. Each H⁺ symbol will represent 0.1 mol of dissolved hydrogen ions. Do *not* draw the solution's water molecules.

Inside each box, draw between 2 and 20 acid molecules, or the appropriate numbers of hydrogen ions and anions, to illustrate the following conditions:

376   **Unit 4**   Air: Chemistry and the Atmosphere

Sample Student Drawings

Strong/concentrated

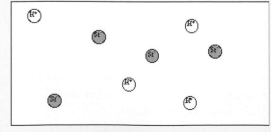

Strong/dilute

376

▶ In the first box, depict a *concentrated strong acid* (HSt) solution.

▶ In the second box, depict a *dilute strong acid* (HSt) solution.

▶ In the third box, depict a *concentrated weak acid* (HWe) solution.

▶ In the fourth box, depict a *dilute weak acid* (HWe) solution.

Use your depictions to answer the following questions:

1. Explain the difference between each pair of words used to describe a solution of an acid or base:

   a. weak, dilute   b. strong, concentrated

2. Calculate the molar concentration (molarity) of hydrogen ions (H^+) depicted in each of your four drawings. Recall that each ion you drew represented 0.1 mol of particles.

3. How would the pH values for the four solutions that you depicted compare to one another?

4. a. Why is it easier to use a single symbol to represent 0.1 mol of particles, rather than trying to draw every particle in 0.1 mol of ions?

   b. How many total particles are actually in 0.1 mol of particles? (Refer to page 161 in Unit 2.)

5. How might your model drawings mislead a viewer about what is actually present in each solution?

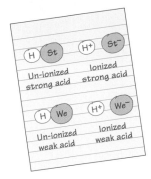

Figure 4.60 *Suggested models used to represent strong and weak acids in solution.*

C.10 ACIDS, BASES, AND BUFFERS

One early mystery associated with acid rain was the observation that the pH of some lakes and streams seemed unaffected by acidic precipitation. What protected these bodies of water from undergoing large changes in pH?

The key to solving this mystery came when researchers realized that bodies of water that suffered acidification due to acid rain (Figure 4.61) had two features in common. First, they were downwind from a dense array of power stations, metal-processing plants, or large cities, all of which produce nitrogen oxides and sulfur oxides. Second, these bodies of water were often surrounded by soils that are unable to neutralize acid carried by the precipitation. If the soil cannot neutralize the acidic precipitation, the lake or stream into which the precipitation drains then becomes acidified.

By contrast, some bodies of water benefit from surrounding and underlying rock and soils that can neutralize the acidic precipitation and, consequently, they are not seriously affected by acid rain. In particular, the effects of acidic precipitation can be greatly reduced by limestone ($CaCO_3$), which reacts with acids to produce soluble calcium hydrogen carbonate:

$$CaCO_3(s) + H_3O^+(aq) \longrightarrow Ca^{2+}(aq) + HCO_3^-(aq) + H_2O(l)$$

However, calcium carbonate can only prevent the pH from changing when an acid is added to the water. If a base is added, there is nothing available to neutralize it and the pH will increase. To keep the pH of a solution relatively steady—that is, neither increasing nor decreasing appreciably if small amounts of base or acid are added—a *buffer* is needed.

 Buffer Action

Figure 4.61 *pH sampling of lake water*

Section C   Acids in the Atmosphere   **377**

2. Answers will depend on the number of ions drawn. Example: A student who drew 2 H^+ ions will calculate

$$\frac{2 \times 0.1 \text{ mol}}{1.0 \text{ L}} = 0.2 \text{ M } H^+$$

3. pH strong, concentrated < pH strong, dilute < pH weak, concentrated < pH weak, dilute

   Students may find that their calculated pH for weak, concentrated acid is less than that calculated for strong, dilute acid. This is possible and quite acceptable for this limited model.

4. a. There would be far too many particles to draw.

   b. 0.1 mol particles is equivalent to 6×10^{22} particles.

5. For most dilute acids, only a small percent of molecules ionize in solution.

C.10 Acids, Bases, and Buffers

A buffer is a system that resists changes in pH when relatively small amounts of acid or base are added to its solution. A buffer must be able to neutralize both acids and bases. Buffers help maintain the pH of ecosystems and body systems.

Buffer Notes   A buffer is a combination of a weak acid and its conjugate base or a weak base and its conjugate acid, often in the form of a salt. For example, acetic acid has a conjugate base of acetate ion, often as sodium acetate. This system resists changes in pH as follows:

Added acid: $H_3O^+ + CH_3CO_2^- \longrightarrow CH_3COOH + H_2O$

Added base: $OH^- + CH_3COOH \longrightarrow CH_3CO_2^- + H_2O$

All buffers are characterized by *buffer capacity,* the amount of acid or base that can be added to a given volume of buffer solution before its pH changes significantly. This depends on the amount of buffer present and on the identity of its components.

Weak/concentrated

Weak/dilute

Investigating Matter

C.11 Buffers

C.11 Buffers Student Worksheet and Data Table

Students compare effects of adding an acid or a base to a buffer solution to similar additions to (unbuffered) water.

Time

30 min

Materials

(For 12 student pairs)

12 24-well wellplates

12 Beral pipets containing distilled water

12 Beral pipets containing 0.1 M NaOH (sodium hydroxide), 0.4 g NaOH in 100 mL solution

12 Beral pipets containing 0.1 M HCl (hydrochloric acid), 0.8 mL concentrated HCl diluted to 100 mL with water

12 Beral pipets filled with a solution prepared by dissolving 5.36 g $Na_2HPO_4 \cdot 7H_2O$ and 2.76 g $NaH_2PO_4 \cdot H_2O$ in 200 mL water

12 Beral pipets containing universal-indicator solution

Universal indicator color charts
Toothpicks

Safety

Students should wear protective goggles and aprons throughout the investigation. *Add acid to water* when diluting hydrochloric acid.

Advance Preparation

Label and fill pipets and place them (tip up) in the wellplate or in an empty cassette tape case for distribution.

A **buffer** is a substance or a combination of substances capable of neutralizing limited quantities of either an acid (H_3O^+) or a base (OH^-) that are added to it without significantly altering its pH value by more than one pH unit. Thus, a buffer must contain two components: (1) an acid to neutralize added base and (2) a base to neutralize added acid. Although calcium carbonate does not act as a true buffer—it cannot prevent added base from increasing the pH—the bicarbonate (HCO_3^-) anion produced serves as a buffer capable of neutralizing *either* added acid or base:

Neutralizing added acid: $H_3O^+(aq) + HCO_3^-(aq) \rightleftharpoons 2\,H_2O(l) + CO_2(g)$

Neutralizing added base: $OH^-(aq) + HCO_3^-(aq) \rightleftharpoons H_2O(l) + CO_3^{2-}(aq)$

In the next investigation, you will observe the unique behavior of buffers and better understand how some bodies of water can withstand the effects of acid rain.

Investigating Matter

C.11 BUFFERS

Introduction

Lab Video: Buffers

In this investigation, you will test a buffer solution. In particular, the results of adding acid and base to water, which serves as the control, will be compared to the results of adding acid and base to a buffered solution. Read the entire procedure and construct a data table suitable for collecting all relevant data.

Procedure

1. Place a wellplate on top of a sheet of white paper. The white paper will help you to observe more easily any color changes during this investigation. (***Caution:*** *The solutions in this activity are corrosive. If you splash anything on your skin, wash the affected area thoroughly with water and promptly inform your teacher.*)

2. Add 20 drops of distilled water to each of two wells. Add one drop of universal indicator to each well that contains water. Record the color of the resulting solutions in your data table. Retain the two solutions.

3. Add 20 drops of buffer solution to each of two other empty wells. This buffer solution contains 0.1 M sodium hydrogen phosphate (Na_2HPO_4) and 0.1 M sodium dihydrogen phosphate (NaH_2PO_4).

4. Add one drop of universal indicator to each well containing buffer solution. Record the resulting colors.

5. Add 5 drops 0.1 M NaOH to one of the previous wells containing water and universal indicator. Note and record the color produced.

6. Carefully counting each drop, slowly add 0.1 M NaOH to one well containing buffer solution and universal indicator until the color just matches the well color produced in Step 5. Record the number of drops required.

Pre-Lab Discussion

Review the function of a buffer using C.10.

Lab Tips

• For best results, students should minimize drop size by using Beral pipets drawn out and trimmed to narrow the pipet stem.

• All references to water are to distilled (or deionized) water.

• Provide universal indicator color charts or tables so students can estimate pH values of their solutions. Students should not try matching the *intensity* of color, only the color itself.

7. Add 5 drops of 0.1 M HCl to the second well that contains water and universal indicator. Record the color produced.

8. Carefully counting each drop, slowly add 0.1 M HCl to the second well that contains buffer solution and universal indicator until its color just matches the well color produced in Step 7. Record the number of drops required.

9. Retain the solutions until you have gathered all data required.

10. Report your group's data to the class as instructed.

11. Dispose of all solutions as directed by your teacher.

12. Wash your hands thoroughly before leaving the laboratory.

Questions

1. What observations suggest the solution you tested is a buffer?

2. a. How many drops of NaOH solution were needed to bring the buffer solution to the same color (or pH value) that was produced by adding 5 drops of NaOH to the distilled water? Explain any difference.
   b. Make the same comparison as in Question 2a for added HCl.

3. The buffer used in this investigation included hydrogen phosphate ions (HPO_4^{2-}). Write an equation that shows how hydrogen phosphate ions could prevent the pH of lake water from decreasing if limited quantities of acid (H_3O^+) were added.

Making Decisions

C.12 CONSIDERING ACID RAIN

As you plan your feature for the *Riverwood High Gazette*, it will be helpful to consider how school bus idling may or may not be linked to acid rain.

1. Isaiah Martin said he heard that bus air pollution creates acid rain (page 300). As you know, sulfur oxides and nitrogen oxides are the primary emissions that lead to acid rain. Does an idling school bus generate either of these gases? Is Mr. Martin correct? Explain.

2. Ms. Powers, principal of Riverwood High School, stated that reducing school bus idling is motivated by concern for students' well-being and for protecting the environment from damage (page 300). To what damage might she be referring?

3. If a "no bus-idling" policy is enforced, will issues of petroleum-burning vehicles and associated air pollution be resolved? Why?

4. At the larger scale of acid rain or global warming, Riverwood idling school bus emissions are relatively small. So why do you think Principal Powers and other citizens believe that a "no bus-idling" policy is useful?

Section C   Acids in the Atmosphere   379

• Universal indicator color changes follow rainbow colors as pH gradually changes from 1 to 13. The mnemonic ROY G. BIV helps students keep the colors straight: Red, Orange, Yellow, Green, Blue, Indigo, Violet. pH 7 produces green.

• If probe ware is available, pH probes can measure the extent of pH changes (if any).

Expected Results

It takes considerably more acid and base to cause buffer solution to change pH appreciably than to make water change its pH correspondingly.

Answers

1. The buffer solution required much more acid or base to change its pH than water.

2. a., b. In each case, much more acid or base is needed to change the pH. The buffer reacts with and neutralizes both acids and bases.

3. $HPO_4^{2-}(aq) + H_3O^+(aq) \longrightarrow H_2PO_4^-(aq) + H_2O(l)$

Post-Lab Discussion

Pool class data so each student benefits from all observations. Each group should report that the buffer system, compared to water, strongly resists pH change.

Making Decisions

C.12 Considering Acid Rain

1. Answers will vary, but should indicate that school bus engines generate NO_x. They may also generate SO_x, particularly if they use diesel fuel.

2. Answers will vary, but may mention acid rain, smog, and the ozone hole. NO_x contributes to both acid rain and smog but *not* to the ozone hole. SO_x is primarily associated with acid rain.

3. No. Buses represent only a small fraction of petroleum-based vehicles, and they generate pollutants while they are moving, even if they do not idle for long. (Point out that without buses, many bus riders would drive personal cars.)

4. Answers will vary, but may involve the "think globally, act locally" idea. Students may mention that exhaust from petroleum burning is considered harmful to human health.

SECTION C SUMMARY

 Section C Supplement

Reviewing the Concepts

1. a. 5.6

  b. Less than 5.6

2. Carbon dioxide reacts with water vapor in the atmosphere to form carbonic acid:

$$CO_2(g) + H_2O(l) \longrightarrow H_2CO_3(aq)$$

3. Natural sources include volcanic eruptions and lighting. Human-generated sources include fossil-fuel burning and industrial processes, such as metal smelting.

4. Reducing fossil-fuel burning and cleaning up industrial exhaust gases

5. Nitrogen oxides, sulfur oxides, and carbon dioxide

6. $SO_3(g) + H_2O(l) \longrightarrow H_2SO_4(aq)$

7. Sketches will vary, but should show pH near 5.6 upwind from the smokestack and lower pH values downwind from the smokestack. Distance from the smokestack is the independent variable (x-axis). pH values should be plotted on the y-axis.

8. a. Base b. Acid c. Neutral d. Acid

9. a. $Ca(OH)_2$ and H_2O

  b. NH_4^+ and OH^-

10. a. $H_2SO_4 + H_2O \longrightarrow H_3O^+ + HSO_4^-$

  b. $HF + H_2O \rightleftharpoons H_3O^+ + F^-$

11. A strong acid is an acid that ionizes completely in water to produce H^+ (H_3O^+) ions. A concentrated acid is an acid with a relatively large number of particles (ions, molecules, atoms) dissolved in a given volume of solution.

12. The hydronium ion consists of a hydrogen ion bonded to a water

---

SECTION C SUMMARY
Reviewing the Concepts

> Rainwater is naturally acidic due to dissolved CO_2, but contaminants in the atmosphere can produce precipitation that is even more acidic than normal.

1. What is the pH range of
  a. typical rainwater?
  b. acid rain?

2. Provide an explanation (including a chemical equation) for why rain is naturally acidic.

> Gaseous sulfur oxides and nitrogen oxides generated from natural and human sources contribute to acid rain.

3. List two natural sources of sulfur oxides and nitrogen oxides and two human-generated sources of these two pollutants.

4. What strategies can reduce emissions of sulfur oxides and nitrogen oxides to the atmosphere?

5. Identify the major acidic components of acid rain.

6. Write a balanced equation representing what happens when SO_3 gas dissolves in water.

7. What pattern would you expect to find among pH measurements of precipitation in the immediate vicinity of an acid-rain-producing smokestack and at regular distances downwind and upwind from the site? Sketch a graph of what you would expect to find.

> Acids produce hydrogen (or hydronium) ions in water, while bases produce hydroxide ions. Strong acids and bases ionize completely; weak acids and bases ionize only partially.

8. Which of the following substances are acids? Which are bases? Which are neutral substances?
  a. LiOH
  b. CH_3COOH
  c. $C_{12}H_{22}O_{11}$ (table sugar)
  d. H_2SO_3

9. Complete the following equations, depicting reactions that yield hydroxide ions:
  a. $??? + ??? \longrightarrow Ca^{2+}(aq) + 2\ OH^-(aq)$
  b. $NH_3(g) + H_2O(l) \rightleftharpoons ??? + ???$

10. Write an equation showing production of hydronium ions as the following acids are mixed with water:
  a. sulfuric (H_2SO_4) acid, a strong acid used in automotive batteries
  b. hydrofluoric (HF) acid, a weak acid sometimes used to etch glass

11. What is the difference between a *strong* acid and a *concentrated* acid?

12. What is the difference between a hydrogen ion and a hydronium ion?

---

molecule—that is, a hydrated hydrogen ion: $H^+ + H_2O \longrightarrow H_3O^+$

13. The concentrations are equal.

14. The hydronium-ion concentration would decrease significantly, because most hydroxide and hydronium ions would react (neutralize each other) to form water.

15. Acidic; it contains more hydronium ions than hydroxide ions.

16. The pH values are simple numbers (usually from 1 to 14) and are more convenient to use.

Acidic solutions contain a higher concentration of hydronium ions than hydroxide ions; basic solutions contain a higher concentration of hydroxide ions than hydronium ions.

13. Compare the concentration of hydroxide ions and hydronium ions in pure water.

14. What would happen to the concentration of hydronium ions in a solution of a strong acid if an equal number of hydroxide ions were added to the solution?

15. One liter of room-temperature solution contains 1×10^{-2} mol H_3O^+ and 1×10^{-12} mol OH^-. Is this solution acidic or basic? Explain.

pH is an expression of the molar concentration of hydronium ions in an aqueous solution. Water solutions with pH 7.0 at room temperature are neutral; those with lower pH are acidic and those with higher pH are basic.

16. Why do chemists often express the acidity of a solution as a pH value rather than as a hydrogen ion concentration?

17. Coffee has a pH of 4.0, and pure water has a pH of 7.0. How many more times acidic is coffee than pure water?

18. A sample of acid rain has a pH of 3.0:

a. What is its hydronium ion concentration?

b. What is its hydroxide ion concentration?

19. Consider the three solutions in the following list, and then answer the questions that follow:

- lemon juice, containing 0.001 M H_3O^+
- stomach fluid, containing 0.1 M H_3O^+
- drain cleaner, NaOH, containing 0.1 M OH^-

a. What is the pH of each solution? See Figure 4.58, page 374.

b. Which solution is most acidic?

c. Which solution is most basic?

Living organisms and the reactions that sustain them may be adversely affected by changes in pH.

20. How would a lake surrounded by limestone respond to acid rain compared to a lake that was surrounded by rock that does not react appreciably with acid rain?

21. Someone proposes that the acid rain problem could be fixed by dissolving large quantities of basic substances in affected lakes. Do you agree? Explain.

22. Cite evidence from Investigating Matter C.2, pages 366–368, that low pH has a harmful effect on plant material.

23. Very acidic solutions can be used to preserve food. Explain how low pH prevents food spoilage.

A buffered solution is capable of neutralizing limited amounts of either added acid or base, thus resisting changes in solution pH.

24. What are the general components of a buffer?

25. $H_2PO_4^-$ acts as a buffer in cellular systems. Write an equation showing the reaction of a $H_2PO_4^-$ ion with

a. hydronium ion.

b. hydroxide ion.

26. Is it better to describe a buffered solution as *resisting* or *preventing* all changes in pH? Explain your answer.

27. Why do some lakes appear unaffected by acid rain?

Section Summary   381

rock that did not react with acid rain would decrease more readily.

21. Answers will vary, but students should support their answers with scientific principles. In theory this approach could work, but it would take a very large amount of basic substances and would only last until all base was neutralized.

22. In *Investigating Matter C.2,* water containing dissolved sulfur dioxide (simulating acid rain) caused an apple peel to discolor. This demonstrated that the acid rain is harmful to the apple, a plant material.

23. Low-pH solutions are harmful to most living organisms, so organisms that cause food spoilage cannot generally survive in highly acidic solutions.

24. A buffer system contains components that can act as acids and as bases and can thus neutralize additions of either. The acid in the buffer system provides H^+ to neutralize the added base, and the base in the buffer system neutralizes the added acid.

25. a. $H_2PO_4^- + H_3O^+ \longrightarrow H_3PO_4 + H_2O$

b. $H_2PO_4^- + OH^- \longrightarrow HPO_4^{2-} + H_2O$

26. Buffers *resist* change in pH. They are limited (by concentration) to their buffer capacity.

27. Some lakes have natural buffering action due to limestone or other materials.

17. Coffee is 10^3 or 1000 times more acidic than water ($10^{-4}/10^{-7} = 10^3 = 1000$).

18. a. 0.001 M $= 10^{-3}$ M

b. 0.000 000 000 01 M $= 10^{-11}$ M

19. a. Lemon juice, 3; stomach fluid, 1; drain cleaner, 13

b. Stomach fluid

c. Drain cleaner

20. A lake surrounded by limestone can neutralize acid rain because calcium carbonate (limestone) reacts with the acid. The pH of a lake surrounded by

Connecting the Concepts

28. Hydrogen hydroxide (HOH), or water, produces equal concentrations of H_3O^+ and OH^- ions.

29. Answers should describe a procedure that tests methane for acidic properties. For instance, moisten blue litmus paper and place it in a container of methane gas.

30. A very dilute solution of a strong acid may have the same number of hydronium ions as a weak acid.

31. Shampoos are buffered to maintain a particular pH to trigger a desired effect on the hair, such as shine. Medicines are usually buffered to control the location in the body where they will dissolve or to protect parts of the gastrointestinal tract.

32. Antacids are basic substances that react with acids in neutralization reactions. Buffers can neutralize both acids and bases.

33. a. 10^{-9} M H_3O^+ to 10^{-5} M H_3O^+
b. 10^4 or 10 000
c. As acidity increases, diversity of fish species decreases, since some species are quite sensitive to changes in pH.

Extending the Concepts

34. Hydrogen cations have a higher charge density than either Na^+ or K^+. Also, hydrogen cations are simply protons, while Na^+ and K^+ have their nuclear charge partially shielded by inner electron shells.

35. Water: Hydronium ion:

Water is a bent molecule. The hydronium ion is trigonal pyramidal, resembling the three legs of a tripod. Molecular shapes can be predicted using Valence Shell Electron Pair Repulsion (VSEPR)

Connecting the Concepts

28. Explain why the substance that could be called *hydrogen hydroxide* has neither acidic nor basic properties. What is a more familiar name for this compound?

29. A methane molecule (CH_4) contains several hydrogen atoms. Describe a laboratory investigation that would allow you to decide whether or not methane behaves as an acid.

30. Explain how it might be possible for a strong acid solution and a weak acid solution to have identical pH values.

31. Why are shampoos and medicines often buffered?

32. In terms of their chemical behavior, compare antacids to buffers.

33. In Unit 1, you learned that most fish can live in water with pH values between 5.0 and 9.0:
a. What range of hydronium-ion concentrations corresponds to this pH range?
b. By what factor does the hydronium-ion concentration differ between these two pH values?
c. Explain how acid rain might affect the distribution of fish species in an affected lake.

Extending the Concepts

34. What characteristics make the hydrogen ion uniquely reactive compared to a sodium or potassium cation with the same 1+ electrical charge?

35. Construct models and draw electron-dot structures of a water molecule and hydronium ion. Compare their shapes, bonding, and interactions.

36. Use the Internet and the library to research and report on serious acid rain effects over the past decade.

37. Examine the list of ingredients for several antacid products. Which ingredients are responsible for neutralizing acids?

38. Is it possible to have a solution with a pH value of *zero*? Does this mean that the solution has no measurable acidity? Explain your answers.

39. Sometimes the zone separating warring or hostile countries is called a "buffer zone." How does that particular use of the word *buffer* compare to a chemist's use of the term?

theory. See **http://www.chem.purdue.edu/gchelp/vsepr/** for information on VSEPR.

36. Effects include acid-rain impact in southwestern China and on the Taj Mahal's 17th-century white marble façade in India.

37. Antacids contain aluminum salts, magnesium salts, $CaCO_3$, or $NaHCO_3$, which neutralize excess stomach acid.

38. Yes. pH = 0 indicates an H_3O^+ concentration of 1 M (10^0 M).

39. In chemistry a buffer maintains a solution in a stable state, despite limited additions of acids or bases. A buffer zone between nations helps maintain peace by maintaining a stable (neutral) area that separates hostile forces.

Air Pollution: Sources, Effects, and Solutions

Polluted air is so common in the United States (see Figure 4.62) that weather reports for some cities include the levels of certain contaminants in the air.

Most air pollutants result from fossil-fuel-based energy production, such as gasoline-powered vehicles or coal-based electricity generation. Depending on where you live, motor vehicles (such as school buses), power plants, or industries may contribute to local air pollution. See Figure 4.63.

Contaminated air often smells unpleasant and looks unsightly. But even when it cannot be smelled or seen, air pollution can be harmful. Air pollution causes billions of dollars of damage every year. It can corrode buildings and machines, and it can stunt the growth of agricultural crops and weaken livestock. Even more grave, air pollution has been associated with diseases such as bronchitis, asthma (Figure 4.64), emphysema, and lung cancer, adding to human suffering and hospital costs worldwide.

Have you had any experiences with air pollution? Take a moment to consider what you know about air quality. What do you think are common sources of contaminated air near where you live? What is the impact of air pollution on public health and on the environment? This section addresses these and other questions.

| **Figure 4.62** *The downtown Los Angeles skyline shrouded in smog.*

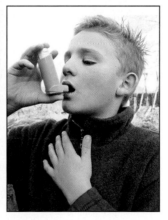

Figure 4.63 *Small-scale, individual activities (such as mowing a lawn) can lead to build-up of air pollution in densely populated cities and towns.*

Figure 4.64 *Air pollution can exacerbate asthma symptoms.*

Section D Air Pollution: Sources, Effects, and Solutions **383**

Air Pollution: Sources, Effects, and Solutions

Section D explores how pollution, particularly that caused by humans, affects air quality. The text considers pollutant sources, control and prevention of air pollution, and the importance of clean air.

As you begin Section D, ask students what they already know about air quality and air pollution. Students will probably be aware of many issues but may not fully understand the science behind their causes and control.

At the end of this section, students will finish writing features for the *Riverwood High Gazette*. If you have chosen to require both first and final drafts, you should allow students one class day to exchange their draft articles with at least two classmates. You may wish to identify criteria by which students judge each other's articles, depending on student experience with peer editing and peer reviewing. You may make the rubric for this culminating activity available now.

Using the Figures

Figures 4.62, 4.63, and 4.64: Use these photographs to discuss students' experiences with air pollution. Some students may suffer from asthma or know someone who does and can speak to air-quality conditions that exacerbate symptoms. Depending on where students live or have traveled, they may have seen a "brown cloud" similar to that in Figure 4.62. The cloud is due to photochemical smog. Ask students for ideas about how photochemical smog forms. At this point, their answers will probably be general. You can point out that photochemical smog often poses problems in highly populated areas that receive considerable sunshine, thus beginning to establish connections between photochemical smog, human activities (specifically, burning fossil fuels), and daylight. Students may mention ground-level ozone (a component of photochemical smog), depending on how "in tune" they are to daily air-quality forecasts. *Cautions:* Air does not need to be colored or smell bad to be considered polluted, and not all air pollutants are generated by human activities. Remind students of this as they examine Figure 4.62.

D.1 Sources of Air Pollutants

This material points out that air contamination can result from human and natural causes. When air contamination occurs faster than natural processes can dispose of it, air pollution becomes a problem. Air pollutants, as the text says, can be classified as primary and secondary. Primary pollutants are contaminants as emitted; secondary pollutants form in the atmosphere from components that may not be hazardous before reacting. Emphasize that this distinction is based on the *origin* of the pollutant, not the *severity* of its effects. Also, some pollutants can be *both* primary and secondary under different circumstances.

A helpful Web site for understanding air-pollutant categories is **http://www.epa.nsw.gov.au/envirom/ prinairpol.htm**.

You might wish to introduce or review (based on students' knowledge of air pollutants) some effects of air pollution. Examples include

• *Minor nuisance:* slight odor and reduced visibility
• *Property damage:* building discoloration, accelerated weathering, metal corrosion
• *Damage to crops:* lower crop yield, plants killed
• *Damage to animals:* eye and respiratory irritation among humans, dead wildlife

D.1 SOURCES OF AIR POLLUTANTS

Many air contaminants such as carbon dioxide, which contribute to rainwater's natural acidity, are the result of natural processes. Natural sources produce more of almost every major air contaminant (except SO_2) than do human sources. In most cases, natural air contamination occurs over wide regions and is seldom noticed. Furthermore, the environment may dilute, transform, or disperse such naturally emitted substances before they accumulate to harmful levels in the air.

By contrast, air pollutants from human activities are usually generated within more localized areas, such as in the vicinity of smokestacks, exhaust pipes, or large population centers. When the amount of an air contaminant overwhelms the ability of natural processes to disperse or dispose of it, air quality can become a serious problem.

Many large cities are prone to high concentrations of air pollutants. If air pollutants generated by activity in large cities were evenly spread over the entire nation, they would have substantially lowered concentrations and be much less noticeable. Unfortunately, weather-related air movement does not produce such even spreading.

Several categories of air contaminants can be identified.

Primary air pollutants directly enter the atmosphere. For example, methane (CH_4) that enters the atmosphere is a by-product of fossil-fuel use and a component of natural gas. Methane is also produced naturally in large quantities by anaerobic bacteria as they break down organic matter, a process that occurs in wetlands, landfills, and even within the digestive systems of animals such as cows and sheep.

Another primary pollutant is actually a class of compounds known as *volatile organic compounds* (VOCs). The term *VOC* refers to a group of hydrocarbons that easily evaporate or that are gaseous at room temperature. Many VOCs released to the atmosphere are unburned fuel molecules emitted from automobiles, trucks, and buses. Release of these compounds has also been linked to natural processes (several types of trees are known to emit large amounts of VOCs) and to human activities that involve easily vaporized liquid hydrocarbons, such as those in some paints, dry-cleaning processes, and near gasoline stations. VOCs are also involved in smog formation, as you will later learn.

Secondary air pollutants are formed in the atmosphere by reactions between primary air pollutants and natural air components. For example, atmospheric sulfur dioxide (SO_2) and oxygen gas react to form sulfur trioxide (SO_3), a secondary air pollutant. Reactions with water in the atmosphere can convert sulfur trioxide to sulfates (SO_4^{2-}) or sulfuric acid (H_2SO_4), a secondary contaminant partly responsible for acid rain.

Particulate pollutants, as shown in Figure 4.65, include microscopic particles that enter the air from either human activities (such as power plants, waste burning, diesel combustion, road building, or mining) or natural processes (such as forest fires, wind erosion, or

> For safety, an odoriferous substance is added to household natural gas, which is mainly methane; the methane itself is odorless.

> As the name indicates, hydrocarbons are made up of C and H. VOCs are primarily composed of these elements, although they may also contain smaller amounts of O, N, and other elements.

> Particulate pollution is also called *particle pollution*.

volcanic eruptions). Common particle pollution includes emissions from smokestacks and vehicle tailpipes, which occasionally are observed as "smoke," but may not always be visible. In fact, virtually undetectable smaller particles that commonly are emitted from diesel-burning vehicles are known as the most dangerous to human health.

Figure 4.65 *Particulate contaminants found in air may include dust, pollen, and soot, all shown here under magnification.*

Synthetic substances are present in air solely as a result of human activity; if not for people, they would not be there at all. For example, fluorine is released in the stratosphere by high-energy ultraviolet photons that interact with a group of synthetic compounds known as **chlorofluorocarbons** (*CFCs*). These compounds will be discussed later in this section. Because no natural sources of stratospheric fluorine are known, the presence of fluorine has provided evidence that CFCs play a key role in stratospheric ozone depletion—a topic that you will consider soon.

Developing Skills

D.2 IDENTIFYING MAJOR AIR CONTAMINANTS

Table 4.7 (page 386) gives a detailed picture of the sources of some major U.S. air contaminants. Use the information provided in Table 4.7 to answer the following questions:

1. Overall, what is the main source of U.S. air contaminants?
2. For which contaminants is one-third or more contributed by
   a. industry?
   b. transportation?
   c. fuel combustion for electrical, industrial, home heating, and other so-called stationary fuel-burning applications?
3. Name one general type of volatile organic compound (VOC) that might be associated with transportation. Explain its source.
4. Based on data in Table 4.7, would the replacement of gasoline-fueled vehicles by gasoline–electric hybrid vehicles eliminate transportation as a source of sulfur dioxide (SO_2) emissions? Why?

What proportion of total air contamination does human activity produce? Automobile use alone contributes about half the total mass of human-generated air contaminants. However, air is also contaminated each time we heat or cool a building, when we use fossil-fuel-based electricity, or even when food items and other products are delivered to retail stores.

Developing Skills

D.2 Identifying Major Air Contaminants

Students analyze data from **Table 4.7** (comparing quantities of pollutants from various human and natural sources, page 386). This is a good opportunity to practice interpreting data from a table. Review this table and ask students some introductory questions before having them complete the activity. Help students realize that choices regarding energy consumption and use of industrial products affect pollution problems.

Answers

1. Transportation
2. a. Pb, VOCs
   b. CO, NO_x, VOCs
   c. NO_x, SO_2
3. Possible answers include gasoline, natural gas, propane, and butane. The release might result from incomplete combustion or from refining or fueling operations (for example, evaporation at gasoline pumps). (Air pollution from VOCs is one reason "topping off" at the gas station is strongly discouraged. The other reason is the possibility of accidentally spilling fuel, creating a fire hazard—which also relates to the volatility of the fuel.)
4. No. Although hybrid vehicles reduce transportation SO_2 emissions, diesel-burning vehicles still contribute to them. Also, hybrid vehicles still burn gasoline and thus produce some SO_2.

SECTION D

D.3 Smog: Hazardous to Your Health

Smog is now generally considered a reduction in air clarity resulting from elevated airborne pollutant levels. Photochemical smog refers specifically to polluted air found over cities resulting from interaction of industrial emissions and automotive exhaust with solar radiation. The major substances involved in photochemical smog include hydrocarbons, nitrogen oxides, and ozone. The type of smog depends on the type of activity, climate, and geography of the area. The text presents the relationship between a temperature inversion and the severity of photochemical smog, along with key ingredients of smog.

SELECTED U.S. AIR POLLUTANTS (IN 10^3 METRIC TONS PER YEAR)

Source	CO	Pb	NO$_x$	VOCs	PM$_{10}$	SO$_2$	Totals
Transportation	69 334	0.513	12 021	7 617	642	1 637	91 764
Fuel combustion							
Electric utilities	404	0.065	4 777	58	245	10 332	15 881
Industrial	1 108	0.015	2 923	168	221	2 625	7 061
Other	2 653	0.374	1 053	868	438	538	5 924
(residential, commercial, institutional)							
Industrial Processes	6 823	2.869	877	7 288	1 127	1 359	20 342
Miscellaneous	18 875	—	523	2 459	19 891	19	41 767
(fires, agriculture and forestry, fugitive dust)							
Totals	79 501	3.559	21 439	17 468	2 829	18 520	

Key: CO   Carbon monoxide
        Pb   Lead
        NO$_x$ Nitrogen oxides
        VOCs Volatile organic compounds
        PM$_{10}$ Particulate matter (<10 μm diameter)
        SO$_2$ Sulfur dioxide

Source: U.S. EPA, *National Air Quality and Emissions Trends Report,* 2001.

| Table 4.7

Figure 4.66 *Donora, PA, at midday in late October, 1948.*

D.3 SMOG: HAZARDOUS TO YOUR HEALTH

Sometimes meteorological conditions interact with air contaminants to form a potentially hazardous condition called **smog.** (The word *smog* is a combination of *smoke* and *fog*). In 1952, a deadly smog over London, England, lasted five days and contributed to the deaths of nearly 4000 people. Four years earlier in the coal-mining town of Donora, Pennsylvania (see Figure 4.66), smog-laden air killed 20 people and hospitalized hundreds of others. Similar, though less deadly, episodes have occurred historically in other cities.

Because substances in smog can endanger health, their levels in the air are of major public interest; many weather forecasters report an *air quality rating*, along with humidity and temperature data. The U.S. Environmental Protection Agency (EPA) has devised the Air Quality Index (AQI) based on concentrations of pollutants that are major contributors to smog in metropolitan areas. Table 4.8 emphasizes that the combined health effects of these pollutants can become quite serious.

		U.S. AIR QUALITY INDICES					
Air Quality Index (AQI) Values	Air Quality Description	Particulate Matter (<10 μm diameter; 24 hour) μg/m³	Sulfur Dioxide (24 hour) ppm	Carbon Monoxide (8 hour) ppm	Ground-Level Ozone (1 hour) ppm	Nitrogen Dioxide (1 hour) ppm	Levels of Health Concern
0–50	Good	0–54	0.000–0.034	0.0–4.4	—	Not reported	Satisfactory; little or no risk.
51–100	Moderate	55–154	0.035–0.144	4.5–9.4	—	Not reported	Acceptable air quality; for some pollutants there may be a moderate health concern for a very small number of people.
101–150	Unhealthful for sensitive groups	155–254	0.145–0.224	9.5–12.4	0.125–0.164	Not reported	Members of sensitive groups* may experience health effects. General public is not likely to be affected.
151–200	Unhealthful	255–354	0.225–0.304	12.5–15.4	0.165–0.204	Not reported	Everyone may begin to experience health effects. Members of sensitive groups* may experience serious health effects.
201–300	Very unhealthful	355–424	0.305–0.604	15.5–30.4	0.205–0.404	0.65–1.24	Health alert; everyone may experience serious health effects.
301–500	Hazardous	425–604	0.605–1.004	30.5–50.4	0.405–0.604	1.25–2.04	Health warnings of emergency conditions. The entire population is likely to be affected.

*High-risk group includes elderly people, children, and those with heart or lung diseases.

Source: Adapted from U.S. EPA, *Air Quality Index: A Guide to Air Quality and Your Health*, 2004.

Table 4.8

Using the Figures

Figure 4.66: You can find more information about the Donora smog disaster at: **http://www.pbs.org/now/science/smog.html**. The smog consisted of SO_2, CO, and metal dust emissions (from plants and coal furnaces in the valley and town), which were trapped by a layer of warm air. During five days, 20 people died and more than 7000 were sickened. Investigations into this disaster led to the first federal clean-air act, passed in 1955.

Using the Figures

Figure 4.67: Ask students to identify some geographic locations that are prone to temperature inversion (coasts, valleys). Discuss whether these locations may also influence the impact of photochemical smog. (For instance, coastal areas tend to be densely populated.) Extensive information about smog is available on the Internet. Some sources include: **http://www.epa.gov/oar/oaqps/ peg_caa/pegcaa03.html**, **http://en.wikipedia.org/wiki/Smog**, **http://www.windows.ucar.edu/tour/ link=/earth/Atmosphere/smog. html&edu=high**, **http://www. smogcity.com/welcome.htm**, and **http://www.epa.gov/NE/airquality/ index.html**.

The term *smog* was originally used to describe any reduction in air clarity, but it now refers to specific hazardous air pollutants (hydrocarbons and nitrogen oxides) that may be present in air even when it appears clear.

Fatality rates in severe smog episodes have been higher than predicted from known hazards of sulfur oxides or particulates alone. According to some researchers, this increase may be due to *synergistic interactions,* where the combined effect of several substances is greater than the sum of their separate effects alone.

A brownish haze that irritated the eyes, nose, and throat and that also damaged crops first appeared in the air above and around Los Angeles, California, in the 1940s. Researchers were puzzled for some time because Los Angeles had no significant industrial or heating activities. However, the city did have many motor vehicles and abundant sunshine. These factors contributed to the formation of *photochemical smog,* which, as you will soon learn, is different than the previously described industrial smog of London or Donora, Pennsylvania. Another factor was that Los Angeles is bordered by mountains on three sides. Although its valley location makes Los Angeles smog-prone, the smog experienced there was much worse than seemed reasonable. There had to be more to this story.

Normally, air at Earth's surface is warmed by solar radiation and by reradiation from surface materials. This warmer, less dense air rises, carrying pollutants away with it. Cooler, less polluted air then moves in below. In a *temperature inversion,* a cool air mass is trapped beneath a less dense warm air mass, often in a valley or over a city (see Figure 4.67).

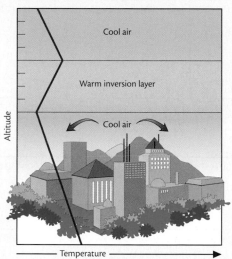

(a) Normal Conditions

Cooler air

Cool air

Warm air

Altitude

Temperature

(b) Temperature Inversion

Cool air

Warm inversion layer

Cool air

Altitude

Temperature

Figure 4.67 *A temperature inversion. Unlike normal conditions (a), in a temperature inversion (b), a layer of cool air is trapped close to Earth's surface below a warm layer, preventing air contaminants from escaping.*

In Los Angeles, the combination of sunny weather and mountains can produce temperature inversions about 320 days annually. During a temperature inversion, air pollutants cannot escape, so their concentrations may rise to dangerous levels. The production and severity of photochemical smog, which can occur even without a temperature inversion (particularly in regions congested with automobiles, such as Los Angeles), are amplified by that accumulation of pollutants.

The simplified equation that follows represents the key ingredients and products of **photochemical smog.** Hydrocarbons, carbon monoxide, and nitrogen oxides from vehicle exhausts are irradiated by sunlight in the presence of oxygen gas. The resulting reactions produce a potentially dangerous mixture, including other nitrogen oxides, ozone, and irritating organic compounds, as well as carbon dioxide and water vapor:

$$\text{Hydrocarbons} + \text{Sunlight} + O_2(g) + CO(g) + NO_x(g) \rightarrow O_3(g) + NO_x(g) + \text{Organic compounds} + CO_2(g) + H_2O(g)$$

Auto exhaust   Oxidizing agents and irritants

> Any reaction initiated by light is a photochemical reaction.

Nitrogen oxides are essential ingredients of photochemical smog. As noted in Section C, the high temperatures and pressures of automotive combustion (nearly 1000 °C and about 10 atm) promote a reaction between nitrogen gas and oxygen gas in the vehicle's engine cylinders that produces the pollutant nitrogen monoxide (NO):

$$N_2(g) + O_2(g) + \text{Energy} \longrightarrow 2\,NO(g)$$

> See Unit 2 (page 149) for background on oxidizing agents. Such materials are also known as oxidants.

Exposed to the atmosphere, nitrogen monoxide gas from the vehicle's exhaust is oxidized to reddish brown nitrogen dioxide gas (NO_2), which often is visible in polluted urban air:

$$2\,NO(g) + O_2(g) \longrightarrow 2\,NO_2(g)$$

The photochemical-smog cycle begins when photons from sunlight—the second essential ingredient—break N–O bonds in NO_2. This forms NO molecules and highly reactive oxygen (O) atoms, also known as *oxygen radicals.*

$$NO_2(g) + \text{Sunlight} \longrightarrow NO(g) + O(g)$$

Oxygen radicals then react with oxygen molecules (O_2) in the troposphere to produce ozone (O_3), just as in the stratosphere:

$$O(g) + O_2(g) \longrightarrow O_3(g)$$

> Radicals are molecules or atoms that contain at least one unpaired electron, causing them to be extremely unstable. Radicals are stabilized by taking electrons from nearby molecules, which can lead to bodily cell damage and also to destruction of the protective ozone layer in the upper atmosphere.

Two harmful and unpleasant components of photochemical smog have now been identified—NO_2 and O_3. Nitrogen dioxide has a pungent, irritating odor at detectable concentrations. Even at relatively low concentrations (0.5 ppm), nitrogen dioxide can inhibit plant growth. At 3 to 5 ppm, this pollutant can cause human respiratory distress after an hour of exposure.

Ozone is a very powerful oxidizing agent (oxidant). At concentrations as low as 0.1 ppm, ozone can crack rubber, corrode metals, and

Making Decisions

D.4 Vehicles and Smog

In this activity, students analyze the graph in Figure 4.68 to determine why the concentration of certain air pollutants varies over a 24-hour period.

Answers

1. a. About 6 A.M. and 9 A.M.
   b. These times correspond to morning rush hours, when traffic peaks.
2. Because it is being physically dispersed, adsorbed onto surfaces, or chemically converted to other substances
3. NO is the source of nitrogen dioxide. Most NO_x emissions from automobiles are in the form of NO. Once released into the atmosphere, NO is further oxidized to nitrogen dioxide, $2NO(g) + O_2(g) \longrightarrow 2NO_2(g)$. As NO is oxidized, its concentration decreases and that of NO_2 increases.
4. a. NO
   b. That nitrogen oxides may be related to ozone formation (in fact, ground-level ozone is formed by reaction of VOCs with nitrogen oxides in intense sunlight).
5. Answers will vary but should indicate that the fueling and operation of buses would contribute to the pollutants in the figure.

Ozone Formation

Ozone produced in photochemical smog remains largely in the troposphere and is commonly called "ground-level" ozone.

damage plant and animal tissues. In terms of human health, relatively low ozone concentrations can cause chest pain, shortness of breath, throat irritation, and coughing. Ozone may also worsen chronic respiratory diseases such as asthma, as well as compromise the body's ability to fight respiratory infections.

Ozone undergoes a complex series of reactions with hydrocarbons, principally VOCs, which are the third essential ingredient of photochemical smog. Hydrocarbons escape from vehicle gasoline tanks and also are emitted due to incomplete gasoline combustion.

The concentrations in air of substances associated with photochemical smog customarily vary over a 24-hour period. In the following activity, you will consider factors that may influence such concentration changes.

Making Decisions

D.4 VEHICLES AND SMOG

Use the data in Figure 4.68 to answer the following questions:

1. a. Between what hours do the concentrations of nitrogen oxides and hydrocarbons peak?
   b. Account for this fact in terms of automobile traffic patterns.
2. Give two reasons why a given pollutant may decrease in concentration over several hours.
3. The concentration maximum for NO_2 occurs at the same time as the concentration minimum for NO. Explain this phenomenon.
4. Although ozone is necessary in the stratosphere to protect Earth from excessive ultraviolet light, at Earth's surface, it is a major component of photochemical smog.

Recall that the concentration unit "ppm" means "parts per million."

Figure 4.68 *Photochemical smog formation.*

a. Using Figure 4.68, determine which substances are at their minimum concentrations when O_3 is at its maximum concentration.

b. What does this suggest about the production of O_3 in polluted tropospheric air?

5. None of the individuals interviewed at the beginning of this unit (see page 300) mentioned smog in conjunction with the school-bus-idling policy. Are the two related? Explain your answer, and be sure to include what you have learned from Figure 4.68.

Many nations, including the United States, have made considerable progress in smog control. Many cities have cleaner air today than they did decades ago. As you read on, you will explore how the reduction and control of air pollutants formerly produced by motor vehicles and other sources have been successfully addressed.

D.5 STATIONARY-SOURCE AIR POLLUTION CONTROL AND PREVENTION

Several policy options can limit and prevent air pollution from stationary sources:

▶ Energy technologies that cause air pollution can be replaced by technologies that do not involve combustion, such as solar power, wind power, or nuclear power.

▶ Pollution from combustion can be reduced by energy-conservation measures, such as extracting more energy from fuels and thereby burning less of them.

▶ Potentially harmful substances can be removed from fuel before burning; for example, most sulfur can be removed from coal.

▶ The combustion process can be modified so that the fuel is more completely burned (oxidized).

▶ Pollutants can be removed after combustion.

All pollution reduction options involve new costs. When evaluating a pollution prevention or control measure, decision makers must answer three key questions: (1) *What would the prevention or control measure cost?* (2) *What benefits would it offer?* (3) *What costs or risks would be involved in* not *using the prevention or control measure?*

Power plants and smelters generate more than half of all particulate matter emitted by human activity in the United States. However, notable progress has been made in cleaning up the air pollution from these sources (and others) in recent years. Since the 1970s, there has been a significant decrease in the amount of most air pollutants in the United States. See Figure 4.69 (page 392).

Manufacturers have used large-scale techniques to reduce particulates emerging from industrial plants. Several cost-effective methods, such as those described next, are used for controlling particulates and other emissions.

D.5 Stationary-Source Air Pollution Control and Prevention

This section offers several strategies to control air pollution from stationary sources and raises the question of relative costs and benefits. It discusses the most cost-effective methods of controlling emissions, including mechanical filtering, electrostatic precipitation, and scrubbing.

Students may possess varied levels of familiarity with pollution-control strategies. Before introducing this content, you may ask them what methods control pollution from stationary sources. This is also a good topic for students to research independently, since control strategies are continually developed and improved.

Another topic related to this issue is Green Chemistry. Rather than controlling the pollutants, one strategy of Green Chemistry is to change processes to avoid generating them.

Some useful links support this content:

Air Pollution Control
http://www.epa.gov/ebtpages/
　airairpoabatement.html
http://www.cleanairworld.org/
　TopicDetails.asp?parent=7
　(many links to control-technology sites)

Green Chemistry
http://www.epa.gov/greenchemistry/
http://chemistry.org/portal/a/c/s/1/
　acsdisplay.html?DOC=
　greenchemistryinstitute\
　index.html
http://www.rsc.org/is/journals/
　current/green/greenpub.htm

ChemQuandary 3

Limiting Reactants and Scrubbers

There should be an excess of $Ca(OH)_2$. If $Ca(OH)_2$ were the limiting reactant, some undesirable $SO_2(g)$ could remain after the reaction is completed.

Investigating Matter

D.6 Cleansing Air

D.6 Cleansing Air Student Worksheet and Data Table

Part I: Electrostatic Precipitation

Materials

Graduated cylinder, glass, 100-mL
Copper wire, bare, 18 gauge, 1 m
Rubber stopper, 1-hole, to fit gradu-
    ated cylinder
Wire cutters
Tesla coil
Smoke source (such as a 1 cm² piece
    of heavy cardboard)

Safety

Everyone should wear protective goggles. Be aware of electric hazard due
to high electrical potential. Keep the
Tesla coil unplugged until ready to
use. Unplug it immediately after use.

Procedure

1. Insert a 1-hole stopper in a clean,
   dry graduated cylinder.
2. Wrap several Cu-wire turns around
   the cylinder. Make a loop at the
   wire's bottom end. Attach a wire
   from the loop to a water faucet
   to create a ground. ***Caution:***
   Ensure that the water-supply line
   is metallic.
3. Cut a Cu wire about 4 cm longer
   than the cylinder depth; make a
   small loop at one end. Insert wire,

Figure 4.69 *Air pollutants in the United States, 1900–2000. One short ton equals 2000 pounds.*

Electrostatic precipitation is currently the most common technique used to control particulate pollutants. Combustion waste products pass through a strong electrical field, where they become electrically charged. The charged particles then collect on plates of opposite charge. This technique can remove 99% (or more) of particulates, leaving only particles with diameters smaller than about one-tenth of a micrometer (0.1 μm, where 1 μm = 1×10^{-6} m). Dust and pollen collectors installed in home ventilation systems are often based on this technique.

Mechanical filtering works much like a vacuum cleaner. Combustion waste products pass through a cleaning room (bag house) where huge filters trap up to 99% of the particles.

Scrubbing is a method that controls particles and also sulfur oxides. In the example of *wet scrubbing* shown in Figure 4.70, sulfur dioxide gas is removed by an aqueous solution of calcium hydroxide, $Ca(OH)_2(aq)$, also known as *limewater*. The sulfur dioxide reacts to form solid calcium sulfite, $CaSO_3$:

$$SO_2(g) + Ca(OH)_2(aq) \longrightarrow CaSO_3(s) + H_2O(l)$$

Scrubbers can remove up to 95% of sulfur oxides. Unfortunately, because of higher operating costs resulting from maintenance and disposal expenses, combined with lower net power production, scrubbers add significantly to the cost of electrical-power generation.

Figure 4.70 *A wet scrubber for removing sulfur dioxide gas and particulates from the exhaust of a coal-fired power plant.*

loop at top, into the graduated cylinder through the stopper. This wire should *not* touch cylinder sides.

4. Remove wire and stopper. Ignite piece of heavy cardboard and drop it into cylin-der; replace wire-stopper assembly.
5. Plug in and start the Tesla coil.
6. Hold the Tesla-coil tip as close as possi-ble to central wire, allowing a spark to

jump to the top wire loop. ***Caution:*** Be very cautious with Tesla coil. Smoke should clear almost immediately.

7. Disassemble the apparatus. The cylinder must be clean and dry before reuse.

Observations for Part I

1. The smoke disappears.
2. The rod turns greenish.

ChemQuandary 3

LIMITING REACTANTS AND SCRUBBERS

In Section B (page 353), you were introduced to the concept of limiting reactants. Consider the stoichiometry involved in removing sulfur dioxide emissions with a wet scrubber (see the equation on page 392). In properly designing this scrubber, which reactant should be designated as the limiting reactant? Why? What would be the consequences if the other reactant were the limiting reactant?

Investigating Matter

D.6 CLEANSING AIR

Introduction

Your teacher will demonstrate two control methods for air pollutants: *electrostatic precipitation* and *wet scrubbing*. Prepare a sketch of each laboratory setup as part of your note-taking for this demonstration.

 Lab Video: Cleansing Air

Part I: Electrostatic Precipitation

1. Observe the generation of smoke and what happens to it. Record your observations.
2. Observe the chemical reaction that takes place on the copper rod. Record your observations.

Part II: Wet Scrubbing

3. As the reaction proceeds, observe the color of the universal indicator in the liquid and the color of the pH paper in each flask. Compare those colors with the color-key information provided with the pH paper. Record your observations.

Questions

1. Write an equation representing the smoke-generating reaction that occurred in Part II between HCl and NH_3.
2. What information did the universal indicator provide about the contents of each flask in Part II?
3. What information did the pH paper in each flask provide?
4. What was the overall effect of the scrubbing, as shown by the acid-base indicators?
5. List two ways in which the quality of the air in the reaction vessel was improved by wet scrubbing.
6. a. What advantages do electrostatic precipitators have over wet scrubbers?
   b. What are their disadvantages?

Section D   Air Pollution: Sources, Effects, and Solutions   393

Thistle tube or long-stem glass funnel
2 pieces of glass tubing with 90° bends ~20 cm apart
Aspirator adapter

Safety

Everyone should wear protective goggles. Ensure adequate ventilation. Wrap flasks with transparent tape. When inserting thistle tubes, use glycerin to lubricate the stem, hold it close to the stopper, and protect your hand with towels.

Procedure

1. Set up the apparatus in the photo.
2. Add 5–10 drops of universal indicator to each collecting flask, then fill with water up to the neck.
3. Place moistened pH paper between the stopper and glass rim, hanging above the water level.
4. Add 10 mL conc. HCl to smoke-generating flask. Immediately stopper it.
5. Pour 10 mL conc. $NH_3(aq)$ through thistle tube; immediately turn on aspirator.

Answers

1. $HCl(g) + NH_3(g) \longrightarrow NH_4Cl(s)$.
2. Solution pH
3. pH of the gases above water
4. pH of the solution and gases above approach neutrality in the second flask.
5. It removes particulate matter and lowers acidity/alkalinity of exhaust gases.
6. a. They yield solid waste, rather than a solution, do not use other reactants and require minimal maintenance.
   b. They require electricity and do not remove SO_2 and NO_2.

Part II: Wet Scrubbing

Materials

1 pkg wide-range Hydrion (pH) paper
5 mL universal indicator solution
10 mL 12.0-M HCl
10 mL 14.8-M $NH_3(aq)$
2 500-mL Erlenmeyer flasks
500-mL filter flask
stoppers, 1-hole to fit filter flask; two 2-hole to fit Erlenmeyer flasks

D.7 Controlling Automobile Emissions

The EPA sets emissions standards for automobiles, and the automobile industry has developed several effective techniques to reduce emissions. Although students may be familiar with the term *catalytic converter,* they may not understand the chemistry supporting its operation. Most modern automobile catalytic converters have both a reduction catalyst and an oxidation catalyst. In the reduction-catalyst portion, oxides of nitrogen form molecular nitrogen and oxygen. In the oxidation-catalyst portion, the products of incomplete combustion—CO and unburned hydrocarbons—are oxidized to CO_2. See also **http://auto.howstuffworks.com/catalytic-converter.htm**. If your school has a technical program involving automobiles, see if its instructors can help you procure and open a used catalytic converter to reveal the catalytic matrix. The honeycomb matrix is quite fascinating and worth sharing with students.

In general, catalysts work by allowing a reaction to take place with a smaller activation energy than would usually be necessary. Use the activation-energy diagram (**Figure 4.72**) to review energy concepts from Unit 3 and explain that the catalyst provides an alternative pathway, with the same starting and ending points, but a lower activation-energy hump. You might want to perform a catalyst demonstration and then ask students to think about how a catalyst accomplishes this lowering of activation energy.

Figure 4.71 *A catalytic converter (top) is installed in an automobile's exhaust system (bottom).*

D.7 CONTROLLING AUTOMOBILE EMISSIONS

The Clean Air Act of 1970 authorized the Environmental Protection Agency to set emissions standards for new automobiles. Maximum allowable limits were set for hydrocarbon, nitrogen oxide, and carbon monoxide emissions. One major contribution toward meeting those standards was the development of the *catalytic converter,* which is a reaction chamber built into the exhaust system of motor vehicles, as shown in Figure 4.71.

As you may recall from Unit 3 (page 254), a catalyst is a material that speeds up a chemical reaction that would proceed far slower without the presence of that catalyst. Enzymes that aid in digesting food and in promoting other bodily functions are organic catalysts. Although a catalyst participates in the chemical reaction, it is not considered a reactant because it emerges unchanged when the reaction is completed.

How can a catalyst speed up a reaction and still remain unchanged? **Collision theory** states that reactions can occur only if molecules collide with sufficient energy and with suitable orientation to disrupt chemical bonds. The minimum energy required for such effective collisions is called the **activation energy.** You can think of the activation energy as an energy barrier that stands between the reactants and products. See Figure 4.72. Reactants must have enough energy to get over the barrier before a reaction can occur. That is, the reactants must have sufficient kinetic energy to participate in effective

Figure 4.72 *Activation-energy diagram for a typical chemical reaction. The activation energy represents the minimum energy needed to initiate the reaction.*

Demonstration Idea

Using a wellplate or small beakers, place a small volume of 3% H_2O_2 in each of several wells or beakers. Designate one as the control, to show that uncatalyzed H_2O_2 decomposition to H_2O and oxygen is extremely slow (you may choose to use liquid detergent as a bubble indicator). Then add a molecular collisions. The higher the energy barrier, the fewer the molecules with sufficient energy to get over it and the slower the overall reaction proceeds.

A catalyst works by providing a different reaction pathway, one with a lower activation energy. In effect, the catalyst lowers the energy barrier. The result is that more molecules now have sufficient energy to react and to form products within a given period of time. In automotive catalytic converters, a few grams of platinum, palladium, or rhodium embedded in a noncatalytic material such as aluminum oxide (Al_2O_3) act as the catalyst.

In the **catalytic converter,** exhaust gases and outside air pass over several solid catalysts that help speed the conversion of potentially harmful gases to harmless products—nitrogen oxides to nitrogen gas, carbon monoxide to carbon dioxide, and hydrocarbons to carbon dioxide and water. Exhaust gases enter the catalytic converter where, for example, nitrogen oxides and carbon monoxide are removed as shown in the following equation.

$$2\ NO(g) + 2\ CO(g) \xrightarrow{\text{Catalyst}} N_2(g) + 2\ CO_2(g)$$

The Clean Air Act amendments of 1990 set new tailpipe emission standards for U.S. automobiles (see Figure 4.73) and also established emission standards for vehicles other than automobiles. Those national tailpipe-emission levels set achievable goals that significantly helped reduce photochemical smog. Between 1993 and 2002, total CO tailpipe emissions decreased 21%. NO_x emissions from transportation decreased 5% within the same period.

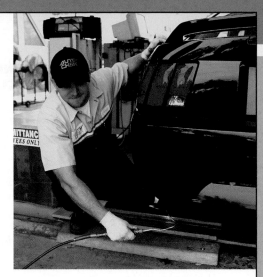

Figure 4.73 *Many cities and towns, and some states, require annual testing of exhaust emissions.*

Transportation is still a major air-pollution source in many states despite improvements made by catalytic converters.

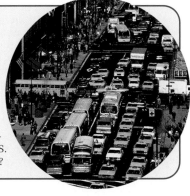

ChemQuandary 4

CONTROLLING AIR POLLUTION

From a practical point of view, why do you think that controlling air pollution from all U.S. automobiles, recreational vehicles, buses, and trucks would be more difficult than controlling air pollution from U.S. power plants and industries?

(large pieces/small pieces, solid/solution) to illustrate the effects of catalyst state and surface area. Increased surface area and heterogeneity (being in a different state from the reactants) tend to increase the catalytic effect.

Some discussion questions include, *Why are catalytic converters made as honeycomb structures?* (to maximize surface area), *What materials can damage catalytic converters?* (Lead—coats surface; unburned fuel or engine oil additives—can plug holes)

ChemQuandary 4

Controlling Air Pollution

It is easy and relatively inexpensive to install, maintain, and update control technologies when relatively few locations and people are involved. However, automobiles, buses, and trucks are widely dispersed and controlled by millions of individuals, which makes it difficult to ensure compliance with standards. Many states require motor vehicle owners/operators to have their vehicle emissions tested for compliance with standards before those vehicles can be registered or operated.

small amount of MnO_2 catalyst to one of the wells or beakers. Ask students to observe the dramatic change in H_2O_2 decomposition rate. Other possible catalysts to investigate in the other wells or beakers include Ag_2O, Pt, KI or KI solution, and even small sections from an automobile catalytic converter. You can vary the catalysts and forms

D.8 Ozone and CFCs: A Continued Success Story

~~~~ **D.8 Content Reading Guide**

Earth's Ozone Shield Ozone accounts for fewer than 10 molecules in every million molecules of air, yet its presence in the stratosphere is essential in protecting humans and other organisms from the harmful effects of ultraviolet (UV) radiation. Though ozone is an irritating pollutant at ground level, in the stratosphere it absorbs UV radiation from the sun. Most atmospheric ozone is found in a layer between 10 and 40 km above Earth's surface.

The thickness of this ozone layer varies with location. In general, it is thinner near the equator and thicker near the poles. The ozone layer also experiences seasonal variation; it tends to be thicker during the spring and thinner during the autumn. The reasons for these variations include atmospheric circulation patterns and solar intensity. The following sites provide more information about the ozone layer: **http://www.epa.gov/ozone/science/sc_fact.html, http://www.ozonelayer.noaa.gov/, http://europa.eu.int/comm/environment/ozone/index.htm**

The text explains formation and decomposition of ozone in the stratosphere, including the role of oxygen free radicals. Becuse they have unpaired electrons, free radicals tend to be unstable and highly reactive. Both oxygen and chlorine form free radicals in the stratosphere. Oxygen radicals tend to combine with oxygen molecles to form ozone, which later forms oxygen molecules and oxygen radicals.

Figure 4.74 Sunscreen products protect skin from the harmful effects of the Sun's ultraviolet rays. This is particularly necessary now that scientists have determined that stratospheric ozone has been significantly depleted.

Figure 4.75 Ultraviolet rays can damage eyes as well as skin. Many sunglasses are made of materials that block UV rays from reaching one's eyes.

D.8 OZONE AND CFCs: A CONTINUED SUCCESS STORY

Although small doses of ultraviolet A and B radiation are necessary for health, too much is dangerous. In fact, if all ultraviolet radiation in sunlight reached Earth's surface, many forms of life would be seriously damaged. Ultraviolet B and C photons, you learned in Section B, have enough energy to break covalent bonds, even within biological structures such as DNA. The resulting chemical changes can cause sunburn and cancer in humans and can damage many biological systems (Figures 4.74 and 4.75).

Earth's Ozone Shield

Fortunately, Earth has an ultraviolet shield in the stratosphere, near the troposphere. The shield consists of a thin region of gaseous ozone (O_3) that absorbs ultraviolet radiation. However, this stratospheric **ozone shield** is a fragile system that contains a remarkably low concentration of ozone. If all ozone molecules in the shield were moved to Earth's surface at atmospheric pressure, they would form a 3-mm layer (about the thickness of this textbook's cover).

This ozone layer is vital to life on Earth. A National Research Council study suggests that for each 1% decrease in stratospheric ozone, a 2% to 5% increase in various forms of skin cancer will occur. Such ozone depletion could also lower yields of some food crops, sharply increase sunburn and eye cataracts, and damage some aquatic plant species.

As sunlight penetrates the stratosphere, high-energy ultraviolet photons react with oxygen gas molecules, splitting them into individual oxygen atoms (the dot in the following equation represents an unpaired electron):

$$O_2 + \text{High-energy UV photon} \longrightarrow \cdot O + \cdot O$$

These reactive oxygen atoms are an example of a **free radical.** Radicals contain unstable arrangements and an odd number of electrons. Radicals quickly enter into chemical reactions that allow them to attain stable arrangements of electrons. For example, oxygen free radicals in the stratosphere can combine with oxygen molecules to form ozone, as the following equation shows. A third molecule (typically N_2 or O_2, represented by M in the equation) carries away excess energy from the reaction, but remains unchanged:

$$O_2 + \cdot O + M \longrightarrow O_3 + M$$

Each ozone molecule formed in the stratosphere can absorb an ultraviolet B photon with a wavelength of less than 320 nm. In this energy absorption, which keeps potentially harmful ultraviolet radiation from reaching Earth's surface, ozone decomposes, producing an oxygen molecule and an oxygen free radical:

$$O_3 + \text{Medium-energy UV photon} \longrightarrow O_2 + \cdot O$$

These products can then continue the reaction cycle by replacing ozone in the protective stratospheric layer:

$$O_2 + \cdot O + M \longrightarrow O_3 + M$$

CFCs and Ozone Depletion

 Ozone Depletion

Some human activities have already affected Earth's stratospheric ozone layer. Riverwood's Isaiah Martin speculated that one possible cause might be bus exhaust.

Actually, the major culprit has been identified as chlorine atoms from chlorinated hydrocarbon molecules known as *chlorofluorocarbons* (CFCs). The Freons, CCl_3F (CFC-11) and CCl_2F_2 (CFC-12), are the most familiar CFCs. Chlorofluorocarbons are synthetic substances that were once widely used (and still are in some countries) as propellants in aerosol cans (see Figure 4.76), as cooling fluids in air conditioners

Rowland and Molina received the 1995 Nobel Prize in chemistry for their pioneering research on stratospheric ozone depletion.

Scientific American Working Knowledge Illustration

Figure 4.76 *Aerosol spray can. Products, such as whipped cream, spray paint, and hair spray, are often packaged in aerosol spray cans. The can contains the product and a volatile liquid and gas, called the propellant. The propellant gas exerts high pressure above the liquid product. (As you know, gaseous particles are constantly in motion and exert pressure as they collide with surfaces.) Left: Propellant gas inside the can normally exerts pressure (green arrows) on can walls and liquid (yellow). Right: As the spray can nozzle is pushed down, a passage opens to the outside atmosphere. Because gas pressure exerted on the liquid is greater than air pressure outside the can, the liquid is propelled up toward the nozzle and exits as sprayed droplets.*

Section D   Air Pollution: Sources, Effects, and Solutions   **397**

compounds absorb UV radiation, dissipating it as heat.

Figure 4.75: UV radiation can damage eyes. Ask students what properties sunglasses should have for UV protection. Answers may include tint or color, darkness, mirror coating, polarization, and UV coating. Students may be surprised to learn that the key feature sunglasses must have to provide UV protection is either a UV coating on the surface of the lens or lenses made of polycarbonate. Photochromic lenses also offer UV protection. Properties such as color, darkness, mirror coating, and polarization have little to no impact on the ability of the lens to absorb UV rays; these properties reduce glare and improve object definition.

Scientific American Working Knowledge Illustration

This Scientific American Working Knowledge illustration explains how aerosol-can propellants work. Ask students to think of desirable properties of propellants. Some include that they are gases at room temperature, are nontoxic and nonflammable, and don't react with or dissolve in the liquid product the aerosol spray delivers. CFCs had these properties and were widely used as propellants until the discovery that CFC molecules—stable in the troposphere—decompose to ozone-destroying chlorine radicals when UV photons irradiate them in the stratosphere.

Using the Figures

Figure 4.74: This photo shows someone applying sunscreen. Have students volunteer what they know about sunscreen and its application to identify knowledge and misconceptions. You might share the following:
• Sunscreens consist of inorganic and/or organic active ingredients.

• Zinc oxide and titanium oxide are inorganic active ingredients that reflect or scatter ultraviolet radiation. (Students should be familiar with reflectivity from Section 4A. Ask why white might be a desirable color for a sunscreen product.)
• Octyl methoxycinnamate (OMC) and oxybenzone are both examples of organic active ingredients found in sunscreens. These

CFCs and Ozone Depletion Isaiah Martin's speculation that bus exhaust could cause ozone depletion is a common misconception. It is easy for students to lump all air pollution problems together (smog formation, acid rain, global warming, and ozone depletion). One common misconception is that the ozone hole causes global warming, because the ozone hole allows more UV rays to reach Earth's surface. Another common misconception is that car and industrial emissions create the ozone hole. Emphasize that each air pollution problem is a separate issue with distinct causes (and requiring a different solution).

As students have learned, ozone is naturally destroyed in the stratosphere due to absorption of UV photons. However, this is one step in a cycle. Ozone re-forms in another step. By itself, oxygen chemistry does not explain the net disappearance of stratospheric ozone.

The main culprits are chlorofluorocarbons (CFCs), which people considered safe because they were nonreactive in the troposphere. However, once in the stratosphere, CFCs become sources of chlorine radicals. These chlorine radicals destroy ozone in a catalytic process—chlorine radicals that react with ozone in one step are re-generated in a later step and can thus continue the ozone-destroying process.

Students may ask how CFCs get to the stratosphere. If CFCs are released mainly in the Northern Hemisphere, why is the ozone hole over Antarctica? And how important are natural sources of chlorine in destroying stratospheric ozone? Scientists had to address all these questions to develop a model that explains stratospheric ozone depletion.

Figure 4.77 *Nobel Prize Winners: F. Sherwood Rowland (top) and Mario Molina (bottom).*

Breaking a C—Cl bond in CFC-11 by a high-energy ultraviolet light photon.

and refrigerators, and as cleaning solvents for computer chips. Developed in the 1930s, nontoxic and nonflammable CFCs quickly replaced toxic ammonia or sulfur dioxide as coolants of choice in refrigerators and air conditioners. For almost half a century, CFCs were well accepted as refrigerants, propellants, and cleaning solvents.

However in the 1970s, two U.S. chemists—F. Sherwood Rowland and Mario Molina (Figure 4.77)—proposed that chlorofluorocarbons (CFCs) posed a threat to the world's protective ozone layer. Since then, extensive research has developed a more complete picture of that threat, as you will soon learn.

A satellite launched later in the 1970s carried instruments to monitor changes in worldwide stratospheric ozone concentrations. By 1986, satellite data showed seasonal ozone reduction, or the formation of a so-called **ozone hole,** in the stratosphere above Antarctica, as shown in Figure 4.78. The data indicated an annual variation in ozone concentration of 1% to 2.5%, well beyond normal variation noted before the production of CFCs. That depletion cycle was observed to increase annually over subsequent years. In fact, by the late 1990s, nearly 70% of stratospheric ozone disappeared for a time over Antarctica, creating an area of ozone depletion as large as North America. More recent evidence shows some thinning of stratospheric ozone over Arctic regions as well, although not to the same extent as over Antarctica.

Several bodies of evidence gathered since the mid-1980s have converged, linking the Antarctic ozone depletion to chlorine atoms obtained from CFCs, not from natural sources. Although CFCs are highly stable molecules in the troposphere, high-energy ultraviolet photons in the stratosphere split chlorine radicals (·Cl) from CFCs by breaking their C–Cl bonds.

The highly reactive chlorine radicals can participate in a series of reactions that destroy ozone by converting it to O_2:

$$2 \cdot Cl + 2 O_3 \longrightarrow 2 \cdot ClO + 2 O_2$$

Figure 4.78 *Total October ozone concentrations in the stratosphere over Antarctica, 1996–2004. Reds and greens indicate high ozone concentrations; blues and purples indicate low ozone concentrations. Lower Dobson units indicate lower ozone concentration.*

398   **Unit 4**   Air: Chemistry and the Atmosphere

First, CFCs need to get from the troposphere to the stratosphere. Their transport may seem unlikely, considering CFCs are heavier than the major components of air (N_2 and O_2). However, constant air turbulence mixes these gases in the lower atmosphere and helps them rise into the stratosphere, mainly in tropical latitudes. Winds then carry them to both poles. Formation of the ozone hole over the South Pole can partly be explained by the presence of Antarctica—a very large land mass completely surrounded by ocean. Very low stratospheric temperatures above Antarctica lead to the formation of polar stratospheric clouds that facilitate chemical changes,

Figure 4.79 *Stratospheric ozone (red) and chlorine monoxide (purple) concentrations over Antarctica.*

The reactive chlorine monoxide radical (·ClO) produced by that ozone-destroying reaction can combine with itself:

$$·ClO + ·ClO \longrightarrow ClOOCl$$

The resulting ClOOCl then can decompose in the presence of solar radiation through a two-step process:

$$ClOOCl + UV\ photon \longrightarrow ·ClOO + ·Cl$$

$$·ClOO + UV\ photon \longrightarrow \quad ·Cl + O_2$$

Note that these last two reactions replace the "2 ·Cl" that was consumed in the first ozone-destroying step. That is, the chlorine free radical (·Cl) emerges unchanged in this series of reactions, even though it participated in them. Thus, the ·Cl serves as a *catalyst* for the destruction of stratospheric O_3. The net result (the arithmetic sum) of all of these reactions can be written this way:

$$2\ O_3 \longrightarrow 3\ O_2$$

Each chlorine radical participates in not just one O_3-destroying reaction, but in an average of 100 000 of these reactions. In so doing, it speeds up ozone destruction, but the chlorine radical remains ultimately unchanged. The net effect is depletion of ozone molecules (O_3) by their conversion into oxygen molecules (O_2), a chemical reaction catalyzed by chlorine radicals released from CFC molecules. See Figure 4.79.

> The "dot" in the symbols ·Cl and ·ClO signifies a single, unpaired electron; the resulting symbol represents a highly reactive free radical.

> A particular chlorine radical is eventually removed from this stratospheric cycle due to other chemical changes, such as its reaction with methane (CH_4) to produce hydrogen chloride, HCl.

causing rapid ozone loss during September and October each year. (Point out that **Figure 4.78** shows the ozone hole during October of three different years.) These conditions do not exist in the northern polar regions; the stratosphere is warmer above the North Pole, resulting in fewer cloud formations and less ozone loss.

Almost all of the chlorine radicals involved in stratospheric ozone depletion can be traced to human sources. Natural sources of chlorine, such as evaporated ocean spray and volcano emissions, dissolve and make their way back to the surface in precipitation. They do not reach the stratosphere. Measurements made in

1985 and 1992 confirm that most stratospheric chlorine can be traced to human sources. One convincing piece of evidence shows that the increase in total stratospheric chlorine between 1985 and 1992 corresponds to the known increases in concentrations of human-made halocarbons during that time.

Using the Figures

Figure 4.77: F. Sherwood Rowland and Mario Molina, along with Paul Crutzen, received the 1995 Nobel Prize in chemistry for their pioneering research on stratospheric ozone depletion.

http://jcbmac.chem.brown.edu/ baird/EnviroChem/OzoneNobelPrize/ NobelPrizeChemistry95.html and **http://www.ogp.noaa.gov/library/ rtnf92.htm** provide information about their research and ozone-depletion history.

Figure 4.78: NASA provides daily updates (including maps like these) at **http://ozonewatch.gsfc.nasa.gov/ index.html**. The Dobson unit (DU) is the most common unit for measuring ozone concentration. It is named after G. M. B. Dobson, one of the first scientists to investigate atmospheric ozone. One DU represents the number of molecules of ozone required to create an ozone layer 0.01 mm thick at STP. Earth's ozone layer has an average thickness of about 300 DU (3 mm).

This type of plot may be unfamiliar to students. Challenge them to think of other data they could plot with a similar technique (population density, electron density, earthquake density, high and low pressure regions). You might display ozone-concentration maps from other months and discuss seasonal differences that appear.

Addressing Ozone Depletion   Since initiation of the Montreal Protocol, buildup of the most significant CFCs in the lower atmosphere has slowed, and in some cases, even reversed. For example, concentrations of a key ozone-depleting compound (CFC-11) are now decreasing. However, due to their robust nature and slow migration to the stratosphere, large concentrations of other ozone-depleting substances remain in the atmosphere and are expected to persist well into this century.

Scientists believe that global compliance with the Montreal Protocol will lead to improvements in the ozone layer, and a recovery should occur around 2050. However, many warn that this matter should not be considered "solved." Many issues related to ozone depletion still merit attention. For example, since CFCs were banned in 1996, a black market smuggling CFCs from developing countries into the United States has steadily grown. Additionally, there has been growing concern regarding the impact on climate that CFC-replacement compounds (such as HFCs, known to be greenhouse gases) might have. Finally, some scientists worry that greenhouse gases and other pollutants may affect ozone loss, particularly in polar regions. The effects of climate change may well cause ozone depletion over Earth's poles to worsen before it gets better.

Addressing Ozone Depletion

Concerned about the growing threat to the stratospheric ozone layer, representatives of the United States and 55 other countries met in Montreal in 1987 and signed an historic agreement, the Montreal Protocol on Substances That Deplete the Ozone Layer, known also as the *Montreal Protocol*. This initial treaty, with amendments in the 1990s (and again later), established a timetable to phase out all new CFC production within developed nations by 1996.

The Montreal Protocol, which over 170 countries have joined, appears to be working. The United States and 140 other nations halted CFC production at the close of 1995. The amended treaty includes a multimillion dollar fund to help developing nations phase out CFC production by 2010 by helping them build industries that do not rely on CFCs.

Another result of the Montreal Protocol restrictions is that chemical research has developed CFC substitutes that will not harm Earth's protective ozone layer. Chemists have synthesized such substitutes by modifying the molecular structures of CFCs.

Air-conditioned vehicles currently manufactured in the United States use CFC substitutes known as *hydrochlorofluorocarbons* (HCFCs) as the coolant. HCFC molecules replace some offending chlorine atoms with atoms of hydrogen and fluorine. The hydrogen atoms allow HCFCs to decompose in the troposphere and reduce the amount of catalytic chlorine free radicals released in the stratosphere. For example, the hydrochlorofluorocarbon CHF_2Cl has only about 5% of the ozone-depleting capacity of CFC-12.

Although some HCFC decomposition occurs in the troposphere, appreciable numbers of undecomposed HCFC molecules still rise into the stratosphere and decompose under exposure to UV radiation, releasing chlorine free radicals. And, like CFCs, HCFCs are greenhouse gases; thus, there is some concern that they may contribute to global warming.

Because of these potential problems, HCFCs are considered as only transitional replacements for CFCs. Montreal Protocol amendments require that companies accelerate phaseout of some HCFCs before 2030 and complete the phaseout of all HCFCs by then.

Thus, chemists continue research for even better CFC substitutes. This research has already produced a group of synthetic compounds known as *hydrofluorocarbons*, HFCs. Molecules of HFCs, such as CH_2FCF_3, contain only carbon, fluorine, and hydrogen atoms. They contain no ozone-depleting chlorine atoms, and the included hydrogen atoms promote HFC decomposition.

CH_2FCF_3, a typical hydrofluorocarbon

D.9 AIR-QUALITY CONCLUSIONS

As you have learned, human activity can have large-scale impact on gases surrounding our planet. Such impact may influence the world's average temperature by altering normal atmospheric concentrations of substances such as carbon dioxide. They increase potential exposure of living systems to ultraviolet radiation by thinning the protective stratospheric ozone layer. Air pollution resulting from human activity can also lead to regional effects, such as acid rain and smog, or even to localized problems, such as the potential health hazards associated with elevated levels of various air pollutants.

Atmospheric chemistry is quite complex and difficult to study. However, increased knowledge of chemical and physical processes involved in the atmosphere, all gained by scientific research, already has helped guide decision making to protect and enhance the vital envelope of gases encircling Earth.

However, what about the decision to prohibit school bus idling at Riverwood High School? Based on what you have learned in this unit, do benefits of that decision outweigh its drawbacks? By now, you have probably formed some thoughts on these issues, as you prepare to write your feature article for the *Riverwood High Gazette*.

> Concerns regarding Earth's air quality will continue into the future; you have gained useful background in this unit to comprehend these issues.

D.9 Air-Quality Conclusions

This material offers concluding remarks on the issue of air pollution and sets the stage for the decision to prohibit school bus idling at Riverwood High School.

Green Chemistry offers some alternatives in the ozone-depletion debate. One principle of Green Chemistry is elimination of solvents and, where necessary, use of safer solvents. Some solvents developed to replace CFCs in electronics applications have been shown to be technically and economically superior.

For more information, see **http://www.epa.gov/ozone/index.html** or **http://www.epa.gov/ozone/snap/index.html**.

SECTION D SUMMARY

 Section D Supplement

Reviewing the Concepts

1. Primary air pollutants enter the atmosphere directly. Secondary air pollutants are formed in the atmosphere by a reaction between primary air pollutants or natural components of air.

2. $2 SO_2 + O_2 \longrightarrow 2 SO_3$

3. a. Primary; burning wood and fossil fuels, decomposition
   b. Primary; burning fossil fuels and natural gas, decomposition
   c. Primary and secondary; automobile emissions
   d. Primary; burning fossil fuels, decomposition

4. Nitrogen oxides, hydrocarbons, oxygen, and CO

5. Abundant sunny days in valleys or near mountains

6. No. Temperature inversions generally occur in valleys or near mountains.

7. Atomic oxygen is formed when sunlight breaks NO_2 into NO and oxygen atoms. The oxygen atoms then react with oxygen molecules to form tropospheric ozone, a component of photochemical smog.

8. By using electrostatic precipitators, mechanical filtering, scrubbing, and source reduction

9. The oxides of nitrogen (such as NO and NO_2)

10. NO, NO_2, and other nitrogen oxides are generally present together in smog. NO_x represents all nitrogen oxides.

11. Using electrostatic precipitators, scrubbing, mechanical filtering, using catalytic converters, driving less, decreasing industrial production, and modifying

SECTION D SUMMARY
Reviewing the Concepts

Air pollution results from contributions of both primary and secondary pollutants.

1. What distinguishes a primary air pollutant from a secondary air pollutant?

2. Write and balance the equation for formation of SO_3 from SO_2 and oxygen gas.

3. Characterize each of the following as a primary or secondary pollutant, and identify its major source:
   a. CO_2 c. NO_x
   b. CH_4 d. H_2S

Photochemical smog can intensify due to temperature inversions and adverse wind patterns.

4. What ingredients are needed to create photochemical smog?

5. What conditions are shared by cities that experience photochemical smog?

6. Are all cities subject to temperature inversions? Explain your answer.

7. What do oxygen free radicals contribute to photochemical smog?

8. What are some ways that photochemical smog can be reduced?

9. What does the formula NO_x represent?

10. Why is the general expression NO_x used, rather than a specific molecular formula?

Air pollution can be affected by everyday activities and by changes in chemical technologies.

11. List five ways that air pollutants from motor vehicles and industries can be reduced.

12. Describe how a catalyst can speed up a chemical reaction.

13. Consider these three air-pollution control technologies: *scrubbers, catalytic converters,* and *electrostatic precipitators.* Which technique is most effective in combating each of the following types of air pollutants?
   a. sulfur oxides
   b. particulates
   c. hydrocarbons

14. Explain how electrostatic precipitators can reduce air pollution.

15. Some Green Chemistry programs seek to prevent pollution before it starts. What are advantages of this strategy over combating existing air pollution?

16. The following list provides some examples of decisions that one might make to reduce personal contributions to air pollution. For each example, identify particular air pollutants involved, and explain how their release will potentially be reduced:
   a. ordering a fast-food lunch inside a restaurant, rather than waiting in a line of cars at the drive-up window
   b. hanging wet laundry outside to dry
   c. avoiding "topping off" a car's gasoline tank by adding more gasoline after the pump stops automatically
   d. buying groceries and other locally produced items
   e. turning off lights, the TV, and other electrical devices when exiting rooms

industrial processes using Green Chemistry concepts.

12. By lowering the activation energy needed for a reaction to proceed, thus increasing the fraction of molecules with sufficient energy to react.

13. a. Scrubbers b. Electrostatic precipitators c. Catalytic converters

14. Gases produced during combustion, containing particulate waste products, pass through a strong electrical field and become charged. The electrically charged particles collect on oppositely charged plates. The particles are then dislodged and collected rather than being emitted with the gases.

Chlorofluorocarbons (CFCs) can destroy stratospheric ozone.

17. Draw Lewis dot structures for CFC-11 and CFC-12.

18. What properties of CFCs made them useful in industry?

19. What are some alternatives for industrial uses of CFCs?

20. Why are problems associated with CFCs regarded as *global* rather than *national*?

21. What is a free radical, and why is it so reactive?

22. Explain how a chlorine free radical can act as a catalyst in the stratosphere.

Connecting the Concepts

23. Explain the pattern in the data shown in Figure 4.79, page 399. If comparable data were obtained in the Northern Hemisphere, would you expect to observe the same pattern?

24. What are advantages and disadvantages of scrubbing as a strategy for air-pollution reduction?

25. Why is the *presence* of ozone regarded as a problem at ground level, while the *absence* of ozone is regarded as a problem in the stratosphere?

26. Find Internet sites that report current patterns of ozone distribution in the stratosphere. Write a report to summarize this current information.

27. How might monitoring practices be different for primary and secondary air pollutants?

28. Which primary and secondary air pollutants are typically produced by diesel engines, such as those that power buses?

Extending the Concepts

29. Why would scrubbing probably *not* be a good strategy for removing NO_x from vehicle exhaust gases?

30. Major automobile manufacturers have abandoned their research and development of pure electric-powered vehicles. Investigate some factors, in terms of total pollution, that led to this decision.

31. Investigate the historical use of refrigerants. What did CFCs replace? What current products have replaced CFCs?

32. Investigate reported progress of phasing out CFCs and HCFCs. What has been accomplished and what challenges remain?

33. What advances recently have been accomplished in the design of internal combustion engines to minimize pollution?

34. Investigate the topic of diesel engines. Are catalytic converters used with diesel engines? If so, do they differ from catalytic converters used with gasoline engines?

35. Investigate differences in the atmospheric movement of CFCs and ozone. How does this movement affect stratospheric conditions?

Section Summary   403

15. Some advantages include eliminating production of additional wastes (such as scrubber sludge), requiring no additional energy, improved process efficiency, and reduced costs.

16. a. Avoid NO_x emissions generated while waiting in line.
b. Avoid SO_2 and NO_x, or VOC and CO emissions, depending on the dryer's source of thermal energy.

c. Reduce VOCs, volatile gasoline fumes from the gas tank or overfilling.
d. Reduce NO_x and particulates emitted by trucks transporting goods.
e. Reduce SO_2, NO_x, and particulates emitted by electrical generating plants due to a decreased demand for electricity.

17. CFC-11 (CCl_3F)   CFC-12 (CCl_2F_2)

18. They are nontoxic, excellent propellants, good nonpolar solvents, and nonflammable.

19. HCFCs and HFCs

20. Once CFCs enter the atmosphere they affect climate worldwide, regardless of original source.

21. It is a chemical species with an unpaired electron, which is associated with a higher energy state (and less stability) than bonded or paired electrons.

22. Chlorine atoms react with ozone to form chlorine oxide, which reacts with oxygen atoms to form oxygen and re-form chlorine atoms. Destruction of ozone now follows a lower-energy pathway, while the chlorine is left unchanged, fulfilling both requirements of a catalyst.

Connecting the Concepts

23. Stratospheric ozone seems to be decreasing, leading to the "ozone hole." A similar pattern might be expected in the Northern Hemisphere; comparable, but less severe, effects have been observed near the North Pole.

24. Advantages include high-efficiency removal of particulate matter, the ability to collect both particulate matter and gaseous pollutants, and the ability to install it at existing plants.
    Disadvantages include the need for more water and energy and sludge (waste) creation.

25. At ground level, ozone is a strong oxidant. At low concentrations, it can crack rubber, corrode metals, and damage plant and animal tissues. The absence

of ozone allows UV radiation to penetrate the stratosphere, resulting in lower yields of some food crops, damage to some aquatic plants, and increased incidence of sunburn, skin cancer, and cataracts.

26. Helpful sites include **www.unep.ch/ozone/** and http://ozone.unep.org/Public_Information/index.asp.

27. Primary air pollutants can be monitored near their sources and near the time of emission. Secondary air pollutants, since they form in the atmosphere, would require measuring some distance from their source or some time after their creation.

28. SO_2, NO_x, particulates, and hydrocarbons

Extending the Concepts

29. There are several reasons: Not all the NO_x formed is in exhaust gases (it forms on outer engine surfaces); water, power, and chemicals are required (as well as a system for mixing them); and waste products are generated. While this is plausible for large-scale emissions, it is impractical for small systems.

30. Pure electric vehicles must be recharged with electricity generated by (usually) coal-burning power plants. Such facilities generate oxides of sulfur and nitrogen as well as particulates. Hybrid electric vehicles recharge their batteries through braking and don't require any electricity from generating plants.

31. Helpful sites include **http://chemcases.com/fluoro/** and **http://www.dupont.com/suva/emea/pdf/ ref_history.pdf.** Student answers should reference

their research and identify replacement refrigerants, which may include HFC-134a and HFC-125.

32. The sites listed in Answer 31 include information on CFC/HCFC phaseout. Other sources include **http://www.epa.gov/ozone/title6/phaseout/ accfact.html** and **http://www.epa.gov/ozone/title6/ phaseout/hcfc.html.**

33. Students may mention catalytic converters, efficiency improvements, and alternate-fuel use.

34. Catalytic converters are available for diesel engines. They differ somewhat from those used for gasoline engines, because diesel catalytic converters must remove larger amounts of particulates and unburned hydrocarbons as well as products of incomplete combustion.

35. CFCs are chemically unreactive under most conditions. This means they can be emitted at ground level and will disperse until they are distributed throughout the atmosphere—including the stratosphere.

    Ozone is extremely reactive, so as it is generated in reactions associated with photochemical smog it does not persist long enough to redistribute through the atmosphere. Ground-level ozone, unfortunately, cannot replace depleted stratsospheric ozone.

PUTTING IT ALL TOGETHER

Bus-Idling Policy and Air Quality

 Putting It All Together: Bus-Idling Policy and Air Quality

As the culminating activity for this unit, students write a feature article for the *Riverwood High Gazette* discussing the new bus-idling policy. Drafts should address emissions and air-quality concerns associated with bus idling and benefits and drawbacks of minimizing bus-idling time. Articles should also address the opinions expressed in the interviews quoted on page 300. Students should use scientific knowledge and appropriate terminology in addressing the bus-idling policy and air-quality issue. Encourage students to use a writing style appropriate to a newspaper and to support their assertions and opinions with evidence. English teachers, journalism teachers, and/or your school newspaper advisor may be willing to provide helpful resources for students as they write their features.

Students should include at least two diagrams or illustrations in their articles. The diagrams or illustrations should support the information in the articles. Some ideas for illustrations (provide these suggestions only if students have considered their options and are still struggling) are:

Carbon cycle

Greenhouse effect

Electromagnetic spectrum

Fate of radiation in the atmosphere

In-out diagram for bus fuel and emissions

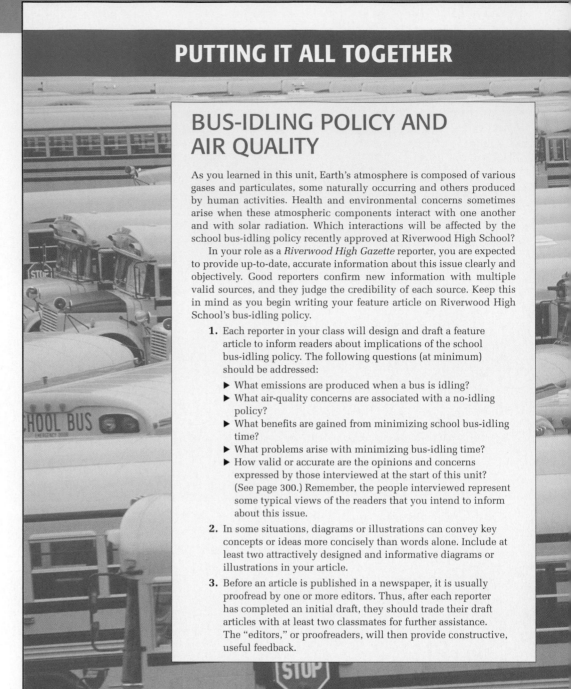

PUTTING IT ALL TOGETHER

BUS-IDLING POLICY AND AIR QUALITY

As you learned in this unit, Earth's atmosphere is composed of various gases and particulates, some naturally occurring and others produced by human activities. Health and environmental concerns sometimes arise when these atmospheric components interact with one another and with solar radiation. Which interactions will be affected by the school bus-idling policy recently approved at Riverwood High School?

In your role as a *Riverwood High Gazette* reporter, you are expected to provide up-to-date, accurate information about this issue clearly and objectively. Good reporters confirm new information with multiple valid sources, and they judge the credibility of each source. Keep this in mind as you begin writing your feature article on Riverwood High School's bus-idling policy.

1. Each reporter in your class will design and draft a feature article to inform readers about implications of the school bus-idling policy. The following questions (at minimum) should be addressed:

   ▶ What emissions are produced when a bus is idling?
   ▶ What air-quality concerns are associated with a no-idling policy?
   ▶ What benefits are gained from minimizing school bus-idling time?
   ▶ What problems arise with minimizing bus-idling time?
   ▶ How valid or accurate are the opinions and concerns expressed by those interviewed at the start of this unit? (See page 300.) Remember, the people interviewed represent some typical views of the readers that you intend to inform about this issue.

2. In some situations, diagrams or illustrations can convey key concepts or ideas more concisely than words alone. Include at least two attractively designed and informative diagrams or illustrations in your article.

3. Before an article is published in a newspaper, it is usually proofread by one or more editors. Thus, after each reporter has completed an initial draft, they should trade their draft articles with at least two classmates for further assistance. The "editors," or proofreaders, will then provide constructive, useful feedback.

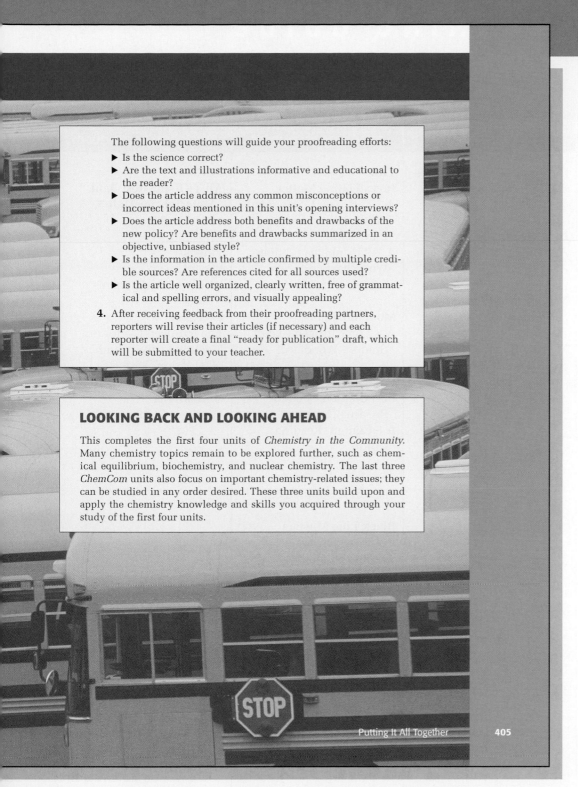

The following questions will guide your proofreading efforts:

▶ Is the science correct?

▶ Are the text and illustrations informative and educational to the reader?

▶ Does the article address any common misconceptions or incorrect ideas mentioned in this unit's opening interviews?

▶ Does the article address both benefits and drawbacks of the new policy? Are benefits and drawbacks summarized in an objective, unbiased style?

▶ Is the information in the article confirmed by multiple credible sources? Are references cited for all sources used?

▶ Is the article well organized, clearly written, free of grammatical and spelling errors, and visually appealing?

4. After receiving feedback from their proofreading partners, reporters will revise their articles (if necessary) and each reporter will create a final "ready for publication" draft, which will be submitted to your teacher.

LOOKING BACK AND LOOKING AHEAD

This completes the first four units of *Chemistry in the Community*. Many chemistry topics remain to be explored further, such as chemical equilibrium, biochemistry, and nuclear chemistry. The last three *ChemCom* units also focus on important chemistry-related issues; they can be studied in any order desired. These three units build upon and apply the chemistry knowledge and skills you acquired through your study of the first four units.

Putting It All Together   405

Once drafted, student articles should be reviewed by other students. You may wish to develop a formal structure for this, so that students receive reviews that provide constructive feedback. You may also decide to require students to submit their reviewed draft attached to the final version of the article to ensure that they completed this aspect of their assignment.

LOOKING BACK AND LOOKING AHEAD

After completing this unit, the remaining three units can be studied in any order. At this point, you may choose to discuss with students the reasons for choosing the units and ideas that will comprise the rest of the course. Common considerations include state and local science standards and content of other high school science courses.

SECTION	CLASS TIME	STUDENT EDITION FEATURES	PROGRAM RESOURCES	MEDIA AND TECHNOLOGY
Section A: **Some Chemistry of Nitrogen** **Objectives** • List the main elements found in fertilizer. • Describe the effect of each ingredient in a typical fertilizer on plant growth. • Describe the nitrogen cycle, specifically referring to processes by which nitrogen gas is fixed (converted into nitrogen-containing compounds). • Predict relative electronegativity trends among several elements. • Determine whether covalently bonded atoms exhibit positive or negative oxidation states, based on their electronegativity values.	5–6 Class Periods	**Developing Skills** A.9 Determining Oxidation States **Investigating Matter** A.3 Fertilizer Components A.7 Phosphates **Modeling Matter** A.6 The Nitrogen Cycle **Making Decisions** A.1 Chemical Processing in Your Life A.5 Plant Nutrients	**TRB** **Investigating Matter** A.3 Fertilizer Components Student Worksheet and Data Table A.7 Phosphates Student Worksheet and Data Table **Modeling Matter** A.6 The Nitrogen Cycle Student Worksheet **Content Reading Guides** Introduction Content Reading Guide A.8 Content Reading Guide **Supplements and Practice** Section A Supplement **Black Line Masters** Electronegativity Values of Elements	**TRCD** **All TRB and Test Bank Materials for Unit 5, Section A** **Videos** Phosphates Fertilizer Components **Exercises** The Nitrogen Cycle Electronegativity and Oxidation State **Animations** Fertilizer Components

SECTION	CLASS TIME	STUDENT EDITION FEATURES	PROGRAM RESOURCES	MEDIA AND TECHNOLOGY
Section B: Nitrogen and Industry **Objectives** • Explain how temperature, reactant concentration(s), and the absence or presence of a catalyst affect reaction rates. • Describe characteristics of a system in dynamic equilibrium. • Use Le Châtelier's Principle to predict shifts in equilibria caused by perturbations to a system. • Describe the Haber-Bosch process for industrial production of ammonia. • Explain why many nitrogen-based compounds are effective chemical explosives. • Describe the main goals of Responsible Care, Green Chemistry, and EPA standards.	**5 Class Periods**	**Developing Skills** B.2 Chemical Systems at Equilibrium B.6 Explosive Nitrogen Chemistry **ChemQuandary 1** The Top Chemicals **Investigating Matter** B.3 Le Châtelier's Principle **Making Decisions** B.9 What Does Riverwood Want?	**TRB** **Investigating Matter** B.3 Le Chatelier's Principle Student Worksheet and Data Table **Content Reading Guides** B.7 Content Reading Guide **Supplements and Practice** B.4 Supplement: Le Chatelier's Principle Section B Supplement	**TRCD** **All TRB and Test Bank Materials for Unit 5, Section B** **Videos** Le Chatelier's Principle **Exercises** Disturbing an Equilibrium **Animations** A Simple Equilibrium—Sugar and Tea Visualizing an Ionic Equilibrium Nitrogenase—an Enzyme Catalyst

SECTION	CLASS TIME	STUDENT EDITION FEATURES	PROGRAM RESOURCES	MEDIA AND TECHNOLOGY
Section C: **Metal Processing and Electrochemistry** **Objectives** • Describe the design of a voltaic cell. • Use the activity series of metals to predict the direction of electron flow within a particular voltaic cell. • Interpret, in terms of half-reactions describing oxidation and reduction, chemical processes by which batteries convert chemical energy to electrical energy. • Describe how electrolysis is used in industry (for example, to reduce aluminum cations to aluminum metal). • Use burden-benefit analysis in decisions about implementing chemical technologies.	5 Class Periods	**Developing Skills** C.4 Getting Charged by Electrochemistry **ChemQuandary 2** Battery Sizes **Investigating Matter** C.2 Voltaic Cells **Making Decisions** C.8 Asset or Liability?	**TRB** **Investigating Matter** C.2 Voltaic Cells Student Worksheet and Data Table **Content Reading Guides** C.1 and C.3 Content Reading Guide C.5 Content Reading Guide **Supplements and Practice** C.1 Supplement: Electrochemical Changes C.3 Supplement: Half-Reactions Section C Supplement	**TRCD** **All TRB and Test Bank Materials for Unit 5, Section C** **Videos** Voltaic Cells **Exercises** Using the metal activity series Maximizing the electrical potential **Animations** Using the metal activity series Constructing a voltaic cell Maximizing the electrical potential
Putting It All Together: A Chemical Plant for Riverwood		**Putting It All Together** • A Chemical Plant for Riverwood?	**TRB** **Putting It All Together** Putting It All Together: Instructions Putting It All Together: Rubric Putting It All Together: Group Worksheet Putting It All Together: Questions for Other Groups Worksheet	**TRCD** **All TRB Materials for Unit 5, Putting It All Together**

Equipment, Expendable Items, and Unususal Materials (per 12 Student Pairs)

Sorted by Item

QUANTITY	ITEM	SECTION USED
325 mL	ammonium molybdate-sulfuric acid reagent	A.7
50 mL	ammonium nitrate (NH_4NO_3), 0.1 M	A.3
20 g	ascorbic acid ($C_6H_8O_6$)	A.7
6	balances, accurate to 0.1 g	A.7
50 mL	barium chloride ($BaCl_2 \cdot 2H_2O$), 0.1 M	A.3
12	beakers, 100 mL	A.3
36	beakers, 400 mL	A.7, B.3
120	Beral pipets	A.3, C.2
12	Bunsen burners	A.3
40 g	calcium chloride, anhydrous ($CaCl_2$)	B.3
100 mL	cobalt(II) chloride hexahydrate ($CoCl_2 \cdot 6H_2O$), 0.1 M	B.3
12	cobalt-blue glass squares	A.3
12	copper strips, medium	C.2
12	copper strips, narrow	C.2
12	copper strips, wide	C.2
50 mL	copper(II) nitrate ($Cu(NO_3)_2$), 0.1 M	C.2
24	dropper bottles	B.3
100 mL	ethanol, 95%	B.3
20 g	fertilizer, granular	A.7
12	graduated cylinders, 10-mL	A.7
12	graduated cylinders, 50-mL or 100-mL	A.7
12	hotplates	A.3, A.7, B.3

Sorted by Item (continued)

QUANTITY	ITEM	SECTION USED
50 mL	hydrochloric acid (HCl), 2.0 M	A.3
100 mL	hydrochloric acid (HCl), 6.0 M	A.3
2 lbs	ice	B.3
12	iron strips	C.2
50 mL	iron(III) nitrate ($Fe(NO_3)_3 \cdot 9H_2O$), 0.1 M	A.3
50 mL	iron(II) sulfate ($FeSO_4 \cdot 7H_2O$), 0.1 M	A.3
50 mL	iron(III) nitrate ($Fe(NO_3)_3$), 0.1 M	C.2
24 strips	litmus paper, red	A.3
50 mL	magnesium nitrate ($Mg(NO_3)_2$), 0.1 M	C.2
12	magnesium strips, 3-cm	C.2
12	nichrome or platinum (Pt) wire loops with handles	A.3
1.0 L	phosphate standard, 10.0 ppm	A.7
50 mL	potassium nitrate (KNO_3), 0.1 M	A.3
100 mL	potassium nitrate (KNO_3), saturated	C.2
50 mL	potassium thiocyanate (KSCN), 0.2 M	A.3
265 mL	silver nitrate ($AgNO_3$), 0.1 M	B.3
5 g	sodium chloride (NaCl)	B.3
50 mL	sodium hydroxide (NaOH), 3.0 M	A.3
50 mL	sodium nitrate ($NaNO_3$), 0.1 M	A.3
50 mL	sodium phosphate ($Na_3PO_4 \cdot 2H_2O$), 0.1 M	A.3

Sorted by Item (continued)

QUANTITY	ITEM	SECTION USED
50 mL	sodium sulfate (Na$_2$SO$_4$·10H$_2$O), 0.1 M	A.3
12	stirring rods	A.7
36	strips of filter paper, 8 mm × 3 cm	C.2
50 mL	sulfuric acid (H$_2$SO$_4$), 6 M	A.3
50 mL	sulfuric acid (H$_2$SO$_4$), concentrated	A.3
12	spatulas	A.7
12	test tube holders	A.3, A.7, B.3
12	test tube racks	A.3, A.7, B.3
84	test tubes (18 × 150 mm)	A.3, A.7, B.3
12	voltmeters	C.2
12 L	water, distilled	A.3, A.7
12	wellplates, 24-well	C.2
24	wire leads with alligator clips	C.2
50 mL	zinc nitrate (Zn(NO$_3$)$_2$), 0.1 M	C.2
12	zinc strips, medium (~ 0.5 cm × 3 cm × 0.1 cm)	C.2
12	zinc strips, narrow (~ 0.25 cm × 3 cm × 0.1 cm)	C.2
12	zinc strips, wide (~ 1 cm × 3 cm × 0.1 cm)	C.2

Equipment, Expendable Items, and Unususal Materials (per 12 Student Pairs)

Sorted by Section

QUANTITY	ITEM	SECTION USED
12	beakers, 100-mL	A.3
48 strips	litmus paper, red	A.3
12	nichrome or platinum (Pt) wire loops with handles	A.3
12	test tube racks	A.3
12	test tube holders	A.3
12	Bunsen burners	A.3
84	test tubes (18 × 150 mm)	A.3
12	cobalt-blue glass squares	A.3
120	Beral pipets	A.3
2.0 L	water, distilled	A.3
50 mL	hydrochloric acid (HCl), 2.0 M	A.3
100 mL	hydrochloric acid (HCl), 6.0 M	A.3
50 mL	sodium hydroxide (NaOH), 3.0 M	A.3
50 mL	sulfuric acid (H_2SO_4), concentrated	A.3
50 mL	iron(II) sulfate ($FeSO_4 \cdot 7H_2O$), 0.1 M	A.3
50 mL	barium chloride ($BaCl_2 \cdot 2H_2O$), 0.1 M	A.3
50 mL	potassium thiocyanate (KSCN), 0.2 M	A.3
50 mL	sulfuric acid (H_2SO_4), 6 M	A.3

Sorted by Section (continued)

QUANTITY	ITEM	SECTION USED
50 mL	sodium phosphate ($Na_3PO_4 \cdot 2H_2O$), 0.1 M	A.3
50 mL	sodium nitrate ($NaNO_3$), 0.1 M	A.3
50 mL	sodium sulfate ($Na_2SO_4 \cdot 10H_2O$), 0.1 M	A.3
50 mL	potassium nitrate (KNO_3), 0.1 M	A.3
50 mL	ammonium nitrate (NH_4NO_3), 0.1 M	A.3
50 mL	iron(III) nitrate ($Fe(NO_3)_3 \cdot 9H_2O$), 0.1 M	A.3
12	hot plates	A.3
20 g	ascorbic acid ($C_6H_8O_6$)	A.7
20 g	granular fertilizer	A.7
1.0 L	phosphate standard, 10.0 ppm	A.7
325 mL	ammonium molybdate-sulfuric acid reagent	A.7
10 L	water, distilled	A.7
60	test tubes (18 × 150 mm)	A.7
12	test tube holders	A.7
12	test tube racks	A.7
12	wire gauze squares	A.7
36	beakers, 400-mL	A.7

SUPPLY LIST

Sorted by Section (continued)

QUANTITY	ITEM	SECTION USED
12	graduated cylinders, 10-mL	A.7
12	graduated cylinders, 50-mL or 100-mL	A.7
12	stirring rods	A.7
12	hot plates	A.7
6	balances	A.7
12	spatulas	A.7
12	wax pencils for labeling test tubes	A.7
12	test tubes (18 × 150 mm)	B.3
12	test tube holders	B.3
24	beakers, 400-mL	B.3
12	hot plates	B.3
2 lbs	ice	B.3
24	dropper bottles	B.3
100 mL	cobalt(II) chloride hexahydrate ($CoCl_2 \cdot 6H_2O$), 0.1 M	B.3
40 g	calcium chloride, anhydrous ($CaCl_2$)	B.3
265 mL	silver nitrate ($AgNO_3$), 0.1 M	B.3
5 g	sodium chloride (NaCl)	B.3
100 mL	ethanol, 95%	B.3

Sorted by Section (continued)

QUANTITY	ITEM	SECTION USED
12	wellplates, 24-well	C.2
48	Beral pipets	C.2
50 mL	zinc nitrate $(Zn(NO_3)_2)$, 0.1 M	C.2
50 mL	copper(II) nitrate $(Cu(NO_3)_2)$, 0.1 M	C.2
50 mL	iron(III) nitrate $(Fe(NO_3)_3)$, 0.1 M	C.2
50 mL	magnesium nitrate $(Mg(NO_3)_2)$, 0.1 M	C.2
12	copper strips, wide	C.2
12	copper strips, medium	C.2
12	copper strips, narrow	C.2
12	zinc strips, wide	C.2
12	zinc strips, medium	C.2
12	zinc strips, narrow	C.2
12	magnesium strips, 3-cm	C.2
12	iron strips	C.2
12	voltmeters	C.2
24	wire leads with alligator clips	C.2
36	strips of filter paper, 8 mm × 3 cm	C.2
100 mL	potassium nitrate (KNO_3), saturated	C.2

UNIT 5
INDUSTRY: APPLYING CHEMICAL REACTIONS

Introduction to the Unit

Industrial chemistry encompasses a wide range of manufacturing processes, including refining petroleum (addressed in Unit 3), extracting metals from their ores (addressed in Unit 2), and producing polymers (see Unit 3) and pharmaceuticals. This unit focuses on the industrial processes associated with producing synthetic inorganic fertilizers and preparing aluminum from bauxite ore.

This unit gives students opportunities to evaluate operations of EKS, a nitrogen products company, and WYE, a metal production corporation. As students evaluate EKS and WYE, they revisit and expand on their previous knowledge of atoms, electrons, ions, electronegativity, reduction–oxidation reactions, activity series, chemical reactions, and thermochemistry. New concepts introduced in this unit include the nitrogen cycle, colorimetry, concentration, oxidation numbers, kinetics, equilibrium, Le Châtelier's Principle, and electrochemistry. Topics directly related to industrial chemistry, such as chemical engineering, Green Chemistry, Responsible Care, and benefit-burden analysis, are also incorporated.

UNIT 5

Industry: Applying Chemical Reactions

HOW do chemical industries convert substances into other useful materials by large-scale manufacturing?

SECTION A
Some Chemistry of Nitrogen (page 410)

? The town of Riverwood seeks to generate new employment opportunities. Two large chemical companies are interested in locating in Riverwood. In this unit, you will learn about issues Riverwood must address before the town invites either company to build a chemical plant in the community.

The unit culminates in a Riverwood Town Council meeting, where students decide whether EKS or WYE will be invited to locate in Riverwood based on their understanding of the chemistry and risks and benefits involved in operating such large-scale plants.

Because it is impossible to demonstrate industrial processes adequately in the classroom, use some of these strategies:

• Obtain DVDs, videos, or films of industrial processes to view with your class. *The World of Chemistry* videotapes and TV Ontario's videotapes are good sources.

• Arrange field trips to nearby industrial plants involved in such businesses as electroplating, jewelry making, electronics, and aluminum processing.

• Arrange for classroom visits by knowledgeable individuals such as industrial chemists, electroplating and electrolysis workers, and silversmiths.

• Invite students to "shadow" a professional industrial chemist or chemical engineer or assign students to mentors for a short time.

Using the Unit Project

Two newspaper commentaries set the stage for the major storyline of the unit—companies EKS and WYE are interested in opening chemical manufacturing plants near Riverwood. In the commentaries, two Riverwood residents express differing opinions on this possibility.

You may wish to read these articles as a class to help students become engaged with the story, which will provide the "need-to-know" for the entire unit. Based on these two articles, ask students (either as a class or in small groups) to list advantages and disadvantages of allowing either EKS or WYE to have a plant near Riverwood. You can revisit and reevaluate this list during the unit as students become more informed about the chemistry and risks and benefits associated with EKS and WYE.

EKS or WYE?
More Job Options for Riverwood

A *RIVERWOOD NEWS* COMMENTARY BY GRETA B. LEDERMAN

Riverwood Resident

Several weeks ago, the town council announced that two industrial firms were interested in building chemical manufacturing plants in Riverwood: EKS Nitrogen Products Company and WYE Metals Corporation. Because of a lack of employment opportunities in Riverwood, many of your friends and neighbors have expressed relief at this news.

Greta Lederman

When the Riverwood Corporation declared bankruptcy last year, many residents lost their jobs. Although some have found new jobs, many have not. The unemployment rate in Riverwood has hovered near 15% for most of the past year.

Can anything be done to boost our local economy? Yes. We can allow one of these eager companies to build a chemical plant in our town. New jobs would be created for chemists, chemical technicians, and office personnel. Each company claims it would need to hire about 200 new employees.

In addition, both companies confirm that they plan to occupy the former Riverwood Corporation site. Recently, the Riverwood Corporation parking lot seems to attract only weekend flea-market vendors and people selling used cars.

We need more job opportunities; no one denies that. But some people may wonder whether a chemical plant is the best option for Riverwood. Why not a furniture manufacturer or a book warehouse? Aren't chemical plants dangerous?

The reality is that no other companies have expressed an interest in locating in Riverwood. EKS and WYE are attracted by our well-educated workforce and by our access to abundant resources and electrical energy, among other factors. Both companies are well suited to our community.

Both companies have strong safety and environmental records. They are members of the American Chemistry Council's Responsible Care initiative. They both advocate green technologies.

We have a unique opportunity to choose between two companies that are competing to locate here. Usually it's the reverse—two or more cities competing for one company. Learn more about each company. Visit the Web site of each company and attend the scheduled citywide discussions.

If you still have doubts, notice how this news has affected your friends and neighbors. A new sense of hope has emerged over the recent weeks. Let's turn weeks of hope into years of Riverwood prosperity.

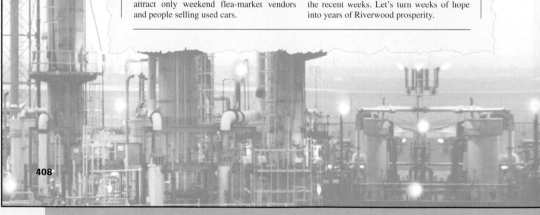

EKS or WYE?
New Jobs May Become too Costly

A *RIVERWOOD NEWS* COMMENTARY BY PAK JIN-WOO
Riverwood Resident

Although no one can deny that our Riverwood community needs a source of new jobs, it's foolish to invite either EKS Nitrogen Products Company or WYE Metals Corporation to locate here to manufacture, respectively, ammonia or aluminum, without first considering all the consequences.

Pak Jin-Woo

The promise of 200 new jobs is alluring. However, all of these jobs would be in only one company. What will happen if there's a decline in the market for ammonia or aluminum?

Either of the proposed Riverwood plants would be small compared to other plants operated by EKS and WYE in other cities. Thus, the Riverwood plant would probably be among the first to be shut down if an economic slowdown occurs. If that happens, the Riverwood area would quickly return to the same economic situation it is in now.

Wouldn't it be more prudent to distribute those 200 jobs among several different companies? Let's learn from our recent experience with the city's former principal employer, the now-bankrupt Riverwood Corporation.

Although long-term economic health is important, we must question the potential safety and environmental risks that each of these two chemical plants would pose to our community.

For instance, ammonia production requires very high pressures and temperatures. Although accidents are uncommon, the potential consequences of an explosion or spill are still great. Several illnesses and even deaths of workers have been documented at ammonia plants.

Aluminum production also involves risks to its workers. For every 100 employees, job-related illnesses and injuries involve, on average, about 20 workers annually. Which 40 Riverwood residents would be included in this statistic if we allow an aluminum plant to be established here?

Perhaps the greatest long-term concern is the potential for environmental harm. Ammonia-based contamination of the Snake River could, for example, cause another fish-kill crisis.

Along the same lines, manufacturing aluminum metal produces, among other things, toxic carbon monoxide gas. What might happen if the company mishandles the containment of this gas?

I realize that not all of these scenarios are likely to occur. However, we must be absolutely willing to accept the consequences should something negative happen. With what level of risk are you and your friends willing to live?

As you can infer from the newspaper commentaries, two companies want to establish a chemical plant in Riverwood. EKS Nitrogen Products Company wants to establish a plant that produces ammonia. WYE Metals Corporation would build an aluminum-production plant. As both commentators acknowledge, either company would offer at least 200 new job opportunities to the Riverwood community. However, as the commentaries suggest, job creation is not the only factor to consider.

Later in this unit, you will help to decide whether to invite EKS or WYE (or neither company) to operate a plant in Riverwood. The chemistry you learn in this unit will prepare you to make informed decisions about the risks and benefits of operating such plants. Keep in mind the concerns in the two commentaries as you learn about the chemistry involved in manufacturing ammonia and aluminum.

409

As in other units, this story line lends itself to connections with current and/or local events. During the unit, you may ask students to find and bring in articles that relate to Riverwood's decision-making process. Students can share these articles with the class through short presentations or by posting them on a bulletin board. Current information on industrial chemistry and community issues around those industries will reinforce in students' minds that concerns in the imaginary town of Riverwood are relevant in their own lives.

Some Chemistry of Nitrogen

Introduction Content Reading Guide

The main focus of Section A is to let students explore methods chemical industries use. Through these methods, industries apply fundamental chemical principles to produce useful products.

The solutions for *Investigating Matter A.7* give best results when prepared several days in advance. Consider preparing them as you begin Section A; they will keep indefinitely.

Using the Figures

Figure 5.1: Initiate the activity in *Making Decisions A.1* by asking students to identify substances in this photo that have *not* been altered in some way.

Making Decisions

A.1 Chemical Processing in Your Life

This introductory activity invites students to think about the impact of the chemical industry on their lives.

Items students may list as being "unaltered" include water, milk, fresh and organic produce, grains, meat and fish; helium (for balloons); firewood; and houseplants.

Answers

1. a. Unless you grow your own food, spin your own fibers, or buy items from individuals who do, most purchased items are packaged in chemically processed paper, cardboard, or plastics.
   b. Packaging can be essential in maintaining product quality—freshness, integrity, and purity—

SECTION A

Some Chemistry of Nitrogen

In the first four units, you learned that chemistry is concerned with the composition and properties of matter, changes in matter, and the energy involved in those changes. In this unit you will explore how chemical industries use chemical knowledge and reactions to produce a wide range of useful material goods on a large scale.

In particular, this unit offers you an opportunity to evaluate the chemical operations of EKS and WYE. This knowledge will help you later as you debate whether or not a new chemical plant should locate in Riverwood, and, if so, which one.

Making Decisions

A.1 CHEMICAL PROCESSING IN YOUR LIFE

To become more aware of how pervasive the products of chemical processing are in everyday life, list five items or materials around you that have *not* been manufactured, processed, or altered from their natural form. Start by considering everyday items, such as clothes, objects in your home, modes of transportation, books, foods, communication devices such as phones and computers, and sports and recreation equipment—all things you routinely encounter.

Now answer the following questions. Be prepared to share and discuss your answers in class.

1. a. Which items on your list were wrapped, boxed, or shipped in materials that had been manufactured (Figure 5.1)? Explain.
   b. Is the packaging or shipping material essential or simply a convenience? Why?

2. In what ways might each item or material on your list be better than or inferior to a manufactured, processed, or synthetic alternative? Consider factors such as cost, convenience, availability, and quality.

3. If a product is "100% natural," does that necessarily mean it was not involved in any processing or chemical or physical changes? Why? Support your answer with at least one example.

A.2 CHEMICAL PRODUCTS

Consider the items you listed in Making Decisions A.1. There are very few things that we use regularly that have not been modified in some way. This is the chemical industry's focus—transforming natural resources into useful products to meet a wide variety of needs and purposes. The chemical industry also creates new substances and materials as replacements for natural ones. For example, plastics often replace wood or metals, and synthetic fibers often replace cotton or wool.

Figure 5.1 *The chemical industry manufactures many products, some of which are used in shipping and supplying food products.*

---

during shipping and storage. Some packaging can be a convenience that facilitates easier handling of goods.

2. In most cases, synthetic products cost less than their natural alternatives (examples: nylon vs. silk, synthetic vitamins vs. natural). Often, natural materials come from particular regions, requiring additional transport compared to locally produced synthetics. In some instances, synthetic materials are more abundant than their natural counterparts, resulting in a lower price per unit. Thus synthetic products can also be more convenient than natural alternatives.

Even though the chemical industry is a worldwide, multibillion-dollar enterprise that affects everyone's daily life through its products and economic impact, most people are not aware of what happens when new materials are produced. This raises questions about how chemical industries operate, how they manufacture new products, and what those products contain.

The modern chemical industry employs well over a million people worldwide. Over the past 80 years, it has grown through mergers of smaller companies and creation of new companies. During that time, the industry's focus has expanded from a limited range of basic products to more than 70 000 products. Hundreds of chemical companies form the third largest manufacturing group in the United States; only industries that produce machinery and electrical equipment are larger. Indeed, if we include the food and petroleum industries in the chemical-industry category, this represents the world's *largest* industry.

Most chemical products reach the public indirectly because they are used to produce other consumer materials. For instance, the automobile and home-construction industries use enormous supplies of industrial chemicals. They use paints and plastics for automobile body parts such as bumpers, dashboard panels, upholstery and carpeting, and synthetic rubber in tires. Home construction involves large quantities of plastics for carpeting and flooring, insulation, siding, window frames, piping, and appliances. It also involves using paints, metals, and air-conditioning coolants. Figure 5.2 shows a range of products from various chemical industries.

Figure 5.2 *The chemical industry produces many materials that have useful properties.*

3. "100% natural" does not mean that no chemical processing occurred; it only indicates that the product has no synthetic additives. In fact, almost all natural products have undergone some chemical processing. Examples include 100% natural cereals and vitamins and all-cotton or all-wool clothing.

This question provides an opportunity to emphasize two points: All matter is made of chemical substances, and assuming it is pure, a given synthetic compound is identical to the natural version of the same compound.

A.2 Chemical Products

The chemical industry changes natural materials into useful products and creates new products to replace natural materials. A.2 discusses the modern chemical industry and its status as a worldwide, multi-billion-dollar enterprise. Some substances produced by the chemical industry reach the public directly, but many chemical products reach the public indirectly—they are used in production of other materials. For example, sulfuric acid is used in producing fertilizers and manufacturing lead–acid batteries. Chlorine, also widely produced, is used to manufacture disinfectants and bleaching agents. **Figure 5.2** shows several products of chemical industry, including paints and plastics, used in manufacturing and consumer goods.

One segment of the chemical enterprise is the food industry. The role of fertilizers in food production and the choice of appropriate fertilizers are discussed. Complete fertilizers contain the three main elements that plants need for optimal growth—nitrogen, phosphorus, and potassium—in the form of anions and cations. Fertilizers may also include filler material (possibly clay pellets,

Quality of manufactured/processed materials compared to their natural alternatives can vary significantly. Most manufacturers aim to provide material that is at least of comparable quality (example: synthetic rubber for natural). In some instances, synthetic materials have additional properties that allow them to be more useful than their natural alternatives (example: some butterlike products are enhanced to provide cholesterol-lowering benefits). Finally, a blend of natural and synthetic sometimes provides a desirable combination of cost and quality (example: clothing made by blending cotton with synthetic fibers).

ash, or granular limestone) or additional nutrients such as magnesium, sulfur, calcium, manganese, zinc, boron, and iron.

Investigating Matter

A.3 Fertilizer Components

 A.3 Fertilizer Components Student Worksheet and Data Table

Students use the techniques of qualitative analysis to determine whether six nutrient ions (NO_3^-, PO_4^{3-}, SO_4^{2-}, NH_4^+, Fe^{3+}, K^+) are present in a fertilizer. In Part I, students will perform tests on known solutions of these ions to become familiar with each confirming test. In Part II, students will perform the same tests to determine whether an unknown fertilizer solution contains the ions.

Time

50 min

Materials

(For 12 student pairs)

12 100-mL beakers
48 litmus paper strips, red
12 nichrome or platinum (Pt) wire loops, each attached to a cork stopper or handle
12 Bunsen burners
12 hot plates
84 18 × 150 mm test tubes (assuming tubes are washed and reused)
12 test tube racks
12 test tube holders
12 squares of cobalt-blue glass
120 Beral pipets
50 mL 2 M HCl for cleaning nichrome wires (8.3 mL conc. HCl/50 mL solution)

Test Solutions

100 mL 6.0 M HCl (50 mL conc. HCl/100 mL solution)

You will learn about aluminum production in Section C.

Fertilizer Components

Figure 5.3 *This label indicates that this fertilizer contains 4% nitrogen, 5% P_2O_5, 2% K_2O, and 1% iron.*

Ideal for roses, azaleas, camellias, ferns, fuchsias, begonias, and other acid or shade loving plants.

GUARANTEED ANALYSIS
Total Nitrogen (N)...4.00%
Available Phosphoric Acid (P_2O_5) 5.00%
Potash (K_2O)...2.00%
Iron (Fe)...1.00%

Derived from processed organic materials: Ammonium Nitrate, Ammonium Phosphate, Sulfate of Potash, and Iron Sulfate.

DIRECTIONS
Apply evenly by hand around base of plant out to drip line and water in well. A 1/8" deep layer around plant three times annually. For potted plants apply 2 tablespoons full per 6" pot.
LAWN & DICHONDRA — Apply by hand or spreader 2-1/2 lbs. per 100 sq. ft. (10 x 10). A 1 lb. coffee can holds approximately 2-1/2 lbs. of 4-5-2.

Reporting P and K as P_2O_5 and K_2O (as in Figure 5.3) is traditional and originates from early research on fertilizers. When chemists burned fertilized plants to ash and then analyzed the ash, they obtained the masses of P_2O_5 and K_2O.

You used confirming tests in water testing in Unit 1 (see page 42).

In Riverwood, the two industrial companies under consideration manufacture products involving nitrogen and aluminum. Among the products manufactured by EKS Nitrogen Products Company are nitric acid and ammonia, which are often used in chemical reactions that produce other materials. By contrast, the sheet aluminum produced by WYE Metals Corporation is most often used directly in its manufactured form.

EKS is committed to producing high-quality nitrogen-based fertilizer in Riverwood at a reasonable cost, using the best available technologies. Fertilizer may sound unappealing as a product, but its manufacture and sale represent a multi-million-dollar business that employs thousands of people worldwide and affects the lives of nearly everyone, from farmers and gardeners to food producers and consumers.

How can you decide whether a particular fertilizer is best for a specific application, such as on houseplants, lawns, or cornfields? One way is to find out if the fertilizer contains the proper ingredients. Complete fertilizers, such as those manufactured by EKS, contain the three main elements growing plants need—*nitrogen, phosphorus,* and *potassium*—as well as trace ions and filler material.

Figure 5.3 shows the label of a typical commercial fertilizer bag. The numbers on the label indicate the percent values of key ingredients contained in the fertilizer: nitrogen, N; phosphorus, P (expressed as percent P_2O_5); and potassium, K (expressed as percent K_2O). The proportion of each component varies according to crop needs. Most lawn grasses need nitrogen; a 20–10–10 fertilizer is a good choice for lawns. Phosphorus is especially useful in promoting fruit and vegetable growth, so some gardeners prefer a 10–30–10 mixture over a balanced (10–10–10) fertilizer.

Many plant nutrients provided in fertilizers are in the form of cations and anions. Cations are likely to include potassium (K^+), ammonium (NH_4^+), and iron(II) (Fe^{2+}) or iron(III) (Fe^{3+}); anions include nitrate (NO_3^-), phosphate (PO_4^{3-}), and sulfate (SO_4^{2-}).

In the following laboratory investigation, you will use confirming tests to determine whether a fertilizer solution contains specified nutrients.

50 mL 3.0 M NaOH (60 g NaOH/500 mL solution)
50 mL conc. H_2SO_4 in dropper bottles
50 mL 0.1 M $FeSO_4$ (1.4 g $FeSO_4 \cdot 7H_2O$/50 mL solution)
50 mL 0.1 M $BaCl_2$ (1.2 g $BaCl_2 \cdot 2H_2O$/50 mL solution)
50 mL 0.2 M KSCN (0.5 g KSCN/50 mL solution)
50 mL 6 M H_2SO_4

Known Ion Solutions

50 mL 0.1 M Na_3PO_4 (1.9 g $Na_3PO_4 \cdot 2H_2O$/50 mL solution)
50 mL 0.1 M $NaNO_3$ (4.3 g $NaNO_3$/50 mL solution)
50 mL 0.1 M Na_2SO_4 (1.6 g $Na_2SO_4 \cdot 10H_2O$/50 mL solution)
50 mL 0.1 M KNO_3 (0.50 g KNO_3/50 mL solution)

A.3 FERTILIZER COMPONENTS

Investigating Matter

Introduction

You will test a fertilizer solution for six particular ions (three anions and three cations). In Part I you will perform tests on known solutions of those ions to become familiar with each confirming test. In Part II you will decide which ions are present in an unknown fertilizer solution. Read the complete procedure and prepare a suitable data table to record your observations.

🔴 **Lab Video: Fertilizer Components**

Procedure

Part I. Ion Tests

1. Prepare a warm-water bath by adding about 30 mL of water to a 100-mL beaker. Place the beaker on a hot plate. The water must be warm, but it should not boil. Control the hot plate accordingly. You will use this bath in Step 6d.

2. Obtain a Beral pipet set containing test solutions of each of six known ions: nitrate (NO_3^-), phosphate (PO_4^{3-}), sulfate (SO_4^{2-}), ammonium (NH_4^+), iron(III) (Fe^{3+}), and potassium (K^+). Observe and record the colors of all six solutions.

BaCl₂ Test

Several of the ions you are studying in this investigation can be identified first by their reaction with barium cations (Ba^{2+}) and then their behavior in the presence of an acid.

3. a. Add 2 to 3 drops of each test solution to six separate, clean test tubes. Add 2 to 3 drops of distilled water to a seventh clean test tube to serve as a blank.

    b. Test each solution individually by adding 1 to 2 drops of 0.1 M barium chloride ($BaCl_2$) solution (see Figure 5.4). Record your observations.

    c. Add 3 drops of 6 M hydrochloric acid (HCl) to each of the seven test tubes. *Caution: 6 M HCl is very corrosive. If any splashes on your skin, wash it off thoroughly with water and inform your teacher. Do not inhale any HCl fumes.* Record your observations.

    d. Dispose of the solutions as instructed, then clean and rinse the test tubes.

A *blank* was explained and used in a Unit 1 investigation (see page 42).

| **Figure 5.4** *Adding drops to a test tube.*

---

50 mL 0.1 M NH_4NO_3 (0.40 g NH_4NO_3/ 50 mL solution)

50 mL 0.1 M Fe $(NO_3)_3$ (2.0 g $Fe(NO_3)_3 \cdot 9H_2O$/50 mL solution)

Distilled water for preparing solutions and rinsing test tubes, 2.0 L

Unknown "fertilizer solutions" in Beral pipets, labeled with a code number. See Advance Preparation.

Safety

Students should wear protective goggles and aprons throughout the investigation.

Concentrated sulfuric acid is extremely hazardous: Students should use it only under strict supervision. We recommend that teachers dispense the concentrated sulfuric acid in Step 3c. Exercise caution when handling 6 M HCl and 3 M NaOH. Both hydrochloric acid and sodium hydroxide may damage skin. Barium compounds are toxic. Students should exercise caution when handling the $BaCl_2$ solution.

Advance Preparation

Label Beral pipets and fill them with the test solutions (except for concentrated sulfuric acid) and the six known ions. (If student teams are to use sulfuric acid, it should be supplied in dropper bottles made specifically for concentrated sulfuric acid.) Place the pipets in a wellplate (or a cassette tape case) with the points up to avoid spillage.

The $FeSO_4$ should be freshly prepared. Otherwise, the brown-ring test does not work well.

For the unknowns, use any available (and safe) solutions that contain the appropriate ions. Samples of commercial fertilizers are *not* recommended for the unknowns because some contain insoluble matter, time-released substances, or ions that interfere with the simple identifying tests suggested in this procedure. Ion concentrations in the unknown solutions should be at least 0.1 M. Examples include (a) a solution that contains both 0.1 M NH_4NO_3 and 0.1 M Na_3PO_4 (testing positive for NH_4^+, NO_3^-, and PO_4^{3-}) and (b) a solution of 0.1 M $Fe_2(SO_4)_3$ (testing positive for Fe^{3+} and SO_4^{2-}). It is not necessary to prepare a different unknown for each student team.

Prepare the unknown solutions and place them in coded Beral pipets. Tell students to record the code for their unknown in their laboratory report.

If necessary, clean the used flame-test wires with a higher concentration of HCl, such as 12 M, after student use.

Lab Tips

• Students will need to create fairly detailed data tables to record their observations in this investigation. You may decide to ask students to create their data tables in advance and present them for checking prior to the investigation. In the $BaCl_2$ test, ensure that students record separate results for the addition of $BaCl_2$ and for the subsequent addition of HCl.

• Encourage students to label the test tubes to reduce the chances of mix-ups. Stress that students must keep careful records of the solutions in each test tube so they will be able to draw conclusions based on their data. Making good observations is also crucial in this qualitative investigation—students should describe initial colors of solutions, color changes, and precipitate formations in detail.

Brown-Ring Test

In the presence of nitrate ions (NO_3^-), mixing iron(II) ions (Fe^{2+}) with sulfuric acid (H_2SO_4) produces a distinctive result—a brown ring. You can use this *brown-ring test* to detect nitrate ions in a solution.

4. a. Add eight drops of sodium nitrate ($NaNO_3$) solution to a small, clean test tube. Place eight drops of distilled water in a second small, clean test tube, which will serve as a blank.

   b. Add about one milliliter of iron(II) sulfate ($FeSO_4$) solution to each of the two test tubes. Gently swirl to mix the contents of each tube.

   c. Have your teacher carefully pour about one milliliter of concentrated sulfuric acid (H_2SO_4) along the inside of each test tube wall so the acid forms a second layer under the undisturbed solution already in the tube (Figure 5.5).

   ⚠ *Caution: Concentrated H_2SO_4 is a very strong, corrosive acid. If any contacts your skin, immediately wash affected areas with abundant running tap water and inform your teacher.*

   d. Allow the test tubes to stand, undisturbed, for 1 to 2 min.

   e. Observe any change that occurs at the interface of the two liquid layers. Record your observations.

5. Dispose of the solutions as instructed, then clean and rinse the test tubes.

Figure 5.5 *To minimize mixing, concentrated sulfuric acid is allowed to run down the inside surface of the test tube. Possessing a larger density than water, concentrated sulfuric acid forms a layer beneath the water.*

NaOH and Litmus Test

Now you will investigate which of the three cations (NH_4^+, Fe^{3+}, or K^+) you can identify by observing their characteristic behavior in the presence of a strong base.

6. a. Add four drops of each cation test solution to three separate, clean test tubes. Add four drops of distilled water to a fourth clean test tube, which will serve as a blank.

   b. Moisten four strips of red litmus paper with distilled water; place them on a watch glass.

   c. Add 10 drops of 3 M sodium hydroxide (NaOH) directly to

   ⚠ the solution in one of the four test tubes. *Caution: 3 M NaOH is corrosive. If any splashes on your skin, wash it off thoroughly with water and inform your teacher. Do not allow any NaOH solution to contact the test tube lip or inner wall. Immediately stick one of the four premoistened red litmus-paper strips from Step 6b across the top of the test tube. The strip must not contact the solution.*

   d. Warm the test tube gently in a hot water bath for 1 min. Wait 30 s and then record your observations.

   e. Repeat Steps 6c and 6d for each of the other three test tubes.

Flame Test

You can identify many metal ions by the characteristic color they emit when heated in a burner flame. For example, it is common to use a flame test to identify potassium ions.

EXPECTED RESULTS						
TEST	**ION TESTS**					
	NH_4^+	Fe^{3+}	K^+	NO_3^-	PO_4^{3-}	SO_4^{2-}
Color	NC	Brown	NC	NC	NC	NC
$BaCl_2$	NC	NC	NC	NC	ppt	ppt
$BaCl_2$ and HCl	NC	NC	NC	NC	ppt dissolved	ppt remained
Brown-ring test	X	X	X	brown ring	X	X
NaOH and litmus	blue litmus	NC	NC	X	X	X
Flame test			violet	X	X	X
Flame test and cobalt glass			pink	X	X	X
KSCN test	NC	red	NC	NC	NC	NC
NC: no change X: test was not performed ppt: precipitate						

7. a. Obtain a platinum or nichrome wire inserted into glass tubing or a cork stopper, which serves as its handle.

b. Set up and light a bunsen burner. Adjust the flame to produce a light blue, steady inner cone and a luminous, pale blue outer cone.

c. To clean the wire, place about 10 drops of 2 M hydrochloric acid (HCl) in a small test tube. ***Caution: 2 M HCl is corrosive. If any splashes on your skin, wash it off thoroughly with water and inform your teacher. Do not inhale any HCl fumes.*** Dip the wire into the hydrochloric acid and then heat the wire tip in the burner flame. Position the wire at the intersection of the two parts of the flame, not in the center cone. As the wire heats bright red, the burner flame may become colored, as illustrated in Figure 5.6. The characteristic colors are due to metallic cations held on the wire's surface.

Figure 5.6 *Completing a flame test. Metallic ions emit characteristic colors when heated*

d. Continue dipping the wire into the acid solution and inserting the wire into the flame until there is little or no change in flame color as the wire heats to redness.

The lack of color change in the flame indicates that the wire is clean.

e. Place 7 drops of potassium ion solution into a clean test tube. Dip the cool, cleaned wire into this solution. Then insert the wire into the flame. Note any change in the flame color, the intensity of the color, and the estimated time (in seconds) that the color was visible.

f. Repeat the potassium-ion flame test, this time observing the burner flame through cobalt-blue or didymium glass (Figure 5.7). Again, note the color, intensity, and duration of the color. Your partner can hold the wire in the flame while you observe through the colored glass. Then exchange roles. Record all observations.

The colored glass may make the characteristic potassium flame color easier to see against the color of the burner flame.

Figure 5.7 *The emission produced by excited potassium ions is best observed through cobalt glass.*

• Test tubes must be rinsed thoroughly with distilled water before using them a second time. Remind students to clean the test tubes thoroughly as they finish their work.

• The burner setting should be adjusted to produce a hot, blue flame. A hot platinum or nichrome wire will itself display color. Students should record the color that appears *before* the wire is red hot.

• Remind students that red litmus paper turns blue (or slightly violet) in base.

Section A Some Chemistry of Nitrogen **415**

Answers

1. Answers will depend on the unknowns provided. Students should refer to specific observations from Part II that match test results in Part I as evidence to support their answers.

2. Answers will depend on unknown composition, but should list fertilizer ingredients containing phosphate, potassium, or nitrate ions. Examples include ammonium phosphate $((NH_4)_3PO_4)$, monopotassium phosphate (KH_2PO_4) and potassium nitrate (KNO_3).

3. A white precipitate in the barium chloride test indicates the presence of either phosphate or sulfate. If the precipitate then dissolves in 6 M hydrochloric acid, the phosphate ion is present.

4. Soluble. In the investigation, barium chloride is added to a solution containing nitrate ions. No precipitate forms, suggesting that barium nitrate is soluble in water.

5. These tests provide only qualitative information about whether a fertilizer contains certain nutrients. They do not provide information about the quantities of nutrients contained. Deciding whether a fertilizer is suitable for a particular use requires quantitative information.

Post-Lab Discussion

Ask students how using data tables helped them to determine the ions present in the unknown sample. You may decide to ask students to share their results with each other and data that led them to their conclusions. This is also an ideal opportunity to challenge students to identify and discuss potential sources of error in this investigation.

KSCN Test

In Unit 1 (page 44), you learned that when potassium thiocyanate (KSCN) is added to an aqueous solution containing iron(III) ions (Fe^{3+}), a deep red color appears due to the formation of $[FeSCN]^{2+}$ cations. Appearance of this characteristic color confirms the presence of iron(III) in a solution.

8. a. Place 3 drops of iron(III)-containing solution into a clean test tube. Place 3 drops of water into a second clean test tube.
   b. Add 1 drop of 0.1 M KSCN solution to each test tube. Record your observations.
   c. Dispose of the solutions as instructed, then clean and rinse the test tubes.

Part II. Tests on an Unknown Fertilizer Solution

1. Obtain a Beral pipet containing an unknown fertilizer solution. Record its code number. Your unknown solution contains one of the cations and one of the anions that you tested in Part I. Observe and record the color (if any) of the unknown solution.

2. Complete suitable laboratory tests of the fertilizer solution to identify the two unknown ions it contains. Record all observations and conclusions. Repeat a particular test, if you wish, to confirm your initial observations.

3. Dispose of all solutions used in this investigation as directed by your teacher.

4. Wash your hands thoroughly before leaving the laboratory.

Questions

1. Identify the ions that were present in your unknown fertilizer sample, citing evidence from your investigation.

2. Look up the components of common commercial fertilizers and provide the name and formula for two of the ingredients that contain one or both of the ions in your fertilizer sample. For example, sodium chloride (NaCl) would supply sodium ions (Na^+) and chloride ions (Cl^-) to a solution, while potassium carbonate (K_2CO_3) would furnish potassium ions (K^+) and carbonate ions (CO_3^{2-}).

3. Using evidence collected in your investigation, describe a test you could complete to verify whether a fertilizer sample contains phosphate ions (PO_4^{3-}).

4. Is barium nitrate, $Ba(NO_3)_2$, soluble or insoluble in water? Cite specific evidence from your investigation to support your answer.

5. Explain why the kind of data gathered in this investigation about a specific fertilizer solution is inadequate for you to judge whether the fertilizer is suitable for a particular use.

In this procedure, students played roles of analytical chemists, positions that would be available at a new Riverwood plant. Analytical chemists complete qualitative and quantitative tests to determine the identity and quantity of matter in a sample.

Some analytical chemists create and identify these procedures.

The analyses in this investigation involved tests based on chemical reactions ("wet" chemistry). Modern analyses also involve computer-interfaced instrumentation.

A.4 FERTILIZER AND THE NITROGEN CYCLE

Each year EKS manufactures about 3 million tons of ammonia and more than 1.5 million tons of nitric acid. Most is used to manufacture fertilizers sold to farmers and gardeners.

The purpose of all fertilizers is to add nutrients to soil so growing plants have adequate supplies. The raw materials that growing crops use are mainly carbon dioxide from the atmosphere and water and nutrients from the soil. Plant roots absorb water and nutrients such as phosphate, magnesium, potassium, and nitrate ions.

Phosphate becomes part of the energy-storage molecule ATP (adenosine triphosphate) and the nucleic acids RNA and DNA. Magnesium ions are a key component of chlorophyll, which is essential for photosynthesis. Potassium ions—found in the fluids and cells of most living things—help maintain a growing plant's ability to convert carbohydrates from one form to another and to synthesize proteins. Nitrate ions aid vigorous plant growth and supply nitrogen atoms that are incorporated into proteins. Figure 5.8 illustrates how plants use these nutrients.

> Liquified ammonia can also be directly applied to soil as a fertilizer.

Potassium (K)
- Promotes cell-wall thickening, protecting plants against cold temperatures, pests, and disease
- Regulates water use and nutrient movement in cells
- Activates plant enzymes involved in processes such as photosynthesis and respiration

Phosphorus (P)
- Promotes production of blooms, flowers, seeds, and root development
- Component of DNA, RNA, and ATP

Nitrogen (N)
- Promotes new green growth
- Component of proteins, DNA, RNA, ATP, and chlorophyll

Adenosine triphosphate (ATP)—provides energy for cellular reactions

Figure 5.8 *All plants depend on certain nutrients participating as reactants in vital chemical reactions.*

A.4 Fertilizer and the Nitrogen Cycle

The primary purpose of any fertilizer is to add enough nutrients to soil to provide plants an adequate supply. This material examines the role each primary plant nutrient (nitrogen, phosphorus, and potassium) in a typical fertilizer plays to ensure production of strong, healthy plants. Farmers use chemical fertilizers to increase the growth and yield of crops. Fertilizer use has been a key factor in enabling the United States to remain a major world food producer.

Plants need nitrogen, in the form of NH_4^+ or NO_3^-, to synthesize both proteins and nucleic acids. Nitrogen is also a component of chlorophyll, a pigment needed for photosynthesis. Nitrogen deficiency can cause yellowing of leaves (called *chlorosis*) due to the lack of chlorophyll, and can stunt plant growth.

Phosphorus, typically in the form of PO_4^{3-}, is found in compounds such as nucleic acids and ATP. It also participates in photosynthesis and respiration. Phosphorus deficiency stunts plant growth and darkens foliage due to accumulation of chlorophyll.

Potassium, in the form of K^+, helps maintain electrical neutrality of cells and assists in osmosis between cells. It also participates in activation of enzymes. Potassium deficiency causes reduced growth and brown leaf edges due to disturbances in water transport and enzyme activity.

Magnesium, in the form of Mg^{2+}, is a component of chlorophyll molecules. It also participates as a cofactor in the activity of many plant enzymes. Magnesium deficiency results in yellowing of leaves due to lack of chlorophyll.

SECTION A

Using the Figures

Figure 5.9: Elemental nitrogen is an extremely stable molecule—much energy is required to convert it into other forms (nitrogen-containing compounds). In nature, this energy sometimes comes in the form of lightning. The challenge to industrial chemists has been to find efficient processes for converting elemental nitrogen into other, usable compounds, where the cost of energy invested in the process does not exceed the value of final products. Revisiting this challenge would be a good lead-in to *Section A.8,* which discusses industrial nitrogen-fixing processes.

Figure 5.9 *Energy supplied by lightning facilitates reactions between atmospheric nitrogen and oxygen. This is one way to "fix" nitrogen, that is, to incorporate it into nitrogen-based compounds.*

> Proteins are large molecules made up of various combinations of 22 different amino acids.

Proteins are a major constituent of all living organisms, including plants. In plants, proteins usually account for 5–20% of the plant's mass. Nitrogen makes up about 16% of the mass of those protein molecules.

Although nitrogen gas (N_2) is abundant in the atmosphere, it is so chemically stable (unreactive) that plants cannot use it directly. However, nitrogen gas can be *fixed*—that is, combined with other elements to produce nitrogen-containing compounds that plants can use chemically. Lightning or combustion can fix atmospheric nitrogen (see Figure 5.9) by causing it to combine with other elements, especially oxygen. Some plants called *legumes,* such as clover and alfalfa, have nitrogen-fixing bacteria in their roots.

Scientists are exploring biological methods for making atmospheric nitrogen more available to plants. These methods include engineering some microorganisms and plants to contain genes that will direct the production of nitrogen-fixing enzymes. Having such enzymes would allow plants or their bacteria to produce their own nitrogen-based fertilizers, just as the bacteria associated with legumes do.

When ammonia (NH_3) and ammonium ions (NH_4^+) enter soil from decaying matter and from other sources (see Figure 5.10), soil bacteria oxidize them to nitrate ions. Plants reduce nitrate ions to nitrite ions (NO_2^-) and then to ammonia. They then use ammonia directly to synthesize amino acids. Unlike humans or other animals, many plants are able to synthesize all their needed amino acids by using ammonia or nitrate ions as their initial nitrogen-containing reactants.

Figure 5.10 *Many U.S. farmers routinely apply anhydrous liquid ammonia fertilizer to their fields.*

When organic matter decays, much of the released nitrogen recycles among plants and animals, and some returns to the atmosphere. Thus, some nitrogen gas removed from the atmosphere through nitrogen fixation eventually cycles back to the atmosphere.

The Nitrogen Cycle

The **nitrogen cycle** consists of the following steps:

1. Nitrogen-fixing bacteria that live in legume root nodules or in soil convert atmospheric nitrogen (N_2) to ammonia molecules or ammonium ions. Alternatively, lightning converts N_2 to nitrogen oxides (NO_x).

> Nitrifying bacteria are found in many plants, blue-green algae, some marine algae, and lichens.

2. Various soil bacteria oxidize ammonia and ammonium ions to nitrite ions and then to nitrate ions.

3. Plants take in nitrate ions from the soil, and subsequently incorporate nitrogen atoms in synthesizing proteins and other nitrogen-containing compounds.

4. The nitrogen passes along the food chain to animals that feed on these plants and to animals that feed on other animals.

5. When those plants and animals die, bacteria and fungi take up and use some of the nitrogen from plant/animal proteins and other nitrogen-containing molecules. The remaining nitrogen atoms are released from the decaying matter as ammonium ions and ammonia gas.

> Some nitrogen atoms recycle through the living world without returning to the atmosphere.

6. Denitrifying bacteria convert some ammonia, nitrite ions, and nitrate ions back to nitrogen gas, which returns to the atmosphere.

A.5 PLANT NUTRIENTS

Making Decisions

Consider and answer the following questions:

1. Why do some farmers alternate plantings of legumes and grain crops over several growing seasons (Figure 5.11)?

2. Why is it beneficial to return unused parts of harvested crops to the soil?

3. How might research on new ways to fix nitrogen help lower farmers' operating costs?

4. What consequences might result from over-fertilizing?

Figure 5.11 *A contour strip farm in Wisconsin. Legumes (green) and grain (gold) are rotated over several growing seasons. How might this practice be beneficial?*

Section A   Some Chemistry of Nitrogen   **419**

Answers

1. Legumes have nitrogen-fixing bacteria in their roots. These bacteria increase the amount of usable nitrogen available to plants in the soil. If such crops are alternated with plants (such as grain crops) that extract nitrogen compounds from the soil, the soil's net store of available nitrogen remains relatively constant.

2. Non-harvested plant parts contain nitrogen, phosphorus, potassium, and other nutrients originally extracted from the soil by the growing plant. By plowing the plants back into the soil, farmers make these nutrients available for the next season's crops, requiring less fertilizer than would otherwise be the case.

3. If scientists developed plants capable of fixing nitrogen, energy costs would decrease because less fertilizer would be needed and less tractor fuel would be consumed in applying fertilizer to the soil.

4. Overfertilizing can cause overgrowth of vegetation or toxicity to vegetation. Also, run-off containing nitrates and phosphates can pollute nearby bodies of water, and excess fertilizer in surface water can increase algae growth in streams and lakes. When the excess algae die, the oxygen level in the water decreases. This in turn kills fish and other aquatic animals.

Making Decisions

A.5 Plant Nutrients

Using the Figures

Figure 5.11: If only one type of crop, such as grains (nitrogen-extracting) or legumes (nitrogen-fixing), was planted in the same soil over several years, an imbalance in the natural nitrogen cycle would develop. This could have a negative impact on the surrounding environment and could decrease crop growth over time.

These questions highlight the value of using chemical technologies to work with nature.

Modeling Matter

A.6 The Nitrogen Cycle

A.6 The Nitrogen Cycle Student Worksheet

This activity begins by comparing the nitrogen cycle to the carbon and hydrological cycles. The main idea is that the nitrogen cycle is a natural recycling system that supplies a useable form of nitrogen to plants (nitrogen fixation).

Students then construct their own visual models of the nitrogen cycle. Before they start, you may decide to revisit as a class the carbon and hydrologic cycles to refamiliarize students with representations of cyclical processes. Students exchange their visual models and answer questions. These questions help students think critically about clarity, detail, and ease of interpretation in any good model or diagram. Answers to all of the questions will vary based on students' experience.

Modeling Matter

A.6 THE NITROGEN CYCLE

In Unit 1, you learned how the hydrologic cycle can purify water (pages 86–87). You also learned in Unit 4 that carbon-containing molecules change as carbon atoms cycle among living and nonliving components of Earth (page 348–349). For instance, plants transform carbon found as CO_2 into complex molecules, such as carbohydrates. Carbon is also chemically bound as dissolved CO_2 in the oceans and as carbonate rocks in Earth's crust (Figure 5.12).

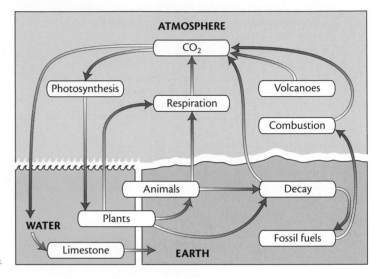

| **Figure 5.12** *The carbon cycle.*

In addition to studying the hydrologic and carbon cycles, you examined diagrams illustrating those processes. Such visual models help you organize related information, allowing you to easily trace interactions and connections.

You have just learned that nitrogen atoms also cycle among the atmosphere, soil, and organisms. However, a visual model depicting this nitrogen-cycle information has not been presented. In this activity you will create that missing diagram.

Look at Figure 5.12 and also figures on pages 87 and 348. Notice how they depict the hydrologic and carbon cycles. Then review Fertilizer and the Nitrogen Cycle A.4 (pages 417–419) in this unit (and earlier textbook material if needed) to guide your completion of the following steps.

1. Construct your own diagram of the nitrogen cycle.
   a. Use arrows to show the direction of flow as nitrogen atoms cycle among the atmosphere, soil, and living organisms.
   b. Include symbols and names for key molecules and ions at each cycle stage.
   c. Use pictures and color as needed to clarify details in your model.
   d. Make your model easy to follow. A classmate should be able to summarize the steps correctly by referring to your diagram.
2. Exchange your model with a classmate's model.
3. Select an appropriate starting point on your classmate's diagram and trace nitrogen through its cycle.
4. Repeat Step 3, but use your classmate's diagram to write a description of the key steps in the nitrogen cycle. Your written description should be limited to information contained in your classmate's diagram, even if some features are different from those in your diagram.
5. Exchange diagrams and written descriptions with your classmate. You now have the nitrogen-cycle diagram you originally drew and your classmate's written description based on it.
6. Compare the difficulty you experienced in completing these two tasks:
   a. transforming the book's description of the nitrogen cycle into your diagram
   b. transforming your classmate's diagram of the nitrogen cycle into a written description
7. How closely did your classmate's written description reflect the actual structure and details of your diagram? Explain.
8. Compare the description that your classmate wrote about your diagram with the description of cycle steps on page 419.
   a. Compared to the textbook description, did your classmate's description omit or add any details or steps? Explain.
   b. Which description is more detailed? Explain.
9. Based on your classmate's description,
   a. how easy and convenient was your diagram to interpret and follow? Explain.
   b. how could you modify your diagram to improve its accuracy and clarity? Explain.
10. Considering your answers to Question 9, make any needed changes to your diagram so it more clearly illustrates the nitrogen cycle.

In Investigating Matter A.3, you identified some major ions present in fertilizer. In the next investigation you will complete a more detailed study of one of these ions—the phosphate anion (PO_4^{3-}).

> In what ways is this step similar to drawing a map for someone who asks you to provide directions to travel to a particular location?

> This is similar to using a drawn map to navigate unfamiliar territory. What are the consequences of missing details or inadequate labeling in such a map?

Variations

After students revise their nitrogen-cycle models, divide the class into groups to discuss and decide which visual model best illustrates the cycle. Then each group could construct a larger "best model" to display in the classroom and compare with those of other groups.

You may prefer to organize students into small groups to complete the activity. Give groups large sheets of paper, markers, and crayons to construct their models. Larger paper makes it easier for the entire group to participate in the construction process. Students working in groups may prefer to do a rough draft in which they collaboratively work out the details of their diagram. During the exchange process, groups exchange models.

Section A   Some Chemistry of Nitrogen   **421**

Investigating Matter

A.7 Phosphates

A.7 Phosphates Student Worksheet and Data Table

Using colorimetric techniques, students determine the mass and percent phosphate in a fertilizer solution. In colorimetry, investigators relate the intensity of a solution's color to the concentration of a known colored solution. Students prepare standard samples with a range of phosphate concentrations and color intensities. They determine the concentration of an unknown fertilizer solution by comparing its color intensity to that of the standard samples.

Time

50 min

Materials

(For 12 student pairs)

20 g ascorbic acid

20 g granular fertilizer (20–20–20); or others as available; as an alternative, a mixture of 80 g NH_4NO_3 and 380 g $Na_3PO_4 \cdot 12H_2O$

1.0 L 10.0-ppm standard phosphate buffer solution

325 mL ammonium molybdate–sulfuric acid reagent

10 L distilled water

60 test tubes (18 × 150 mm)

12 test tube holders

12 test tube racks

36 400-mL beakers

12 10-mL graduated cylinders

12 50-mL or 100-mL graduated cylinders

12 spatulas

12 stirring rods

12 hot plates

6 balances

12 wax pencils

See page 412 for background on the components of commercial fertilizers, including phosphorus.

Lab Video: Phosphates

Figure 5.13 *The intensity of colors in several different solutions of known concentration can be used to estimate an unknown solution concentration.*

A.7 PHOSPHATES

Introduction

We can partially evaluate the quality of fertilizers by examining the percentage (by mass) of essential nutrients they contain. In this investigation, you will analyze a fertilizer solution to determine the mass and percent phosphate ($PO_4{}^{3-}$) contained in it.

Phosphate is a component of several critically important biomolecules, including DNA, RNA, ATP, and proteins. In DNA and RNA, phosphate links other molecular units together in long chains that store genetic information. In ATP, phosphate ions help store chemical energy. Changes in phosphate-ion concentration can also affect an enzyme's effectiveness in catalyzing a particular reaction. Thus, phosphate serves as a "chemical switch," turning particular chemical reactions on or off.

Colorimetry, the method you will use to determine a fertilizer sample's phosphate content, is based on the fact that the intensity of a solution's color is directly related to the concentration of the colored substance. To analyze colorless phosphate ions this way, you will first convert all phosphate ions to a new, colored ion. Then you will compare the color intensity of the unknown solution to the intensities of solutions with known phosphate concentrations—that is, to a set of phosphate-based *color standards* (see Figure 5.13).

If the color intensities of the sample and standard appear identical, then the phosphate concentrations must also be the same. Likewise, if the color intensity of the unknown sample is lower than that of the standard, the unknown sample has the lower of the two phosphate concentrations. One strategy of this laboratory procedure is to reduce the unknown phosphate solution concentration sufficiently through dilution so its color intensity will be within the range of the prepared color standards.

Procedure

1. Label five clean test tubes: *10 ppm, 7.5 ppm, 5.0 ppm, 2.5 ppm,* and *x ppm.*

2. Prepare a water solution of the unknown sample by placing 0.50 g of solid fertilizer in a 400-mL beaker. Add 250 mL of distilled water. Stir until the sample completely dissolves.

As prepared in Step 2, your fertilizer solution is too concentrated to analyze by colorimetry. In other words, milliliter for milliliter, your solution contains considerably more phosphate ion than you can evaluate by the known color standards you will use later. Therefore, you will have to prepare a more dilute fertilizer solution for analysis, one that is only 1/50 as concentrated.

Here is a very impractical way to accomplish that dilution goal of 1/50 concentration: Imagine adding distilled water (with stirring) to

---

Safety

Students should wear protective goggles and aprons throughout the investigation.

Advance Preparation

For optimum results, make the solutions a week ahead of time. They can be stored indefinitely.

Standard Phosphate Solution

To prepare the standard phosphate solution: dissolve 0.916 g K_2HPO_4 in a small volume of water and then dilute to 1.00 L in a volumetric flask. After this solution is thoroughly dissolved, dilute a 20.0 mL sample from it to 1.00 L, which produces 1 L of standard (10.0 ppm) phosphate solution:

your 250-mL fertilizer solution until its volume becomes 50 times larger. The phosphate concentration would, indeed, be 1/50 of its initial value. However, you would probably be dismayed to discover that the diluted volume would be almost 13 L (0.250 L × 50 = 12.5 L)—over three gallons!

Fortunately, there is a more sensible dilution strategy. As you complete Steps 3 and 4, think about how this procedure accomplishes the same dilution goal more successfully.

3. Measure 5.0 mL of your unknown fertilizer solution. Retain the remaining solution (in case you need to start over).

4. Pour this 5.0-mL sample of fertilizer solution into a clean 400-mL beaker. Then add 245 mL of distilled water, measuring that volume with a graduated cylinder. Stir thoroughly.

5. Pour 20 mL of this diluted fertilizer solution into the test tube labeled *x ppm*.

6. Your teacher has already prepared a supply of 10-ppm phosphate-ion standard solutions. Pour 20 mL of that standard solution in the test tube labeled *10 ppm*.

7. Given supplies of 10-ppm solution and distilled water, decide what volumes of 10-ppm solution and distilled water you should measure and mix to prepare 20.0-mL samples, respectively, of 7.5-ppm, 5.0-ppm, and 2.5-ppm phosphate solutions. Write out your plan.

8. Ask your teacher to check your written plan. After receiving your teacher's approval, prepare the three solutions. Pour each standard solution into its appropriately labeled test tube.

9. Place a 400-mL beaker half-full of water on a hot plate. Start heating the water but do not allow the water to boil. You will use this warm-water bath in Step 12.

10. Add 2.0 mL of ammonium molybdate–sulfuric acid reagent to each of the four test tubes containing phosphate standards and to the diluted unknown solution.

11. Add a few crystals of ascorbic acid (no more than the size of a pencil eraser) to each tube. Using a rinsed and dried stirring rod each time, stir to dissolve.

> Ascorbic acid is another name for Vitamin C.

12. Carefully place your five test tubes into the warm-water bath held in the beaker on the hot plate. Continue heating the tubes in the water bath until a blue color develops in the 2.5-ppm solution. Do not allow the water to boil. Turn off the hot plate.

13. Using a test-tube holder, remove the test tubes from the water bath and place them in numerical order in a test-tube rack.

14. Compare the color intensity of the unknown solution ('*x ppm*') with the intensities of the four color-standard solutions. Place the unknown-solution test tube between the two tubes containing standard solutions that you judge to have the closest-matching color intensities to the unknown.

ANSWERS FOR PROCEDURE STEP 7 (PAGE 423— DILUTIONS OF 10-ppm STANDARD SOLUTION)

STANDARD	QUANTITY OF 10-ppm STANDARD	QUANTITY OF WATER
7.5 ppm	15	5
5.0 ppm	10	10
2.5 ppm	5	15

0.916 g K_2HPO_4 × (95.0 g PO_4^{3-}/174 g K_2HPO_4) × (1.00 g PO_4^{3-}/1000 g solution in first dilution) × (20.0 mL first solution/1000 mL final dilute solution) = 10.0 ppm

Ammonium Molybdate–Sulfuric Acid Reagent

To prepare ammonium molybdate solution:

1. Dissolve 7.5 g of ammonium molybdate, $(NH_4)_2MoO_4$, in 75 mL distilled water. Set solution aside to cool in an ice bath.

2. Slowly, with mixing, add 125 mL of ice-cold 18 M H_2SO_4 to 125 mL of ice-cold distilled water. *Caution:* Diluting concentrated sulfuric acid generates considerable heat and may produce splattering if you do not add the acid *slowly with continual stirring.* Perform this dilution with care. Add acid to water, not water to acid.

3. Slowly add cold sulfuric acid solution (with stirring) to the ice-cold ammonium molybdate solution. Keep the ammonium molybdate solution in an ice bath during this step.

Pre-Lab Discussion

If students have difficulty conceptualizing colorimetry, display test tubes with food-coloring–water mixtures serially diluted and labeled with concentration values. Then, show students a solution whose food-coloring concentration is "unknown" and ask them to figure out its concentration.

Highlight the connection between this investigation and earlier qualitative work students completed involving fertilizer.

Check student procedures for diluting the standard phosphate solution. Some students may need help with the notion of a dilution series.

Lab Tips

• Since the solution color intensity is affected by the time it boils, agree on some consistent method of heating to ensure comparable results for all teams. One good reference point is the appearance of the first bubble of boiling. As color becomes more intense, it is more difficult to see differences among the standard samples.

• If a spectrophotometer is available, students can collect and plot data to obtain an absorption curve for phosphate standards—absorbance versus concentration (ppm). It may be easier to read percent transmittance (%T) on an analog spectrophotometer scale. If so, %T can be converted to absorbance (A), using $A = -log(\%T/100)$. 610-nm wavelength gives maximum absorbance. Students can then use this absorption curve to find sample values. This is a good opportunity for sharing class data and allowing students to compare their concentrations with values generated by a spectrophotometer and a standard curve and to introduce common instrumentation used in many analytical laboratories.

Expected Results

Using 20–20–20 fertilizer, the actual value of phosphate as diphosphorus pentoxide (P_2O_5) is 20%. Student results customarily range from 17 to 25%.

Answers

1. Possible answers include coffee, tea, juices, powdered drinks, and household cleaners with coloring added.

2. It provides reproducible, quantitative data.

Recall that *ppm* represents parts per million, or, as here, $g\ PO_4^{3-}$ per 10^6 g solution.

15. Estimate the concentration (ppm) of your unknown phosphate solution from the known color standards. For example, if the unknown solution color falls between the 7.5-ppm and 5.0-ppm color standards, you might decide to call it *6 ppm* (or 6 g PO_4^{3-} per 10^6 g solution). Record the estimated phosphate ion concentration in ppm.

16. Discard your solutions as directed by your teacher.

17. Wash your hands thoroughly before leaving the laboratory.

Data Analysis

1. Calculate the mass (in grams) of phosphate present in your original 250-mL fertilizer solution (or in the original 0.50-g solid fertilizer sample). Note that you need to use a multiplication factor of 50 to compensate for the fact that you used only 1/50 of the original fertilizer sample (see Step 3). In other words, the phosphate concentration in the original fertilizer must have been 50 times greater than the value found for the solution in the *x ppm* test tube. Thus the calculation becomes

$$\text{mass of phosphate (in grams)} = \frac{??\ \text{g phosphate}}{10^6\ \text{g solution}} \times 250\ \text{g solution} \times 50$$

In place of *??*, substitute the value of the unknown solution concentration (in ppm) you obtained in Step 15. Record your calculated mass of phosphate.

2. Based on your calculated mass, find and record the percent phosphate (by mass) in your original 0.50-g fertilizer sample.

Questions

1. Name two common household solutions for which you can estimate their relative concentrations just by observing their color intensities.

2. Chemists often use an instrument called a *colorimeter* to determine solution concentrations. A **colorimeter** measures the quantity of light that can pass through an unknown sample and compares it to the quantity of light that can pass through a known standard solution. What advantages does a colorimeter offer over use of the human eye?

3. Explain this statement: "The accuracy of results of a colorimetric analysis depends, in part, on the care taken in preparing the standards used in the analysis."

4. In Investigating Matter A.3 (page 413), the tests were *qualitative* and were used only to indicate whether particular ions were present. How could you modify an ion test involving the formation of a colored solution so it would be *quantitative*—indicating the concentration of ion present?

---

3. Colorimetric analysis depends on comparing an unknown to a known series of concentrations. Without carefully prepared color standards, experimental data will be erroneous.

4. The test could yield quantitative results if the sample quantity were carefully measured and known solutions were carefully prepared for comparison.

5. In Step 3, you measured 1/50 of the total fertilizer solution volume and set aside the rest. Consider this seemingly simpler alternative: In Step 2 you could have taken 1/50 of the starting mass of fertilizer (0.50 g × 1/50 = 0.010 g) and then omitted Steps 3 and 4 completely. What are possible disadvantages of this shorter, more direct procedure?

A.8 FIXING NITROGEN BY OXIDATION–REDUCTION

Fertilizer Sources

Using commercial ammonia for fertilizer has had a huge impact on agriculture and world food supplies. World ammonia production has increased dramatically over the last 50 years, as farmers have increased their use of fertilizer to meet the food needs of growing populations. The U.S. chemical industry annually produces about 40 billion pounds of ammonia, mostly dedicated to making fertilizer.

Before modern methods of manufacturing ammonia were developed, nitrogen-containing fertilizers came from either animal waste or nitrate compounds. Large quantities of such compounds came from Chilean guano beds (Figure 5.14). At the turn of the 20th century, speculation arose that guano beds would be depleted by about 1930, raising fears of an agricultural crisis and the spectre of world famine. Actually, the advent of commercial ammonia production largely eliminated dependence on all natural nitrate sources.

In seeking ways to fix nitrogen gas artificially, scientists in 1780 first combined atmospheric nitrogen and oxygen by exposing them to an electric spark. However, the cost of electricity made this too expensive for any commercial use. A less expensive method, the *Haber-Bosch process* replaced it. From 1912 to 1916, Fritz Haber and Karl Bosch in Germany developed the technique for making ammonia directly from hydrogen gas and nitrogen gas, according to this equation:

$$N_2(g) + 3\,H_2(g) \rightleftharpoons 2\,NH_3(g)$$

> Liquified ammonia can also be directly applied to soil as a fertilizer. See Figure 5.10, page 418.

Figure 5.14 *Guano (seabird dung) deposits were one of the first commercial sources of fertilizer.*

Post-Lab Discussion

Emphasize the wide use of colorimetric methods. Colorimeters are used to quantitatively determine solution concentration. Light of a selected wavelength passes through the sample, and investigators measure the proportion absorbed. Colorimetric techniques rely on the relationship of the quantity of light absorbed to the solution concentration. Many modern colorimeters are linked to computers, making data analysis immediate. Colorimeters are used in water analysis, color control of dyes and paints, and quality analysis of diamonds.

Quantitative data are also important in farming. Colorimetry gives accurate data on soil composition, such as phosphate concentrations in fertilizers and soils. pH meters can inform farmers of soil pH.

A.8 Fixing Nitrogen by Oxidation–Reduction

A.8 Content Reading Guide

The stability of the triple bond in $N_2(g)$ makes this bond difficult to break. The Haber-Bosch process accomplishes this and subsequently forms ammonia. Due to this industrial process, ammonia is among the most widely produced substances in the United States. The text uses the Haber-Bosch process to review the concepts of oxidation and reduction.

---

5. Measuring smaller quantities of solid fertilizer introduces greater error into the investigation. Seemingly tiny measuring errors in a small quantity of solid fertilizer can lead to large percent errors. Measuring a large quantity of fertilizer originally, and then diluting, then taking 1/50th of total fertilizer solution volume, allows manipulation of larger quantities of material. Small errors then have less impact on results.

Re-introduce the concept of electronegativity. Students may need guidance to realize that elements with lower electronegativities undergo oxidation more readily. Elements with higher electronegativities undergo reduction more readily.

Students may also need help with the idea that positive oxidation states correspond to a loss of electrons and negative oxidation states result from a gain of electrons. Remind students that electrons are negatively charged and that loss of a negative particle results in a more positive product. Gain of a negative particle results in a more negative product. Refer students to the mnemonics *OIL RIG (Oxidation Is Loss, Reduction Is Gain)* and *LEO says GER (Loss of Electrons is Oxidation, Gain of Electrons is Reduction).*

Using the Figures

Figure 5.15: Encourage students to closely examine trends in electronegativity values. Ask them to compare values for metals and nonmetals. Does it make sense that metals, with low electronegativity values, tend to lose electrons, forming cations, when combined with nonmetals in ionic compounds? Ask students to suggest possible explanations for the trends. For instance, in a molecule containing an N—O bond, why might the oxygen atom have greater pull on shared bonding electrons? (Oxygen has one more proton in its nucleus than nitrogen, which increases attractions between the oxygen nucleus and shared electrons.) Examine trends moving down a group. An increase in the number of protons does *not* lead to a higher electronegativity value. Why? The main effect here is the increase in the atom's size.

Oxidation–Reduction

In the Haber-Bosch reaction of nitrogen gas with hydrogen gas, electrons are involved in an oxidation–reduction reaction. As you know, atoms that apparently lose their share of electrons are involved in a process called *oxidation* (see page 147). For example, the conversion of metallic sodium atoms (Na) into sodium ions (Na^+) is oxidation because electrically neutral sodium atoms are oxidized to $+1$ sodium ions by the loss of one electron per atom. Recall that the opposite process—the apparent gaining of electrons—is called *reduction*. The formation of chloride ions (Cl^-) from electrically neutral chlorine atoms is an example of reduction. Electrons can be transferred to or from particular atoms, molecules, or ions. The products of such oxidation–reduction reactions also include atoms, molecules, or ions.

You can judge the relative tendency of a covalently bonded atom to attract electrons within compounds based on that element's *electronegativity* (see page 71). Nonmetallic elements typically have higher electronegativities than do metallic elements. Figure 5.15 shows the electronegativity values for some common elements.

> Regardless of how the electron-transfer occurs, the same oxidation-reduction principles apply.

Figure 5.15 *Electronegativity values of selected elements.*

Electronegativity & Oxidation State

Oxidation Number

A convenient, yet arbitrary, way to express the degree of oxidation or reduction of particular atoms is by assigning each atom an **oxidation state.** The higher (more positive) the oxidation state becomes, the more

Recall that electrons are grouped into shells (Unit 3, page 221). First-period elements have valence electrons residing in the first shell; second-period elements have valence electrons in the second shell, etc. As the total number of shells increases, so does the atom's size. The nuclei of larger atoms, being more distant from the shared bonding electrons (and also shielded by inner electron shells), exert a weaker attractive force on bonding electrons than the nuclei of smaller atoms.

an atom has become oxidized. The lower (less positive) the atom's oxidation state becomes, the more the atom has become reduced.

In binary compounds (compounds composed of two elements), we assign atoms of the element with the lower electronegativity a **positive oxidation state,** corresponding to an apparent loss of electrons. Likewise, we assign atoms of the more electronegative element a **negative oxidation state,** corresponding to an apparent gain of electrons.

Consider the key chemical change in the Haber-Bosch process, as depicted with electron-dot formulas and space-filling models:

$$:N:::N: \quad + \quad 3\,H:H \quad \longrightarrow \quad 2\,:\overset{\textstyle H}{\underset{\textstyle H}{N}}:H$$

$$N_2 \quad + \quad 3\,H_2 \quad \longrightarrow \quad 2\,NH_3$$

Note that each nitrogen atom in N_2 shares six electrons with another nitrogen atom, resulting in a triple covalent bond. Both nitrogen atoms exert equal attraction for these shared electrons. Each nitrogen atom in N_2 has a **zero oxidation state.** (This is true of any atom of an element that is not bonded to any other element.) The two nitrogen atoms share their bonding electrons equally; there is no separation of electrical charge. As the reaction progresses, each nitrogen atom becomes covalently bonded to three hydrogen atoms. Each bonded nitrogen and hydrogen atom shares an electron pair, but they do not share the pair equally. Nitrogen atoms (electronegativity value = 3.0) have a greater attraction for these shared electrons than do hydrogen atoms (electronegativity value = 2.1). Thus, the nitrogen atom in each NH_3 molecule acquires a greater portion of shared electrons than does each hydrogen atom.

Consequently, the nitrogen atom in NH_3 is assigned a negative oxidation state. Likewise, each hydrogen atom in NH_3 has lost some share of bonding electrons due to the reaction; hydrogen is assigned a positive oxidation state. Thus, the oxidation state of an atom in a particular substance depends on the identity of neighboring atoms to which it is covalently bonded.

The Haber-Bosch process converts nitrogen gas molecules into more useful ammonia molecules, a form of *fixed* nitrogen. Once nitrogen is chemically combined with another element, it can be readily converted to other nitrogen-containing compounds.

For example, under proper conditions, ammonia will react with oxygen gas, forming nitrogen dioxide:

$$4\,NH_3(g) + 7\,O_2(g) \longrightarrow 4\,NO_2(g) + 6\,H_2O(g)$$

Demonstration Idea: A Traffic Light Reaction

This demonstration vividly illustrates oxidation–reduction reactions with eye-catching color changes. Gently swirl a flask containing a pale yellow solution, and the solution turns red. Shake the flask, and the solution turns green.

Procedure

Wear protective goggles and an apron throughout this demonstration.

1. Place 50 mL solution A in a 250-mL flask.

2. Add 5–10 mL solution B. Before mixing with solution A, the solution should be light yellow.
3. Stopper the flask.
4. Gently swirl the flask to produce the red color.
5. Give the flask a vigorous shake to produce the green color.

Reactions

The indicator is reduced by alkaline dextrose, which results in a yellow product. When the flask is swirled, oxygen gas dissolves; the indicator is oxidized and forms an intermediate (red color). Shaking the flask introduces more oxygen, which further oxidizes the indicator to green. Upon standing, dextrose reduces the indicator back to its original yellow.

Solutions

Solution A: 3 g dextrose (glucose) and 5 g NaOH in 250 mL water
Solution B: 1.0% solution indigo carmine indicator; dissolve 1 g indigo carmine in 100 mL water.

Tips

• If the red color does not persist, increase the added quantity of Solution B.
• The "traffic light" system has an advantage over similar reactions: It doesn't require using a magnetic stirrer.
• Do not exceed the recommended volume of Solution A.

Questions for Students

1. Is this a redox reaction? If so, what is oxidized and what is reduced?
2. What role does the indicator play?
3. What happens when the flask is swirled? Shaken?
4. Will this reaction eventually stop working if the stopper remains in the flask?

Developing Skills

Additional Activity

Invite students to conduct library and/or Internet research on the Haber-Bosch process to reinforce the difference between industrial- and laboratory-scale chemistry.

Developing Skills

A.9 Determining Oxidation States

Positive and negative oxidation states are related to the concept of electronegativity. The oxidation state refers to a hypothetical electrical charge assigned to atoms in a chemical species based on the assumption that all bonding electrons "belong" to the more electronegative atom in each bond. The idea is *not* that such electrical charges actually form, but that the more electronegative atom exerts more attraction for shared electrons in each covalent bond.

In this activity, students decide whether an element should be assigned a positive or negative oxidation state in a given compound by comparing electronegativity values. Note that students do *not* assign oxidation *numbers* in this activity.

Encourage students to look for trends in electronegativity values based on arrangements in the periodic table. For example, all metals are relatively low in electronegativity. Nonmetals have relatively greater electronegativities.

This is an oxidation–reduction reaction. In forming NO_2, the nitrogen atom in ammonia has apparently been oxidized; it has lost part of its share of electrons. Why does this occur? Because oxygen is more electronegative than is nitrogen (O = 3.5; N = 3.0), oxygen attracts bonding electrons more strongly than does nitrogen. Each oxygen atom is considered to be reduced; each oxygen atom has gained more control of its bonding electrons than it originally had in O_2.

Developing Skills

A.9 DETERMINING OXIDATION STATES

Sample Problem 1: *Which element in sulfur dioxide (SO_2) has a positive oxidation state?*

Figure 5.15 (page 426) indicates that sulfur's electronegativity value is 2.5 and oxygen's is 3.5. In sulfur–oxygen covalent bonding, sulfur has the weaker electron-attracting ability. Therefore, sulfur is assigned a positive oxidation state in SO_2.

Sample Problem 2: *The following equation represents the reaction of sulfur with oxygen gas to produce sulfur dioxide gas:*

$$S_8(s) + 8\ O_2(g) \longrightarrow 8\ SO_2(g)$$

Why do chemists consider this reaction as an oxidation–reduction reaction in which sulfur is oxidized?

The oxidation state of sulfur changes from zero (in the pure element) to a positive value in the product, sulfur dioxide (see Sample Problem 1)—sulfur has been oxidized. By contrast, oxygen gas becomes reduced; it has become reduced from a zero oxidation state to a negative oxidation state.

Now answer the following questions:

1. Consider each of the following covalent compounds. Using the electronegativity values from Figure 5.15, decide which element in each compound has (i) a positive oxidation state and which has (ii) a negative oxidation state:

   a. ammonia, NH_3
   b. hydrogen chloride, HCl
   c. hydrogen fluoride, HF
   d. oxygen difluoride, OF_2
   e. iodine trifluoride, IF_3
   f. phosphorus trifluoride, PF_3

> The element sulfur is found in eight-atom rings, S_8.

2. Each of the following compounds includes a metallic element and a nonmetallic element. Select the element in each compound possessing (i) a positive oxidation state and (ii) a negative oxidation state.

   a. sodium iodide, NaI
   b. lead(II) fluoride, PbF_2
   c. lead(II) sulfide, PbS
   d. potassium oxide, K_2O
   e. iron(III) chloride, $FeCl_3$
   f. sodium phosphide, Na_3P
   g. sodium chloride, NaCl

3. Consider your answers to Questions 1 and 2. What conclusions can you draw about the oxidation states of metals and nonmetals in binary compounds?

4. Consider the chemical equation $8\,Ni + S_8 \longrightarrow 8\,NiS$.

   a. Does this equation represent an oxidation–reduction reaction?
   b. If so, identify the element oxidized and the element reduced. If not, explain why.

5. The element iron is part of an essential system of energy transfer within human cells. In that system, Fe^{2+} ions are converted to Fe^{3+} ions. Does that change represent an oxidation or a reduction?

6. Within the nitrogen cycle (see page 419), nitrogen gas (N_2) undergoes particular chemical reactions in which it is oxidized and other reactions in which it is reduced. Identify, by name and formula, a nitrogen-cycle product that forms by nitrogen gas being

   a. oxidized.
   b. reduced.

Answers

1.	Positive	Negative
a.	H	N
b.	H	Cl
c.	H	F
d.	O	F
e.	I	F
f.	P	F

2.	Positive	Negative
a.	Na	I
b.	Pb	F
c.	Pb	S
d.	K	O
e.	Fe	Cl
f.	Na	P
g.	Na	Cl

3. When a metal and a nonmetal form a binary compound, the metal has a positive oxidation state, and the nonmetal has a negative oxidation state.

4. a. Yes
   b. Nickel is oxidized, and sulfur is reduced.

5. Oxidation. It can be viewed as losing electrons; the oxidation state becomes more positive.

6. a. For example, nitrite ions (NO_2^-)
   b. For example, ammonia, NH_3, and ammonium ions, NH_4^+

SECTION A SUMMARY

Reviewing the Concepts

 Section A Supplement

1. N, K, and P
2. It contains 20% nitrogen, 10% phosphorus (as P_2O_5), and 15% potassium (as K_2O) by mass.
3. In early analyses, plant fertilizers were burned to ash and the mass of K_2O obtained. The convention persisted.
4. Phosphate ions become part of ATP, RNA, and DNA. Potassium ions activate enzymes and maintain water/ion balance. Nitrogen is used to synthesize amino acids.
5. The proportion of each nutrient in fertilizer varies according to the crop's needs.
6. $BaCl_2$ tests, phosphates and sulfates; brown-ring test, nitrate ions; NaOH and litmus, ammonium ions; flame tests, potassium ions; KSCN test, Fe^{3+} ions
7. To synthesize proteins and nucleic acids; as a component of chlorophyll.
8. Atmospheric N_2 is unreactive, thus plants cannot use it. Fertilizers provide usable nitrogen.
9. To convert atmospheric N_2 into nitrogen compounds
10. By nitrogen-fixing bacteria, combustion, and lightning
11. NO_3^-, NH_4^+
12. a. Plants obtain it from ammonia or nitrate ions in the soil. Animals obtain it from foods.
    b. Plants synthesize them from nitrogen-containing ions. Animals obtain them from proteins in their diets.
13. To convert NH_3, nitrite, and nitrate to N_2
14. Atmospheric N is converted to ammonia or nitrogen oxides. NH_3 or NH_4^+ is oxidized to nitrite and nitrate ions. Plant roots absorb

---

SECTION A SUMMARY
Reviewing the Concepts

Fertilizers contain many essential plant nutrients.

1. List the three main elements in fertilizer.
2. What would the expression *20–10–15* mean if found on a fertilizer label?
3. Why is potassium content expressed as percent K_2O in fertilizer?
4. Describe the role in plant growth of each of the three essential elements in a typical fertilizer.

5. Why is it useful for fertilizers, such as 7–7–7 and 20–10–10, to be available with different compositions?
6. List each test completed in Investigating Matter A.3 (page 413), along with the ions that the test identified.

Nitrogen is transformed chemically as it cycles through living systems and the physical environment.

7. Why do plants need nitrogen?
8. Given the fact that nitrogen is abundant in the atmosphere, why is it included in fertilizers?
9. What does it mean to *fix* nitrogen gas?
10. List three ways in which atmospheric nitrogen can be fixed.
11. List two nitrogen-containing ions that are useful to plant growth.

12. How do plants and animals differ in the ways they obtain
    a. nitrogen?
    b. amino acids?
13. What is one role of denitrifying bacteria in the environment?
14. Summarize the steps of the nitrogen cycle.

The relative tendency of an atom to attract electrons within a covalent chemical bond can be estimated by the electronegativity of that element.

15. Referring to Figure 5.15 (page 426), identify the element that is *most* electronegative.
    a. Identify the element's symbol and name.
    b. Is this element a metal or nonmetal?
16. Referring to Figure 5.15, identify the element that is *least* electronegative.
    a. Identify the element's symbol and name.
    b. Is this element a metal or nonmetal?

17. Describe how electronegativity values for elements change as one moves
    a. from left to right across any period of the periodic table.
    b. down a group of the periodic table.
18. Arrange each of the following sets of elements in order of their increasing attraction for electrons within a bond:
    a. silicon, sodium, and sulfur
    b. nitrogen, phosphorus, and potassium
    c. bromine, fluorine, lithium, and potassium

NO_3^- from soil. N passes through the food chain to animals. When plants and animals die, some N is assimilated by bacteria and fungi. Remaining N is released as NH_4^+ or NH_3. Some N is returned to the atmosphere as nitrogen gas.

15. a. F; fluorine b. Nonmetal
16. a. Fr or Cs; francium or cesium b. Metal
17. a. values increase b. values decrease
18. a. Na, Si, S b. K, P, N c. K, Li, Br, F

19. Zero
20. a. It becomes more positive.
    b. It becomes more negative.
21. If the atom is the more electronegative element in a bond, it is reduced. If the atom is the less electronegative element in another bond, it is oxidized.
22. Nonmetal
23. a. H_2O, H(+), O(−) b. NH_3, H(+), N(−) c. CO_2, C(+), O(−) d. $MgCl_2$, Mg(+), Cl(−)

Assigning oxidation states is a convenient way to identify oxidation or reduction of atoms in reactions.

19. What is the oxidation state of an atom in its elemental form (that is, not combined with an atom of another element)?

20. How does the oxidation state of an atom change when the atom is
   a. oxidized?
   b. reduced?

21. How is it possible for the same element to be oxidized in one reaction and reduced in another?

22. What type of element (metal or nonmetal) is more often found in negative oxidation states when bonded to atoms of other elements?

23. For each of the following compounds, write its chemical formula and identify which element has a positive oxidation state and which has a negative oxidation state.
   a. water
   b. ammonia
   c. carbon dioxide
   d. magnesium chloride

The chemical industry transforms elements and compounds into other useful materials.

24. List four different ways that the chemical industry is involved in the production of a box of breakfast cereal.

25. Look around wherever you are sitting right now and identify four things you see that are products of the chemical industry.

26. What is the ultimate use of most of the ammonia produced in the United States?

27. What was the most common source of ammonia before the 20th century?

28. Write the chemical equation that represents the main reaction in the Haber-Bosch process.

Connecting the Concepts

29. Describe one advantage and one disadvantage of using commercial fertilizer instead of manure to fertilize crops.

30. The quantity of phosphorus in fertilizer is reported as *percent P$_2$O$_5$*.
   a. What is the percent phosphorus in P$_2$O$_5$?
   b. Fertilizers are burned (oxidized) for analysis, and the burning produces P$_2$O$_5$. In what form is the phosphorus actually found in the original fertilizer?

31. Describe a procedure for determining whether a soil sample contains any fixed nitrogen.

32. Compare the fertilizer tests you completed in this unit to the ion tests in Unit 1 (page 42). In what ways are these tests similar and in what ways are they different?

33. A magazine article claims that "oxygen is needed for all oxidation reactions." Do you agree or disagree with that statement? Support your answer with evidence.

34. What does the electronegativity of an electrically neutral atom indicate about its tendency to become oxidized?

35. In general, how do the electronegativities of metallic and nonmetallic elements compare?

36. Consider the Haber-Bosch process.
   a. Write the Lewis-dot structure for each reactant and product involved.
   b. Using the concept of electronegativity, determine which atoms in that reaction have a positive oxidation state and which have a negative oxidation state.

37. How does the concept of a limiting reactant apply to the use of fertilizers?

38. Why is colorimetry effective in measuring the concentration of only certain kinds of solutions?

Section Summary   431

---

plete a test with NaOH and litmus. Ammonium ions will turn red litmus blue in the presence of NaOH.

32. Similarities: Confirming tests, qualitative, test for ions. Differences: Fertilizer tests detect more ions using a greater variety of methods.

33. Disagree: Any atom that can be considered to give up electrons during a reaction undergoes oxidation, whether the electrons are given up to oxygen or another more electronegative element.

34. Atoms of lower electronegativity have a lesser tendency to attract electrons in a bond and may lose control of electrons and become oxidized.

35. Metallic elements tend to have lower electronegativities than do nonmetallic elements.

36. a. N$_2$:   H$_2$:   NH$_3$:
    :N:::N: H:H   H:N:H
                         H

   b. In ammonia, nitrogen has a negative oxidation state, and hydrogen has a positive oxidation state.

37. Fertilizers are used to avoid negative impacts of limiting reactants within plants.

38. Colorimetry is based on comparing color intensity, so it cannot be used to determine concentrations of colorless solutions.

---

24. Growing grains, processing grains, synthesizing additives, producing the packaging.

25. Examples include paper, pens, desks, cosmetics, clothing, and electronics.

26. Directly or indirectly as fertilizer

27. Animal waste

28. N$_2$(g) + 3 H$_2$(g) $\rightleftarrows$ 2 NH$_3$(g)

Connecting the Concepts

29. Advantages: known composition, can compensate for soil deficiencies. Disadvantage: Expense.

30. a. 43.64% $\%P = \dfrac{(2 \times 30.97)}{141.94}$

   b. Phosphate, PO$_4^{3-}$.

31. Test for nitrates using the brown-ring test. To test for ammonium ions, com-

Extending the Concepts

39. a. In all cycles, mass is conserved.

b. In the water cycle, all changes are physical. In the C cycle, chemical change is common during photosynthesis, respiration, decomposition, and combustion. In the N cycle, chemical change is common during fixation, oxidation, and denitrification.

c. In the water cycle, organisms have limited involvement. Bacteria in the soil convert dissolved organic compounds into simpler compounds, purifying water. In the C and N cycles, participating organisms include animals, plants, and bacteria.

40. Vegetarians eat plants, which have synthesized their own food. Nonvegetarians eat animals that have consumed plants and/or other animals. Vegetarians' diets involve fewer prior energy conversions, so some claim they use food more efficiently.

41. The Haber-Bosch process provided a convenient source of ammonia for making military munitions. This method of producing military explosives allowed Germany to continue fighting after the British navy terminated its shipping linkages to Chilean nitrate deposits.

42. Diagrams should include a light-tight sample chamber, a light source, and a photo detector.

43. a. There is enough magnesium in soil.

b. Such nutrients include iron, carbon, calcium, and manganese.

44. The top plant fertilizer ingredients are P, K, and N. Human nutrients include Ca, Cl, Mg, P, K, Na, and S, along with a dozen or so vitamins, such as B12, E, and biotin.

Extending the Concepts

39. You have considered three major natural cycles: water, carbon, and nitrogen. Compare these cycles with respect to

a. conservation of mass,
b. types of chemical change, and
c. participating organisms.

40. Why do some vegetarians claim that their diets make more economical use of world food resources than do the diets of nonvegetarians?

41. Some historians claim that development of the Haber-Bosch process prolonged World War I. Explain.

42. Research and draw a diagram of the basic parts of a colorimeter, which is a simple version of a *spectrophotometer*.

43. a. Magnesium is a key component of chlorophyll in green plants. Explain why magnesium is generally not included in commercial fertilizers.

b. Identify some other substances required by growing plants that are not included in fertilizers.

44. Review the list of ingredients in a multipurpose vitamin capsule for humans and compare this to the ingredients in a typical commercial fertilizer. Suggest reasons for the similarities and differences you find.

45. How does lightning fix nitrogen?

46. Research and report on denitrifying bacteria. Include their typical habitats and any unusual characteristics.

---

45. Lightning provides the necessary energy for the reaction of nitrogen with oxygen to form nitrogen oxides, such as nitric oxide (NO) and nitrogen dioxide (NO_2).

46. Denitrifying bacteria can grow under aerobic conditions (in the presence of oxygen); under anaerobic conditions, they respire using the nitrate ion. A wide range of bacteria are capable of denitrification and include species of the genera *Bacillus, Enterobacter, Salmonella,* and *Pseudomonas.* Denitrifying organisms are often found where O_2 is absent, but there is a rich source of nitrate ions and organic material to oxidize.

Nitrogen and Industry

As you have learned, many industrial raw materials are extracted from Earth's crust (such as minerals, precious metals, sulfur, and petroleum), oceans (for example, magnesium and bromine), and atmosphere. Nitrogen gas and oxygen gas, both obtained by low-temperature distillation of liquefied air, are valuable starting materials in the production of ammonia and nitric acid. As you will soon learn, producing ammonia also depends on understanding implications of reversible reactions and chemical equilibrium.

B.1 KINETICS AND EQUILIBRIUM

Producing ammonia from nitrogen gas and hydrogen gas is a chemical challenge. As you learned in Section A, molecular nitrogen (N_2) is very stable. This means that nitrogen fixation, the chemical combination of nitrogen gas with other elements, has a substantial activation-energy barrier. As you learned in Unit 4 (page 394), a reaction with a large energy barrier requires either that the reactant particles have substantial kinetic energy or that a catalyst reduces the energy required to initiate the reaction.

The reaction of nitrogen gas with hydrogen gas is also difficult because some ammonia molecules tend to decompose back to nitrogen gas and hydrogen gas during the synthesis reaction. As you learned in Unit 4 (page 375), this kind of reaction—one in which products re-form reactants at the same time that reactants form products—is known as a *reversible reaction*. The double arrows used in the following equation indicate that both forward and reverse reactions occur simultaneously:

$$N_2(g) + 3\ H_2(g) \rightleftharpoons 2\ NH_3(g)$$

How do chemists and chemical engineers, whether at EKS Nitrogen Products Company or elsewhere, overcome these obstacles to produce ammonia?

Kinetics: Producing More Ammonia in Less Time

The rate at which nitrogen fixation occurs determines the time required for a certain amount of ammonia to form. The **reaction rate** expresses how fast a particular chemical change occurs. The study of reaction rates is often referred to as chemical **kinetics.**

For chemical reactions to occur, reactant molecules, atoms, or ions must collide with one another. According to collision theory, the reaction rate depends on the collision frequency and the energy involved in each collision (Figure 5.16).

Figure 5.16 *For a chemical reaction to occur, reactant particles must collide with proper orientation and sufficient energy.*

You first learned about collision theory in Unit 4 (page 394). According to this theory, the reaction rate also depends on the orientation of the colliding molecules.

Nitrogen and Industry

This section examines the synthesis of ammonia from nitrogen and hydrogen gas, an example of a reversible reaction used for commercial production of a useful product.

Students are introduced to kinetics, equilibrium, Le Châtelier's Principle, and Green Chemistry.

B.1 Kinetics and Equilibrium

Several important concepts are developed here. Students learn about reversible reactions, kinetics, equilibrium, and Le Châtelier's Principle. The concepts of kinetics and chemical equilibrium are used to explain how chemists overcame obstacles to producing ammonia.

Using the Figures

Figure 5.16: Use this figure as an example of an analogy for collision theory. Ask students to identify features of the bumper-car analogy that correspond to specific aspects of collision theory as well as to critique limitations of this analogy. This may help them to become more thoughtful when developing their own analogies for collision theory.

Kinetics: Producing More Ammonia in Less Time   Kinetics is introduced to help set the stage for some difficulties associated with ammonia production. Collision theory explains that a reaction's kinetics depend on collision frequency and the energy involved in each collision. Although not mentioned in the text (except briefly within the Figure 5.16 caption), reaction rate also depends on the proper *orientation* of reacting molecules. Catalysts act by lowering the activation energy. Ask students to create analogies that describe the factors within collision theory that influence the rate of a reaction. Encourage students to also identify limitations to their analogies. (See **Using the Figures, Figure 5.16**.)

Equilibrium: Favoring the Forward Reaction Some students may struggle with the notion of chemical equilibrium. A common student misconception is that equilibrium only occurs if the *concentrations* of reactants and products are equal. Reemphasize that equilibrium occurs when the *rate* of the forward reaction equals the *rate* of the reverse reaction. An indicator of equilibrium is *no net change* in concentrations of reactants or products. Some students may need visual cues to conceptualize equilibrium. The demonstration on page 435 is one way to address misconceptions about equilibrium.

Using the Figures

Figure 5.18: Students could critique using escalators as an analogy for equilibrium. (One criticism may be that not all people are familiar with escalators!)

Scientific American Conceptual Illustration

This *Scientific American* illustration depicts dynamic equilibrium involving two opposing physical processes—evaporation and condensation. You can set up a similar display of two Erlenmeyer flasks in the classroom a few weeks (or days, depending on local humidity) before teaching equilibrium. Ensure that both flasks are filled to the same level with water, and then stopper one flask. Direct students' attention to the flasks every few days (or more often) to observe any changes. Then, when you're ready to introduce the concept of equilibrium, invite students to discuss their observations

Figure 5.17 *A catalyst reduces the size of the activation-energy barrier involved in synthesizing ammonia from its elements.*

All reversible reactions in closed containers eventually reach equilibrium if conditions such as temperature remain constant.

Visualizing an Iconic Equilibrium

Increasing concentrations of reactants speeds up reaction rates by increasing the number of collisions. High temperatures increase the reaction rate by providing more reacting molecules with sufficient energy to overcome the activation-energy barrier. Catalysts, on the other hand, increase the reaction rate by lowering the activation-energy barrier required for the reaction to occur, as shown in Figure 5.17.

Although a higher reaction temperature increases the average kinetic energies of the nitrogen and hydrogen molecules that react to form ammonia, ammonia itself becomes increasingly unstable at higher temperatures. The result is that ammonia decomposes back to nitrogen gas and hydrogen gas. If the reaction takes place at lower temperatures, fewer nitrogen and hydrogen molecules have enough energy to overcome the activation energy barrier, thus slowing the net rate of ammonia formation (even though less ammonia decomposes at that lower temperature). What can we do to increase the rate and yield of ammonia production?

The major breakthrough that led to profitable ammonia production was the discovery of a suitable catalyst. Catalysts made it possible to produce ammonia at lower temperatures (450–500 °C), thus slowing the rate of ammonia decomposition. Fritz Haber and his colleagues spent a great deal of time and effort in the early 1900s systematically searching for good catalysts. Today, the ammonia industry commonly employs iron as an ammonia synthesis catalyst.

Equilibrium: Favoring the Forward Reaction

Any reversible reaction appears to stop when the rate at which product forms equals the rate at which product reverts back to reactants—that is, when reactants and products attain *dynamic equilibrium*. At equilibrium, both the forward and the reverse reactions continue, but there is no further change in the amounts of reactants or products. At the point of dynamic equilibrium, the two opposing changes are in exact balance, as modeled in Figures 5.18 and 5.19.

Figure 5.18 *A system at dynamic equilibrium involves two ongoing processes acting in opposition to one another.*

and explain what they observed in each flask. They will probably say that water evaporates from the open flask, but that "nothing" happens in the stoppered flask.

At this point, turn the discussion to the model in this figure or simply present this figure as a possible model and invite students to interpret and comment on it.

Scientific American Conceptual Illustration

Figure 5.19 Dynamic equilibrium. *In the stoppered flask (left), we observe no overall change in the water level because its evaporation rate equals its rate of condensation. Water contained in the open flask (right) slowly escapes from the flask as water vapor. This happens because the rate of evaporation of water molecules is greater than the rate of condensation—this system is not in equilibrium. The closed system in the stoppered flask is, by contrast, an example of dynamic equilibrium.*

The net amount of ammonia formed from a certain amount of nitrogen gas and hydrogen gas at a fixed temperature is limited. One way to increase the amount of ammonia produced is to cool the ammonia as soon as it forms until it turns to a liquid and remove it from the reaction chamber. This prevents ammonia from decomposing back into nitrogen gas and hydrogen gas. If ammonia is continuously removed, the rate of the reverse reaction (decomposition of ammonia) is significantly decreased because there is less gaseous ammonia available to decompose. This causes the overall reaction (see equation page 433) to favor the production of more ammonia.

Section B   Nitrogen and Industry   **435**

think at the particulate level and emphasize that, in terms of evaporation and condensation, some water molecules gain enough energy to leave the water surface, but at the same rate that gaseous water molecules return to the water surface and condense back to liquid. (c) For reactions that have attained dynamic equilibrium, reactant molecules still move, collide, and turn into product molecules and vice versa.

Demonstration Idea

Place two large, equally sized, transparent tanks at the front of the classroom. Fill one with water and leave the other empty (or nearly empty). Adding food coloring to the water often makes this demonstration easier to view. Give two student volunteers one cup each. The students, in synchronization, scoop water from their designated tank and transfer that water to the other tank. The student assigned the empty tank must still go through the motion of scooping water and emptying it into the opposite tank. The overall objective for each student is to empty his or her tank. Over time, students note that the water in each tank reaches a level from which it doesn't move, despite continued scooping and transferring. This demonstration illustrates that the rates of forward and reverse reactions (that is, the volume of water scooped from both tanks) are equal at equilibrium. It also illustrates the concept of *dynamic* equilibrium.

Emphasize several points: (a) Systems at dynamic equilibrium do not appear to change (in this physical case, the water level in the stoppered flask remains constant; for a chemical reaction, the concentrations of reactants and products remain constant). However, that does not mean "nothing" is happening. (b) Encourage students to

Le Châtelier's Principle   The text uses Le Châtelier's Principle to describe how ammonia manufacture can be controlled to produce the maximum amount of product at minimum expense. Optimal strategies for producing ammonia include:

1. Maintaining a high concentration of reactants (N and H)

2. Removing the product from the reaction vessel as it forms. Ammonia condenses at a higher temperature than either hydrogen or nitrogen, so the reaction vessel is cooled to liquefy and remove ammonia.

3. Strict temperature control. Low temperatures favor the forward reaction (producing ammonia). High temperatures favor the reverse reaction. Therefore, temperatures must be low enough to inhibit product decomposition but high enough to provide activation energy needed for the forward reaction.

4. Using a catalyst to speed up the reaction. The lowered temperature (see Point 3) makes it more difficult for molecules to obtain activation energy. Since catalysts lower the needed activation energy, more collisions become effective.

5. Controlling pressure. Pressure must be high enough to increase total molecular collisions and therefore encourage product formation. However, very high pressures are costly and introduce safety hazards for workers.

Consider using the video by TV Ontario on chemical equilibrium—especially Segment 6, "The Haber Process," which covers the chemical and historical events mentioned in Section B.

Shifting the position of an equilibrium system is often described by the direction of the favored reaction. If the disturbance causes the forward reaction to be favored, the equilibrium is shifted to the right side of the equation. If the reverse reaction is favored, the equilibrium is shifted to the left side of the equation.

Disturbing an Equilibrium

This example illustrates that a system at equilibrium can often be disturbed by changing the concentration of either reactants or products or by changing the temperature of the system. When one of these disturbances occurs, it causes either the forward or the reverse reaction rate to become larger than the other and thus to be favored over the other—a change that *partially counteracts* the initial effect of the disturbance. Thus, the initial equilibrium position is shifted. This effect, first described by the French chemist Henri Le Châtelier in 1884, is commonly called *Le Châtelier's Principle.*

The external disturbance imposed on a system at equilibrium, sometimes called a *stress,* may be a change in the concentration of a particular reactant or product, a change in the temperature of the system, or (for a system including gases) a change in the total pressure. According to **Le Châtelier's Principle,** *the predicted shift in the equilibrium position is always in the direction that partially counteracts the imposed change in conditions.* In the industrial production of ammonia, removal of ammonia (a change in its concentration inside the reaction vessel) results in the initial equilibrium position being shifted in favor of products. In the language of Le Châtelier's Principle, the removal of ammonia is partially counteracted by the system, thus producing *more* ammonia.

Another external disturbance (stress) used to increase ammonia production is to add reactant molecules (nitrogen gas and hydrogen gas) continuously at high pressure. This higher pressure of reactant gases means the number of nitrogen and hydrogen gas molecules per unit volume is increased, thereby increasing the concentration of the reactants. The frequency of molecular collisions increases, which favors the forward reaction, and thus increases the amount of ammonia formed. This change can be viewed as partially counteracting the initial increased pressure because the total number of gas molecules have been decreased. (Four molecules of gas—three molecules H_2 and one molecule N_2—are replaced by two molecules of NH_3 gas.)

In many cases, changing the system's temperature can also cause an equilibrium system to shift. The direction of that effect can be predicted based on whether the forward reaction is exothermic or endothermic. For example, the synthesis of ammonia is exothermic:

$$N_2(g) + 3\ H_2(g) \rightleftharpoons 2\ NH_3(g) + Heat$$

Heat (thermal energy) can be regarded as a product of the forward (left to right) reaction. Raising the temperature would tend to favor the reverse (right to left) reaction, a chemical change that absorbs heat. Consequently, less ammonia is formed at conditions of higher temperatures. Remember, though, that the temperature must be high enough to provide the nitrogen and hydrogen molecules with adequate kinetic energy to react. A delicate balance is needed; the temperature must be high enough to produce significant amounts of ammonia but not so high that it promotes an excessive rate of ammonia decomposition.

B.2 CHEMICAL SYSTEMS AT EQUILIBRIUM

Developing Skills

Sample Problem: *For the following equilibrium system, describe three changes you could make to increase the formation of nitric oxide gas, NO(g), at equilibrium.*

$$Heat + 2\ NO_2(g) \rightleftharpoons 2\ NO(g) + O_2(g)$$

We need to consider factors that will cause the equilibrium to shift to the right, favoring NO production. Based on Le Châtelier's Principle, these factors apply: (1) The system could be heated to a higher temperature. (2) The concentration of NO_2 could be increased. (3) The concentration of O_2 or NO could be decreased.

Now answer the following questions:

1. For each equilibrium system, describe three changes you could make to favor the forward reaction.
   a. $2\ SO_2(g) + O_2(g) \rightleftharpoons 2\ SO_3(g) + Heat$
   b. $H_2(g) + Cl_2(g) \rightleftharpoons 2\ HCl(g) + Heat$

2. Examine the graph in Figure 5.20:
   a. What generalization can you make about the effect of temperature on the yield of ammonia?
   b. Do you think your generalization would remain valid for temperatures much lower than 400 °C? Explain your answer.
   c. What generalization can you make about the effect of total pressure on the yield of ammonia?
   d. What combination of temperature and pressure results in the highest ammonia yield?

3. For Questions 1a and 1b, describe three changes you could make to favor each reverse reaction.

Figure 5.20 *Ammonia production in the system $N_2(g) + 3\ H_2(g) \rightleftharpoons 2\ NH_3(g) + Heat$. The graph depicts the effect of pressure and temperature changes on the percent NH_3 present at equilibrium.*

Developing Skills

B.2 Chemical Systems at Equilibrium

Students apply Le Châtelier's Principle to chemical equilibrium systems.

Answers

1. a. Increase the concentration of SO_2 or O_2, decrease the concentration of SO_3 by removing product, or cool the system.
   b. Increase the concentration of H_2 or Cl_2, decrease the concentration of HCl by removing product, or cool the system.

2. a. Lower temperatures increase the yield.
   b. No. Temperatures need to be high enough for molecules to possess activation energy for effective collisions.
   c. Higher pressures result in higher yields.
   d. Lower temperatures (400 °C) and higher pressures (500 atm)

3. a. Decrease the concentration of SO_2 or O_2 by removing them as they form, increase the concentration of SO_3, or heat the system.
   b. Decrease the concentration of H_2 or Cl_2 by removing them as they form, increase the concentration of HCl, or heat the system.

SECTION B

B.3 Le Châtelier's Principle

B.3 Le Chatelier's Principle Student Worksheet and Data Table

Students explore Le Châtelier's Principle with an equilibrium system.

Time

30 min

Materials

(For 12 student pairs)

12 test tubes (18 × 150 mm)

12 test tube holders

24 400-mL beakers

12 hot plates

Ice (2 lbs)

24 dropper bottles

265 mL 0.1 M $AgNO_3$ (4.5 g $AgNO_3$/ 265 mL solution)

5.0 g NaCl

0.1 M $CoCl_2$ Tincture Components

(See Preparation Instructions Below)

2.37 g $CoCl_2 \cdot 6H_2O$

40 g $CaCl_2$ anhydrous

100 mL 95% ethanol

Pre-Lab Discussion

Review conditions affecting an equilibrium system, using Le Châtelier's Principle.

Safety

Students should wear protective goggles and lab aprons throughout this investigation. They should handle silver nitrate with care; it stains clothing and skin.

Advance Preparation

Prepare 0.1 M $CoCl_2$ tincture by dissolving 2.37 g $CoCl_2 \cdot 6H_2O$ in 100 mL 95% ethanol. Add about 40 g anhydrous $CaCl_2$. Swirl until the solution is deep blue. Decant

solution into dropper bottles for student use. Slightly more than 40 g $CaCl_2$ may be needed if the supply of solid $CaCl_2$ is partially hydrated.

Set up hot-water baths in advance. The bath should be no higher than 70 °C—well below boiling. Also set up ice-water baths in advance.

Investigating Matter

B.3 LE CHÂTELIER'S PRINCIPLE

 Lab Video: Le Châtelier's Principle

Introduction

In this investigation of a system at equilibrium, you will use what you have learned about Le Châtelier's Principle to explore the effects of changing concentration and temperature on the position of an equilibrium system. The chemical system that you will investigate is described by the following equilibrium equation involving *complex ions*:

$$Heat + [Co(H_2O)_6]^{2+}(aq) + 4\ Cl^-(aq) \rightleftharpoons [CoCl_4]^{2-}(aq) + 6\ H_2O(l)$$

A **complex ion** is composed of a single central atom or ion, usually a metal ion, to which other atoms, molecules, or ions are attached. Part of your task will be to decide which complex ion above—$[CoCl_4]^{2-}$ or $[Co(H_2O)_6]^{2+}$—is blue and which is pink.

Procedure

1. Prepare a hot-water bath (60–70 °C) to use in Step 4.
2. Add 20 drops of 0.1 M cobalt(II) chloride ($CoCl_2$) solution to a clean, dry test tube. Record the color.
3. Add 7 drops of 0.1 M silver nitrate ($AgNO_3$) solution to the same test tube. **Caution:** *$AgNO_3$ solution can stain your skin or clothing. Handle with care.* Gently swirl the tube to ensure good mixing. Record the color.
4. Heat the tube in a hot-water bath for 30 s. Record the color.
5. Remove the tube from the hot-water bath. Add approximately 0.3 g sodium chloride (NaCl). Gently agitate the tube. Heat the solution for 30 s in the hot-water bath. Record the color.
6. Place the test tube in a beaker containing ice water for 30 s. Record the color.
7. Reheat the test tube in the hot-water bath. Record the color.
8. Dispose of the mixture in the test tube as directed by your teacher.
9. Wash your hands thoroughly before leaving the laboratory.

Questions

In answering the following questions, refer to your observations and to the equilibrium equation contained in the Introduction.

1. Which reaction (forward or reverse) was favored by cooling the solution?
2. Which reaction was favored by adding more chloride ions?
3. What is the identity of the white precipitate that formed in Step 3? (*Hint:* Refer to Unit 1, page 44.)

Answers

1. The reverse reaction; cooling the solution favors the reaction liberating heat.
2. The forward reaction; it counteracts the stress of increased Cl^- concentration.
3. Silver chloride, AgCl(s)

4. Why did adding AgNO₃ solution affect the equilibrium, even though neither Ag⁺ ions nor NO₃⁻ ions appear in the equilibrium equation? Write an equation to support your answer.

5. Why did the solution's color change after heating in Step 5 but not in Step 4?

6. a. Which complex ion is pink: $[CoCl_4]^{2-}$ or $[Co(H_2O)_6]^{2+}$?
   b. Which complex ion is blue?

   Provide evidence that supports both of your answers.

B.4 INDUSTRIAL SYNTHESIS OF AMMONIA

Large-scale ammonia production involves much more than allowing nitrogen gas and hydrogen gas to react in the presence of a catalyst. First, of course, the plant must obtain a continuous supply of the reactants. Nitrogen gas, which represents 78% of Earth's atmosphere, is liquefied from air through a series of steps involving cooling and compression. As you will soon learn, hydrogen gas can be obtained chemically from natural gas (mainly methane, CH_4). Opening an ammonia plant in Riverwood would mean building a pipeline from a natural gas source (or distribution center) to the chemical plant.

To produce hydrogen gas, chemical engineers first treat natural gas to remove sulfur compounds; then they allow methane to react with steam:

$$Heat + CH_4(g) + H_2O(g) \rightleftharpoons 3\,H_2(g) + CO(g)$$

In modern ammonia plants, this endothermic reaction takes place at 200–600 °C and at pressures of 200–900 atm. Technicians, such as the one shown in Figure 5.21, must carefully control the ratio of methane to steam to prevent the formation of carbon compounds that would lower the yield of hydrogen gas.

Carbon monoxide, a product of the hydrogen-generating reaction shown above, is converted to carbon dioxide, which is accompanied by the production of additional hydrogen gas:

$$CO(g) + H_2O(g) \rightleftharpoons H_2(g) + CO_2(g)$$

All the hydrogen gas produced is then separated from carbon dioxide and from any unreacted methane.

In the Haber-Bosch process (see page 425), the reactants (hydrogen gas and nitrogen gas) are first compressed to high pressures (150–300 atm). Ammonia forms as the hot gases (at about 500 °C) flow over an iron catalyst. Ammonia gas is removed by converting it, by means of cooling and added pressure, to liquid ammonia, which is then removed from the reaction chamber, thus reducing the rate of ammonia decomposition. Unreacted nitrogen gas and hydrogen gas are recycled, mixed with additional supplies of reactants, and passed through the reaction chamber again.

Figure 5.21 *This technician checks conditions within an industrial chemical storage system. What evidence suggests that safety is a priority?*

The CO_2 formed in this reaction can be removed in several ways, including allowing it to react with calcium oxide (CaO or lime), which forms solid calcium carbonate ($CaCO_3$), or by dissolving the CO_2 gas at high pressure in water.

methane (CH_4); however, the CH_4-to-steam ratio must be controlled carefully to prevent forming other compounds. Although this process is used in industrial NH_3 synthesis, it is not very efficient; it produces only 20–30% NH_3.

The Haber-Bosch process requires close monitoring by chemists, chemical engineers, and technicians. The temperature and pressure must be carefully controlled to maximize NH_3 produced and minimize safety hazards. The catalyst surface must also be "clean" so optimal amounts of N_2 and H_2 are adsorbed. Adsorbed impurities interfere with and lower yield.

Fritz Haber, a German physical chemist, received the 1918 Chemistry Nobel Prize for this method. Carl Bosch, an industrial chemist, shared a 1931 Nobel Prize with Friedrich Bergius for their high-pressure studies.

This material may be interesting to students planning to study engineering later. Chemical engineers develop processes and equipment for chemical manufacturing and also monitor production.

Using the Figures

Figure 5.21: A technician wears protective goggles and a hard hat, called *PPE* (personal protective equipment). The tank before him is labeled with its contents and a National Fire Protection Association (NFPA) label. Each NFPA color represents a hazard factor; the numbers indicate the degree of hazard (from 0 to 4). Yellow = *reactivity hazards,* red = *fire hazards,* blue = *health hazards.* According to this label, toluene is stable (low reactivity), readily ignitable, and hazardous to health.

 B.4 Supplement: Le Chatelier's Principle

4. Ag⁺ removes Cl⁻ (a reactant) from solution. More reactant is thus produced.
   $$Ag^+(aq) + Cl^-(aq) \longrightarrow AgCl(s)$$

5. In Step 5 heating, $[CoCl_4]^{2-}$ forms (Step 6). It did not change in Step 4 because Ag⁺ removed most Cl⁻ from solution, preventing $[CoCl_4]^{2-}$ from forming.

6. a. $[Co(H_2O)_6]^{2+}$ b. $[CoCl_4]^{2-}$

B.4 Industrial Synthesis of Ammonia

NH_3 is synthesized by the Haber-Bosch process. N_2 from air reacts with H_2 at elevated temperatures (500 °C) and high pressure (150–300 atm) in the presence of iron oxides and Al_2O_3 catalysts. The required H_2 is produced by reaction of steam with

B.5 Nitrogen's Other Face

This material features the uses of nitrogen compounds as explosives, emphasizing the work of Alfred Nobel and his family. *Explosions* are rapid, exothermic reactions in which the volume of hot, gaseous products is much greater than the volume of the original solid or liquid reactants. In explosives containing nitrogen, it is released upon explosion as stable $N_2(g)$ molecules.

Using the Figures

Figure 5.23: *All but one* of these structures contain one or more nitrogen atoms bonded to carbon and several oxygen atoms. *All* of these structures contain nitrogen in a less stable environment than that of elemental nitrogen. Each compound is either a solid or a liquid. Upon explosion, when they quickly convert to more stable, gaseous nitrogen molecules, the rapid increase in volume contributes to the destructive force of the explosive.

The text discusses air bags. Sodium azide is an ionic compound of sodium (Na^+) and azide ions (N_3^-). Azide anions are very unstable and will readily react to form the more stable nitrogen gas, N_2. In an air bag, sensors detect the impact of a collision. These sensors turn on an electrical circuit, which provides the spark that ignites the sodium azide. Nitrogen gas formed in this process fills the bag at a velocity of 150–250 mph. This process, from start to finish, must be completed within 40 ms (milliseconds). When the reaction is complete, the nitrogen gas leaves the air bag through small vents. The purpose of this deflation is to create a softer impact zone for the driver or passenger.

B.5 NITROGEN'S OTHER FACE

The Haber-Bosch process has provided relatively inexpensive ammonia for a variety of applications. For example, ammonia reacts directly with nitric acid to produce ammonium nitrate, a substitute for natural nitrates traditionally used as fertilizers.

$$\underset{\text{Ammonia}}{NH_3(g)} + \underset{\substack{\text{Nitric} \\ \text{acid}}}{HNO_3(aq)} \longrightarrow \underset{\substack{\text{Ammonium} \\ \text{nitrate}}}{NH_4NO_3(aq)}$$

> About 80% of NH_3 produced is used in fertilizer and 5% is used in explosives. What other uses for NH_3 might account for the other 15%?

The widespread availability of ammonia and nitrates has changed the course of warfare as well as of agriculture. Ammonia is a reactant in the production of explosives, most of which are nitrogen-containing compounds (see Figures 5.22 and 5.23). The development of the Haber-Bosch process provided a convenient source of ammonia for making both fertilizers and military munitions. This allowed Germany to continue fighting in World War I even after its shipping connections to Chilean nitrate deposits were cut off by the British Navy.

Nitrogen-based explosives also have non-hostile, and even life-saving, uses. Air bags in automobiles are one such modern application. An air bag quickly inflates like a big pillow during a collision to reduce injuries to the driver and passengers. The uninflated air-bag assembly contains solid sodium azide, NaN_3. In a collision, sensors initiate a sequence of events that rapidly decompose the sodium azide to form a large volume of nitrogen gas:

$$3\,NaN_3(s) \longrightarrow Na_3N(s) + 4\,N_2(g)$$

Figure 5.22 *Explosive substances, such as those used here, are used in many mining and construction operations.*

Figure 5.23 *Structural formulas of some common substances used as explosives. What similarities are shared by these chemical structures?*

Nitrogen gas quickly inflates the air bag (to about 50 L) within 50 ms (0.05 s) after the collision starts (see Figure 5.24).

The forces released by nitrogen-based explosives also blast roadbeds through solid rock during highway construction. To cut through the stone faces of hills and mountains, road crews drill holes, drop in explosive canisters, and then detonate the explosives.

Explosions in general result from the rapid formation of gaseous products from liquid or solid reactants. Detonating an explosive such as sodium azide, dynamite, or nitroglycerin produces gases that occupy more than a thousand times the volume of the original solid or liquid.

Many compounds used as explosives involve nitrogen atoms in a positive oxidation state and carbon in a negative oxidation state within the same reactant molecule. This creates conditions for the release of vast quantities of energy. The energy released in this type of explosive reaction is due in part to the formation of N_2, a highly stable molecule.

The powerful explosive nitroglycerin (see Figure 5.23) was invented in 1846. However, it was too sensitive (unstable) to be useful; one never knew when it was going to explode. The Nobel family built a laboratory in Stockholm to explore ways to control this unstable substance (Figure 5.25). Although the father and his four sons were interested in explosives, one son, Alfred, was the most persistent experimenter.

Carelessness led to accidental explosions. One killed Alfred's brother Emil. The city of Stockholm finally insisted that Alfred move his experimenting elsewhere. Determined to continue research to make nitroglycerin less unpredictable and dangerous, Alfred rented a barge and performed experiments in the middle of a lake.

Alfred finally discovered that mixing oily nitroglycerin with a finely divided solid (diatomaceous earth) caused nitroglycerin to become stable enough for safe transportation and storage. However, the nitroglycerin would still explode if a blasting cap activated it. This new, more stable form of nitroglycerin carried a new name—*dynamite*.

A new era in explosives had begun. At first, dynamite served peaceful uses in mining and in road and tunnel construction (see Figure 5.22). By the late 1800s, dynamite also found destructive use in warfare.

Figure 5.24 *Automobile air bags deploy due to nitrogen gas released from a nitrogen-based explosive compound.*

Chemical explosions are often rapid, exothermic oxidation–reduction reactions that produce large volumes of gaseous product.

Figure 5.25 *The production of nitroglycerin, devised by Alfred Nobel, was a dangerous process that needed careful monitoring. Note the one-legged stool that ensured that the attendant didn't fall asleep on the job.*

Nitroglycerin and dynamite are also mentioned. Nitroglycerin was first created by Ascanio Sobrero in 1846 by treating glycerol (from animal fat) with a mixture of nitric and sulfuric acid. This highly exothermic reaction will result in an explosion of nitroglycerin, unless the mixture is cooled while the reaction is taking place. Nitroglycerin is extremely unstable; it is quite sensitive to shock and heat. This instability means that nitroglycerin explosions can be quite unpredictable. When nitroglycerin explodes, the gases carbon dioxide, oxygen, water vapor, and nitrogen are produced.

Nitroglycerin was extremely popular during the second half of the 19th century; it was more energetic than gunpowder. Nobel was able to establish several factories in Europe dedicated to nitroglycerin production. The many accidents at Nobel's manufacturing plants evoked considerable concern; several countries banned or proposed a ban on nitroglycerin. Nobel worked to try to stabilize nitroglycerin to minimize accidents. He mixed diatomaceous earth (silicon-rich remains of tiny marine animals) with nitroglycerin to form a paste having significantly higher stability. He named this mixture *dynamite*.

Nitrogen chemistry provides excellent examples of the ways that a particular chemical technology can be used for either constructive or destructive purposes.

Developing Skills

B.6 Explosive Nitrogen Chemistry

In this activity, students analyze the stoichiometry of the explosion of nitroglycerin.

Answers

1. The reaction begins with 4 mol reactant and produces 29 mol gaseous products. Therefore, 1 mol nitroglycerin produces approximately 7.25 mol gaseous products (3 mol CO_2, 1.5 mol N_2, 2.5 mol H_2O, and 0.25 mol O_2).

2. 1 mol nitroglycerin produces 7.25 mol gaseous products × 22.4 L/mol = 162 L, so the volume increases approximately 1600 times [(162 L of gaseous product)/0.1 L (of liquid reactant)].

3. 8 × 1600 = 13 000 times

4. The very large, sudden volume increase exerts enormous destructive force in the vicinity of the explosion.

B.7 From Raw Materials to Products

B.7 Content Reading Guide

The text states that four factors (engineering, profitability, waste, and safety) are involved in scaling up laboratory reactions to industrial-size processes. The need to reduce chemical waste in manufacturing as mandated by the EPA has led to reprocessing waste materials and, incidentally, additional financial benefits for companies.

Military use of his invention caused Alfred Nobel considerable anguish and motivated him to use his fortune to benefit humanity. His will specified that his money be dedicated to annual international prizes for advances in physics, chemistry, physiology and medicine, literature, and peace. (The Swedish parliament later added economics as an award category.) Nobel prizes, first awarded in 1901, are still regarded as the highest honors individuals can receive in these fields. Table 5.1 lists recent Nobel Prize recipients in chemistry, together with their contributions to chemical science.

Table 5.1 *Afred Nobel's will established several annual awards, one of which is bestowed upon those who "shall have made the most important chemical discovery or improvement."*

NOBEL LAUREATES IN CHEMISTRY, 2001–2005		
Year	**Awardees**	**Contributions**
2005	Yves Chauvin, France, Institut Français du Pétrole; Robert H. Grubbs, United States, California Institute of Technology; and Richard R. Schrock, United States, Massachusetts Institute of Technology	Development of the metathesis method in organic chemistry, reducing potentially hazardous waste through "Green-Chemistry" synthesis methods
2004	Aaron Ciechanover and Avram Hershko, Israel, Technion-Israel Institute of Technology; and Irwin Rose, United States, University of California, Irvine	Discovery of ubiquitin-mediated protein degradation
2003	Peter Agre, United States, Johns Hopkins University School of Medicine; and Roderick MacKinnon, United States, Rockefeller University	Discoveries about channels in cell membranes
2002	John B. Fenn, United States, Virginia Commonwealth University; Koichi Tanaka, Japan, Shimadzu Corporation; and Kurt Wüthrich, Switzerland, Swiss Federal Institute of Technology	Development of analytical methods for identification and structure analyses of biological macromolecules
2001	William S. Knowles, United States, Monsanto Company; and Ryoji Noyori, Japan, Nagoya University	Work on chirally catalyzed hydrogenation reactions
	K. Barry Sharpless, United States, The Scripps Research Institute	Work on chirally catalyzed oxidation reactions

B.6 EXPLOSIVE NITROGEN CHEMISTRY

Developing Skills

The following equation describes the explosion of nitroglycerin:

$$4\ C_3H_5(NO_3)_3(l) \longrightarrow 12\ CO_2(g) + 6\ N_2(g) + 10\ H_2O(g) + O_2(g) + Energy$$
Nitroglycerin

1. How many total moles of gaseous products form in the explosion of one mole of nitroglycerin?

2. One mole of gas at standard temperature and pressure occupies 22.4 L. One mole of liquid nitroglycerin occupies approximately 0.1 L. By what factor does the volume increase when one mole of nitroglycerin explodes? (Assume temperature remains constant.)

3. When nitroglycerin explodes, the actual temperature increase causes gas volume to increase eight times more than the factor you just calculated in Question 2. By what combined factor does the total volume suddenly increase during an actual nitroglycerin explosion?

4. How do your answers to Questions 2 and 3 help explain the destructive power of a nitroglycerin explosion?

B.7 FROM RAW MATERIALS TO PRODUCTS

Some chemical reactions you have observed in this chemistry class are essentially the same as reactions used in industry to synthesize chemical products. However, chemical reactions in industry must be scaled up to produce very large quantities of high-quality products at low cost.

Four considerations become crucial in attempting to scale up chemical reactions: *engineering*, *profitability*, *waste*, and *safety*. Sometimes an industrial reaction is conducted as a *batch process*, a single run of converting reactants to products (see Figure 5.26, top). You completed such reactions to produce esters in Unit 3 (page 275). Additional batch runs can produce more product. The early industrial production of nylon was also a batch process.

More commonly and less expensively, industrial reactions can involve a *continuous process:* Reactants flow steadily into the reaction chamber, and products continuously flow out (see Figure 5.26, bottom). Engineers carefully control the rate of flow, time, temperature, and catalyst composition to ensure a successful continuous-production operation.

Figure 5.26 *On an industrial scale, materials can be made through a batch process (top) or a continuous process (bottom). What benefits might each production method offer?*

Using the Figures

Figure 5.26: The top photo shows cheese being produced by a *batch process.* Cheese vats are filled with rennet-treated milk. (Rennet contains the enzyme *chymosin*, which coagulates milk.) Cutting and stirring produces a cheese curd, which is then placed into molds. The bottom photo depicts a *continuous process* by which ceramics are manufactured. Continuous processes are typically less expensive and more conducive to high production over less time. Batch processes can be used to synthesize small quantities of more dangerous (thus less desirable) intermediates, which can then be completely used up.

ChemQuandary 1

The Top Chemicals

In addition to mass or weight, relative production levels could be ranked in terms of volume, cost, density, or amount (moles). Each ranking would yield a different order based on particular physical and chemical properties of the substances.

Chemical engineers face many challenges in designing manufacturing systems for industry. In your classroom laboratory, the small quantity of thermal energy generated by a reaction in a test tube or wellplate may seem insignificant. However, in exothermic industrial processes, thousands of liters may react in huge vats. Engineers have to anticipate and manage the release of large quantities of heat. Otherwise, reaction temperatures may rise, creating potentially dangerous, costly, and destructive situations.

The chemical industry also faces challenges in dealing with unwanted materials that result from chemical processes. When reactions occur on an industrial scale, large quantities of waste can accumulate. A major responsibility of the Environmental Protection Agency (EPA) is regulating the cleanup of hundreds of chemical-waste sites in the United States (Figure 5.27). Those sites are legacies of earlier times when a common attitude was "out of sight, out of mind."

When the EPA put an end to such releases, many chemical industries discovered that, with some additional processing, they could turn some previously unwanted materials or products into valuable commodities. Former "waste" compounds can often become intermediates in producing useful substances. Thus, instead of contaminating the environment, such wastes-turned-resources offer new sources of income. Additionally, recently developed catalysts and new or modified processes have allowed manufacturers to increase their efficiency and decrease the amounts of starting materials (reactants) they need.

Chemical manufacturers have learned that pollution prevention pays off. For example, 3M Corporation, a major producer and user of chemical materials, has maintained a pollution prevention program for more than 25 years. During that time, 3M has saved nearly a billion dollars by eliminating more than 1.5 billion pounds of pollutants. 3M's goal now is to approach zero pollution. Most of these pollution-prevention suggestions have come directly from 3M employees.

Figure 5.27 *The Environmental Protection Agency (EPA) regulates and monitors pollutants, including those associated with industrial processes.*

ChemQuandary 1

THE TOP CHEMICALS

Table 5.2 lists the top-produced chemical substances in the United States. Notice that production is reported in billions of pounds. What quantities other than mass or weight could you use to compare the relative production levels of chemical materials? How would the relative rankings be affected— if at all—if you used each quantity?

TOP 25 CHEMICAL SUBSTANCES PRODUCED IN THE UNITED STATES

Rank	Name	Formula	Billions of Pounds
1	sulfuric acid	H_2SO_4	95.2
2	nitrogen	N_2	75.7
3	oxygen	O_2	57.7
4	ethene (ethylene)	C_2H_4	51.7
5	calcium oxide (lime)	CaO	45.0
6	ammonia	NH_3	39.5
7	phosphoric acid	H_3PO_4	28.8
8	propene (propylene)	C_3H_6	28.7
9	chlorine	Cl_2	25.7
10	sodium hydroxide	$NaOH$	23.0
11	sodium carbonate	Na_2CO_3	21.4
12	1,2-dichloroethane (ethylene dichloride)	$C_2H_4Cl_2$	19.5
13	methyl *tert*-butyl ether (MTBE)	$C_5H_{12}O$	18.9
14	nitric acid	HNO_3	18.7
15	urea	$(NH_2)_2CO$	17.6
16	ammonium nitrate	NH_4NO_3	17.2
17	vinyl chloride	C_2H_3Cl	17.0
18	benzene	C_6H_6	16.3
19	ethylbenzene	C_8H_{10}	13.0
20	methanol	CH_3OH	12.5
21	styrene	C_8H_8	11.4
22	terephthalic acid	$C_8H_6O_4$	8.7
23	formaldehyde	H_2CO	8.6
24	hydrochloric acid	HCl	8.6
25	toluene	$C_6H_5CH_3$	8.1

Based on data for 1998, *U.S. Chemical Industry Handbook*, Chemical Manufacturers Association, 1999 (Table 2.17, page 44).

Table 5.2 *The U.S. chemical industry produces billions of pounds of chemical substances annually.*

Using the Figures

Table 5.2: Sulfuric acid is listed as the top substance produced in the United States. A large proportion of this sulfuric acid is used to manufacture agricultural fertilizers. Other uses for sulfuric acid include purifying petroleum, manufacturing lead storage batteries, and metallurgy.

A useful extension activity would be to assign students (or small groups of students) one of the substances in the table. Students can investigate its common uses and present this information to the class.

B.8 Green Chemistry and Responsible Care

To make informed decisions concerning their community, students should be aware of industry's expected community responsibilities. The chemical industry is obliged to produce useful products while causing as little environmental damage as possible and also minimal harm to public health. On the other hand, citizens should understand industry's requirements and the extent of society's need for its products and services. Therefore, communities and industries should work together to prevent emissions before they occur, rather than cleaning them up after they occur.

Figure 5.28 *Industrial processes must be carefully monitored.*

The American Chemical Society's Green Chemistry Institute promotes education and research that encourages Green-Chemistry practices.

Green Chemistry

B.8 GREEN CHEMISTRY AND RESPONSIBLE CARE

On learning that EKS and WYE may want to locate plants in Riverwood, the town council created a draft of general criteria that either company must meet. These criteria are based, in part, on two national initiatives regarding the chemical industry's social and technical responsibilities.

The first initiative, Green Chemistry, addresses the chemistry involved in an industrial process and its effects on humans and the environment. The second initiative, Responsible Care, considers how industries can safely and productively contribute to communities.

The impact of these initiatives can be partly monitored by the EPA's Toxics Release Inventory (TRI). The TRI is a state-by-state database of annually reported releases of about 600 toxic materials into the air, water, or land by more than 21 000 facilities. Anyone, including citizens of Riverwood, interested in monitoring local releases of toxic materials can consult this TRI database.

Green Chemistry encourages monitoring all industrial practices (Figure 5.28). The goal is to make chemical production less hazardous to human health and to the environment. This initiative is sometimes termed *Benign by Design*. In meeting the objectives of Green Chemistry, industries also try to make their processes more efficient and profitable.

Principles guiding Green Chemistry include these general points:

▶ It is better to prevent waste than treat it or clean it up after it forms.

▶ Synthetic methods should be designed so that the desired product contains as much of the material used in the process as possible.

▶ Whenever feasible, reactants used and waste generated should be as benign as possible.

▶ Solvents and other potentially hazardous substances should be made unnecessary wherever possible and innocuous where not possible.

▶ Energy requirements should be recognized for their environmental and economic impact and should be minimized wherever possible.

▶ Catalysts should be used whenever appropriate.

▶ Raw materials (reactants) should be obtained from renewable resources wherever possible.

▶ Chemical products should be designed so that if they decompose, the resulting products are not harmful.

▶ Chemical processes should be designed to minimize the chance for chemical accidents, including accidental releases, explosions, and fires.

These principles encourage work that has already devised new industrial techniques, such as bleaching paper without using chlorine, recycling cellulose-based wastes into fuels, synthesizing drugs and polymers more efficiently, and developing reduced-risk pesticides highly specific for certain pests.

Responsible Care, initiated in 1988, is an international program in which chemical manufacturing companies voluntarily agree to public scrutiny and evaluation according to specific criteria. In the United States, member companies and partners of the American Chemistry Council (ACC) pledge to follow these principles:

▶ To seek and incorporate public input regarding products and operations.

▶ To provide chemicals that can be manufactured, transported, used, and disposed of safely.

▶ To make health, safety, the environment, and resource conservation critical considerations for all new and existing products and processes.

▶ To provide information on health or environmental risks and pursue protective measures for employees, the public, and other key stakeholders.

▶ To work with customers, carriers, suppliers, distributors, and contractors to foster the safe use, transport, and disposal of chemicals.

▶ To operate facilities in a manner that protects the environment and the health and safety of employees and the public.

▶ To support education and research on the health, safety, and environmental effects of products and processes.

▶ To work with others to resolve problems associated with past handling and disposal practices.

▶ To lead in the development of responsible laws, regulations, and standards that safeguard the community, workplace, and environment.

▶ To practice Responsible Care by encouraging and assisting others to adhere to these principles and practices.

As with Green Chemistry, adhering to the Responsible-Care pledge has encouraged many companies to increase safety for their workers and their surrounding communities, reduce the quantity of waste they generate, and achieve greater overall efficiency.

The next activity will help you develop criteria that any chemical industry interested in establishing a plant in Riverwood should meet.

For a recent article on developments in Green Chemistry, see Terrence J. Collins and Chip Walter, "Little Green Molecules," *Scientific American,* March 2006, pages 82–90. The article describes enzymelike catalysts being used to destroy pollutants in rivers.

More information on the Responsible Care Program can be obtained from:

American Chemistry Council
1300 Wilson Blvd
Arlington, VA 22209
http://www.americanchemistry.com/

Making Decisions

B.9 What Does Riverwood Want?

This activity provides a preliminary perspective for the Town Council meeting to be held at the close of this unit. Students should start to identify relevant arguments for the presence (or absence) of EKS or WYE in Riverwood. Assign students to work in small groups, possibly in groups similar to those in Unit 1 (pages 104–105).

Student answers will differ depending on principles chosen. Students should be able to communicate clearly the rationale behind their choice of expectations. They should also give reasons for their classifications of those expectations as either mandatory or desirable. You might wish to ask student groups to share results of their work with the entire class.

Making Decisions

B.9 WHAT DOES RIVERWOOD WANT?

The first of several town meetings to discuss the possibility of a chemical plant in Riverwood is coming up soon. Representatives from EKS and WYE and town council members will attend. All interested local citizens are also encouraged to attend.

1. Examine and compare the principles of Green Chemistry with those of the Responsible Care program (pages 446–447).

   a. Identify at least six expectations that the town council should clearly communicate to any chemical company that wants to locate in Riverwood.

   b. Classify your expectations as either 'mandatory' or simply 'desirable.'

2. Related to the expectations that you identified in Question 1, identify at least two questions that you would like to ask company representatives.

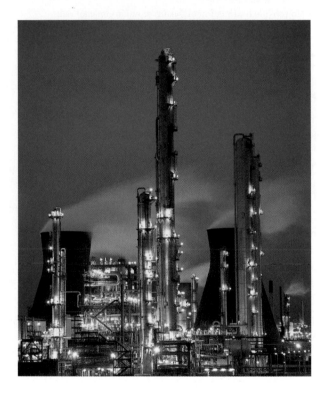

SECTION B SUMMARY
Reviewing the Concepts

The rate of a particular reaction depends on temperature, reactant concentration(s), and the influence of a catalyst.

1. What is meant by the *rate* of a reaction?
2. What does *chemical kinetics* mean?

3. Explain why reactions tend to speed up
   a. with increased temperature.
   b. with increased concentration.
   c. when a suitable catalyst is added.

When a system is in dynamic equilibrium, the rate of the forward reaction equals, and is thus balanced by, the rate of the reverse reaction.

4. What is equal about equilibrium?
5. What is dynamic about dynamic equilibrium?

6. How can you tell if chemical equilibrium is represented in a chemical equation?
7. What do *forward* and *reverse* mean when speaking about an equilibrium system?

Le Châtelier's Principle can be used to predict a shift in the equilibrium position of a reversible reaction.

8. Summarize Le Châtelier's Principle.
9. List three types of stress that can be applied to an equilibrium system.
10. Consider the following system at equilibrium:

    $$PCl_3(g) + Cl_2(g) \rightleftharpoons PCl_5(g) + Heat$$

    What effect (if any) will each of the following changes have on the position of that equilibrium system?
    a. adding more Cl_2
    b. lowering the temperature
    c. removing some PCl_5 as it forms
    d. decreasing the total pressure

11. Consider the following system at equilibrium:

    $$C(s) + H_2O(g) + Heat \rightleftharpoons CO(g) + H_2(g)$$

    What effect (if any) will each of the following changes have on the position of that equilibrium system?
    a. lowering the temperature
    b. adding steam at constant volume to the equilibrium system
    c. adding a catalyst
    d. increasing the total pressure

12. What is the effect of removing some heat from an exothermic reaction that is at equilibrium?

Section Summary   449

SECTION B SUMMARY

 Section B Supplement

Reviewing the Concepts

1. How fast a particular chemical change occurs
2. The study of reaction rates

3. a. Greater numbers of molecules have the necessary activation energy to participate in the reaction, and there are more collisions.
   b. The probability of collisions between two reactants with adequate activation energy increases.

   c. A catalyst lowers activation energy, so more reactants have the requisite activation energy to participate in the reaction.
4. At equilibrium, the rate of the forward reaction is equal to the rate of the reverse reaction. At the point of dynamic equilibrium, opposing changes are in balance.
5. It is characterized by continuous change. Changes in both directions (forward and reverse) occur at equal rates.
6. It is symbolized by a double arrow.
7. *Forward* refers to the reaction that occurs when substances on the left side of the equilibrium arrow react to form the substances on the right side of the arrow. *Reverse* refers to right-side substances reacting to form left-side substances.
8. Le Châtelier's Principle states that when a stress is imposed on a system at equilibrium, the shift in the equilibrium position is in the direction that partially counteracts the stress.
9. Pressure, temperature, and concentration
10. a. It will shift to the right (forward reaction favored).
    b. It will shift to the right.
    c. It will shift to the right.
    d. It will shift to the left (reverse reaction favored).
11. a. It will shift to the left (reverse reaction favored).
    b. It will shift to the right (forward reaction favored).
    c. No change; the reaction rate will increase equally in both directions.
    d. It will shift to the left (reverse reaction favored).
12. This favors the forward reaction, increasing the amount of product formed.

13. Nitrogen gas is liquefied from air. Hydrogen gas must be obtained from natural gas, mainly methane, CH_4.

14. a. High pressures
b. Low temperatures

15. It serves as a stress on the equilibrium system, resulting in production of more ammonia.

16. Ammonia production is exothermic. If temperatures are high, the reverse reaction (decomposition of ammonia) becomes favored.

17. Rapid formation of gaseous products, occupying many times the volume of liquid or solid reactants, and temperature increases.

18. Nitrogen molecules are very stable, with strong triple bonds holding nitrogen atoms together. Nitrogen-based explosives contain nitrogen atoms relatively weakly bonded to carbon and oxygen atoms. Breaking weak bonds and forming strong bonds (in N_2) releases large quantities of energy. Also, nitrogen-based explosives are solids or liquids, which occupy small volumes compared to explosion products, many of which are gases.

19. He experimented with nitroglycerin and increased its stability by combining it with diatomaceous earth to make dynamite.

20. $1.0 \text{ g NaN}_3 \times \dfrac{1 \text{ mol NaN}_3}{64.99 \text{ g NaN}_3} \times$

$\dfrac{4 \text{ mol N}_2}{3 \text{ mol NaN}_3} \times \dfrac{22.4 \text{ L}}{1 \text{ mol N}_2} = 0.46 \text{ L}$

21. 1. Seeking and incorporating public input regarding products and operations
2. Providing information on health or environmental risks and pursuing protective measures for employees, the public, and other key stakeholders
3. Supporting education and research on the health, safety,

| Ammonia is commonly produced industrially by Haber-Bosch process.

13. What are the sources of the reactants for Haber-Bosch process?

14. The Haber-Bosch process works most effectively under particular conditions. What are optimal conditions for

a. pressure?
b. temperature?

15. What is the advantage of removing ammonia from the reaction mixture as it forms in the Haber-Bosch process?

16. Why does the yield of ammonia decrease if the Haber-Bosch process is conducted at too high a temperature?

| Nitrogen compounds are commonly used in explosives.

17. What are the characteristics of a chemical explosion?

18. What two characteristics of nitrogen are responsible for the particular effectiveness of nitrogen-based explosives? Explain.

19. What were Alfred Nobel's main contributions to chemistry?

20. Consider the equation for the principal reaction that quickly causes an automobile air bag to inflate:

$$3 \text{ NaN}_3(s) \longrightarrow \text{Na}_3\text{N}(s) + 4 \text{ N}_2(g)$$

What volume of nitrogen gas (at STP) would an air-bag reaction involving 1.0 g NaN_3 produce?

| Initiatives such as Responsible Care, Green Chemistry, and EPA standards stress conservation, safety, and pollution prevention in decisions regarding manufacturing, storing, transporting, and disposing of chemical materials.

21. Identify four principles of Responsible Care that differ from Green-Chemistry principles.

22. "An ounce of prevention is worth a pound of cure." Explain how this saying relates to the Green-Chemistry initiative.

23. Provide an example of how following Green-Chemistry principles can help a chemical-manufacturing company become more profitable.

---

and environmental effects of products and processes
4. Leading in development of responsible laws, regulations, and standards that safeguard the community, workplace, and environment

22. It basically says that, in the long run, less money, energy, and time are required to prevent waste than to clean it up.

23. Using the principles of Green Chemistry encourages development of new, more efficient, time- and money-saving industrial techniques and products.

Connecting the Concepts

24. a. It shifts right b. It shifts left.
c. It shifts left. d. It shifts right.

Connecting the Concepts

24. Consider the following equilibrium system:

$$2 SO_2(g) + O_2(g) \rightleftharpoons 2 SO_3(g) + Heat$$

Explain how this equilibrium system would be affected by

a. adding more molecules of oxygen gas at constant volume.

b. increasing the temperature.

c. increasing the volume of the reaction vessel.

d. increasing the total pressure on the system.

Extending the Concepts

28. Compare the nitrogen-supply crisis of the early 20th century to current concerns about petroleum supplies.

29. Before chemists can convert methane to nitrogen gas, they must remove sulfur-containing compounds. How is sulfur removed from natural gas? Why is this necessary? Include and explain relevant chemical equations as part of your answer.

30. In several situations, an industrial by-product has become a valuable commodity. Discuss, in detail, one example.

31. Select two common substances that the chemical industry produces (Table 5.2, page 445) and investigate uses of these substances.

25. Scaling up a reaction to production levels involves many challenges not necessarily apparent at the lab scale. Discuss three such challenges faced by chemical engineers at EKS Nitrogen Products Company.

26. Refrigerated food lasts longer than food stored at room temperature. Explain.

27. Many explosive compounds contain nitrogen atoms in a positive oxidation state and carbon atoms in a negative oxidation state. What happens to the oxidation states of each type of atom if these compounds explode?

32. Describe some examples or analogies, other than chemical reactions, of dynamic equilibria.

33. The Toxics Release Inventory (TRI) is available from the EPA. Use the TRI to judge how much your state or metropolitan area has accomplished in reducing emissions from manufacturing facilities.

34. A *pressure cooker* reduces the total time needed to cook foods. Investigate the design of a pressure cooker and explain why it speeds up cooking times.

35. Select three Green-Chemistry or Responsible-Care principles and, for each, describe how you could apply and follow a comparable principle in your daily activities.

Extending the Concepts

28. In each case a resource was only available from foreign sources that were temporarily restricted.

29. The process is often referred to as *gas sweetening*. A common method involves treating natural gas with amine solutions that dissolve sulfur-containing compounds. Sulfur can also be removed by adsorption with activated charcoal. Sulfur-containing compounds form sulfur oxides (SO_x) when burned in air. These can react with water and contribute to acid rain. $SO_2(g) + H_2O(l) \rightleftharpoons H_2SO_3(aq)$ and $SO_3(g) + H_2O(l) \rightleftharpoons H_2SO_4(aq)$

30. Sample answer: Sulfur is a by-product of petroleum processing. It is used in manufacturing rubber, for agricultural purposes, and in metallurgy.

31. Information sources include **www.webelements.com** and **www.answers.com**.

32. Examples include birth and death rates or money earned and money spent.

33. See **www.epa.gov/tri/**

34. Pressure cookers allow water to be heated to temperatures above its normal boiling point, speeding up "cooking" reactions.

35. Possible answers:

• It is better to prevent waste than to treat or clean up waste. Use glasses, plates, and silverware instead of disposable cups, plates, and cutlery.

• Whenever it is feasible, reactants used and waste generated should be as benign as possible. Use household cleansers that do not harm the environment and that minimize health hazards for users.

25. Challenges include disposing of large volumes of waste; greater hazards to workers due to increased quantities of reactants and products; greater cost due to increased equipment and reactant needs; and modifying processes to increase yield while maintaining profitability.

26. Decreases in temperature reduce rates of spoiling reactions.

27. Nitrogen atoms in a positive oxidation state undergo reduction, so their oxidation state becomes more negative. Carbon atoms in a negative oxidation state undergo oxidation; their oxidation state becomes more positive.

Metal Processing and Electrochemistry

Aluminum, the metal produced by WYE, is reduced from its ore by electrolysis. Students study two types of electrochemical processes—voltaic cells and electrolysis. The conceptual development within this section will help students to understand how electrochemistry affects the chemical industry and their lives.

C.1 Electrolysis and Voltaic Cells

C.1 and C.3 Content Reading Guide

The electrical energy for electrolysis comes from hydroelectric or other power-generating plants. Another source of electricity is voltaic cells, although they would not generate enough electricity for aluminum production.

Electrolytic cells (like those used to reduce aluminum metals) and voltaic cells (like those in batteries) involve opposite processes. Electrolytic cells involve converting electrical energy to chemical energy (to cause a nonspontaneous redox reaction). Voltaic cells involve converting chemical energy (from a spontaneous redox reaction) to electrical energy.

Metal Processing and Electrochemistry

Yᴏᴜ have learned how EKS Nitrogen Products Company produces ammonia using the Haber-Bosch process. Such a chemical plant could affect Riverwood both positively and negatively. You will now learn more about WYE Metals Corporation. Then you will be able to determine whether EKS or WYE (or neither company) should be invited to build a chemical plant near Riverwood.

In producing sheet aluminum, WYE specializes in **electrochemistry,** chemical changes that produce or are caused by electrical energy. The following discussions and laboratory investigation provide background on electrochemistry principles. This information will help you understand how WYE's proposed new plant would operate.

C.1 ELECTROLYSIS AND VOLTAIC CELLS

WYE Metals Corporation proposes to produce aluminum metal using oxidation–reduction methods. Because aluminum is the most abundant metallic element in Earth's crust, such production might sound easy. However, aluminum in Earth's crust is not found in its elemental form. Instead it is found in clay soils and is industrially extracted from the ore bauxite (Figure 5.29), in which aluminum ions (Al^{3+}) are strongly bonded to other atoms. Extraction of aluminum metal involves **electrolysis,** in which passing an electrical current through a solution of ions (an **electrolyte**) causes a chemical reaction. In this case, the flow of electrons reduces Al^{3+} ions in the electrolyte to aluminum metal, $Al(s)$ (Figure 5.30).

Electrolysis requires considerable electrical energy, so the cost of electricity is a factor in plant location. The hydroelectric plant at the Snake River Dam generates considerably more electricity than needed by Riverwood and its surrounding communities. To encourage WYE Corporation to consider locating in Riverwood, power company officials have offered WYE large quantities of electrical power at very competitive rates.

In Unit 2, Investigating Matter B.5 (page 142), you learned that some metals lose electrons (become oxidized) more readily than others; that is, some metals are more chemically active than others. The relative tendencies of metals to release electrons can be summarized in the *activity series* of metals (see Table 5.3). A metal higher in the activity series will give up electrons more readily than will a metal that is lower. For example, according to Table 5.3, aluminum atoms are oxidized (lose electrons) more easily than are iron atoms.

Connecting two metals from different positions on the activity series in a voltaic cell creates an electrical potential between the

Figure 5.29 *Aluminum metal can be obtained from bauxite, an aluminum-containing ore. Bauxite is a mixture mainly of aluminum oxides and aluminum hydroxides.*

Figure 5.30 *Aluminum ingots are produced by an oxidation–reduction process.*

Figure 5.31 A voltaic cell

The activity series, introduced in Unit 2, is used as a point of reference to decide on the ease of metal oxidation. In Unit 2, students learned that metals higher on the activity series are more reactive than those lower on the activity series. In this unit, students make the connection between a metal's activity and the ease of its oxidation.

Using the Figures

Figures 5.29 and 5.30: Use these photos to illustrate that compounds of an element can have drastically different physical properties from those of the pure element. Bauxite (in Figure 5.29) certainly appears different in color and texture from aluminum (Figure 5.30). Encourage students to think of other physical properties that might differ (conductivity, melting point, boiling point, etc.).

C.1 Supplement: Electrochemical Changes

ACTIVITY SERIES OF COMMON METALS

Metal	Products of Metal Reactivity
Li(s)	$\longrightarrow$ Li$^+$(aq) + e^-
Na(s)	$\longrightarrow$ Na$^+$(aq) + e^-
Mg(s)	$\longrightarrow$ Mg^{2+}(aq) + 2 e^-
Al(s)	$\longrightarrow$ Al^{3+}(aq) + 3 e^-
Mn(s)	$\longrightarrow$ Mn^{2+}(aq) + 2 e^-
Zn(s)	$\longrightarrow$ Zn^{2+}(aq) + 2 e^-
Cr(s)	$\longrightarrow$ Cr^{3+}(aq) + 3 e^-
Fe(s)	$\longrightarrow$ Fe^{2+}(aq) + 2 e^-
Ni(s)	$\longrightarrow$ Ni^{2+}(aq) + 2 e^-
Sn(s)	$\longrightarrow$ Sn^{2+}(aq) + 2 e^-
Pb(s)	$\longrightarrow$ Pb^{2+}(aq) + 2 e^-
Cu(s)	$\longrightarrow$ Cu^{2+}(aq) + 2 e^-
Ag(s)	$\longrightarrow$ Ag$^+$(aq) + e^-
Au(s)	$\longrightarrow$ Au^{3+}(aq) + 3 e^-

Table 5.3 *The higher a metal is positioned in the activity series, the more readily it can give up one or more electrons, as shown.*

 Using the Metal Activity Series

 Constructing a Voltaic Cell

Electrolysis uses electrical energy to cause a nonspontaneous reaction. A voltaic cell generates electrical energy through a spontaneous reaction.

metals. Electrical potential (volts) is somewhat like water pressure in a pipe. Just as pressure causes water to flow in the pipe, **electrical potential** "pushes" electrons through the wire connecting the two metals. The greater the difference between the chemical activities of the two metals, the greater the electrical potential that the cell generates.

The differing tendency of metals to lose electrons allows an oxidation–reduction reaction to generate electrical energy. You can make a simple device called a **voltaic cell** from two half-cells connected in a circuit (see Figure 5.31). Each **half-cell** contains a metal partially immersed in a solution of ions of that metal. For example, one half-cell could contain copper metal immersed in a solution of Cu^{2+} ions. Another could contain a piece of zinc metal immersed in a solution of Zn^{2+} ions. You know from Unit 2, page 142, that the oxidation–reduction reaction between Cu^{2+} and Zn readily occurs. By separating these reactants into half-cells, the electrons are forced to flow through a wire and provide electrical energy to an external circuit.

A barrier prevents the solutions in the two half-cells from mixing. A wire connects the two metals, which act as **electrodes,** and allows electrons to flow between them, as shown in Figure 5.31. Such an electron flow constitutes an **electric current.** To complete the circuit and maintain a balance of electrical charges within the system, the two half-cells must be connected by a **salt bridge.** Dissolved ions in the salt bridge complete the internal electrical circuit by allowing ions to move freely between the half-cells, preventing build up of electrical charge near the electrodes. Without the flow of ions, a positive electrical charge would build up in one half-cell and a negative electrical charge would build up in the other half-cell. That situation would prevent any further flow of electrons in the wire.

Section C Metal Processing and Electrochemistry **453**

SECTION C

Investigating Matter

C.2 Voltaic Cells Student Worksheet and Data Table

C.2 Voltaic Cells

In this investigation, students construct and test several electrochemical cells. This investigation applies oxidation–reduction concepts to the generation of electrical energy.

Time

50 min

Materials

(For 12 student pairs)

12 24-well wellplates

48 Beral pipets

50 mL 0.1 M copper(II) nitrate [1.2 g Cu(NO₃)₂·3H₂O/50 mL sol'n]

50 mL 0.1 M zinc nitrate [1.5 g Zn(NO₃)₂·6H₂O/50 mL sol'n]

50 mL 0.1 M magnesium nitrate [1.3 g Mg(NO₃)₂·6H₂O/50 mL sol'n]

50 mL 0.1 M iron(III) nitrate [2.02 g Fe(NO₃)₃·9H₂O/50 mL sol'n]

12 wide copper strips (1 cm × 3 cm × 0.1 mm)

2 medium copper strips (0.5 cm × 3 cm × 0.1 mm)

12 narrow copper strips (0.25 cm × 3 cm × 0.1 mm)

12 wide zinc strips (1.0 cm × 3 cm × 0.25 mm)

12 medium zinc strips (0.5 cm × 3 cm × 0.25 mm)

12 narrow zinc strips (0.25 cm × 3 cm × 0.25 mm)

12 3-cm lengths of magnesium ribbon

12 iron strips, 0.5 cm × 3 cm (or small iron nails)

12 voltmeters

24 small alligator clips with fine wire leads

36 strips of filter paper, 8 mm × 3 cm

Saturated KNO₃ solution (about 35 g/100 mL water)

Investigating Matter

C.2 VOLTAIC CELLS

In this investigation, you will construct several voltaic cells and measure and compare the electrical potentials that they generate. You will also explore factors that may help determine the actual electrical potential a particular voltaic cell generates.

Lab Video:
Voltaic Cells

Procedure

Part I: Constructing a Voltaic Cell

(Figure 5.32 shows a completed cell.)

1. Add 1 mL of 0.1 M Cu(NO₃)₂ to one well in a wellplate.
2. Add 1 mL of 0.1 M Zn(NO₃)₂ to an adjacent well.
3. Clean strips of Cu and Zn with steel wool.
4. Add a Cu strip (electrode) to the well containing Cu(NO₃)₂ solution.
5. Add a Zn strip (electrode) to the well containing Zn(NO₃)₂ solution.
6. Drape a small strip of filter paper saturated with KNO₃ solution between the wells containing the two solutions. Ensure that each end of the filter paper strip is immersed in one of the two solutions. Do not allow the metal strips to touch each other or the filter paper.

Figure 5.32 *The voltaic cells you will complete resemble the one depicted here. Voltaic cells result in spontaneous flow of electrons from the metal of higher activity to ions of the less-active metal.*

7. Obtain a voltmeter and two insulated wires with alligator clips connected at each end. Attach one end of each wire to a separate voltmeter terminal.
8. Attach one wire from the voltmeter to the copper electrode. Lightly touch the second wire to the zinc electrode. If the needle deflects in the direction of a positive potential or if the digital readout is positive, attach the second clip to the zinc metal. If the needle deflects in a negative direction (or the readout value is negative), reverse the clip connections to the electrodes.
9. Record the electrical potential indicated by the voltmeter.

Safety

Students should wear protective goggles and aprons throughout the investigation.

Advance Preparation

Prepare the solutions. Label and fill Beral pipets with the appropriate solutions. Place them in a wellplate (or cassette tape case) with tips up. Soak filter-paper strips in saturated KNO₃ solution to make salt bridges.

Lab Tips

• If using analog meters, remind students to avoid allowing the voltmeter needle to deflect in a negative direction for any length of time; this damages the meter. You may wish to

Part II: Measuring Electrical Potentials

10. Using what you learned in Part I about building a voltaic cell, construct additional cells and measure electrical potentials generated by voltaic cells composed of all possible combinations of the half-cells listed below. (See Figure 5.33.) Record your data.

    a. 0.1 M Cu(NO₃)₂ and Cu strip
    b. 0.1 M Zn(NO₃)₂ and Zn strip
    c. 0.1 M Mg(NO₃)₂ and Mg strip
    d. 0.1 M Fe(NO₃)₂ and Fe sample (a nail)

Part III: Investigating Electrode Size Effects

11. Based on Parts I and II, design a laboratory investigation, accompanied by an appropriate data table, to explore whether an electrode's size influences the total electrical potential (volts) generated by a cell and, if so, how you can describe that effect. Base your design on copper and zinc metal electrodes of different widths: 0.25 cm (narrow), 0.50 cm (medium), and 1.0 cm (wide).

12. Set up and conduct your investigation. Record your data.

13. Dispose of your experimental materials as directed by your teacher.

14. Wash your hands thoroughly before leaving the laboratory.

Questions

1. a. In Part II, you constructed voltaic cells using copper and three other metals: zinc, magnesium, and iron. List these cells in order of decreasing electrical potential (highest cell potential first).
   b. Explain the resulting list in terms of the relative activities of the metals involved.

2. Would the electrical potential generated by cells composed of each of the following pairs of metals be larger or smaller than that of the Zn–Cu cell? Refer to Table 5.3 (page 453).

   a. Zn and Cr   b. Zn and Ag   c. Sn and Cu

3. How did changing the size of the zinc and copper electrodes affect the measured electrical potential? Explain and provide evidence supporting your answer.

4. Could an Ag–Au cell serve as a commercially feasible voltaic cell? Explain and provide evidence for your answer.

Figure 5.33 *Representative metal electrodes used in this investigation.*

Maximizing the Electrical Potenial

they generate the greatest cell potential.

2. a. Smaller b. Greater c. Smaller

3. Size change has no observable effect. Students should refer to voltmeter readings as evidence.

4. No. There is not much difference in the tendencies of silver and gold to lose electrons. The battery would also be very expensive.

Post-Lab Discussion

Ask students to formulate a conclusion from their data about factors affecting electrical potential. Although groups' results may differ slightly, the rank orders should be the same. The activity series places elements in order of decreasing tendency to lose electrons, so results reported are consistent with the elements' arrangement in the activity series. Mg loses electrons more readily than does Zn, which, in turn, loses electrons more readily than does Fe. Ensure that students understand that in a voltaic cell, electrons flow spontaneously from one metal to another. The greater the electrical potential (potential difference), the more volts generated by the cell.

EXPECTED RESULTS		
NEGATIVE LEAD	**POSITIVE LEAD**	**VOLTS**
Medium Cu	Mg	2.7
Medium Cu	medium Zn	1.1
Medium Cu	Fe	0.8
Narrow Cu	Mg	2.7
Narrow Cu	narrow Zn	1.1
Narrow Cu	Fe	0.8
Wide Cu	Mg	2.7
Wide Cu	wide Zn	1.1
Wide Cu	Fe	0.8

acquaint students with various features of voltmeters prior to the investigation.

• Remind students that electrical potentials varying by several hundredths of a volt are really the same. This may present a prime opportunity to discuss measurements, significant digits, and error.

• Remind students to clean and rinse the wellplates immediately after using. The used metals may be collected in an appropriately labeled container.

Answers

1. a. Mg/Cu, Zn/Cu, and Fe/Cu
   b. Mg, Zn, and Fe are all above Cu in the activity series, so they lose electrons more readily than Cu. Mg and Cu have the greatest difference in electronegativity, so

C.3 Voltaic Cells and Half-Reactions

A voltaic cell allows the chemical energy of a spontaneous oxidation–reduction reaction to do electrical work. Voltaic cells are made from various combinations of metals and ions. The metals and ions used in specific voltaic cells, in part, are selected based on differences in their relative tendencies to lose electrons. The greater the difference between the reactivity (or relative ease of oxidation) of the two metals, the greater the tendency for electrons to move between them, and the greater the electrical potential generated. Use this opportunity to encourage students to reflect on the activity series and their results from *Investigating Matter C.2*. They should be able to see the relationship between volts generated and the relative proximity of participating metals on the activity series.

Volts and *voltaic cells* are named for the Italian scientist Alessandro Volta (1745–1827). He was one of the first to construct cells of this type. The term *galvanic cell* is often used interchangeably with *voltaic cells*. *Galvanic cells* are named for Luigi Galvani (1737–1798), another Italian scientist who completed some of the earliest research on electricity.

TV Ontario videos on electrochemistry contain useful segments about electrochemical cells (both lab- and industrial-scale) and related topics. See the *ChemCom* CD-ROM for an activity related to voltaic cells.

One way to remember these electrode processes: Note that **a**node and its associated process (**o**xidation) both begin with vowels, while **c**athode and its process (**r**eduction) both start with consonants.

Figure 5.34 **RED**uction always occurs at the **CAT**hode.

Developing Skills

C.3 VOLTAIC CELLS AND HALF-REACTIONS

In the voltaic cells you constructed in the laboratory, each metal immersed in a solution of its ions represented a half-cell. The activity series predicts that zinc is more likely to be oxidized (lose electrons) than copper. Thus, in the zinc–copper cell you investigated, oxidation (electron loss) occurred in the half-cell with zinc metal immersed in zinc nitrate solution. Reduction (electron gain) took place in the half-cell of copper metal in copper(II) nitrate solution. The half-reactions (individual electron-transfer steps) for that cell are:

$$\text{Oxidation half-reaction: } Zn(s) \longrightarrow Zn^{2+}(aq) + 2\ e^-$$

$$\text{Reduction half-reaction: } Cu^{2+}(aq) + 2\ e^- \longrightarrow Cu(s)$$

The electrode at which oxidation takes place is the *anode*. Reduction occurs at the *cathode*. (See Figure 5.34.)

The overall reaction in the zinc–copper voltaic cell is the sum of the two half-reactions, added so that the electrical charges balance—the total electrons lost and gained are the same—resulting in a net electrical charge of zero.

$$Zn(s) \longrightarrow Zn^{2+}(aq) + 2\ \cancel{e^-}$$
$$Cu^{2+}(aq) + 2\ \cancel{e^-} \longrightarrow Cu(s)$$
$$\overline{Zn(s) + Cu^{2+}(aq) \longrightarrow Zn^{2+}(aq) + Cu(s)}$$

Because a barrier separates the two reactants (Zn and Cu^{2+}) in the cell, the electrons released by zinc must travel through the external wire to reach (and reduce) the copper ions.

The greater the difference in the reactivity of the two metals in a voltaic cell, the greater the tendency for electron transfer to occur, and the greater the electrical potential (volts) of the cell. A zinc–gold voltaic cell, therefore, would generate a larger electrical potential than a zinc–copper cell. (See Table 5.3, page 453, to compare the placement of these metals in the activity series.)

C.4 GETTING CHARGED BY ELECTROCHEMISTRY

Each of the following questions deals with voltaic cells, their properties, and equations to describe them.

Sample Problem: *Consider a voltaic cell containing lead metal (Pb) immersed in lead(II) nitrate solution, $Pb(NO_3)_2$, and a half-cell containing silver metal (Ag) in silver nitrate solution, $AgNO_3$.*

    a. *Predict the direction of electron flow in the wire connecting the two metals.*

    b. *Write equations for the two half-reactions and the overall reaction.*

    c. *Which metal is the anode and which is the cathode?*

✎ **C.3 Supplement: Half-Reactions**

The answers are as follows:

a. Table 5.3 (page 453) shows that lead is a more active metal than is silver. Therefore, lead will be oxidized, and electrons will flow from lead to silver.

b. One half-reaction involves forming Pb^{2+} from Pb, as shown in Table 5.3. The other half-reaction produces Ag from Ag^+, which can be written by reversing the equation in Table 5.3 and doubling it so electrons lost and gained are the same:

$$Pb(s) \longrightarrow Pb^{2+}(aq) + 2e^-$$
$$2\,Ag^+(aq) + 2e^- \longrightarrow 2\,Ag(s)$$
$$\overline{Pb(s) + 2\,Ag^+(aq) \longrightarrow Pb^{2+}(aq) + 2\,Ag(s)}$$

c. In the cell reaction, each Pb atom loses two electrons. Pb is therefore oxidized, making it the anode. Each Ag^+ ion gains one electron; a reduction reaction. Because reduction takes place at the cathode, Ag must be the cathode.

Now answer the following questions.

1. Predict the direction of electron flow in a voltaic cell made from each specified pair of metals partially immersed in solutions of their ions.
   a. Al and Sn
   b. Pb and Mg
   c. Cu and Fe

2. A voltaic cell uses tin (Sn) and cadmium (Cd) as the electrodes. The overall equation for the cell reaction is as follows:

   $$Sn^{2+}(aq) + Cd(s) \longrightarrow Cd^{2+}(aq) + Sn(s)$$

   a. Write the two half-reaction equations for this cell.
   b. Which metal, Sn or Cd, loses electrons more readily?

3. Sketch a voltaic cell composed of a $Ni\text{–}Ni(NO_3)_2$ half-cell linked to a $Cu\text{–}Cu(NO_3)_2$ half-cell.

4. For each voltaic cell designated below, identify the anode and the cathode. Assume that each voltaic cell uses appropriate ionic solutions.
   a. Cu–Zn cell
   b. Al–Zn cell
   c. Mg–Mn cell
   d. Au–Ni cell

> The total electrons consumed in reduction equals the total electrons liberated in oxidation. Overall, the voltaic cell based on these two half-reactions involves twice as many silver ions reduced as lead atoms oxidized.

Developing Skills

C.4 Getting Charged by Electrochemistry

In this activity, students apply their understanding of redox reactions to electrochemical cells. Help students to see that electrochemical cells involve redox reactions without becoming overwhelmed by details. Remind them to refer to **Table 5.3** (page 453) to determine which metal is more active (and therefore easier to oxidize).

Answers

1. a. From Al to Sn
   b. From Mg to Pb
   c. From Fe to Cu
2. a. $Sn^{2+}(aq) + 2\,e^- \longrightarrow Sn(s)$ (reduction)
   $Cd(s) \longrightarrow Cd^{2+}(aq) + 2\,e^-$ (oxidation)
   b. Cd loses electrons more readily.
3. Drawings should resemble **Figure 5.31** (page 453), but with $Ni\text{—}Ni(NO_3)_2$ and $Cu\text{—}Cu(NO_3)_2$.
4. a. Anode = Zn, cathode = Cu
   b. Anode = Al, cathode = Zn
   c. Anode = Mg, cathode = Mn
   d. Anode = Ni, cathode = Au

C.5 Batteries

Dry cells and alkaline batteries are discussed. You can create a display of dissected batteries for students. **Caution:** Do not let students touch caustic and corrosive materials in the batteries.

You can remind students that the voltaic cells constructed in *Investigating Matter C.2* (page 454) were cells that generated electricity. This electricity, measured by volt-meters, could do useful work, such as lighting a small bulb or light-emitting diode. You may demon-strate this by inserting a small light-bulb into the circuit of a voltaic cell set up during the activity. Then point out that batteries are portable voltaic cells that produce electricity used in cars, radios, telephones, and cordless devices.

Volta invented the first battery in 1799. This battery consisted of a stack of alternating disks of Zn and Cu with each pair separated by a salt-water soaked cloth. A wire was attached to either end.

People use lithium ion batteries in laptops, cellular telephones, radios, and other portable devices. These batteries can provide more electrical potential than a NiCad bat-tery of the same size. The anode is often graphite-based, and the cath-ode may be lithium oxide. The elec-trolyte contains lithium ions. Like NiCad batteries, they are recharge-able. Technology for this type of bat-tery continues to evolve. Lithium metal batteries are also available, but they can be hazardous. Challenge students to come up with the chemi-cal reason behind hazards of lithium metal batteries. Students should connect the hazards with the reac-tivity of lithium.

458

$$2\,MnO_2 + H_2O + 2\,e^- \longrightarrow Mn_2O_3 + 2\,OH^-$$

Graphite rod ⎫
MnO₂ paste ⎬ Cathode

KOH paste

Zinc can (Anode)

$$Zn + 2\,OH^- \longrightarrow Zn(OH)_2 + 2\,e^-$$

Figure 5.35 *An alkaline battery. What substances are contained in this fresh alkaline battery? How will those substances change as the battery is used?*

C.5 BATTERIES

Voltaic cells are a convenient way to convert chemical energy to electrical energy. The cells can fit in small, portable containers. We can use various combinations of metals and ions to make commercial voltaic cells. In ordinary *dry cells*—often called *batteries*—zinc is the anode, and a graphite rod surrounded by a water-based paste of manganese(IV) oxide (MnO_2) and graphite serves as the cathode. A mixture of ammonium chloride and zinc chloride in an aqueous paste serves as the electrolyte. Alkaline batteries, common in portable music players, have similar zinc and graphite–MnO_2 electrodes, but the electrolyte is an alkaline (basic) aqueous potassium hydroxide (KOH) electrolyte paste. See Figure 5.35.

Both zinc–MnO_2 dry cells and alkaline bat-teries generate an electrical potential of 1.54 V. The following oxidation–reduction equations describe the chemical changes involved.

Dry Cell

Oxidation: $\qquad\qquad Zn(s) \longrightarrow Zn^{2+}(aq) + 2\,e^-$

Reduction: $2\,MnO_2(s) + 2\,NH_4^+(aq) + 2\,e^- \longrightarrow 2\,MnO(OH)(s) + 2\,NH_3(g)$

Overall: $Zn(s) + 2\,MnO_2(s) + 2\,NH_4^+(aq) \longrightarrow Zn^{2+}(aq) + 2\,MnO(OH)(s) + 2\,NH_3(g)$

Alkaline Battery

Oxidation: $\qquad Zn(s) + 2\,OH^-(aq) \longrightarrow Zn(OH)_2(s) + 2\,e^-$

Reduction: $2\,MnO_2(s) + H_2O(l) + 2\,e^- \longrightarrow Mn_2O_3(s) + 2\,OH^-(aq)$

Overall: $Zn(s) + 2\,MnO_2(s) + H_2O(l) \longrightarrow Zn(OH)_2(s) + Mn_2O_3(s)$

ChemQuandary 2

BATTERY SIZES

Each battery in this photo gener-ates the same electrical potential, 1.5 V. So why does anyone need 1.5-V batteries larger than the smallest one? Wouldn't it save space, weight, and perhaps even resources to restrict consumer use to the smallest batteries?

C.5 Content Reading Guide

Dry cells and alkaline batteries are called *primary batteries.* They generate electrical potential only as long as all starting materials (reactants) remain. When the limiting reactant (see Unit 4, page 353) is depleted, primary batteries cannot be recharged.

By contrast, nickel–cadmium (NiCad) and automobile batteries are rechargeable; we can return their systems to their original states and thus reuse the batteries. The common NiCad rechargeable battery is based on a nickel–iron battery that Thomas Edison developed in the early 1900s. The NiCad battery anode is cadmium, and the cathode is nickel oxide. These electrodes have a rolled design (Figure 5.36) that increases surface area and, thus, increases the generated current (electron flow).

When this battery operates, Cd and NiO_2 are converted to $Cd(OH)_2(s)$ and $Ni(OH)_2(s)$. These solid products cling to the electrodes, allowing them to convert back to reactants when you connect the used battery in a recharging circuit. In recharging, an external electrical potential causes electrons to flow in the opposite direction, thus reversing the reaction (see Figure 5.37). Although you can recharge NiCad batteries many times, some of the same processes that prevent recharging of primary batteries can take their toll and eventually reduce the efficiency of recharging.

Figure 5.36 *Cross-section of a NiCad battery.*

Cathode (NiO₂)   Anode (Cd)
         Separator

NiCad batteries should be recycled to prevent the cadmium, which is toxic, from leaching into groundwater.

Scientific American Conceptual Illustration

Figure 5.37 Rechargeable batteries. *When a nickel-metal hydride (NiMH) battery is recharged, the charging circuit removes electrons (red) from the positive electrode (green) composed of nickel(II) hydroxide. This process oxidizes the Ni^{2+} to Ni^{3+}. Electrons are supplied to the negative electrode (blue). This causes a hydrogen-absorbing metal alloy to become reduced. When this battery is discharged during use, electron flow is reversed. The nickel(II) hydroxide gains electrons, while the metal hydride loses electrons.*

Using the Figures

Figure 5.35: This cross-section of an alkaline battery, along with the half-reactions, should help students visualize how batteries work and what happens when batteries "die." As the battery is used, solid films of Mn_2O_3 and $Zn(OH)_2$ form at the cathode and anode, respectively. Eventually, the amount of reactant (for each half-reaction) will diminish, and the reactions shown will no longer be possible. The flow of electrons ceases.

ChemQuandary 2

Battery Sizes

Different applications require batteries of various sizes. Powering a lightweight radio for jogging will be different from powering a large wall clock. Also, some applications may need greater total capacity (battery hours times load current), which a larger battery can provide.

Scientific American Working Knowledge Illustration

Follow the electron-flow arrows with students in each illustration (charging and discharging). These equations describe the half-reactions and overall reactions involved in discharging a NiMH battery:

$$NiOOH + H_2O + e^- \longrightarrow Ni(OH)_2 + OH^-$$

$$MH + OH^- \longrightarrow M + H_2O + e^-$$

$$MH + NiOOH \longrightarrow M + Ni(OH)_2$$
(overall E = 1.35 V)

Using the Figures

Figure 5.38: Students should be familiar with the concept of energy conversions from Unit 3. In a car, the original source of energy to recharge the battery is combustion of gasoline. This is converted to mechanical energy within the engine; some of the mechanical energy is then converted to electrical energy that causes electrons to flow back through the battery, regenerating Pb and PbO_2. The product of the half-reactions at both the anode and the cathode of this battery is $PbSO_4$. At the anode, elemental lead is oxidized in the production of $PbSO_4$. At the cathode, PbO_2 is reduced to form $PbSO_4$. Because it can exist in multiple oxidation states, lead is involved in both half-reactions.

Lead-acid batteries are found in trucks, aircraft, motorcycles, self-starting lawnmowers, and motorized golf carts.

A 12-V automobile battery, known as a *lead-acid battery*, is composed of a series of six electrochemical cells. As illustrated in Figure 5.38, each cell consists of an anode of uncoated lead (Pb) plates and a cathode of lead plates coated with lead(IV) oxide (PbO_2). The electrodes are immersed in a dilute solution of sulfuric acid (H_2SO_4), the electrolyte in this system.

When the vehicle's ignition is turned on, the electrical circuit is completed. As electrons travel from one electrode to the other, they provide energy for the car's electrical systems. Metallic lead at the anode is oxidized to Pb^{2+}. The freed electrons travel through the wire to the lead(IV) oxide cathode, reducing Pb^{4+} in PbO_2 to Pb^{2+}. Lead ions (Pb^{2+}) produced at both electrodes then form $PbSO_4$ by reacting with the electrolyte, as shown in the following equations.

Oxidation: $\qquad\qquad Pb(s) + SO_4^{2-}(aq) \longrightarrow PbSO_4(s) + 2\,e^-$

Reduction: $\quad PbO_2(s) + SO_4^{2-}(aq) + 4\,H^+(aq) + 2\,e^- \longrightarrow PbSO_4(s) + 2\,H_2O(l)$

Overall: $\quad PbO_2(s) + Pb(s) + 4\,H^+(aq) + 2\,SO_4^{2-}(aq) \longrightarrow 2\,PbSO_4(s) + 2\,H_2O(l)$

You can sometimes recognize a run-down or dead car battery by observing layers of solid white $PbSO_4$ coating the electrodes.

If an automobile battery is used too long without being recharged, it runs down; that is, the redox reaction stops. Lead(II) sulfate eventually coats the electrodes, which reduces their ability to react and produce a current and electrical potential. In an automobile, recharging is accomplished by an alternator or generator, which converts some mechanical energy from the vehicle's engine into electrical energy that forces electrons to move in the opposite direction through the battery. This reverses the direction of the battery's chemical reactions (see Figure 5.38).

Figure 5.38
Discharging and recharging an automobile battery. What furnishes the energy to recharge this battery?

DISCHARGING

PbO_2 (cathode):
$PbO_2(s) + SO_4^{2-}(aq) + 4\,H^+(aq) + 2\,e^- \longrightarrow PbSO_4(s) + 2\,H_2O(l)$

Pb (anode):
$Pb(s) + SO_4^{2-}(aq) \longrightarrow PbSO_4(s) + 2\,e^-$

CHARGING

PbO_2 (anode):
$PbSO_4(s) + 2\,H_2O(l) \longrightarrow PbO_2(s) + SO_4^{2-}(aq) + 4\,H^+(aq) + 2\,e^-$

Pb (cathode):
$PbSO_4(s) + 2\,e^- \longrightarrow Pb(s) + SO_4^{2-}(aq)$

Lead-acid batteries can pose dangers if rapidly charged by an outside source of electrical energy. Hydrogen gas, formed by the reduction of H^+ in the acidic electrolyte, is released at the lead electrode. A spark or flame can ignite the hydrogen gas, causing an explosion. This is one reason you must be careful to avoid sparks when using jumper cables to start a vehicle with a dead battery.

C.6 INDUSTRIAL ELECTROCHEMISTRY

Chlorine and Sodium Hydroxide Production

One economically significant application of electrolysis in the chemical industry is the *chlor-alkali process*. In this process, sodium chloride dissolved in water (a solution known as *brine*) is electrolyzed, producing chlorine gas (Cl_2) at the anode and hydrogen gas (H_2) at the cathode (Figure 5.39). Positive sodium ions and negative hydroxide ions remain in solution. The hydroxide ions replace the chloride ions lost from the brine as chlorine gas, thus maintaining the charge balance, as shown by the following equation:

Electrical energy + $2\ Na^+(aq) + 2\ Cl^-(aq) + 2\ H_2O(l) \longrightarrow 2\ Na^+(aq) + 2\ OH^-(aq) + H_2(g) + Cl_2(g)$

This electrolysis reaction generates three widely produced industrial substances: hydrogen gas, chlorine gas, and sodium hydroxide.

We can use the hydrogen gas and chlorine gas produced in the chlor-alkali process without additional purification because no other gases are released by this reaction. We must purify the sodium hydroxide because it remains in solution with unreacted sodium chloride.

Figure 5.39 *Electrolysis of aqueous NaCl to produce $H_2(g)$, $Cl_2(g)$, and NaOH(aq).*

From: Kotz, J.C. and Treichel, P.: *Chemistry & Chemical Reactivity*, Saunders College Publishing, Fort Worth, TX, 1999.

C.6 Industrial Electrochemistry

This material focuses on the electrolysis of brine (aqueous NaCl), and on the industrial production of aluminum using the Hall-Héroult process. Both of these processes involve using electrical energy to cause chemical change. Emphasize that the processes discussed here are virtually the reverse of the process involved in voltaic cells.

The electrolysis of brine is discussed first. Chlorine gas produced by this process is mainly used for producing polyvinyl chloride (PVC), inorganic compounds, and chloromethanes (common organic solvents). Sodium hydroxide (also known as *caustic soda*) is used to produce organics, soaps, bleach, and mineral oils. The products should be common to student experience. Refer students to **Table 5.2** (page 445). Have them locate both chlorine and sodium hydroxide among the top 25 chemical substances produced in the United States and thus appreciate the magnitude of the chlor-alkali process.

In the electrolysis of brine, the end product is sodium hydroxide rather than sodium due to the extreme activity of sodium, making it easier to produce sodium hydroxide and hydrogen gas from the reduction of water. To produce sodium metal, molten (*not* aqueous) sodium chloride must undergo electrolysis. Sodium metal is used in synthesizing both organic and inorganic compounds.

The Hall-Héroult process is responsible for many aluminum products—and led to locating aluminum plants near electric power plants. Emphasize that although the scale of operations is vastly different, the same reactions occur on laboratory benches as in industrial plants.

The Bayer process takes bauxite ore, which contains oxides of aluminum, silicon, iron and titanium, and isolates the aluminum oxide (alumina) used as the starting material in the Hall-Héroult process.

Within two months after Hall developed his process, Paul-Louis Héroult, a young French scientist, independently developed the same process. These two workers, linked through their common discovery, also shared the same birth and death years (1863–1914).

Originally, the large industrial electrolysis cells for the chlor-alkali process included mercury cathodes. Before people understood the environmental hazards of metallic mercury, they dumped it into rivers and lakes while renewing the cells. Mercury is no longer used in chlor-alkali cells. Research chemists and chemical engineers modified the chlor-alkali process considerably, replacing both electrodes, and developed new permeable polymer membranes that separate the anode and cathode compartments (Figure 5.39, page 461).

Aluminum Production

The industrial production of aluminum, the focus of WYE Metals Corporation, is another major process that uses electrical energy to produce chemical change. It is very difficult to reduce Al^{3+} held by ore into pure metal, $Al(s)$. Aluminum was first isolated as a metal in the 1820s by an expensive and potentially dangerous process that used highly reactive sodium or potassium metal as the reducing agent. As a result, for more than 60 years, aluminum was very expensive, despite the fact that aluminum is the most plentiful metal ion in Earth's crust. Aluminum was even used in jewelry, including the French crown jewels and the Danish crown. In 1884, a 2.8-kg (6-lb) aluminum cap was installed on top of the Washington Monument in Washington, D.C., as ornamentation and as the tip of a lightning-rod system. At that time, the aluminum cap cost considerably more than did the same mass of silver.

The challenge for industrial users was how to produce aluminum at a much lower cost. No common substance gives up electrons readily enough to reduce aluminum cations to aluminum metal. For example, carbon, an excellent reducing agent for metal compounds such as iron oxide or copper sulfide, cannot reduce aluminum compounds.

A young chemist named Charles Martin Hall solved the problem. In 1886, within a year after graduating from Oberlin College (Ohio), Hall devised a method for reducing aluminum using electricity (Figure 5.40). Hall's breakthrough was in discovering that aluminum oxide (Al_2O_3), which melts at 2000 °C, dissolved in molten cryolite (Na_3AlF_6) at 950 °C. The lower temperature meant that he had found an easier way to get aluminum ions from aluminum ore into solution for electrolysis. Hall's discovery became the basis of a rapidly growing aluminum industry. He founded the Aluminum Company of America (Alcoa) and was a multimillionaire when he died in 1914.

In the Hall-Héroult process, aluminum oxide (bauxite) is dissolved in molten cryolite in a large steel tank lined with carbon. The carbon tank lining is given a negative electrical charge by a source of electrical current. This carbon cathode transfers electrons to aluminum ions, reducing them to molten metal. The molten aluminum sinks to the bottom, where it is periodically drawn off.

The anode, also made of carbon, is oxidized during the reaction. As the reaction consumes the tips of the carbon-rod anodes, the rods are gradually lowered deeper into the molten cryolite bath.

The half-reactions for producing aluminum metal by the Hall-Héroult process are as follows:

$$4 \; Al^{3+}(melt) + 12 \; e^- \longrightarrow 4 \; Al(l)$$

$$3 \; C(s) + 6 \; O^{2-}(melt) \longrightarrow 3 \; CO_2(g) + 12 \; e^-$$

Ions from cryolite carry the electric current in the molten mixture.

Before that industrial process was devised, only about 1000 kg of aluminum was produced annually worldwide. In 1884, one pound of aluminum metal sold for about $12, a significant sum in those days. Within three years of their discovery, Hall and Héroult each started commercial operations, creating a worldwide aluminum production rate of one million tons annually by the turn of the 20th century (see Figure 5.41, page 464). The price of aluminum plummeted. Five years after large-scale production started, aluminum sold for 70 cents per pound. Thus, this process opened doors for wide-ranging uses of aluminum: from beverage cans and stepladders to foil wrap and aircraft components.

The designation "(melt)" indicates that at very high cryolite temperatures, ions in the bauxite can dissolve and thus are free to move within the molten material.

Figure 5.40 *The Hall-Héroult process for producing aluminum.*

Section C   Metal Processing and Electrochemistry   **463**

C.7 Moving Toward Greener Methods

The chemical industry is obliged to produce useful products or services while causing as little damage as possible to the environment and to public health. Independent outside organizations monitor compliance with industry standards. An international program (ISO 14000) is in the process of developing a single set of environmental-management system standards that will be implemented worldwide. As responsible citizens, students should know the risks and benefits associated with the chemical industry and weigh those risks and benefits to make wise decisions.

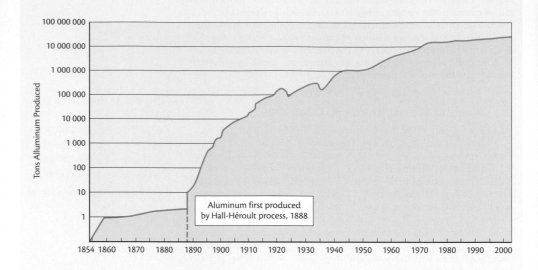

Figure 5.41 *Worldwide aluminum production.*

More than 10 billion kilograms (over 22 billion pounds) of aluminum are produced in the United States each year, requiring about $2 billion worth of electrical energy (about 20 cents per kilogram of aluminum metal produced). Because aluminum plants use such large quantities of electricity, they are often located near sources of hydroelectric power. Electricity from hydropower generally costs less than that generated from the combustion of fossil fuels. Many U.S. aluminum plants are located in the Pacific Northwest because of the hydroelectric power sources there. WYE Metals Corporation is interested in Riverwood due to the availability of hydroelectric power and the town's proximity to aluminum-ore sources.

C.7 MOVING TOWARD GREENER METHODS

As you learned earlier in this unit, industries, governments, and citizens in the United States and elsewhere have recognized their joint responsibility to ensure that chemical products are manufactured with maximum benefit and minimum risk to society. The EPA's Design for Environment program, which includes Green Chemistry (pages 446–447), has already influenced the way chemical-processing, printing, and dry-cleaning industries conduct business.

The chemical industry has developed new synthesis methods based on using safe starting materials to replace toxic or environmentally unsafe substances. Green Chemistry focuses on preventing environmental pollution directly at the point of manufacturing. In this approach, and in others such as Responsible Care (page 447), the chemical industry works as a social partner to sustain development and international trade without damaging the environment.

New Green Chemistry-based processes use more environmentally benign reactants than do traditional processes and create waste products that are less damaging to the air and water. For example, chemical processes can now use D-glucose, ordinary table sugar, to replace benzene, a known carcinogen. The D-glucose serves as a raw material for synthesizing other reactants that are used to produce nylon and various medicinal drugs. Also, in some processes, chemists can substitute nontoxic food dyes for catalysts composed of toxic metals such as lead, chromium, and cadmium.

Isocyanates are substances used to make polyurethanes, which in turn are used to produce seat cushions, insulation, and contact lenses. Carbon dioxide can replace phosgene, a toxic gas, in manufacturing isocyanates. Green Chemistry has led to methods for synthesizing industrial chemicals using water as a solvent instead of toxic alternatives, whenever possible, and for employing materials that can be recycled and reused, thus significantly reducing waste-disposal problems.

The chemical industry has the responsibility to make products in ways that are as hazard-free as possible. The chemical industry must deal honestly with the public to ensure that people clearly understand risks and benefits of chemical operations. Chemistry companies also must assure consumers that their products are safe when used as intended.

Chemical industries must comply with relevant laws and regulations, as well as with voluntary standards set by many manufacturers themselves. Independent, outside organizations, such as the International Organization for Standardization (ISO) in Geneva, Switzerland, encourage worldwide compliance.

No initiatives of the chemical industry or the government can eliminate all risks involved in manufacturing chemical substances, any more than we can completely eliminate the risks of automobile travel. However, knowing the risks, continuing to explore the sources of and alternatives to those risks, and prudent decision making all remain essential.

As users of the industry's chemical products, all consumers share these responsibilities. Having studied some basic concepts about the manufacturing of chemical products, you can now turn to using such knowledge to weigh risks and benefits of particular decisions—to you, to the community, and to the environment.

In 1998, the occupational injury and illnesses rate of the U.S. chemical industry was less than half that of U.S. manufacturing industries as a whole.

C.8 Asset or Liability?

The main purpose of this activity is not just to challenge students to make a decision about the proposed plants; it also is to encourage students to consider issues affecting their decisions about chemical plants in Riverwood and to consider possible outcomes of those decisions. The text provides extensive information on several such issues. Encourage students to think of others and to offer explanations.

One way to organize this exercise is on a 2 × 2 matrix labeled as "high priority" and "low priority" vertically and "unlikely occurrence" and "likely occurrence" horizontally. Students can plot each factor on this matrix. This exercise can be done individually, followed by class sharing. Another option is to complete the entire activity in small groups or in a whole-class discussion.

Making Decisions

C.8 ASSET OR LIABILITY?

If you were a Riverwood citizen, what would be your view? Should the town invite a chemical plant to locate in Riverwood? On what basis should such a decision be made?

To clarify this challenge, it is helpful to consider and evaluate both benefits and burdens—positive and negative factors—associated with any choice. Then you will be ready to address key questions that confront Riverwood citizens as they decide on their choices.

Positive Factors

▶ The Riverwood economy would improve. Either plant would employ about 200 local residents. This would add about $8 million to Riverwood's economy annually. In addition, each plant employee would indirectly provide jobs for another four people in local businesses. This is very desirable because 15% of Riverwood's labor force of 21 000 is currently unemployed.

▶ Farming costs might go down. Each year farmers in the Riverwood area spread 700 tons of fertilizer (see Figure 5.42). The fertilizer comes from a fertilizer plant 200 miles away. Transport costs increase farmers' expenses by $15 for each ton of ammonia-based fertilizer. Local farmers thus stand to save about $10 000 annually in transportation costs.

Figure 5.42 *Fertilizers used to increase yields of farm crops are cost-effective due to large-scale fertilizer production by chemical industries.*

- New local industries could result. With direct access to aluminum locally, entrepreneurs might start a factory to make aluminum window frames and siding for home construction. Without significant transportation costs for raw materials, such a company could establish itself in the market by selling its products at lower prices. The factory would probably hire 30–45 employees, mainly shop workers and drivers, adding $700 000 annually to the local economy.

- As a commercial refrigerant, ammonia is used to produce large quantities of ice. Ready access to ammonia supplies could support a commercial ice-making plant in Riverwood. Such a company might employ 25–35 individuals, principally drivers and some plant workers, which could add $500 000 annually to Riverwood's economy.

- Riverwood air quality might improve. A Riverwood ammonia plant would require natural gas, and a natural-gas transmission company could build a pipeline to deliver the gas (mainly methane, CH_4). Residents have traditionally burned fuel oil in their home furnaces, but they could convert to natural gas. If all 11 000 Riverwood homes and businesses burned natural gas rather than oil, emissions of sulfur dioxide and particulate matter would decrease significantly.

- The tax base would improve. Although tax incentives are part of the appeal of a Riverwood site, the aluminum or ammonia plant will still contribute to the town's tax base. This will provide a large increase in revenues for the community.

Negative Factors

- Rates of worker-related injuries and accidents could increase. Ammonia is manufactured at high pressures and high temperatures. At ordinary temperature and pressure, ammonia gas is extremely toxic at high concentrations. Large amounts of ammonia released due to an accident on the road or at the plant could injure or kill workers and other community members within the vicinity. Several cases of work-related injury or illness or even death in ammonia-based fertilizer plants have been reported annually.

- Aluminum itself is nontoxic, but its production has its own dangers. Molten aluminum is drawn from large electrolytic cells. As the carbon anodes burn off in cryolite bath, toxic carbon monoxide gas may be produced as a by-product and must be handled properly. Mining and transporting aluminum ore may also involve risk of injury. Aluminum-production illness and injury rates annually are approximately 20 per 100 full-time employees. (The injury and accident rates in aluminum- and ammonia-based fertilizer production, by contrast, are both lower than rates found in motor-vehicle manufacturing, meat packing, or steel foundries.)

Section C   Metal Processing and Electrochemistry   **467**

▶ Water quality might suffer. If ammonia, ammonia-bearing wastewater, or wastes from aluminum production leaked into the Snake River, the resulting water contaminants could threaten aquatic life.

▶ Aluminum or ammonia markets might decline. Aluminum is commercially valuable because it is inexpensive, resists corrosion, and has low density. The market for aluminum is driven by applications such as those in the building trades (including insulation, window casings, reinforcement strips, and ventilation devices), transportation (including sheeting for truck trailers, campers, and mobile homes), and packaging. If aluminum substitutes emerged (from new alloys, plastics, or ceramics) in any of these major areas, the demand for aluminum would weaken.

▶ The fertilizer industry is among the largest consumers of ammonia. Current fertilizer-intensive agricultural methods have created controversy. In some cases, crop yields have declined despite use of increased quantities of synthetic fertilizer. Some farmers have elected to use less synthetic fertilizer, so ammonia demand may decline in coming years.

Considering Burdens and Benefits

The poet William Wordsworth used the phrase *Weighing the mischief with the promised gain . . .* in judging technological advancements (railroads, new in his time). Since the dawn of civilization, people have often accepted the burdens of new technologies to gain technology's benefits. Fire, one of civilization's earliest useful devices, gave people the ability to cook, warm themselves, and forge tools from metals. Yet fire out of control can destroy property and life. Every technology offers its benefits at a price.

One way to identify an acceptable new technology or venture is to evaluate it, finding an option that has a relatively low probability of producing harm—that is, it delivers benefits that far outweigh the burdens. Unfortunately, benefit–burden analysis—weighing what Wordsworth called *mischief* against *promised gain*—is not an exact science.

> In many cases, electing not to make a decision is, in fact, also a decision—one accompanied by its own burdens and benefits.

For instance, some technologies may present high burdens immediately, while others may be associated with chronic, low-level risks for years or even decades. Many burdens are impossible to predict or assess with certainty. Individuals can control some potential burdens, but others must be addressed and controlled at regional or national levels. In short, it is quite difficult to conduct a thorough burden–benefit analysis. However, complete these activities:

1. Based on what you have learned in this unit, work in groups to create two lists for each chemical plant; one summarizing benefits and one summarizing burdens/risks.

2. Review your summaries of the burdens/risks. Are any negative factors completely unacceptable? If so, the plant associated with that risk or burden is probably not a viable option for Riverwood.

3. Within each list, mark the most valuable benefits with a plus symbol and the most serious burdens with a minus symbol.

4. Also consider the likelihood of occurrence of each benefit and burden. A burden that is fairly minor but almost certain to occur might merit more consideration than a burden that is more serious but extremely unlikely. Using a scale from *1* (highly unlikely) to *5* (extremely likely), rate each item on your lists in terms of its likelihood of occurrence.

5. Based on your responses to Questions 3 and 4, decide your personal position on the question of building a chemical plant near Riverwood. Discuss your view with your group.

6. As a class, discuss whether Riverwood should invite a chemical plant to the community. Be sure that the concerns of students who do not share the opinion of the majority are also heard and considered.

Section C   Metal Processing and Electrochemistry   **469**

SECTION C SUMMARY

✎ Section C Supplement

Reviewing the Concepts

1. The process in which an electrical current is passed through a solution of ions, causing a nonspontaneous redox reaction

2. A cell in which electrical energy is generated through a spontaneous chemical reaction

3. One portion of the electrochemical cell in which oxidation or reduction occurs

4. a. An ion-containing structure that electrically connects the two separated solution compartments of a voltaic cell

   b. Because it completes the circuit and maintains a balance of electrical charges within the system. Without the flow of ions from the salt bridge, a positive electrical charge would build up in one half-cell, and a negative electrical charge would build up in the other half-cell. This would impede further flow of electrons through the external wire.

   c. Saturating filter paper in a solution of an ionic compound (such as KNO_3) that does not react with any component of the voltaic cell

5. If two half-cells are separated from one another but connected by a wire, electrons flow from one cell to the other cell via the wire. This flow of electrons constitutes an electrical current.

CHEMISTRY at Work

Searching for Solutions in Chemistry

Todd Blumenkopf has applied his chemistry knowledge in many different ways, in and out of the laboratory, during his 20-year career in the pharmaceutical industry.

Someday, when you reach for a pill to relieve an aching muscle or a headache, you might have Todd Blumenkopf to thank. Todd, who has used a wheelchair throughout his life, is a research chemist at Pfizer, Inc. Todd and his laboratory staff have worked on medications that reduce the swelling, or inflammation, of joints and muscles.

Todd and his colleagues in the Research Division worked to conceive of and synthesize new compounds that target the enzymes and receptors that contribute to certain disease states in the body. Each compound is tested *in vitro* (in an artificial environment outside the body) and *in vivo* (in the living body of an animal) to determine whether the compound produces desirable results without unwanted side effects.

After a drug has passed the required laboratory testing, researchers collect additional data about the drug to file with the Food and Drug Administration (FDA).

More recently, Todd took a position in Pfizer to identify and establish research collaborations with universities and biotechnology companies. Pfizer is thus able to expand opportunities to discover, develop, and market new drugs, while smaller companies and university research groups partner with Pfizer to complete the expensive clinical trials required to determine that a potential drug is both efficacious and safe.

As a child, Todd had a strong interest in science. His parents encouraged him to pursue a career in the profession, in part because they felt his disability might be met with less resistance in science than in other fields. As he progressed in his studies, he chose a career in pharmaceuticals. After receiving his Ph.D. and completing some postdoctoral work, Todd began his career as a research chemist. He now works at Pfizer's pharmaceutical research and development headquarters in New London, Connecticut.

Todd also works on the American Chemical Society's Committee on Chemists with Disabilities, which sponsors the development of materials and other efforts to improve opportunities in the chemical sciences for individuals with disabilities.

Todd believes the qualities needed for success in chemistry research are curiosity, creativity, and motivation. He also stresses the importance of patience and perseverance, since the process of developing a new product from an initial idea can take many years.

470   **Unit 5**   Industry: Applying Chemical Reactions

6.

Cu electrode — Ag electrode — Salt bridge

Solution containing Cu^{2+} ions (for instance, copper (II) sulfate, $CuSO_4$)

Solution containing Ag^+ ions (for instance, silver nitrate, $AgNO_3$)

7. a. No. As the electrode size increases or decreases, the electrical potential produced does not vary.

   b. Yes. Electrical potential is directly related to the relative differences in ten-

SECTION C SUMMARY
Reviewing the Concepts

Electrochemistry involves chemical changes that produce or are caused by electrical energy.

1. What is electrolysis?
2. What is a voltaic cell?
3. What is a half-cell?
4. Voltaic cells require a salt bridge.
   a. What is a salt bridge?
   b. Why is a salt bridge necessary for the operation of a voltaic cell?
   c. Describe one way to make a salt bridge.

5. How are half-cells linked to produce electricity?
6. Diagram a simple Ag–Cu voltaic cell. Label electrodes, solutions, and salt bridge.
7. Considering your results in Investigating Matter C.2 (page 454), does the electrical potential produced by a voltaic cell depend on the
   a. size of the electrodes? Explain.
   b. specific metals used? Explain.

The activity series of metals can be used to predict the direction of electron flow within a particular voltaic cell.

8. In a voltaic cell, what process takes place at the
   a. anode?   b. cathode?
9. Sketch a voltaic cell made from Ni and Zn in solutions of their ions. Label anode and cathode (identifying each metal) and show the direction of electron flow.

10. Predict the direction of electron flow in a voltaic cell made from each of these metal pairs in solutions of their ions. See Table 5.3 (page 453).
    a. Ag and Sn   c. Cu and Pb
    b. Cr and Ag

Batteries, which consist of one or more voltaic cells, provide convenient, portable ways to energize many common electrical devices.

11. What is the source of electrical energy in a battery?
12. Two types of voltaic cells are dry cells and alkaline batteries.
    a. List three similarities of these two cell types.
    b. How do these cells differ?
13. Write half-reaction equations for each of these oxidation–reduction processes. For each, identify (i) what is oxidized and (ii) what is reduced.
    a. $Pb(s) + Cu^{2+}(aq) \longrightarrow Pb^{2+}(aq) + Cu(s)$
    b. $Cr(s) + 3\ Ag^{+}(aq) \longrightarrow Cr^{3+}(aq) + 3\ Ag(s)$

14. Consider the following equation:

$$PbO_2(s) + Pb(s) + 4\ H^+(aq) + 2\ SO_4^{2-}(aq) \longrightarrow 2\ PbSO_4(s) + 2\ H_2O(l)$$

   a. In what type of battery does this reaction occur?
   b. What is (i) oxidized and (ii) reduced?
   c. Does this equation represent the charging or discharging of the battery?
   d. Identify the substance that you might observe as a white coating on battery electrodes.
   e. Under what conditions could this battery produce hydrogen gas?

Section Summary   471

---

10. a. From Sn to Ag
    b. From Cr to Ag
    c. From Pb to Cu
11. Chemical energy generated by the spontaneous chemical reaction that serves as the basis of the battery's design.
12. a. Both types generate an electrical potential of 1.54 V, have zinc anodes, and have graphite–MnO_2 cathodes.
    b. The electrolyte in dry cells is an aqueous paste of ammonium chloride and zinc chloride. In alkaline batteries, the electrolyte is an aqueous, alkaline paste of potassium hydroxide.
13. a. $Pb(s) \longrightarrow Pb^{2+}(aq) + 2\ e^-$
    Oxidation
    $Cu^{2+}(aq) + 2\ e^- \longrightarrow Cu(s)$
    Reduction
    b. $Cr(s) \longrightarrow Cr^{3+}(aq) + 3\ e^-$
    Oxidation
    $3\ Ag^+(aq) + 3\ e^- \longrightarrow 3\ Ag(s)$
    Reduction
14. a. An operating lead-acid battery
    b. The lead in the lead dioxide (spongy lead) is being reduced (gaining electrons); metallic lead is being oxidized (losing electrons).
    c. Discharging
    d. Lead sulfate, $PbSO_4(s)$
    e. When it is being charged by an outside source, hydrogen ions $H^+(aq)$ may be reduced to hydrogen gas, $H_2(g)$ at the lead dioxide electrode.

---

dencies of the two metals to lose electrons (become oxidized). If that difference is high, the electrical potential is high; if that difference is low, the electrical potential is low.

8. a. Oxidation
   b. Reduction

9. **Cathode:** Ni electrode   ← Electron flow   **Anode:** Zn electrode

Salt bridge

Solution containing Ni^{2+} ions (for instance, nickel (II) nitrate, $Ni(NO_3)_2$)

Solution containing Zn^{2+} ions (for instance, zinc nitrate, $Zn(NO_3)_2$)

SECTION C

15. Hydrogen gas, chlorine gas, and sodium hydroxide

16. Mercury is no longer used in chlor-alkali cells.

17. It was very difficult to isolate aluminum metal from its ore.

18. Aluminum processes require a large quantity of electricity

19. a, b. $4\ Al^{3+}(melt) + 12\ e^- \longrightarrow 4\ Al(l)$ [reduction]

$3\ C(s) + 6\ O^{2-}(melt) \longrightarrow 3\ CO_2(g) + 12\ e^-$ [oxidation]

c. $4\ Al^{3+}(melt) + 3\ C(s) + 6\ O^{2-}(melt) \longrightarrow 4\ Al(l) + 3\ CO_2(g)$

d. Electrons

e. Electrons cause the reduction of $Al^{3+}(melt)$ into $Al(s)$.

f. $378\ g\ Al \times \dfrac{1\ mol\ Al}{26.98\ g} \times \dfrac{4\ mol\ Al^{3+}}{4\ mol\ Al(l)} \times \dfrac{12\ mol\ e^-}{4\ mol\ Al^{3+}} = 42.0\ mol\ electrons$

20. a. Positive aspects include lower farming costs due to the proximity of fertilizer and the establishment of a commercial ice-making plant. Negative factors include potentially dangerous high pressures and temperatures for ammonia production, and ammonia-bearing waste water.

b. Producing aluminum can make it more feasible for local window and siding companies to establish themselves near these plants. Also, jobs associated with aluminum manufacturing and recycling can be numerous. Two negative aspects are the large quantities of electricity needed for electrolysis of alumina and dangers of molten aluminum and carbon monoxide.

21. One change is using D-glucose instead of benzene, a carcinogen, in synthesizing medicines and nylon.

| Electrolysis is a useful application of electrochemistry.

15. What three products does the chlor-alkali industrial process generate?

16. How was the chlor-alkali process changed to address environmental concerns?

17. Why was aluminum so expensive in the early 19th century, despite its abundance as an element in Earth's crust?

18. Why are aluminum-producing plants generally located in areas with inexpensive electrical power?

19. Consider the Hall-Héroult process.
   a. Write the half-reaction equations.
   b. Label each equation as an oxidation or reduction.
   c. Write the overall redox equation.
   d. What component is missing from this equation?
   e. What is the role of that component?
   f. How many moles of electrons would you need to reduce enough Al^{3+} ions to produce a 378-g roll of aluminum foil?

| Burden–benefit analysis is useful in weighing both positive and negative consequences when making decisions.

20. List two positive and two negative aspects of the technologies involved in producing
   a. ammonia.   b. aluminum.

21. Describe a specific change that the chemical industry has implemented in response to the principles of Green Chemistry.

Connecting the Concepts

22. Consider voltaic cells and electrolytic cells (cells where electrolysis occurs).
   a. How are they similar?
   b. How do they differ?
   c. Sketch a diagram of each type of cell and highlight the differences. (*Hint:* Refer to Investigating Matter, pages 202 and 454)
   d. Are these processes opposites? Explain.

23. Why is reducing aluminum oxide more difficult than reducing copper(II) oxide?

24. Describe the economic and societal impact of the Hall-Héroult process.

25. Why is recycling aluminum more cost-effective than processing aluminum ore by the Hall-Héroult method?

26. Explain how you can test the condition of a lead storage battery with a *hydrometer*, which measures liquid density. (*Hint:* Sulfuric acid solutions are more dense than liquid water.)

27. Why do batteries eventually stop operating? Explain in terms of limiting reactants.

28. Why are some batteries rechargeable and some not?

29. Identify one benefit and one burden or risk associated with each of the following:
   a. Playing high-school basketball
   b. Driving a car
   c. Jogging
   d. Receiving a dental X-ray
   e. Applying pesticides to garden plants
   f. Using food preservatives

472   **Unit 5**   Industry: Applying Chemical Reactions

Connecting the Concepts

22. a. Both involve movement of electrons in a redox reaction.

b. Voltaic cells are spontaneous and involve the flow of electrons from more active reactants to less active reactants. Electrolytic cells involve the flow of electrons from less active reactants to more active reactants; these are non-spontaneous changes.

c. Examples of electrolytic cells can be found in **Figure 2.51** (page 197, electroplating) and **Figure 5.40** (page 463, aluminum production). Sketches of voltaic cells can be found in **Figure 5.31** (page 453) and in Answers 6 and 9 above. Key differences: (1) Electrolytic cells require

Extending the Concepts

30. Identify the top four substances produced by the chemical industry in the United States. List two uses of each of those substances.

31. Identify and report on three commercial uses of chlorine gas. Are there alternatives to these uses that do not involve chlorine?

32. Find out how aluminum metal is welded. What techniques involved in welding aluminum differ from those used in welding other metals?

33. Investigate how the printing and dry-cleaning industries are changing their operations to become more environmentally sensitive and responsible.

34. Identify several technologies in your community. Use the risk-assessment table below to assign an appropriate letter to each activity. Discuss your decisions and compare your rankings with those made by others.

Assessment of Possible Risks Involved with an Activity or Technology

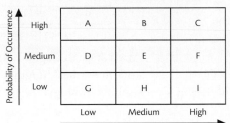

cantly increased the quantity of aluminum that could be produced at relatively low cost. Plentiful, inexpensive aluminum metal is used in innumerable common applications.

25. Recycling requires less electrical energy than reducing the metal from its ore.

26. Over time, there is less sulfuric acid in the battery due to its reaction with lead ions at both electrodes. If the battery is fully charged, the density of the electrolyte solution will be closer to that of sulfuric acid. Discharged batteries will have densities closer to that of water.

27. A battery will stop operating when one of the reactants is fully consumed (the limiting reactant).

28. Primary batteries (alkaline and dry cells) work only as long as the reactants have not been used up. They do not use reversible reactions. A rechargeable battery produces solid products that cling to the electrodes. The process can be reversed by connecting the battery to an external electrical potential, which causes electrons to move in the opposite direction, recharging the battery.

29.   *Benefit*
   a. Exercise, teamwork
   b. Getting you where you want to go
   c. Exercise, weight control
   d. Locate cavities
   e. Kills pests, improves yield
   f. Food lasts longer
   Burden/Risk
   a. Injury
   b. Cost, accidents
   c. Injury
   d. Exposure to radiation
   e. Damage to environment
   f. Undesirable side effects

Section Summary   **473**

a power supply to force electrons to flow from the anode to the cathode, and voltaic cells do not, and (2) the anode and cathode must be separated in voltaic cells. In an electrolytic cell, the anode and cathode reside in one container and are in contact with the same solution.
d. They are opposite in that voltaic cells convert chemical energy to electrical

energy; electrolytic cells use electrical energy to complete a chemical change.

23. Because aluminum metal is more active than copper metal. There is no common substance that gives up electrons readily enough to reduce aluminum ions to aluminum metal.

24. The Hall-Héroult process reduced the cost of producing aluminum and signifi-

Extending the Concepts

30. *Sulfuric acid:* manufacturing fertilizer, refining petroleum; *nitrogen:* manufacturing ammonia, liquid nitrogen for cooling; *oxygen:* used in acetylene torches, used in oxygen tents for medical purposes; *ethene:* fuel, raw materials for polyethylene

31. Chlorine gas can be used to disinfect, to bleach items, to extract raw gold. Iodine (or bromine) can be used instead of chlorine for water disinfection. Hydrogen peroxide can be used for bleaching. Bromine can be used to extract elemental gold from its ore.

32. When being welded, aluminum must be bathed in a noble gas to prevent it from oxidizing. The shielding gas is generally delivered through the head of the welding torch.

33. Green Chemistry strives to reduce pollution in these industries by reinventing chemical processes, using safer solvents, reducing waste, and generating less toxic by-products. Student answers should provide details.

34.

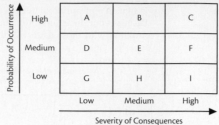

Assessment of Possible Risks Involved with an Activity or Technology

Answers will depend on the community involved and on student judgment of risks associated with each technology.

PUTTING IT ALL TOGETHER

A Chemical Plant for Riverwood?

Town Council Meeting Detailed instructions for this activity are in the student text. Because this is the second town-meeting activity, students should complete it with less teacher direction. Several options are available for structuring this culminating activity. One option is to assign each student to a group—Town Council, EKS, WYE, Riverwood Industrial Development Authority, Riverwood Environmental League, Riverwood Taxpayer Association—and allow each group to prepare a presentation. Based on arguments presented by each group, the Town Council discusses and votes on whether either chemical plant will be invited to Riverwood.

Tips

• Allow some class time for students to organize and assign roles within each group.
• Monitor the discussion so that one person or group does not dominate. Thirty-five to 45 minutes should be enough time to bring out all important points from the groups.

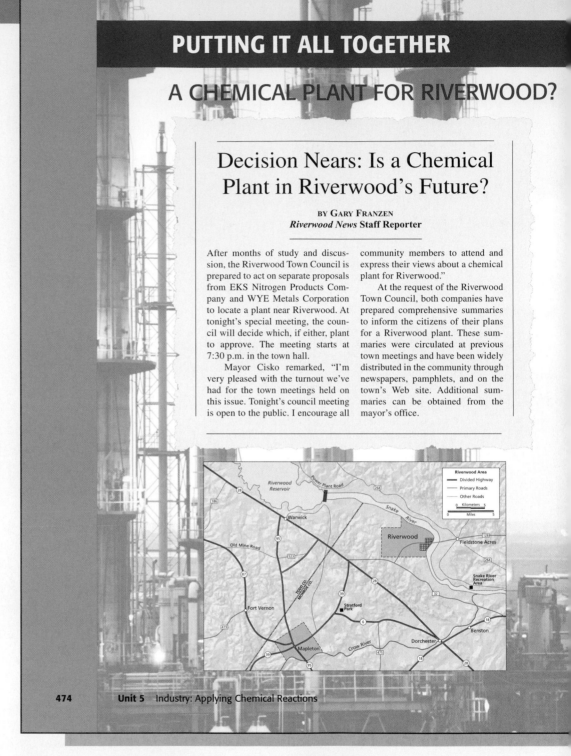

Decision Nears: Is a Chemical Plant in Riverwood's Future?

BY GARY FRANZEN
Riverwood News **Staff Reporter**

After months of study and discussion, the Riverwood Town Council is prepared to act on separate proposals from EKS Nitrogen Products Company and WYE Metals Corporation to locate a plant near Riverwood. At tonight's special meeting, the council will decide which, if either, plant to approve. The meeting starts at 7:30 p.m. in the town hall.

Mayor Cisko remarked, "I'm very pleased with the turnout we've had for the town meetings held on this issue. Tonight's council meeting is open to the public. I encourage all community members to attend and express their views about a chemical plant for Riverwood."

At the request of the Riverwood Town Council, both companies have prepared comprehensive summaries to inform the citizens of their plans for a Riverwood plant. These summaries were circulated at previous town meetings and have been widely distributed in the community through newspapers, pamphlets, and on the town's Web site. Additional summaries can be obtained from the mayor's office.

 Putting It All Together: Instructions

 Putting It All Together: Rubric

 Putting It All Together: Group Worksheet

 Putting It All Together: Questions for other Groups Worksheet

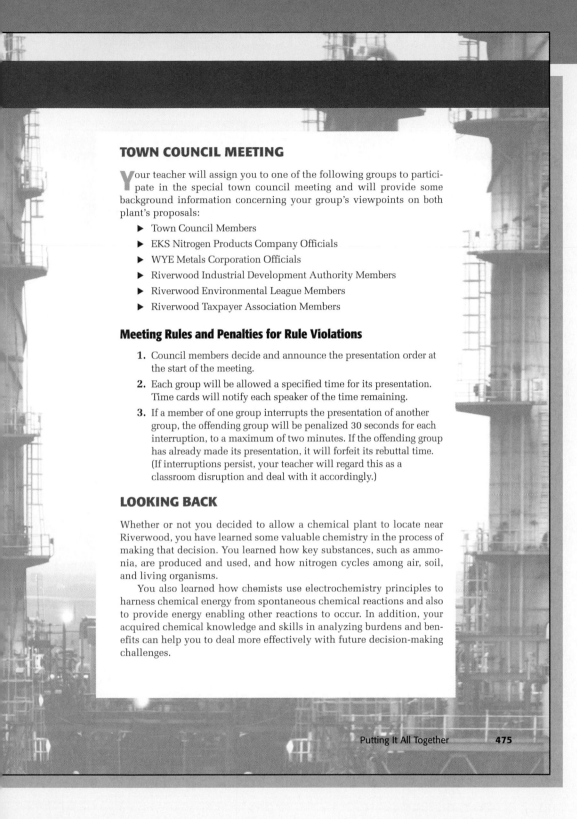

TOWN COUNCIL MEETING

Your teacher will assign you to one of the following groups to participate in the special town council meeting and will provide some background information concerning your group's viewpoints on both plant's proposals:

- ▶ Town Council Members
- ▶ EKS Nitrogen Products Company Officials
- ▶ WYE Metals Corporation Officials
- ▶ Riverwood Industrial Development Authority Members
- ▶ Riverwood Environmental League Members
- ▶ Riverwood Taxpayer Association Members

Meeting Rules and Penalties for Rule Violations

1. Council members decide and announce the presentation order at the start of the meeting.

2. Each group will be allowed a specified time for its presentation. Time cards will notify each speaker of the time remaining.

3. If a member of one group interrupts the presentation of another group, the offending group will be penalized 30 seconds for each interruption, to a maximum of two minutes. If the offending group has already made its presentation, it will forfeit its rebuttal time. (If interruptions persist, your teacher will regard this as a classroom disruption and deal with it accordingly.)

LOOKING BACK

Whether or not you decided to allow a chemical plant to locate near Riverwood, you have learned some valuable chemistry in the process of making that decision. You learned how key substances, such as ammonia, are produced and used, and how nitrogen cycles among air, soil, and living organisms.

You also learned how chemists use electrochemistry principles to harness chemical energy from spontaneous chemical reactions and also to provide energy enabling other reactions to occur. In addition, your acquired chemical knowledge and skills in analyzing burdens and benefits can help you to deal more effectively with future decision-making challenges.

LOOKING BACK

Invite students to look back and compare the knowledge they now have gained with the background they initially brought to this course. In addition to learning about chemistry skills and concepts, they should now have a better idea of the importance of chemistry and technology in their world. Students should now be more able to continue weighing risks and benefits to deal more effectively, as responsible citizens, with future challenges.

SECTION	CLASS TIME	STUDENT EDITION FEATURES	PROGRAM RESOURCES	MEDIA AND TECHNOLOGY
Section A: **The Nature of Atoms** **Objectives** • Define and describe *radioactivity*. • Distinguish between ionizing and nonionizing radiation. • Describe the structure of the atom, including characteristics of the major subatomic particles (protons, neutrons, and electrons). • Describe Rutherford's gold-foil experiment, including how its results led to a new model of the atom. • Define *isotope* and *radioisotope.* • Interpret a given isotope in terms of its atom's total protons and neutrons. • Calculate the average molar mass of an element, given isotopic molar masses and abundance data.	**6 Class Periods**	**Developing Skills** A.5 Interpreting Isotopic Notation A.8 Molar Mass and Isotopic Abundance **ChemQuandary 1** Scientific Discoveries **Modeling Matter** A.6 Isotopic Pennies **Making Decisions** A.9 Fact or Fiction?	**TRB** **Modeling Matter** A.6 Isotopic Pennies Student Worksheet **Content Reading Guides** A.1 through A.3 Content Reading Guide A.8 Content Reading Guide **Supplements and Practice** A.4 and A.5 Supplement: Atomic Architecture A.7 and A.8 Supplement: Finding Average Atomic Weight Section A Supplement	**TRCD** **All TRB and Test Bank Materials for Unit 6, Section A** **Exercises** Radioactivity The Gold Foil Experiment **Animations** The Gold Foil Experiment

SECTION	CLASS TIME	STUDENT EDITION FEATURES	PROGRAM RESOURCES	MEDIA AND TECHNOLOGY
Section B: **Nuclear Radiation** **Objectives** • Define and describe *background radiation,* including some of its sources. • Describe the effect of ionizing radiation on human tissue. • Distinguish among alpha, beta, and gamma radiation and their effects on living tissue. • Describe the effects of shielding, length of exposure, and proximity on the impact of alpha, beta, and gamma radiation. • Describe how various radioactive emissions affect the composition of the nucleus. • Write, complete, and balance nuclear equations describing changes in the composition of nuclei that are involved in radioactive emissions. • List and describe methods for detecting and measuring ionizing radiation.	6 Class Periods	**Developing Skills** B.6 Nuclear Balancing Act **ChemQuandary 2** Radiation Exposure Standards **Making Decisions** B.2 Your Annual Ionizing-Radiation Dose B.10 Ensuring Public Safety **Investigating Matter** B.4 Alpha, Beta, and Gamma Radiation B.9 Cloud Chambers	**TRB** **Investigating Matter** B.4 Alpha, Beta, and Gamma Student Worksheet and Data Table B.9 Cloud Chambers Student Worksheet and Data Table **Making Decisions** B.2 Your Annual Ionizing-Radiation Dose Student Worksheet **Content Reading Guides** B.7 Content Reading Guide B.9 Content Reading Guide **Supplements and Practice** B.5 and B.6 Supplement: Nuclear Balancing Act Section B Supplement	**TRCD** **All TRB and Test Bank Materials for Unit 6, Section B** **Videos** Alpha, Beta, and Gamma Radiation Cloud Chambers **Exercises** Detecting Radiation Shielding of Radiation Radiation Emitted by Everyday Objects

SECTION	CLASS TIME	STUDENT EDITION FEATURES	PROGRAM RESOURCES	MEDIA AND TECHNOLOGY
Section C: **Using Radioactivity** **Objectives** • Define and describe *half-life*. • Given its half-life, calculate the amount of a particular radioisotope that remains after a specified time. • Describe how radioisotopes are used as diagnostic tracers in medicine. • Describe how radioisotopes are used to kill cancerous cells. • Describe the process of nuclear transmutation. • Write, complete, and balance nuclear transmutation equations.	**5 Class Periods**	**Developing Skills** C.3 Applications of Half-Lives C.7 Nuclear-Bombardment Reactions **ChemQuandary 3** Carbon-14 Dating **ChemQuandary 4** Using Radioisotopes in Medicine **ChemQuandary 5** Transmutation of Elements **Modeling Matter** C.2 Understanding Half-Life **Making Decisions** C.9 Opinions About Radioactivity	**TRB** **Content Reading Guides** Section C Content Reading Guide **Supplements and Practice** C.1 Supplement: Half-Life C.6 Nuclear Bombardment Reactions Section C Supplement	**TRCD** **All TRB and Test Bank Materials for Unit 6, Section C** **Exercises** Half-Lives of Radioisotopes Carbon-14 Dating

SECTION	CLASS TIME	STUDENT EDITION FEATURES	PROGRAM RESOURCES	MEDIA AND TECHNOLOGY
Section D: **Nuclear Energy: Benefits and Burdens** **Objectives** • Define and describe *nuclear fission*. • Write a balanced nuclear equation for a fission reaction. • Describe how electricity is generated in a nuclear power plant. • Define and describe *nuclear fusion*. • List and describe types of nuclear waste, including their sources. • List, describe, and evaluate methods for disposal of nuclear wastes, including burdens and benefits of each.	**5 Class Periods**	**Developing Skills** D.7 Disposing of High- and Low-Level Waste **ChemQuandary 6** Risk-Free Travel? **Modeling Matter** D.2 The Tumbling Domino Effect **Making Decisions** D.5 The Safest Journey	**TRB** **Content Reading Guides** D.3 Content Reading Guide D.6 Content Reading Guide Section D Content Reading Guide **Supplements and Practice** Section D Supplement	**TRCD** **All TRB and Test Bank Materials for Unit 6, Section D** **Animations** A Nuclear Power Plant
Putting It All Together: Communicating Scientific and Technical Information	**2 Class Periods**	**Putting It All Together** Communicating Scientific and Technical Information	**TRB** **Putting It All Together** Putting It All Together: The Risks and Benefits of Nuclear Technology Rubric	**TRCD** **All TRB Materials for Unit 6, Putting It All Together**

Equipment, Expendable Items, and Unusual Materials (per 12 Student Pairs)

Sorted by Item

QUANTITY	ITEM	SECTION USED
100 mL	alcohol (ethyl or isopropyl)	B.9
12 sets	alpha, beta, and gamma radiation sets	B.4
12	balance, accurate to 0.1 g	A.6
12	bottles, squeeze (for alcohol)	B.9
12	cloud chamber kits	B.9
12	container or box (plastic or cardboard) with lid	C.2
12	forceps	B.9
12 dozen	dominoes	D.2
10 pounds	dry ice	B.9
12	forceps	B.4, B.9
24	glass plates (about 5 cm square, 0.1 cm thick)	B.4
1 box	gloves, disposable	B.4, B.9

Sorted by Item (continued)

QUANTITY	ITEM	SECTION USED
1 package	graph paper	B.4
12	cardboard pieces (about 5 cm square, 0.1 cm thick)	B.4
24	lead plates (about 5 cm square, 0.1 cm thick)	B.4
12	light source, high intensity (bright flashlight)	B.9
12	meter sticks	B.4
1200	pennies	C.2
72	pennies, post-1982	A.6
72	pennies, pre-1982	A.6
12	radiation counters	B.4
12	radiation source (usually part of cloud chamber)	B.9
12	containers, opaque, sealable (possibly film canisters)	A.6

Equipment, Expendable Items, and Unusual Materials (per 12 Student Pairs)

Sorted by Section

QUANTITY	ITEM	SECTION USED
12	balance	A.6
72	pennies, post-1982	A.6
72	pennies, pre-1982	A.6
12	containers, opaque, sealable (possibly film canisters)	A.6
12 sets	alpha, beta, and gamma radiation sets	B.4
24	glass plates (about 5 cm square, 0.1 cm thick)	B.4
1 package	graph paper	B.4
12	cardboard pieces (about 5 cm square, 0.1 cm thick)	B.4
24	lead plates (about 5 cm square, 0.1 cm thick)	B.4
12	meter sticks	B.4
12	radiation counters	B.4
12	forceps	B.4

Sorted by Section (continued)

QUANTITY	ITEM	SECTION USED
1 box	gloves, disposable	B.4
100 mL	alcohol (ethyl or isopropyl)	B.9
12	bottles, squeeze (for alcohol)	B.9
12	cloud chamber kits	B.9
12	forceps	B.9
10 pounds	dry ice	B.9
1 box	gloves, disposable	B.9
12	light source, high intensity (bright flashlight)	B.9
12	radiation source (usually part of cloud chamber)	B.9
12	container or box (plastic or cardboard) with lid	C.2
1200	pennies	C.2
12 dozen	dominoes	D.2

UNIT 6
ATOMS: NUCLEAR INTERACTIONS

Atoms: Nuclear Interactions confronts one of the most highly charged issues in modern society: the use of nuclear energy and technology. This unit traces the history and development of nuclear energy and technology, from discovery of radioactivity to modern-day reactors and fusion, with emphasis on exploring risks and benefits of nuclear technologies. The facts and principles explored in this unit will, without question, remain applicable to students beyond this course. Call students' attention to the fact that, as adults, they may need to make informed decisions about the introduction and/or use of nuclear technology in their communities. Remind students of the general *ChemCom* theme, that scientific understanding alone will not provide answers to complex societal problems and technological issues, but it can provide a rational basis for public debate and action.

A major goal of this unit is to provide insight into the nature of atoms by developing facts and principles related to nuclear science and technology. Atomic structure, isotopes, radiation, and chemical bonding are revisited and explored in greater detail.

UNIT 6

Atoms: Nuclear Interactions

WHAT discoveries led to a modern understanding of the composition of atoms?

SECTION A
The Nature of Atoms (page 480)

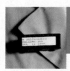

WHY does human exposure to some types of radiation cause health problems?

SECTION B
Nuclear Radiation (page 497)

HOW do the rates of radioactive decay influence decisions about using nuclear radiation?

SECTION C
Using Radioactivity (page 521)

WHAT risks and benefits accompany uses of nuclear energy?

SECTION D
Nuclear Energy: Benefits and Burdens (page 541)

? A citizen's group wants to ban all nuclear radiation from Riverwood and its surrounding area. Turn the page to learn what you might contribute to the community's discussions of the group's proposals.

The unit introduces radioactivity, radioisotopes, half-life, nuclear transformation, the impact of radiation on human health, and medical applications of nuclear technology. Students use facts and principles explored during the unit to weigh potential benefits of nuclear technology against potential harm it poses to individuals, society, and the environment. Students will also confront and evaluate commonly held misconceptions about nuclear technology.

The Putting It All Together activity challenges students to prepare and present information about nuclear science and technology to a senior-citizen group. The purpose of this presentation is to enable senior citizens to make informed decisions about nuclear energy and, more directly, to encourage students to consolidate and review their learning.

As a preassessment, you may have students classify the statements on the CANT flyer (page 478) as true or false. This is a very useful way to identify student misconceptions at the start of the unit. You may then ask students to reevaluate their pre-assessment responses at the close of the unit and reflect on what they have learned.

Using the Unit Project

Unit 6 opens with a flyer from the Citizens Against Nuclear Technology (CANT). This group, whose goal is to ban all uses of nuclear energy and nuclear materials in the Riverwood area, is planning an "informative" meeting to discuss its proposal. Students assume the role of Riverwood High School chemistry students and prepare a presentation that provides background information about nuclear science and technology for senior citizens in the community. These senior citizens plan to attend the CANT meeting; they want enough information that they can question CANT members. During the unit, students will learn facts and principles about nuclear change and nuclear technology that enable them to prepare an accurate presentation for these senior community members.

The CANT flyer presents statements about nuclear technology that vary in validity. As students progress through this unit, they will evaluate the accuracy and clarity of these statements. This information will also be useful as students plan their presentation.

Citizens Against Nuclear Technology (CANT)
invite you to an informative seminar on banning the use of all nuclear energy and materials in the Riverwood area.
See you Friday, 7:00 p.m., Town Council Hall

Do you know whether each statement below is true or false? If not, you could be in danger of serious nuclear exposure!

1. Home smoke detectors contain radioactive materials.
2. Radioactive materials and radiation are unnatural—they did not exist on Earth until created by scientists.
3. All radiation causes cancer.
4. Human senses can detect radioactivity.
5. Individuals vary widely concerning how they are affected by exposure to radiation.
6. Small amounts of matter change to immense quantities of energy released by nuclear weapons.
7. Physicians can distinguish cancer caused by radiation exposure from cancer resulting from other causes.
8. Medical X-rays are dangerous.
9. Nuclear power plants create serious hazards to public health and to the environment.
10. An improperly operated nuclear power plant can explode like a nuclear weapon.
11. Some nuclear wastes must be stored for centuries to prevent dangerous radioactivity from escaping.
12. New, dangerous elements are being invented every day.
13. Nuclear power plants produce material that could be converted into nuclear weapons.
14. All nuclear medical techniques are highly dangerous.

A local Riverwood organization, the Citizens Against Nuclear Technology (CANT), has organized to prevent all uses of nuclear power, the disposal of nuclear waste, food irradiation, and nuclear medicine in the Riverwood area. The flyer reproduced on the opposite page is a sample of the organization's effort to communicate with the residents of the Riverwood area.

Some Riverwood citizens are wary about the restrictions that CANT proposes because they fear that such restrictions would hinder access to a full range of medical diagnosis and treatment options. The grandmother of Ms. Lynn Paulson, a Riverwood High School chemistry teacher, is among these citizens. She asked Ms. Paulson whether any of her chemistry students could provide some background about nuclear science and technology to the senior-citizen community. Several senior citizens are planning to attend the announced CANT meeting, but they would like to acquire some background knowledge and be ready to question CANT representatives about their proposal. Ms. Paulson has agreed to help. In this unit, you and your classmates will assume the role of Riverwood High School chemistry students preparing a community presentation.

The chemistry you have learned thus far involves chemical changes due to sharing or transferring outer-shell electrons among atoms. You will encounter very different *changes* in this unit—changes associated with nuclei (rather than electrons) of atoms. This unit examines nuclear radiation, radioactivity, and nuclear energy, plus implications of their use and development.

As you progress through this unit, record the ideas and applications you decide to share in your presentation. In particular, focus on the assertions contained in the CANT flyer. You may also focus on issues that are of interest to your audience.

Several activities contribute to students' successful completion of the culminating activity. In Making Decisions A.9 (page 493), students first attempt to classify CANT flyer assertions as either factual or fictitious based on their study of radioactive nuclei and ionizing and nonionizing radiation. In Making Decisions B.10 (page 517), students again consider the CANT flyer statements and evaluate the appropriateness of several government proposals designed to protect the public from radiation hazards. In Making Decisions C.9 (page 536), students respond to several erroneous statements about nuclear technology. You may decide to ask students to complete these three Making Decisions activities in the same groups in which they will complete the final project. This will help cultivate group collaboration and ownership.

The Nature of Atoms

Section A introduces processes associated with changes in nuclei of atoms that result in emission of nuclear radiation and nuclear energy. Additionally, students explore atomic structure, isotopes, and isotopic abundance.

From discussing work by Roentgen, Rutherford, and Becquerel, students learn that some scientific discoveries are accidental and that, in searching for answers to one question, scientists often stumble on other questions that are more interesting. Students also gain appreciation for the use of scientific processes in these investigations.

A.1 A Great Discovery

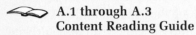 **A.1 through A.3 Content Reading Guide**

This material provides historical background on the discovery of radioactivity, including the fascinating revelation that Becquerel's crucial experiment, the exposure of photographic film by uranium, was somewhat of an accident. However, Becquerel's knowledge and curiosity led him to investigate the cause of the accident and thus make a discovery.

Using the Figures

Figure 6.2: Phosphorescent objects that glow under black lights contain compounds that are first excited by ultraviolet and high-energy visible light and then re-emit the absorbed energy as lower-energy forms of visible light. Electrons within the compounds absorb incoming UV radiation and are promoted to higher energy levels. Rather than relaxing

---

SECTION

A | The Nature of Atoms

In this section, you will learn how both well-planned experiments and chance observations led to the current model of the atom's structure and to the discovery of radioactivity. Determining and describing the structure of atoms rank among the greatest scientific accomplishments of the past centuries. The stories of these discoveries will help you understand atomic and nuclear chemistry and how researchers have used methods of science in their investigations.

A.1 A GREAT DISCOVERY

The history of modern atomic investigation began with the study of **radiation**, which constitutes the emission of energetic particles or electromagnetic waves (such as visible light, X-rays, and microwaves). Scientists have long been interested in light—because of its essential role in life—and other types of radiation. By the end of the 19th century, scientists had already studied many types of radiation from a variety of sources.

In 1895, a series of observations significantly broadened scientific understanding of radiation. The German physicist W. K. Roentgen was studying **fluorescence,** a phenomenon where certain materials emit light when struck by radiant energy, such as ultraviolet rays (Figures 6.1 and 6.2). Roentgen found that certain materials fluoresced when exposed to beams of **cathode rays** emitted from the cathode when electricity passed through an evacuated glass tube (see

You learned about electromagnetic radiation in Unit 4 (see page 337).

Figure 6.1 *French physicist Henri Becquerel's investigations of fluorescence led to the discovery of radioactivity.*

Older computer monitors and TV screens were based on a version of the cathode-ray tube.

Figure 6.2 *Ultraviolet light shining on particular objects, such as certain fabrics, produces fluorescence—visible light emitted by material exposed to such electromagnetic radiation.*

480   **Unit 6**   Atoms: Nuclear Interactions

---

back to their initial state and re-emitting energy equal to the original UV radiation absorbed, these electrons relax to an energy level between the initial and excited states. After reaching the intermediate energy

level, the electrons do eventually relax to their initial energy state—emitting light lower in energy than the originally absorbed UV light. In the case of this figure, laundry additives that get clothes "whiter than

480

Figure 6.3). A few years after Roentgen's work, cathode rays were identified as beams of electrons.

Roentgen was working with a cathode-ray tube covered by black cardboard. He observed an unexpected glow of light on a piece of paper across the room. The paper was coated with a fluorescent material, and Roentgen expected it to glow when exposed to radiation. However, visible radiation could not pass through the black cardboard covering the cathode-ray tube, and the fluorescent paper was not in the path of electrons in the tube. Roentgen hypothesized that some other radiation passing through the black cardboard had been emitted by the cathode-ray tube. He named the mysterious radiation *X-rays*, where *X* represented the unknown radiation. Scientists now know that **X-rays** are a form of high-energy electromagnetic radiation.

Figure 6.3 *A beam of electrons moves from the cathode (left) to the anode (right). The visible light emitted results from collisions of electrons with the fluorescent screen inside the tube. The deflection of the beam by a magnet indicates that the beam particles have a negative electrical charge. Collision of the electron beam with the glass or anode produces X-rays.*

In modern X-ray devices, the X-rays are generated when an electron beam strikes a metal target, which is often made of tungsten.

Further experiments revealed that these X-rays could penetrate many materials but could not easily pass through dense materials such as lead or bone. Scientists soon realized how useful these X-rays could be in medicine. In fact, one early X-ray image Roentgen obtained was of his wife's hand. Figures 6.4 and 6.5 show some modern X-ray images.

Figure 6.5 *An X-ray image of a human jaw. Such images help dentists detect cavities and other dental problems.*

Figure 6.4 *These X-ray images reveal a pair of normal human legs (left) and a pair of broken legs (right). Development of this useful medical diagnostic tool emerged from the study of fluorescence.*

Section A   The Nature of Atoms   **481**

a beam, and this beam is deflected to scan the surface at the viewing end (anode), which is lined with phosphorescent material (it emits light when exposed to electrons). The beam in all modern tube-type TVs is steered by electromagnets. (For more information on CRTs, refer to **http://en.wikipedia.org/wiki/Cathode_ray_tube.**)

Figures 6.4 and 6.5: When X-rays (a type of ionizing radiation) interact with materials in the human body, electrons are ejected from those materials, and ions are formed. The newly formed, charged entities can then promote a variety of damaging reactions within our cells, which can result in various diseases or even birth defects in offspring. Health professionals have determined that humans are able to recover from minor damage incurred by brief, limited exposure to X-rays. However, individuals who may be exposed to repeated or long-term doses of X-rays should take necessary precautions, such as using protective lead-based vests or shields.

Ask students how many have experienced an X-ray. Ask them to share what they observed about the procedures during this process. In particular, what steps did technicians take to protect the patient and themselves? As part of this discussion, have students weigh the relative risks versus the information gained from this medical technique.

Medical applications of ionizing radiation are further explored in Section C.

white" absorb UV light and emit light of a different energy. Thus, a white shirt washed in such detergents "glows" when exposed to UV light.

Figure 6.3: Cathode-ray tubes (CRTs) are used in computer displays, video monitors, televisions, and oscilloscopes. Within a television, electrons are carefully directed into

A.1 Continued

The discovery of radioactivity demonstrates how scientific investigations are often interrelated. In this case, Roentgen's X-rays prompted Becquerel to seek X-rays emitted by fluorescent materials, such as uranium. Becquerel's photographic plates were exposed by the uranium salts he was investigating. The photographic plates were composed of silver halides (AgCl, AgBr, or AgI), compounds sensitive to radiant energy. Any radiation more energetic than infrared radiation causes a photochemical reaction, resulting in the reduction of silver ions to silver atoms during subsequent photographic development. In Becquerel's experiment, this reduction darkened the photographic plate. Thus, the uranium salts must have emitted some type of radiant energy, as Becquerel hypothesized.

Becquerel concluded that the concept of fluorescence could not explain his findings. The photographic plates were exposed in the presence of the uranium salts, even in the absence of sunlight. A discussion of Becquerel's discoveries should highlight the difference between fluorescence (which stops as soon as the source of radiation is removed) and radioactivity (which involves spontaneous emission of particles). Becquerel was co-awarded the Nobel Prize for Physics in 1903. The 1903 Nobel Prize for Physics was also given to Pierre and Marie Curie for their study of Becquerel's radiation.

Roentgen's discovery intrigued other scientists, including the French physicist Henri Becquerel. Because X-rays could produce fluorescence, Becquerel wondered if fluorescent minerals might give off X-rays as they fluoresce. In 1896, Becquerel placed in sunlight some crystals of a fluorescent mineral that contained uranium. He then wrapped an unexposed photographic plate in black paper and placed the mineral crystals on top of the wrapped plate. If the mineral did emit X-rays, they would penetrate the black paper and the exposed film would darken, even though the film was shielded from light.

Cloudy weather prevented Becquerel from completing his experiments. He stored the wrapped photographic plates in a drawer with the uranium-containing mineral. After several days, he decided to develop some of the stored plates, thinking that perhaps some fluorescence might have persisted, causing some fogging of the photographic plates. When Becquerel developed the plates, he was astounded. Instead of faint fogging, the plates had been strongly exposed. Figure 6.6 illustrates the chain of events in Becquerel's investigation.

Figure 6.6 *Becquerel's investigation. Becquerel placed a fluorescent mineral in direct sunlight (a), then put it on an unexposed, wrapped photographic plate (b). Radiation exposed the plate (c). On a cloudy day (d), the wrapped plate was placed in a drawer with the mineral and kept from light (e), however, the mineral sample still exposed the photographic plate (f).*

Figure 6.7 *Many minerals exhibit fluorescence when exposed to ultraviolet light.*

Fluorescence stops as soon as the external radiation (in this case, from the Sun) is removed from the object. Thus, a fluorescent mineral in a desk drawer should not cause such an intense exposure. Scientists at that time could not offer a satisfactory explanation for Becquerel's observations. Becquerel suspected that the rays that exposed the photographic plates in the drawer were more energetic and had much greater penetrating ability than did X-rays. Thus he interrupted his study of X-rays to investigate the mysterious radiation apparently given off by the uranium-containing mineral. Although he was unable to explain it, Becquerel had discovered **radioactivity,** which is now known to involve the spontaneous emission of particles and energy from atomic nuclei. This phenomenon is distinctly different from X-ray production or fluorescence (Figure 6.7).

Becquerel suggested that Marie Curie (Figure 6.8), a graduate student working with him, attempt to isolate the radioactive component of pitchblende, a uranium ore, for her PhD research. Her preliminary work was successful; her physicist husband, Pierre Curie, changed his research focus to join her on the pitchblende project. Working together, Marie and Pierre Curie discovered that the level of radioactivity in pitchblende was four to five times greater than that expected from its known uranium content. The Curies suspected the presence of another radioactive element. After processing more than a thousand kilograms of pitchblende, they isolated tiny quantities (measured in milligrams) of two previously unknown radioactive elements. These elements later became known as polonium (Po) and radium (Ra).

Marie Curie first proposed the term "radioactivity."

Figure 6.8 *Marie Curie discovered two highly radioactive elements—radium (named for the radiation it emitted) and polonium (named for her native Poland). Her work earned her two Nobel Prizes.*

ChemQuandary 1

SCIENTIFIC DISCOVERIES

What do the following events have in common with Becquerel's discovery of radioactivity?

1. As Charles Goodyear experimented with natural rubber (a sticky material that melts when heated and cracks when cold), a mixture of the rubber and sulfur came in contact with a hot stovetop. He noted that the rubber and sulfur mixture did not melt. *Vulcanization,* a process which makes rubber more durable, resulted from this observation.

2. Roy Plunkett, a research chemist, used gaseous tetrafluoroethene ($F_2C{=}CF_2$) from a storage cylinder, but the gas flow stopped long before the cylinder should have completely emptied. He cut open the cylinder and discovered a new, white solid that is now known as polytetrafluroroethene or *Teflon.*

Products made with Teflon

3. James Schlatter, a research chemist trying to produce an antiulcer drug, accidentally got some of the substance on his fingers. When he later licked his fingers to pick up a piece of paper, his fingers tasted very sweet, and he correctly linked the sweetness to the antiulcer drug. Instead of finding an antiulcer drug, he had discovered *aspartame,* an artificial sweetener.

Section A   The Nature of Atoms   **483**

SECTION A

ChemQuandary 1

Scientific Discoveries

Each described discovery is similar to Becquerel's uranium work in that something unexpected happened. In all cases, observed events were discrepant with current scientific explanations. Becquerel did not expect the plates to be exposed, nor did Goodyear expect sulfur to harden rubber. Plunkett did not expect to find a polymer of tetrafluoroethane, nor did Schlatter expect to find artificial sweetener when he licked his fingers. Make the point that careful observation helps us uncover deeper scientific principles from seemingly ordinary events or mistakes. Pasteur's statement, "Chance favors the prepared mind," and Fleming's statement, "One sometimes finds what one is not looking for" are useful nuggets of advice for all scientists.

Other chance discoveries include the following: Louis Pasteur, vaccination; Alexander Fleming, penicillin; and Luigi Galvani, electrical current. These cases and others may be used as topics for additional student research.

A.2 Nuclear Radiation

Students first encountered the electromagnetic spectrum and radiation in Unit 4 when they investigated how solar energy interacts with Earth's atmosphere. In this unit, students refer to the electromagnetic spectrum as they focus on the energies of types of ionizing and nonionizing radiation. Use page 484 to make sure that students are familiar with the differences between ionizing and nonionizing radiation.

Three types of nuclear radiation are introduced—alpha particles, beta particles, and gamma rays. Ernest Rutherford, the scientist who developed the modern model of the nuclear atom, discovered both alpha and beta particles through his study of radioactivity in uranium compounds. The differences among these three types of nuclear radiation are explored later in Section B.

Figure 6.9 *The electromagnetic spectrum. Microwaves, infrared radiation (from heat lamps), and X-rays are all examples of electromagnetic radiation.*

Figure 6.10 *Sunburn often results from overexposure of skin to ultraviolet radiation.*

A.2 NUCLEAR RADIATION

Many people respond with alarm and even panic when they hear the word *nuclear*. In addition, the general term *radiation*, which is sometimes used to refer particularly to *nuclear radiation* can also cause anxiety. In reality, radiation falls into two general types: *ionizing radiation* and *nonionizing radiation*.

Electromagnetic radiation in the visible and lower-energy regions of the spectrum (see Figure 6.9) is **nonionizing** (long-wavelength) **radiation.** Nonionizing radiation transfers its energy to matter, causing atoms or molecules to vibrate (infrared radiation), move their electrons to higher energy levels (visible radiation), or heat up (such as in microwave ovens). Although this radiation is generally considered safe, excessive exposure can be harmful. Sunburn, for example, results from an overexposure to nonionizing radiation from the Sun (Figure 6.10). In fact, intense microwave and infrared radiation can cause lethal burns.

Ionizing radiation, which includes high-energy electromagnetic radiation (short-wavelength ultraviolet radiation, X-rays, and gamma rays) and all nuclear radiation, carries more energy and potential for harm than nonionizing radiation. Energy from ionizing radiation can eject electrons from atoms and molecules, forming molecular fragments and ions. These fragments and ions can be highly reactive. If formed within a living system, they can disrupt normal cellular chemistry, causing serious cell damage.

Nuclear radiation is a form of ionizing radiation that is caused by changes in the nuclei of atoms. In chemical reactions, the atomic number (number of protons) does not change; an atom of aluminum (13 protons) always remains an aluminum atom, and an iron atom (26 protons) always remains an iron atom. However, atoms with unstable nuclei—radioactive atoms—can spontaneously change their identities. A radioactive atom changes spontaneously through disintegration of its nucleus, which results in the emission of high-speed particles and energy. When this happens, the identity of the radioactive atom often changes; an atom of a different element forms. This process is **radioactive decay.** The emitted particles and energy make up **nuclear radiation.**

Ernest Rutherford showed in 1899 that nuclear radiation included at least two different types of emissions, which he named *alpha rays* and *beta rays*. Shortly afterward, scientists discovered a third kind of nuclear radiation: *gamma rays*.

Researchers allowed the three types of nuclear radiation to pass through magnetic fields to investigate their electrical properties. Scientists already knew that when electrically charged particles move through a magnetic field, the magnetic force deflects them. See Figure 6.11. Scientists also knew that positively charged particles are deflected in one direction, negatively charged particles are deflected in the opposite direction, and electrically neutral particles and electromagnetic radiation are not deflected. Further experiments revealed that alpha emissions were composed of positively charged particles, and that beta emissions were composed of negatively charged particles. Thus these two types of emissions are referred to as **alpha particles** and **beta particles** (not *rays* as originally named). **Gamma rays,** not deflected by a magnetic field, have no electric charge; they are high-energy electromagnetic radiation similar to X-rays.

By thus describing the nature of radioactivity, scientists toppled an old theory (a common event in scientific progress—new knowledge replaces old knowledge). Once scientists knew about alpha particles, beta particles, and gamma rays, they became convinced that atoms, which were originally thought to be the smallest, most fundamental units of matter, must be composed of even *smaller* particles.

From the results of another experiment, the *gold-foil investigation,* Rutherford proposed a fundamental model of the atom that is still useful today. To do so, he developed an ingenious, indirect way to "look" at the structure of atoms.

> The nuclei of unstable atoms are sources of nuclear radiation.

 Radioactivity

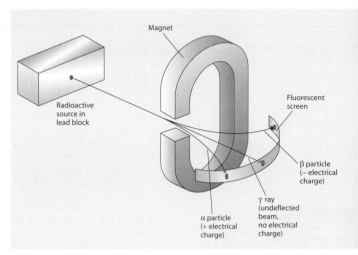

Figure 6.11 *Behavior of alpha (α) particles, beta (β) particles, and gamma (γ) rays passing through a magnetic field.*

> Alpha (α), beta (β), and gamma (γ) are the first three letters of the Greek alphabet.

Using the Figures

Figure 6.10: Students may have already heard or read about issues related to ultraviolet radiation, sunburns, and sunscreen. Ask them to share what they know about UVA, UVB, and UVC rays. UVC rays have wavelengths between 100 and 290 nm. These are the highest in energy of the three types of ultraviolet radiation, have the highest potential to inflict damage on living tissue, and are absorbed by the ozone layer before reaching Earth's surface. Historically, UVB radiation (290 to 320 nm) has been associated with sunburns; sunscreens have protected against this window of the electromagnetic spectrum. Recent studies have indicated that both UVB *and* UVA rays are linked to skin cancer. Therefore, health professionals strongly recommend using sunscreens that shield against both UVA (320 to 400 nm) and UVB rays.

A.3 The Gold-Foil Experiment

This material elucidates (through example) the idea that experimental observations are sometimes unexpected when based on a current model. Discovering the nucleus was not the purpose of the gold-foil experiment. Rutherford was investigating how alpha particles behave with metals. He expected that most of the alpha particles would travel through the gold foil without deflection and that a small percent of alpha particles would scatter slightly. He based this expectation on prevailing thought that positive and negative species were distributed equally throughout the atom and that these electrical charges would only exert very weak influence on moving alpha particles. The unusual deflections prompted Rutherford to propose the existence of a very massive and very small positively charged region—the nucleus. To help students visualize the physical arrangement of the investigation, focus on **Figures 6.13** and **6.14.** You may also display a transparency of the gold-foil experiment.

Additional Information

Rutherford used his experimental results to develop the modern nuclear model of the atom. The Bohr model of the atom, developed by Niels Bohr, a student of Rutherford, includes the speculation that electrons travel around the nucleus much as planets orbit the sun. The Bohr model also advanced the concept of definite electronic energy levels within atoms. While ade-

A.3 THE GOLD-FOIL EXPERIMENT

The Gold Foil Experiment

Prior to Rutherford's research, scientists had tried to explain the arrangement of electrons and positively charged particles within atoms in several ways. In the most widely accepted model, the atom was viewed as a volume of positive electrical charge, with the negatively charged electrons embedded within, like peanuts in a candy bar. In the late 1800s this model was known as the "plum pudding" model because it resembled the distribution of raisins within that traditional English dessert.

About 1910, Rutherford decided to test the plum pudding model. Working in Rutherford's laboratory in Manchester, England, Hans Geiger and Ernest Marsden focused a beam of alpha particles—the most massive of the three types of nuclear radiation—at a thin sheet of gold foil only 0.000 04 cm (about 2000 atoms) thick (see Figure 6.12). Geiger and Marsden used a zinc sulfide-coated screen to detect the alpha particles after they passed through the gold foil (see Figure 6.13). The screen emitted a flash of light where each alpha particle struck it. By observing the tiny light flashes at different positions with respect to the gold foil, Geiger and Marsden deduced the paths of the alpha particles as they interacted with the gold foil.

Rutherford expected alpha particles to be scattered slightly as they were deflected by the gold atoms in the foil, producing a pattern similar to water being sprayed from a nozzle. However, he was in for quite a surprise. First, most of the alpha particles passed straight through the gold foil as if nothing were there (see Figure 6.14). This implied that most of the volume occupied by the gold atoms was essentially empty space. But Rutherford was even more surprised that a few alpha particles, about 1 in every 20 000, bounced *back* toward the source. He described his astonishment this way: "It was almost as incredible as if you fired a 15-inch [artillery] shell at a piece of tissue paper and it came back and hit you."

Whatever repelled these deflected alpha particles must have been extremely small because most of the alpha particles went straight through the foil. Yet the particles encountered by alpha particles must also have been very massive (as compared to the alpha particles) and most likely possessed a positive electrical charge because they tended to repel positively charged alpha particles.

> Alpha rays and beta rays are more commonly referred to as particles because they possess measurable mass.

Figure 6.12 *Gold foil, similar to gold leaf being applied here, was used in Rutherford's early investigations of atomic structure.*

quately describing structure of the atom on a basic level, the Bohr model did have shortcomings and raised numerous unanswered questions. Further experimentation led to the current model of the atom, the quantum mechanical model. This model treats electrons as waves and depicts electrons in terms of probability distributions

Figure 6.13 *The alpha-particle scattering experiment led Rutherford to conclude that the atom is largely empty space with an incredibly dense, positively charged nucleus at its center.*

From these results, Rutherford developed the modern model of the *nuclear atom*. He named the tiny, dense, positively charged region at the center of the atom the *nucleus*. He envisioned that electrons orbited the nucleus, somewhat like planets orbit the Sun. Figure 6.14 illustrates how the nuclear model explained the results of the gold-foil experiment, and also features of the nuclear model of the atom.

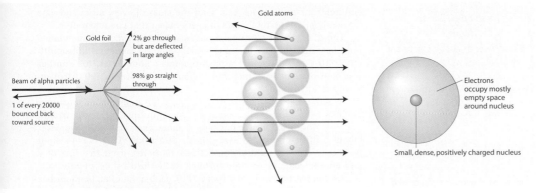

A.4 ARCHITECTURE OF ATOMS

Since Rutherford's time, scientific understanding of atomic structure has expanded and changed somewhat. Rutherford's model of a central, dense nucleus surrounded mostly by empty space is still valid. Subsequent research has shown that the idea of orbiting electrons is incorrect. The general regions in which electrons are most likely to be found can be described, but the particular movements or locations of electrons cannot be described.

Figure 6.14 *Result of the alpha-particle scattering experiment. Most alpha particles passed through the foil but a few were deflected, some at very large angles (left). Proposed model (middle) to account for the results. Nuclear model of the atom (right).*

A.4 Architecture of Atoms

This material identifies components of the nucleus and explains isotopes in terms of mass numbers. Nuclear notation can be used to help identify the number of neutrons in a given isotope. Analogies can help students gain a sense of atomic scale. Emphasize several points:

• Atoms are very small. If people were the size of atoms, the entire population of the world (approximately 6 billion) would fit on the head of a pin.

• Most of the volume occupied by an atom is essentially empty space. If the nucleus were the size of a billiard ball, the average electron would be located about 0.5 km (about 1/3 mile) away.

• Protons and neutrons account for most of the mass of all atoms (and therefore of all matter). The mass of each is approximately 2000 times greater than that of an electron.

• Encourage students to devise other appropriate analogies. A brief review of the structure of atoms versus ions may be beneficial at this point.

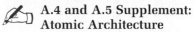 **A.4 and A.5 Supplement: Atomic Architecture**

whose charge density reflects the likelihood of finding an electron. The Website **http://science.howstuffworks.com/atom.htm** is a useful source of historical information on discoveries in physics and chemistry that led to modern understanding of the atom.

Supplementary Activity: The Black Box

This activity simulates how scientists use indirect evidence to infer properties that our senses cannot directly perceive. The focus of this activity is to encourage students to use evidence-based reasoning to solve a problem.

Time

30–45 min

Materials

(For 12 student pairs)

Twenty-four sealed, coded boxes (cigar or shoe boxes), each containing one, two, or three unconstrained objects such as small scissors, a small rubber ball, a small fork, a plastic comb, a large paper clip, cotton balls, or a small key. You might also use common laboratory materials such as test tube holders, flame spreaders, and rubber stoppers. Commercially available black boxes could also be used.

Procedure

1. Before the activity begins, discuss how studying atomic structure is analogous to dealing with a black box.
2. Challenge students to propose what (if anything) is inside their black boxes *without opening them*. Encourage students to first make controlled observations (what they hear, feel, etc., as they carefully shake or manipulate the boxes, for example). Allow students to investigate their black boxes in any way they can without actually opening them (for instance, students could run a magnet along one side) and to suggest other tests they could perform if they had the proper equipment (such as taking an

THREE COMPONENTS OF ATOMS			
Particle	**Location**	**Electrical Charge**	**Molar Mass (g/mol)**
Proton	Nucleus	+1	1
Neutron	Nucleus	0	1
Electron	Outside nucleus	−1	0.0005

Table 6.1 *The proton, neutron, and electron are subatomic particles.*

Neutrons are actually slightly more massive than are protons.

Protons: positive electrical charge
Neutrons: no electrical charge
Electrons: negative electrical charge

In most periodic tables, the atomic number is written above the symbol of each element.

Further research revealed that the nucleus is composed of two types of particles: *neutrons,* which are electrically neutral, and *protons,* which possess a positive charge. These particles, as well as *electrons,* are called **subatomic particles.** Protons and neutrons have about the same mass, 1.7×10^{-24} g. Although this mass is incredibly small, it is much greater than the electron's mass, which is 9.1×10^{-28} g. As shown in Table 6.1, one mole of electrons (6.02×10^{23} electrons) has a mass of only 0.0005 g. The same number of protons or neutrons would have a mass of about 1 g. In other words, a proton or a neutron is about 2000 times more massive than is an electron. Thus protons and neutrons account for nearly all the mass of every atom and also for nearly all of the total mass of every object that you encounter.

The diameter of a typical atom is about 10^{-10} m, and an average nuclear diameter is 10^{-14} m, which is only one ten-thousandth ($10^{-14}/10^{-10}$) of the entire atom's diameter. Looking at this another way, the nucleus occupies only about one trillionth (10^{-12}) of an atom's total volume.

Imagine that a billiard ball represents the diameter of an atom's nucleus. On that scale, electrons surrounding this billiard-ball nucleus would extend out in space more than one-half kilometer (about a third of a mile) away in all directions. This is consistent with the observation that most alpha particles, each the size of a helium nucleus, passed right through Rutherford's sheet of gold foil.

As you learned in Unit 2 (page 120), each atom of an element has the same number of protons in its nucleus, and each element has a unique number of protons. This number, called the *atomic number,* identifies the element. For example, each carbon atom nucleus contains six protons; therefore, the atomic number of carbon is 6.

All atoms of a given element do not necessarily have the same number of neutrons in their respective nuclei. Recall that atoms of the same element with different numbers of neutrons are called *isotopes* of that element. Naturally occurring carbon atoms, each containing six protons, may have six, seven, or even eight neutrons. The composition of these three carbon isotopes is summarized in Table 6.2. Figure 6.15 shows their nuclei.

X-ray). After generating a list of observations, prompt students to make inferences about what is in their boxes. They should specify the general size and composition of each object. Each inference should be supported by evidence (observations) from students' manipulation of the black boxes. Help students distinguish between observation and inference.

Post-Activity Discussion

Focus on how the activity simulated the work of atomic scientists rather than on stu-

THREE CARBON ISOTOPES

Name	Total Protons (Atomic Number)	Total Neutrons	Total Protons & Neutrons (Mass Number)	Total Electrons
Carbon-12	6	6	12	6
Carbon-13	6	7	13	6
Carbon-14	6	8	14	6

Table 6.2 *Composition of three carbon isotopes.*

Isotopes are distinguished by their different mass numbers. The *mass number*, as you learned in Unit 2 (page 120), represents the total number of protons and neutrons in an atom. The three carbon isotopes in Table 6.2 have mass numbers 12, 13, and 14, respectively. To specify a particular isotope, the atomic number and the mass number are written in front of the element's symbol in a particular way. For example, an isotope of carbon (C) with an atomic number 6 and a mass number 12 is written as follows:

$$^{12}_{6}\text{C}$$

An atom of strontium with an atomic number 38 and mass number 90 would be symbolized as follows:

$$^{90}_{38}\text{Sr}$$

Another way to identify a particular isotope is to write the name or symbol of the element followed by a hyphen and its mass number. For example, an isotope for carbon may be called carbon-12, C-12, or ^{12}C. The symbols, names, and nuclear composition of some isotopes are summarized in Table 6.3.

Carbon-12

Carbon-13

Carbon-14

Figure 6.15 *Nuclei of three carbon isotopes, containing, respectively, 6, 7, and 8 neutrons (gray) and 6 protons (blue).*

SOME COMMON ISOTOPES

Symbol	Name	Total Protons (Atomic Number)	Total Neutrons	Total Protons + Neutrons (Mass Number)	Total Electrons
$^{7}_{3}$Li	Lithium-7	3	4	7	3
$^{16}_{8}$O	Oxygen-16	8	8	16	8
$^{20}_{10}$Ne	Neon-20	10	10	20	10
$^{67}_{31}$Ga	Gallium-67	31	36	67	31
$^{138}_{56}$Ba	Barium-138	56	82	138	56
$^{195}_{78}$Pt	Platinum-195	78	117	195	78
$^{201}_{81}$Tl	Thallium-201	81	120	201	81
$^{208}_{82}$Pb	Lead-208	82	126	208	82

Table 6.3 *Names, symbols, and nuclear composition of some isotopes.*

Section A   The Nature of Atoms   **489**

Answers

1. Hearing, touch (feeling the impact of moving objects on the container walls)
2. The structure of the atom is like a black box that scientists cannot open to examine its contents. (And no one is available to tell them if they're correct or not!)
3. Indirect evidence is used to formulate explanations (theories) about the natural world whenever events occur beyond the range of our perceptions. The time it takes for events to occur may be too short (kinetic molecular theory) or too long (plate tectonics), or the objects of interest may be too small (atomic theory) or too large (the universe).

Demonstration Idea

A useful variation on the black box activity involves suspending a disposable object (key, paper clip, fork, comb, scissors, rubber ball) inside a sealed shoe box. Cut rigid construction paper strips (white) 50–55 cm long by 7 cm wide to fit through slits in the back of the box, serving as an imaging screen. Spray paint (modeling alpha particles) through a hole in the front of the box to create a "shadow image" of the concealed object. This demonstration reinforces the notions of a source and a target, and illustrates the process of shooting something into the atomic "black box" to acquire information about its structure and contents.

dents who believed that they succeeded in their task. Ask students to explain how they arrived at their answers. *Do **not** disclose the actual contents of the sealed boxes!* Scientists are unable to check the "correctness" of their work—all they have to go on is indirect observations and inferences.

Questions

1. Which senses did you use to gather most observational data?
2. How does this activity resemble the efforts of scientists in exploring atomic and molecular structures?
3. Name some theories about the nature of the world that are based primarily on indirect evidence.

Developing Skills

A.5 Interpreting Isotopic Notation

This activity gives students practice using isotopic notation and illustrates that higher-atomic-number atoms have larger neutron/proton ratios than atoms of elements with lower atomic numbers.

Answers

1. See table below.
2. a. Roughly a 1:1 ratio.
   b. More neutrons than protons.

Modeling Matter

A.6 Isotopic Pennies

 A.6 Isotopic Pennies Student Worksheet

This simulates finding the isotopic composition of an element. Students find the proportion of pre-1982 pennies in a sealed 10-penny container.

Materials

(For 12 student pairs)

12 sealed opaque containers (coded) with different 10-coin mixtures of pre-1982 and post-1982 pennies (35-mm film canisters are ideal)

72 pre-1982 pennies

72 post-1982 pennies

Balance, accurate to 0.1 g

Advance Preparation

Pre-weigh each empty container and provide the mass for students to use in calculations. Fill containers in advance, using various combinations of pre-1982 and post-1982 pennies. Use coding to identify the containers.

Avoid 1982 pennies, since some have pre-1982 composition; others are similar to post-1982 pennies. To allow for mass variance of separate pennies, students can

490

A.5 INTERPRETING ISOTOPIC NOTATION

Sample Problem: *Suppose you know that one product of a certain nuclear reaction is an isotope containing 85 protons and 120 neutrons. The atom therefore has a mass number of 205 (85 p + 120 n). What is the symbol of this element?*

$$^{205}_{85}?$$

Consulting the periodic table, you find that the atomic number 85 represents the element astatine (At).

$$^{205}_{85}\text{At}$$

1. Prepare a summary chart similar to Table 6.3 (page 489) for the following six isotopes. (Consult the periodic table for any needed information.)

   a. $^{12}_{?}\text{C}$ d. $^{24}_{12}?$
   b. $^{14}_{7}?$ e. $^{202}_{?}\text{Hg}$
   c. $^{16}_{?}\text{O}$ f. $^{238}_{92}?$

2. Using Table 6.3 as a source of information, what general relationship do you note between the total number of protons and total number of neutrons for atoms of

   a. lighter elements with atomic numbers less than 20?
   b. heavier elements with atomic numbers greater than 50?

A.6 ISOTOPIC PENNIES

You learned earlier (Unit 2, page 113) that pre-1982 and post-1982 pennies have different compositions. As you would probably expect, these pennies also have different masses. In this activity, a mixture of pre- and post-1982 pennies will model or represent atoms of a naturally occurring mixture of two isotopes of the imaginary element *coinium*. Using the pennies, you will simulate one way scientists determine the relative amounts of different isotopes in a sample of an element.

You will receive a sealed container of 10 pennies that contains a mixture of pre-1982 and post-1982 pennies (Figure 6.16). Your container might hold any particular atomic mixture of these two isotopes. Your task is to determine the isotopic composition of *coinium—without opening the container.*

Figure 6.16 *How many pre- and post-1982 pennies are in your 10-coin sample of coinium?*

SYMBOL	NAME	TOTAL PROTONS	TOTAL NEUTRONS	MASS NUMBER	TOTAL ELECTRONS
$^{12}_{6}\text{C}$	Carbon-12	6	6	12	6
$^{14}_{7}\text{N}$	Nitrogen-14	7	7	14	7
$^{16}_{8}\text{O}$	Oxygen-16	8	8	16	8
$^{24}_{12}\text{Mg}$	Magnesium-24	12	12	24	12
$^{202}_{80}\text{Hg}$	Mercury-202	80	122	202	80
$^{238}_{92}\text{U}$	Uranium-238	92	146	238	92

▶ Your teacher will give you some pre-1982 and post-1982 pennies, and a sealed container with a mixture of 10 pre- and post-1982 pennies, and will tell you the mass of the empty container. Record this information and the code number of your sealed container.

▶ Determine the isotopic composition of the element *coinium*. That is, find the percent pre-1982 and percent post-1982 pennies in your container. There is more than one way to find these answers.

Now answer these questions:

1. Describe the procedure that you followed to find the percent composition of *coinium*.

2. What property of *coinium* is different in its pre- and post-1982 forms?

3. Name at least one other familiar item that could serve as a model for isotopes.

A.7 ISOTOPES IN NATURE

Most elements in nature are mixtures of isotopes. Some isotopes of an element may be radioactive, while others are not. All isotopes of an element behave virtually the same way chemically, because they have the same electron distribution and differ only slightly in mass. If one considers chemical changes only, knowledge of isotopes is not particularly helpful. The atomic weight of an element, as shown on the periodic table, represents averages based on the relative natural abundances of the isotopes of that element (see Figure 6.17 for lithium).

Marie Curie originally thought that only heavy elements were radioactive. It is true that naturally occurring **radioisotopes** (that is, radioactive isotopes) are more common among the heavy elements. In fact, all naturally occurring isotopes of elements with atomic numbers greater than 83 (bismuth) are radioactive. However, many natural radioisotopes are also found among lighter elements. Modern technology has made it possible to create a radioisotope of any element. Table 6.4 lists some naturally occurring radioisotopes and their isotopic abundances.

What is the relationship between an element's molar mass and the percent abundance of the element's isotopes? To calculate the molar mass of an element, it is helpful to use the concept of a *weighted average*, as illustrated in Developing Skills A.8.

SOME NATURAL RADIOISOTOPES

Isotope	Abundance (%)
Hydrogen-3	0.000 13
Carbon-14	Trace
Potassium-40	0.0012
Rubidium-87	27.8
Indium-115	95.8
Lanthanum-138	0.089
Neodymium-144	23.9
Samarium-147	15.1
Lutetium-176	2.60
Rhenium-187	62.9
Platinum-190	0.012
Thorium-232	100

| Table 6.4

3
Lithium
Li
6.94

7.59 %   92.41 %
Li-6   Li-7

Figure 6.17 *Lithium's atomic weight is a weighted average of the molar masses of its two isotopes, Li-6 and Li-7. Most lithium atoms (92.41%) are Li-7, thus lithium's atomic weight is closer to 7 than to 6.*

No stable (nonradioactive) isotopes have yet been found for elements with atomic numbers of 83 or greater.

Section A   The Nature of Atoms   491

---

weigh 10 pre-1982 pennies and 10 post-1982 pennies and use an *average* mass of each in calculations.

Some students may devise a non-math "brute-force" approach to this task—they weigh *all* combinations (1 new, 9 old; 8 new, 2 old; etc.), then compare their mass with this table of known masses. You may allow this approach.

Answers

1. One approach: Total mass pennies = (total pre-1982 pennies)(mass of one pre-1982 penny) + (total post-1982 pennies)(mass of one post-1982 penny). Explanation: There are 10 pennies per container. If (p) represents total pre-1982 pennies, then (10 − p) represents total post-1982 pennies. Total mass of all pre-1982

pennies = total pre-1982 pennies (p) × (mass of one pre-1982 penny). Likewise, total mass of post-1982 pennies = the number of post-1982 pennies (10 − p) × (mass of one post-1982 penny). Thus, total mass of *all* pennies (pre- and post-1982) = (p)(mass of pre-1982 penny) + (10 − p) (mass of post-1982 penny). Students solve for p, total pre-1982 pennies, and then find 10 − p, total post-1982 pennies.

Students may elect a non-math approach (see above) to find total pre-1982 and post-1982 pennies.

2. Mass

3. Auto tires, soft-drink containers, paper clips, buttons, or any class of related objects with different masses, but similar appearance and identical function

A.7 Isotopes in Nature

Most elements are mixtures of isotopes. Although isotopes of an element have identical chemical properties, their masses differ due to different total neutrons. Some isotopes are radioactive (radioisotopes); others are not. Typically, radioactivity is linked to particular neutron/proton ratios and forces holding nuclei together.

Atomic (or molar) masses represent a *weighted average* of isotopes of an element. The contribution of an isotope to an element's atomic mass is related to its percent abundance. For example, carbon's most common isotope is C-12; the atomic weight of carbon is 12.01. This value is slightly larger than 12, suggesting that there are small amounts isotopes more massive than C-12.

Developing Skills

A.8 Molar Mass and Isotopic Abundance

This activity gives students practice in calculating the average molar mass of an element from isotopic molar masses, and in determining the percent abundance of isotopes from an element's molar mass and isotopic molar masses. Depending on students' abilities and comfort with mathematical problem solving, you may choose to work through the sample problems to model this type of calculation.

Answers

1. Student data. Students should use the formula in the text.
2. Student data
3. Answers 1 and 2 should be the same.
4. a. It should be closer to 11, since more than 80% of boron atoms are boron-11 isotopes.
   b. Molar mass = (0.1990)(10.0 g/mol) + (0.8010)(11.0 g/mol) = 10.80 g/mol
5. a. It should be closest to 238. The molar mass should be closest to the mass of the most abundant isotope.
   b. Molar mass = (0.9928)(238.1 g/mol) + (0.0071)(235.0 g/mol) + (0.000054)(234.0 g/mol) = 238.1 g/mol

---

Developing Skills

A.8 MOLAR MASS AND ISOTOPIC ABUNDANCE

You can calculate the average molar mass—and of the coins in the element *coinium* from the Modeling Matter activity on page 490—by using the mathematical relationship introduced in the sample problem below.

Sample Problem 1: *Consider an isotopic mixture of copper. Naturally occurring copper (Cu) consists of 69.1% copper-63 atoms and 30.9% copper-65 atoms. The molar masses of these two isotopes are:*

$$Copper\text{-}63 = 62.93 \text{ g/mol}$$

$$Copper\text{-}65 = 64.93 \text{ g/mol}$$

What is the average molar mass of naturally occurring copper?
The equation for finding average molar masses is as follows:

$$\text{Molar mass} = \begin{pmatrix}\text{Fractional} \\ \text{abundance} \\ \text{of isotope 1}\end{pmatrix} \times \begin{pmatrix}\text{Molar mass} \\ \text{of isotope 1}\end{pmatrix} + \begin{pmatrix}\text{Fractional} \\ \text{abundance} \\ \text{of isotope 2}\end{pmatrix} \times \begin{pmatrix}\text{Molar mass} \\ \text{of isotope 2}\end{pmatrix} + \dots \text{(for each isotope involved)}$$

Since there are two naturally occurring copper isotopes, the average molar mass of copper can be calculated as follows:

$$\text{Molar mass of Cu} = (0.691)(62.93 \text{ g/mol}) + (0.309)(64.93 \text{ g/mol}) = 63.5 \text{ g/mol}$$

The decimal fractions must add up to 1. Why?

Sample Problem 2: *For the coinium example, suppose that you found that the composition of the mixture was 0.40 (40%) pre-1982 pennies and 0.60 (60%) post-1982 pennies. What is the average mass of a penny?*

The equation setup is shown here, using the 40/60 coin mixture:

$$\text{Average penny mass} = (0.40) \times (\text{Mass of pre-1982 penny}) + (0.60) \times (\text{Mass of post-1982 penny})$$

1. Calculate the average mass of a penny in your *coinium* mixture.
2. Calculate the average mass of a penny in your mixture another way: Divide the total mass of your entire penny sample by 10.
3. Compare the average masses that you calculated in Questions 1 and 2. These results should convince you that either calculation leads to the same result. If not, consult your teacher.
4. Naturally occurring boron (B) is a mixture of two isotopes. (See the table at the top of the next page.)
   a. Do you expect the molar mass of naturally occurring boron to be closer to 10 or to 11? Why?
   b. Calculate the molar mass of naturally occurring boron.

 **A.7 and A.8 Supplement:
Finding Average Atomic Weight**

5. Naturally occurring uranium (U) is a mixture of three isotopes.

   a. Do you expect the molar mass of naturally occurring uranium will be closest to 238, 235, or 234? Why?

   b. Calculate the molar mass of naturally occurring uranium.

ISOTOPE MOLAR MASS AND ABUNDANCE		
Isotope	Molar Mass (g/mol)	% Natural Abundance
Boron-10	10.0	19.90%
Boron-11	11.0	80.10%
Uranium-234	234.0	0.0054%
Uranium-235	235.0	0.71%
Uranium-238	238.1	99.28%

Making Decisions

A.9 FACT OR FICTION?

Look again at the statements at the start of this unit (page 478). Answer the following questions about the CANT flyer. This will help you start preparing your presentation for Riverwood senior citizens (see Figure 6.18).

1. Identify the specific statements on the flyer that you can now conclusively identify as either true or false. For each statement,

   a. list two pieces of evidence that helped you make your decision.

   b. list two public concerns about the statement that you plan to address in your presentation.

2. a. Choose one statement from the flyer that you understand more completely now, but are still unable to confirm or deny.

   b. What else do you need to know before you can make a decision about that statement?

3. How helpful do you think it will be to discuss the history of some discoveries that you studied in this section when you talk to the Riverwood senior citizens? Explain your answer.

4. a. Which new terms introduced in this section will you explain as part of your presentation?

   b. Select two terms from your answer to Question 4a. Prepare an explanation of each term that your audience will understand. Describe examples or real-world applications that you may use in your explanation.

Figure 6.18 *What does your research lead you to conclude about the accuracy of statements made in the flyer? (See page 478.)*

The history of science is full of discoveries that build on earlier discoveries. The discovery of radioactivity was such an event. The investigations of Roentgen, Becquerel, the Curies, and Rutherford led to new knowledge and a better understanding of atomic structure. As you start to consider some current applications of nuclear radiation, think about the evidence and reasoning that supported these scientific advancements.

Section A   The Nature of Atoms   493

Making Decisions

A.9 Fact or Fiction?

Their answers will help students prepare the presentation for Riverwood senior citizens. Encourage students to keep a folder dedicated to the Making Decisions activities throughout the unit. Having access to their previous work and thoughts on the CANT statements will be beneficial when students begin to work on the culminating activity. You may have students complete this task individually or in small groups. Also consider assigning students to the same groups in which they will complete the final project to encourage productive, collaborative work.

Answers

1. a. Answers will vary, but the following statements can be classified as fully *false* based on information contained in Section A:
   "Radioactive materials and radiation are unnatural—they did not exist on Earth until created by scientists." Radioactive materials exist in nature. The first nuclear scientists extracted radioactive material from tons of pitchblende.
   "All radiation causes cancer." Radiation only leads to cancer when it is sufficiently energetic and exposure limits are exceeded. All living matter is exposed to natural background radiation all the time.
   "Human senses can detect radioactivity." Human senses cannot detect alpha and beta particles or gamma waves. We need special instruments to detect and measure radiation.

   b. Students may refer to the CANT flyer, may express concerns of their own, or may raise concerns they have heard in other venues. Public concerns may touch on issues of health, safety, the environment, and economics.

2–4. Help students clarify their ideas about the topic and make plans for their presentation.

SECTION A SUMMARY

✎ **Section A Supplement**

Reviewing the Concepts

1. Becquerel wrapped a photographic plate in black paper, then put it next to a fluorescent mineral. He stored the plate and mineral in a drawer for several days. Unexpectedly, the film showed faint fogging when developed.

2. Radium, polonium, and uranium

3. The spontaneous emission of particles and energy from atomic nuclei

4. Alpha particles, beta particles, and gamma rays

5. They were deflected in a magnetic field as if they were positively charged.

6. It is not deflected by a magnetic field and has no electrical charge.

7. Knowledge about alpha and beta particles convinced scientists that atoms must be composed of even smaller particles.

8. a. Ionizing radiation can eject electrons from molecules, leading to formation of ions. Examples include UV radiation, X-rays, and gamma rays.
   b. Nonionizing radiation transfers its energy to matter and causes molecules to vibrate, rotate, translate, or move electrons to higher energy levels; the matter often increases in temperature. Examples include visible, microwave, and infrared radiation.

9. Because fragments formed on absorption of ionizing radiation are highly reactive and can damage living systems

10. Nonionizing: a, d; ionizing: b, c

11. The reactive particles it creates disrupt normal cell chemistry.

12. A beam of alpha particles was focused at a thin sheet of gold foil. A zinc-sulfide screen sur-

rounded the gold foil and fluoresced where each alpha particle struck it. The paths of the alpha particles could be deduced from locations of these flashes of light.

13. a. They passed through the gold foil.
    b. Most of the volume occupied by gold atoms is empty space.

14. a. They bounced back toward the source.
    b. There must be a dense, positively charged structure within the atom.

15. He proposed that atoms consist of a small, positively charged nucleus surrounded by negatively charged particles.

16. Drawings for before the experiment should show electrons and protons evenly distributed through the atom.

SECTION A SUMMARY
Reviewing the Concepts

Radioactive nuclei are unstable and undergo spontaneous changes in their structure.

1. Describe the sequence of events that led to Becquerel's discovery of radioactivity.

2. What three radioactive elements did the Curies find in pitchblende?

3. Define *radioactivity*.

4. List three types of nuclear radiation.

5. How did scientists determine that alpha particles have a positive electrical charge?

6. In what way is gamma radiation different from alpha and beta radiation?

7. How did the idea that the atom is the smallest particle of matter change after the discovery of radioactivity?

Radiation can be classified as either *ionizing* or *nonionizing,* depending on the type of energy it transmits.

8. Define and give an example of
   a. *ionizing radiation.*
   b. *nonionizing radiation.*

9. Why is ionizing radiation regarded as more dangerous than nonionizing radiation?

10. Classify each of the following as ionizing or nonionizing radiation:
    a. visible light   c. gamma rays
    b. X-rays   d. radio waves

11. How does ionizing radiation damage living cells?

Rutherford's gold-foil experiment results led to a new model of the atom.

12. Describe Rutherford's gold-foil experiment.

13. a. What happened to most of the alpha particles observed in the gold-foil experiment?
    b. What did Rutherford conclude from this observation?

14. a. What happened to about 1 in every 20 000 alpha particles in the gold-foil experiment?
    b. What did Rutherford conclude from this observation?

15. What was the general structure of the atom that Rutherford proposed?

16. Sketch models to show the concept of an atom before and after Rutherford's gold-foil experiment.

17. What characteristic of alpha particles made them desirable as the beam in Rutherford's gold-foil experiment?

Most elements in nature are a mixture of isotopes. Some isotopes are radioactive.

18. Give the correct isotopic notation for copper-65.

19. Calculate the total neutrons present in an atom of sulfur-34.

20. Copy the following table and determine the value of each coded letter, *a* through *p*:

Symbol	Total Protons	Total Neutrons	Mass Number
$^2_1$H	*a*	1	*b*
$^{37}_c$Cl	*d*	*e*	*f*
^g_hTc	43	56	*i*
$^{137}_j$Cs	*k*	*l*	*m*
^n_oAg	47	60	*p*

Connecting the Concepts

24. A local politician proposes to ban all radiation in your community. Explain why this proposal has little chance of success.

25. Why is it possible to receive a suntan from ultraviolet radiation but not from radio waves?

26. How does the gold-foil experiment demonstrate the importance of evidence regarding events that cannot be directly observed?

21. How do the nuclei of carbon-12, carbon-13, and carbon-14 differ?

22. Consider the symbol $^{190}_{78}$Pt.
    a. What does the superscript 190 indicate?
    b. What does the subscript 78 indicate?
    c. How many neutrons are in a Pt-190 nucleus?

23. Neon (Ne) is composed of three isotopes with the following molar masses and relative abundances: Ne-20 (19.99 g/mol), 90.51%; Ne-21 (20.99 g/mol), 0.27%; and Ne-22 (21.99 g/mol), 9.22%.
    a. Based on these data, should neon's atomic weight be closest to 20, 21, or 22? Why?
    b. Calculate the actual atomic weight of neon. Show your calculations.

27. Describe how the development of atomic theory illustrates the way scientific discoveries build on previous scientific knowledge and experiments.

28. In what way is fluorescence different from radioactivity?

29. In what way is a cathode-ray tube similar to a
    a. modern X-ray device?
    b. television tube?

Section Summary   495

---

21. In numbers of neutrons
22. a. Mass number (total protons and neutrons in the nucleus)
    b. Atomic number (total protons)
    c. 112
23. a. 20, because the most abundant isotope is Ne-20
    b. (19.99 g/mol)(0.9051) + (20.99 g/mol)(0.0027) + (21.99 g/mol)(0.0922) = 18.09 + 0.057 + 2.03 = 20.18 g/mol

Connecting the Concepts

24. "All radiation" includes the entire electromagnetic spectrum. That would mean banning radio transmissions, microwave ovens, visible light, and infrared heat lamps as well as *sunlight*.

25. Radio waves are nonionizing, while UV rays can be ionizing. Skin "tans" when many skin molecules release increased quantities of the pigment melanin after exposure to UV radiation.

26. Using the gold-foil experiment, Rutherford and co-workers concluded that the atom has a small, positively charged nucleus and that most of the volume of an atom is empty space, based on indirect evidence about the structure of atoms.

27. Becquerel's observations led to questions about the nature of atomic structure, which led to further research by Rutherford and others.

28. In fluorescence, particular materials emit light when they are struck by radiant energy. These materials cease to emit light when radiant energy is removed. In radioactivity, atomic nuclei spontaneously emit particles and energy.

29. a. Both use a beam of electrons to excite some substances.
    b. Both use a beam of electrons to excite some substances.

Drawings for after the experiment should show a small, dense nucleus and electrons surrounding the nucleus, but most of the atom's volume as empty space.

17. They have high velocities, are relatively massive, possess an electrical charge, and can be readily detected.

18. $^{65}_{29}$Cu

19. 18 neutrons (34 − 16 = 18)

20.

SYMBOL	TOTAL PROTONS	TOTAL NEUTRONS	MASS NUMBER
	a = 1		b = 2
c = 17	d = 17	e = 20	f = 37
g = 99, h = 43			i = 99
j = 55	k = 55	l = 82	m = 137
n = 107, o = 47			p = 107

Extending the Concepts

30. Gold is very dense but not a very active metal. It is extremely malleable and can be hammered into a thin sheet only a few atoms thick.

31. The kind of scattering Rutherford observed would not have occurred with beta particles. Beta particles are negatively charged (electrons) and would not have been repelled by the positively charged nucleus.

32. The neutron has no electrical charge; we cannot observe it interacting with electrically charged objects.

33. a. In Thomson's "plum pudding" model, negatively charged particles are embedded in a uniformly positively-charged sphere.

b. The quantum mechanical model includes the dense, positively-charged nucleus of Rutherford and depicts electrons probability clouds.

Extending the Concepts

30. Investigate the properties of gold and discuss why Rutherford probably selected that metal as an alpha-particle target.

31. Imagine that Rutherford proposed using beta particles rather than alpha particles in the gold-foil experiment. What result would you predict?

32. The neutron was discovered decades after the proton and electron were discovered. What made discovering the neutron such a challenge?

33. Compare earlier models of the atom with

a. Rutherford's model.
b. the currently accepted model of the atom.

Nuclear Radiation

Of nearly 2000 known isotopes, there are more radioactive (unstable) isotopes than there are nonradioactive (stable) isotopes. Actually, most isotopes you encounter are not radioactive. However, naturally occurring radioisotopes expose everyone to low levels of radiation. This radiation is from radioisotopes in building materials (such as brick and stone) in schools and homes (see Figure 6.19); in air, land, and sea; in foods you eat; and even within your own body. Because the human senses cannot detect nuclear radiation, various devices to detect and measure its intensity have been developed.

B.1 EXPOSURE TO IONIZING RADIATION

When radioisotopes spontaneously decay, they usually emit alpha, beta, and/or gamma radiation. The type and intensity of the radiation emitted helps to determine possible medical and industrial applications of particular radioisotopes. Each type of nuclear radiation also poses distinct hazards to human health.

A relatively constant level of radioactivity, called **background radiation,** is always present around and within you. Everyone receives background radiation at low levels from natural sources and from sources related to human activity. You will always experience at least some exposure to ionizing radiation.

Natural sources of background ionizing radiation include:

- High-energy particles from outer space that bombard Earth.
- Radioisotopes in rocks, soil, and groundwater: uranium (U-238 and U-235), thorium (Th-232), and the radioactive isotopes that form as they decay.
- Radioisotopes in the atmosphere: radon (Rn-222) and its decay products, including polonium (Po-210).
- Naturally occurring radioisotopes in foods and in the environment, such as potassium-40 and carbon-14.

Radiation Emitted by Everyday Objects

Figure 6.19 *Bricks are a common source of background ionizing radiation.*

Figure 6.20 *Air travel increases human exposure to ionizing radiation.*

Nuclear Radiation

This section introduces students to the nature and properties of three common types of nuclear radiation—alpha particles, beta particles, and gamma rays. It discusses the level of radiation considered safe for humans in terms of background radiation and exposure standards. The text presents some consequences of exposure to radiation, leading to a discussion of devices that detect and measure radiation intensity. Laboratory investigations provide opportunities for students to use these devices.

B.1 Exposure to Ionizing Radiation

Humans are exposed regularly to low-level natural background radiation due to the spontaneous decay of radioactive elements from natural sources in the environment. Additional exposure occurs to radiation generated from human activities, such as medical X-rays or industrial activities. The text compares the SI units used to measure radiation exposure (gray and sievert) to radiation absorbed dose (rad) and its effect on living organisms (rem). Although the level of background radiation from natural and human sources is well below the limits set by the U.S. government as reasonably safe, it is prudent to avoid unnecessary exposure to ionizing radiation.

Using the Figures

Figures 6.19 and 6.20: Bricks can contain up to 2200 Bq/kg Ra-226 (**http://www.uic.com.au/nip59.htm**). As an introduction to *Making Decisions B.2* (pages 500–501), you could invite students to think of possible sources of background radiation they encounter in their lives.

Additional Information

The units to use for measuring radiation depend on the quantity or effect being measured. The gray, sievert, rem, and rad are all mentioned in the student text. Both the gray (Gy) and the rad (radiation absorbed dose) are measures of the quantity of energy absorbed per kilogram of tissue. One gray equals one joule per kilogram of tissue. The gray is named after Louis Harold Gray, a student of Ernest Rutherford, who did research on the biological effect of neutrons. With colleagues, he discovered that damage done by neutrons to human systems was a function of both dose and dose rate. One rad is equal to one-hundredth of a gray.

Both the sievert (Sv) and rem are units expressing the extent of tissue damage that radiation causes. The sievert is named for Rolf Sievert, a medical radiation physicist who developed a chamber for measuring radiation dose. Like Gray, he was interested in the biological effects of radiation and application of radiation therapies in cancer treatment. *Rem* stands for the **r**oentgen **e**quivalent **m**an—a nod to another early pioneer in nuclear chemistry, Wilhelm Conrad Roentgen.

Other units commonly used for measuring radiation include the becquerel (Bq) and the curie (Ci). The becquerel is the SI unit expressing the number of decay events per second. The curie also expresses the number of decay events per second and is more useful because it is a larger unit. One curie equals 3.7×10^{10} Bq.

The total radioisotopes released to the environment from fossil-fuel power plants is greater than the total released from nuclear power plants.

The units *rad* and *rem* are abbreviations for roentgen absorbed dose and roentgen equivalent man.

Advances in science and technology have created additional sources of background radiation, such as:

▶ Residual radioactive fallout from aboveground nuclear-weapon testing.

▶ Increased exposure to radiation during high-altitude airplane flights (see Figure 6.20).

▶ Radioisotopes released into the environment from both fossil fuel and nuclear power generation as well as other nuclear technologies.

▶ Radioisotopes released through the disturbance and use of rocks in mining and in making cement, concrete, and sheet rock.

Because of its effect on living tissue, it is important to monitor the amount of ionizing radiation to which people are exposed over time. The **gray** (Gy) is the SI unit that expresses the quantity of ionizing radiation absorbed by a particular sample, typically human tissue. An absorbed dose of one gray is defined as one joule of energy absorbed per kilogram of body tissue.

Not all forms of ionizing radiation, however, produce the same effect on living organisms. For example, alpha radiation will cause more harm internally to living organisms than will the same quantity of gamma radiation. The **sievert** (Sv) is the SI unit that expresses the ability of radiation—regardless of type or activity—to cause ionization in human tissue. Any exposure to radiation that produces the same detrimental effects as one gray of gamma rays represents one *sievert* of exposure. It is usually most convenient to express exposure in sieverts; this unit facilitates direct comparisons across different types of ionizing radiation.

While the SI units for radiation exposure are the gray and the sievert, two other units have traditionally been used in the U.S.: the *rad* and the *rem* (see Table 6.5). The **rad** (like the gray) expresses the absorbed dose of radiation, and the **rem** (like the sievert) indicates ionizing effects on living organisms. Both the rad and the rem are one-hundredth of their corresponding SI units.

| Table 6.5

UNITS OF RADIATION DOSAGE

Unit	Unit Expresses:		Definition
	Absorbed Dose	Ionizing Effects	
sievert (Sv)		X	1 Sv = dose equivalent of absorbed radiation that causes same biological effects as 1 Gy of gamma rays
rem		X	1 rem = 10^{-2} Sv
millirem (mrem)		X	1 mrem = 10^{-3} rem = 10^{-5} Sv
gray (Gy)	X		1 Gy = 1 J of energy absorbed per kilogram of body tissue
rad	X		1 rad = 10^{-2} Gy

Figure 6.21 *All living things contain some radioactive isotopes, including these that are located in particular parts of the human body.*

Thyroid
Iodine-131

Lungs
Radon-222
Uranium-238
Plutonium-239
Krypton-85

Muscles
Potassium-40
Cesium-137

Liver
Cobalt-60

Bones
Radium-226
Strontium-90
Phosphorus-32
Carbon-14

Even though one rem is only one-hundredth as large as one sievert, it is still much larger than typical radiation exposures. Normal human exposures are so small that doses are expressed in units of *millirem* (mrem), where 1 mrem = 0.001 rem. One millirem of any type of radiation produces essentially the same biological effects, whether the radiation is composed of alpha particles, beta particles, or gamma rays.

Some ionizing radiation comes from within your own body, as depicted in Figure 6.21. On average, people living in the United States receive about 360 mrem per person annually; about 300 mrem (83%) come from natural sources of radiation. Figure 6.22 shows the approximate proportion from each source.

It is in your best interest to avoid unnecessary ionizing radiation exposure. What ionizing radiation level is considered reasonably safe? The U.S. government's background radiation limit for the general public is 500 mrem (0.5 rem) per year for any individual. The U.S. average exposure value of 360 mrem falls below this. The established U.S. limit for an individual's annual maximum safe workplace exposure is 5000 mrem (5 rem).

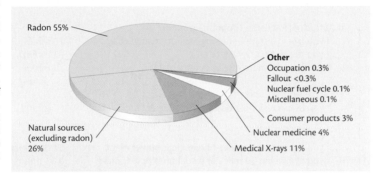

Radon 55%

Other
Occupation 0.3%
Fallout <0.3%
Nuclear fuel cycle 0.1%
Miscellaneous 0.1%

Consumer products 3%

Nuclear medicine 4%

Medical X-rays 11%

Natural sources (excluding radon) 26%

Figure 6.22 *Sources of ionizing radiation in the United States.*

ChemQuandary 2

RADIATION EXPOSURE STANDARDS

Why might radiation exposure standards for some individuals be different from those for the general public? Why do the standards differ for those who are exposed in their workplace?

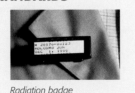

Radiation badge

ChemQuandary 2

Radiation Exposure Standards

Individuals who have more rapidly dividing cells, such as children and pregnant women, are more at risk from a given dose of radiation than the general population. On the other hand, for people needing benefits of radiation treatment, higher doses may be worth the risks. Also, for practical (including economic) reasons, occupationally exposed individuals (such as medical X-ray technicians and scientists handling radioactive pharmaceuticals, defense program workers, and civilian workers in nuclear power plants) are allowed to receive higher, though apparently still safe, doses.

Making Decisions

B.2 Your Annual Ionizing-Radiation Dose

The purpose of this activity is to raise student awareness of the sources and quantities of radiation in the everyday environment. The activity reinforces the fact that human senses cannot detect ionizing radiation, although emissions are constantly present. Using the table provided, students estimate their annual radiation dose in mrem, analyze the sources, and then consider ways to reduce the quantity of their exposure. Students also compare their results to the U.S. ionizing-radiation limit. Encourage students to share this table with friends and family members. Interesting discussions may follow from the realization that exposure to ionizing radiation is quite customary and, in fact, inevitable. A reproducible worksheet is provided in the TRB and on the TRCD for this activity. You may also instruct students to use a separate sheet of paper, but in either case remind students not to write in their books.

Answers

1. a. Answers will vary. Most should be below the U.S. limit of 500 mrem annually.
   b. Individual answers are expected here, comparing values with the standard 360 mrem/y.

Making Decisions

B.2 YOUR ANNUAL IONIZING-RADIATION DOSE

On a sheet of paper, list the numbers and letters of each category in the table on the following two pages. Then fill in the blanks on your sheet with appropriate quantities. Add all these quantities to estimate your annual ionizing-radiation dose.

YOUR ANNUAL IONIZING-RADIATION DOSE		
Common Sources of Radiation		**Your Annual Dose (mrem)**

1. Where You Live

a. Cosmic Radiation (from outer space)
Your exposure depends on elevation. These are annual doses.

sea level	26 mrem	4000–5000 ft	47 mrem
0–1000 ft	28 mrem	5000–6000 ft	52 mrem
1000–2000 ft	31 mrem	6000–7000 ft	66 mrem
2000–3000 ft	35 mrem	7000–8000 ft	79 mrem
3000–4000 ft	41 mrem	8000–9000 ft	96 mrem

_____ mrem

b. Terrestrial Radiation (from the ground)

If you live in a state bordering Gulf or Atlantic coasts	16 mrem
If you live in AZ, CO, NM, or UT	63 mrem
If you live anywhere else in continental U.S.	30 mrem

_____ mrem

c. House Construction

If you live in a stone, adobe, brick, or concrete building	7 mrem

_____ mrem

d. Power Plants

If you live within 50 miles of a nuclear power plant	0.009 mrem
If you live within 50 miles of a coal-fired power plant	0.03 mrem

_____ mrem

2. Food, Water, Air
Internal Radiation (based on average values)

a. from food (C-14, K-40) and water (radon dissolved in water)	40 mrem	_____ mrem
b. from air (radon)	200 mrem	_____ mrem

YOUR ANNUAL IONIZING-RADIATION DOSE (Continued)

Common Sources of Radiation		Your Annual Dose (mrem)
3. How You Live		
Weapons test fallout*	1 mrem	_____ mrem
Travel by jet aircraft (per hour of flight)	0.5 mrem	_____ mrem
If you have porcelain crowns or false teeth	0.07 mrem	_____ mrem
If you wear a luminous wristwatch	0.06 mrem	_____ mrem
If you go through airport security (each time)	0.002 mrem	_____ mrem
If you watch TV*	1 mrem	_____ mrem
If you use a video display (computer screen)*	1 mrem	_____ mrem
If you live in a dwelling with a smoke detector	0.008 mrem	_____ mrem
If you use a gas camping lantern with an old mantle	0.2 mrem	_____ mrem
If you wear a plutonium-powered pacemaker	100 mrem	_____ mrem
4. Medical Uses (radiation dose per procedure)		
X-rays: Extremity (arm, hand, foot, or leg)	1 mrem	_____ mrem
Dental	1 mrem	_____ mrem
Chest	6 mrem	_____ mrem
Pelvis/hip	65 mrem	_____ mrem
Skull/neck	20 mrem	_____ mrem
Barium enema	405 mrem	_____ mrem
Upper GI	245 mrem	_____ mrem
CT scan (head and body)	110 mrem	_____ mrem
Nuclear medicine (e.g., thyroid scan)	14 mrem	_____ mrem
Your Estimated Annual Radiation Dose		_____ *mrem*

*The value is less than 1 mrem but adding that value would be reasonable.
Adapted from American Nuclear Society (2000). Copyright 2000 American Nuclear Society.

1. Compare your annual ionizing-radiation dose to the
   a. U.S. limit of 500 mrem per person annually.
   b. average background radiation value (360 mrem).

2. a. Why is it useful to keep track of how many X-rays you receive annually?
   b. What geographic factors might decrease your annual ionizing-radiation dose?

3. a. What lifestyle changes could reduce a person's exposure to ionizing radiation?
   b. Would you decide to make those changes? Explain.

Section B   Nuclear Radiation   **501**

2. a. This is an effective way to monitor one's annual exposure to radiation. (You may choose to discuss with students the advisability of inquiring about the necessity of each medical and dental X-ray, and ensuring that technicians use shielding for body parts not being X-rayed.)
   b. Living at lower altitudes, living in nonmasonry structures, living away from nuclear power plants, and living near the Gulf Coast or Atlantic Ocean. Point out that even after making these changes, the resulting reduction in exposure would still be very small. The values in the table also suggest that making these changes would not result in a substantial change in one's annual radiation dose.

3. a. Answers may include flying less frequently (which may involve switching to automobile transportation, which is associated with *other* hazards), moving to lower elevations, switching to a wood-constructed home, or refraining from watching TV or using a computer.
   b. Answers will vary. In many cases, students would not make these changes because the activity may be necessary or the changes will alter their lifestyles. Students may also indicate they would not make changes because they will not necessarily result in a substantially lower annual radiation dose.

B.3 Ionizing Radiation: How Much Is Safe?

The damage ionizing radiation does to human tissue depends on the quantity of radiation received and the energy associated with that radiation. The biological effects of large doses of ionizing radiation include changes to DNA, which may result in birth defects, cancer, and other diseases. One problem associated with assessing radiation damage is that low-level radiation does not produce unique effects that are easy to distinguish from the results of other injuries or illnesses. Also, it often takes years for symptoms to appear.

B.3 IONIZING RADIATION: HOW MUCH IS SAFE?

The two main factors that determine tissue damage due to ionizing radiation are *radiation density* (the number of ionizations within a given volume) and *dose* (the quantity of radiation received).

Gamma rays and X-rays are ionizing forms of electromagnetic radiation that penetrate deeply into human tissue. Ionizing radiation causes tissue damage by breaking bonds in molecules. At low levels of ionizing radiation, only a few molecules are damaged. In most low-dose cases, a body's systems can repair the damage. As the dose received increases, the total number of molecules affected by the radiation also increases. Generally, the damage to proteins and nucleic acids is of greatest concern because of their role in body structures and functions. Proteins form much of the body's soft tissue structure and compose enzymes, molecules that control the rates of cellular chemical reactions. If a large number of protein molecules are destroyed within a small region, too few functioning molecules may remain to enable the body to heal itself in a reasonable time (see Figure 6.23).

> See Unit 7 for more information on proteins and enzymes.

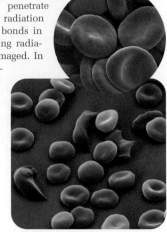

Figure 6.23 *Mutations are caused by damage to DNA which can result from exposure to radiation. Here, blood cells are deformed (normal cells are shown above) as a result of a mutation.*

Table 6.6 *These four factors determine the actual effects of particular ionizing-radiation exposure.*

BIOLOGICAL DAMAGE FROM IONIZING RADIATION	
Factor	**Effect**
Dose	Most scientists assume that an increase in radiation dose produces a proportional increase in risk.
Exposure time	The more a given dose is spread out over time, the less harm it does.
Area exposed	The larger the body area exposed to a given radiation dose, the greater the damage.
Tissue type	Rapidly dividing cells, such as blood cells and germ cells, are more susceptible to radiation damage than are slowly dividing or nondividing cells, such as nerve cells. Fetuses and children are more susceptible to radiation damage than are adults.

Nucleic acids in DNA can be damaged by ionizing radiation. Minor damage causes **mutations,** which are changes in the structure of DNA that may result in the production of altered proteins. Mutations often kill the cell in which they occur. If the cell is a sperm or ovum, a mutation may lead to birth defects in offspring. Some mutations can lead to *cancer,* a disease in which cell growth and metabolism are out of control. When the DNA in many body cells is severely damaged, cells cannot synthesize new proteins to replace the damaged ones, and the organism or person dies.

> DNA molecules control cell reproduction and the synthesis of proteins.

Table 6.6 lists factors determining the extent of biological damage from ionizing radiation. Table 6.7 summarizes the biological effects of large doses of ionizing radiation. Because the values in Table 6.7 are so large, they are reported in rems, not millirems.

Large ionizing-radiation doses can have drastic effects on humans. Conclusive evidence that such doses produce increased cancer rates has been gathered from uranium miners and nuclear-accident victims. Some of the first cases of exposure to large doses of ionizing radiation occurred among workers who used radium compounds to paint numbers on watch dials that would glow in the dark (see Figure 6.24). The workers used their tongues to smooth the tips of their paintbrushes and unknowingly ingested small amounts of radioactive compounds. Later, these workers began to lose hair and became quite weak. Sometimes this exposure even led to death.

IONIZING-RADIATION EFFECTS	
Dose (rem)	**Effect**
0–25	No immediate observable effects.
25–50	Small decreases in white blood cell count, causing lowered resistance to infections.
50–100	Marked decrease in white blood cell count; development of lesions.
100–200	Radiation sickness: nausea, vomiting, and hair loss; blood cells die.
200–300	Hemorrhaging, ulcers, death.
300–500	Acute radiation sickness; 50% of those exposed die within a few weeks.
>700	100% die.

Table 6.7 *You can see how the consequences of radiation exposure change as dose increases.*

> Becquerel discovered a red spot on his chest after carrying a radium sample in his breast pocket. The dangers of ionizing radiation were unknown at that time.

Figure 6.24 *These women painted radioactive radium onto watch dials so the watches could be read in the dark. Their exposure to ionizing radiation from radium often resulted in illness. Modern glow-in-the-dark watches do not contain radium.*

Using the Figures

Figures 6.23 and 6.24: Ask students whether they know of comparable situations in which health issues are now linked to activities previously thought to be safe. Some examples involve cigarettes, lead-based paints, leaded gasoline, asbestos insulation, and thalidomide. Encourage students to discuss how these types of situations might be prevented in the future and what factors might make them difficult to prevent. Emphasize the task of a science-literate citizenry to monitor and participate in situations where science and public health intersect.

Note: If students question whether or not Figure 6.23 shows sickled blood cells caused by sickle-cell anemia, tell them that sickle-cell anemia is caused by an inherited mutation, not by a radiation-induced mutation.

Investigating Matter

B.4 Alpha, Beta, and Gamma Radiation

B.4 Alpha, Beta, and Gamma Student Worksheet and Data Table

This investigation acquaints students with characteristics of three types of emissions from radioactive materials. In Part 1, students compare the penetrating abilities of alpha, beta, and gamma radiation. In Part 2, they determine the effect of distance on radiation intensity, and in Part 3 they compare the radiation-shielding effects of lead and glass. As they account for background radiation in their observations, remind students of a fact introduced in *Making Decisions B.2*—their everyday environments contain natural radiation.

Only a few detectors are sensitive to all three types of ionizing radiation. Alpha radiation is commonly the hardest to detect. Thus, depending on available equipment, you may have difficulty demonstrating alpha-particle detection. If equipment is in short supply, you may demonstrate this procedure. This activity addresses several important concepts, so students should at least observe a demonstration.

Note: The American Nuclear Society conducts a special program to distribute working Geiger-Mueller counters to schools. Visit **http://www. ans.org/pi/edu/teachers/workshops/** for more information. Your school's physics department or local college or university physics department may also have Geiger counters available for loan.

Time

50–90 min

Materials

(For 12 student pairs)

12 radiation counters

504

12 alpha, beta, gamma radiation source sets

12 meter sticks

12 lead plates (5 cm × 5 cm × 0.1 cm)

24 glass plates (5 cm × 5 cm × 0.3 cm)

12 pieces of cardboard (5 cm × 5 cm × 0.1 cm)

Vernier calipers (optional) for measuring the exact thickness of plates

12 sheets of graph paper

12 forceps or crucible tongs (for handling isotopes)

24 pairs disposable safety gloves

Leukemia, a rapidly developing cancer of white blood cells, is commonly associated with exposure to high doses of ionizing radiation. Exposure also promotes other forms of cancer, anemia, heart problems, and cataracts (opaque spots on an eye lens).

Considerable controversy continues regarding whether very low doses of ionizing radiation, such as those from typical background sources, can cause cancer. Most of the data on cancer incidence have been based on human exposure to high doses of radiation; these data are extrapolated to much lower doses. Few studies have directly linked low radiation doses with cancer development. Most scientists agree that typical background levels of ionizing radiation are safe for most people. Some authorities argue that any increase above normal background levels increases the probability of developing cancer.

Investigating Matter

B.4 ALPHA, BETA, AND GAMMA RADIATION

Laboratory Video: Alpha, Beta, and Gamma Radiation

Introduction

An early device used to detect radioactivity still used today is the Geiger-Mueller counter (Figure 6.25). As illustrated in Figure 6.26, ionizing radiation that strikes the detector produces electrical signals. In this investigation, a counter (or similar device) will detect the penetrating abilities of different types of ionizing radiation through cardboard, glass, and lead.

Figure 6.25 *Using a Geiger-Mueller counter to measure radiation dose.*

Ionizing radiation enters the counter's detecting tube (or probe), producing an electrical signal. Most radiation counters register these signals as both audible clicks and meter readings. The intensity of the radiation is indicated by the number of electronic signals or counts per minute (cpm).

You must first take a reading of background radiation to establish a *baseline* before taking readings from a known radioactive source. You then subtract the background count from each radioactive-source reading to find the actual radiation level emitted by that source.

With proper handling, radioactive materials in this investigation pose no danger to you. Nuclear materials are strictly regulated by state and federal laws. The radioactive sources you will use emit only very small quantities of radiation; using them requires no special license.

High voltage

+

–

Path of ionizing radiation

Figure 6.26 *As ionizing radiation passes into a Geiger-Mueller detector tube, ions form in the gas inside. Positive ions are attracted to the tube's negatively charged outer wall, while negative ions are attracted to the positively charged center. These electrically charged particle movements constitute a pulse of electrical current. Each pulse is detected and counted.*

Safety

Students should always wear protective goggles, aprons, and gloves when handling radioactive materials throughout this investigation. (*Note:* The students shown in **Figures 6.27** and **6.28** are not wearing gloves or goggles because they are not handling samples, but all students should be encouraged to wear protective equipment throughout the investigation.)

Nevertheless, you should handle all radioactive samples with great care, including wearing protective gloves. Do not allow the radiation counter to come in direct contact with any radioactive material. Check your hands with a radiation monitor before you leave the laboratory.

Procedure

Part 1: Penetrating Ability

1. Read the following procedure and construct a data table suitable for recording all relevant data.

2. Set up the apparatus shown in Figure 6.27. There should be space between the source and the detector for several sheets of glass or metal.

3. Turn on the counter; allow it to warm up for at least 3 min. Determine the intensity of background radiation by counting the clicks for one minute without any radioactive sources present. Record this background-radiation value in counts per minute (cpm) in your data table.

4. Put on protective gloves. Using forceps, place a gamma-ray source on the ruler at a point where it produces nearly a full-scale reading. Observe the meter for 30 s and estimate the number of counts per minute detected over this period. Record this approximate value. Then subtract the background reading from that value and record the corrected results.

5. Without moving the radiation source, place a piece of thin cardboard (or an index card) between the detector and the source, as shown in Figure 6.28.

6. Observe the meter for 30 s. Record the typical reading. Then correct the reading for background radiation and record the corrected result in your data table.

7. Repeat Steps 5 and 6, replacing the cardboard with a glass or plastic sheet.

8. Repeat Steps 5 and 6, replacing the cardboard with a lead sheet.

9. Repeat Steps 4 through 8, using a beta-particle source.

10. Repeat Steps 4 through 8, using an alpha-particle source.

Figure 6.27 *You will need to determine the level of radiation detected in the absence of shielding.*

Figure 6.28 *How will the type of shielding affect the level of detected radiation?*

Section B Nuclear Radiation **505**

Lab Tips

- Adjust laboratory procedures for the apparatus available. Not all detectors will measure all forms of radiation.
- Cover lab tables with butcher paper for these nuclear investigations.
- Radioactive sources sealed in plastic disks are available from most commercial school-science suppliers.
- Most lead plates available for shielding are 1 mm thick.
- Because even a few cm of air will block alpha particles, the thick glass of the counter probe will not permit their detection. You can order a very thin glass plate or totally remove the glass plate on the end of the counter probe so students can discover how several cm of air can act as a barrier to alpha particles.
- Since the radioactive sources used will probably be weak, the total time needed may have to be extended from 30 seconds to several minutes. If possible, it is better to count clicks rather than just record an average meter reading. The use of gloves in this investigation is not only to shield students from radiation, but also to protect the sample from contamination. With sealed commercial sources, there is little risk of this type of contamination.
- If student readings are highly variable, instruct them to take additional readings.
- Take great care to ensure that the radioactive materials you and your students handle present no dangers.
- Be sure that no extraneous radioactive materials come in contact with your radiation counter. The counter can become contaminated with radiation and record higher-than-normal background readings.

Part 1 Answers

1. Lead greatly reduces the levels of alpha, beta, and gamma radiation. Cardboard greatly reduces alpha radiation levels. Glass reduces the levels of alpha and beta radiation.
2. Gamma radiation is the most penetrating; alpha radiation is the least penetrating.
3. a. Lead is most effective. It reduced the levels of all three types of radiation.
   b. Cardboard is least effective. It can only reduce alpha (the least penetrating) radiation.
4. Density and thickness

Part 2 Answers

5. Intensity decreased by a factor of four.
6. No. Redoubled, it is approximately one-sixteenth the original.
7. The intensity varies inversely with the square of the distance ($I = k/d^2$).

Part 2: Effect of Distance on Intensity

11. Read the following procedure and construct a data table suitable for recording all relevant data.
12. Using forceps, place a radioactive source designated by your teacher at a ruler distance (usually about 5 cm) that produces nearly a full-scale reading.
13. Observe the reading over 30 s. Determine the average number of counts per minute (cpm) and record that value. Then correct this reading by subtracting the background value. Record your corrected values.
14. Move the source so its distance from the detector is doubled.
15. Observe the reading over 30 s. Record the average value and the corrected value.
16. Move the source two more times, so the original distance is first tripled, then quadrupled, recording the initial and corrected readings after each move. (For example, if your first reading was at 2 cm, you would also take readings at 4, 6, and 8 cm.)
17. Graph your data, plotting corrected cpm values on the *y*-axis and distances from the source to the detector (in cm) on the *x*-axis.

Figure 6.29 *Relationship between distance from the source (left) and radiation intensity. Intensity is expressed as counts per minute within a given area. Note how the same quantity of radiation spreads over a larger area (B vs. A) as distance from the source increases.*

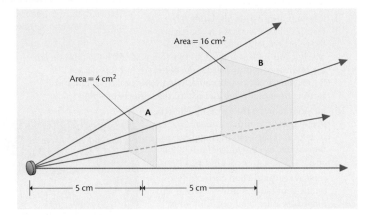

Part 3: Shielding Effects

18. Read the following procedure and construct a data table suitable for recording all relevant data.
19. Using forceps, place a radioactive source designated by your teacher on the ruler to give nearly a full-scale reading.
20. Take a typical reading over 30 s. Determine the number of counts per minute (cpm), correcting for background radiation. Record your actual and corrected values.

21. Place a glass sheet between the source and the detector. Do not change the distance between the detector and the source. Take an average reading over 30 s. Then determine and record the corrected number of counts per minute.

22. Place a second glass sheet between the source and the detector. Take an average reading over 30 s. Determine and record the corrected number of counts per minute.

23. Repeat Steps 21 and 22, using lead sheets rather than glass sheets.

24. Wash your hands thoroughly and check your hands with a radiation monitor before leaving the laboratory.

Questions for Part 1

1. Which shielding materials were effective in reducing the intensity of each type of radiation? Support your answers with data or observations.

2. How do the three types of radiation that you tested compare in terms of their penetrating ability?

3. Of the shielding materials tested, which do you conclude is the
   a. most effective in blocking radiation? Cite supporting evidence.
   b. least effective in blocking radiation? Cite supporting evidence.

4. Based on your observations, what properties of a material appear to affect its radiation-shielding ability?

Questions for Part 2

Analyze the graph that you prepared in Step 17:

5. By what factor did the intensity of radiation (measured in counts per minute) change when the initial distance was doubled?

6. Did this same factor apply when the distance was doubled again?

7. State the mathematical relationship between distance and intensity, using the factor identified in Question 5 and information in Figure 6.29.

Questions for Part 3

8. How effective was doubling the shield thickness in blocking the radiation intensity by
   a. glass?   b. lead?

9. A patient receiving an X-ray is covered by a protective shield (Figure 6.30).
   a. What material would be a good choice for this apron?
   b. Why?

10. a. Which type of ionizing radiation from a source outside the body is likely to be most dangerous to living organisms?
    b. Why? Give evidence to support your answer.

A *factor* is a number by which a value is multiplied to give a new value.

Figure 6.30 *What type of body shielding is used as this dental X-ray is obtained?*

Section B   Nuclear Radiation   **507**

Part 3 Answers

8. a. Doubling the glass shield thickness made little difference.
   b. Doubling the lead shield thickness reduced the intensity of the radiation.

9. a. Lead
   b. Lead is very dense and can stop high-energy radiation such as gamma rays and X-rays.

10. a. Gamma radiation
    b. It has the greatest penetrating ability and the greatest energy per unit, so it can cause the most cellular and molecular disruption. Alpha radiation poses a serious problem if taken into the body through air passages or swallowing. Although it has less penetrating power, it has greater ionizing potential because of the massive size of alpha particles.

Post-Lab Discussion

Ask students to share the conclusions based on their collected data for each part of the investigation. Focus class discussion on trends in the data and inferred characteristics of each type of ionizing radiation.

B.5 Natural Radioactive Decay

The text further explains characteristics of alpha, beta, and gamma decay. Remind students that radioactive decay occurs because the nuclei of some isotopes are unstable. These nuclei attain stability by undergoing radioactive decay. Radioactive decay—in which one element is converted into another— is also called *nuclear transmutation*. Students may need help remembering the events associated with each type of decay. Encourage students to use **Table 6.8** when they have to predict the results of a particular nuclear disintegration reaction.

The text introduces the concept of balanced nuclear equations. In Unit 2, students learned that mass is conserved in chemical reactions. Emphasize that both atomic and mass numbers are conserved in nuclear reactions, but the identity of elements may change. After working through examples of nuclear equations, draw attention to **Figure 6.35** (page 510), which summarizes the uranium-238 radioactive decay series.

B.5 NATURAL RADIOACTIVE DECAY

Shielding of Radiation

> Because of their relatively large mass, slower velocities, and large (2+) electrical charge, alpha particles lose most of their energy within a short distance.

> Ionic charges, such as the 2+ of an alpha particle, are usually not included in nuclear equations.

You know that alpha particles are positively charged. Why is this so?

An alpha particle is composed of two protons and two neutrons; it is identical in composition to the nucleus of a helium-4 atom. Since alpha particles have no electrons, they have a double-positive electrical charge and are often symbolized as a doubly charged helium-4 atom, $^{4}_{2}He^{2+}$. Alpha radiation (also called *alpha emission*) is released by many radioisotopes of elements with atomic numbers greater than 83.

Compared to a beta particle, an alpha particle has 5 to 50 times more energy and is over 7300 times more massive. However, the larger and slower alpha particles are easy to stop when they are outside the body. Once inside the body, however, the electrical charge and energy of alpha particles can cause great damage to tissues. This damage occurs over very short distances (about 0.025 mm).

Because alpha particles are very powerful tissue-damaging agents once inside the body, alpha emitters in air, food, or water are particularly dangerous to human life. Fortunately, outside the body, alpha particles are easy to block. As you noted in Investigating Matter B.4 (page 504), alpha particles are even stopped within a few centimeters by air.

Figure 6.31 illustrates a radium-226 nucleus emitting an alpha particle. During this process, the radium nucleus loses two protons, so its atomic number drops from 88 to 86, and it becomes an isotope of a different element, radon. In addition to losing two protons, radium-226 loses two neutrons, so its mass number drops by 4. The net result is the formation of radon-222. The decay process can be represented by the following nuclear equation:

$$^{226}_{88}Ra \longrightarrow \quad ^{4}_{2}He \quad + \quad ^{222}_{86}Rn$$

Radium-226   Alpha particle   Radon-222

Atoms of two elements—helium and radon—have been formed from one atom of radium. (A radium compound is shown in Figure 6.32) Note that atoms are *not* necessarily conserved in nuclear reactions, as they are in chemical reactions. Atoms of different elements can appear on both sides of a nuclear equation. Total mass numbers and atomic numbers, however, *are* conserved. In the above equation for radium-226 decay, the reactant mass number equals the sum of mass numbers of products (226 = 4 + 222). Also, the atomic number of radium-226 equals the sum of atomic numbers of products (88 = 2 + 86). Both relations hold true for all nuclear reactions.

Figure 6.31 *Alpha-particle emission by radium-226. Consequently, its mass number decreases by four (2 p + 2 n) and its atomic number decreases by two (2 p).*

Figure 6.32 *Radium's name comes from the fact that small amounts of radium compounds, such as that on this antique watch face, emit enough radiation to glow in the dark. (See Figure 6.24, page 503.)*

Beta particles are fast-moving electrons emitted from a nucleus. Because they are so much lighter than alpha particles and travel at very high velocities, beta particles have much greater penetrating ability than do alpha particles. On the other hand, beta particles are not as damaging to living tissue.

During **beta decay,** a neutron in a nucleus decays to a proton and an electron. The proton remains in the nucleus, but the electron is ejected. The electron emitted from the nucleus is a beta particle. The following equation describes the process:

$$\underset{\text{Neutron}}{{}_{0}^{1}n} \longrightarrow \underset{\text{Proton}}{{}_{1}^{1}p} + \underset{\substack{\text{Beta particle} \\ \text{(electron)}}}{{}_{-1}^{0}e}$$

Due to its negligible mass and negative electrical charge, a beta particle is assigned a mass number of 0 and an "atomic number" (nuclear charge) of -1. The net nuclear change due to beta emission is that a neutron is converted to a proton.

The following equation shows a nucleus of lead-210 undergoing beta decay: The nucleus loses one neutron and gains one proton. The mass number remains unchanged at 210, but the atomic number increases from 82 to 83. The new nucleus thus formed is that of bismuth-210:

$$\underset{\text{Lead-210}}{{}_{82}^{210}\text{Pb}} \longrightarrow \underset{\text{Bismuth-210}}{{}_{83}^{210}\text{Bi}} + \underset{\substack{\text{Beta particle} \\ \text{(electron)}}}{{}_{-1}^{0}e}$$

Once again, the sum of all mass numbers remains the same in this nuclear equation (210 on each side), and the sum of atomic numbers (the nuclear charge) remains unchanged (82 on each side).

Alpha and beta decay often leave nuclei in an energetically excited state. This type of excited state is described as *metastable* and is designated by the symbol *m*. For example, the symbol ^{99m}Tc represents a technetium isotope in a metastable or excited state. Energy from isotopes in such excited states is released as gamma rays—high-energy electromagnetic radiation that has as much or more energy than X-rays. Because gamma rays have neither mass nor charge, their release does not change the mass balance or charge balance in a nuclear equation. Table 6.8 summarizes the general changes involved in natural radioactive decay.

> Note that *n, p,* and *e* are symbols, respectively, for a neutron, a proton, and a beta particle. An emitted electron (beta particle) can also be symbolized by the Greek letter beta, ${}_{-1}^{0}\beta$

> Tc-99m is the most widely used radioisotope in medical diagnostic studies. Its half-life is 6h.

| Table 6.8

CHANGES RESULTING FROM NUCLEAR DECAY				
Decay Type	Symbol	Change in Atomic Number	Change in Total Neutrons	Change in Mass Number
Alpha	${}_{2}^{4}\text{He}^{2+}, \alpha$	Decreases by 2	Decreases by 2	Decreases by 4
Beta	${}_{-1}^{0}e, \beta$	Increases by 1	Decreases by 1	No change
Gamma	γ	No change	No change	No change

Students may be curious about other types of radioactive decay. *Proton emission* decreases the mass and atomic numbers by one and is accompanied by transmutation of an element. This type of decay is rare and typically only occurs in neutron-deficient nuclei. Neutron emissions, also rare, occur when an atom contains excess neutrons and a neutron is ejected from the nucleus. This type of emission decreases the mass number of each atom by one and does not result in a transmutation. The result is a new isotope of the element.

Make sure students understand that while gamma rays are the most penetrating, the relatively massive alpha particles have impact over a greater area.

Given that radioactive decay is a dynamic process occurring beyond the limits of human vision, computer and film simulations can be effective aids to enhance student understanding. For instance, see the animations at **http://www.eas.asu. edu/~holbert/eee460/eee460.html** and **http://isotopes.lbl.gov/education/ glossary/glossaryf.htm**.

B.5 and B.6 Supplement: Nuclear Balancing Act

Figure 6.33 *Relative penetrating ability of alpha (α) particles, beta (β) particles, and gamma (γ) rays. Gamma rays are the most penetrating; alpha particles the least.*

Gamma rays are the most penetrating of these three forms of ionizing radiation. Under most circumstances, however, they cause the least damage to tissue over comparable distances. Why is this so? Tissue damage is related to the extent of ionization created by the radiation, and is expressed as the number of ionizations within each unit of tissue. Alpha particles, which create the highest levels of ionization per tissue unit, cause considerable damage over a short range. However, protecting against them is easy. Beta and gamma radiation do less damage over a longer range, but it is more difficult to protect against them. The relative penetrating abilities of the three types of ionizing radiation are shown in Figure 6.33.

Figure 6.34 *Uranium ore contains U-238 and U-235 isotopes, each of which participates in a decay series, producing several generations of radioactive decay products.*

New isotopes produced by radioactive decay may also be radioactive and therefore undergo further nuclear decay. Uranium (U) (see Figure 6.34) and thorium (Th) are *parents* (reactants) in three natural **decay series** that start with U-238, U-235, and Th-232, respectively. Each decay series ends with formation of a stable isotope of lead (Pb). The decay series starting with uranium-238 contains 14 steps, as shown in Figure 6.35.

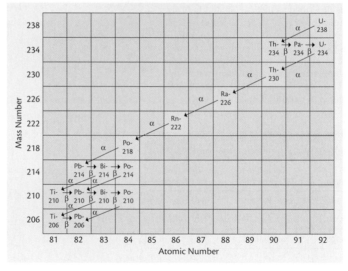

Figure 6.35 *The uranium-238 decay series. Diagonal lines show alpha decay; horizontal lines show beta decay. Here is how to interpret this chart: Locate radon-222 (Rn-222). The arrow pointing left shows that this isotope decays to polonium-218 by alpha (α) emission. This nuclear equation applies:*

$$^{222}_{86}Rn \longrightarrow\ ^{218}_{84}Po +\ ^{4}_{2}He.$$

B.6 NUCLEAR BALANCING ACT

The key to balancing nuclear equations is recognizing that both atomic numbers and mass numbers are conserved. Use the information in Table 6.8 (page 509) to complete the following exercise.

Sample Problem: *Cobalt-60 is one source of ionizing radiation for medical therapy. Complete this equation for the beta decay of cobalt-60:*

$$^{60}_{27}Co \longrightarrow \; ^{\;\;0}_{-1}e + ?$$

Beta emission causes no change in mass number. Therefore, the new isotope will also have a mass number of 60. Thus the unknown product can be written as $^{60}?$. Because the atomic number increases by one during beta emission, the new isotope will have atomic number 28, one more than cobalt's atomic number. The periodic table indicates that atomic number 28 is nickel (Ni). The final equation is:

$$^{60}_{27}Co \longrightarrow \; ^{\;\;0}_{-1}e + ^{60}_{28}Ni$$

Now answer these questions:

1. Write the appropriate symbol for the type of radiation given off in each reaction.

   a. The following decay process illustrates how archaeologists date the remains of ancient biological materials. Living organisms take in carbon-14 and maintain a relatively constant amount of it over their lifetimes. After death, no more carbon-14 is taken in, so the amount gradually decreases due to decay:

   $$^{14}_{6}C \longrightarrow \; ^{14}_{7}N + ?$$

   b. The following decay process takes place in some types of household smoke detectors:

   $$^{241}_{95}Am \longrightarrow \; ^{237}_{93}Np + ?$$

2. The two decay series beginning with Th-232 and U-238 are believed responsible for much of the thermal energy generated inside Earth. (Thermal contributions from the U-235 series are negligible; the natural abundance of U-235 is low.)

   Complete the following equations, which represent the first five steps in the Th-232 decay series, and identify the missing items *A, B, C, D,* and *E.* Each code letter represents a particular isotope or a type of radioactive emission. For example, in the first equation, Th-232 decays by emitting alpha radiation to form *A.* What is *A?*

   a. $^{232}_{90}Th \longrightarrow \; ^{4}_{2}\alpha + A$ d. $D \longrightarrow \; ^{4}_{2}He + ^{224}_{88}Ra$
   b. $^{228}_{88}Ra \longrightarrow \; ^{\;\;0}_{-1}e + B$ e. $^{224}_{88}Ra \longrightarrow E + ^{220}_{86}Rn$
   c. $^{228}_{89}Ac \longrightarrow C + ^{228}_{90}Th$

> Thorium oxide (ThO$_2$) was used in gas-light mantles and more recently in outdoor camping lanterns, since it glows brilliant white as the fuel burns.

> An alpha particle can be symbolized as either $^{4}_{2}He$ or $^{4}_{2}\alpha$.

B.6 Nuclear Balancing Act

This activity provides student practice in balancing nuclear equations. Explain that during beta decay, a neutron is transformed into a proton and an electron. Since the new proton remains in the nucleus, the atomic number increases by one, while the mass number remains the same. The mass number remains constant because the number of neutrons decreases by one and the number of protons increases by one. The consequence is formation of a different element. You may choose to work through several sample problems to model the process of balancing nuclear equations and ensure students' understanding.

Answers

1. a. $^{\;\;0}_{-1}e$
   b. $^{4}_{2}\alpha$
2. a. $^{228}_{88}Ra$
   b. $^{228}_{89}Ac$
   c. $^{\;\;0}_{-1}e$
   d. $^{228}_{90}Th$
   e. $^{4}_{2}He$ or $^{4}_{2}\alpha$

B.7 Radon

B.7 Content Reading Guide

Radon has been classified by many national and international health organizations as a human carcinogen.

There are two types of radon sampling techniques. Passive radon testing devices do not need electricity to function. In most passive devices, the testing occurs over a finite period, and the device (or a part of it) must be sent to a laboratory for analysis and calculation of radon levels. The most common types of passive radon testing devices include charcoal canisters, charcoal liquid scintillation devices, and alpha-track detectors. In the charcoal-based devices, the radon and its decay products are adsorbed onto the charcoal surface. In the laboratory, technicians determine the quantity of radioactive material adsorbed onto the charcoal surface and use it to calculate radon levels. In alpha-track detectors, a plastic film is marked by alpha particles that strike it. The number of sites where contact is made is counted in the laboratory and indicates the level of radioactive material.

Active radon sampling devices need power to function. They can detect and immediately record radon and the products of its radioactive decay continuously. This type of device is more expensive.

B.7 RADON

The gaseous element radon, which is the most massive of the noble gases, has always been a component of earth's atmosphere. It is a radioactive decay product of uranium. In the 1980s, unusually high concentrations of radioactive radon gas found in a relatively small number of U.S. homes became a public health concern.

Radon is produced as the radioisotope uranium-238 decays in the soil and in building materials. Once it is emitted, radon is transported throughout the environment in many ways. Some radon produced in the soil dissolves in groundwater. In other cases, radon gas seeps into houses through cracks in foundations and basement floors (see Figure 6.36).

In older houses, outdoor air entering through gaps in doors and windows can dilute the radon gas. However, to conserve energy, newer houses are built more airtight than are older houses. In a tightly sealed house, radon gas cannot mix freely with outdoor air or escape from the house. Consequently, radon gas concentrations may reach higher levels in newer homes. Remedies for high radon levels in houses include increasing ventilation and sealing cracks in floors (see Figure 6.37). Inexpensive radon test kits are available for home use.

You can locate this radioactive decay product as Rn-222 in Figure 6.35, page 510.

Figure 6.36 *Radon gas is naturally released from certain soils containing radioisotopes. Radon gas (red arrows) can enter a house by many paths.*

Loose fitting pipe

Crack

Radon gas can enter a house through many paths

Floor drain

Sump

Figure 6.37 *Radon's high density and the fact that it enters a residence through foundation cracks means this radioactive gas can be removed by installing a venting system that withdraws air from the basement.*

The most serious danger of radon gas results from reactions that occur after it is inhaled. Radon decays to produce, in succession, radioactive isotopes of polonium (Po), bismuth (Bi), and lead (Pb). When radon gas is inhaled, it enters the body and is transformed, through radioactive decay, into these toxic heavy-metal ions, which cannot be exhaled as gases. These radioactive heavy-metal ions also emit potentially damaging alpha particles within the body.

Estimates indicate that about 6% of homes in the United States have radon levels higher than the exposure level recommended by the U.S. Environmental Protection Agency (EPA). See Figure 6.38. It is estimated that 10–15% of annual U.S. deaths from lung cancer are linked to the effects of indoor radon gas. These figures, although sobering, should be kept in perspective; about 80% of all U.S. lung-cancer deaths annually are attributed to cigarette smoking.

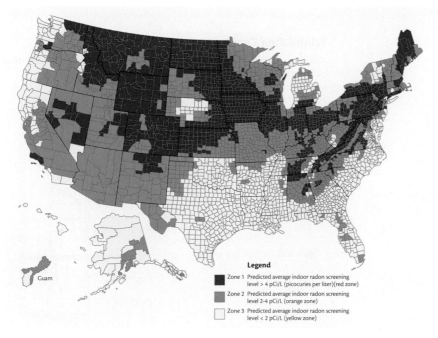

Legend

Zone 1 Predicted average indoor radon screening level > 4 pCi/L (picocuries per liter)(red zone)

Zone 2 Predicted average indoor radon screening level 2-4 pCi/L (orange zone)

Zone 3 Predicted average indoor radon screening level < 2 pCi/L (yellow zone)

Figure 6.38 *Map highlighting U.S. areas by county that have experienced radon problems.*

The radon issue is worth exploring with students for these reasons:
• It is a present-day problem.
• It is a case where nature is the source of the pollution, not humans.
• It illustrates how solving one problem (high home energy bills) can sometimes create a new one.
• It provides a useful context for discussing risk-benefit analysis and the concept of comparative risks.

Several Websites offer information about radon, its chemistry, associated health risks, and how these risks can be reduced. These include:
www.epa.gov/radon
www.radon.com/
http://www.cancer.gov/cancertopics/ factsheet/Risk/radon

Using the Figures

Figures 6.36 and 6.37: Depending on your geographical region, radon may be a common concern—particularly in home buying. Ask students to share any experiences they have had in dealing with radon. Encourage them to ask their parents if their basement was ever checked for radon. If radon is detected, homeowners can install a mitigation system in which strategically placed pipes and fans vent radon from the basement out through the roof.

B.8 Nuclear Radiation Detectors

The text describes ionization, scintillation, and solid-state radiation detectors. A Geiger counter is an ionization counter that can detect alpha, beta, and gamma radiation. Scintillation counters emit light when radiation strikes them, and a photomultiplier tube counts these flashes of light. Solid-state detectors monitor changes in movement of electrons when they are exposed to ionizing radiation and then count them electronically. In both cloud and bubble chambers, ionizing radiation makes visible paths. In a cloud chamber, the passing of ionizing radiation results in a trail of condensed vapor, while in a bubble chamber, the ionizing radiation delivers just enough energy to boil a cooled liquid.

Investigating Matter

B.9 Cloud Chambers

B.9 Cloud Chambers Student Worksheet and Data Table

 B.9 Content Reading Guide

In this investigation, students construct a simple device for indirectly observing ionizing radiation. The objective is to use a simple chamber supersaturated with 2-propanol (isopropyl alcohol) vapor and observe condensation trails left by ionizing radiation emitted by the source.

Time

45 min

Detecting Radiation

B.8 NUCLEAR RADIATION DETECTORS

The only way to detect radioactive decay is to observe the results of nuclear radiation interacting with matter. In each of the following detection methods, visible and/or electronically detectable changes in matter enable a technician to determine when such radiation is present.

Geiger-Mueller Tubes and Counters

The Geiger-Mueller tube contains argon gas that is ionized when nuclear radiation enters the tube. The ionized gas conducts an electric current; an electrical signal (counts per minute) is generated as the ions and components of radiation pass through the tube.

Film Badges

You learned earlier in this unit that emissions from radioactive materials will expose photographic film. Workers who handle radioisotopes wear film badges or other detection devices to monitor their exposure. The more ionizing radiation workers encounter, the greater the extent of exposure in their film badges. If workers receive doses in excess of the federal limits, they are temporarily reassigned to jobs that minimize their future exposure to ionizing radiation.

Scintillation Counters

Another detection approach involves devices called **scintillation counters** that contain solid substances whose atoms emit light when they are excited by ionizing radiation. In modern scintillation counters, the flashes of light are detected electronically. The scintillation counter probe illustrated in Figure 6.39 has a sodium iodide (NaI) detector that emits light when ionizing radiation strikes it.

Figure 6.39 *A scintillation counter probe. Ionizing radiation causes flashes of light (scintillations) in the detector (NaI crystal). Each light flash is converted to an electron pulse that is increased many times as it moves through the photomultiplier tube.*

- Intensified electron beam
- Photomultiplier tube
- Electron path
- Photocathode
- Phosphor (NaI)
- Light flashes
- Window

Materials

(For 12 student pairs)

12 cloud-chamber kits (see Advance Preparation)

100 mL 2-propanol

1 lb dry ice (thin slabs)

6–12 high-intensity light sources (20 W or greater)

12 dispenser (squeeze) bottles for 2-propanol

24 pairs disposable safety gloves

12 forceps

Solid-State Detectors

In another technique, **solid-state detectors** monitor changes in the movement of electrons through silicon-based semiconductors as they are exposed to ionizing radiation. These detectors are often used in research laboratories.

Cloud Chambers

Ionizing radiation can also be detected in a cloud chamber. You will learn about this detection method in the following investigation.

Investigating Matter

B.9 CLOUD CHAMBERS

Introduction

A **cloud chamber** is a container filled with air saturated with water or another vapor, similar to saturated air on a very humid day. If cooled, this air becomes supersaturated with vapor. This is an unstable condition (see page 55). When a radioactive source is placed near a cloud chamber filled with supersaturated air, the radiation ionizes gas molecules in the vapor as the radiation passes through the chamber. Vapor condenses to liquid on the ions that are formed, leaving a white trail along each passing radioactive emission, thus revealing the path of the particle or ray. Figure 6.40 is an image of particle tracks under such conditions.

 Laboratory Video: Cloud Chambers

Cloud-chamber trails resemble the vapor trails from high-flying aircraft.

Figure 6.40 *A cloud chamber, showing many particle trails created by ionizing radiation. The radioactive source is located on the left side.*

Section B   Nuclear Radiation   **515**

Lab Tips

• Students need only to *dampen* the felt band and base disk with alcohol, avoiding direct contact with the radiation source. Place the lid on the chamber and warm it with your hands before placing it on dry ice. You may need to adjust the height of the radioactive source inside the chamber to obtain a good result. If available, a small piece of old lantern mantle (newer ones do not work) can be used as a radioactive source. The dry ice should be crushed unless you have a smooth block. Obtain good contact between the dry ice and the bottom of the cloud chamber. The light source should be directed at an oblique angle rather than straight down.

• Practice is necessary to ensure success with this investigation. Rubbing the outside of the chamber with a silk cloth to promote a charged atmosphere may help.

• See the *ChemCom* CD-ROM for a video sequence of a cloud chamber in action.

Advance Preparation

Obtain cloud chambers and dry ice. (Cloud-chamber kits, including the radiation source, may be purchased. Sometimes dry ice can be purchased from ice cream stores or supermarkets. Check the telephone directory to find a local source.) Place the radioactive source in the cloud chamber with forceps. Use thick gloves and/or tongs to handle dry ice and *do not* allow students to handle dry ice.

Answers

1. The length, direction, and intensity will differ.
2. Alpha particles, owing to their large mass and size and relatively slow speed.
3. It reduces the temperature of the gases inside the closed chamber. This allows vaporized alcohol to supersaturate the air. The supersaturated gaseous mixture will condense to a liquid with the slightest disturbance, such as ions speeding through the chamber.

Post-Lab Discussion

Discuss conditions that support the direct observation of ion vapor trails (supersaturation) and the historical use of cloud chambers. See **http://www.sciencemuseum.org.uk/ on-line/electron/section3/1911b.asp**, **http://en.wikipedia.org/wiki/Cloud_ chamber**, or **http://www-outreach.phy. cam.ac.uk/camphy/cloudchamber/ cloudchamber_index.htm** for more information.

Making Decisions

B.10 Ensuring Public Safety

In this activity, students discuss a series of proposals for protecting the public from radiation. You may appoint students to small groups for this exercise (perhaps the same groups in which they will give their final presentation). Encourage students to draw on knowledge gained in Sections A and B to address the appropriateness of each proposal. This activity will help students think critically about nuclear technology and prepare for their end-of-unit presentation.

Figure 6.41 *A cloud chamber allows the path of ionizing radiation to be viewed with the naked eye or photographed.*

The cloud chamber you will use consists of a small plastic container and a felt band moistened with 2-propanol (isopropyl alcohol). The alcohol evaporates faster than does water, so it saturates the enclosed air more readily. You will chill the cloud chamber with dry ice to promote supersaturation and cloud formation (Figure 6.41).

Procedure

1. Fully moisten the felt band inside the cloud chamber with isopropyl alcohol. Also place dark paper on the chamber bottom and moisten it with a small quantity of alcohol.
2. Using gloves and forceps, quickly place a radioactive source in the chamber.
3. To cool the chamber, place it on a flat surface of crushed dry ice, ensuring that the chamber remains level.
4. Leave the chamber on the dry ice for 3–5 min.
5. Your teacher will adjust the room lighting. Focus a light source at an oblique angle (not straight down) through the container to illuminate the chamber base. If you do not observe any vapor trails, shine the light through the side of the chamber.
6. Observe the air inside the chamber near the radioactive source. Record your observations.

Questions

1. What differences, if any, did you observe among the tracks?
2. Which type of radiation do you think would make the most visible tracks? Why?
3. What is the purpose of the dry ice?

B.10 ENSURING PUBLIC SAFETY

Making Decisions

Consider again the statements found in the CANT flyer (page 478) and also your planned presentation to the senior citizens of Riverwood. Within a small group of classmates, discuss the appropriateness of each of the following proposals for protecting the public from radiation hazards. For each proposal, identify statements in the CANT flyer that might encourage public groups to make such a proposal.

1. Because all radiation is bad, government regulators should ban exposure to all forms of radiation.

2. Although there are several different types of ionizing radiation (alpha, beta, and gamma), government standards for protecting the public against possible dangers should treat all radiation exposures identically.

3. Because nuclear radiation can be harmful, physicians should be required by law to inform patients of any medical procedure that involves nuclear radiation. Patients can then reject the treatment if they have concerns about their exposure to radiation (Figure 6.42).

4. The government should provide a waste-disposal site for permanently storing all wastes that have ever been identified as radioactive (Figure 6.43).

Figure 6.42 *Nuclear technology is widely used in medicine.*

In this section you studied the origins of ionizing radiation, sources of exposure to ionizing radiation, and some possible consequences of that exposure. Keep these ideas and concerns in mind as you explore uses of nuclear radiation in the next section.

Figure 6.43 *Should the government be responsible for permanently storing all wastes that have ever been identified as radioactive?*

Answers

1. All radiation is not bad, and even if it were, it is impossible to "ban" it with legislation. Radiation is all around us, some natural and some a consequence of human activity. Radiation comes in many forms and intensities. Depending on the nature of the radiation, its properties range from harmless to deadly. Statements 2 and 3, although false, might prompt a public group such as CANT to make such a proposal.

2. All radiation is not the same, and it would be wasteful to regard all radiation as if it were. Some has little penetrating ability, so it would be wasteful to use abundant shielding to block it. The radiation may be expended by the time protection is in place. Statements 2 and 3, although false, might prompt a group such as CANT to make such a proposal.

3. Patients must always weigh risks and benefits. Nearly all medical treatment involves some risk, from adverse drug reactions to surgical complications. Statements 3, 5, and 14 might prompt a public group such as CANT to make such a proposal.

4. Just because something is radioactive does not mean it should be placed in a specialized waste site. If that were true, many of our homes and household fixtures would end up in such a site. Statement 11 might prompt a public group such as CANT to make such a proposal.

   The flyer contains some half-truths and generalizations that can prompt inappropriate calls for action.

SECTION B SUMMARY

Reviewing the Concepts

1. A constant level of radioactivity that results from natural sources and from sources related to human activity

2. Building materials, air, land, food, the human body.

3. Altitude, soil type, mineral deposits, and other natural factors vary. Regional fallout and contamination also play a role.

4. It is not possible. Background radiation is everywhere—in soil, water, air, food, etc.

5. a. 500 mrem   b. 0.0005 Sv

6. Sieverts

7. a. 2.5 mrem b. 116 mrem
   c. 7.03 mrem

8. Through cracks in foundations and basements

9. Energy-efficient homes are nearly air-tight. As a result, radon gas cannot be diluted through mixture with outdoor air and cannot escape from the house.

10. If a large number of protein or DNA molecules are destroyed within a small region, the body may not be able to heal itself. Damaged DNA may lead to cancer.

11. An alteration in the structure of DNA.

12. Ionizing radiation may damage DNA, resulting in mutations.

13. Dose, exposure time, area exposed, and tissue type.

14. Rapidly dividing cells, such as blood cells and sex cells, are most susceptible. Cells in fetuses and children are more susceptible to radiation damage because they divide rapidly due to growth.

15. a. Between 100 and 200 rem
    b. Between 100 000 and 200 000 mrem

SECTION B SUMMARY
Reviewing the Concepts

Radioisotopes in the environment create background radiation.

1. Define *background radiation*.

2. List five sources of background radiation.

3. Why does background radiation vary from one region to another?

4. Is it possible to eliminate background radiation? Explain.

5. What is the established U.S. background radiation limit for the general public expressed in
   a. mrem?
   b. Sv?

6. In what SI units is exposure to background radiation expressed?

7. What radiation dose would you receive
   a. during a five-hour jet aircraft flight?
   b. from a CT scan and a chest X-ray?
   c. if you lived in a brick house 25 mi (40 km) from a coal-fired power plant for one year?

8. How does radon gas get into houses?

9. Why do radon levels tend to be higher in energy-efficient houses?

Ionizing radiation has sufficient energy to break chemical bonds.

10. Why is the breaking of chemical bonds in living cells by ionizing radiation harmful?

11. What is a *mutation*?

12. How does ionizing radiation lead to an increase in mutation rates?

13. List the four factors that determine the extent of biological damage from radiation.

14. What types of human tissue are most susceptible to radiation damage?

15. At what radiation dose level would a person begin to experience nausea and hair loss? Express your answer in units of
    a. rem.
    b. mrem.

Alpha, beta, and gamma radiation have different properties that determine their effects on living tissues.

16. Which type or types of ionizing radiation would
    a. be stopped by a glass window pane?
    b. penetrate a cardboard box?
    c. penetrate a thin sheet of plastic but not a thin sheet of lead?

17. Explain why materials that emit alpha radiation are more dangerous inside the body than outside the body.

18. What is the relationship between radiation intensity and distance from the radiation source?

19. Suppose a beta source gives a corrected radiation reading of 640 cpm at a distance of 3 cm. Predict the corrected reading at a distance of
    a. 6 cm.
    b. 12 cm.

16. a. Alpha and beta radiation
    b. Beta and gamma radiation
    c. Beta radiation

17. Alpha particles have little penetrating ability. If the source is outside of the body, skin blocks their entry. However, if the source is internal, alpha particles can travel short distances and damage tissue.

18. Intensity varies inversely with the square of the distance.

19. a. 160 cpm b. 40 cpm

20. a. Two neutrons and two protons.
    b. $_2^4$He and α

21. a. A fast-moving electron emitted from a nucleus.
    b. $_{-1}^{0}e$ and β

22. A neutron is converted to a proton by emitting a beta particle.

23. Emission of an alpha particle is accompanied by the loss of two protons, which

The emission of nuclear radiation changes the composition of the nucleus.

20. a. What is the composition of an alpha particle?
   b. List two symbols used to represent an alpha particle.

21. a. What is a beta particle?
   b. List two symbols used to represent a beta particle.

22. How is a beta particle formed?

23. Why does the emission of an alpha or beta particle create an atom of a different element?

24. Copy and complete the following nuclear equations.
   a. $^6_3\text{Li} + ^1_0 n \longrightarrow ^4_2\text{He} + \underline{\hspace{1cm}}$
   b. $^{42}_{19}\text{K} \longrightarrow ^0_{-1}e + \underline{\hspace{1cm}}$
   c. $^{235}_{92}\text{U} \longrightarrow \underline{\hspace{1cm}} + ^{231}_{90}\text{Th}$
   d. $^1_0 n + \underline{\hspace{1cm}} \longrightarrow ^{142}_{56}\text{Ba} + ^{91}_{36}\text{Kr} + 3\,^1_0 n$

Ionizing radiation may be detected by its interaction with matter using a variety of methods.

25. Describe how each of the following devices can detect the presence of ionizing radiation:
   a. Geiger-Mueller tube and counter
   b. scintillation counter
   c. solid-state detector
   d. cloud chamber
   e. film badge

26. Would you expect alpha, beta, and gamma radiation to produce the same kinds of trails in a cloud chamber? Explain your answer.

Connecting the Concepts

27. High-level radioactive wastes are generally stored deep underground. Suggest two ways in which this method serves to keep people safe from excessive exposure to ionizing radiation.

28. In the 1940s and 1950s, some shoe stores invited customers to check the adequacy of shoe fit by X-raying their feet. Why did shoe stores discontinue that practice? (That shoe-store device was called a *fluoroscope*.)

29. Are the effects of shielding and distance the same for both ionizing and nonionizing radiation? Explain your answer.

30. Radon is an inert noble gas that is relatively harmless to living things. Explain why its presence in homes constitutes a health hazard for occupants.

31. Describe fundamental differences between nuclear and chemical reactions.

32. A student sets up a cloud chamber and sees no white trails. What are some possible explanations for this result?

33. Two students live next door to each other. One receives three times more annual radiation than the other. Explain how this could be possible.

34. Why do radiation detectors register counts even though no apparent source of radioactivity is in the vicinity?

35. A heavy apron is provided for a patient who receives a dental X-ray.
   a. What element is probably used in the apron?
   b. What is the purpose of the apron?
   c. Why does the dentist or hygienist leave the room while the X-ray device is turned on?

Section Summary   519

26. Alpha particles will produce more visible tracks due to their larger mass and size, and relatively slow speed. Gamma rays lack mass and do not form a track.

Connecting the Concepts

27. Radioactive materials decay with half-lives that cannot be changed by any known means. Most nuclear wastes must be isolated for thousands of years from both human (terrorism and war) and natural (water seepage and geological shifts) intrusions. The shielding materials must block beta and gamma radiation and withstand thermal, mechanical, and chemical stress.

28. X-rays are high-energy electromagnetic radiation (ionizing). People learned to avoid unnecessary exposure.

29. In general, yes. Both vary inversely with the square of the distance. They are stopped by various thicknesses of shielding, but nonionizing radiation has lower energy and can be stopped with less shielding.

30. Radon is radioactive. It undergoes natural decay by alpha emission. The main health risk is cancer. The risk of developing cancer increases as the level of radon concentration and the length of exposure (time) increases. The products of radon decay (polonium, bismuth, and lead) are solid particles that can become trapped in lungs, where they may continue to do damage even after the original source of radon is removed.

31. Nuclear reactions involve decay of atomic nuclei (through radioactivity) to form another

changes the identity of the element. Emission of a beta particle is accompanied by an increase in the number of protons, also changing the identity of the element.

24. a. ^3_1H b. $^{42}_{20}\text{Ca}$ c. ^4_2He d. $^{235}_{92}\text{U}$

25. a. Gas is ionized by radiation entering the tube, which produces an electrical signal as the radiation passes through the probe.
   b. The counter detects light emitted by excited atoms of the detector.
   c. It detects movement of electrons through a semiconductor.
   d. Ionizing radiation ionizes air as it passes through a chamber. The vapor condenses on the ions, leaving a "trail."
   e. The radiation strikes silver salts, causing a chemical reaction and color change in the photographic film.

(Answers continued on page 520)

element. Atomic number and mass number are conserved, but the identity of atoms involved typically changes. In a chemical reaction, atoms change arrangement but not identity. In some chemical reactions, electrons may change locations, but the number of protons (the identity of the atom) never changes. At the beginning and end of a chemical reaction, the same atoms are present in exactly the same quantities.

32. The temperature is not low enough to condense the vapor in the air. The air is not saturated (it must be supersaturated). The source giving off beta or gamma particles is inactive. The light is not at the correct angle (optimal position is at an oblique angle).

33. Determining factors might include the type of material from which each house is built (wood, glass, concrete, brick), the design of the house (built on slab, basement, amount and kind of insulation), and differences in lifestyles (frequency of air travel, extent of TV watching and video-game playing, number and type of medical and dental treatments).

34. Because of background radiation in the environment

35. a. Lead
b. To block (shield against) harmful radiation
c. To avoid being exposed or becoming overexposed to ionizing radiation

Extending the Concepts

36. Suntan is the body's defense against damaging UV radiation. Both are usually associated with UV radiation, which is energetic enough to disrupt some molecular bonds within skin cells. If DNA molecules are disrupted and mutations occur,

Extending the Concepts

36. In terms of radiation, how is a sunburn different from a suntan? How do sunscreens work to prevent both?

37. Identify the five fastest-growing metropolitan areas in the United States. Rank them according to the average level of ionizing radiation exposure that inhabitants in similar houses receive.

38. Investigate and explain whether or not beta particles can be distinguished from electrons.

39. Why does ionizing radiation break some chemical bonds but not others?

skin cancer may result. Sunscreens effectively block harmful UV radiation.

37. Resources for answering this question are at **http://www.census.gov/population/ www/cen2000/briefs.html**.

38. Beta particles are equivalent to high-speed electrons. The difference is that beta particles originate in the nucleus, and electrons are outside the nucleus.

39. Low levels of ionizing radiation break few bonds. As radiation scatters, only some of the energy is absorbed by chemical bonds. Bonds only break if radiation delivers enough energy to overcome the attractive forces between nuclei and electrons.

Using Radioactivity

Each radioisotope decays and emits ionizing radiation at its own special rate. Scientists have devised convenient ways to measure, analyze, and report how rapidly (or slowly) particular radioisotopes decay. In this section you will learn about radioactive decay rates, a characteristic that helps determine how useful or hazardous a radioisotope may be.

C.1 HALF-LIFE: A RADIOACTIVE CLOCK

How long does it take for a sample of radioactive material to decay? There is no simple answer to this question. However, by understanding how radioactive materials decay, scientists can predict how long a radioisotope used in a medical diagnostic test, for example, will remain active within the body; plan the long-term storage requirements for hazardous nuclear wastes; and estimate the ages of old organisms, civilizations, or rocks.

In 1904, Ernest Rutherford proposed the concept of *half-life* to describe the random process of radioactive decay. **Half-life** expresses the total time within which a radioactive atom has a 50-50 chance to undergo radioactive decay. Because one gram of any element contains well over 10^{21} atoms, the typical sample size involves a very large number of atoms. *Half-life* and *radioactive decay rate* have different meanings. Under normal conditions, the half-life for a particular radioisotope remains constant, while the radioactive decay rate represents the total number of atoms that have decayed within a certain period of time. The decay rate gradually decreases as the number of radioactive atoms decreases over time.

Statistics related to very large numbers provide two other useful ways to interpret half-life. The first—and perhaps most common—interpretation is that one half-life is the time required for one-half of the total radioactive atoms originally present in a sample to decay. The second interpretation is that at the end of one half-life, the rate of radioactive decay in a sample will decrease to one-half its original value. Table 6.9 lists the half-lives of several radioisotopes.

Half-Lives of Radioisotopes

DECAY EQUATIONS AND HALF-LIVES FOR FIVE RADIOACTIVE ISOTOPES

Radioisotope	Decay Equation	Half-Life
Hydrogen-3	$^3_1\text{H} \longrightarrow {}^3_2\text{He} + {}^0_{-1}e$	12.3 y
Carbon-14	$^{14}_6\text{C} \longrightarrow {}^{14}_7\text{N} + {}^0_{-1}e$	5.73×10^3 y
Phosphorus-32	$^{32}_{15}\text{P} \longrightarrow {}^{32}_{16}\text{S} + {}^0_{-1}e$	14.3 d
Potassium-40	$^{40}_{19}\text{K} \longrightarrow {}^{40}_{20}\text{Ca} + {}^0_{-1}e$	1.28×10^9 y
Radon-222	$^{222}_{86}\text{Rn} \longrightarrow {}^{218}_{84}\text{Po} + {}^4_2\text{He}$	3.82 d

| Table 6.9

Section C   Using Radioactivity   521

Using Radioactivity

Section C Content Reading Guide

In this section, students examine varied applications of radioactivity. The half-life of a radioactive sample influences how useful or harmful an isotope may be. This section addresses radioactive half-life conceptually and in terms of useful estimates and calculations. Applications of radioisotopes, including carbon-14 dating and medical uses of radioactive tracers, are discussed. The section concludes by exploring transmutation of elements and artificial radioactivity.

C.1 Half-Life: A Radioactive Clock

Half-life is the time required for one-half of original atoms to decay. Students may have heard of half-life but may not thoroughly understand it. Allow time for a brief discussion to correct misconceptions, such as that (a) one half of the material changes in one half-life and the other half during the next half life, and (b) atoms disappear rather than being changed into a decay product. Keep the calculations simple to avoid obscuring the concept. The goal in this segment is for students to understand the process by which radioactive material decays. They will then use this knowledge to assess the potential hazards or usefulness of a particular radioisotope.

Additional Information

Half-life and the *rate of radioactive decay* are different concepts. The rate of radioactive decay is an extensive property (such as mass) that depends on the quantity of material. It expresses the total atoms decaying over a specified time in units such as counts per minute (cpm). In other words, one metric ton of U-238 has a decay rate one million times greater than that of one gram of U-238, because the larger sample has a million times more atoms.

Half-life is an intensive property (such as density). It does not depend on the quantity of material. Both a metric ton of U-238 and one gram of U-238 have the same half-life. To prevent student confusion, avoid associating half-life values with decay rates. Instead, clearly explain half-life and refer to that idea consistently.

Carbon-14 Dating

We can use carbon-14 dating to determine the age of once-living organic (carbon-containing) materials. Metals cannot be dated using carbon-14 dating, as they contain no carbon.

After 50 000 years, C-14 would have gone through 8.7 half-lives, and the quantity of C-14 remaining is too small to yield accurate results.

Carbon-14 dating is dependable because the decay rate of C-14 is exceptionally consistent. It is not affected by heat, pressure, concentration, or any other external factor.

Modeling Matter

C.2 Understanding Half-Life

This activity models the exponential decay curve of radioactive samples through several half-lives. The "decaying atoms" are pennies; a decay event occurs every time a coin flips from heads to tails. This simulation makes the point that atomic decay is a statistical phenomenon. We can never be certain which particular atom will survive and which will decay at any given time.

The activity will take about 30 min. Each student group will need 80 pennies and a plastic container with lid or a cardboard box. M & M candies can serve as an alternative to pennies. If you use M & Ms, the printed side and non-printed side of each candy piece is its distinguishing trait. Students should be careful not to shake M & Ms too aggressively—the candy may disintegrate.

The relative abundance of C-14 has remained reasonably constant over thousands of years because C-14 is constantly being produced in the upper atmosphere by cosmic rays interacting with nitrogen atoms, while C-14 atoms are also undergoing radioactive decay.

Because the decay rate is directly related to the number of C-14 atoms present, scientists usually express the decay rate rather than the number of C-14 atoms.

Although it is not possible to predict when a particular radioactive atom will decay, each way of thinking about half-life is equally valid when working with the large numbers of atoms in typical chemical samples. The decay of carbon-14 is represented by the following equation:

$$^{14}_{6}C \longrightarrow ^{14}_{7}N + ^{0}_{-1}e$$

All living matter contains carbon and, therefore, a small amount of radioactive C-14. Thus, all living organisms emit a small but constant level of radioactivity. In living matter, decaying C-14 atoms are constantly replaced by new carbon atoms. After death, no new carbon atoms are taken in. The radioactive C-14 atoms continue to decay, so the longer an organism has been dead, the fewer C-14 atoms it contains.

Table 6.9 (page 521) indicates that C-14's half-life is 5730 years. If an organism contains 50.0 billion atoms of carbon-14 at the time of death, half of those atoms will have decayed after 5730 years pass, leaving 25.0 billion atoms of carbon-14. During the next 5730 years, another one-half of the atoms will decay, leaving 12.5 billion atoms of carbon-14. Therefore, if a sample from a previously living organism contains only one-fourth the number of C-14 atoms expected in a living organism, we can estimate that the sample is about 11 460 years old—that is, two half-lives must have passed since the organism died.

CARBON-14 DATING

It is not possible to determine the age of every artifact using carbon-14 dating. What kinds of materials might be good candidates for carbon-14 dating? What are some materials you could not date using carbon-14? Why does carbon-14 dating have a practical limit of about 50 000 years?

Every radioisotope has a specific half-life that is constant under normal circumstances. Half-lives of radioisotopes can be as short as a fraction of a second or as long as several billion years. For example, the half-life of polonium-212 is 3×10^{-7} seconds, while that of uranium-238 is 4.5 billion years. Thus, in one year all the atoms in a small sample of polonium-212 will probably have decayed, while well over 99% of the original uranium-238 atoms will still be present.

After 10 half-lives, only about 1/1000 or 0.1% of the original radioisotope atoms are still left to decay. (You can verify that statement with your own calculations.) This means that the rate of an isotope's radioactive decay has dropped to 0.1% of its initial level. This reduced level is

---

✏️ **C.1 Supplement: Half-Life**

often considered safe because it roughly approaches the level of normal background radiation.

Because there is no way to change the radioactive decay rate significantly for a particular isotope, radioactive waste disposal (or storage) can pose challenging problems, especially for radioisotopes with very long half-lives. You will examine that issue later in this unit.

In the following activity, you will model and explore the concept of half-life with heads-up and heads-down coins.

> In 2004, scientists reported that they could decrease the half-life of beryllium-7 by half a day (a 1% change) by trapping it in an electron-rich environment.

Modeling Matter

C.2 UNDERSTANDING HALF-LIFE

In this activity you will receive 80 pennies and a box. Place all pennies heads up to represent the starting sample of *headsium*. Assume each heads-up penny represents an atom of radioactive *headsium*. Its decay produces a tails-up penny—*tailsium*. Each shake of the closed box containing pennies represents one half-life. During this time a certain number of *headsium* nuclei will decay—flip over—to produce *tailsium*. You will investigate the relationship between the passage of time and the quantity of radioactive nuclei (heads-up pennies) that decay.

Complete these steps with your pennies:

1. Prepare a data table for recording the undecayed *headsium* and decayed *tailsium* atoms after each of four half-lives. Include initial values for passage of 0 half-lives.

2. Place the 80 pennies heads up in the box.

3. Close the box and shake it vigorously.

4. Open the box. Remove all atoms that decayed into *tailsium*. Record the number of undecayed (*headsium*) and decayed (*tailsium*) atoms after this first half-life.

5. Repeat Steps 3 and 4 three more times. You will now have simulated the passage of four half-lives. Record your results for each half-life.

6. Follow your teacher's instructions to obtain pooled class data for total undecayed *headsium* atoms remaining after each half-life.

7. Using your own data and the class-pooled data, prepare a graph by plotting the number of half-lives on the *x*-axis and the number of undecayed atoms remaining after each half-life on the *y*-axis. Plot and label two graph lines—one representing your own data and the other representing pooled class data.

Now answer these questions, based on your data:

1. a. Describe the appearance of your two graph lines. Are they straight or curved?
   b. Which set of data—yours or the pooled class data—provides a more convincing demonstration of half-life? Why?

Section C Using Radioactivity **523**

Part of this activity involves distinguishing between the usefulness of individual data vs. aggregated class data. Create a place in the classroom (on the chalkboard, butcher paper, or an overhead transparency) where groups can post their data to share with the class. When all group data are posted, instruct students to average the pooled data for each half-life. Then have them use this information to create a graph with two plotted lines, one line representing the group's own data and the other representing pooled class data.

Student graphs represent a radioactive decay curve. Ensure that students understand the random nature of radioactive decay. One cannot know when a given atom will decay but can predict the decay behavior for a large aggregate of atoms. The greater the total number of atoms, the better one can predict the decay behavior.

You can also use various computer and video simulations. If a computer-graphing program is available, consider asking students to use computers to generate their graphs.

Answers

1. a. They curve downward.
   b. The pooled class data should produce a smoother curve with data points that better approximate half of the particles undergoing decay during each half-life, as a consequence of including a larger number of atoms.

2.

Number of half-lives	Headsium nuclei remaining
0	600
1	about 300
2	about 150
3	about 75

3.

Number of half-lives	Headsium nuclei remaining
0	3000
1	about 1500
2	about 750
3	about 375
4	about 187

Four half-lives must have passed.

4. Similarities: The simulation is similar to actual radioactive decay in that during any half-life there is a 50–50 chance that a particular atom will decay. Nuclear decay is a chance occurrence. Differences: This simulation involves only 80 pennies; the half-life of any radioisotope is based on a much larger number of nuclei. Using pooled data in the simulation helps adjust for this. Also, identification and separation of radioactive atoms are not as simple as in this simulation.

5. Use an object with more than two sides, such as dice or sugar cubes with one side marked. Following each shake students would notice that the number of "decayed" nuclei would be much less than the half observed when using pennies. In fact, a "half life" for multiple-sided objects might involve two, three, or four shake cycles.

6. a. Four. (100% ⟶ 50.0% ⟶ 25.0% ⟶ 12.5% ⟶ 6.25%)

b. i. Yes. Only about 0.1% of the original sample would remain, but even a small sample of material contains a sizable number of atoms.

ii. No. (To have one radioactive nucleus left after 100 half-lives, about 1.3×10^{30} nuclei would be required in the original sample.)

2. About how many *headsium* nuclei would remain after three half-lives, if the initial sample had 600 *headsium* atoms?

3. If 190 *headsium* nuclei remain from an original sample of 3000 *headsium* nuclei, about how many half-lives must have passed?

4. Describe one similarity and one difference between your model based on pennies and actual radioactive decay. (*Hint:* Why did you pool the class data?)

5. How could you modify this model to demonstrate that different isotopes have different half-lives?

6. a. How many half-lives would be needed for one mole of a radioisotope to decay to 6.25% of the original number of atoms?

b. Is it likely that any of the original radioactive atoms would still remain after

i. 10 half-lives? Explain your answer.

ii. 100 half-lives? Explain your answer.

7. a. In this simulation, can you predict when a particular *headsium* nucleus will "decay"?

b. If you could follow the fate of an individual atom in a sample of radioactive material, could you predict when it would decay? Why or why not?

8. What other ideas could model the concept of half-life?

Developing Skills

C.3 APPLICATIONS OF HALF-LIVES

Use what you learned about half-life to answer the following questions. Figure 6.44 may help.

Sample Problem: *The half-life of O-15 is 2.0 min; its radioactive decay produces N-15. How much O-15 will remain after 5.0 min, if the original sample contained 14.0 g O-15?*

First determine the total number of half-lives that 5.0 min represents:

$$5.0 \ \text{min} \times \frac{1 \ \text{half-life}}{2.0 \ \text{min}} = 2.5 \ \text{half-lives}$$

Because the total number of half-lives is not an integer, use Figure 6.44 to estimate the proportion of O-15 remaining. Locate 2.5 half-lives on the *x*-axis. From that point, move directly upward on the graph until you touch the curved line. Then move left until you intersect the *y*-axis. Read this point from the graph: about 0.18. This means that 18% of the original O-15 sample remains:

$$(14.0 \ \text{g O-15}) \times 0.18 = 2.5 \ \text{g O-15 remain}$$

7. a. No.

b. No. A half-life value projects only how long it will take for half of a sample of atoms to decay, not *which* atoms will decay.

8. If you have 1000 automobiles and half break down every 10 years, the half-life of the automobile is 10 years. Students will suggest other ways.

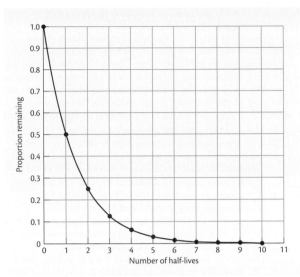

Figure 6.44 *This graph depicts the quantity of radioactive material remaining vs. total half-lives that have passed. What proportion of material would remain after four half-lives?*

You can check to see whether an answer of 2.5 g makes sense: After one half-life, 7.00 g O-15 would remain in the sample (the remaining mass represents N-15). After two and three half-lives, respectively, 3.50 g and 1.75 g O-15 would remain. The answer we found, 2.5 g, is between 3.50 g and 1.75 g, which is what we would expect.

1. Suppose you received $1000 (see Figure 6.45) and could spend one-half in the first year, one-half of the balance in the second year, and so on. (*Note:* One year corresponds to one half-life in this analogy.)

   a. If you spent the maximum allowed annually, at the end of which year would you have $31.25 left?

   b. How much money would be left after ten half-lives?

2. Potassium is a necessary nutrient for all living things and is the seventh most abundant element on earth's surface, composing about 1.5% of its crust. About 0.01% of natural potassium atoms are the radioisotope potassium-40. K-40 has a half-life of nearly 1.3 billion (1.3×10^9) years.

   a. Assuming earth is about 4.5 billion years old, how much of the K-40 at earth's formation remained after one half-life?

   b. Roughly how many times more K-40 was present when earth formed than is present now?

Figure 6.45 *If you initially had $1000 and spent half the money each year, how many years would it take until you had only $125?*

Developing Skills

C.3 Applications of Half-Lives

In this activity, students practice calculating half-lives. You may decide to complete several sample calculations to model the procedures.

Answers

1. a. Fifth year ($500 $\longrightarrow$ $250 $\longrightarrow$ $125 $\longrightarrow$ $62.50 $\longrightarrow$ $31.25)

   b. $0.98 (sixth year $15.62, seventh year $7.81, eighth year $3.91, ninth year $1.95, tenth year $0.98)

2. a. One-half of natural K-40 atoms

   b. 4.5 billion years represents 3.46 half-lives. Using **Figure 6.44,** about 9% of the original K-40 atoms would still be present, so (100%/ 9% =) 11 times as many K-40 atoms existed when Earth formed.

Using the Figures

Figure 6.45: With a half-life of one year, it takes three years of spending before $1000 would be reduced to $125. After one year (one half-life), $500 would remain. This is reduced to $250 after the second year; and $125 would remain after the third year.

3. a. i. Zero—1963   One—1992
   Two—2021   Three—2050
   Four—2079   Five—2107
   ii. 1963–100.0%   1992–50.0%
   2021–25%   2050–12.5%
   2079–6.25%   2107–3.13%

b. i. Students can read values from the graph. The value for 2005 was approximately 35%.
   ii. Approximately 3%
c. i. The graph in **Figure 6.44** uses half-lives rather than years on the *x*-axis.
   ii. They have similar shapes.

C.4 Radioisotopes in Medicine

The expanding use of radioisotopes in medicine is beneficial. They serve as diagnostic tools and as a therapeutic treatment of cancer.

Radioisotope tracers are diagnostic tools that usually have short half-lives so that they decay quickly when

3. Strontium-90 is one of many radioisotopes generated by nuclear-weapon explosions. This isotope is especially dangerous if it enters the food supply. Strontium behaves chemically like calcium, because these elements are members of the same chemical family. Thus, rather than passing through the body, radioactive strontium-90 is incorporated into calcium-based material, such as bone. A nuclear test-ban treaty in 1963 ended most above ground weapons testing. But some Sr-90 released in previous testing is still present in the environment.

a. Sr-90 has a half-life of 28.8 y. Track the decay of Sr-90 atoms that were present in the atmosphere in 1963 as follows:
   i. Using 1963 as year zero, when 100% of released Sr-90 was present, identify the years that represent the completion of one, two, three, four, and five half-lives.
   ii. Calculate the percent of the original 1963 Sr-90 radioisotope present at the end of each half-life.
b. Plot the percent of the original 1963 Sr-90 radioactivity level on the *y*-axis and the years 1963 to 2110 on the *x*-axis. Connect the data points with a smooth curve.
   i. What percent of Sr-90 formed in 1963 is present now?
   ii. What percent will remain in 2100?
c. Compare your graph to that shown in Figure 6.44 (page 525).
   i. How do the two graphs differ?
   ii. In what ways are they the same?

C.4 RADIOISOTOPES IN MEDICINE

For several decades following the discovery of X-rays and radioactivity, the public was fascinated by these scientific developments. In fact, some patent medicines advertised that they contained radium, claiming supposed benefits of that substance. Unfortunately, some older patent medicines actually contained radioactive materials and were very hazardous.

The careful use of ionizing radiation and radioisotopes can be quite effective in medical diagnosis and treatment (see Figures 6.46 and 6.47). Such uses can be classified as either *diagnostic* or *therapeutic*. Diagnostic use helps doctors understand what is happening inside the body (see Figure 6.48), while therapeutic use involves treating a medical condition.

Figure 6.46 *Injection of a radioisotope allows noninvasive imaging of internal organs.*

A common diagnostic application uses *radioisotope-tracer studies*, based on detecting a radioisotope in particular parts of the body. Knowing that certain elements collect in specific parts of the body (for example, calcium in bones and teeth), physicians can investigate a given part of the body by using an appropriate radioisotope as a **tracer.** In a tracer study, the physician places radioisotopes with short half-lives in a patient's body. Such studies can identify cellular abnormalities and help physicians select appropriate therapies.

Tracers have properties that make them ideally suited to this task. First, radioisotopes behave the same as stable (non-radioactive) isotopes of the same element. Researchers can apply a solution of an appropriate tracer isotope to the body, or they can feed or inject the patient with a biologically active compound containing the radioactive tracer element. A detection system, as shown in Figure 6.46, then allows a medical technician to track the tracer's location throughout the body.

For example, iodine-123 is used to diagnose problems of the thyroid gland, which is located in the neck. A patient drinks a tracer solution containing sodium iodide (NaI), in which some of the iodide ions are the radioisotope I-123. The physician, using a radiation detection system, monitors the rate at which this tracer is taken up by the thyroid. A healthy thyroid will incorporate a known amount of iodine. An overactive or underactive thyroid will take up, respectively, more or less iodine. The physician compares the measured rate of I-123 uptake by the patient to the normal rate for an individual of the same age, gender, and weight, and then takes appropriate therapeutic action.

Technetium-99m (Tc-99m), a synthetic radioisotope, is the most widely used diagnostic radioisotope in medicine. It has replaced exploratory surgery as a way to locate tumors in the brain, thyroid, and kidneys. *Tumors* are areas of runaway cell growth; technetium concentrates where cell growth is fastest. A bank of radiation detectors around the patient's body can pinpoint the Tc-99m at the tumor's precise location.

Figure 6.47 *Radioisotopes are prepared and used with knowledge of their half-lives, thus ensuring appropriate levels of activity as tracers.*

Figure 6.48 *Nuclear-medicine scan of bones of the entire human body.*

imaging has been completed. The radiation emitted must be intense enough to be measurable. The text notes that the most widely used radioisotope is technetium-99m; over 80% of nuclear-medicine diagnostic tests involve Tc-99m. This radioisotope has a short (six-hour) half-life and emits primarily easily detectable gamma rays. It has a versatile chemistry that allows it to serve a variety of diagnostic functions.

Technetium-99m is an artificially produced radioisotope formed by commercially available molybdenum/technetium generators kept onsite at medical facilities. It can be produced as needed in single doses. Refer students to the other medical radioisotopes used as tracers in **Table 6.10** (page 529).

Using the Figures

Figures 6.46, 6.47, and 6.48: Students may already have some knowledge of one or more of these medical applications of radioactive isotopes—through their own or a friend or relative's experiences. Invite students to share such experiences. However, be sensitive to emotional responses to the health problems associated with these medical practices.

Therapeutic radioisotopes use the energy associated with decay to destroy malignant cells. These radioisotopes differ from tracers. Therapeutic radioisotopes must produce sufficient energy to destroy diseased cells. The text describes external treatment with radioisotopes: Gamma beams from Co-60 can be used to irradiate an area of malignant cells. Internal treatment with radioisotopes often involves implanting a radiation source in the target area. The energy emitted through decay kills cells within the immediate vicinity of the implant.

The use of radioisotopes in medicine dates back to the early 1900s, when radium was used as therapy for skin lesions caused by tuberculosis. The Web site **http://www.cancer.gov/cancertopics/factsheet/Therapy/radiation** is a good source for radiotherapy information.

ChemQuandary 4

Using Radioisotopes in Medicine

The rate of decay of any radioactive isotope is fixed. Using the radiation emitted does not "use up" more radiation from the sample, just as an increase in the total people warming themselves from a campfire does not "use up" firewood fuel any faster.

Physicians use *therapeutic radioisotopes* because they emit radiation that carries sufficient energy to destroy living tissue. In some cancer treatments, doctors kill cancerous cells with ionizing radiation. For thyroid cancer, a patient is administered a concentrated internal dose of radioiodine, which collects in and destroys the cancerous portion of the thyroid gland. In other cancer treatments, physicians may direct an external beam of ionizing radiation (from cobalt-60) at the cancerous spot. Physicians must administer treatments with great care; high-radiation doses also kill normal cells.

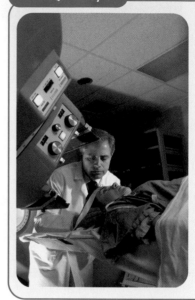

ChemQuandary 4

USING RADIOISOTOPES IN MEDICINE

One source of ionizing radiation is cobalt-60, which kills rapidly dividing cells. Consider two equally sized Co-60 samples shipped to two hospitals at the same time.

At one hospital, the Co-60 is used to treat dozens of individuals, while at the other hospital it is used only once or twice. Why would *both* hospitals dispose of their Co-60 samples after five years?

Radiosodium is usually administered as a sodium chloride solution.

Other medical applications include use of radiosodium (Na-24) to detect circulatory system abnormalities and radioxenon (Xe-133) to help locate lung embolisms (blood clots) and abnormalities. Table 6.10 summarizes medical uses for several radioisotopes.

You have learned that ionizing radiation, like that observed in a cloud chamber (page 515), is emitted from an unstable, radioactive isotope that eventually changes to a stable, nonradioactive atom. Do you think it would be possible to reverse that process, converting a stable isotope into an unstable, radioactive isotope? Think about it. This question will be addressed later in this section.

| Table 6.10

SELECTED MEDICAL RADIOISOTOPES

Radioisotope	Half-Life	Uses
Used as Tracers		
Technetium-99m	6.01 h	Measure cardiac output; locate strokes and brain and bone tumors
Gallium-67	78.3 h	Diagnosis of Hodgkin's disease
Iron-59	44.5 d	Determine the rate of red blood cell formation (these contain iron); anemia assessment
Chromium-51	27.7 d	Determine blood volume and life span of red blood cells
Hydrogen-3 (tritium)	12.3 y	Determine the volume of the body's water; assess vitamin D usage in body
Thallium-201	72.9 h	Cardiac assessment
Iodine-123	13.3 h	Thyroid function diagnosis
Used for Radiation Therapy		
Cesium-137	30.1 y	Treat shallow tumors (external source)
Phosphorus-32	14.3 d	Treat leukemia, a bone cancer affecting white blood cells (internal source)
Iodine-131	8.0 d	Treat thyroid cancer (external source)
Cobalt-60	5.3 y	Treat shallow tumors (external source)
Yttrium-90	64.1 h	Treat pituitary gland cancer internally with ceramic beads

C.5 Nuclear Medicine Technologies

PET scans have been used in many major areas of medical research, including addiction, eating disorders, attention deficit hyperactivity disorder, aging, and neurodegenerative disorders such as Alzheimer's disease. The radioisotope most commonly used is fluorine-18. Its half-life is 110 min.

C.5 NUCLEAR MEDICINE TECHNOLOGIES

Computers touch nearly all aspects of modern life. For example, health and medical science now employ two nuclear medicine technologies that rely heavily on computers to make sense of the large quantities of data obtained. These technologies are *positron emission tomography* (see Figure 6.49, page 530), which involves radioisotopes, and *magnetic resonance imaging*.

SECTION C

Scientific American Working Knowledge Illustration

While positrons are an exotic form of matter, they find routine use in PET scans. The radioisotope (fluorine-18) used is incorporated into a glucose molecule. Since active cells consume more glucose than inactive ones, PET scans can provide information about where active cells (often tumors) are concentrated. Have students critique this image regarding scales of representation. Glucose molecules are depicted for visual placement, but are much too large relative to the cells. Positrons and electrons are also much larger than actual size. The electron being annihilated is depicted without the atom or molecule with which it was associated.

An internet image search for "PET scan" will provide a large array of interesting applications of PET scans.

Tomography refers to producing a three-dimensional image of an internal object of interest.

Positron emission tomography (PET) scans are based on a very unusual form of radioactive decay involving a few particular radioisotopes. Although most radioisotopes emit alpha, beta, and/or gamma radiation, a few radioisotopes emit radiation in the form of *positrons*. **Positrons** originate in the nucleus and have the same mass as beta particles (electrons). However, positrons differ from electrons in fundamental ways. Positrons have a positive electrical charge, while electrons are negatively charged. And positrons are not made of matter as we commonly understand it.

Scientific American Working Knowledge Illustration

Figure 6.49 *Positron emission tomography (PET). Cancerous tissue can be detected using positron emission tomography (PET) scans. In this illustration, a brain tumor is identified by detecting gamma radiation emitted when positrons collide with electrons. As depicted in the particulate-level representation (bottom image), sugar molecules are tagged with a radioisotope tracer that emits positrons (yellow spheres). When a positron collides with an electron (blue spheres) in the immediate vicinity, both particles are destroyed and produce two gamma rays (depicted as yellow waves). The gamma-ray pair is then detected.*

Positrons are composed of *antimatter*. When a positron encounters an electron, both particles are annihilated (destroyed) and produce two gamma rays that are emitted in opposite directions. PET detects these gamma-ray pairs and, with the help of computers, determines where they originated. By observing a large number of such events, a computer-generated image gradually emerges.

The radioisotope tracer that emits positrons in PET scans is attached to a sugar molecule. Physicians can accurately determine the movement of each tagged sugar molecule as it progresses through the body. Because cancers grow faster than normal tissues, cancerous tissue metabolizes more sugar in a given time than does normal tissue. The radioisotope tracer (sugar tag) eventually becomes more concentrated in regions of the body containing cancerous tissue. PET technology can thus detect and display metabolic activity. Doctors can use this information to investigate brain functioning without invasive surgery.

Magnetic resonance imaging (MRI) does not employ ionizing radiation; it relies on the properties of protons. MRI is an application of a laboratory process known as *nuclear magnetic resonance* (NMR), which was developed in the mid-twentieth century. NMR is a noninvasive technique that can identify atoms within a sample without altering the sample itself.

MRI imagery can produce useful images of soft tissues. A major benefit of MRI is that it does not rely on ionizing radiation. Unlike most other nuclear-medicine technologies, MRI uses radio waves of very low energies and involves no known health risks. Some patients were hesitant to undergo this procedure when it was called by its original name, nuclear magnetic resonance, due to fear evoked by the term *nuclear*. This unfounded fear prompted the name change to magnetic resonance imaging.

C.6 ARTIFICIAL RADIOACTIVITY

In 1919, Ernest Rutherford enclosed nitrogen gas in a glass tube and bombarded the sample with alpha particles. After analyzing the gas remaining in the tube, he found that some nitrogen atoms had been converted to an isotope of oxygen, according to the following equation:

$$^{4}_{2}\text{He} + ^{14}_{7}\text{N} \longrightarrow ^{17}_{8}\text{O} + ^{1}_{1}\text{H}$$

Helium-4 (alpha particle)　Nitrogen-14　Oxygen-17　Hydrogen-1

Emphasize that MRI does not depend on ionizing radiation, but on radio waves of very low frequencies, produced when a strong magnetic field interacts with atomic nuclei. Plan a field trip to an MRI lab or have a technician visit the class to talk about MRI and/or PET scans. The Web site **http://electronics. howstuffworks.com/mri.htm** has an excellent description of the science involved in MRI procedures.

C.6 Artificial Radioactivity

The text gives a brief history of the development of nuclear chemistry, beginning with Rutherford's investigations with alpha particles and transmutation, which had been some alchemists' historic quest.

High potential-energy barriers make synthesis of elements difficult. Two methods can overcome these barriers, using high temperatures in millions of kelvins (approximating temperatures of stars) and using high speeds. High speeds have been easier to achieve. High speeds overcome repulsions that occur on bombardment of a nucleus with positively charged particles. Particle accelerators accelerate these charged particles to the necessary speeds. Neutrons are also commonly used to bombard nuclei in transmutation reactions, as they eliminate the problem of repulsion. Several U.S. government laboratories conduct research related to particle accelerators and neutron bombardment, including Oak Ridge National Laboratory, Fermi National Accelerator Laboratory, and Lawrence Livermore National Laboratory. Each laboratory has a Web site with more information: **www.ornl.gov**, **www.fnal.gov**, and **www.llnl.gov**.

Using the Figures

Figure 6.50: You may choose to discuss further the work of the Joliot-Curies. For example, the phosphorus-30 they produced has a half-life of 3.5 min. The Joliot-Curies earned the 1935 Nobel Prize in chemistry for this and related research. Irene Joliot-Curie, like her mother, died of leukemia associated with her work. See **http://nobelprize.org/chemistry/ laureates/1935/joliot-curie-bio.html**, **http://www.chemheritage.org/ classroom/chemach/atomic/ joliot.html**, and **http://en.wikipedia. org/wiki/Irene_Joliot-Curie** for further information.

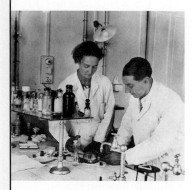

Figure 6.50 Irène and Frédéric Joliot-Curie produced the first synthetic radioisotope in 1934.

Reactions may release more than one ejected particle. For example, see the Cm-246 reaction on the next page.

Rutherford had produced the first synthetic or artificial **transmutation** of an element; that is, the first documented conversion of one element to another. He continued this work but was limited by the moderate energies of alpha particles then available. By 1930, scientists had developed particle accelerators that could produce highly energetic particles for bombardment reactions. Using these higher-energy particles, scientists then created many other synthetic atoms, some of which were radioactive.

The first **synthetic radioisotope** (one not occurring in nature) was produced in 1934 by French physicists Irène and Frédéric Joliot-Curie (the daughter and son-in-law of Marie and Pierre Curie; see Figure 6.50). They bombarded aluminum atoms with alpha particles, producing radioactive phosphorus-30 and neutrons:

$$^{27}_{13}\text{Al} + {}^{4}_{2}\text{He} \longrightarrow {}^{30}_{15}\text{P} + {}^{1}_{0}n$$

Since then, researchers have accomplished many transformations of one element to another and have synthesized new radioactive isotopes of various elements. Many of the diagnostic radioisotopes noted in Table 6.10 (page 529) are synthetic. Technetium-99m, for example, is both a synthetic element and a radioisotope.

Most synthetic radioisotopes are produced by bombarding elements with neutrons, which are captured by target nuclei. This process requires less energy than many other bombardment reactions because neutrons have no electrical charge and are not repelled by the positive charge of the nucleus. Such reactions produce radioactive nuclei that tend to emit beta particles, thus changing the atomic number and producing a different element.

The following examples show the formation of two synthetic radioisotopes often used as medical tracers, calcium-45 and iron-59.

$$^{44}_{20}\text{Ca} + {}^{1}_{0}n \longrightarrow {}^{45}_{20}\text{Ca}$$

$$^{58}_{26}\text{Fe} + {}^{1}_{0}n \longrightarrow {}^{59}_{26}\text{Fe}$$

Nuclear-bombardment reactions generally involve four particles:

▶ *Target nucleus:* the stable isotope that is bombarded.
▶ *Projectile particle* (bullet): the particle fired at the target nucleus.
▶ *Product nucleus:* the isotope produced in the reaction.
▶ *Ejected particle:* the lighter nucleus or particle emitted from the reaction.

For example, consider the Joliot-Curies' production of the first synthetic radioactive isotope, phosphorus-30. The four types of particles involved are identified as follows:

$$^{27}_{13}\text{Al} \quad + \quad {}^{4}_{2}\text{He} \quad \longrightarrow \quad {}^{30}_{15}\text{P} \quad + \quad {}^{1}_{0}n$$

Aluminum-27	Alpha particle	Phosphorus-30	Neutron
target nucleus	**projectile particle**	**product nucleus**	**ejected particle**

C.6 Supplement: Nuclear Bombardment Reactions

C.7 NUCLEAR-BOMBARDMENT REACTIONS

Developing Skills

Sample Problem: *Nobelium (No) can be produced by bombarding curium (Cm) atoms with nuclei of a low-mass element. What element serves as the projectile particle in this reaction?*

$$^{246}_{96}Cm + ? \longrightarrow {}^{254}_{102}No + 4{}^{1}_{0}n$$

Because the sum of the product atomic numbers is 102, the projectile must have the atomic number 6, to make the sum of the reactant atomic numbers also 102. Therefore, the projectile must be carbon (atomic number = 6). The total mass numbers of products is 258 (254 + 4), indicating that the projectile must have been carbon-12 (258 − 246 = 12). The completed equation is as follows:

$$\underset{\substack{\text{Target}\\\text{nucleus}}}{^{246}_{96}\text{Cm}} + \underset{\substack{\text{Projectile}\\\text{particle}}}{^{12}_{6}\text{C}} \longrightarrow \underset{\substack{\text{Product}\\\text{nucleus}}}{^{254}_{102}\text{No}} + \underset{\substack{\text{Ejected}\\\text{particles}}}{4{}^{1}_{0}n}$$

Complete the following equations by supplying the missing numbers or symbols. Name each particle. Then identify the target nucleus, projectile particle, product nucleus, and ejected particle.

1. $^{59}_{27}? + {}^{?}_{1}n \longrightarrow {}^{60}_{?}?$ (Scientists produce most medically useful isotopes by bombarding stable isotopes with neutrons. This process converts the original nuclei to radioactive forms of the same element.)

2. $^{96}_{42}? + {}^{?}_{1}H \longrightarrow {}^{97}_{43}? + {}^{1}_{0}?$ (Until it was synthesized in 1937, technetium was only an unfilled gap in the periodic table; all its isotopes are radioactive. Any technetium originally on earth has decayed. Technetium, the first element artificially produced, is now used in industry and medicine.)

3. $^{58}_{?}? + {}^{209}_{?}Bi \longrightarrow {}^{?}_{109}Mt + {}^{1}_{0}?$ (In 1992, a research group in Darmstadt, Germany, created element 109 by bombarding bismuth-209 nuclei. The name Meitnerium (Mt) honors Lise Meitner, the Austrian physicist who first proposed the idea of nuclear fission. See page 541.)

Not only does the ability to transform one element into another provide new and powerful technological capabilities, it also has changed our view of elements (see Figure 6.51).

As you learned earlier, completing nuclear equations involves balancing atomic numbers and mass numbers.

Figure 6.51 *Collisions of nuclear particles can be studied with bubble chambers. Mixtures of liquefied noble gases (at low temperatures) boil and produce streams of tiny bubbles as they absorb energy from particles involved in these collision investigations.*

Using the Figures

Figure 6.51: In this photo, a bubble-chamber scanner works at the Fermi National Accelerator Laboratory (Fermilab) near Chicago, Illinois. She sits at a table onto which a bubble-chamber photograph is projected from overhead. A tracker ball enables her to move the image in any direction, and a computer allows her to call up the photographs. Her responsibility is to measure track positions, lengths, angles, and curvatures. These data enable physicists to identify the particles producing the tracks.

Section C   Using Radioactivity   533

Developing Skills

C.7 Nuclear-Bombardment Reactions

Students write equations for bombardment reactions using the four types of particles involved in those reactions.

Answers

	TARGET NUCLEUS		PROJECTILE PARTICLE		PRODUCT NUCLEUS		EJECTED PARTICLE
1.	$^{59}_{27}\text{Co}$	+	$^{1}_{0}n$	$\longrightarrow$	$^{60}_{27}\text{Co}$		
2.	$^{96}_{42}\text{Mo}$	+	$^{2}_{1}\text{H}$	$\longrightarrow$	$^{97}_{43}\text{Tc}$	+	$^{1}_{0}n$
3.	$^{58}_{26}\text{Fe}$	+	$^{209}_{83}\text{Bi}$	$\longrightarrow$	$^{266}_{109}\text{Mt}$	+	$^{1}_{0}n$

ChemQuandary 5

Transmutation of Elements

People could change lead and iron atoms into gold, but the method would be far too expensive to be profitable due to huge equipment and energy costs. Reactions of the type used to produce elements 109–114 could conceivably be employed. In one hypothetical reaction, $n + Pb \longrightarrow Au + Li + 4\,n$.

C.8 Extending the Periodic Table

People have made the transuranic elements by bombarding heavy nuclei with such particles as helium nuclei. Other methods of producing these elements include successive neutron capture, which results from continuous bombardment of a heavy nucleus with low-energy neutrons. Scientists have produced still other transuranic elements in nuclear explosions, where a heavy nucleus such as uranium is bombarded with neutrons emitted from the explosion. Some transuranium elements are quite unstable and readily decay. People have produced only a few atoms of some of these elements, so little is known about them.

People have used transuranium elements and their isotopes in a variety of applications. For example, they have used plutonium-239 as a fuel to generate nuclear power and americium-241 to diagnose thyroid disorders and to make smoke detectors.

With expansion of the periodic table, conflict has frequently emerged over naming the new elements. Some scientists would argue that discovering or creating

ChemQuandary 5

TRANSMUTATION OF ELEMENTS

Ancient alchemists searched in vain for ways to transform (transmute) lead or iron into gold. Has such transmutation now become a reality? From what you know about nuclear reactions, do you think that lead, iron, or mercury atoms could be changed to gold? If so, try to write equations for the possible reactions.

C.8 EXTENDING THE PERIODIC TABLE

Since 1940, nearly 20 **transuranium** elements—with atomic numbers greater than the atomic number of uranium (92)—have been added to the periodic table. These elements have been synthesized in nuclear reactions, usually conducted in accelerators known as *cyclotrons* (see Figure 6.52). From 1940 to 1961, Glenn Seaborg and coworkers at the University of California–Berkeley synthesized and identified ten new elements with atomic numbers 94 to 103, a prodigious feat. None of those new elements occurs naturally. All were made by high-energy bombardment of heavy nuclei with various particles. For example, alpha-particle bombardment of plutonium-239 produced curium-242:

$$^{239}_{94}\mathrm{Pu} + {}^{4}_{2}\mathrm{He} \longrightarrow {}^{242}_{96}\mathrm{Cm} + {}^{1}_{0}n$$

Seaborg and coworkers also identified over 100 new isotopes of various elements.

Figure 6.52 *Cyclotrons allow scientists to investigate high-energy bombardment of heavy nuclei with various particles. Cyclotron particle masses and collision energy increased dramatically over the past decades.*

Bombarding Pu-239 with neutrons yielded americium-241, a radioisotope now used in home smoke detectors:

$$^{239}_{94}\text{Pu} + 2\ ^{1}_{0}n \longrightarrow\ ^{241}_{95}\text{Am} + \ ^{0}_{-1}e$$

Seaborg received the 1951 Nobel Prize in Chemistry for his work. Albert Ghiorso, a colleague of Seaborg, led the way in producing several new elements beyond lawrencium (element 103). One is element 106, produced by bombarding a californium-249 target with a beam of oxygen-18 nuclei to produce an isotope of element 106. To honor Seaborg's pioneering work, element 106 was named *seaborgium* (Sg). Glenn Seaborg, shown in Figure 6.53, has been called the father of the modern periodic table.

Traditionally, the discoverer of an element selects its name. For example, when Marie Curie first discovered element 84, she named it *polonium* (Po) in honor of Poland, her home country.

Figure 6.53 *Glenn Seaborg and coworkers at the University of California-Berkeley synthesized and identified ten new elements beyond uranium. Can you identify any transuranium elements that they may have created?*

transuranic elements is the culmination of innumerable research efforts and findings, rather than the work of one group or one individual. This is due to continual communication and exchange of ideas among individuals within the scientific community (via research journals and scientific meetings), creating an environment where new ideas or discoveries are founded on accumulated information and knowledge from many sources. Many scientists enjoy and endorse this free exchange of ideas and mutual collaboration. However, it is interesting to consider how other factors (such as politics, ego, and national pride) can creep into scientific activity when recognition for a specific discovery is at stake.

Using the Figures

Figure 6.53: Glenn Seaborg was a professor at the University of California at Berkeley and cofounder and chairman of the Lawrence Hall of Science (among numerous achievements—in fact, he has appeared in the *Guinness Book of Records* for having the longest entry in *Who's Who in America*). The transuranium elements Seaborg and his group created include americium, curium, berkelium, californium, einsteinium, fermium, mendelevium, nobelium, and seaborgium. When *seaborgium* was officially accepted as the name for element 106 in 1997, it was the first time an element had been named for a living person. Seaborg called it his greatest honor. He died (at age 86) in 1999.

Making Decisions

C.9 Opinions about Radioactivity

This activity will help students to prepare for this unit's culminating activity. By now, students should be able to evaluate the community-member opinions, particularly with respect to relevant science concepts. Ask students to compare their responses with those of other class-mates. Possible answers follow.

1. Isotopes are all around us; they occur naturally; some are radioactive, while others are not. Sources of radioisotopes include groundwater, air, rocks, sand, and stars. Our own bodies contain radioisotopes.

2. Radioactive isotopes are a part of building materials, medical and dental X-rays, television sets, and air travel. It is impossible to completely avoid radioactive materials.

3. The production of new elements has expanded our understanding of the atomic nucleus.

Scientific research, like other human endeavors, can involve strong personalities, competition, and controversy.

Several scientific laboratories have claimed to have synthesized elements with atomic numbers greater than 92. For example, laboratories in both the former Soviet Union and the United States claimed the discovery of elements 104 and 105. USSR scientists proposed naming them *kurchatovium* (Ku) and *dubnium* (Db), while U.S. scientists proposed the names *rutherfordium* (Ru) and *hahnium* (Ha). The International Union of Pure and Applied Chemistry (IUPAC) examined the claims and supporting evidence for element discovery before recommending the official names. In 1997 the IUPAC approved the names *rutherfordium* and *dubnium*.

At present, the IUPAC recognizes official names and symbols for the first 111 elements. Although claims for the discovery of other elements have been filed, the IUPAC has not yet recommended their official names. Scientists temporarily identify such unnamed elements by Latin prefixes indicating their atomic numbers. For example, element 112 is temporarily named *ununbium* (un = 1, un = 1, bi = 2), which is symbolized as *Uub* until IUPAC officially recognizes the original discovery of that new element.

The production of transuranium elements has enriched our understanding of the atomic nucleus. With the synthesis and identification of elements beyond atomic number 92, the periodic table has expanded to fill the actinide series as well as nearly all of period 7.

The name proposed by discoveries of element 111—*roentgenium* (Rg)—was approved by IUPAC in 2004. It honors W. K. Roentgen, who discovered X-rays. Roentgen, you may recall, was the first scientist you learned about in this unit (see page 480).

Making Decisions

C.9 OPINIONS ABOUT RADIOACTIVITY

Some older people tend to associate nuclear technologies with the use of atomic weapons at the close of World War II and with the atomic-weapon threats of the Cold War in the 1950s and beyond. Some of these people are likely to be in the audience when you speak to the Riverwood senior citizens.

The following opinions might be expressed by such community members. Decide how you would respond to each opinion, using knowledge you have gained in this unit.

1. "I'm against having any isotopes in Riverwood. They're too dangerous."

2. "I don't want to live near anything that is radioactive."

3. "I don't know why scientists keep trying to make new elements; all the new ones are radioactive."

4. "I don't understand how cancer can be treated with radiation. I thought radiation *caused* cancer."

5. "We must outlaw radioactive material altogether to completely eliminate the possibility of a nation or terrorists using radioactive material to harm others."

Join with a classmate and share your responses to each opinion. How are your responses similar? How are they different?

Figure 6.54 *How can each of these images suggest ways to respond to the concerns of Riverwood's citizens?*

4. Radioisotopes can kill cancerous cells. Physicians carefully select these radioisotopes based on the area of the body to be treated, and administer them with care to avoid exposing healthy cells to ionizing radiation.

5. Radioactive material is all around us and would be impossible to outlaw. Furthermore, outlawing radioactive material would prohibit access to many medical technologies.

SECTION C

SECTION C SUMMARY

 Section C Supplement

Reviewing the Concepts

1. The time required for 50% of a given sample of radioactive isotopes to decay

2. C-14 decays naturally, with a half-life of 5730 y. As long as a plant or animal is alive, the amount of C-14 in the organism is the same as C-14 in the atmosphere. After it dies, the C-14 it loses through radioactive decay is not replaced. Therefore, we can use the fraction of C-14 remaining to determine the age of the dead organism.

3. a. 100%
   b. About 98%

4. a. About 4%
   b. Virtually none

5. 42.9 days

6. Rn-222 has a half-life of 3.82 days (**Table 6.9,** page 521).
   a. 2.3 mol
   b. 0.28 mol
   c. Less than 0.035 mol

7. This radioisotope concentrates where cell growth is fastest, so it helps pinpoint tumors in the brain, thyroid, and kidney.

8. Fe-59 is used to monitor the rate of red blood cell formation (it is a component of hemoglobin) and to diagnose anemia.

9. A healthy thyroid incorporates some iodine. When a patient receives a solution containing a radioactive iodine tracer (I-123), doctors can compare the actual rate of tracer uptake to the rate in a healthy thyroid.

10. Sodium ions are normally found dissolved in blood. Xenon, a noble gas, would not damage sensitive tissue.

SECTION C SUMMARY
Reviewing the Concepts

| Half-life is used to characterize radioisotopes.

1. Define *half-life*.
2. How can the concept of half-life be used to determine a material's age?
3. The half-life of carbon-14 is 5730 years. Provide a rough estimate of the percent of the C-14 radioisotope that would be left after
   a. 24 h.
   b. 100 y.
4. The half-life of astatine-209 is 5.4 h. Estimate the percent of At-209 that would be left after
   a. 24 h.
   b. 100 y.
5. Phosphorus-32 has a half-life of 14.3 d. How long would it take for 1/8 of a sample of P-32 to remain unchanged?
6. Given a sample of 4.5 mol radon-222, how many moles of Rn-222 would remain undecayed after
   a. 3.82 d?
   b. 15.3 d?
   c. 28.0 d?

| Radioisotopes can be used as tracers for diagnostic purposes.

7. How is metastable Tc-99m useful in medical diagnosis?
8. How is iron-59 used for diagnostic purposes?
9. Why do physicians use a radioisotope of iodine to detect thyroid problems?
10. Radioactive sodium chloride is appropriate for diagnosing circulatory problems, while radioactive xenon is helpful in searching for lung problems. Explain why each is used for its specific applications.
11. Medical personnel are selecting a radioisotope for diagnostic use. Why is each of the following considerations important in selecting the most suitable radioisotope?
    a. half-life
    b. mode of decay
    c. chemical properties of the element

| Ionizing radiation emitted by some radioisotopes can be used for medical treatment.

12. How are cancer cells different from normal cells?
13. How do physicians use ionizing radiation to treat cancer?
14. What could happen if the source of ionizing radiation used to treat cancerous growth were
    a. too weak?
    b. too strong?
15. Name three radioisotopes that radiologists can use externally to treat cancer.

11. a. The isotope must have short half-life, decay rapidly, and leave the patient's body quickly.
    b. Since alpha particles can cause extensive damage inside the body, the tracer should not decay by alpha emission.
    c. Chemical properties must be the same as those of chemically stable isotopes of the element.

12. Cancer cells divide faster.
13. Ionizing radiation kills the cancer cells.
14. a. It would not kill all of the cancer cells.
    b. It would damage normal cells.
15. Cobalt-60, iodine-131, and phosphorus-32

The conversion (transmutation) of one element to another can be accomplished by bombarding atomic nuclei with subatomic particles or other nuclei.

16. Define *transmutation*.

17. Why was Rutherford's ability to complete transmutations limited compared to the Curies' transmutation abilities?

18. Why are neutrons frequently used as projectiles in transmutation reactions?

Connecting the Concepts

20. A student wrote this statement in a homework assignment: "After one half-life, half of the mass of a material has disappeared." Do you agree or disagree? Explain.

21. Would carbon dating help scientists determine the age of dinosaur remains? Explain.

22. Explain why an externally applied alpha emitter is an ineffective treatment for tumors deep within the body.

23. Graph the data in the following table and determine the
a. half-life of thorium-234.
b. minimum number of days required for thorium-234 to decay to 20% of its original activity.

Elapsed Time (days)	% Thorium-234 Activity Remaining
0	100
7	82
16	60
28	45
42	30
62	17
94	7

19. Copy and complete each of the following transmutation equations:

a. _____ $\longrightarrow$ $^{4}_{2}\alpha + ^{259}_{104}Rf$
b. $^{238}_{92}U \longrightarrow$ _____ $+ ^{234}_{90}Th$
c. $^{210}_{83}Bi \longrightarrow ^{0}_{-1}\beta +$ _____
d. $^{95}_{40}Zr \longrightarrow$ _____ $+ ^{95}_{41}Nb$
e. _____ $\longrightarrow$ $^{4}_{2}\alpha + ^{214}_{80}Hg$

24. Scientists using carbon-14 dating generally do not use it to extend back further than seven half-lives.

a. Explain why.
b. What is the maximum number of years a substance can be dated using carbon-14 dating?

25. A radiologist injects a patient's bloodstream with a radioisotope tracer sample registering 10 000 cpm of radioactivity. Soon after, a technician draws 6.0 mL of blood, and the sample shows an activity of 10 cpm. What is the patient's total blood volume, assuming essentially no decrease in the activity of the radioisotope occurred during this clinical procedure?

Connecting the Concepts

20. Disagree. After one half-life, half the atoms have decayed. Most of the original mass is still present in decay products.

21. No. Dinosaurs lived too long ago, beyond the range of C-14 dating accuracy.

22. The skin blocks transmission of alpha particles.

23.

a. About 25 d
b. 50–52 d

24. a. After seven half-lives, the amount of the original sample remaining to analyze will be less than 1%.
b. 7 × 5730 y = 40 110 y

25. The radioactivity of the 6.0 mL blood is 1000 times less than that of the original material injected. Assuming the injected sample became evenly distributed throughout the patient's blood supply—and assuming the radioisotopes did not decay significantly during the short time before the blood was drawn—the patient's total blood volume would be 1000 × 6 mL (or 6 L).

16. The process by which one element is converted into another element

17. Rutherford had access only to low-energy alpha particles. The Curies were able to use higher-energy particles to complete transmutations due to development of particle accelerators.

18. They are electrically neutral and are not repelled by positively charged nuclei.

19. a. $^{263}_{106}Sg$
b. $^{4}_{2}He$
c. $^{210}_{84}Po$
d. $^{0}_{-1}\beta$
e. $^{218}_{82}Pb$

Extending the Concepts

26. a. PET uses radioisotope tracers that emit positrons. The positrons encounter electrons and produce gamma-ray pairs. A computer will detect where these gamma-ray pairs form and produce an image. MRI uses low-energy radio waves to produce images of body tissues.

b. PET can provide information about brain functioning and tumor growth. MRI can provide data based on differences in how normal and abnormal tissues in the area of investigation respond to alternations in the magnetic field.

c. In MRI, there is no exposure to ionizing radiation. In PET, patients are exposed to a radioisotope with a short half-life.

27. Radioisotopes of oxygen could be introduced into CO_2 or H_2O made available to the growing plant. Then one could use a radiation-detection system to trace radioactive oxygen atoms as they move through the living plant and out again.

28. Based on knowledge of decay products and the type of emissions, scientists complete equations involving the decay products to identify the original element.

29. This treatment brings out color and removes imperfections. Changing the color of gemstones is legal, but the stones must then be stored long enough for radioactivity to decrease. Gamma radiation produced by the decay of Co-60 is often used to irradiate gems.

30. a. The process is too expensive.
b. No.

31. The lightest nuclides that exhibit stability have almost equal numbers of protons and

Extending the Concepts

26. Compare PET and MRI in terms of
 a. their method of operation.
 b. data they provide for diagnosis.
 c. radiation exposure for a patient.

27. Scientists originally were uncertain whether the oxygen gas produced during photosynthesis came from CO_2, H_2O, or both. How could radioisotope tracers be used to help settle that uncertainty?

28. A newly discovered element with an extremely short half-life is detected by analyzing its decay products. Explain how scientists can "work backward" to identify the original element.

29. Many gemstones are irradiated. Research and report on the reasons for this process.

30. Gold and other precious metals can be created from other metals by nuclear transformations.
 a. So why don't commercial firms do this as a source of profit?
 b. Is the synthetic precious metal distinguishable from the naturally occurring precious metal?

31. Research how the proton–neutron ratio is related to the stability of an atomic nucleus. Describe how you could use this ratio to predict the type of radioactive decay a particular atomic nucleus undergoes.

32. List foods that are currently irradiated with nuclear radiation before they are marketed for human consumption. Describe the process and evaluate its risks and benefits.

neutrons. Heavier nuclides require up to 50% more neutrons than protons for stability. Alpha radiation mostly comes from nuclei that have too many protons or too few neutrons. Neutron-rich nuclei tend to decay by beta emission.

32. Irradiated foods include fruits, vegetables, and spices. Poultry and red meat are also FDA approved for irradiation. During irradiation, radiant energy kills

harmful bacteria such as *E. coli, Campylobacter,* and *Salmonella.* The process also can control insects and parasites, reduce spoilage, and inhibit ripening and sprouting. Irradiation can reduce levels of thiamin, but not enough for concerns about vitamin deficiency. Living cells are damaged or killed in the process, which affects the viability of seeds, such as those in alfalfa sprouts.

Nuclear Energy: Benefits and Burdens

In the 1930s, a bombardment reaction involving uranium unlocked a new energy source and led to the development of both nuclear power and nuclear weapons. This event marked the start of the nuclear age. How did scientists first unleash the enormous energy of the atom, and how have nuclear engineers harnessed atomic energy for both useful and destructive purposes?

D.1 UNLEASHING NUCLEAR FORCES

Shortly before the start of World War II, German scientists Otto Hahn and Fritz Strassman bombarded uranium with neutrons in the hope of creating a more massive nucleus and, thus, a new element. Much to their surprise, they found that one reaction product was atoms of barium, with only about half the atomic mass of the original target uranium atoms.

The first to understand what had happened was the Austrian physicist Lise Meitner (Figure 6.55), then living in Sweden, who had previously worked with Strassman and Hahn. Meitner and her nephew Otto Frisch suggested that neutron bombardment had split the uranium atom into two parts of nearly equal mass. Other scientists quickly verified Meitner's explanation.

Hahn and Strassman had actually triggered an array of related reactions. One of the reactions that produced barium is:

Figure 6.55 *Lise Meitner was first to suggest that nuclei might split due to neutron bombardment.*

Lise Meitner fled to Sweden when Nazis assumed control of Germany and Austria.

$$^{1}_{0}n \; + \; ^{235}_{92}U \; \longrightarrow \; ^{140}_{56}Ba \; + \; ^{93}_{36}Kr \; + \; 3\,^{1}_{0}n \; + \; \text{Energy}$$

Neutron   Uranium-235   Barium-140   Krypton-93   Neutrons

$+ \quad \text{Energy}$

Nuclear Energy: Benefits and Burdens

 Section D Content Reading Guide

Students learn of the immense quantity of energy locked inside atomic nuclei, and how that energy is released via chain reactions in nuclear power plants, in nuclear weapons, and within the Sun and other stars. They examine major components of a nuclear power plant and explore the risks and benefits of nuclear reactions, including problems associated with high- and low-level waste disposal.

After the close of this section, students create a presentation in the culminating activity to help Riverwood residents draw

---

conclusions about the nuclear concerns raised by CANT. You may choose to allow class time for students to work in their groups during Section D. Depending on class size, you may assign each group one or several CANT statements. One to two class periods should be adequate for students to receive their statement assignment(s) and create their presentations. Research and responses to these statements were initiated during Making Decisions activities (pages 493, 517, and 536–537) earlier in the unit.

D.1 Unleashing Nuclear Forces

This part introduces students to the *strong force,* which holds protons and neutrons together in the nucleus. This force can be unleashed by bombarding a fissionable nucleus, causing the nucleus to split into two new nuclei. This event is accompanied by release of a large quantity of energy. The text compares the energy changes in nuclear reactions to those of conventional chemical reactions. You may wish to emphasize that a small quantity of mass, if converted into energy, yields an enormous quantity of energy, according to the equation $E = mc^2$. (See the margin note on page 543 for a sample calculation.) This accounts for the large quantity of energy that accompanies fission or fusion.

Elicit students' impressions of nuclear power, nuclear weapons, and any popular uses of the terms *critical mass* and *chain reaction.* Then use **Figure 6.57** and the text material to clarify these concepts and the relationships among them.

Note that sustaining nuclear fission in chain reactions (by providing a sufficient quantity of fissionable isotope or critical mass, page 544) is the strategy on which both nuclear reactors and nuclear weapons operate. The key difference is that nuclear reactors are based on carefully controlled chain reactions, while nuclear weapons are based on initiation of uncontrolled chain reactions.

A quantity in excess of the critical mass is termed *supercritical mass.* In this situation, chain reactions are able to accelerate due to the large quantity of fissionable material and the large number of neutrons available to strike additional nuclei. In nuclear weapons, supercritical masses form as multiple subcritical masses of fissionable material quickly come together in the presence of a neutron-emitting source.

Fission of U-235 produces many other pairs of nuclei, such as Te-137 and Zr-97.

Not all nuclei are fissionable. U-235 is the only naturally occurring isotope that undergoes fission with lower-energy (thermal) neutrons. However, many synthetic nuclei (e.g., U-233, Pu-239, and Cf-262) also fission under neutron bombardment.

If one kilogram of U-235 fissions, a mass of about one gram would be converted into energy.

Splitting an atom into two smaller atoms is called **nuclear fission.** Scientists soon found that the uranium-235 nucleus can fission (split) into numerous pairs of smaller nuclei. The uranium usually did not split into two equal halves, but into one element accounting for about 60% of uranium's mass (such as barium) and another element equivalent to about 40% of uranium's mass (such as krypton). Here is another example of a nuclear fission reaction involving uranium-235:

$$_{0}^{1}n \; + \; _{92}^{235}U \; \longrightarrow \; _{54}^{143}Xe \; + \; _{38}^{90}Sr \; + \; 3\,_{0}^{1}n \; + \; \text{Energy}$$

Neutron Uranium-235   Xenon-143 Strontium-90 Neutrons

The nuclear fission of heavy atoms such as uranium releases a huge quantity of energy. Gram for gram, the released energy is at least a *million* times more than the energy of any chemical reaction. This is what makes nuclear explosions so devastating and nuclear energy so powerful.

Why does a nuclear reaction release much more energy than does a chemical reaction? Recall what you know about chemical reactions, such as burning petroleum. Chemical reactions involve breaking chemical bonds in reactants and making new chemical bonds in products. When bonds are stronger in products than in reactants, energy is released, often as thermal energy (heat). Thus, chemical energy is converted into thermal energy. There is no overall energy loss or gain. Similarly, mass is conserved in a chemical reaction. The nucleus of each atom, and thus its identity, remains intact in all chemical reactions. As a result, the number of atoms of each element remains unchanged; the atoms simply become rearranged. Balanced chemical equations illustrate this conservation of atoms and mass.

Nuclear reactions are also based on conserving energy and mass. However, during nuclear fission, very small quantities of mass are converted into appreciable energy. Where does this energy originate?

The origin of nuclear energy lies in the force that holds protons and neutrons together in the nucleus. This force, called the **strong force,** is fundamentally different from, and a thousand times stronger than, the electrical forces that hold atoms and ions together in chemical bonds. The strong force operates over very short distances, extending only across an atom's nucleus.

The forces holding nuclear particles together in the two atomic nuclei produced during U-235 fission are stronger than those in the nucleus of the uranium atom that was split. A small loss of mass results from forming two new nuclei and is converted into large quantities of released energy.

How much mass and energy are involved? The mass loss is very small, often less than 0.1% of the total mass of the fissioning atom. Even so, the conversion of these small quantities of mass into energy accounts for the vast power of nuclear reactions.

Albert Einstein's famous equation relates mass and energy: $E = mc^2$. This equation indicates that the energy released (E) equals the mass lost (m) multiplied by the speed of light (a very large number) squared (c^2). If one gram of matter were fully converted to energy, the energy released would equal that produced by burning 700 000 gal of high-octane gasoline!

Such nuclear energy release has been harnessed by engineers to generate electricity (see Figure 6.56) and to create atomic weapons. However, the fission of one nucleus does not produce enough energy for practical use. How are fission reactions sustained to involve much larger quantities of nuclei?

Note from the equations on page 541–542 that another product of nuclear fission is the release of neutrons. These emitted neutrons can sustain the fission reaction by serving as reactants to split additional fissionable nuclei, which produce additional neutrons, which can split additional fissionable nuclei, and so on. The result is a **chain reaction** (see Figure 6.57).

> One gram of mass loss (1×10^{-3} kg) times the speed of light (3×10^8 m/s) squared equals 9×10^{13} J of energy.

Figure 6.56 *The core of a fission reactor, based on a nuclear chain reaction, emits visible light due to ionizing radiation released.*

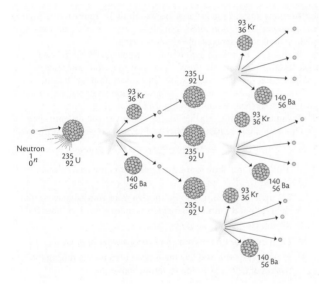

Figure 6.57 *A nuclear chain reaction. A neutron colliding with a uranium-235 nucleus initiates the reaction (left). The reaction continues and grows, as emitted neutrons encounter and split the nuclei of other fissionable atoms.*

Section D   Nuclear Energy: Benefits and Burdens   **543**

Using the Figures

Figure 6.56: The blue reactor core glow effect is known as Cerenkov radiation, named after the Russian scientist who developed the theory explaining the phenomenon. Nuclear fission releases a tremendous amount of energy due to differences in binding energy between reactant and product nuclei. Some of this energy is in excited fission products, which decay and produce beta particles. These beta particles can be emitted with kinetic energies whose velocities exceed the speed of light in water. This results in emission of blue light and the characteristic blue reactor core glow. (See **http://www.nuc.umr.edu/reactor/reactor.html** for more information.)

Figure 6.57: Use this figure to ensure that students understand how a chain reaction works and to prepare them for Modeling Matter D.2. Point out that each fission event produces high-energy neutrons that can initiate another fission event. Discuss potential fates of these neutrons (energy loss, absorption by non-fissionable nuclei) and link these fates to the requirement for a critical mass of fissionable material.

D.2 The Tumbling Domino Effect

This activity demonstrates the concept of *expanding* versus *limited* chain reactions. Give each student group a standard set of 28 dominoes. You may need two or three sets of dominoes for an adequate class demonstration.

Answers

1. a. No answer is required.

b. Student drawings

c. Each domino that fell caused two additional dominoes to fall.

d. Each neutron produced two additional neutrons, which can then bombard two additional U-235 nuclei and emit four more neutrons. This produces an *expanding* (out-of-control) chain reaction; the number of falling dominoes increases with each row.

e. The model does not represent new nuclei formed during the chain reaction. This model is two-dimensional; nuclear fission extends three-dimensionally. Little energy is released by the falling dominoes (fortunately!).

2. a.–c. No answer required.

d. Student drawings

e. A few dominoes may fall, but the "reaction" stops quickly when a domino is missing.

f. If there are not enough fissionable atoms in proximity, neutrons will not bombard a fissionable target. The chain reaction stops.

g. This would require "enriching" the domino sample so a greater proportion of total dominoes contains seven dots.

Recall, however, that most of an atom is empty space. The probability that a neutron from a fission reaction will hit and split another fissionable nucleus depends on how much fissionable material is available. Unless a certain **critical mass** (minimum quantity) of fissionable material is present, the neutrons are not likely to encounter enough fissionable nuclei to sustain the reaction. However, if a critical mass of fissionable material is present, a chain reaction can occur, as depicted in Figure 6.57, page 543. Shortly after the first fission reactions were explained in 1939, scientists recognized that they could employ large-scale nuclear reactions in military weapons. Germany and the United States soon initiated projects to build atomic bombs during World War II. In 1945, U.S. planes dropped two such bombs onto Hiroshima and Nagasaki in Japan, which led rapidly to the end of the war.

More recently, nuclear engineers have used the energy produced by nuclear fission chain reactions to generate electricity. They carefully monitor and control the rate of fission for such uses. Nuclear power plants harness the enormous energy produced by nuclear fission reactions, while also minimizing the risks of an uncontrolled chain reaction. You will soon learn more about these design features.

D.2 THE TUMBLING DOMINO EFFECT

Chain reactions sustain nuclear fission reactions in applications such as electrical power generation and atomic weapons. In this activity, dominoes will model some aspects of a chain reaction.

Each domino that falls represents a nucleus that has been split through fission. Figure 6.58 shows one way that you could set up the dominoes so that making one domino fall causes all other dominoes also to fall. Because you will model a specific fission reaction, your models will not match the one depicted in Figure 6.58.

The uranium-235 nucleus can fission into over 100 different pairs of atoms. One way, for example, produces tellurium-137 and zirconium-97:

$$\frac{1}{0}n + \frac{235}{92}U \longrightarrow \frac{137}{52}Te + \frac{97}{40}Zr + 2\frac{1}{0}n + Energy$$

1. As this equation shows, splitting *one* U-235 nucleus releases *two* neutrons.

a. Set up all the dominoes you receive from your teacher so that each falling domino will make two more erect dominoes fall.

b. Sketch your setup.

c. Push over the first domino and record what happens.

d. Explain how this models the release of neutrons during the fission of U-235 as in the equation above.

e. What aspects of the U-235 fission reaction are not modeled by the behavior of your domino setup?

2. Now you will assemble a critical mass of atoms (dominos) to initiate a chain reaction.

   a. Set up the dominoes as in Step 1a.

   b. Assume that only dominoes (atoms) with seven total dots are fissionable.

   c. Remove all dominoes from your setup that do not have seven dots.

   d. Sketch your new setup.

   e. Push over the first domino and record what happens.

   f. In what way does this model help clarify the idea of *critical mass?*

   g. How can you ensure that you have a critical mass of "fissionable" dominoes in a particular setup?

3. Suppose you need to control the total neutrons emitted so that fission is just sustained.

   a. Set up the dominoes as in Step 1a.

   b. Devise a plan so that only *half* the dominoes will fall when you push over one domino. You should not remove any dominoes that are already set up.

   c. Describe and sketch your strategy.

   d. Try your plan and record what happens.

   e. What stopped the dominoes from falling?

   f. Use a domino model to describe how to control fission chain reactions.

4. Compare the domino arrangements in Questions 1 and 3.

   a. Which is a better model of an atomic-weapon explosion? Explain.

   b. Which is a better model of fission in a nuclear power plant? Explain.

5. Propose another way to model a nuclear chain reaction.

   a. Explain how your model illustrates features of a nuclear chain reaction.

   b. Explain some limitations of your model.

Figure 6.58 *Domino behavior can model key characteristics of a chain reaction.*

3. a. No answer required

   b. Each falling domino can strike only one other domino. Students can do this by placing a barrier between it and the second domino it would strike, analogous to a control rod.

   c. Answers will vary.

   d. Half the dominoes fall.

   e. A falling domino strikes one domino, but not the second domino from the Question 1 setup.

   f. Control rods absorb some neutrons to prevent them from striking other uranium nuclei.

4. a. The arrangement in Question 1 models the explosion of a nuclear weapon, in which a tremendous amount of energy is released in a very short time.

   b. The arrangement in Question 3 models a nuclear power plant. In this case, the energy is released over a longer period of time and is kept under control.

5. One model might be to spread news via a phone tree (where each person calls, for example, two others) vs. one-way calling. If one person is not at home, the chain reaction stops for that branch. Other ideas include loaded mousetraps with Ping-Pong balls within a closed container.

   a. This simulation is like a nuclear chain reaction in that the action proceeds spontaneously at ever-increasing rates.

   b. The simulation is limited in that it does not produce new substances or release appreciable quantities of energy.

SECTION D

D.3 Nuclear Power Plants

✐ D.3 Content Reading Guide

The text explains the essential components and operation of nuclear power plants. Make sure students understand that the primary difference between a nuclear power plant and a fossil-fuel based power plant is the source of thermal energy used to boil water and produce steam. You can find useful animations of operating nuclear power plants at **http://www.nrc.gov/reactors/power.html** and **http://science.howstuffworks.com/nuclear-power3.htm**.

Using the Figures

Figure 6.59: Ask students to compare this photograph with **Figure 6.54** at the bottom of page 537. Which photo best fits their mental picture of a nuclear power plant? Many people mistake the water cooling tower (not pictured here, but pictured in Figure 6.54 with steam coming out) with the location where nuclear fission occurs. The photograph on this page focuses on the more conventional-looking building that houses the nuclear fuel and accompanying reactions.

Figure 6.59 *A nuclear power plant. Notice the reactor containment building with its domed roof.*

D.3 NUCLEAR POWER PLANTS

The first nuclear power reactors were designed and built during World War II. Since then, commercial companies have built many nuclear reactors to generate electricity, such as the nuclear power plant shown in Figure 6.59. In 2004, slightly more than 100 commercial nuclear reactors were generating electricity in the United States. Figure 6.60 shows where these reactors are located. On a global scale, an estimated 441 nuclear reactors in over 30 nations produce about one-sixth of the world's electricity.

Most conventional power plants generate electricity by burning fossil fuels to boil water and produce steam. A nuclear power plant operates in much the same way. However, instead of using fossil-fuel combustion to boil water, **nuclear power plants** use thermal energy released from nuclear-fission reactions to heat water and produce steam. The steam spins turbines of giant generators, producing electricity.

The essential parts of a nuclear power plant, diagrammed in Figure 6.61, include the fuel rods, control rods, moderator, generator, and cooling system.

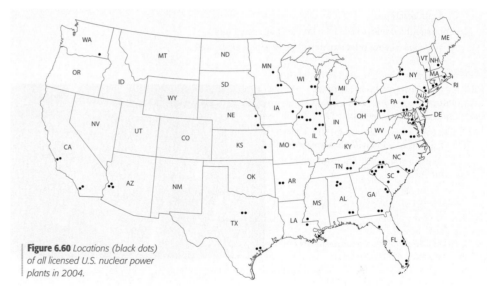

Figure 6.60 *Locations (black dots) of all licensed U.S. nuclear power plants in 2004.*

Figure 6.61 *Components of a nuclear power plant. Note the water flowing between the reactor and steam generator (red), and between the steam generator and outside body of water (blue). This water flow is important in controlling the power-plant operating temperature.*

A Nuclear Power Plant

Figure 6.60: Ask students to locate the nearest nuclear power facility to their school and to examine the placement of nuclear power plants across the United States. Students may note that the general location of nuclear power plants coincides with areas of larger population and thus higher energy demands. Some states appear to be more "accepting" of nuclear energy than others.

Fuel Rods

Coal-fired power plants burn thousands of tons of coal daily. By contrast, nuclear reactor fuel occupies a small fraction of the volume needed for coal and is replenished only about once annually. Nuclear reactor fuel is small uranium dioxide (UO_2) pellets about the size and shape of short pieces of chalk. The energy in one uranium fuel pellet equals the energy in one ton of coal or 126 gal of gasoline (see Figure 6.62, page 548). One nuclear power plant uses as many as 10 million fuel pellets. These pellets are arranged inside long, narrow steel cylinders—the *fuel rods*. The fission chain reaction occurs inside these rods (see Figure 6.61).

Most uranium dioxide in fuel pellets is composed of the nonfissionable uranium-238 isotope. Only 0.7% of natural uranium is U-235, the fissionable isotope. In reactor fuel rods, U-235 composition has been enriched to about 3%, which is only a small fraction of total fuel-rod material. It is sufficient to sustain a chain reaction, but far less than enough to cause a nuclear explosion.

> Weapons-grade uranium usually contains 90% or more of the fissionable U-235 isotope.

Section D   Nuclear Energy: Benefits and Burdens   **547**

The just over 100 fully licensed U.S. nuclear power reactors are of two types: pressurized water reactors (PWRs) and boiling water reactors (BWRs). Most are PWRs. Coolant water under pressure is heated via fission within the PWRs; this water circulates through a heat exchanger where it boils water contained in a second cooling loop. The steam produced powers the turbines. In this design, water from the reactor never interacts with the turbines. In BWRs, coolant water in the reactor core is heated; the steam that results spins the turbines directly.

Figure 6.62 *The total energy released by one nuclear fuel pellet (top) is equivalent to the energy released by combustion of either of these quantities of fossil fuel.*

Figure 6.63 *A nuclear reactor core.*

Control Rods

The nuclei of some elements, such as boron or cadmium, can absorb neutrons very efficiently. Such materials are placed in *control rods,* which regulate the number of neutrons available for causing fission. Moving the control rods up or down (see Figure 6.63) between the fuel rods regulates the rate of the nuclear chain reaction. The reaction can be completely stopped by dropping the control rods all the way down between the fuel rods and absorbing nearly all neutrons released as U-235 fissions.

Moderator

In addition to fuel rods and control rods, the core of a nuclear reactor contains a *moderator,* which slows down high-speed neutrons. This allows the fuel rods to more efficiently absorb neutrons, enhancing the probability of fission.

Heavy water (with the formula D_2O, where D represents the hydrogen-2 isotope, deuterium), regular water (termed light water by nuclear engineers), and graphite (carbon) are the three most commonly used moderator materials.

Generator

In commercial nuclear reactors, the fuel rods and control rods are usually surrounded by a system of circulating water. In simpler reactors, the heat released by the fuel rods boils this water, and the resulting steam spins the turbines of the electrical generator. In another type of reactor, this water is superheated under pressure and does not boil. Instead, it circulates through a heat exchanger, where it boils the water contained in a second cooling loop. This type of reactor is illustrated in Figure 6.61 (page 547).

Cooling System

Steam moves past the turbines and travels through pipes where it is cooled by water drawn from a nearby body of water. The cooled steam condenses to liquid water and circulates inside the generator. So much thermal energy is generated that some steam must also be released into the air. The largest and most prominent features of most nuclear power plants are tall, gracefully curved concrete cylinders, called cooling towers, where excess thermal energy is released. Some observers mistakenly assume that the cooling tower is the nuclear reactor.

A nuclear reactor is designed to prevent the full escape of radioactive material if a malfunction causes the release of radioactive material, including cooling water, within the reactor itself. The core of a nuclear reactor is surrounded by concrete walls two to four meters thick. Further protection is provided by enclosing the reactor in a building with thick walls of steel-reinforced concrete designed to withstand a chemical explosion or an earthquake. The reactor building is also capped by a domed roof that can withstand high internal pressure.

The well-known nuclear accident in 1986 at one of the four reactors at the Ukraine's Chernobyl power plant occurred because too many control rods were withdrawn from the reactor and were not replaced fast enough. There was little control of the fission process, resulting in the buildup of considerable steam. The resulting explosion was not nuclear, but was due to the buildup of high-temperature steam and to the chemical reactions that it triggered. Unfortunately, the plant had been built without a surrounding concrete containment building, unlike currently operating U.S. reactors, so a large quantity of nuclear material from the reactor was also released directly into the environment.

Nuclear fission is not the only way to liberate nuclear energy. Soon you will learn about the kind of nuclear reaction that fuels the stars (and, indirectly, fuels all living matter).

> The white plumes seen rising from such cooling towers are condensed steam, not smoke.

> In the Chernobyl accident, one chemical reaction that caused trouble was high-temperature steam reacting with carbon from the moderator, producing CO and H_2. When H_2 mixed with air, it became explosive.

People have tried to create other types of nuclear power reactors, but no new designs have been approved for commercial use. Two high-profile nuclear reactor designs are high-temperature gas-cooled reactors (HTGRs) and breeder reactors. High-temperature gas-cooled reactors use a gas such as helium to cool the reactor and, in some cases, to power the turbines. Higher temperatures within the reactor make it a potential industrial heat source as well as a means of producing electricity. Breeder reactors produce energy by fission reactions and, in addition, use neutrons produced in the fission process to make new fuel, notably plutonium-239. The use of this type of reactor has provoked serious debate in the United States, in part due to fears regarding terrorist theft of the weapons-grade Pu-239.

CHEMISTRY at Work

Nuclear Power in Action: Submarines

With the possible exception of the space shuttle, nothing has as much technology crammed into as small a space as a nuclear-powered submarine. Nevertheless, you can be fully trained to operate the nuclear propulsion system on a submarine by the time you are 19—that is, if you pass Navy Lieutenant Mike Arnold's class. After six months of intensive training on land in Charleston, South Carolina, Lieutenant Arnold's students are ready for a challenging career under the oceans.

What Does a Submariner Do?

Before becoming a trainer at the Nuclear Power Training Unit, Navy Lieutenant Mike Arnold spent three years as a junior officer on the nuclear submarine *USS L. Mendel Rivers.* There he directed the operation of the nuclear propulsion plant, piloted through some of the most beautiful regions of the oceans, and, along with his crewmates, carried out defense missions.

Each submariner has a particular duty called a *watch*. Each watch is so distinct and essential to the mission of the submarine that the entire crew on duty operates as a single entity. Individuals work in six-hour shifts, around the clock; no watch is ever left unattended.

Why Do Submarines Use Nuclear Power, While Most Ships, Land Vehicles, and Aircraft Have Combustion Engines?

Submarines must generate their own electricity and propel themselves underwater for months at a time. The key to the role of nuclear power, however, is the word *underwater*. Burning fuel (combustion) requires oxygen, but there is no way to provide enough usable oxygen underwater to fuel lengthy trips. Thus, controlled nuclear reactions are used to power submarines. Some of this energy is also used to generate electricity to operate the equipment and make life possible for the crew. For example, oxygen gas and freshwater are made from seawater using energy generated by nuclear reactions.

Steam

Turbine

Secondary radiation shield

Radiation shield

Reactor

Steam generator

Primary coolant pump

Feed pump

Condenser

How Does the Nuclear Propulsion System Onboard a Submarine Work?

On a submarine, the turbines that generate electricity and the propellers are spun by steam. The energy used to make this steam comes from the controlled fission of uranium atoms in the core of the nuclear reactor. The design of the nuclear reactor is classified information, but the principles are not.

The heat generated by the fission reaction is transferred to water in a highly pressurized loop of piping called the *primary loop*. This water enters a steam generator, where it transfers heat to water running through a separate loop of piping, the *secondary loop*. The water in the primary loop goes back to the reactor. The water in the secondary loop is converted to steam and heads for the turbines, where the energy from the steam is converted to electricity and mechanical energy. The steam then goes through a condenser, where seawater is used to cool the steam to its liquid state, the condensed liquid heads back to the steam generator, and the cycle continues.

Questions to Explore

1. Investigate the dimensions of a submarine and find out how many crew share the living space during a typical voyage.

2. The world's first nuclear-powered submarine, the *USS Nautilus,* was launched in 1955. However, submarines were used in the Civil War, and even Alexander the Great's soldiers are said to have used them. Search the Web to learn how submarines were powered before the advent of nuclear propulsion.

3. Since the end of the Cold War era, some scientists have used Navy submarines for their underwater research. Find out what they have been studying at ocean depths by searching www.pbs.org/wgbh/nova/subsecrets/inside.html. While you are at this site, take a virtual tour of a submarine.

Section D   Nuclear Energy: Benefits and Burdens   **551**

SECTION D

D.4 Nuclear Fusion

This material explores nuclear fusion as an energy source. It describes the tremendous energy promise of fusion plants, as well as difficulties associated with their use. The appeal of generating electricity via nuclear fusion is that fusion reactors would produce neither the troublesome air pollutants of fossil-fuel plants nor the long-lived radioactive waste created by fission reactors. Mid-1970s forecasts of having full-scale fusion power plants by the year 2020 are now regarded as unrealistically optimistic by most experts. Promising announcements of "cold fusion" in the 1990s also proved to be unfounded.

ITER, which means "the way" in Latin, a joint project of the People's Republic of China, the European Union and Switzerland, India, Japan, the Republic of Korea, the Russian Federation, and the United States, is an effort to conduct fusion research. The project was organized under the auspices of the International Atomic Energy Agency (IAEA). Design work has been conducted in Germany and Japan; the actual device will be built in Cadarache, France. ITER is an intermediate step between current research in plasma physics and fully operational fusion-based power plants of the future. For more information, visit **http://www.iter.org**.

D.4 NUCLEAR FUSION

In addition to releasing energy by splitting massive nuclei (fission), large quantities of nuclear energy can be generated by *fusing,* or combining, small nuclei. **Nuclear fusion** involves forcing two relatively small nuclei to combine into a new, more massive nucleus. As with fission, the energy released by nuclear fusion can be enormous, again due to the conversion of mass into energy. Gram for gram, nuclear fusion liberates even more energy than does nuclear fission—between three and ten times more energy (Figure 6.64).

Scientific American Conceptual Illustration

Figure 6.64 Nuclear fission and fusion. *Fusion (top) occurs when smaller nuclei (protons in blue, neutrons in grey) combine to form larger nuclei. Fission (bottom) occurs when a neutron of appropriate energy collides with certain large nuclei, creating two smaller nuclei. Both processes can release large quantities of energy, according to Einstein's famous equation, $E = mc^2$, where m is the mass converted into energy (E) and c is the speed of light. However, the total energy released decreases as the nuclei involved approach iron-56, the most stable nucleus.*

Nuclear fusion powers the Sun and other stars (Figure 6.65). Scientists believe that the Sun formed when a huge quantity of interstellar gas, mostly hydrogen, condensed under the force of gravity. As the volume of gas decreased, its temperature increased to about 15 million degrees Celsius, and hydrogen nuclei began fusing into helium. The nuclei that fused together were all positively charged and tended to repel one another. The high temperature gave each nucleus considerable kinetic energy, which helped overcome the repulsions.

Once fusion was started, the Sun began to shine, converting nuclear energy into radiant energy. Scientists estimate that the Sun, believed to be about 4.5 billion years old, is about halfway through its life cycle.

Figure 6.65 *The Sun's energy is produced by continuous nuclear-fusion reactions.*

The nuclear-fusion reactions occurring in the Sun are rather complicated, but the end result is the conversion of hydrogen nuclei into helium nuclei. The overall result can be summarized by this equation:

$$4\,^1_1\text{H} \longrightarrow \,^4_2\text{He} + 2\,^{\,0}_{+1}e + \text{Energy}$$

Hydrogen-1   Helium-4   Positrons

How much energy does such a nuclear fusion reaction produce? Comparing the total mass of reactants to the total mass of products reveals that 0.006 900 5 g is lost when one gram of hydrogen-1 atoms fuse to produce one gram of helium-4 atoms. Using Einstein's equation, $E = mc^2$, the energy released through the fusion of one gram of hydrogen atoms (one mole H) is 6.2×10^8 kJ. Here is one way to put this very large quantity of energy into perspective: The nuclear energy released from the fusion of one gram of hydrogen-1 equals the thermal energy released by burning nearly 5000 gal of gasoline or 20 tons of coal.

Powerful military weapons incorporate nuclear fusion. The hydrogen bomb, also known as a *thermonuclear device,* is based on a fusion reaction that uses the thermal energy from the explosion of a small atomic (fission) bomb to initiate fusion.

Invite students to compare the processes of *fusion* and *fission*. Ask them to describe the reactants and products. Discuss the neutrons produced in fission and the role they play in initiating fission of other nuclei. Note that while fusion does not depend on neutrons, repulsive forces between nuclei being fused must be overcome. The consequence of this is that controlled, sustained fusion, to date, has not been conducted on Earth.

Using the Figures

Figure 6.65: It is fascinating to consider fusion processes that take place on the sun—where 600 million tons of hydrogen is converted into 596 million tons of helium every second. The "lost" 4 million tons is mass converted into energy (to calculate how much, multiply the mass deficit in grams by the speed of light [m/s] squared, based on Einstein's equation). The energy released is so great that 40 000 W of light is emitted by each square inch of the sun's surface. The sun has steadily emitted this light for the last 4.5 billion years, and—as far as scientists know—will continue to do so for several billion years longer (**http://observe.arc.nasa.gov/nasa/exhibits/sun/sun_5.html**).

Section D   Nuclear Energy: Benefits and Burdens   **553**

Making Decisions

D.5 The Safest Journey

This activity points out that risks and benefits enter every aspect of our lives. How we deal with risks may be related to information from news media and other sources that shape our perceptions. For example, even though traveling by air is much safer than traveling an equivalent distance by automobile, most people still consider air travel more dangerous.

Answers

1. a. Bicycle: (in text)
   Auto: (500 mi) × (0.000 001 risk factor)/(100 mi) = 0.000 005 risk factor
   Train: (500 mi) × (0.000 001 risk factor)/(120 mi) = 0.000 004 2 risk factor
   Bus: (500 mi) × (0.000 001 risk factor)/(500 mi) = 0.000 001 risk factor
   Airline: (500 mi) × (0.000 001 risk factor)/(1900 mi) = 0.000 000 26 risk factor
   b. Scheduled airline travel
   c. Bicycling

2. a. Traveling by bicycle is cheapest; cars, trains, and buses are faster than bicycles; and transportation by scheduled airlines is the fastest and most worry-free—in terms of personal responsibility for "driving"—but it can be expensive.
   b. Bicycle travel is most risky, due to collisions with cars or road hazards. Cyclists are relatively unprotected, especially without helmets. Car crashes are common; risk of injury increases if no seat belts are worn, the driver is intoxicated, or in bad weather conditions. Plane crashes are infrequent but most passengers die when they occur.

Figure 6.66 *A deuterium-tritium fuel pellet placed in the path of a laser beam, to initiate fusion.*

Can the energy of nuclear fusion be harnessed for beneficial purposes, such as producing electricity? This remains to be seen. Scientists have spent more than five decades pursuing this possibility. They have tried many schemes, but have not yet succeeded. The major difficulties have been maintaining the high temperatures needed for fusion while also containing the reactants and fused nuclei. Figure 6.66 shows one of these fusion experiments. The nuclear fusion facility at Princeton University has achieved temperatures sufficient to initiate fusion, but so far the total quantity of energy put into the process is more than the total energy released.

If scientists finally succeed in controlling nuclear fusion in the laboratory, there is still no guarantee that fusion reactions will become a practical source of energy. Low-mass isotopes needed to fuel such reactors are plentiful and inexpensive, but confinement of the reaction could be very costly. Furthermore, although the fusion reaction itself produces less radioactive waste than does nuclear fission, capturing the positrons and shielding the heat of the reaction could generate nearly as much radioactive waste as that produced now by fission-based power plants.

In splitting and fusing atoms, the nuclear energy that fuels the universe has been unleashed. Much good has arisen from it, but so have scientific, social, and ethical questions. Along with great benefits come great risks. How much risk is worth any potential benefits? In the next activity you will analyze risks and benefits associated with deciding how to travel, to see a friend.

> Electing not to make a decision is, in fact, also a decision—one with its own risks and benefits.

Making Decisions

D.5 THE SAFEST JOURNEY

Suppose you want to visit a friend who lives 500 mi (800 km) away, using your safest means of transportation. Insurance companies publish reliable statistics on the safety of different methods of travel. Using Table 6.11, answer the following questions:

RISK OF TRAVEL	
Mode of Travel	**Distance (Miles) Traveled at Which One Person in a Million Will Suffer Accidental Death***
Bicycle	10
Automobile	100
Train	120
Bus	500
Scheduled Airline	1900

*On average, chance of death is increased by 0.000 001.

Table 6.11 *The extent of risk associated with travel depends both on the risk of an accident and on the total time spent in that mode of travel.*

1. Assume there is a direct relationship between distance traveled and chance of accidental death (that is, assume that doubling the distance doubles your risk of accidental death).

   a. What is the risk factor (chance of accidental death) for traveling 500 mi by each mode of travel listed in the table? For example, Table 6.11 shows that the risk factor for biking increases by 0.000 001 for each 10 mi traveled. Therefore, the bike-riding risk factor in visiting your friend would be

   $$500 \text{ mi} \times \frac{0.000\ 001 \text{ risk factor}}{10 \text{ mi}} = 0.000\ 05 \text{ risk factor}$$

   b. What is the safest mode of travel (the one with the smallest risk factor)?
   c. What is the riskiest mode of travel (the one with the largest risk factor)?

2. a. List some benefits associated with each mode of transportation.
   b. List some risks associated with each mode of transportation.
   c. In your view, do benefits of riskier ways to travel outweigh their increased risks? Explain your reasoning.
   d. Identify some situations in which assumptions made in Question 1 would be invalid.

3. Do you think the statistics in Table 6.11 will apply 25 years from now? Explain.

4. What factors, beyond the risk to personal safety, would you include in a risk-benefit analysis before you decided on how to travel?

5. a. Which mode of travel would you choose? Why?
   b. Would another person's risk-benefit analysis always lead to your decision? Why or why not?

Section D   Nuclear Energy: Benefits and Burdens   **555**

c. Students answers will vary, depending on personal preferences. Some benefits of the riskier ways to travel (such as by automobile) include personal mobility, schedule flexibility, and ample luggage capacity.

d. Some roads are much more dangerous than others. Some airlines have poor safety records. Weather conditions can increase the risk of travel.

3. Probably not, given increasing population and increased automobile transportation and air travel. On the other hand, new technologies, such as proposed "smart highways" that guide vehicles electronically, might make transportation safer or provide new options.

4. Possible answers include cost (including meals and overnight expenses), time, responsibility for vehicle, space, payload (luggage, load), freedom to stop or detour, exercise, pleasure, lack of worry regarding mechanical breakdown.

5. a. Answers will vary.
   b. No, because each person places different priorities and values on each mode of transportation. Sometimes the perceived importance of a trip is worth accepting increased risks.

ChemQuandary 6

Risk-Free Travel?

There is no risk-free way to visit a friend. Even deciding *not* to visit a friend may pose risks. A conscious decision not to take a risk may put one in a position of greater risk because of unknown events. For example, if you decide to stay home, a tree might fall on your house. In addition, not visiting friends could negatively affect your quality of life, which also should be weighed against travel risks. The idea here is to minimize total risk by taking a more knowledgeable approach toward known risks.

Students may be surprised to learn that traffic fatalities per passenger mile were approximately 30 times higher in the pre-automobile days than today (30 deaths per 108 passenger miles on horses), or roughly equivalent to the fatality rate for motorcycles. There is no such thing as a risk-free ride.

Disabuse students of the misconception of "gamblers' logic." Just because the risk of accident may be one per thousand miles, it does not mean that after traveling a thousand miles you are "due" for an accident. The risk is the same for each mile.

ChemQuandary 6

RISK-FREE TRAVEL?
Is there any way to travel to visit your friends or relatives that would be completely risk-free?

Would it actually be safer not to visit them at all? Why?

D.6 NUCLEAR WASTE: PANDORA'S BOX

Imagine that you live in a home that was once clean and comfortable, but now you have a major problem: You cannot throw away your garbage. The city forbids garbage removal because it has not decided what to do with the garbage. For nearly 50 years, your family has compacted, wrapped, and saved the garbage as efficiently as possible, but you are running out of room. Some bundles leak and are a health hazard. What can be done?

The U.S. nuclear power industry, the nuclear weapons industry, and medical and research facilities have a similar problem. Spent (used) nuclear fuel and radioactive waste products have been accumulating for nearly 50 years (see Figure 6.67). Some of these materials are still highly radioactive, while other materials—even initially—display low levels of radioactivity. It is uncertain where these materials, regardless of radioactivity levels, will be permanently stored or how soon.

Figure 6.67 *Although low-level radioactive waste does not require the same disposal methods as do spent fuel rods from nuclear reactors, serious hazards are posed by improper disposal of such wastes.*

Nuclear Wastes

Two broad categories of nuclear waste are *high-level* and *low-level*. **High-level nuclear wastes** are either (a) *products of nuclear fission,* such as those generated in a nuclear reactor; or (b) *transuranics,* products formed when the original uranium-235 fuel absorbs neutrons. For example, plutonium-239 is a transuranic material. **Low-level nuclear wastes** have much lower levels of radioactivity. These wastes include used nuclear laboratory protective clothing, diagnostic radioisotopes, and air filters from nuclear power plants. Figure 6.68 illustrates the composition of radioactive wastes in the United States.

Figure 6.68 emphasizes distinguishing *waste volume* from *radioactivity level* when considering nuclear wastes; high volume does not necessarily mean high radioactivity. For example, Figure 6.68 shows that military defense efforts produce the largest volume of radioactive wastes (57%), but this waste contributes slightly more than 4% of the total radioactivity in nuclear wastes. On the other hand, spent fuel from nuclear reactors occupies less than 1% of the volume of all radioactive wastes, yet it contributes 96% of the total radioactivity. Moreover, high-level nuclear wastes also can have extended half-lives, some as long as thousands of years.

Current Disposal Methods

Because high-level and low-level nuclear wastes have different characteristics, people dispose of them differently. We can put low-level wastes into sealed containers and bury the containers in lined trenches 20 ft deep. Low-level military nuclear waste is disposed of at federal sites maintained by the Department of Energy. Since 1993, each state is responsible for the disposal of its own low-level commercial nuclear wastes. Groups of states in several regions have formed compacts in which all members use a disposal site in one state for low-level wastes from all compact members.

High-level nuclear waste disposal requires a very different approach. Spent nuclear fuel presents the greatest challenge. A commercial nuclear reactor (power plant) typically produces about 30 tons of spent fuel annually. That means that commercial nuclear power plants now operating in the United States generate roughly 3100 tons of waste annually. Approximately 22 000 tons of spent fuel are already stored in 34 states. Eventually, of course, the components of nuclear power-plant reactors will also become nuclear waste.

U.S. Radioactive Wastes: Volumes and Radioactivities

Volumes

- High-level commercial waste 0.05%
- Low-level commercial waste 38%
- High-level defense waste 8%
- Spent fuel* 0.2%
- Transuranics 5%
- Low-level defense waste 49%

■ Commercial   ▢ DOE/Defense

Radioactivities

- High-level commercial waste 0.1%
- High-level defense waste 4%
- Transuranics 0.02%
- Low-level commercial waste 0.02%
- Low-level defense waste 0.05%
- Spent fuel** 96%

*Including spacing between fuel assembly rods.
**DOE/Defense program to reprocess spent fuel is not shown

Figure 6.68 *Volumes and radioactivities of radioactive waste.*

D.6 Nuclear Waste: Pandora's Box

D.6 Content Reading Guide

The text introduces students to a highly controversial and pressing issue—high-level nuclear waste disposal. Even if all processes resulting in high-level nuclear waste were to end tomorrow, previously generated waste would still constitute an issue requiring continued attention. Encourage students to watch for newspaper articles pertaining to this topic. Given the nature of radioactive decay (particularly long half-lives), the problem will not go away in the foreseeable future.

The U.S. Department of Energy sponsors various projects for studying nuclear waste disposal. For example, the National Spent Nuclear Fuel Program studies four areas: packaging and transport, interim and long-term storage, accurate waste characterization, and compliance with safety and regulatory requirements. The program's Web site is **http://www.nsnfp.inel.gov/**. The U.S. Nuclear Regulatory Commission also provides general information on nuclear waste at **http://www.nrc.gov/waste.html**.

You may wish to find up-to-date information on the Yucca Mountain Project or to give students the opportunity to investigate and evaluate information sources about Yucca Mountain and other waste-management projects mentioned in the text. The following Web sites are possible starting points for further investigating nuclear waste disposal.

Yucca Mountain   http://www. ocrwm.doe.gov/ymp/index.shtml is sponsored by the Office of Civilian Radioactive Waste Management of the U.S. Department of Energy and has a Youth Zone for K–12 students. **http://www.yuccamountain.org** is sponsored by the Yucca Mountain Information Office of Eureka County, Nevada. **http://www.epa.gov/ radiation/yucca/** is a site that is somewhat technical, but useful in showing how the Environmental Protection Agency views its role in protecting public health around Yucca Mountain.

SOME RADIOISOTOPES FOUND IN SPENT FUEL RODS	
Isotope	**Half-Life**
Plutonium-239	24 110 y
Strontium-90	28.8 y
Barium-140	12.8 y

| Table 6.12

Each nuclear reactor site already employs this cooling process for wastes.

Vitrification is conversion of material into a glassy solid by application of heat.

The U.S. nuclear weapons program contributed about 20 million liters of additional stored waste. The volume of military waste is much greater than the amount of commercial waste. This waste is in the form of a sludge—the waste product of extracting plutonium from spent fuel rods in military reactors. (Nuclear weapons are created from the plutonium.) As radioisotopes in the waste gradually decay, they emit radiation and thermal energy. In fact, without external cooling, such waste can become hot enough to boil. This makes military waste containment a continual challenge.

Operators must replace up to one-third of a nuclear reactor's fuel rods annually. This is necessary because the uranium-235 fuel becomes depleted as fissions occur and because accumulated fission products interfere with the fission process. The spent fuel rods are highly radioactive, with some isotopes continuing to decay for many thousands of years. Table 6.12 lists the half-lives of three radioisotopes produced by nuclear fission. All of these and many more are contained in spent fuel rods.

By federal law, nuclear reactor waste must be stored on-site, usually in nuclear waste storage tanks, until a permanent repository is created. Available storage space on-site is limited, however. The federal government is responsible for the final storage of high-level radioactive waste, but it has not yet opened permanent long-term disposal sites for high-level wastes. Legal negotiations, congressional debates, and developmental work are in process to develop such a site at Yucca Mountain, Nevada. High-level nuclear wastes may eventually be stored there deep underground.

Investigating Long-Term Disposal Methods

The method of long-term radioactive waste disposal favored by the U.S. government (and by many other nations) is *mined geologic disposal.* The radioactive waste would be buried at least one kilometer below earth's surface and at least one kilometer from any water table in vaults that would presumably remain undisturbed.

To prepare radioactive waste for burial, spent fuel rods would first be allowed to cool for several decades in very large tanks of water. Over time, many of the radioisotopes would essentially decay, lowering the radioactivity level to a point where technicians could safely handle the materials. Such on-site nuclear waste storage would be only temporary; the tanks would require too much maintenance to remain safe for more than several decades.

Next, technicians would lock cooled radioactive wastes inside packages engineered to be leak-proof. The currently favored method is to transform the wastes by *vitrification* (see Figure 6.69) into a type of solid ceramic. Although the encased material would still be highly radioactive, the waste would be much less likely to leak or leach into the environment because of the glasslike envelope encasing it. Technicians could seal the vitrified radioactive wastes in containers made of glass, stainless steel, or concrete. The Savannah River vitrification plant in South Carolina is the world's largest facility of its kind. France has used vitrification for over a decade (nuclear reactors produce about 78% of France's electricity).

Nowhere in the world, however, has nuclear waste been permanently buried. The challenge is to find technically, politically, and socially acceptable sites. The Japanese government has even considered deep-ocean burial.

Figure 6.69 *One strategy to prevent radioactive waste from entering water supplies is to vitrify the waste—that is, convert it into a glassy solid.*

Some geologic sites formerly assumed to be stable enough for radioactive waste disposal were later discovered to be unsafe. For example, technicians buried some plutonium at Maxey Flats, Kentucky, in a rocky formation that geologists believed would remain stable for thousands of years. Within a decade, however, some buried plutonium had migrated dozens of meters away.

What are current plans to resolve our long-term nuclear waste disposal problems? By U.S. law, Congress has selected two sites for permanent radioactive waste disposal from options provided by the Department of Energy. These sites, located in regions of presumed geologic stability (see Figure 6.70), are the Waste Isolation Pilot Plant near Carlsbad, New Mexico, and Yucca Mountain, Nevada, an extinct volcanic ridge 100 miles northwest of Las Vegas.

Both proposals have generated considerable debate and controversy about site locations and the means of transporting radioactive wastes to them. Scientists, engineers, citizens, and politicians will continue to address legal, environmental, and engineering issues before making final decisions about these sites.

It will probably be at least 2010 before a suitable site is fully approved to receive high-level nuclear wastes for long-term storage.

Figure 6.70 *Storing nuclear waste requires an underground site that will minimize contact with local water resources and remain geologically stable over many centuries. This poses formidable challenges; the waste will remain dangerously radioactive for thousands of years.*

Waste Isolation Pilot Plant   This facility, near Carlsbad, New Mexico, is not as widely covered as Yucca Mountain. Two relevant Web sites are **http://www.wipp/energy.gov/**, a Department of Energy site, and **http://www.emnrd.state.nm.us/ EMNRD/Wipp/FAQ.htm**, a State of New Mexico–sponsored site about nuclear waste transportation.

Maxey Flats Nuclear Disposal Site This waste facility operated from 1963 to 1977. It is now one of the largest federal Superfund cleanup sites in the country. For a sample of how the Environmental Protection Agency reports on these sites, visit **http://www.epa.gov/region4/waste/ npl/nplky/maxfltky.htm**.

Section D   Nuclear Energy: Benefits and Burdens   **559**

D.7 Disposing of High- and Low-Level Waste

In this activity, students analyze the characteristics of U.S. radioactive wastes (using **Figure 6.68** on page 557) and evaluate priorities for dealing with different types of nuclear waste.

1. a. By volume: 38% + 49% = 87%
   b. By volume: 8% + 5% + 0.05% = 13%
2. Defense waste
3. Commercial and defense
4. Evaluate student answers according to how well they defend their answers with evidence. High-level wastes constitute a small fraction of the total volume, but the greater portion of radioactivity. It would make sense to deal with it first. On the other hand, the greater volume of low-level waste is costly to store and requires attention, even though the radioactive levels are lower.

SECTION D SUMMARY

 Section D Supplement

Reviewing the Concepts

1. The process of splitting an atomic nucleus into two smaller nuclei
2. Uranium-235, plutonium-239, uranium-233, californium-252
3. $^{235}_{92}U + ^{1}_{0}n \longrightarrow ^{87}_{35}Br + ^{146}_{57}La + 3\,^{1}_{0}n$
4. Because it involves the strong force holding neutrons and protons in the nucleus, which is much stronger than the electrical force that holds atoms and ions together in chemical bonds.
5. $E = mc^2$, where E = energy, m = mass, and c = speed of light
6. The *strong force* is much stronger than the electrical force that holds

D.7 DISPOSING OF HIGH- AND LOW-LEVEL WASTE

Use Figure 6.68 (page 557) to answer the following questions:

1. Approximately what percent of nuclear waste is
   a. low-level waste?
   b. high-level (including transuranic) waste?
2. Which waste source accounts for the greatest volume of high-level nuclear waste?
3. Which two waste sources account for most of the low-level nuclear waste?
4. Should high-level or low-level nuclear wastes receive greater attention? Explain your answer.

atoms and ions together in chemical bonds, and it operates over very short (nuclear) distances.

7. A chain reaction is a self-propagating reaction where the products of one reaction initiate the next. When fissionable material such as U-235 is bombarded with neutrons, its nuclei split into lighter isotopes, accompanied by more neutrons. These neutrons split other U-235 nuclei, setting off a chain reaction.

8. A chain reaction requires the fissionable nuclear mass to be near enough or large enough to capture neutrons.

9. They burn fossil fuels to boil water and produce steam. The steam spins the turbines of giant generators, producing electricity.

SECTION D SUMMARY
Reviewing the Concepts

Some relatively large nuclei, when bombarded by neutrons, undergo nuclear fission.

1. What is *nuclear fission*?
2. Name three isotopes that can undergo nuclear fission.
3. Write a balanced nuclear equation for the fission of U-235 by a neutron, producing Br-87, La-146, and several neutrons.
4. Why does a nuclear reaction release more energy than does a chemical reaction?
5. State Einstein's mass-energy relationship and explain the meaning of each symbol.
6. Name the force that holds nuclear particles together and describe its characteristics.
7. Describe characteristics of a nuclear chain reaction.
8. Why is a critical mass of fissionable material needed to sustain a nuclear chain reaction?

The electricity produced by nuclear power plants originates from the energy released by fission in controlled chain reactions.

9. Describe how most conventional (non-nuclear) power plants generate electricity.
10. State the equivalent quantities of coal and petroleum needed to produce the total energy contained in one nuclear fuel pellet.
11. Why is U-235 used in nuclear power plants?
12. How does each of the following affect neutrons in a nuclear power plant?
    a. control rods
    b. moderator
13. Why is it impossible for the fuel in a nuclear power plant to cause a nuclear explosion?
14. List the three common moderators used in nuclear power plants.
15. The core of a nuclear reactor is surrounded by thick concrete walls. Give three reasons for these walls.
16. What is the composition of the white plumes often seen rising from nuclear power-plant towers?

Nuclear fusion is the combination of two relatively small nuclei into a new, more massive nucleus.

17. Why are high pressures and temperatures needed to initiate fusion reactions?
18. How much more energy can nuclear fusion produce than nuclear fission?
19. Why isn't nuclear fusion currently practical for generating electricity in power plants?
20. State the equivalent quantities of coal and gasoline needed to produce the energy released by the fusion of one gram of hydrogen-1.
21. What is a *thermonuclear weapon*?
22. Explain why both of these statements are true:
    a. Nuclear fusion has not been used as an energy source on earth.
    b. Nuclear fusion is earth's main energy source.

Section Summary   **561**

---

10. The energy in one nuclear fuel pellet is equivalent to the energy in one ton coal or 126 gal gasoline.
11. U-235 is an abundant naturally occurring radioisotope that can undergo fission.
12. a. Control rods regulate the number of neutrons available for fission by absorbing some neutrons. Placing control rods fully among the fuel rods absorbs nearly all neutrons and stops the chain reaction.
    b. The moderator slows down high-speed neutrons and enhances the likelihood of nuclear fission.
13. Nuclear-reactor fuel pellets are only 3% U-235. Weapons-grade uranium is enriched to 90% U-235, enough to initi-

---

ate an uncontrolled chain reaction and, consequently, a nuclear explosion. The uranium used in nuclear power plants is just sufficient to sustain the chain reaction, but not enough to provoke a nuclear explosion.

14. Heavy water, regular water, and graphite
15. The walls (a) prevent escape of radioactive material in the case of malfunction, (b) withstand a chemical explosion (extreme overpressure) and (c) withstand natural disasters such as earthquakes and hurricanes.
16. The plumes are steam from heated cooling water.
17. The nuclei that fuse are all positively charged and repel one another. High pressure brings the nuclei close enough to fuse. High temperature gives each nucleus enough kinetic energy to overcome repulsions.
18. Three to ten times as much
19. Currently, in research fusion reactors, the quantity of energy put into the process is greater than the total energy released.
20. 5000 gal gasoline or 20 tons coal
21. A weapon based on a fusion reaction initiated by the energy released when a small atomic (fission) bomb explodes.
22. a. Nuclear fusion is not yet available as an economically feasible source of energy.
    b. Because energy from the sun drives most physical and chemical processes on earth, and because this energy is derived from solar nuclear fusion reactions, nuclear fusion is already the main energy source on earth.

23. a. High-level nuclear wastes are transuranic isotopes or products of nuclear fission. Low-level nuclear wastes include, for example, used nuclear laboratory protective clothing, diagnostic radioisotopes, and air filters from nuclear power plants.
    b. The major difference is their radioactivity, or quantity of ionizing radiation they release.

24. Defense and commercial activities

25. a. 0.2%   b. 96%

26. Fuel is depleted as fission occurs, and accumulated fission products interfere with fission.

27. High-level waste must cool, then be stored on site until a permanent repository is prepared. Low-level waste is sealed in containers and buried in lined trenches.

28. This treatment makes it unlikely that wastes will leak or leach into the environment.

29. a. Yucca Mountain, NV, and the Waste Isolation Pilot Plant near Carlsbad, NM
    b. They are remote and geologically stable.

Connecting the Concepts

30. *Fission* means splitting radioisotopes, by neutron bombardment, into lighter isotopes. *Fusion* means combining lighter isotopes to form heavier isotopes.

31. It does not destroy atoms (they're conserved); the material would still be radioactive.

32. The waste continues to decay. Half-life varies widely, which affects disposal and shielding requirements.

33. In nuclear fusion, two hydrogen nuclei join under high temperature and pressure, producing a helium atom.

The permanent disposal of nuclear waste poses challenging problems and issues.

23. a. List and describe the two categories of nuclear wastes.
    b. What is the major difference between them?

24. In the United States, what are the two largest sources of radioactive waste? Refer to Figure 6.68, page 557.

25. Refer to Figure 6.68. Spent fuel makes up what percentage of total U.S. radioactive wastes by
    a. volume?
    b. radioactivity?

26. Why do technicians have to regularly replace nuclear fuel pellets even if the pellets are still radioactive?

27. Compare current methods for disposing of high- and low-level nuclear wastes.

28. Why is vitrification a preferred method for handling and storing nuclear wastes?

29. a. Where are two potential U.S. sites for permanent radioactive waste disposal?
    b. Why were these particular sites selected?

Connecting the Concepts

30. Explain the difference between nuclear *fission* and nuclear *fusion*.

31. Sometimes burning is a good way to dispose of some types of extremely toxic material. Why would burning be an unacceptable plan for destroying nuclear waste?

32. Explain why the disposal of nuclear waste is a challenging issue in many nations. Use the concepts of radioactive decay, half-life, and radiation shielding in your answer.

33. How does nuclear fusion compare to a chemical reaction in which two hydrogen atoms combine to form a hydrogen molecule, H_2?

34. Construct a diagram showing energy transformations involved in producing electricity in a nuclear power plant. How would your diagram differ for a coal-fired power plant?

35. A simple way to minimize the need for long-term storage of radioactive waste might seem to be speeding up all radioactive decay rates involved. Why won't this plan work?

36. What are some factors complicating the cleanup of abandoned or improperly stored nuclear waste?

Extending the Concepts

37. Research how other countries dispose of their high-level nuclear waste and evaluate their methods in terms of risks and benefits.

38. When confronting problems surrounding high-level nuclear waste disposal, students sometimes propose loading the waste in a rocket and shooting it into the Sun. What are some risks and benefits of this plan?

39. Fusion reactions that produce iron and lighter elements can take place in the core of an ordinary star. However, elements with higher atomic numbers generally result from violent stellar explosions. Explain the difference.

40. What would be some advantages of nuclear fusion over nuclear fission for producing electricity?

41. In the late 20th century, a group of scientists mistakenly claimed they had accomplished "cold fusion." Research this event and its scientific impact.

42. Investigate conditions needed to sustain a critical-mass chain reaction in
    a. a nuclear reactor.
    b. a nuclear weapon.

---

34. Diagrams should show nuclear energy converted to thermal energy in radioactive decay, thermal energy (used to produce steam) converted into mechanical energy (as steam spins turbines), and mechanical energy converted into electrical energy as rotating turbines produce electricity.

In a coal-fired power plant, chemical energy (in chemical bonds among carbon atoms) is converted to thermal energy as coal burns. The remaining steps are the same.

35. There is no way to change the rate of radioactive decay.

36. The continuous decay of radioactive waste and contamination of groundwater

Extending the Concepts

37. France, Belgium, and the UK use vitrification. Australia invented, and England may start using, SynRoc (a ceramic that incorporates radioactive waste into its crystal structure). Risks and benefits are similar for both. The waste is still radioactive, so protective measures still must be taken. Possible benefits are that both methods make it unlikely that nuclear wastes will leak or leach into the environment. Many countries are still seeking (and planning for) permanent repositories for their high-level nuclear waste.

38. Risks include high cost and the possibility of a launch accident that would spread radioactive waste. Benefits include not having the waste on Earth.

39. Energies even greater than those in normal stars are required to fuse nuclei to produce elements with atomic numbers greater than that of iron. This difference is related to the binding energy curve. See **http://en.wikipedia.org/wiki/Binding_energy** or **http://hyperphysics.phy-astr.gsu.edu/HBASE/nucene/nucbin.html#c2** for more information.

40. With fusion, we would not run out of fuel; fusion produces a stable, nonradioactive, and nonreactive product (He), which would eliminate concerns about pollution and waste.

41. "Cold fusion" would conceivably provide an endless source of non-polluting energy at low cost. In 1989, Martin Fleischmann and Stanley Pons announced discovery of cold fusion. It rapidly became the science news story of the decade. But the excitement and kudos quickly vanished when others determined that the findings were invalid. Amid accusations of fraud and incompetence, the scientific establishment shunned the work of Fleischmann and Pons. The two scientists soon dropped from public attention (**http://www.wired.com/wired/archive/6.11/coldfusion.html**).

42. a. Necessary conditions include a moderator such as water to slow neutrons down, since fast neutrons are less likely to be absorbed and can lead to termination of the chain; adequate, high-purity, appropriately shaped fission fuel; and minimization of non-fission capture.

b. All the factors in Answer 42a, plus rapid conversion of subcritical masses of fissionable material into supercritical masses to promote an uncontrolled (explosive) chain reaction.

PUTTING IT ALL TOGETHER

COMMUNICATING SCIENTIFIC AND TECHNICAL INFORMATION

Throughout your chemistry studies up to this point, you have used scientific ideas to evaluate and draw your own conclusions regarding published claims in the CANT flyer. Your final task in this unit is to prepare and present what you have learned to help some Riverwood residents draw their own conclusions about nuclear concerns.

As you already know, your audience is composed of senior citizens at a local community center. They are concerned that regulations proposed by CANT will affect their ability to receive a full range of medical care. They are also alarmed by some CANT claims about nuclear waste disposal.

The senior citizens have invited your class to address the scientific aspects of statements made in the flyer from CANT so that they can evaluate the group's message more completely.

Unit 6
Overview

YOUR PRESENTATION

Each student group will be responsible for responding to one or more CANT statements. In preparing your presentation, coordinate with other groups working on statements that involve similar ideas.

For each statement, your presentation should address these points:

1. Decide whether the flyer statement is *true, false,* or *partially true.*

2. Explain the science or technology that the statement involves. For example, for statements about nuclear power plants, you should review how such plants work; for statements about radiation, you should explain different types of radiation.

3. Prepare a replacement statement, if necessary, that more accurately and evenhandedly addresses the same topic/issue.

Design your presentation to be understandable by adults with at least a high school education that most likely was completed many years ago.

When possible, include visual aids and everyday examples and applications. Also devise a way to evaluate the effect of your presentation. Try to assess whether or not the audience, following your presentation, is better able to make informed decisions regarding nuclear policies for Riverwood.

Putting It All Together   563

PUTTING IT ALL TOGETHER

 Putting It All Together: Risks and Benefits of Nuclear Technology Rubric

Communicating Scientific and Technical Information

One goal of *ChemCom* is to help students *apply* their science knowledge and skills to their everyday lives. This culminating activity is a good example of this process. Ideally, students will create a presentation that both reflects their knowledge and informs their audience. You may provide students with one or two class sessions to create a presentation around their given statement(s). Encourage students to use results of Making Decisions activities earlier in the unit (pages 493, 517, and 536–537) as resources. Be sure they assess the truth of their CANT statement(s), explain the technology related to the statement, and devise a more satisfactory replacement statement. Students may request materials to support their presentations. Consider providing a scoring rubric for presentations in advance so that students become aware of project expectations and plan to consider and address those expectations.

Consider arranging to take your class to an actual senior-citizen center and inviting students to make their presentations. Plan to distribute copies of the CANT flyer (page 478) to the audience and ask them to decide, before the presentations, whether the statements are true, false, or partially true. Alternatively, consider arranging for students to make their presentations to another class (such as a science or social science "modern problems" course).

563

SECTION	CLASS TIME	STUDENT EDITION FEATURES	PROGRAM RESOURCES	MEDIA AND TECHNOLOGY
Section A: Food as Energy **Objectives** • Describe how calorimetry is used to determine the energy stored in a particular food. • Calculate energy involved, temperature change, or specific heat capacity, given appropriate calorimetry data. • Describe main processes and reactions involved as energy flows from the sun to growing plants, then in turn to herbivores, carnivores, and decomposers. • Describe how chemical energy is derived from oxidation of carbohydrates and fats.	**5 Class Periods**	**Developing Skills** A.6 Energy in Action **Investigating Matter** A.3 Snack-Food Energy **ChemQuandary 1** How Does Your Garden Grow? **Making Decisions** A.2 Diet and Food Groups A.8 Gain Some, Lose Some	**TRB** **Investigating Matter** A.3 Snack Food Energy Student Worksheet and Data Table **Making Decisions** A.2 Food Inventory Student Worksheet A.2 Diet and Food Groups Student Worksheet A.9 Energy Intake and Expenditure Student Worksheet **Content Reading Guides** A.4 and A.5 Content Reading Guide A.8 Content Reading Guide **Supplements and Practice** A.3 Supplement: Calorimetry Section A Supplement **Black Line Masters** Sample Food Diary 1 Sample Food Diary 2	**TRCD** **All TRB and Test Bank Materials for Unit 7, Section A** **Exercises** The Energy Value of Food **Videos** Food Energy in a Potato Chip

SECTION	CLASS TIME	STUDENT EDITION FEATURES	PROGRAM RESOURCES	MEDIA AND TECHNOLOGY
Section B: **Energy Storage and Use** **Objectives** • Describe the general structure of a carbohydrate molecule. • Distinguish among monosaccharide, disaccharide, and polysaccharide structures. • Describe the general structure and components of a fat molecule. • Describe saturated and unsaturated fats. • Describe hydrogenation. • Distinguish between cis and trans isomers. • Explain how structural differences in fat and carbohydrate molecules account for their different properties and energy content. • Identify a limiting reactant, given the equation and reaction conditions.	**5 Class Periods**	**Developing Skills** B.4 Calories from Fat B.6 Fats in the Diet B.9 Limiting Reactants in Chemical Reactions **Making Decisions** B.10 Analyzing Fats and Carbohydrates **ChemQuandary 2** Fat-Free Food? **Modeling Matter** B.8 Limiting-Reactant Analogies	**TRB** **Making Decisions** B.10 Analyzing Fats and Carbohydrates Student Worksheet **Modeling Matter** B.8 Limiting Reactant Analogies Student Worksheet **Content Reading Guides** Section B Content Reading Guide **Supplements and Practice** B.7 Supplement: Limiting Reactants Section B Supplement	**TRCD** **All TRB and Test Bank Materials for Unit 7, Section B** **Exercises** Carbohydrates: Structure & Function Fats: Structure & Function **Animations** Carbohydrates: Structure & Function Fats: Structure & Function

SECTION	CLASS TIME	STUDENT EDITION FEATURES	PROGRAM RESOURCES	MEDIA AND TECHNOLOGY
Section C: **Proteins, Enzymes, and Chemistry** **Objectives** • Describe the general structure of a protein molecule. • Describe the formation of a peptide bond. • Describe how amino acids in food are converted to proteins within the body. • Describe how some protein molecules (enzymes) serve as catalysts. • Describe the effect of temperature and pH on enzymes' catalytic behavior.	**5 Class Periods**	**Developing Skills** C.4 Analyzing Daily Protein Requirements **Investigating Matter** C.5 Enzymes C.7 Amylase Tests **Making Decisions** C.8 Protein Content **ChemQuandary 3** A Problem to Chew On **Modeling Matter** C.2 Molecular Structure of Proteins	**TRB** **Investigating Matter** C.5 Enzymes Student Worksheet and Data Table C.7 Amylase Tests Student Worksheet and Data Table **Making Decisions** C.8 Protein Content Student Worksheet **Content Reading Guides** C.1 and C.3 Content Reading Guide **Supplements and Practice** Section C Supplement	**TRCD** **All TRB and Test Bank Materials for Unit 7, Section C** **Videos** Enzymes Amylase Tests **Exercises** Constructing a Protein Amylase: A Biological Protein Catalyst **Animations** Constructing a Protein

SECTION	CLASS TIME	STUDENT EDITION FEATURES	PROGRAM RESOURCES	MEDIA AND TECHNOLOGY
Section D: **Other Substances in** **Foods** **Objectives** • Describe how some vitamins act as coenzymes within the body. • Explain why a particular vitamin is either fat soluble or water soluble. • Describe how titration can be used to determine the amount of solute in a particular solution. • List key minerals and explain their importance to the body. • List and describe main uses of food additives. • Describe how paper chromatography separates and identifies mixture components.	**7 Class** **Periods**	**Developing Skills** D.2 Vitamins in the Diet D.5 Minerals in the Diet D.10 Food Additive Survey **Investigating Matter** D.3 Vitamin C D.7 Analyzing Food-Coloring Additives **Making Decisions** D.11 Analyzing Vitamins and Minerals **ChemQuandary 4** Nitrite Additives	**TRB** **Investigating Matter** D.3 Vitamin C Student Worksheet and Data Table D.7 Analyzing Food Coloring Additives Student Worksheet and Data Table **Making Decisions** D.11 Analyzing Vitamins and Minerals Student Worksheet **Content Reading Guides** D.1 and D.4 Content Reading Guide D.6, D.8 and D.9 Content Reading Guide **Supplements and Practice** Section D Supplement	**TRCD** **All TRB and Test Bank** **Materials for Unit 7,** **Section D** **Videos** Vitamin C Food Coloring Analysis **Exercises** Vitamins and Solubility Food Coloring Analysis Molecular Design of an Artificial Sweetener **Animations** Vitamins and Solubility Molecular Design of an Artificial Sweetener
Putting It All Together: School Vending Choices: Guiding PTSA's Decisions		**Putting It All Together** • School Vending Choices: Guiding PTSA's Decisions	**TRB** **Appendix** Analyses of Food Diaries 1 and 2 **Putting It All Together** Putting It All Together Supplement PTSA Report Rubric	**TRCD** **All TRB Materials for** **Unit 7, Putting It All** **Together**

Equipment, Expendable Items, and Unusual Materials (per 12 Student Pairs)

Sorted by Item

QUANTITY	ITEM	SECTION USED
2.3 g	amylase	C.7
1	apple	C.5
12	balances	A.3
12	beakers, 250-mL	C.7
300 mL	Benedict's solution	C.7
24	boiling chips	C.7
12	bottles, wide-mouth (or glass jars)	D.7
60 mL	buffer solution, pH 2	C.7
60 mL	buffer solution, pH 4	C.7
60 mL	buffer solution, pH 7	C.7
60 mL	buffer solution, pH 8	C.7
60 mL	buffer solution, pH 10	C.7
1 lb	candy, M&Ms	D.7
1 lb	candy, Skittles	D.7
1 pkg	chromatography paper, 1 in wide	D.7
1	food coloring, blue	D.7
1	food coloring, green	D.7
1	food coloring, red	D.7

Sorted by Item (continued)

QUANTITY	ITEM	SECTION USED
1	food coloring, yellow	D.7
12	graduated cylinders, 10-mL	D.3
12	graduated cylinders, 10-mL	C.7
12	hot plates	C.7
120 mL	hydrogen peroxide (H_2O_2), 3%	C.5
5 lbs	ice	A.3
12	index cards, 3" × 5"	A.3
0.5 lbs	liver, raw	C.5
1 box	matches, long-stem	A.3
36	pipets, Beral	D.3, D.7
12	paper clips	A.3
1 g	potassium iodate (KIO_3)	D.3
1 g	potassium iodide (KI)	D.3
1	potato, white or baking	C.5
12	rings	A.3
12	ring stand	A.3
12	rubber stoppers to fit bottles (or glass jars)	D.7
12	soft-drink cans with pull tabs	A.3

Sorted by Item (continued)

QUANTITY	ITEM	SECTION USED
150 mL	starch solution, 0.1%	C.7
150 mL	starch solution, 1%	D.3
12	stirring rods	A.3
24	stoppers to fit test tubes (16 × 125 mm), with inserted glass tubing	C.5
12	stoppers, cork, approximately size 20	A.3
60	stoppers, rubber, to fit test tubes	C.7
6 mL	sulfuric acid (H_2SO_4), 3 M	D.3
12	test tube holders	C.7
24	test tubes (16 × 125 mm)	C.5
60	test tubes (16 × 125 mm)	C.7
12	thermometers, alcohol, −10 to 110 °C	A.3
1 box	toothpicks	D.3, D.7
1	vitamin C tablets (60 or 100 mg)	D.3
12	wellplates, 24-well	D.3, D.7
1 pkg	yeast	C.5

SUPPLY LIST

Equipment, Expendable Items, and Unusual Materials (per 12 Student Pairs)

Sorted by Section

QUANTITY	ITEM	SECTION USED
12	balances	A.3
5 lbs	ice	A.3
12	index cards, 3" × 5"	A.3
1 box	matches, long-stem	A.3
12	paper clips	A.3
12	rings	A.3
12	ring stand	A.3
12	soft-drink cans with pull tabs	A.3
12	stirring rods	A.3
12	stoppers, cork, approximately size 20	A.3
12	thermometers, alcohol, −10 to 110 °C	A.3
1	apple	C.5
120 mL	hydrogen peroxide (H_2O_2), 3%	C.5
0.5 lbs	liver, raw	C.5
1	potato, white or baking	C.5

Sorted by Section (continued)

QUANTITY	ITEM	SECTION USED
24	stoppers to fit test tubes (16 × 125 mm), with inserted glass tubing	C.5
24	test tubes (16 × 125 mm)	C.5
1 pkg	yeast	C.5
2.3 g	amylase	C.7
12	beakers, 250-mL	C.7
300 mL	Benedict's solution	C.7
24	boiling chips	C.7
60 mL	buffer solution, pH 2	C.7
60 mL	buffer solution, pH 4	C.7
60 mL	buffer solution, pH 7	C.7
60 mL	buffer solution, pH 8	C.7
60 mL	buffer solution, pH 10	C.7
12	graduated cylinders, 10-mL	C.7
12	hot plates	C.7
60	stoppers, rubber, to fit test tubes	C.7
12	test tube holders	C.7
60	test tubes (16 × 125 mm)	C.7
150 mL	starch solution, 0.1%	C.7

Sorted by Section (continued)

QUANTITY	ITEM	SECTION USED
12	graduated cylinder, 10-mL	D.3
1 g	potassium iodate (KIO_3)	D.3
1 g	potassium iodide (KI)	D.3
150 mL	starch solution, 1%	D.3
1	vitamin C tablets (60 or 100 mg)	D.3
6 mL	sulfuric acid (H_2SO_4), 3 M	D.3
36	pipets, Beral	D.3, D.7
1 box	toothpicks	D.3, D.7
12	wellplates, 24-well	D.3, D.7
12	bottles, wide-mouth (or glass jars)	D.7
1 lb	candy, M&Ms	D.7
1 lb	candy, Skittles	D.7
1 pkg	chromatography paper, 1 in wide	D.7
1	food coloring, blue	D.7
1	food coloring, green	D.7
1	food coloring, red	D.7
1	food coloring, yellow	D.7
12	rubber stoppers to fit bottles (or glass jars)	D.7

UNIT 7
FOOD: MATTER AND ENERGY FOR LIFE

Introduction to the Unit

The main focus of this unit is the chemistry of foods. Students investigate the chemistry of fats, carbohydrates, proteins, minerals, and vitamins as they review and analyze a three-day diet inventory. You may decide to provide three-day diet inventories for student analyses or direct students to analyze their own diets. Two sample inventories are provided on the IRCD. Students also explore how food they eat provides energy for life and growth. As they progress through this unit, students draw upon and apply topics introduced and explored in previous units, including organic chemistry, thermochemistry, stoichiometry, and catalysis.

In Section A, students explore food as an energy source and use calorimetry to determine energy content of popular snack-food items. In Section B, they investigate how chemical energy is stored and used in both carbohydrate and fat molecules. Students investigate the role of proteins in maintaining life and growth in Section C. In Section D, they explore the chemistry of other substances, such as vitamins, minerals, and additives, in foods.

UNIT 7

Food: Matter and Energy for Life

The organizing issue for this unit centers on food vending machines. The Vending Machine Policy Planning Committee for Riverwood High School will establish new policies on foods in school vending machines. As members of this committee, students prepare an overview of a typical high school student's diet and recommend vending machine foods.

HOW is food energy stored, transferred, and released?

SECTION A
Food as Energy (page 568)

WHAT chemical roles do carbohydrates and fats play in human metabolism?

SECTION B
Energy Storage and Use (page 583)

WHY are protein molecules essential to living organisms?

SECTION C
Proteins, Enzymes, and Chemistry (page 604)

WHAT roles do vitamins, minerals, and additives play in foods we eat?

SECTION D
Other Substances in Foods (page 619)

The Riverwood High School Parent-Teacher-Student Association (PTSA) requests your help on school vending machine policies. In this unit, you will analyze a typical student diet and make recommendations based on this analysis. Turn the page to find out more.

Using the Unit Project

In this unit's culminating project, students serve as members of the Riverwood High School Vending Machine Policy Planning Committee. The planning committee is involved with a timely issue. Many schools and school districts are currently addressing this topic.

To make sound recommendations and write a comprehensive report, students review and analyze a three-day food inventory throughout this unit. In each section, students analyze the inventory in terms of such characteristics as energy, carbohydrate, fat, protein, mineral, and vitamin content. Each student should also refer to the *combined results* of student analyses as he or she prepares to advise planning committee members.

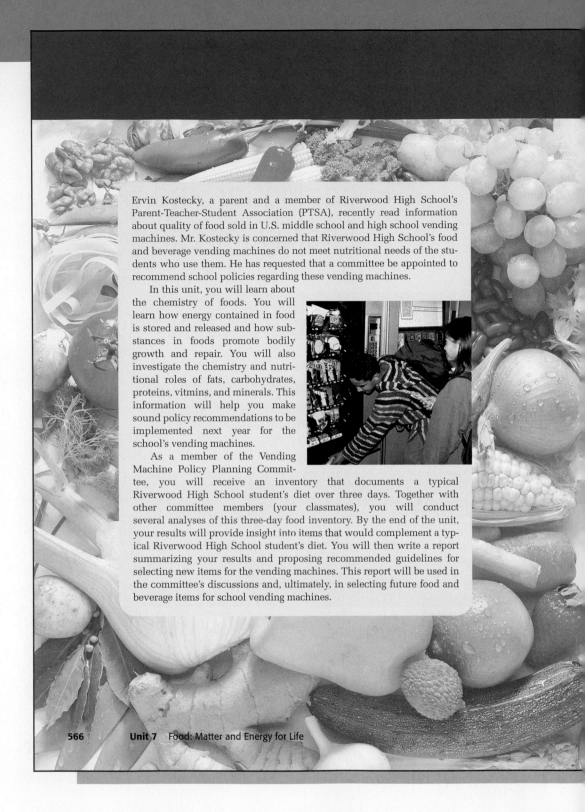

Ervin Kostecky, a parent and a member of Riverwood High School's Parent-Teacher-Student Association (PTSA), recently read information about quality of food sold in U.S. middle school and high school vending machines. Mr. Kostecky is concerned that Riverwood High School's food and beverage vending machines do not meet nutritional needs of the students who use them. He has requested that a committee be appointed to recommend school policies regarding these vending machines.

In this unit, you will learn about the chemistry of foods. You will learn how energy contained in food is stored and released and how substances in foods promote bodily growth and repair. You will also investigate the chemistry and nutritional roles of fats, carbohydrates, proteins, vitmins, and minerals. This information will help you make sound policy recommendations to be implemented next year for the school's vending machines.

As a member of the Vending Machine Policy Planning Committee, you will receive an inventory that documents a typical Riverwood High School student's diet over three days. Together with other committee members (your classmates), you will conduct several analyses of this three-day food inventory. By the end of the unit, your results will provide insight into items that would complement a typical Riverwood High School student's diet. You will then write a report summarizing your results and proposing recommended guidelines for selecting new items for the vending machines. This report will be used in the committee's discussions and, ultimately, in selecting future food and beverage items for school vending machines.

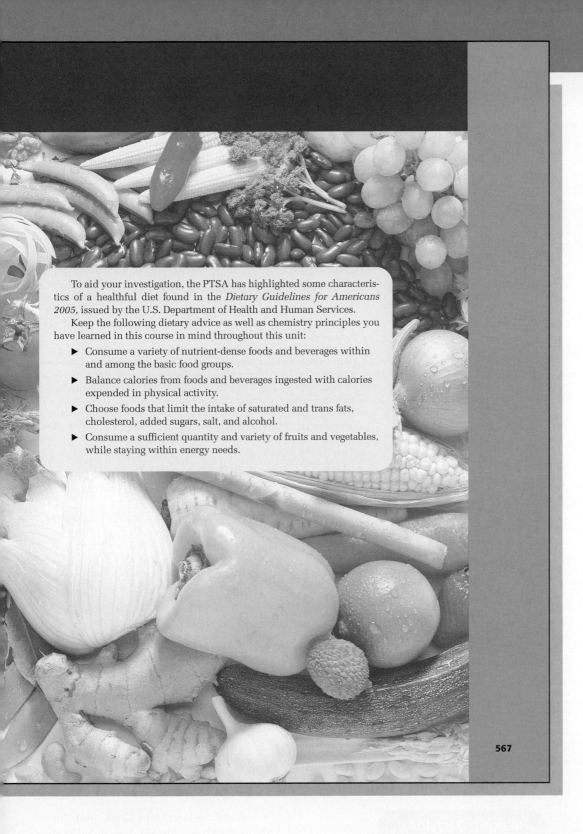

To aid your investigation, the PTSA has highlighted some characteristics of a healthful diet found in the *Dietary Guidelines for Americans 2005*, issued by the U.S. Department of Health and Human Services.

Keep the following dietary advice as well as chemistry principles you have learned in this course in mind throughout this unit:

▶ Consume a variety of nutrient-dense foods and beverages within and among the basic food groups.

▶ Balance calories from foods and beverages ingested with calories expended in physical activity.

▶ Choose foods that limit the intake of saturated and trans fats, cholesterol, added sugars, salt, and alcohol.

▶ Consume a sufficient quantity and variety of fruits and vegetables, while staying within energy needs.

Help students maintain good organization as they progress through the unit. Students may need particular assistance as they gather information for the unit's culminating activity. You might give students labeled folders for organizing components of their food inventory analysis.

567

Food as Energy

Students find the energy in a snack food with calorimetry. They also explore energy flow from sun to food and then to us and learn about relationships between glucose consumed and ATP that provides energy for activity. Energy intake and use are also related to diet and exercise.

A.1 Food Groups

The new *Dietary Guidelines for Americans* and new *Food Pyramid* both urge increased intake of fruits and vegetables, whole grains, and low-fat milk and milk products. Also emphasized are decreased intake of high-fat, high-sugar foods and increased physical activity. The new *Food Pyramid* is based on age, gender, and activity level. The Website **www.mypyramid.gov** permits entry of age, gender, and activity level to yield a personalized pyramid.

Using the Figures

Figure 7.2: Ask students to summarize the message of *MyPyramid*. They should focus on relative widths of rainbow-colored pyramid segments, *not* widths of labels below. Ask them to write an extended caption for this figure or a phone-conversation script in which they describe the message of the figure to a friend who hasn't seen it. (For example, "We should eat a lot of bread and grains, vegetables, and milk products. Fruit should also make up a large portion of what we eat, followed by meat, beans, and eggs. Foods that contain fats, oils, and sweets should only be a small portion. Exercise is also important; the figure shows a person walking up stairs.")

Food as Energy

Where does the energy required for walking, running, playing sports, and even sleeping and studying come from? The answer is obvious: It comes from the food you eat. As you begin to analyze the three-day food inventory, you will learn the chemistry that will allow you to understand where that energy originates, how food energy is stored and used, and how decisions about eating can affect your well-being.

A.1 FOOD GROUPS

When considering foods, people often focus on particular categories, or *food groups*. A healthful diet includes foods from a variety of groups, such as those shown in Figure 7.1. Why? Figure 7.2 highlights the groups. What do you already know about the nutrient and energy contents of foods in each group?

Although it is healthful to consume foods from a variety of groups, the *Dietary Guidelines for Americans 2005* advise that people should increase their daily intake of fruits and vegetables, whole grains, and nonfat or low-fat milk and milk products. In addition, the *Dietary Guidelines* call for decreasing intake of foods rich in fats and sugars.

Some foods listed in the three-day inventory may be represented by categories in Figure 7.2, but others are not. Where would you classify foods not included in Figure 7.2? What range of food groups is represented in the diet you are analyzing? Find out in the next activity.

> The term *diet* does not necessarily imply a weight-loss plan; it refers to the pattern of food and drink one regularly consumes.

Figure 7.1 *An assortment of healthful foods.*

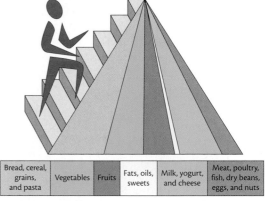

Bread, cereal, grains, and pasta | Vegetables | Fruits | Fats, oils, sweets | Milk, yogurt, and cheese | Meat, poultry, fish, dry beans, eggs, and nuts

Figure 7.2 *MyPyramid, a 2005 revision of the Food Pyramid*

Making Decisions

A.2 Diet and Food Groups

Students study a three-day inventory of food consumption, and analyze the proportion of each food group it represents. You have three classroom options:

• Ask students to track their own diets. Even students with all dietary advantages may make poor choices. However, some students may not wish to disclose what they eat, possibly due to embarrassment about lower household income, culturally diverse food selections, overeating, or other eating disorders. This is why the TRB and TRCD contain sample food diaries.

A.2 DIET AND FOOD GROUPS

Making Decisions

Your three-day food inventory analysis begins with the "big picture." That is, before analyzing the foods in terms of their characteristics—such as energy, fat, carbohydrate, protein, mineral, or vitamin content—you will determine what proportions of each food group the food inventory includes.

In particular, you will investigate whether a variety of food groups is represented within the inventory or if one or two food groups constitute most of the food. Your teacher may give you a prepared three-day food inventory. However, if you analyze a different food inventory (your own or one that you devise), these suggestions will help you:

▶ List each food item, snack, beverage, and dietary supplement consumed during each of three successive days.

▶ Express the quantity of each food item by estimating the number of servings, mass, or volume of the food or beverage. When possible, use food labels on each item to guide your quantity estimates.

For each item in the three-day inventory, indicate the food group to which it belongs. Also indicate if there are items that cannot be classified in any listed category (such as snacks or soft drinks). You may need to investigate food items about which you are unsure. Then complete the following steps:

1. Construct a data table so that the total quantity consumed within each food group can be easily recorded. Include four columns, one for each day, and one for the daily average over the three days.

2. Record the quantity consumed within each food group for each day. Then calculate and enter the average quantity for each group over the three days.

3. Using your data from Step 2, which food group or groups
   a. represent most of the foods within the diet?
   b. are minimally represented in the diet or not at all?

4. Overall, is there a reasonable balance of food groups in the inventory? If not, what dietary substitutions would lead to greater variety among food groups?

5. Complete the following steps for food items that were difficult to assign to a particular food group:
   a. List the item and the food group to which the item was assigned.
   b. Explain why it was difficult to assign this item to a food group.
   c. Explain how you decided to which group to assign each item.

6. Is it better to analyze food consumed over three consecutive days or only for one day? Explain.

7. Under what circumstances would basing your food analysis on a particular three-day average be misleading?

Section A Food as Energy **569**

• Ask students to create a typical or "ideal" teen diet.

• Give students a sample inventory representing a typical diet.

Students will work with this three-day food inventory throughout the unit. Do not ask students to share personal food-intake details with others. Wait until they analyze their diets before collecting class data or individual results. You may decide to give students a blank data table that lists report requirements.

Students usually have difficulty estimating serving sizes. Fill a large beaker to the brim with water; place it in a shallow pan. Then have each student make a fist and put it into the beaker. Water will overflow into the pan. The volume of overflowed water equals fist volume. It is useful to measure volume in *cups,* a typical (non-metric) serving unit used in nutrition tables.

Some foods may "belong to" several groups. A pepperoni pizza has bread, dairy, vegetables, and meat. Students should analyze such "combination" foods carefully. Encourage them to make the best match possible when analyzing their foods. It is not always possible to find a precise description of foods they have eaten.

Student worksheets for all Making Decisions activities in Unit 7 can be found in the TRB and on the TRCD. These worksheets are designed to help students organize data collected and analyzed throughout the unit.

Answers

1. Student data tables
2–4. Data and answers will vary.
5. a. Students may include items such as pizza (combination of food groups) or diet soft drinks (which don't fit any food group).
   b. Students may say that combination foods, like pizza, are difficult to place in a single food group. For food items like diet soft drinks, students may realize that they don't fit any group. Suggest that those items, such as regular soft drinks, with significant sugar or fructose corn syrup, be placed in the Fats, Oils, and Sweets group.
   c. Student explanations should support their food-group assignments.
6. Analyzing food eaten over three days yields averages that reflect food choices and energy consumption in a normal diet.
7. Students may not eat foods representative of a regular diet due to changes in eating schedules, travel, or illness.

569

Investigating Matter

A.3 Snack-Food Energy

A.3 Snack-Food Energy Student Worksheet and Data Table

Students use calorimetry to find the energy content of a popular snack food. They completed two calorimetry investigations in Unit 3—heat of combustion of paraffin (page 248) and heat of combustion of biodiesel (page 286). Suggest that they use procedures from previous investigations as guides for devising procedures here. Many snacks can be tested for food-energy content. Effective snack items are high in sugar/fat/oil and burn readily. *Caution:* Some people have severe allergic reactions to nuts; burning nuts can be hazardous to those individuals.

Time

50 min

Materials

(For 12 student pairs)

(Materials are based on Unit 3 procedures.)

12 12-oz empty soft-drink cans (with pull tabs)

12 ring stands and rings

12 thermometers, alcohol, −10 to 110° C

12 balances

5 lbs ice

Matches

12 paper clips

12 corks, size 20

Safety

Students should wear protective goggles and aprons in this investigation. They should handle thermometers carefully (non-mercury ones if possible) and avoid using them to stir. Caution students to manipulate the can carefully to avoid cuts from

---

A.3 SNACK-FOOD ENERGY

Figure 7. 3 *Part of the label from a popular snack food. Note the mass and total Calories contained in one serving.*

Introduction

Figure 7.3 shows part of a food label from a common snack food. Note the number of grams per serving; then note the Calories (150), which is the quantity of energy contained in one serving. How is this food-energy value determined? How much energy does 150 Cal actually represent?

The quantity of energy contained in a particular food can be determined by carefully burning a known mass of the item under controlled conditions and measuring how much thermal energy is released. You completed a similar investigation in Unit 3 when you determined a candle's heat of combustion (see Figure 7.4). This procedure is known as *calorimetry*, and the measuring device is called a *calorimeter*.

Figure 7.4 *Unit 3 laboratory device used to measure thermal energy released by a burning candle.*

Procedure

In this investigation, you will determine the energy contained in a sample of a snack food. Use the candle-burning procedure (pages 248–249) and this information to guide you as you design a procedure to determine the energy contained in this particular snack sample. *(Caution: Do not use any nut-based snack food for this investigation; some students may be allergic to such items.)* Before starting the investigation, complete the following steps:

▶ Write a complete procedure for determining the energy contained in this snack food.

▶ Sketch your laboratory setup.

▶ Construct a data table to record all necessary measurements and observations for two separate trials.

▶ Have your teacher check and approve your procedure and data table. After your teacher approves your procedure, you may start the investigation. Conduct two trials.

Lab Video: Food Energy in a Potato Chip

---

metal edges. They should also be careful as they burn the snack food. Large flames are possible. They should tie back long hair and roll up sleeves.

Advance Preparation

If tap water is warmer than about 10 °C below room temperature, prepare a large volume of chilled water. Remind students not to transfer ice into the soft-drink can. Ask students to bring in one or two clean, empty soft-drink cans *with intact pull tabs.*

Pre-Lab Discussion

Have students review calorimeter-based investigations (pages 248 and 286) in Unit 3, particularly setups and sources of experimental error. Encourage students to devise a stable holder for their snack-food sample, using paper clips and corks provided. The sample should be positioned as far as possible from the cork so that the cork will not ignite. Students should present procedures and data tables for your approval before they start.

Data Analysis

If you know the mass of water and its temperature change, you can calculate the quantity of thermal energy that caused the temperature change. In this laboratory investigation, we assume that

Energy to heat the water = Energy released by the burning snack item

That assumes, of course, that no thermal energy is lost during this process.

You can calculate the quantity of thermal energy absorbed by the water sample from the specific heat capacity of water and the mass and temperature change of the water. Recall from Unit 3 that the specific heat capacity of liquid water is about 4.2 J/(g·°C). Thus, it takes about 4.2 J to raise the temperature of 1 g water by 1 °C. If you know the mass of water heated and its temperature change, you can calculate the thermal energy absorbed by the water. If necessary, refer to pages 249–250 to remind yourself how to complete this calculation.

Use data collected in this investigation to complete the following calculations:

1. Determine the mass (in grams) of the heated water.
2. Calculate the water's overall temperature change.
3. Calculate the total energy (in joules) required to heat the water.
4. The food **Calorie**, or *Cal* (written with an uppercase C), listed on food labels, is a much larger energy unit than the joule. One Calorie equals 4184 J, which can be conveniently rounded to 1 Cal = 4200 J.
   a. Calculate the total Calories used to heat the water.
   b. How many Calories were released by burning the item?
5. a. Calculate the energy released, expressed as Calories per gram (Cal/g) of snack item burned, for each trial.
   b. Calculate the average Calories per gram for the snack item.
   c. Use reported values from the package label to calculate the declared Calories per gram for the snack item.
   d. Calculate the percent difference between the declared value found on the label and your average experimental value:

$$\% \text{Difference} = \frac{|\text{Experimental value} - \text{Label value}|}{\text{Label value}} \times 100\%$$

Questions

1. Which aspects of your laboratory setup and procedure might account for any difference between your Cal/g value and the corresponding label value?
2. How could your laboratory setup and procedure be improved to increase the accuracy of your results?
3. Consider the snack item shown in Figure 7.5. What procedural changes would be necessary to find the Calories per gram in the snack item shown?

> The precise specific heat capacity of water is 4.184 J/(g·°C).

> The calorie (cal), another common energy unit, is about one-fourth the size of a joule (1 cal = 4.184 J). One Calorie (1 Cal), which is a unit still used in the United States for food-energy values, equals one kilocalorie (1 kcal), or 1000 cal.

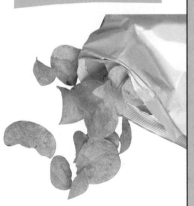

Figure 7.5 *Describe how you would determine the quantity of energy contained in these potato chips.*

Section A   Food as Energy   571

Sample Data Analysis

(Student Results Will Vary)

1. 97.90 mL heated water × 1.000 g/mL = 97.90 g heated water
2. 25.0 − 2.0 °C = 23.0 °C
3. (97.90 g) × (23.0 °C) × 4.18 J/(g·°C) = 9400 J
4. a. (9400 J) × (1 Cal/4184 J) = 2.25 Cal
   b. At least 2.25 Cal. Some thermal energy released by the burning snack was lost to the surroundings.
5. a. Using the sample data: 4.3 Cal/g
   b. Answers will vary (look for a similar calculation for each trial).
   c. Answers depend on the food item used.
   d. Answers will vary; 20 to 50% is typical.

Answers

1. Aspects include (but are not limited to) thermal energy loss to the environment, thermal energy absorption by the can, and large distances between the burning snack food and calorimeter.
2. Decrease the distance between the sample and calorimeter or modify the calorimeter so that more thermal energy from burning is transferred to the water. A better design might include a combustion chamber surrounded by water (as in a bomb calorimeter), but this is impossible with equipment used here. Results would be more accurate if heat absorbed by the Al can is also accounted for (if students have not already done this).
3. If students used potato chips, no changes would be necessary. Students might suggest breaking large chips into smaller pieces to better control burning. Depending on how they suspended their original sample, they might suggest a different "snack holder" design.

Lab Tips

• Try potato chips, corn chips, *small* marshmallows. Large chips or marshmallows are *not* recommended. Two or more groups can test the same item and compare results.

• Extension: Some students may be interested in the thermal energy absorbed by the can. They should find the can mass before adding water. The thermal energy released by burning food equals the thermal energy absorbed by the water and can (and, technically, by surrounding air). Specific heat capacity of Al = 0.902 J/(g(°C).

Sample Data and Calculations

Mass of snack burned	0.52 g
Mass of water in can	97.90 g
Initial water temp.	2.0 °C
Final water temp.	25.0 °C

The snack-food package label is used to find Cal/serving and the percent difference.

571

Post-Lab Discussion

The calculations in Investigating Matter A.3, pages 570–571, may pose difficulties for students due to the differing energy units used. It may help the class or small groups if you model the stepwise calculations described in the student text. Since students are already familiar with using specific heat capacity in units of J/(g·°C), they are first asked to find energy content in joules (see Unit 3). However, food energy is reported in the U.S. in Calories (with a capital *C*). This quantity is much larger than a joule: 1 Calorie = 4180 J = 1000 cal.

No more than two significant figures should be reported in the calculated results. Student results from calorimetry activities similar to this often lack precision. Regardless, the technique still gives students a good concept of calorimetry and the energy content of foods.

Food chemists use calorimetry and other methods to estimate the energy values of foods. One drawback of calorimetry is that it does not account for digestibility factors. Rather, it gives the maximum energy contained within a sample of snack food. For instance, only a small portion of the components of chewing gum is digestible and a source of energy for the body, but calculations based on burning a gum sample would reflect energy given off by both digestible and non-digestible components. It may be a good extension activity for students to research other methods by which they could determine the energy value of foods.

✍ **A.3 Supplement: Calorimetry**

Figure 7.6 *Energy from the Sun was used to convert water and carbon dioxide into the molecules that constitute these onions. What type(s) of energy conversion may happen next?*

A diagram similar to that in Figure 7.7, showing the energy involved in the combustion of methane, appears on page 240.

A.4 ENERGY FLOW: FROM THE SUN TO YOU

The snack item you burned released enough energy to raise the temperature of a sample of water by several degrees Celsius. Where did that energy come from?

The ultimate answer is easy: All food energy originates from sunlight. Through **photosynthesis,** green plants capture and use solar energy to make large molecules from smaller, simpler ones (see Figure 7.6). Recall from Unit 4 (page 348) that green plants, through photosynthesis, use solar energy to convert water and carbon dioxide into carbohydrates and oxygen gas. Although a variety of carbohydrates are produced, an equation for photosynthesis usually depicts the production of glucose:

$$6\ CO_2 + 6\ H_2O + \text{Solar energy} \longrightarrow C_6H_{12}O_6 + 6\ O_2$$

Carbon dioxide　　Water　　　　　　　　　Glucose　　Oxygen gas

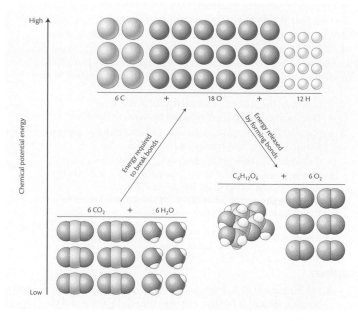

Figure 7.7 *Photosynthesis. Breaking bonds within carbon dioxide and water molecules requires energy. Energy is released when atoms combine to form glucose and oxygen molecules. The first step (bond breaking) requires more energy than the second step (bond forming) releases, so the overall process of photosynthesis is endothermic.*

A.4 Energy Flow: From the Sun to You

📖 **A.4 and A.5 Content Reading Guide**

Sunlight is the source of food energy originally captured by photosynthesis. The over-all process of photosynthesis is endothermic; it requires more energy to break bonds in carbon dioxide and water molecules than is released when glucose and oxygen molecules form. The original quantity of energy captured from solar radiation decreases as

For this reaction to occur, bonds between the carbon and oxygen atoms in carbon dioxide molecules and between the oxygen and hydrogen atoms in water molecules must be broken. The atoms must then recombine in a different arrangement to form glucose and oxygen molecules. Recall from Unit 3 that breaking bonds always requires energy, whereas bond formation releases energy. In photosynthesis, the bonds in carbon dioxide and water molecules require more energy to break than is released when chemical bonds in glucose and oxygen molecules form. The energy needed to drive this endothermic reaction, as the photosynthesis equation indicates, comes from the Sun. The potential energy diagram in Figure 7.7 shows the energy relationships in this process.

The Sun's radiant energy is converted to chemical energy stored within bonds of carbohydrate molecules. Living organisms release this chemical energy when they consume and metabolize carbohydrate molecules, converting them into lower-energy CO_2 and H_2O molecules. This chemical energy can be measured via calorimetry, as you did in Investigating Matter A.3. Material in A.5 addresses metabolism in more detail.

Energy originally delivered as sunlight continues to flow through ecosystems as carnivores (meat-eating animals) consume plant-eating animals. Eventually, plants and animals die and decay; organisms that aid in decomposition use the remaining stored-up energy. Thus, energy flows from the Sun to plants to herbivores and then to carnivores and decomposers.

The Sun's captured energy is dispersed and becomes less available as it is transferred from organism to organism. For example, as energy flows from one organism to another, some energy is dispersed into the environment as thermal energy. You may be surprised to learn that only a small fraction (about 10–15%) of food energy consumed by organisms is used for growth—for converting smaller molecules to larger molecules that become part of an animal's structure. Over half the energy contained in consumed food is used to digest food molecules. The supply of useful energy declines as energy continues to transfer away from its original source—the Sun. Figure 7.8 illustrates this decline in available energy.

> For a discussion of energy involved in chemical reactions, see pages 238–241.

> How would a potential energy diagram for the process of metabolism look?

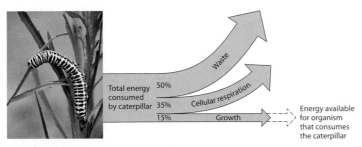

Figure 7.8 *The energy used by this caterpillar originated as solar energy. However, not all incident solar radiation is converted into usable energy. First, only a portion of the Sun's energy is actually stored as chemical energy in molecules within this plant. Next, only a fraction of that stored chemical energy is actually used by the caterpillar.*

Section A Food as Energy **573**

this energy transfers from one organism to another through the food chain. A brief review of endothermic and exothermic reactions (see Unit 3, pages 239–241) may be beneficial at this point. This review should include the idea that the energy involved in chemical reactions depends on the relative strengths of bonds in reactants versus bonds in products.

Using the Figures

Figure 7.6: The most likely answer to the caption question is that the carbohydrates in these onions will be converted into CO_2 and H_2O when consumed and that in conjunction with this transformation, there are many "next steps" for the energy involved, including energizing biological processes, conversion to thermal energy, or storage in fat molecules. In addition to answers along those lines, remind students that biodiesel fuel is commonly made from corn and other "crops" that one might consider similar to onions.

Figure 7.8: Challenge students to trace energy use in a caterpillar. It may be easiest to start at the bottom to think about how energy is used for growth (the result of building larger structures, such as tissue, from molecules ingested). It is somewhat surprising that of all the energy consumed by this organism, only 15% will be available to the next organism that consumes it. Next, ask students to consider what it means for energy to be used for cellular respiration (additional information is coming up in A.5). This is energy used at the cellular level to complete tasks such as transporting molecules, disposing waste, and synthesizing new molecules (like those that end up as part of the caterpillar's structure, resulting in its growth). Half of the energy consumed leaves the caterpillar as waste—expelled thermal energy or undigested food.

ChemQuandary 1

How Does Your Garden Grow?

As plants grow, solar energy is stored as chemical energy in molecules. A common student misconception is that most of the materials plants use for growth come from soil, instead of CO_2 in air. Review the classic investigation of Jan Baptista van Helmont (1580–1644). He weighed 200 pounds of soil, planted a small willow tree in the soil, and allowed it to grow for five years until the tree weighed 169 pounds. He reweighed the soil; its mass was essentially unchanged.

Additional ChemQuandary

How does energy flow through ecosystems? As an example, ask students how the number of tiger lilies in the world compares to the number of tigers in the world.

Discussion: There are millions of tiger lilies but relatively few tigers. This is because larger organisms require more energy, which means they consume large quantities of plants or prey. As the population of plant or prey is often limited, the number of larger organisms is also limited to smaller populations.

Figure 7.10 *Some foods that contain carbohydrates (top), and some foods rich in fats (bottom).*

Carbon dioxide and water are also produced from burning petroleum, coal, and other fossil fuels. See page 349.

This equation is the reverse of the equation for photosynthesis. See Figure 4.43, page 348.

ChemQuandary 1

HOW DOES YOUR GARDEN GROW?

From a chemical viewpoint, consider this question: As garden plants grow, what is the source of the material that causes their mass to increase?

A.5 ENERGY RELEASE AND STORAGE

Some energy in the food you eat is used soon after you consume it (Figure 7.9). The rest of the energy may be stored for later needs. These available reserves of bodily energy are mainly in fats and, to a much smaller extent, in carbohydrates. Figure 7.10 shows some foods rich in carbohydrates and fats.

Whether your body uses energy from food recently ingested or from stored fat, the release of energy from these molecules depends on a series of chemical reactions inside your cells. In *cellular respiration,* plants and animals use oxygen to break down complex organic molecules into carbon dioxide and water molecules. The energy required to break chemical bonds in reactant molecules is less than the energy released when chemical bonds in carbon dioxide and water form. Thus, energy is released in cellular respiration. You can think of this exothermic process as the reverse of the process shown in Figure 7.7 (page 572):

Figure 7.9 *A portion of the energy in food is expended soon after eating, particularly when engaging in energy-demanding activities such as bicycling. The remaining energy is then stored for later activity.*

Organic compounds + Oxygen $\longrightarrow$ Carbon dioxide + Water + Energy

Specialized structures within each cell use the energy released to carry out a variety of tasks, such as energizing reactions, transporting molecules, disposing waste, storing genetic material, and synthesizing new molecules. That energy ultimately allows you to walk, talk, run, work, and think; it also provides energy to power your heart, lungs, brain, and other organs.

Carbohydrates, fats, and proteins can all be processed as fuel for your body. We will now examine cellular respiration through the oxidation of glucose, a carbohydrate. The overall equation, based on the oxidation of one mole of glucose is as follows:

$$C_6H_{12}O_6(aq) + 6\ O_2(g) \longrightarrow 6\ CO_2(g) + 6\ H_2O(l) + 686\ \text{Calories}$$

Figure 7.11 *Products containing glucose.*

This equation actually summarizes a sequence of more than 20 linked chemical reactions catalyzed by more than 20 different enzymes. Glucose (Figure 7.11) becomes oxidized molecule by molecule within cells throughout your body.

The energy needed to perform individual cellular functions is much less than the energy released by "burning" glucose molecules. Between its release from these energy-rich molecules and its later use in cells, energy is stored in biomolecules of adenosine triphosphate (ATP), shown in Figure 7.12.

As indicated by the following equation, more energy is required to break chemical bonds in adenosine diphosphate (ADP) and HPO_4^{2-} than is released when water and ATP form. The difference in these bond energies equals 7.3 Cal, which suggests that an ATP molecule can be regarded as an energy-storage site because energy is released when the reaction proceeds in the opposite direction.

$$7.3 \text{ Cal} + \text{ADP(aq)} + HPO_4^{2-}\text{(aq)} \longrightarrow H_2O\text{(l)} + \text{ATP(aq)}$$

Hydrogen
phosphate ion

When this reaction is reversed, each mole of ATP releases 7.3 Cal. This conveniently small quantity of energy, compared to the 686 Cal produced as 1 mol of glucose is oxidized, is used to energize particular cellular reactions. Some of these reactions require less energy than that supplied by a single ATP molecule, whereas other steps require the total energy released by several ATP molecules.

Oxidation of one mole of glucose produces enough energy to add 38 mol of ATP to short-term cellular energy storage. Each day, your body stores and later releases energy from at least 6.02×10^{25} molecules (100 mol) of ATP.

ATP

ADP

Figure 7.12 *Ionic forms of ATP and ADP. The colored atoms on ATP's left side are removed when ADP forms.*

> Biomolecules such as ATP are compounds produced by chemical reactions associated with living systems.

SECTION A

A.5 Energy Release and Storage

Cellular respiration includes the concept of energy change, especially in various types of food molecules. The discussion of ATP and ADP should tie together students' previous biology knowledge. If students have not studied biology, you may need to introduce cellular respiration.

A fraction of the energy released during cellular respiration is stored in the chemical bonds in adenosine triphosphate (ATP). Hydrolysis of ATP to form adenosine diphosphate (ADP) releases that stored energy to drive various protein-mediated processes, including muscle contraction, maintaining osmotic pressures across cell membranes, and biomolecular syntheses. The rest of the energy obtained from cellular respiration is released as thermal energy.

A.6 Energy in Action

Students use **Table 7.1** to calculate the amount of energy expended during various activities. The calculations continue to move students away from using formulas and toward quantitative reasoning. Some students may find these types of calculations difficult. Model the sample problem for students before asking them to solve the numbered problems. It may help some students to work through the problems in groups of two or three students.

A.6 ENERGY IN ACTION

Table 7.1 summarizes the average energy expended during various activities. Use the information provided in the table to answer questions appearing on the following page.

| Table 7.1

ENERGY EXPENDED IN VARIOUS ACTIVITIES				
Energy Expended (in Calories per Minute) for Individuals of Different Body Mass				
Activity	46 kg (100 lb)	55 kg (120 lb)	68 kg (150 lb)	82 kg (180 lb)
Sleeping	1	1	1	1
Sitting	1	1	1	2
Playing volleyball	2	3	4	4
Weight lifting	2	3	4	4
Walking (17 min/mi)	3	4	5	6
Skateboarding	4	5	6	7
Swimming	5	6	7	9
Wrestling	5	6	7	9
Bicycling (moderate)	6	7	8	10
Playing soccer	6	7	8	10
Doing step aerobics	6	7	8	10
Playing tennis	6	7	8	10
Playing basketball	6	8	10	12
Playing football	6	8	10	12
Playing ice hockey	6	8	10	12
Doing martial arts	8	10	12	14
Jogging (8 min/mi)	10	12	15	18

Sample Problem: *Table 7.1 indicates that a 55-kg (120-lb) person burns 5 Cal/min while skateboarding (Figure 7.13).*

    a. *This energy is supplied by ATP. If the oxidation of each mole of glucose ($C_6H_{12}O_6$) produces 38 mol ATP, how many moles of glucose will be needed to provide the energy for one hour of skateboarding?*

    b. *What mass of glucose does your answer to Question a represent? The mass of one mole of glucose is 180 g.*

To begin, find the moles of ATP needed for one hour of skateboarding:

$$\frac{5\text{ Cal}}{1\text{ min}} \times \frac{60\text{ min}}{1\text{ h}} = 300\text{ Cal/h}$$

$$\frac{300\text{ Cal}}{1\text{ h}} \times \frac{1\text{ mol ATP}}{7.3\text{ Cal}} = 41\text{ mol ATP/h}$$

Because 38 mol ATP can be obtained from each mole of glucose, the skateboarder's need for 41 mol ATP can be met by slightly more than one mole of glucose:

$$41\text{ mol ATP} \times \frac{1\text{ mol glucose}}{38\text{ mol ATP}} = 1.1\text{ mol glucose}$$

What mass of glucose does that represent? Because the skateboarder needs more than one mole of glucose, that mass must be greater than 180 g:

$$1.1\text{ mol glucose} \times \frac{180\text{ g glucose}}{1\text{ mol glucose}} = 200\text{ g glucose}$$

Now answer the following questions:

1. Assume your body produces approximately 100 mol ATP daily.
   a. How many moles of glucose are needed to produce that amount of ATP?
   b. What mass of glucose does your answer to Question 1a represent?

2. One minute of muscle activity requires about 0.0010 mol ATP for each gram of muscle mass. How many moles of glucose must be oxidized to energize 454 g (1 lb) of muscle to dribble a basketball for one minute?

3. a. How many hours do you typically sleep each night?
   b. How many Calories do you use during one night of sleep? (Refer to Table 7.1.)
   c. How many moles of ATP does this require?
   d. What kinds of activity require energy while you are sleeping?

Figure 7.13 *How much energy is expended in one hour of skateboarding?*

More than 200 g glucose would actually be needed because the energy-transfer steps are not 100% efficient.

Answers

1. a. Because one mole of glucose produces 38 mol ATP, 2.6 mol glucose are needed to produce 100 mol ATP.

   $$100\text{ mol ATP} \times \frac{1\text{ mol glucose}}{38\text{ mole ATP}} =$$
   2.6 mol glucose

   b. $2.6\text{ mol glucose} \times$
   $$\frac{180\text{ g glucose}}{1\text{ mol glucose}} = 468\text{ g glucose},$$
   approximately 470 g glucose

2. $454\text{ g muscle mass} \times$
   $$\frac{0.0010\text{ mol ATP}}{1\text{ g muscle mass}} \times \frac{1\text{ mol glucose}}{38\text{ mol ATP}} =$$
   0.012 mol glucose

3. a. Individual answers; 6–10 h typically
   b. Answers will vary; sample calculation assumes 8 h sleep for a 120-lb individual:

   $$8\text{ h} \times \frac{60\text{ min}}{1\text{ h}} \times \frac{1\text{ Cal}}{1\text{ min}} = 480\text{ Cal}$$

   c. $480\text{ Cal} \times \dfrac{1\text{ mol ATP}}{7.3\text{ Cal}} =$

   66 mol ATP
   d. Breathing, movement, metabolism

Section A   Food as Energy   577

A.7 Energy In, Energy Out

Students are introduced to the idea that energy consumed is roughly balanced by energy expended during various activities. When students compare total energy consumed with total energy expended during physical activity, they find one of three resulting effects: maintenance of body weight, weight gain, or weight loss. Students should realize that a minimum quantity of energy is required for normal, resting-state body processes.

Students may be familiar with several commercial diet plans. It may be useful to compare some of these diets for their meal regimen and physical activity requirements (if any).

Making Decisions

A.8 Gain Some, Lose Some

Students explore the relationship between energy expenditure during physical activity and energy intake during eating. Students also complete calculations that reinforce the value of assessing both duration of activity and an individual's weight in this context.

Answers

1. Total calories = 250 Cal + 125 Cal = 375 Cal

  a. Assuming a 150-pound person:

  i. $375 \text{ Cal} \times \dfrac{1 \text{ min}}{4 \text{ Cal}} \times \dfrac{1 \text{ h}}{60 \text{ min}} =$ 1.6 h

  ii. $375 \text{ Cal} \times \dfrac{1 \text{ min}}{5 \text{ Cal}} \times \dfrac{1 \text{ mi}}{17 \text{ min}} =$ 4.4 mi

  iii. $375 \text{ Cal} \times \dfrac{1 \text{ min}}{7 \text{ Cal}} \times \dfrac{1 \text{ h}}{60 \text{ min}} = 0.89 \text{ h}$

A.7 ENERGY IN, ENERGY OUT

People follow various diets for different reasons. Some people may want to lose weight; others may want to gain weight. Still others put little thought into what they eat; instead, they merely eat for convenience or pleasure.

Some foods are needed to deliver important molecules to the body, regardless of their energy value. By contrast, other foods provide only energy. This latter category, which includes sugar-sweetened soft drinks, is sometimes described as furnishing "empty Calories."

If you want to lose weight, you must consume less energy than you expend. If your goal is to gain weight, you must do the opposite. If losing weight or gaining muscle mass is desired, then regular physical activity, such as that shown in Figure 7.14, is needed in addition to the particular diet you follow. Now you will explore the interplay between personal activity and diet.

> If you eat 100 Cal per day more than you burn up, you will gain about a pound each month.

Figure 7.14 *Technology is available for monitoring total energy expenditure.*

Making Decisions

A.8 GAIN SOME, LOSE SOME

Look again at Table 7.1 on page 576. The quantity of energy expended depends on the duration of a given activity and the person's body mass. For example, during one hour of soccer playing, a 55-kg (120-lb) person expends 420 Cal, whereas a 68-kg (150-lb) person expends 480 Cal in the same activity.

Use the information provided in Table 7.1 to answer the following questions.

Sample Problem: *A 46-kg student usually takes 10.0 min to bike home from school. Would this student burn more Calories by jogging home instead (at 8 min/mi for 15.0 min)?*

  Bicycling requires 6 Cal/min × 10.0 min = 60 Cal.

  Jogging requires 10 Cal/min × 15.0 min = 150 Cal.

Thus, jogging home burns more energy per trip—90 Cal more.

---

b. $375 \text{ Cal} \times \dfrac{1 \text{ lb}}{3500 \text{ Cal}} = 0.11 \text{ lb}$

c. $16 \text{ weeks} \times \dfrac{0.14 \text{ lb}}{\text{week}} = 2.2 \text{ lbs}$

2. a. Lower intake of some other high-energy foods in the regular diet.

  b. This would compensate for the energy in the ice cream.

c. Some students may suggest maladaptive methods, such as skipping meals, drinking abundant water, or regurgitating food, which can damage health. Also, foods skipped in such a plan might have greater nutritional value than the sundae.

3. a. $6 \text{ glasses} \times 250 \text{ mL} \times \dfrac{1.0 \text{ g}}{1 \text{ mL}} =$ 1500 g water

1. Consider eating an ice-cream sundae (Figure 7.15). Assume that two scoops of your favorite ice cream provide 250 Cal; the topping adds 125 Cal more.

   a. Assume that your regular diet (without that ice-cream sundae) just maintains your current body weight. If you eat the ice-cream sundae and wish to "burn off" those extra Calories,

      i. for how many hours would you need to lift weights?

      ii. how far should you walk at 17 min/mi?

      iii. for how many hours would you need to swim?

   b. One pound of weight gain is equivalent to 3500 Cal. If you choose not to exercise, how much weight will you gain from eating the sundae?

   c. Now assume that you consumed a similar sundae once per week for 16 weeks. If you do not exercise to burn off the added Calories, how much weight will you gain?

2. Question 1 implies that eating an ice-cream sundae will cause weight gain unless you complete additional exercise.

   a. Can you think of a plan that would allow you to consume the sundae, do no additional exercise, and still *not* gain weight?

   b. Explain your answer.

   c. What concerns would you have about this plan?

3. Suppose you drank six glasses (250 mL each) of ice water (0 °C) on a hot summer day.

   a. Assume your body temperature is 37 °C. How many joules of thermal energy would your body use in heating that ice water to body temperature? Recall that the specific heat capacity of water is about 4.2 J/(g·°C).

   b. How many Calories is this? Recall that 1 Cal equals about 4200 J.

   c. A serving of french fries contains 240 Cal. How many glasses of ice water would you need to drink to "burn off" the Calories consumed in one serving of french fries?

   d. Given your answer to Question 3c, does drinking large quantities of ice water seem like a reasonable strategy to lose weight? Explain.

4. Identify your favorite activity from Table 7.1. How many minutes would you need to engage in that activity to burn off the Calories in one serving of french fries (see Question 3c)?

Figure 7.15 *How does an extra helping of ice cream affect your daily balance between energy intake and expenditure?*

Section A   Food as Energy   **579**

Energy used to heat water = 1500 g × (37 °C − 0 °C) × 4.2 J/(g·°C) = 230 000 J

b. 230 000 J = 55 Cal

c. $240 \text{ Cal} \times \dfrac{6 \text{ glasses}}{55 \text{ Cal}} = 26 \text{ glasses}$

d. No. One would need to consume very large quantities of water. Nutritionists recommend drinking eight glasses of water daily. However, drinking *very* large quantities of water can be dangerous as it can lead to a condition called *hyponatremia* (literally, "low sodium," which disrupts proper functioning of the nervous system).

4. Answers will vary.

A.9 Energy Intake and Expenditure

Students evaluate their three-day food inventory for energy content by:
• calculating average and total daily Calorie intake.
• calculating total Calories supplied by each food group.
• determining if weight would be gained or lost.

Provide students with a nutrition guide such as *Nutritive Values of Foods*, U.S. Department of Agriculture. You can download this publication from **http://www.nal.usda. gov/fnic/foodcomp/Data/HG72/hg72_ 2002.pdf**. Many cookbooks have guides, or you can purchase inexpensive guides at many grocery stores.

Several Websites also have online diet analysis tools. The USDA Center for Nutrition Policy and Promotion provides *Dietary Guidelines for Americans, 2005*, 6th Edition, and also offers *My Pyramid Tracker,* a useful tool for analyzing diets at **http://www. mypyramidtracker.gov/default.htm**. At this site, students can create a username and password and save their data over an extended time. This site will also allow students to monitor physical activity over days, weeks, or months. A related site hosts the *USDA Food Composition Database*. This database can be searched online or downloaded from **http://www.ars. usda.gov/ba/bhnrc/ndl.**

During this activity, encourage students to take complete notes and answer the questions thoroughly. This energy analysis will become a resource as students complete their written reports for the Riverwood High School Vending Machine Policy Planning Committee in the unit's culminating activity.

Energy Value of Food

A.9 ENERGY INTAKE AND EXPENDITURE

Based on the chemical knowledge you have gained, you can find the total energy consumed in the three-day food inventory and estimate the energy expended based on typical activity levels.

Using appropriate resources suggested by your teacher, calculate and record the food energy (Calories) contained in each item in the three-day inventory.

1. Calculate the total Calories consumed each day.

2. Calculate the average Calories consumed per day.

3. Using your results from A.2 (page 569), how many Calories per day (on average) are supplied by each food group?

4. Using Table 7.1 and other resources provided by your teacher, develop a list of typical daily activities for a high school student and record how much energy is expended during each activity listed.

5. Based on your list prepared in Question 4, calculate the total Calories expended over an average day. Calories are expended not only during the activities listed but also by normal, resting-state body processes. Be sure to include this expenditure in your calculation.

Figure 7.16 *The balance between energy intake and expenditure affects one's body mass.*

6. a. Based only on Calories consumed and expended, decide whether the three-day inventory you are evaluating would be appropriate for weight maintenance (see Figure 7.16). Explain your answer.

   b. Identify and describe any limitations in your analysis that may affect your decision in Question 6a.

7. Based on your analysis thus far, what types of items would you recommend for the Riverwood High School vending machines in terms of the energy they provide?

SECTION A SUMMARY

 Section A Supplement

Reviewing the Concepts

1. Calories, calories, joules

2. Student sketches should resemble the soft drink can setup used in Investigating Matter A.3. They should label, at minimum, a thermometer to monitor temperature change and water to absorb thermal energy.

SECTION A SUMMARY
Reviewing the Concepts

Calorimetry can be used to determine the quantity of energy contained in a particular food sample.

1. List three common units used to express the energy content of food.

2. Sketch a simple calorimeter and label the purpose of each component.

3. Why is it important to know accurately the mass of water used in a calorimeter?

4. What is the mathematical relationship between a *Calorie* and a *calorie*?

5. Convert the following energy quantities:
   a. 4375 cal to Cal
   b. 76 932 J to Cal
   c. 289 Cal to J
   d. 12 226 000 cal to kJ

6. What is meant by the *specific heat capacity* of water?

7. a. How much thermal energy (in joules) is required to increase the temperature of a 115-g liquid water sample by 10.0 °C?
   b. Suppose that a 2.0-g food sample was burned in a calorimeter to provide the thermal energy involved in Question 7a. Assume all thermal energy released was used to heat the water.
      i. How many calories per gram were in the food sample?
      ii. How many Calories per gram were in the food sample?

All food energy originates from sunlight and is stored and released through a series of chemical reactions.

8. What process captures sunlight and transforms it into chemical energy?

9. Write a chemical equation for the production of glucose through photosynthesis.

10. Is photosynthesis an endothermic or exothermic chemical change? Explain.

11. Keeping in mind the law of conservation of energy, describe what happens to the food energy consumed by living creatures.

12. What is meant by an "energy-rich" molecule?

13. What is the relationship between photosynthesis and cellular respiration? Write chemical equations that support your answer.

14. What is the difference, in terms of molecular composition and stored energy, between ADP and ATP?

15. How do ADP and ATP permit the controlled use of energy from glucose?

The energy required for a physical activity depends on the particular activity, the total time involved, and the mass of the person engaged in the activity.

16. How much total energy (in Calories) is expended by a 68-kg (150-lb) person swimming for 35 min?

17. How much total energy (in joules) is expended by a 46-kg (100-lb) person walking for 56 min?

18. People expend energy even when they sit perfectly still. Why?

19. How many moles of ATP are required to provide energy for an 82-kg (180-lb) student to sit in class for 45 min?

20. Explain why two people performing exactly the same physical exercise may not burn the same total Calories.

21. Suppose a 55-kg (120-lb) person, whose regular diet and exercise just maintains body weight, adds one chocolate candy bar containing 354 Cal to their diet each day for 30 days without increasing the level of exercise. Predict how much weight the person will gain in 30 days.

Section Summary   581

---

9. $6\ CO_2 + 6\ H_2O$ + solar energy $\longrightarrow$ $C_6H_{12}O_6 + 6\ O_2$

10. Endothermic. It requires the addition of energy.

11. Food energy is either stored in the bonds of new molecules or released as thermal energy.

12. A molecule that stores a relatively large quantity of energy. Fats and carbohydrates, for example, are energy-rich molecules.

13. Photosynthesis and respiration are essentially reverse processes.
In photosynthesis: $6\ CO_2 +$ $6\ H_2O$ + energy $\longrightarrow C_6H_{12}O_6 +$ $6\ O_2$
In respiration: $C_6H_{12}O_6 +$ $6\ O_2 \longrightarrow 6\ CO_2 + 6\ H_2O$ + energy

14. ATP has an additional phosphate group. ATP also has relatively more stored energy. Some of this energy is released in converting ATP to ADP.

15. The energy needed by a cell is much less than the energy released by oxidation of a glucose molecule. The energy released during the oxidation of a glucose molecule is stored in ATP molecules until the cell needs it.

16. $35\ min \times \dfrac{7\ Cal}{min} = 250$ Calories

17. $56\ min \times \dfrac{3\ Cal}{min} \times \dfrac{4184\ J}{1\ Cal} =$ 700 000 J

18. Energy is required to carry on body functions such as breathing, eating, digesting food, synthesizing new molecules, and disposing of waste materials.

19. $45\ min \times \dfrac{2\ Cal}{min} \times \dfrac{1\ mol\ ATP}{7.3\ Cal} =$ 20 mol ATP

20. The Calories expended depend on the duration of the activity, the weight of the person exercising, and the technique employed in performing the exercise.

21. $\dfrac{354\ Cal}{day} \times 30\ days = 10\ 620\ Cal \times$ $\dfrac{1\ lb}{3500\ Cal} = 3.03$ lbs

---

3. The quantity of energy calculation depends on water's temperature change, mass, and specific heat capacity.

4. One (1) Calorie equals 1000 calories, or one (1) kilocalorie.

5. a. 4.375 Cal
   b. 18.405 Cal
   c. 1 210 000 J
   d. 51 154 kJ

6. The quantity of thermal energy needed to raise the temperature of 1 g water by 1 °C

7. a. $115\ g \times 10.0\ °C \times 4.18\ \dfrac{J}{g \cdot °C} = 4810\ J$

   b. i. $4810\ J \times \dfrac{1\ cal}{4.18\ J} = 1150\ cal;$

   $\dfrac{1150\ cal}{2.0\ g} = 580\ cal/g$

   ii. $580\ \dfrac{cal}{g} \times \dfrac{1\ Cal}{1000\ cal} = 0.58\ Cal/g$

8. Photosynthesis

Connecting the Concepts

22. The two are similar in that hydrocarbons and oxygen react to yield CO_2, H_2O, and energy. Cellular respiration occurs at much lower temperatures and in a series of separate reactions under controlled conditions within the cell.

23. It *indirectly* measures the quantity of thermal energy; energy gained by the calorimeter is assumed equal to the thermal energy released by the food or fuel.

24. a. Energy transferred could be imperceptible.
b. The thermal capacity of liquid water would be exceeded—it may start to boil.

25. Apples and chocolate contain different total Calories per gram, contributing to differing weight gain.

26. a. The diagram would be reversed.
b. Respiration is exothermic; photosynthesis is endothermic.

27. Breathing is part of cellular respiration; it supplies O_2 and removes CO_2. Other than that, the processes are distinct.

28. Only 10–15% of energy that an organism consumes is used for growth. A fish must eat 10 pounds of flies to make 1 pound of fish.

29. Low-Calorie food contains less energy than comparable food products, which may lead to weight loss.

30. No. Human bodies can digest only some types of substances; other substances are indigestible and unable to provide us with energy.

Connecting the Concepts

22. Compare the process of cellular respiration to combustion.

23. Does calorimetry directly measure the quantity of thermal energy liberated by a food or fuel? Explain.

24. Describe problems that could arise in calorimetry by using
a. a very small food sample.
b. a very large food sample.

25. A student argues that eating a certain mass of chocolate or eating the same mass of apples results in the same gain in body weight. Explain why this is incorrect.

26. Figure 7.7 (page 572) shows an energy diagram for photosynthesis.
a. Construct a similar energy diagram for cellular respiration.
b. Compare the energy diagrams for photosynthesis and cellular respiration.

27. The term *respiration* is sometimes used to mean "breathing." What is the relationship, if any, between cellular respiration and breathing?

28. In reference to a local seafood restaurant, someone remarked, "When you eat a pound of fish, you're eating ten pounds of flies." Aside from its questionable value as a meal-promoting strategy, how accurate is this message? Why?

29. Explain why reduced-Calorie food products are sometimes described as *lite* or *light*, even though Calories are not a unit of mass.

30. You used similar calorimetry procedures in Unit 3 and in this unit to find the energy content of candles and food products, respectively. Does that imply that anything you can burn to heat water can also be used to fuel your body's metabolism? Explain.

Extending the Concepts

31. a. In what sense does the challenge of world hunger involve an "energy crisis"?
b. In what sense is it a "resource crisis"?

32. Research and report on the difference between *under*nourishment and *mal*nourishment. Could either term ever apply to an overweight person?

33. From an energy standpoint, are there advantages to eating low on the food chain? For example, is it energetically more favorable to use 100 lb of grain or 100 lb of beef as a food source? Explain.

34. Why is it not possible to consume only pure ATP and eliminate some steps in metabolism?

35. Investigate the characteristics of a professionally designed chemistry laboratory calorimeter. Sketch its essential parts and explain its operation.

36. For hibernating animals, the storage of fat is critical to survival. Investigate a particular animal species to find out how it stores optimal quantities of fat for hibernation.

37. A student decides to lose some weight by not wearing a coat in cold winter weather. What knowledge of food energy might have inspired this idea? Does this plan have merit? Explain.

Extending the Concepts

31. a. Providing "fuel" to power humans is similar to providing fuel to power vehicles or to heat homes.
b. Most hunger experts agree that world hunger is a resource issue governed by political and economic factors, rather than the resulting inadequate food supplies.

32. In *undernourishment,* individuals receive less than the minimum quantity of food essential for sound health and normal growth. In *malnourishment,* individuals do not receive adequate quanities of necessary nutrients. Overweight individuals could be malnourished if their diets lack healthful foods.

Energy Storage and Use

You are now ready to explore how the chemical energy contained in foods is stored, transferred, and used. Keep in mind the three-day food inventory you are evaluating and think about how this new knowledge may apply to your analysis.

B.1 CARBOHYDRATES: ONE WAY TO COMBINE C, H, AND O

All **carbohydrates** are composed of carbon, hydrogen, and oxygen. Glucose, which is the key energy-releasing carbohydrate in biological systems, has the molecular formula $C_6H_{12}O_6$. When such formulas were first established, chemists noted a 2:1 ratio of hydrogen atoms to oxygen atoms in carbohydrates, the same as in water. They were tempted to write the glucose formula as $C(H_2O)_6$, implying a chemical combination of carbon with six water molecules. Chemists even invented the term "carbohydrates" (water-containing carbon substances) for glucose and related compounds. Although chemists later determined that carbohydrates contained no water molecules, the name persisted. However, like water, carbohydrate molecules *do* contain O—H bonds in their structures.

Carbohydrate molecules may be simple sugars, such as glucose (see Figures 7.17 and 7.18), or chemical combinations of two or more simple sugar molecules. Simple sugars are called **monosaccharides,** molecules usually containing five or six carbon atoms. Glucose (like most other monosaccharides) exists principally in a ring form; however, glucose can also exist in a chain form, as shown in Figure 7.18. Do both forms have the same molecular formula?

> Sugars, starch, and cellulose are examples of carbohydrates.

Figure 7.17 *Many fruits and vegetables contain simple sugars such as glucose and fructose.*

Ring form   Chain form

Figure 7.18 *Structural formulas for glucose. This carbohydrate, like most simple sugar and disaccharide molecules, is found primarily in ring form. How do ring and chain structures compare with one another?*

Section B   Energy Storage and Use   583

port a full hibernation interval and calculate the quantity of energy involved.

37. The body must liberate calories to keep warm. To lose weight, individuals must burn more calories than they take in. The potential weight lost this way would be quite small relative to the discomfort endured. You might have students estimate the energy loss relative to the drift toward hypothermia for given scenarios. Hypothermia charts are available in many survival, marine, or outdoor resource books or Websites.

Energy Storage and Use

📖 Section B Content Reading Guide

In this section, students examine the composition of carbohydrates, their function in the body, and their classification as monosaccharides, disaccharides, and polysaccharides. Students also explore the composition and structure of fats and their function in the body. The text discusses differences between saturated and unsaturated fats and the concept of cis–trans isomerism. It introduces the concept of limiting reactants and applies it to reactions in living systems. Finally, students revisit their three-day food inventories and analyze their diets for fat and carbohydrate composition.

B.1 Carbohydrates: One Way to Combine C, H, and O

Carbohydrate structure brings students back to photosynthesis as the energy-storing process in foods. The section presents different types of saccharides, including polysaccharides, and gives some nutritional advice.

33. Eating low on the food chain is more efficient from an energy perspective. For example, producing 100 kg beef requires growing nearly 10 times that mass of grain.

34. ATP cannot be stored.

35. Commercial calorimeters are insulated to effectively capture thermal energy liberated by the food sample. They also

are designed to completely burn food that doesn't burn well on its own and to precisely measure the temperature changes.

36. Many animals have sufficiently low metabolism and high fat stores that allow them to hibernate for long periods of time. Students should be able to find the quantity of fat some animals need to sup-

Simple sugars can exist in a linear chain, or the chain can link to make a ring form, which is more stable. The two forms have the same molecular formula. These simple sugars serve as monomers in the formation of disaccharides and in the formation of polysaccharides, often referred to as *complex carbohydrates*. Common disaccharides include sucrose (table sugar) composed of a glucose molecule and a fructose molecule and lactose (milk sugar) composed of glucose and galactose. When these disaccharides undergo digestion in the body, the linkages between the two simple sugars are the first to be cleaved. Individuals who suffer from lactose intolerance do not produce adequate amounts of the enzyme that helps break this linkage; gastrointestinal discomfort results. Products containing this enzyme are commercially available, so lactose-intolerant individuals may still enjoy foods that contain lactose, such as milk, ice cream, and cheese.

The simple sugar subunits can bond together in two different ways in disaccharides and polysaccharides. The difference between linkages in starch and cellulose molecules is small but critical. In digestible starch, both rings are

> Condensation reactions were highlighted in Unit 3, pages 274–277, in the formation of esters and condensation polymers.

Sugar molecules composed of two monosaccharide units bonded together are called **disaccharides.** They are formed by a condensation reaction between two monosaccharides. Sucrose (table sugar, $C_{12}H_{22}O_{11}$) is a disaccharide composed of the ring forms of glucose and fructose, as illustrated in Figure 7.19.

Figure 7.19 *The formation of sucrose. Note that particular -OH groups react (shown in red), resulting in elimination of one H₂O molecule.*

> All polysaccharides are polymers of monosaccharide molecules.

The reaction that forms disaccharides—a condensation reaction—can also cause monosaccharides to form polymers. Such polymers, not surprisingly, are called **polysaccharides** (see Figure 7.20). Starch, which is a major component of grains and many vegetables, is a polysaccharide composed of glucose units. Cellulose, which is the fibrous or woody material of plants and trees, is another polysaccharide formed from glucose.

Figure 7.20 *Structural formulas for starch and cellulose, two polysaccharide molecules.*

Carbohydrates: Structure and Function

The major types of carbohydrates are summarized in Table 7.2. Compare the bonds in starch with those in cellulose. Due to structural differences, starch is easily digested by the body (see Figure 7.21), whereas cellulose is indigestible by humans. Such indigestible types of carbohydrates are commonly called *fiber*.

Carbohydrates and fats are the primary high-energy substances in the human diet. One gram of a carbohydrate provides 4 Cal of food energy. Nutritionists recommend that about 45–65% of dietary Calories come from high-fiber carbohydrates. Worldwide, most people obtain carbohydrates by eating grains such as rice, corn bread, wheat tortillas, bread, pasta, and beans. Other sources of carbohydrates include fruits, milk, and yogurt. Meats contain a small quantity of *glycogen,* the carbohydrate by which animals store glucose.

People in the United States tend to obtain more of their carbohydrates, on average, from wheat-based breads, potatoes, sugar-laden snacks and desserts, and soft drinks than is common in many other parts of the world. Currently, the average U.S. citizen consumes more than 65 kg (145 lb) of sugar annually, mainly from candy, desserts, and soft drinks.

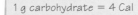

1 g carbohydrate = 4 Cal

Figure 7.21 *Breads and other foods contain starch, which is a digestible polysaccharide. Cellulose (found in wood, paper, and cotton) is a polysaccharide that humans cannot digest. What is a structural difference between digestible polysaccharides (such as starch) and cellulose?*

| Table 7.2

THE COMPOSITION OF COMMON CARBOHYDRATES			
Classification and Examples	**Composition**	**Formula**	**Common Name or Source**
Monosaccharides		$C_6H_{12}O_6$	
Glucose	—		Blood sugar
Fructose	—		Fruit sugar
Galactose	—		—
Disaccharides	Monosaccharides	$C_{12}H_{22}O_{11}$	
Sucrose	Fructose + glucose		Cane sugar
Lactose	Galactose + glucose		Milk sugar
Maltose	Glucose + glucose		Germinating seeds
Polysaccharides	Glucose polymers	—	
Starch			Plants
Glycogen			Animals
Cellulose			Plant fibers

attached to the connecting oxygen (this is similar to an ether functional group) so that the oxygen is below both rings (this is called the *alpha linkage*). In cellulose, the oxygen is above one ring and below the other (the *beta linkage*). See **Figure 7.20**. Human enzymes can cleave the linkages in starch molecules but not in cellulose molecules. Ruminant animals, such as sheep, cows, and horses, can digest cellulose.

Using the Figures

Figures 7.19 and 7.20: Students first learned of condensation polymers in Unit 3 (page 274). Use Figure 7.19 to remind students how monosaccharides react to form disaccharides and polysaccharides via elimination of water molecules. Then note that Figure 7.20 shows only three repeating glucose units (the monomer for both starch and cellulose). For both natural polymers, the structures extend in both directions (depicted by bonds extending from the oxygen ends). Also highlight how a seemingly small difference in structure (orientation around the ether linkage) leads to vast differences in properties (humans can digest starch but not cellulose).

CHEMISTRY at Work

Food for Thought

The next time you chew gum, drink a canned or bottled beverage, or eat a bowl of your favorite breakfast cereal, think about corn. Gum, soda, cereal, ketchup, cookies, pastries, bread, and many other processed foods and drinks are sweetened or colored with products made from corn. Everything you eat and drink has connections to a farm, even if those ties are not readily apparent.

Sue Adams and her husband John work year-round to run an 1100-acre farm in Atlanta, Illinois. To protect the environment, they use integrated pest management and practice a technique called *no-till farming*—planting new crops directly in the residue of previously harvested crops. This method saves on labor and fuel. More importantly, this farming method reduces the loss of valuable topsoil and moisture, which dramatically reduces the need for materials such as fertilizers, pesticides, and herbicides.

In the spring, Sue and John plant half of their fields in corn and the other half in soybeans. As soon as the crops begin to grow, they scout the fields for evidence of damage by pests and, where necessary, apply special crop protection products that decompose quickly in sunlight. Just like a chemist in a laboratory, Sue carefully monitors and measures how these products are used to ensure maximum protection for the crops and the environment.

> Sue and John practice a precise, high-tech agriculture that is used on many of today's farms.

Ever Think of a Satellite as a Farming Tool?

Sue and John also follow a precise, high-tech agriculture system that is used on many of today's farms. One example is their use of global positioning system (GPS) technology. The GPS employs computers, monitoring units, and radio signals to send, receive, and process information from satellites to study objects on Earth's surface. On their farm, Sue uses GPS technology to plot with great precision which areas of her fields require additional fertilizers or other treatment. She even has a specially equipped all-terrain vehicle that can record and access information while she is out in the field.

Using GPS data, Sue and John apply fertilizer only to those areas of the farm that need it, minimizing the quantity of fertilizer they introduce to the environment. Such increased precision has also reduced the costs of fertilizing (materials, equipment, fuel, and labor) by as much as ten dollars an acre.

Earth and Its Food Supply: What's the Forecast?

In the 1700s, an English economist, Thomas Malthus, published his "Essay on the Principle of Population." The widely read pamphlet argued that unchecked population increases geometrically (1, 2, 4, 8, 16, . . .), while food supplies increase arithmetically (1, 2, 3, 4, 5, . . .). Malthus's theory suggested that one day the world might be unable to feed itself. Indeed, world population has grown significantly. In 1800, the world's population was about 1 billion; by 1999, it reached 6 billion.

> Malthus's theory suggested that one day the world might be unable to feed itself.

In small groups, discuss answers to these questions.

1. Malthus' prediction has not become reality, at least for a majority of the world's inhabitants. Was any part of his thinking flawed, especially with regard to human population growth? Explain.

2. The world's population by the year 2020 will probably be almost 8 billion people. Why do you suppose there is renewed interest in Malthus's theory?

3. One of the issues with increased population is the total land required for human residence versus that needed for cropland. What new techniques might farmers, in collaboration with municipal planners, develop to allow for the space needed by both humans and agriculture?

4. No-till farming is said to have several advantages. Why do you suppose it has taken until now for farmers to use no-till techniques instead of the traditional technique of plowing fields?

5. In what ways do the Adamses' farming techniques reflect principles of Green Chemistry, that is, to prevent environmental problems before they occur?

6. a. What are direct advantages to the Adamses of using a greener, high-tech approach to farming?

   b. What are advantages to society of using these techniques?

B.2 Fats: Another Way to Combine C, H, and O Atoms

Students explore the distinction between the meanings of *fat* as used in common language and as used by scientists. Both fats and carbohydrates are composed of C, H, and O; however, the atoms are arranged differently. Ask students to identify the functional groups in fats. Encourage them to revisit Unit 3, Section C (pages 261–278) regarding functional groups.

Fat molecules, also known as *triglycerides,* can differ tremendously based on the fatty acids present and the bonding within those fatty acids. The fatty-acid characteristics directly influence the properties of the triglyceride.

B.2 FATS: ANOTHER WAY TO COMBINE C, H, AND O ATOMS

Unlike the terms *carbohydrate* and *protein*, *fat* has acquired its own general (and somewhat negative) meaning. From a chemical viewpoint, however, *fats* are just another major category of biomolecules with special characteristics and functions.

A significant part of a normal human diet, fats are present in meat, fish, poultry, oils, dairy products, nuts, and grains. When more food is consumed than is needed to satisfy energy requirements, much of the excess food energy is stored in the body as fat molecules. If food intake is not enough to meet the body's energy needs, then stored fat is "burned" to release energy to make up the difference.

Fats are composed of carbon, hydrogen, and oxygen atoms—the same three elements that compose carbohydrates. Fat molecules, however, contain fewer oxygen atoms and more carbon and hydrogen atoms. Thus, fats have a greater number of carbon-hydrogen bonds and fewer carbon-oxygen (and oxygen-hydrogen) bonds than do carbohydrate molecules. You can confirm this by comparing the structure of glyceryl tripalmitate, which is a typical fat molecule, shown in Figure 7.22, to that of glucose or starch molecules (Figures 7.18 and 7.20, respectively).

When an organic substance is burned, it reacts with oxygen to form carbon dioxide, water, and thermal energy. Similarly, when fats, carbohydrates, and proteins are "burned" in the body, they are converted into carbon dioxide, water, and energy.

Fats: Structure and Function

Figure 7.22 *The structural formula for glyceryl tripalmitate, a typical fat molecule.*

Figure 7.23 *Formation of a typical fat molecule, a triglyceride. The colored atoms interact to form the fat molecule plus water.*

Glycerol   Palmitic acid   Glyceryl tripalmitate (a typical fat)   Water

Generally, fat molecules are nonpolar and only sparingly soluble in water. As you can see from Figure 7.22, fats have long hydrocarbon portions that prevent them from dissolving in polar solvents such as water. Their low water solubility and high energy-storing capacity give fat molecules, unlike carbohydrates, chemical properties similar to those of hydrocarbons.

The chemical properties of a fat molecule are due largely to the *fatty acid* groups in the molecule. **Fatty acids** are a class of organic compounds composed of long hydrocarbon chains with a carboxylic acid group (COOH) at one end. Two fatty acids are shown in Figure 7.24.

Figure 7.24 *Typical fatty acids.*

Palmitic acid

Linolenic acid

The typical fat molecule, a **triglyceride,** is a combination of a three-carbon alcohol molecule called *glycerol* and three fatty acid molecules.

1 Glycerol molecule + 3 Fatty acid molecules $\longrightarrow$
    1 Triglyceride (fat) molecule + 3 Water molecules

The formation of a triglyceride is shown in Figure 7.23. Each fatty acid molecule forms an ester linkage as it reacts with an —OH group of glycerol. This produces one water molecule per ester linkage. The main product of this condensation reaction is a triglyceride composed of three ester groups. Although the three fatty acids depicted in Figure 7.23 are identical, fats can contain two or three different fatty acids.

Because they have more carbon-hydrogen bonds than carbon-oxygen bonds, fats contain more stored energy per gram than do carbohydrates. In fact, one gram of fat contains over twice the energy stored in one gram of carbohydrate; 1 g fat is equivalent to 9 Cal, compared to 4 Cal for each gram of carbohydrate. Consequently, you must run more than twice as far or exercise twice as long to "work off" a given mass of fat compared to what you must do to "work off" the same mass of carbohydrate. For example, a typical glazed doughnut contains 11.6 g fat. Thus, the glazed doughnut has 11.6 g fat $\times$ 9 Cal/g fat = 104 Cal of energy from fat. It is not surprising that your body uses fat molecules to store excess food energy efficiently.

In general, the terms "fat" and "triglyceride" are used interchangeably.

The reaction that produces a fat molecule is similar to the reaction you observed in Unit 3 that produced the methyl salicylate ester (page 276).

Like carbohydrates, fats serve as an energy source. However, fats provide more than twice the energy/gram of carbohydrates, due to fewer carbon–oxygen bonds and more carbon–hydrogen bonds in fats. Fat molecules are necessary for proper functioning of the body. Fats provide "essential" fatty acids, which function in growth and development, so they are especially important to infants and toddlers. Fat also helps in absorption of fat-soluble vitamins. Fat serves as an efficient way to store excess food energy. Avoid getting involved at this time in discussing how *good* or *bad* fats are, as this is developed more in upcoming material.

Section B   Energy Storage and Use   **589**

B.3 Saturated and Unsaturated Fats

While all fat molecules contain a glycerol backbone, fatty acids may differ significantly among fat molecules. Fatty acids can be of different lengths and may have varying degrees of saturation. Saturated fats contain saturated fatty acids (that is, there are no carbon–carbon double bonds, maximizing total hydrogen atoms within the structure). Unsaturated fats contain some unsaturated fatty acids (with at least one carbon–carbon double bond). Both types of fats occur naturally.

Saturated fats are found in animal products such as whole milk, cheese, butter, and meats and in some plant-based products (such as coconut and palm oil). Saturated fats raise the level of LDL cholesterol, a waxy substance that may form deposits in arteries and cause blockages leading to coronary disease. You may discuss the popularity of fast foods, which can be high in saturated fats.

Research suggests that unsaturated fats, found primarily in plant products, may contribute to cardiovascular health when used in place of saturated fats. However, consumption of all fats should be monitored; they deliver over twice as much food energy as carbohydrates.

B.3 SATURATED AND UNSATURATED FATS

Recall from Unit 3 that hydrocarbons can be saturated (containing only single carbon-carbon bonds) or unsaturated (containing double or triple carbon-carbon bonds). Likewise, hydrocarbon chains in fatty acids are either saturated or unsaturated. Look again at the fatty acids in Figure 7.24 (page 589). Can you identify each as either saturated or unsaturated?

Fats containing saturated fatty acids are called **saturated fats;** those containing some unsaturated fatty acids are known as **unsaturated fats.** A **monounsaturated fat** contains just one C=C double bond in its fatty acid components. A **polyunsaturated fat** contains two or more C=C double bonds in the fatty acid portion of a triglyceride molecule. Based on these definitions, is the fat depicted in Figure 7.22 (page 588) saturated, monounsaturated, or polyunsaturated?

Oils are fats that are liquids

Key: ■ Saturated fat   ■ Polyunsaturated fat   ■ Monounsaturated fat

Source: *Food Technology,* April 1989.

Figure 7.25 *The percent of polyunsaturated fat in fats from selected plant and animal sources.*

Triglycerides in animal fats are nearly all saturated and are solids at room temperature. However, fats from plant sources commonly are polyunsaturated or monounsaturated. In general, higher levels of unsaturation are associated with oils that have lower melting points. At room temperature these polyunsaturated fats are liquids. (See Figure 7.25).

Using the Figures

Figure 7.25: The proportion of saturated fat affects physical properties of fats. Saturated-fat molecules have a more linear shape and can pack together more readily, enhancing attractions (intermolecular forces) among fat molecules. Sources of fats with a high percent of saturated fats tend to be solids at room temperature. Unsaturated-fat molecules contain at least one C=C double bond, which puts a "kink" in molecular shape. These molecules cannot pack

Due to their C=C double bonds, unsaturated fats undergo addition reactions; saturated fats cannot undergo addition reactions. Thus, these two types of fats participate differently in body chemistry. Unsaturated fat molecules are much more chemically reactive. Increasing evidence suggests that saturated fats may contribute more to health problems than do some unsaturated fats. Saturated fats are associated with formation of *arterial plaque*, which are deposits of fatty material in blood vessel walls (see Figure 7.26). The result is a condition commonly known as "hardening of the arteries," or *atherosclerosis*, which is a particular threat to coronary (heart) arteries and arteries leading to the brain.

Figure 7.26 *An artery cross section, showing plaque (grey) on walls.*

Developing Skills

B.4 CALORIES FROM FAT

A sample of butter (Fig 7.27) provides the following nutritional values for one serving, which is defined as 1 tablespoon (tbsp) or 14 g:

Total fat	10.9 g	Polyunsaturated fat	0.4 g
Saturated fat	7.2 g	Calories	100

Sample Problem: *Calculate the percent of polyunsaturated fat contained in the total fat in butter.*

To find the answer, divide the mass of polyunsaturated fat by the mass of total fat in butter and convert it to a percent value:

$$\frac{0.4 \text{ g}}{10.9 \text{ g}} \times 100\% = 4\%$$

Thus, approximately 4% of butter's total fat is polyunsaturated.

1. Calculate the percent of saturated fat in the total fat in butter.
2. The saturated and polyunsaturated fat percent values don't total 100%.
   a. What does the "missing" percent value represent?
   b. How many grams of fat does this represent?
3. Calculate the total percent fat in one serving of butter.
4. The *Dietary Guidelines 2005* suggest that from 20-35% of total Calories in human diets should come from fats. A way to evaluate this is to compare total Calories from fat to total Calories delivered in that food serving.
   a. Determine the total Calories from fat in 1 tbsp butter.
   b. Calculate the percent of total Calories obtained from butter fat.
5. One serving (14 g) of margarine has 10 g fat and 90 Cal.
   a. Find the percent of Calories obtained from margarine fat.
   b. Compare the percent of total Calories from margarine fat to that value from butter fat.

Figure 7.27 *What type of fat is primarily found in butter?*

Recall that 1 g fat = 9 Cal

Most fats, according to the *Dietary Guidelines*, should come from polyunsaturated and monounsaturated fatty acids, supplied by fish, nuts, and legumes.

Developing Skills

B.4 Calories from Fat

The calculations in this activity highlight that nearly all Calories in butter and margarine are from fat.

Answers

1. $\dfrac{7.2 \text{ g}}{10.9 \text{ g}} \times 100\% = 66\%$ saturated fat

2. a. There must be some monounsaturated fat in butter.
   b. $10.9 \text{ g} - (0.4 \text{ g} + 7.2 \text{ g}) = 3.3 \text{ g}$

3. $\dfrac{10.9 \text{ g}}{14 \text{ g}} \times 100\% = 78\%$ fat

4. a. $10.9 \text{ g} \times 9 \dfrac{\text{Cal}}{\text{g}} = 98.1 \text{ Cal}$
   b. $\dfrac{98.1 \text{ Cal}}{100 \text{ Cal}} = 98.1\%$

5. a. $10 \text{ g} \times 9 \dfrac{\text{Cal}}{\text{g}} = 90 \text{ Cal};$

   $\dfrac{90 \text{ Cal}}{90 \text{ Cal}} \times 100\% = 100\%$

   b. The percents are about the same. Fat in margarine is generally more unsaturated, so may be somewhat more healthful, but some margarine contains higher amounts of trans-fatty acids that have been linked to higher risks of coronary disease. Nutritionists continue to debate whether margarine or butter is a better dietary option.

together as closely as more linear saturated fats, so they experience fewer attractions (intermolecular forces) and tend to be liquids at room temperature. Fats near the top of Figure 7.25, containing a higher percent unsaturated fats, are liquids. Fats listed lower (containing a higher percent saturated fats) are solids at room temperature. Use this as an example of how molecular structure affects physical properties.

B.5 Hydrogenation

Hydrogenation is the process by which hydrogen atoms are added to C=C bonds in unsaturated fat molecules. The process exposes plant oils to hydrogen at high temperatures in the presence of a catalyst (typically nickel). Some C=C double bonds are thus converted to single bonds. Full hydrogenation is seldom completed as it leads to very brittle, hard products. Partial hydrogenation is most common. The hydrogenated molecules lose some kinks and bends and can pack more closely. A liquid fat undergoes conversion to a more solid product. This conversion affects the texture and consistency of many popular food items and allows food producers to replace animal fats with vegetable oils, which are very abundant. The process also extends shelf life of many vegetable oils; the double bonds in unsaturated fats make these molecules prone to oxidation and subsequent spoilage. Hydrogenation creates margarine from liquid vegetable oils. Partially hydrogenated fats are found in many processed foods.

B.5 HYDROGENATION

Partial **hydrogenation** adds hydrogen atoms to some C=C bonds in vegetable oil triglyceride molecules. The reaction with hydrogen converts a C=C double bond to a C—C single bond. Because this decreases the total unsaturated (C=C) sites, the partially hydrogenated product becomes more saturated, and the original liquid oil becomes semisolid. The ability to change an oil from a liquid to a solid, depending on the extent of hydrogenation, allows food manufacturers to control the consistency and softness of their food products. Such partially hydrogenated fats are formed in margarine, vegetable shortening, deep-fried foods, and many snack foods.

The reaction between hydrogen and C=C double bonds in a polyunsaturated fat is typical of how C=C bonds in most alkenes react. Generally, C=C bonds in alkenes can be converted to C—C single bonds when they react with a variety of substances, including hydrogen.

You learned in Unit 3 (page 268) that a double bond in an alkene prevents adjacent carbon atoms in the double bond from rotating around the bond axis. The double-bonded carbon atoms align as shown in Figure 7.28. This inflexible arrangement between carbon atoms creates the possibility of *cis–trans isomerism*.

Figure 7.28 *The structural formula for ethene.*

In **cis–trans isomerism,** two identical functional groups can be in one of two different molecular positions. Both groups can be on the same side of the double bond (the cis isomer), or they can be across the double bond from each other (the trans isomer), as illustrated in Figure 7.29.

cis-2-pentene   *trans*-2-pentene

Figure 7.29 *A comparison of cis-2-pentene and trans-2-pentene. Note positions of the functional groups.*

In the example of 2-pentene, each arrangement creates a different compound, even though the compounds have identical molecular formulas (C_5H_{10}). In *cis*-2-pentene, the molecule has the two hydrogen atoms on the same side (cis) of the double-bond plane. (See Figure 7.29.) In *trans*-2-pentene, the two hydrogen atoms are positioned on opposite sides (trans) of the double-bond plane.

Cis–trans isomerism, which was just described for an alkene, is also possible in unsaturated fats because fatty acid chains often contain C=C bonds. Unsaturated fatty acids in foods that have not been hydrogenated typically have their double bonds in the cis arrangement, as shown in Figure 7.30. During hydrogenation, some cis double bonds break and reform in the trans arrangement. Although questions have arisen about the nutritional safety of *trans*-fatty acids, studies addressing these concerns have not produced conclusive answers. However, the *2005 Dietary Guidelines* advise that people should "keep *trans*-fatty acid consumption as low as possible."

Currently, most U.S. citizens obtain about 33% of their total food Calories from fats, near the upper limit of 35% recommended by the *Dietary Guidelines*. Additionally, the *Guidelines* suggest that less than 10% of total food Calories should come from saturated fats.

High fat consumption is a factor in several modern health problems, including obesity and atherosclerosis. Most dietary fat consumed in the United States comes from processed meat, poultry, fish, and dairy products. Fast foods and deep-fried foods—such as hamburgers, french fries, fried chicken, and many snack items—add even more dietary fat. In addition, if your intake of food energy is higher than what you expend in physical activity, your body converts excess proteins and carbohydrates into fat for storage.

Figure 7.30 *Cis- and trans- fatty acids.*

Non-hydrogenated unsaturated fats typically are found as cis isomers. During hydrogenation, some cis double bonds break and reform in a trans configuration. Research suggests that trans fat, much like saturated fat, can increase the level of LDL cholesterol in the bloodstream and increase risks of coronary heart disease. Many food companies have removed trans fats from their products. Students may have seen packages of popular snack-food items declaring "Trans-Free" or "No Trans Fats."

To reduce and/or eliminate trans fats, some manufacturers have combined fully hydrogenated vegetable oils with liquid vegetable oils to create semisolid products. These approximate the consistency and usefulness of partially hydrogenated fats. Starting in 2006, the FDA required that all food labels include the amount of trans fat per serving, just below the listing for saturated fat.

Using the Figures

Figures 7.29 and 7.30: Provide model kits and invite students to construct molecules depicted in these figures to help them better visualize the three-dimensional molecular geometry associated with cis and trans C=C double bonds.

Developing Skills

B.6 Fats In the Diet

In this activity, students compare the fat content of ice cream and frozen yogurt.

Answers

1. Ice cream: $\dfrac{19\ \text{g}}{115\ \text{g}} \times 100\% =$ 17% fat

   Frozen yogurt: $\dfrac{6.0\ \text{g}}{112\ \text{g}} \times 100\% =$ 5.4% fat

2. a. Yogurt meets the guideline and ice cream does not.

   Ice cream: $19\ \text{g} \times 9\ \dfrac{\text{Cal}}{\text{g}} = 171\ \text{Cal};$

   $\dfrac{171\ \text{Cal}}{310\ \text{Cal}} \times 100\% = 55\%$

   Yogurt: $6\ \text{g} \times 9\ \dfrac{\text{Cal}}{\text{g}} = 54\ \text{Cal};$

   $\dfrac{54\ \text{Cal}}{200\ \text{Cal}} \times 100\% = 27\%$

   b. No, neither meets the guideline.

   Ice cream: $11\text{g} \times 9\ \dfrac{\text{Cal}}{\text{g}} = 99\ \text{Cal};$

   $\dfrac{99\ \text{Cal}}{310\ \text{Cal}} \times 100\% = 32\%$

   Yogurt: $2.5\ \text{g} \times 9\ \dfrac{\text{Cal}}{\text{g}} = 22\ \text{Cal};$

   $\dfrac{22\ \text{Cal}}{200\ \text{Cal}} \times 100\% = 11\%$

ChemQuandary 2

Fat-Free Food?

According to the International Ice Cream Association, classic ice cream must contain at least 10% milk fat by mass. Low-fat ice cream must contain no more than 4.2% fat, and nonfat ice cream must be less than 1% fat. Most nonfat ice creams declare "no fat content."

Developing Skills

B.6 FATS IN THE DIET

Your favorite ice-cream flavor is available as frozen yogurt. The advertising promotes frozen yogurt as a "reduced-fat alternative" to ice cream. Here are the nutritional data:

	Serving	Calories	Saturated Fat	Unsaturated Fat
Ice cream	115 g	310	11 g	8 g
Frozen yogurt	112 g	200	2.5 g	3.5 g

1. Calculate and compare the total percent fat (by mass) contained in each dessert.

2. Another way to compare these two desserts is to examine the percent of Calories from fat in each.

   a. Does either ice cream or frozen yogurt meet the guideline of 35% or less Calories from fat?

   b. Does either dessert meet the guideline of 10% or less Calories from saturated fat?

> Recall that 1 g of fat contains 9 Cal of food energy.

ChemQuandary 2

FAT-FREE FOOD?

You compared ice cream to frozen yogurt in terms of their fat content. You might consider *fat-free* ice cream as another frozen dessert. Consider this ice-cream label carefully. Is fat-free ice cream actually fat free? How do you know? What will happen to the food energy provided by fat-free ice cream if it is not immediately used by the body? Do you think it is wise to base a diet entirely on fat-free foods? Why or why not?

B.7 LIMITING REACTANTS

Biochemical reactions in your body convert fats, carbohydrates, and—under extreme dietary conditions—proteins in foods you eat into energy. These biochemical reactions, like all chemical reactions, require the presence of a complete set of reactants to produce the desired product. Furthermore, the amount of product produced by a chemical reaction depends on the amounts of reactants present.

Think about baking a cake and consider the following recipe:

2 cups flour	1 tablespoon baking powder
2 eggs	1 cup water
1 cup sugar	1/3 cup oil

If food energy is not immediately used by the body, it passes through as waste or is stored as fat. Just because a food is declared as *fat-free* does not mean it lacks carbohydrates or proteins; those unused Calories may be stored as fat.

The proper combination of these quantities (and some thermal energy) will produce one cake. What if you have 14 cups flour, 4 eggs, 9 cups sugar, 10 tablespoons baking powder, 10 cups water, and $3\frac{1}{3}$ cups oil? How many complete cakes can you bake?

Well, 14 cups of flour is enough for 7 cakes (2 cups flour per cake). And there is enough sugar for 9 cakes (1 cup sugar per cake). The supplies of baking powder, water, and oil are sufficient for 10 cakes. However, it is not possible to make 10, 9, or even 7 cakes with the available ingredients.

Why? Because only 4 eggs are available, which is enough for 2 cakes. The supply of eggs limits the number of cakes you can make. Excess quantities of other ingredients (flour, sugar, baking powder, water, and oil) remain unused. If you want more than 2 cakes, you will need more eggs.

In chemical terminology, the eggs in this cake-making analogy represent the *limiting reactant* (also called the *limiting reagent*). The **limiting reactant** is the starting material (reactant) that is used up entirely when a particular chemical reaction occurs. This starting material *limits* how much product can form.

In chemical reactions, just as in baking, materials react in certain fixed ratios. These ratios are referred to as the **stoichiometry** of the reaction. The ratios are indicated in chemical equations by the coefficients given for each substance. Consider the equation for the cellular respiration ("burning") of glucose:

$$C_6H_{12}O_6 \;+\; 6\,O_2 \;\longrightarrow\; 6\,CO_2 \;+\; 6\,H_2O \;+\; \text{Energy}$$

1 Glucose molecule   6 Oxygen molecules   6 Carbon dioxide molecules   6 Water molecules

Sample Problem: *Suppose you have 5 glucose molecules available to react with 60 oxygen molecules. Which substance will become the limiting reactant in this reaction?*

From the equation, you can see that 1 glucose molecule reacts with 6 oxygen molecules. That means that 5 glucose molecules would require 30 oxygen molecules to react completely. On the other hand, to use up all 60 oxygen molecules, 10 glucose molecules are required. Which of these two scenarios is actually possible in this reaction? In other words, which reactant—oxygen or glucose—will be used up completely in this reaction?

Because 60 oxygen molecules are available, all the glucose can react, with some oxygen left unreacted. Alternatively, to react completely, the 60 oxygen molecules would require 10 glucose molecules; however, only five glucose molecules are available. Thus, glucose is the limiting reactant. Because the reaction stops after the five glucose molecules react with 30 oxygen molecules, 30 oxygen molecules will remain unreacted ('excess') at the end of the reaction.

> Recall from Unit 4 that stoichiometry involves quantitative relationships among reactants and products in a reaction described by its chemical equation.

> Limiting reactants were introduced in Unit 4, page 353.

B.7 Limiting Reactants

The concept of limiting reactants (first introduced in Unit 4—see page 353) is presented in the form of a recipe. This non-science analogy will help some students grasp the concept. The text applies the concept to chemical equations and then to nutrients and living systems. You may work through both the recipe analogy and the sample problem with students to ensure that they clearly see similarities in the two situations.

In light of possible end-of-year time limitations, student needs, or your own content preferences, you may omit this material on limiting reactants. Skipping B.7–B.9 will not adversely affect student understanding of remaining *ChemCom* material.

B.7 Supplement: Limiting Reactants

B.8 Limiting-Reactant Analogies

 B.8 Limiting-Reactant Analogies Student Worksheet

In this activity, students practice predicting the amounts of products obtained, based on the limiting reactant. Students consider two non-chemical systems before extending their understanding to cellular respiration of glucose. All models contain limitations; students are again challenged to consider those limitations.

If students experience difficulty, suggest that they calculate how much product is possible for each reactant and compare their results. You may decide to work through one question with students to model the reasoning they should use to solve limiting-reactant problems.

Answers

1. a. Flour
   b. 7
   c. 12 eggs, 2 cups sugar, 3 table-spoons baking soda, 3 cups water, 1 cup oil
2. a. Napkins, b. Napkins, c. 19
3. a. 12, b. 15 CO_2 and 15 H_2O
4. a. Student pictures for cake making should show 2 cups flour + 2 eggs + 1 cup sugar + 1 tbsp baking powder + 1 cup water + 1/3 cup oil yields 1 cake. Pictures for the lunch box should show 1 sandwich + 3 cookies + 2 napkins + 1 milk carton + 1 cardboard container yielding 1 carryout lunch box.
   b. Answers will vary, but students may suggest that using familiar items helps them relate to things they cannot see (molecules).

The idea of limiting reactants applies equally well to living systems. The shortage of a key nutrient or reactant can severely affect the growth or health of plants and animals. In many biochemical processes, a product from one reaction becomes a reactant for other reactions. If a reaction stops because one substance is completely consumed (the limiting reactant), all reactions that follow it will also stop.

Fortunately, in some cases, alternate reaction pathways are available. If the body's glucose supply is depleted, for example, glucose metabolism cannot occur. One backup system oxidizes stored body fat in place of glucose. More drastically, under starvation conditions, structural proteins are broken down and used for energy. Producing glucose from protein is much less energy efficient than producing glucose from carbohydrates; if dietary glucose becomes available later, glucose metabolism reactions start up again.

Alternate reaction pathways are not a permanent solution. If the intake of a vital nutrient is consistently inadequate, that nutrient may become a limiting reactant in biochemical processes and affect personal health.

B.8 LIMITING-REACTANT ANALOGIES

In Unit 4, you considered a container filled with super-bounce balls as an analogy for the kinetic molecular behavior of gases (see page 325). Another analogy, a cake recipe, introduced you to the idea of limiting reactants. Think about this and other limiting-reactant analogies (see Figure 7.31) as you answer the following questions.

Figure 7.31 *What are key ingredients needed to make this triple-stacker s'more? How could the "limiting reactant" concept apply here?*

1. Consider the cake-making analogy (pages 594–595). Assume that you have 26 eggs and the quantities of all the other ingredients, as previously specified.
    a. Which ingredient now limits the total number of cakes you can make?
    b. How many total cakes can you make under the conditions specified?
    c. When the limiting reactant is fully consumed, how much of each other ingredient will be left over?

2. A restaurant prepares carry-out lunch boxes. Each box consists of 1 sandwich, 3 cookies, 2 paper napkins, 1 milk carton, and 1 container. The current inventory is 60 sandwiches, 102 cookies, 38 napkins, 41 milk cartons, and 66 containers.
    a. As carry-out lunch boxes are prepared, which item will be used up first?
    b. Which item is the limiting reactant?
    c. How many complete carry-out lunch boxes can be assembled from this inventory?

5. a. Yes, a lunch box can still be prepared.
    b. You may still be able to produce an edible cake.
    c. No, you cannot produce any product if you completely use up a reactant.
    d. Particular ingredients or items in the non-chemical analogies are not necessarily essential for making a product. You could make substitutions or sell a reduced product if you run out of one component.

3. Now consider the cellular respiration of glucose:

$$C_6H_{12}O_6 + 6\ O_2 \longrightarrow 6\ CO_2 + 6\ H_2O + Energy$$

    a. Suppose that 2 glucose molecules are available for this reaction. How many oxygen molecules would be needed to completely react with these 2 glucose molecules?

    b. Assume that 15 oxygen molecules are available to react. How many carbon dioxide and water molecules can be made from that amount of oxygen and unlimited glucose? (*Hint:* Draw representations of all molecules available to react.)

4. Consider the cake-making and lunch-box analogies as they relate to chemical reactions.

    a. Using pictures or symbols, write a balanced equation to represent each of these analogies. (*Note:* Your pictures should convey information comparable to that conveyed by a chemical equation.)

    b. Describe one way in which these analogies help you to understand the notion of limiting reactants as applied to chemical reactions.

5. As you know, useful analogies also have limitations.

    a. Consider the lunch-box analogy. Even if you run out of one item, can you use the other items to prepare carry-out lunches that people would still buy and eat? Explain.

    b. Consider the cake-making analogy. If you run out of one ingredient, can you still use the other ingredients to make an edible cake? Explain.

    c. Consider the glucose reaction. If one reactant is used up, or if you have less than the reaction requires (for instance, one glucose molecule but only three oxygen molecules), could any product be produced? Explain.

    d. Considering your answers to Questions 5a through 5c, write a statement that summarizes a major limitation of both the cake-making and lunch-box analogies as they relate to actual chemical reactions.

6. Now it is your turn to devise a limiting-reactant analogy. Think about a limiting-reactant problem that you may encounter in everyday life.

    a. Identify what item or product you are trying to create.

    b. List all the reactants you will need.

    c. Then identify the limiting reactant and how many other reactants are left over when the reaction is completed.

> How could a restaurant entice patrons to buy a "lunch" box if they ran out of sandwiches? What if the restaurant had sufficient sandwiches, but ran out of cookies?

In chemical reactions, making a substitution would completely change the product, if you could make a substitution at all. Running out of one substance completely halts the chemical reaction.

6. Answers will vary. A simple machine, birdhouse, or first-aid kit would work well. You could ask students to exchange and solve another student's limiting-reactant problem.

Demonstration Idea: Limiting Reactants

This demonstration provides a chemical example of the limiting reactant concept, involving readily observed chemical changes. Use a protective shield during this demonstration. Ensure that no flames are in use when the balloons are emptied.

Materials

8 culture tubes
8 round balloons
50 mL 3 M hydrochloric acid
    (12.5 mL conc. HCl/50 mL sol'n)
55 cm magnesium ribbon

Procedure

Practice this demonstration before doing it for students. The steps are not difficult, just slightly awkward.

    Fill culture tubes with the volumes of hydrochloric acid listed below or on page 598, clearly label them by number, and place them in test-tube racks. Fold each specified strip of Mg ribbon so it fits inside an uninflated balloon. Take care to avoid piercing the balloon with sharp edges of the Mg ribbon.

Part A: Constant Amount HCl, Variable Amount Mg

Tube 1: 5 mL 3 M HCl + 2.5 cm Mg
    ribbon

Tube 2: 5 mL 3 M HCl + 5.0 cm Mg
    ribbon

Tube 3: 5 mL 3 M HCl + 10.0 cm Mg
    ribbon

Tube 4: 5 mL 3 M HCl + 15.0 cm Mg
    ribbon

[Demonstration continues on page 598]

SECTION B

Part B: Constant Amount Mg, Variable Amount HCl

Tube 5: 2 mL 3 M HCl + 5.0 cm Mg ribbon

Tube 6: 4 mL 3 M HCl + 5.0 cm Mg ribbon

Tube 7: 6 mL 3 M HCl + 5.0 cm Mg ribbon

Tube 8: 10 mL 3 M HCl + 5.0 cm Mg ribbon

Complete the following manipulation one tube at a time: Allow the balloon to hang down so the Mg ribbon doesn't prematurely fall into the test tube. Carefully stretch the neck of the balloon containing the Mg ribbon over the lip of the culture tube. Try to keep air out of the balloon as you attach it. Then manipulate the balloon to allow the Mg ribbon to fall into the acid. Note the relative volume of hydrogen gas generated (as indicated by the balloon volume) and how much of the original Mg ribbon is consumed in each case. Repeat for each tube in the set.

Finally, display and compare all the tube-balloon systems. Invite students to interpret the results in terms of the limiting-reactant concept. Ask students (after they have carefully observed all tubes) which reactant apparently limited the production of hydrogen in Part A tubes (1–4). Then invite them to analyze Part B tubes (5–8) similarly. Also, help students understand how this demonstration helps clarify the limiting-nutrient ideas developed in the textbook.

B.9 LIMITING REACTANTS IN CHEMICAL REACTIONS

A chemical equation can be interpreted not only in terms of *molecules* (as discussed in Section B.7) but also in terms of *moles* and *grams* (as shown on pages 164–165). For example, the oxidation reaction for glucose can be interpreted in terms of moles of reactants and products:

$$C_6H_{12}O_6 \quad + \quad 6\,O_2 \quad \longrightarrow \quad 6\,CO_2 \quad + \quad 6\,H_2O \quad + \quad \text{Energy}$$

| 1 mol Glucose molecules | 6 mol Oxygen molecules | 6 mol Carbon dioxide molecules | 6 mol Water molecules | |

Molar masses can be used to convert the molar amounts to grams:

$$C_6H_{12}O_6 \quad + \quad 6\,O_2 \quad \longrightarrow \quad 6\,CO_2 \quad + \quad 6\,H_2O \quad + \quad \text{Energy}$$

| 1 mol = 180 g | 6 mol (6×32.0 g) = 192 g | 6 mol (6×44.0 g) = 264 g | 6 mol (6×18.0 g) = 108 g | |

> The sum of the reactant masses (180 g + 192 g) equals the sum of the product masses (264 g + 108 g). Why must this be so?

This equation provides information about stoichiometric relationships among the molecules that remain the same regardless of the reacting amounts involved. For example: If only 90.0 g (0.500 mol) glucose were oxidized (half the mass above), only 96.0 g (3 mol) O_2 would be needed.

As illustrated by the following sample problem, these relationships can also help you identify the limiting reactant.

Sample Problem 1: *How much CO_2 can be produced if 100.0 g glucose reacts as completely as possible with 100.0 g O_2? Which is the limiting reactant—oxygen or glucose?*

Start by calculating how much CO_2 could be produced if *each* reactant were fully consumed. The total amount of products formed depends on the amount of the reactant used up first (the limiting reactant). When the limiting reactant is totally consumed, no more products can be produced. Calculating the amount of product that theoretically could be produced from each individual reactant makes it easy to identify the limiting reactant. That is, by comparing the results of these calculations, the *least* amount of product formed identifies the limiting reactant.

Consider how much CO_2 could be produced if glucose fully reacts (assume that sufficient oxygen is available):

$$100.0 \text{ g glucose} \times \frac{1 \text{ mol glucose}}{180.0 \text{ g glucose}} \times \frac{6 \text{ mol } CO_2}{1 \text{ mol glucose}} = 3.333 \text{ mol } CO_2$$

Determine how much CO_2 could be produced if the O_2 fully reacts (assume that sufficient glucose is available):

$$100.0 \text{ g } O_2 \times \frac{1 \text{ mol } O_2}{32.0 \text{ g } O_2} \times \frac{6 \text{ mol } CO_2}{6 \text{ mol } O_2} = 3.12 \text{ mol } CO_2$$

We find that 100.0 g O_2 produces less CO_2 than 100.0 g glucose would produce. That suggests that when 100.0 g O_2 combine with 100.0 g glucose, O_2 is the reactant that is used up first. When all the O_2 has reacted, the reaction stops, with some excess glucose still present.

Sample Problem 2: *How much glucose remains unreacted when the reaction just described finally stops?*

Here is one way to determine this. First, find how much glucose reacts with the O_2:

$$100.0 \text{ g } O_2 \times \frac{1 \text{ mol } O_2}{32.0 \text{ g } O_2} \times \frac{1 \text{ mol glucose}}{6 \text{ mol } O_2} \times \frac{180 \text{ g glucose}}{1 \text{ mol glucose}} = 93.7 \text{ g glucose}$$

Then, find how much glucose remains unreacted:

(100.0 g glucose initially) − (93.7 g glucose reacted) = 6.3 g glucose left over

Now try the following problems:

1. Lactose, the milk sugar, is a disaccharide (see Table 7.2, page 585). In the human body, the enzyme lactase (see Figure 7.32) helps hydrolyze a lactose molecule into one molecule each of two different monosaccharides: glucose and galactose:

$$\underset{\substack{\text{Lactose} \\ \text{342 g/mol}}}{C_{12}H_{22}O_{11}} \;+\; \underset{\substack{\text{Water} \\ \text{18 g/mol}}}{H_2O} \;\xrightarrow{\text{lactase}}\; \underset{\substack{\text{Glucose} \\ \text{180 g/mol}}}{C_6H_{12}O_6} \;+\; \underset{\substack{\text{Galactose} \\ \text{180 g/mol}}}{C_6H_{12}O_6}$$

You are investigating this reaction. During one trial, you combine 1.5 g lactose and 10.0 g water with a lactase enzyme.

a. Identify the limiting reactant in this trial.
b. How many moles of glucose will this reaction produce?
c. How many grams of glucose will be produced?
d. After the reaction stops, which reactant will be left over; that is, which reactant was in excess?
e. How many moles of that substance will be left unreacted?

2. Imagine you also are investigating how the body digests fat. The process starts with hydrolyzing the triglyceride. Each molecule reacts with three molecules of water to form three molecules of fatty acid and one molecule glycerol:

$$\underset{\substack{\text{Glyceryl tripalmitate} \\ \text{806 g/mol}}}{C_{51}H_{98}O_6} \;+\; \underset{\substack{\text{Water} \\ \text{18 g/mol}}}{3\,H_2O} \;\longrightarrow\; \underset{\substack{\text{Palmitic acid} \\ \text{256 g/mol}}}{3\,C_{16}H_{32}O_2} \;+\; \underset{\substack{\text{Glycerol} \\ \text{92 g/mol}}}{C_3H_8O_3}$$

During one trial, you combine 4.0 g glyceryl tripalmitate with 1.0 g water.

a. Identify the limiting reactant in this trial.
b. How many moles of palmitic acid will this reaction produce?
c. What mass (in grams) of palmitic acid will be produced?
d. After the reaction stops, which reactant will be left over; that is, which reactant was initially in excess?
e. How many moles of that substance will remain unreacted?

Figure 7.32 *For "lactose-intolerant" individuals; some dairy products contain added lactase—an enzyme that promotes digestion of lactose.*

> This equation represents the reverse of the triglyceride-forming reaction that you learned about. See Figure 7.23 page 588.

Section B   Energy Storage and Use   **599**

Developing Skills

B.9 Limiting Reactants In Chemical Reactions

This extension of Modeling Matter B.8 applies the concept of a limiting reactant to moles and molecules.

Answers

1. a. $1.5 \text{ g lactose} \times \dfrac{1 \text{ mol lactose}}{342 \text{ g}} \times$

$\dfrac{1 \text{ mol glucose}}{1 \text{ mol lactose}} \times \dfrac{180 \text{ g glucose}}{1 \text{ mol glucose}} =$

0.79 g glucose

$10.0 \text{ g water} \times \dfrac{1 \text{ mol water}}{18.0 \text{ g}} \times$

$\dfrac{1 \text{ mol glucose}}{1 \text{ mol water}} \times \dfrac{180 \text{ g glucose}}{1 \text{ mol glucose}} =$

100 g glucose

Lactose is the limiting reactant.

b. 0.0044 mol

c. 0.79 g

d. Water

e. $1.5 \text{ g lactose} \times \dfrac{1 \text{ mol lactose}}{342 \text{ g}} \times$

$\dfrac{1 \text{ mol water}}{1 \text{ mol lactose}} = 0.0044 \text{ mol water}$

reacts

$10.0 \text{ g water} \times \dfrac{1 \text{ mol}}{18 \text{ g water}} =$

0.556 mol water initially present

Only 0.0044 mol water reacts; that means 0.556 mol − 0.0044 mol = 0.552 mol water will remain.

2. a. $4.0 \text{ g glycerol tripalmitate} \times$

$\dfrac{1 \text{ mol glycerol tripalmitate}}{806 \text{ g glycerol tripalmitate}} \times$

$\dfrac{3 \text{ mol palmitic acid}}{1 \text{ mol glycerol tripalmitate}} \times$

$\dfrac{256 \text{ g palmitic acid}}{1 \text{ mol palmitic acid}} = 3.8 \text{ g}$

palmitic acid

$1.0 \text{ g water} \times \dfrac{1 \text{ mol water}}{18.0 \text{ g water}} \times$

$\dfrac{3 \text{ mol palmitic acid}}{3 \text{ mol water}} \times$

$\dfrac{256 \text{ g palmitic acid}}{1 \text{ mol palmitic acid}} = 14 \text{ g}$

palmitic acid

Glycerol tripalmitate is the limiting reactant.

b. 0.015 mol

c. 3.8 g

d. Water

e. $4.0 \text{ g glycerol tripalmitate} \times$

$\dfrac{1 \text{ mol glycerol tripalmitate}}{806 \text{ g glycerol tripalmitate}} \times$

$\dfrac{3 \text{ mol water}}{1 \text{ mol glycerol tripalmitate}} =$

0.015 mol water is needed

There is 0.056 mol water at the reaction's start, but only 0.015 mol is needed, so 0.041 mol of water remains unreacted.

Making Decisions

B.10 Analyzing Fats and Carbohydrates

Students analyze main energy sources found in their diet inventory from Section A. They will

• determine mass of carbohydrate and percent Calories from carbohydrate.

• determine total mass of fats (saturated and unsaturated).

• calculate average mass of fats.

• calculate average daily energy supplied by fat.

• identify ways to reduce fats in the diet.

Use reference materials identified earlier to help students with these calculations. Student calculations can be verified using the online diet-analysis tools listed for A.9, page 580.

Making Decisions

B.10 ANALYZING FATS AND CARBOHYDRATES

In Section A, you analyzed the energy content of a typical student's three-day diet. Using new information provided in this section, you can now identify the main sources of this energy.

1. Using appropriate resources, determine the mass of carbohydrates (in grams) contained in each item on the three-day food inventory. Then calculate the percent of total Calories provided by carbohydrates. (*Note:* You calculated average Calories per day on page 580.) Report both sets of data in a suitable summary table.

2. If possible, identify the mass (in grams) of fiber in each item. Record these data.

3. Using appropriate resources, determine the mass of fat (in grams) in each item in the inventory. If possible, identify the total mass of saturated and unsaturated fat for each item. Record these data.

4. Calculate the average mass of fat supplied daily by the three-day diet described in the food inventory.

5. a. Calculate the average daily energy (in Calories) supplied by fat.
   b. Based on that value, is food energy from fat less than 30% of the total food energy supplied?

6. Identify possible ways to reduce the quantity of fat in the food inventory you are analyzing.

7. Now think of two possible Riverwood High School vending machine items that are *not* on your inventory.
   a. Find the total mass of carbohydrates (in grams) in each item. If possible, also report the total mass (in grams) of fiber in each item. Record these data.
   b. Determine the mass of fat (in grams) in each item. If possible, report the total mass of saturated and unsaturated fat in each item. Record these data.
   c. Is the food energy from fat less than 30% of the total energy supplied by each item?

SECTION B SUMMARY
Reviewing the Concepts

Carbohydrates, composed of carbon, hydrogen, and oxygen, include sugars, starches, and cellulose.

1. What is the origin of the term *carbohydrate*?
2. Using a shaded oval to represent a single monosaccharide molecule, sketch a model of a
   a. monosaccharide.
   b. disaccharide.
   c. polysaccharide.
3. Name two common monosaccharides and two common disaccharides.

4. All sugars are carbohydrates, but not all carbohydrates are sugars. Explain.
5. What kind of chemical reaction causes monosaccharides to link and produce more complex carbohydrates?
6. Why is starch classified as a polysaccharide?
7. How many Calories would be provided by 25 g carbohydrate?

Fats are composed of carbon, hydrogen, and oxygen atoms that are arranged differently from those atoms in carbohydrates.

8. What are fatty acids?
9. Consider the reaction that forms a typical fat molecule.
   a. List the substances that are combined in this reaction.
   b. How would you classify this reaction?
   c. Name the new functional group formed in this reaction.

10. Fats are examples of triglycerides. Why does that name provide an appropriate description of a fat molecule?
11. How many Calories would be provided by 10.6 g of olive oil?
12. What aspect of their structure makes fats sparingly soluble in water?

Fats may be saturated or unsaturated. Unsaturated fats can be made more highly saturated through hydrogenation.

13. Define, in terms of their carbon-carbon bonds, the terms *saturated fat* and *unsaturated fat*.
14. Distinguish between *monounsaturated* and *polyunsaturated* fats.
15. With what is a saturated fat actually saturated?
16. How does the degree of saturation affect a fat molecule's properties?

17. The ingredient labels on some brands of margarine state that the oil is *partially hydrogenated*.
   a. What property does the product possess as a result of partial hydrogenation?
   b. Why do you think a manufacturer might decide against *completely* hydrogenating margarine?

Section Summary   601

4. All sugars are monosaccharides or disaccharides, which are simple carbohydrates. More complex carbohydrates, such as cellulose and starch, are polymers of glucose but are not classified as sugars.
5. A condensation reaction or dehydration synthesis
6. Because it is composed of many repeating units of glucose (disaccharide) molecules
7. 25 g carbohydrate $\times$ 4 Cal/g = 100 Cal
8. Long-chain hydrocarbons with a carboxylic acid ($—COOH$) at one end
9. a. Glycerol and fatty acids
   b. Condensation reaction
   c. Ester group
10. Glycerol plus three fatty acids make up a *tri*glyceride.
11. 10.6 g olive oil $\times$ 9 Cal/g = 95 Cal
12. Fats are comprised of long, nonpolar hydrocarbon chains that do not appreciably interact with polar water molecules.
13. *Saturated fats* contain only single C—C bonds. *Unsaturated fats* contain at least one double or triple carbon–carbon bond.
14. *Monounsaturated* fats contain just one C=C bond in their fatty acid component. *Polyunsaturated* fats contain two or more C=C double bonds in their fatty acid component.
15. Hydrogen atoms
16. The greater the degree of saturation, the higher the molecule's melting point. Saturated fats are generally solid at room temperature.
17. a. It is more solid than the original oil.
   b. Completely saturated margarine would be more solid and difficult to spread.

SECTION B SUMMARY

 Section B Supplement

Reviewing the Concepts

1. It refers to molecules containing atoms of carbon along with hydrogen and oxygen in the same 2:1 proportion as water.
2. a. Single oval
   b. Two ovals joined together
   c. Many ovals joined together, perhaps with brackets to suggest that they can be many units long
3. Monosaccharides: glucose, fructose, galactose; disaccharides: sucrose, lactose, maltose

18. Cis isomers have functional groups on the same side of the double bond. Trans isomers have functional groups on opposite sides of the double bond.

19. The double bond prevents functional groups on adjacent carbon atoms from rotating around each other. These same functional groups would freely rotate around single bonds.

20. a. Butter, animal fats
b. Plant and fish oils

21. Cis drawings should show a four-carbon chain with methyl groups on the same side relative to the double bond. In trans drawings, the methyl groups are diagonally oriented on opposite sides of the double bond. See pages 592–593.

22.

23. The functional group in fat molecules is most typically an ester group. The functional group in carbohydrates is an alcohol group or a carbonyl group.

24. Fat molecules contain more C—C and C—H bonds than carbohydrates. This means the bonds in fat molecules take less energy to break. More energy is released as C=O and O—H bonds form in CO_2 and H_2O during cellular respiration when fats are used as the fuel. Carbohydrates already contain several C—O and O—H bonds, meaning less energy can be generated during cellular respiration.

25. a. Nonpolar; long-chain hydrocarbons with a carboxyl group at one end.

---

18. What is the difference between cis and trans isomers?

19. Why do cis and trans isomers occur only with a C=C double bond and not with a C—C single bond?

20. What are some natural sources of
a. saturated fats?
b. unsaturated fats?

21. Draw structural formulas for cis and trans isomers of 2-butene, CH_3—CH=CH—CH_3.

22. Draw a structural formula of a fat molecule containing both *cis*- and *trans*-fatty acids.

Differences in structure between fat and carbohydrate molecules account for their different properties and energy content.

23. How are functional groups in fat molecules different from functional groups in carbohydrates? Use structural formulas to clarify your explanations.

24. From a chemical standpoint, explain why fat molecules contain more food energy per gram than do carbohydrate molecules.

25. List two chemical characteristics shared by all
a. fats.
b. carbohydrates.

26. What property of fats makes them good energy-storage molecules?

A chemical reaction involves substances interacting in specific, stoichiometric relationships. The limiting reactant determines how much product can be produced.

27. Is it ever possible to use up *all* reactants in a chemical reaction? Explain.

28. How can a *limiting reactant* be identified?

29. Suppose you want to make a batch of s'mores. The "equation" for producing one s'more is as follows:

2 Graham crackers + 1 Marshmallow
+ 3 Chocolate pieces ⟶ 1 s'more

If you have 12 graham crackers, 25 marshmallows, and 12 chocolate pieces,

a. How many s'mores can you make?
b. Which is the limiting reactant?
c. How much of each excess reactant will be left over?

30. The chemical reaction that quickly inflates an air bag in an automobile accident is

$$2\ NaN_3(s) \longrightarrow 2\ Na(s) + 3\ N_2(g)$$

If 112 g NaN_3 (sodium azide) decomposes according to this equation, what mass $N_2(g)$ will be formed?

31. Consider the reaction of hydrogen gas and oxygen gas to produce water:

$$2\ H_2(g) + O_2(g) \longrightarrow 2\ H_2O(l)$$

a. If 4.0 mol hydrogen gas are combined with 4.0 mol oxygen gas and the reaction described occurs, how many moles of water could be produced?
b. What is the limiting reactant in this reaction?
c. How much of each excess reactant will be left over?

32. One step in an early soap-making method was to allow fireplace wood ashes (containing potash, K_2O) to react with water, producing a highly basic potassium hydroxide (KOH) solution. The equation is as follows:

$$K_2O(s) + H_2O(l) \longrightarrow 2\ KOH(aq)$$

Assume that a 5.4-g sample of K_2O reacts as completely as possible with 9.0 g H_2O.

a. What will be the limiting reactant?
b. What mass (in grams) of potassium hydroxide would be produced?

---

b. Polar; contain multiple alcohol groups.

26. There are more C—H bonds (and fewer C—O bonds) in fats, which means that there are more opportunities to release stored energy through oxidation.

27. It is theoretically possible, although difficult, to start with *exactly* the correct number of molecules of each reactant so that nothing is left over.

28. It is consumed entirely in a chemical reaction.

29. a. 4 s'mores
b. Chocolate pieces
c. 4 graham crackers and 21 marshmallows

30. $112 \text{ g NaN}_3 \times \dfrac{1 \text{ mol NaN}_3}{65.0 \text{ g NaN}_3} \times$

$\dfrac{3 \text{ mol N}_2}{2 \text{ mol NaN}_3} \times \dfrac{28.0 \text{ g N}_2}{1 \text{ mol N}_2} = 72 \text{ g N}_2$

Connecting the Concepts

33. Why would it not be helpful to label a container as "sugar" in a chemical storeroom?

34. Explain how a relatively small number of subunits (fatty acids and monosaccharides) can create so many different kinds of fats and carbohydrates.

35. How do cis–trans isomers compare to the structural isomers that you have learned about? (Recall that isomers were introduced in Unit 3, page 230.)

36. Polysaccharides are examples of naturally occurring polymers.

a. How are they similar to synthetic polymers?

b. How are they different from synthetic polymers?

37. Compare chemical properties of fats to chemical properties of alkanes.

38. Why is the term "burning fat" sometimes used to describe exercising, even though no actual burning is involved?

39. How are chemical equations similar to recipes used for cooking? How are they different?

40. In thinking about the equation $HCl + NaOH \longrightarrow NaCl + H_2O$, one student concluded that 1.0 g HCl should react completely with 1.0 g NaOH. Explain why this reasoning is incorrect.

41. Consider the equation described in Question 31. Specify a pair of starting masses (in grams) for hydrogen gas and oxygen gas so that *both* reactants would completely react in that chemical change.

Extending the Concepts

42. Research three different triglycerides and list the fatty acids in each.

43. Examine the ingredients listed on several food packages in your home. Identify the names of any specific carbohydrates or fats that you recognize.

44. Human consumption of *trans*-fatty acids may be associated with health risks. Investigate and summarize current research regarding this nutritional concern.

45. Fat-like products such as Olestra were designed and marketed as fat replacements in some foods. Investigate the chemistry of these fat substitutes and relate that information to health risks and benefits.

46. Assume that you currently consume 3000 Cal of food energy daily and want to lose 30 lb of body fat within two months (60 days).

a. If you decide to lose that weight only by reducing your intake of food energy (with no extra exercise), how many food Calories, on average, would you have to remove from your daily diet?

b. How many food Calories could you still consume daily?

c. Would the scheme described in Questions 46a and 46b, if followed, be a sensible way to lose weight? Why or why not?

47. Some well-publicized dieting programs use terms such as *net carbs, counting carbs,* and *glycemic index.* Research the meanings of these terms and analyze their dietary usefulness based on the chemistry that you have learned.

31. a. 4 mol

b. H_2

c. 2 mol O_2

32. a. This quantity requires 1.0 g H_2O to react completely.

$$5.4 \text{ g K}_2\text{O} \times \frac{1 \text{ mol K}_2\text{O}}{94.2 \text{ g K}_2\text{O}} \times \frac{1 \text{ mol H}_2\text{O}}{1 \text{ mol K}_2\text{O}} \times \frac{18.0 \text{ g H}_2\text{O}}{1 \text{ mol H}_2\text{O}} =$$

1.0 g H_2O. More H_2O is available, so K_2O is the limiting reactant.

b. $$5.4 \text{ g K}_2\text{O} \times \frac{1 \text{ mol K}_2\text{O}}{94.2 \text{ g K}_2\text{O}} \times \frac{2 \text{ mol KOH}}{1 \text{ mol K}_2\text{O}} \times \frac{56.1 \text{ g KOH}}{1 \text{ mol KOH}} =$$

6.4 g KOH

SECTION B

Connecting the Concepts

33. *Sugar* describes a variety of monosaccharides and disaccharides. This label would not identify a specific sugar.

34. Different combinations create many different molecules, like letters of the alphabet combine to form thousands of words.

35. They have the same molecular formula but different three-dimensional arrangements. Cis–trans isomers are specifically related to the position of functional groups around a carbon–carbon double bond.

36. a. They are made of repeating subunits.

b. They are made in nature, and the types of subunits differ.

37. The carboxyl group allows fats to undergo unique reactions. Alkanes are nonpolar and consist of only C and H atoms; fats contain long C–H chains that are also nonpolar.

38. The term refers to the energy given off by metabolized fats during exercise. The reaction resembles burning but occurs at a much more controlled (slower) rate.

39. Both show the proportions of ingredients, but chemical reactions only involve whole-number ratios. Also, when following a recipe, it is possible to omit ingredients and often still create a viable form of the intended product. This is not possible in chemical reactions.

40. 1 mol HCl = 36 g HCl. 1 mol NaOH = 40 g NaOH. Therefore, 1.0 g HCl will react with 1.1 g NaOH. The equation coefficients refer to the total *molecules* or *moles* of substance that react, not total grams of substance involved.

41. 4.0 g H_2 and 32.0 g O_2, or other masses having a 1:8 mass ratio

603

Extending the Concepts

42. Answers will vary.

43. Answers will vary. Carbohydrate names tend to end in *-ose.*

44. According to the FDA, trans fats behave much like saturated fats; they increase the amounts of LDL cholesterol in the blood, which increases the risk of heart disease.

45. These products are designed so that the body cannot metabolize them. Advertised benefits have included lower fat intake, lower cholesterol, and weight loss. Risks have included gastrointestinal problems and reduced absorption of vitamins and minerals. Encourage students to use several resources (both online and print) as they investigate this topic to ensure balanced perspectives.

46. a. $30 \text{ lb} \times \dfrac{3500 \text{ Cal}}{1 \text{ lb}} = 105\,000 \text{ Cal removed}$ from the diet

$\dfrac{105\,000 \text{ Cal}}{60 \text{ d}} = 1750 \text{ Cal daily}$

b. 3000 Cal (currently consumed) − 1750 Cal (to be eliminated) = 1350 Cal daily

c. No, not without physician supervision. A more gradual scheme of weight loss is less risky.

47. *Net carbs* refers to the total carbohydrates minus portions of similar components such as fiber, glycerin, and sugar alcohols. Since these components have differing effects on blood glucose, monitoring net carbs can be useful for diabetic individuals, but it can be misleading to subtract these components completely. *Counting carbs* is a meal-planning tool used by individuals with diabetes. They track the quantity of carbohydrates they consume in meals and snacks to help manage their blood sugar. Many popular weight-loss programs also require individuals to count carbohydrates they consume. The *glycemic index* ranks carbohydrates based on their immediate effect on blood glucose (blood sugar) level. The index is used both by individuals who are monitoring their weight and by individuals with diabetes, though it is still a controversial topic among nutritionists.

Proteins, Enzymes, and Chemistry

This section focuses on proteins as builder molecules and as enzymes that control rates of biochemical reactions in living organisms. It addresses the structure of proteins with focus on amino acids as protein building blocks. Students analyze protein content of their three-day food inventories.

C.1 Proteins: Function and Structure

 C.1 and C.3 Content Reading Guide

Proteins serve many purposes: They function as catalysts, act as antibodies, and have transport, regulatory, and structural roles. Protein functions are related to their structures. A fundamental feature in a protein's structure is its amino acid sequence. Some 20 amino acids serve as building blocks for proteins in the human body. Because these 20 amino acids can be combined in many ways, there is high diversity among proteins in foods and in our bodies. In fact, there are billions of possible proteins.

Although amino acids share a common structure, their side groups distinguish them. Some amino acids have polar side groups; others have nonpolar side groups. Amino acids are linked through condensation reactions that produce peptide bonds. Students should be familiar with condensation reactions from Unit 3 (page 274), where they studied condensation reactions forming esters.

Be sure students understand the structures of amino acids and their linkage into polypeptides. You can illustrate formation of peptide bonds

with molecular models. In living systems, peptide bond formation is catalyzed by enzymes. While the mechanism is beyond the scope of this course, you can use models to demonstrate one amine combining with a carboxyl group to form an amide (or peptide) bond and a molecule of water. Also use models to demonstrate that the product

still has an amino group and a carboxyl group free to react, and that there are two unique sequences in which they could be connected, AB or BA. Such apparently small differences in sequence can create functional differences in living systems. Using models in this way will assist students with Modeling Matter C.2.

SECTION

C

Proteins, Enzymes, and Chemistry

So far in this unit you have explored how carbohydrates and fats deliver energy that helps to keep you alive. The chemical bonds that store energy are broken, and energy is released in forming new, more strongly bonded molecules. In this section, you will investigate roles that *proteins* play in maintaining your well-being. For instance, proteins control the release of energy stored in foods and provide structure and support to maintain your cells and organs; in short, proteins help sustain life itself.

C.1 PROTEINS: FUNCTION AND STRUCTURE

Whenever you look at a living creature, most of what you see is protein—skin, hair, feathers (Figure 7.33), eyeballs, fingernails, and claws. **Protein** also is a major structural component of human tissue. Inside your body, muscles, cartilage, tendons, and ligaments are composed of protein.

At the cellular level, proteins help make it possible to transport materials into and out of cells. Your immune system depends on the ability of protein molecules to identify foreign substances. The rates of many chemical reactions that your cells require would be too slow were it not for special proteins called *enzymes,* which are biological catalysts present in all cells. In fact, your body contains tens of thousands of different proteins. Table 7.3 lists some major roles that proteins play in the human body.

Proteins are polymers built from smaller molecules called **amino acids.** As Figure 7.34 shows, amino acid molecules contain carbon, hydrogen, oxygen, and nitrogen; a few, like cysteine, also contain sulfur. Just as monosaccharide molecules serve as building blocks for more complex carbohydrates, 20 different amino acids serve as the structural units of all proteins.

All amino acids have several structural features in common, but each amino acid is a unique molecule; four amino acids are shown in Figure 7.34. Every amino acid has two functional groups, the amino group ($-NH_2$) and the carboxylic acid (carboxyl) group ($-COOH$).

Like starch, nylon, and polyester, proteins are condensation polymers (see pages 274–275). The combination of two amino acid molecules with the loss of one water molecule, as illustrated in Figure 7.35, is a typical condensation reaction. The bonds linking amino acid units together are called **peptide bonds.** Proteins are chains of amino acids that vary in length, from ten to several thousand amino acids. Just as the 26 letters of the alphabet combine in different ways to form hundreds of thousands of words, the 20 amino acids can combine in a nearly infinite number of ways to form different proteins that meet many needs of living organisms.

The word *protein* is based on the Greek word *proteios,* which means "of prime importance."

Figure 7.33 *This hummingbird feather is composed of many different proteins.*

Even though hundreds of amino acids have been identified in nature, the human body uses only 20 amino acids.

MAJOR GROUPS OF PROTEINS IN THE HUMAN BODY		
Type	**Function**	**Examples**
Structural proteins		
Muscle	Contraction, movement	Myosin
Connective tissue	Support, protection	Collagen, keratin
Chromosomal proteins	Part of chromosome structure	Histones
Membranes	Control influx, outflow, and communication	Pore proteins, receptors
Transport proteins	Carry needed substances (such as O_2)	Hemoglobin
Regulatory proteins		
Fluid balance	Maintain pH, water, and salt content of bodily fluids	Serum albumin
Enzymes	Control metabolism	Proteases
Hormones	Regulate body functions	Insulin
Protective proteins	Attack foreign bodies (antibodies)	Gamma globulin

| **Table 7.3**

Figure 7.34 *Structural formulas for glycine, alanine, aspartic acid, and cysteine. The amino groups of each are highlighted in blue; the carboxylic acid groups are in red; and green highlights unique side groups that distinguish amino acids from one another.*

| **Figure 7.35** *Formation of a dipeptide from two amino acids (Ala and Cys).*

Section C   Proteins, Enzymes, and Chemistry   **605**

Additional Background Information: Proteins

Proteins are complex macromolecules. The sequence of amino acids in a protein is its *primary structure*. Sections of these chains of amino acids can coil as helices and/or line up to form flat sheets. These conformations within the protein chain are the *secondary structure* of the protein. The secondary structure is the result of interactions between amide hydrogens and the carbonyl oxygens of various amino acids. Two common secondary structures are the α-helix and the β-pleated sheet. Common proteins that contain the α-helical secondary structure are *keratins* that make up hair. Silk fibers contain the β-pleated sheet secondary structure.

Tertiary structure refers to the overall shape of an entire amino acid chain. Interactions among side groups of different amino acids are largely responsible for protein's tertiary structure. Polar side groups interact with other polar side groups or water from the surrounding environment; nonpolar side groups interact with other nonpolar side groups. The result is a compact structure, generally globular.

Any interruption or change in the sequence of amino acids in a protein (its primary structure) can significantly affect its secondary and tertiary structures. The absence or substitution of an amino acid can disrupt and even destroy a protein's function and manifest itself as a disease. An example of this is sickle-cell anemia. When valine replaces glutamic acid in hemoglobin, the overall geometry of the protein changes, and, on the macroscopic level, red blood cells adopt a different shape.

Finally, the *quaternary structure* is the result of aggregation of multiple peptide subunits, each having its own primary, secondary, and tertiary structures. Hemoglobin, present in red blood cells, is an ideal example of this type of structure. Hemoglobin is composed of four separate subunits. Proteins that are only composed of one unit will not display this level of structure.

Modeling Matter

C.2 Molecular Structure of Proteins

Students examine and practice writing structural formulas for amino acids and polypeptides. Considering how many formulas can be devised from only a few amino acids helps students realize how a limited number of amino acids can form staggering numbers of different protein structures.

You may wish to use molecular model kits with students during this exercise. Also, students can view an animation of peptide bond formation either on the *ChemCom* CD-ROM or on the Website.

Answers

1. a.

H₂N—C—C—OH with H and H below the C, and H and O above

Glycine

H₂N—C—C—OH with CH₃ and O above, H below

Alanine

Students should circle the H_2N (amino) group and the COOH (carboxyl) group.

b. Both molecules contain an amino group and a carboxyl group.

c. Alanine has a methyl (CH_3) group in place of the hydrogen atom on glycine.

2. No answer required.

Modeling Matter

Figure 7.36 *Computer-generated space-filling model depicting a polymer of the protein actin. For clarity, each actin monomer (the repeated polymer unit) is shown in a different color.*

Constructing a Protein

C.2 MOLECULAR STRUCTURE OF PROTEINS

Protein molecules differ from one another in the number and types of amino acids they contain and in the sequence in which the amino acids are bonded (see Figure 7.36). However, the way in which amino acids bond to one another to form these long polymers is the same for every protein molecule. You will now investigate how amino acids bond and how the sequence of amino acids affects a protein's structure.

1. Draw structural formulas for glycine and alanine on a sheet of paper. Refer to Figure 7.34, page 605.

   a. Circle and identify the functional groups in each molecule.
   b. How are the two molecules alike?
   c. How do the two molecules differ?

2. Proteins are polymers of amino acids. Examine the equations in Figures 7.35 (page 605) and 7.37 to see how two amino acids join. Notice that the amino group on one amino acid is bonded to the carboxylic acid group on another. This linkage, a *peptide bond,* is shown here:

   —C—OH   H—N—   →   —C—N—   +   H₂O

   Carboxyl group   Amino group   Peptide bond   Water

   | **Figure 7.37** *A carboxyl group combining with an amino group.*

   When two amino acid units are linked by a peptide bond, the product is called a **dipeptide.** Because an amino acid contains at least one amino group and one carboxylic acid group, amino acids can form a peptide bond at either end.

3. Using structural formulas, write the equation for the reaction between two glycine molecules to form a dipeptide. Circle the peptide bond in the dipeptide.

4. Using structural formulas, write equations for possible reactions between a glycine molecule and an alanine molecule.

5. Examine the structural formulas of the dipeptide products you identified in Question 4. Note that each dipeptide still contains a reactive amino group and a reactive carboxylic acid group. These dipeptides can then react with other amino acids, forming even more peptide linkages.

6. Remembering that the carboxylic acid group of the first amino acid forms a peptide bond with the amino group of the second amino acid, explain why the amino acid sequence A-B-C is different from C-B-A.

606   **Unit 7**   Food: Matter and Energy for Life

3.   H—N—C—C—O—H + H—N—C—C—O—H → H—N—C—C—N—C—C—O—H

4. One possibility:

H—N—C—C—O—H + H—N—C—C—O—H → H—N—C—C—N—C—C—O—H

   H glycine   CH₃ alanine   H   CH₃

7. Assuming that you have supplies of three different amino acid molecules—A, B, and C—and that each type of amino acid can be used only once, how many different *tripeptides* (three amino acids linked together) can be formed? Write all possible combinations.

8. Writing the sequence of amino acids by using their chemical names is a time-consuming and tedious process for most protein molecules. Consequently, chemists have devised three-letter (and even one-letter) abbreviations for each amino acid in proteins. For example, a tripeptide with a sequence of glycine–aspartic acid–cysteine is abbreviated *Gly–Asp–Cys*. Using three-letter abbreviations, write down all other possible sequences for these three amino acids.

9. How many *tetrapeptides* (four amino acids bonded together) could be formed from the four amino acids shown in Figure 7.34 (page 605)? Write the possible combinations by using their three-letter abbreviations.

10. The cells in your body build proteins from 20 different amino acids. If each protein can be as long as 10 000 amino acid units, would you estimate the theoretical total of the different proteins your cells could produce to be in the hundreds, thousands, or millions? Explain your answer.

11. How would a living organism benefit from its ability to synthesize so many different proteins? What potential problems do you envision?

Figure 7.38. *Foods, including plant sources, rich in protein.*

bonds to the B subunit via its carboxyl end. In C-B-A, A would bond to B via the amino end. Atoms are arranged differently in these two sequences, indicating different molecules.

7. ABC, BAC, CAB, ACB, BCA, CBA—six combinations

8. Cys-Asp-Gly, Cys-Gly-Asp, Asp-Gly-Cys, Gly-Cys-Asp, Asp-Cys-Gly, Gly-Asp-Cys

9. 24 tetrapeptides:

GlyAlaAspCys	AlaGlyAspCys
GlyAlaCysAsp	AlaGlyCysAsp
GlyAspAlaCys	AlaAspGlyCys
GlyAspCysAla	AlaAspCysGly
GlyCysAlaAsp	AlaCysGlyAsp
GlyCysAspAla	AlaCysAspGly

AspGlyAlaCys	CysGlyAlaAsp
AspGlyCysAla	CysGlyAspAla
AspAlaGlyCys	CysAlaGlyAsp
AspAlaCysGly	CysAlaAspGly
AspCysGlyAla	CysAlaGlyAsp
AspCysAlaGly	CysAlaAspGly

10. Millions. Consider a 10 000-unit protein made up entirely of one amino-acid monomer. Changing it by replacing the last amino acid with one of the other 19 amino acids yields 20 different possible structures. Changing the second to last amino acid yields another 20 possible structures and so on, resulting in $20 \times 10\ 000 = 200\ 000$ different structures simply by changing the amino acid in one location. Thus, far more than millions of possible sequences (on the order of $20^{10\ 000}$ or $1 \times 10^{13\ 000}$) exist.

11. Many arrangements make unique "genetic codings" possible at the molecular level. One problem is that any error in the amino acid sequence can completely change protein characteristics.

A second possibility:

H—N—C—C—O—H +
with H, H, O above and CH₃ alanine

$$H-N-C-C-O-H +$$

(alanine)

$$H-N-C-C-O-H \rightarrow$$

(glycine)

$$H-N-C-C-N-C-C-O-H$$

with CH₃ and H below

5. No answer required.

6. If each amino acid is oriented so that the amine group is on the left and the carboxyl group is on the right, then in the A-B-C sequence the A subunit

SECTION C

C.3 Protein in Your Diet

Since the body cannot store excess protein, individuals must consume a continuous supply. When protein-containing foods are ingested, proteolytic enzymes (proteases) cleave peptide bonds and break long protein chains into amino acids. A very common protease found in the human stomach is pepsin. Other proteolytic enzymes include trypsin, chymotrypsin, and elastase. These digestive enzymes cleave peptide bonds at different locations. Freed amino acids are absorbed through the intestinal walls and used to synthesize new proteins.

Some well-known diets are based on consuming foods high in protein and low in carbohydrates. Some people suggest that these diets work because they force the body into starvation mode, since the brain typically functions on glucose, a simple carbohydrate. When the body runs low on blood glucose, it is forced to use glucose stored in the liver and muscles as glycogen. As the body continues to function without carbohydrates, fat stores will be used for fuel (a process called *ketosis*—ketones are a side product of this metabolism). The extent of weight loss depends on the quantity of fat one has originally stored. There is considerable controversy surrounding these types of diets and, indeed, whether they are good for the body over the long term. Some critics have suggested, for example, that this type of diet may stress the kidneys.

Figure 7.39 *The structural formula for urea.*

Urea

The essential amino acids:

Histidine (for infants)
Isoleucine
Leucine
Lysine
Methionine
Phenylalanine
Threonine
Tryptophan
Valine

Of course, the diet can be altered so that it includes the missing essential amino acid.

Complementary proteins do not need to be consumed at every meal. However, sufficient complementary proteins must be consumed so that the daily protein intake is adequate.

C.3 PROTEIN IN YOUR DIET

What foods are the main protein sources in your diet? To which food groups shown in Figure 7.2 (page 568) do the protein-containing foods in Figure 7.38 (page 607) belong?

When foods containing proteins reach your stomach and small intestine, peptide bonds break. The separated amino acid units then travel through the intestinal walls to the bloodstream, the liver, and then to the rest of the body. Individual cells use these amino acids as building blocks for new proteins.

If you eat more protein than your body requires, or if your body needs to use protein because carbohydrates and fats are in short supply, amino acids are metabolized in the liver. Nitrogen atoms are removed and converted in the liver to urea (Figure 7.39), which is excreted through the kidneys in urine. The remaining portions of the amino acid molecules are either converted to glucose and oxidized, releasing 4 Cal of energy per gram, or stored as fat.

The human body normally can synthesize adequate supplies of 11 of the 20 required amino acids. The other nine, called **essential amino acids,** must be obtained from the diet. If an essential amino acid is in short supply in the diet, that amino acid becomes a limiting reactant in building any protein containing that amino acid. When this happens, the only way the body can make that protein on its own is by breaking down one of its proteins containing that essential amino acid.

Any dietary source of protein that contains adequate amounts of *all* essential amino acids represents a source of **complete protein.** Most sources of animal protein contain all nine essential amino acids in quantities sufficient to meet dietary requirements. Plant protein and some sources of animal protein are *incomplete,* that is, they do not contain adequate amounts of all nine essential amino acids.

No single plant can provide adequate amounts of all the essential amino acids, but certain combinations of plants can. These combinations of foods, which are said to contain **complementary proteins,** are part of many diets around the world (see Figure 7.40).

Figure 7.40 *Complementary proteins provide adequate amounts of all essential amino acids when consumed together in a single day.*

Students examine Dietary Reference Intakes (DRIs) for protein, summarized in **Table 7.4.** Point out that DRIs for protein, much like those for carbohydrates, fats, and Calories, depend on body weight, gender, and activity levels.

Because the human body cannot store amino acids, you must consume some every day. The recommended level of protein intake according to the 2005 *Dietary Guidelines for Americans* is 10–35% of total daily Calories consumed. The consumption of too much protein carries potential health risks. Excess protein causes stress on the two organs that metabolize amino acids: the liver and the kidneys. Excess protein also increases excretion of calcium ions (Ca^{2+}) that function in nerve transmission and help build bones and teeth. A diet with too much protein can even cause dehydration because more fluids are needed for the urinary excretion of urea. This problem is particularly relevant to athletes. Finally, consuming excess protein may lead to an inadequate intake of other nutrients.

In 1997, the Food and Nutrition Board of the National Academy of Sciences created Dietary Reference Intakes (DRIs). The DRIs are quantitative estimates of nutrient intakes for planning and assessing the diets for healthy people. The DRIs for protein shown in Table 7.4, as well as for other nutrients not shown in the table, depend on a person's age and gender. DRIs are based on median heights and weights for a U.S. population of designated age and gender.

Food labels list nutritional information, as shown in Figure 7.41. *Daily values* are based on a daily intake of 2000 Calories and must be adjusted for an individual's body size, age, level of physical activity, and energy demands related to such exercise.

Figure 7.41 *A nutrition label specifying protein content.*

DIETARY REFERENCE INTAKES (DRIs) FOR PROTEIN

Age or Condition	RDA (g/d)[a]
Infants	
0–6 months	9.1
7–12 months	**13.5**
Males	
9–13 years	**34**
14–18 years	**52**
19–70 years	**56**
> 70 years	**56**
Females	
9–13 years	**34**
14–70 years	**46**
> 70 years	**46**
Pregnant	**71**
Nursing	**71**

Note: Recommended Dietary Allowances (RDAs) are in **bold** type. RDAs are set to meet the needs of almost all (97 to 98%) individuals in a group.

[a]Based on 1.5 g/kg body mass per day for infants, 1.1 g/kg body mass per day for ages 1–3, 0.95 g/kg body mass per day for ages 4–13, 0.85 g/kg body mass per day for ages 14–18, 0.8 g/kg body mass per day for adults, and 1.1 g/kg body mass per day for pregnant (using pre-pregnancy weight) and lactating women.

Food & Nutrition Board, National Academy of Sciences: National Research Council, *Dietary Reference Intakes 2004.*

| **Table 7.4**

C.4 ANALYZING DAILY PROTEIN REQUIREMENTS

Use the information in Table 7.4 to answer the following questions:

1. What mass of protein should a person of your age and gender consume each day, on average?
2. For each kilogram of body mass, infants require more protein than adults do. Why should protein values per kilogram of body mass be highest for infants and become lower as a person ages (Figure 7.42)?
3. a. What food do infants consume that meets most of their relatively high protein needs?
   b. What evidence in Table 7.4 supports your answer? Explain.

Developing Skills

Figure 7.42 *Why does an individual's age and developmental stage influence their protein needs?*

Developing Skills

C.4 Analyzing Daily Protein Requirements

In this activity, students apply and interpret DRIs for protein as given in **Table 7.4.**

Answers

1. Answers depend on age and gender: 46 g for 15- to 18-year-old females; 52 g for 15- to 18-year-old males.
2. Infants are more rapidly building new tissues so they need relatively more protein.
3. a. Mother's milk
   b. Nursing (lactating) women require high supplies of protein to produce breast milk.

Using the Figures

Figure 7.42: One's body requires more protein at various stages of life than at others. During growth spurts or other periods of rapid tissue development, needs for amino acid building blocks increase. Pregnant or lactating women, infants, and rapidly growing children or teenagers may require a higher proportion of protein in their diets than average adults require.

Using the Figures

Figure 7.40: Ask students to identify foods that "complement" each other in terms of protein content in each photograph (tofu and rice in the top photo, peanut butter and bread in the bottom photo). Other examples with which students may be familiar include beans and rice, tortillas and refried beans, and wheat pasta and cheese. Dieticians encourage vegetarians to consume complementary protein combinations, since most complete protein sources are animal-based.

C.5 Enzymes

 C.5 Enzymes Student Worksheet and Data Table

Without a catalyst or sunlight, H_2O_2 decomposition proceeds slowly at room temperature. However, the enzyme *catalase* increases the rate. Raw liver, apple, and potato are sources of catalase in this investigation. As the sources are boiled, the catalase denatures. At high temperatures, intermolecular attractions responsible for catalase's tertiary structure become disrupted; the enzyme no longer possesses the shape needed to facilitate H_2O_2 decomposition. Students compare rates of catalyzed and uncatalyzed reactions. The decomposition reaction is $2\ H_2O_2(aq) \longrightarrow 2\ H_2O(l) + O_2(g)$. The rate of gas bubble (O_2) formation conveniently indicates the rate of H_2O_2 decomposition.

Time

30 min

Materials

(For 12 student pairs)

120 mL of 3% hydrogen peroxide (H_2O_2) in brown bottle
24 test tubes (16 × 125 mm)
6 small pieces fresh raw liver
6 small pieces boiled liver
6 small pieces fresh apple
6 small pieces boiled apple
6 small pieces fresh potato
6 small pieces boiled potato
Yeast, 1 package

Safety

Students should wear protective goggles and aprons throughout this investigation.

Lab Video: Enzymes

Introduction

Think of a situation where you had to respond quickly, such as catching an object that fell unexpectedly or getting ready for school when you were late. How do your cells get the energy they need to respond quickly? You have already learned that food is "burned" to meet the body's continuous energy needs. The rate of "burning" can be adjusted from low to high, literally within a heartbeat.

What is the secret behind this impressive performance? It lies with biological catalysts called *enzymes*. Enzymes are able to speed up specific reactions without undergoing any lasting change themselves. In this investigation, you will monitor the rate of an enzyme-catalyzed reaction. In particular, you will investigate how the enzyme *catalase* affects the rate of decomposition of hydrogen peroxide (H_2O_2):

$$2\ H_2O_2(aq) \xrightarrow{\text{Catalase}} 2\ H_2O(l) + O_2(g)$$

You will be assigned a particular material—an apple, a potato, or liver—to test for the presence of catalase. You will test a fresh piece of material and one that has been boiled to investigate whether either material catalyzes the decomposition of hydrogen peroxide.

Read the procedure. Prepare a data table with appropriately labeled columns for your data.

Procedure

1. Obtain two pieces of your assigned food sample: one fresh and one boiled.

2. Label two 16 × 125-mm test tubes: one "fresh," the other "boiled."

3. Add 5 mL 3% hydrogen peroxide (H_2O_2) solution to each test tube. Observe whether any bubbles form (which means a gas is produced). Why does gas formation indicate H_2O_2 decomposition?

4. Add a portion of the fresh material to the appropriate test tube. Insert a stopper containing a segment of glass tubing into the test-tube mouth and arrange tubing as shown in Figure 7.43. Be sure the end of the glass tubing is submerged in a beaker of water.

Figure 7.43 *Setup for enzyme catalysis investigation.*

Advance Preparation

Cut pieces of fresh samples of potato, apple, liver, and yeast. Each piece must fit inside a 16 × 125 mm test tube. Boil a potato, an apple, and a piece of liver. Cool and cut into pieces.

Pre-Lab Discussion

Ask students why H_2O_2 solutions sold in drug stores are in brown bottles. As indicated by the bottle label, H_2O_2 decomposes with age and exposure to light, heat, and dust. Check student data tables before starting.

5. Record the estimated number of bubbles formed per minute in the test tube for a total of 2 min.

6. Repeat Steps 4 and 5 with a portion of boiled material and the second test tube of hydrogen peroxide solution.

7. Discard and dispose of all materials and solutions as directed by your teacher.

8. Wash your hands thoroughly before you leave the laboratory.

Questions

1. What can you conclude about the enzyme's activity when comparing observations of the test with fresh material and boiled material? Cite evidence to support your conclusion.

2. Compare your experimental data with those of other class members who used

   a. the same material.   b. a different material.

3. Why do commercial hydrogen peroxide solutions contain preservatives?

4. Someone tells you that when hydrogen peroxide solution is put on a skin cut, the observed foaming shows that the cut is infected. Explain the actual chemical reason for this observed foaming.

If the same amount of original hydrogen peroxide solution were left undisturbed without adding any catalase-containing material, it would take days for the same extent of hydrogen peroxide decomposition to occur. How do enzymes work so well at catalyzing reactions? Read on.

C.6 HOW ENZYMES WORK

The speed of an enzyme-catalyzed reaction is hard to comprehend. In a single second, one molecule of the enzyme amylase helps to release 18 000 energy-rich glucose molecules from starch:

$$\underset{\text{(portion of a starch molecule)}}{\text{-glucose-glucose-glucose-}} + H_2O \xrightarrow{\text{Amylase}} \underset{\substack{\text{(remaining portion} \\ \text{of a starch molecule)}}}{\text{-glucose-glucose-}} + \text{glucose}$$

How do enzymes (or catalysts in general) work? According to the *collision theory* of reaction rates, chemical reactions can occur only when two reactant atoms or molecules collide with proper energy and orientation. When reactant molecules are large, the appropriate groups on the molecules that react must come together in the correct orientation. If molecules collide randomly, this is not likely to happen; thus the reaction rate will be very slow.

> The names of most enzymes end with -ase. As with any catalyst, the enzyme name is included above the arrow in the equation representing the reaction. This shows that although the enzyme is involved in the reaction, it is not consumed by it.

3. If it did not, it would decompose before it could be transported and sold.

4. Enzymes in the blood catalyze H_2O_2 decomposition. The foaming is O_2 produced during this decomposition.

Post-Lab Discussion

Students may be familiar with H_2O_2 as a topical antiseptic. Some hold a misconception that "bubbling" observed in a wound soaked with H_2O_2 signifies bacterial infection. Bubbling of H_2O_2 simply indicates that it is interacting with blood.

H_2O_2, a strong oxidizing agent, kills cells. *Catalase,* an enzyme, decomposes H_2O_2 before it can do damage. Bacteria and other simple single-celled organisms lack this enzyme. That is why H_2O_2 is a good infection treatment. It kills "bad" cells; "good" cells contain catalase and are unharmed. Some white blood cells can produce H_2O_2 to kill bacteria.

Students should note that boiled food samples did not significantly catalyze H_2O_2 decomposition. Although high temperatures tend to increase the rate of uncatalyzed reactions, enzyme-catalyzed reactions typically occur over a fairly narrow temperature range. High temperatures cause enzymes to denature; they lose biologically active shapes and thus their activity. Some bacteria and algae *(hyperthermophiles)* can survive at high temperatures—to almost 100 °C. Scientists study their enzymes to identify amino-acid sequences in protein structures that function at higher temperatures before they become denatured.

Lab Tip

Provide containers for disposal of raw and cooked samples.

Answers

1. The boiled materials contain denatured enzymes. With fresh materials, the reaction proceeds much more quickly, indicating the presence of a catalyst. (Students should refer to the total gas bubbles (O_2) per minute for raw *vs.* boiled material to offer better supporting evidence for answers.)

2. a. Answers should be the same. Better answers refer to specific data—bubbles per minute.

   b. All tested materials catalyze H_2O_2 decomposition. Generally, liver should be most effective, while apple and potato have closer activities.

C.6 How Enzymes Work

Students explore interactions of an enzyme and its substrate. This material explains how enzymes are *selective*, catalyzing only certain reactions. Enzymes are typically classified according to the type of reaction in which they are involved. Examples include *hydrolases* that catalyze hydrolysis reactions important in digestive processes, *ligases* that catalyze condensation reactions, and *isomerases* that catalyze isomerization processes.

Enzymes properly orient reactant molecules at the active site. This provides an alternative pathway that has lower activation energy, making the enzyme-catalyzed process more efficient and faster than the uncatalyzed reaction. The text describes the *lock and key model* of enzyme activity, but X-ray diffraction evidence suggests that there is some flexibility at active sites. Consequently, the *induced-fit model*, patterned after the lock and key model, describes the active site as less rigid and able to mold itself, to a limited extent, around the substrate.

When the substrate has entered the enzyme's active site, the enzyme weakens substrate bonds, which leads to formation of the *transition state*. The transition state is highly unstable and changes to attain a state of greater stability—the product. The product does not fit into the active site very well and is subsequently released. The enzyme can now accept another substrate molecule.

The rate of enzyme-catalyzed reactions is determined by how fast the enzyme converts the reactant to product and by the relative availability of the enzyme. Temperature

The discussion of automobile catalytic converters on pages 394–395 described how catalysts function; the reaction is speeded up because the catalyst lowers the activation-energy barrier.

Catalysts cause reactions to occur more quickly by properly orienting reactant molecules. Reactions in living cells often involve very large molecules reacting at only one site, so catalysts are essential. Without enzymes or catalysts, many reactions would not occur at all (or at least not at reasonable rates at normal temperatures). Living systems manufacture a large variety of enzymes, each tailored to assist a particular cellular reaction (Figure 7.44).

In general, enzymes function as follows:

▶ A reactant molecule—known as the **substrate**—and the enzyme come together. The substrate molecule fits into the enzyme at an **active site**, where the substrate molecule's key functional groups are properly positioned (Figure 7.45).

▶ The active site of an enzyme determines what kind of reaction the enzyme is able to catalyze. The three-dimensional structure of the enzyme—how the amino acids in the protein polymer arrange themselves and interact—forms a "lock" into which only certain "keys" can fit. In other words, only substrates with the right shape will fit the active site of a particular enzyme.

▶ The enzyme interacts with the substrate, weakening critical bonds and making the reaction more energetically favorable.

▶ The substrate is changed into product(s) as weakened bonds break and stronger ones form. One or more products then depart from the enzyme surface, freeing the enzyme to interact with other substrate molecules. Each enzyme molecule can participate in numerous reactions without any permanent change to its structure. Because of this regenerating (recycling), enzymes are needed in much smaller amounts than are reactants.

Each enzyme is selective. It catalyzes only certain reactions, even though substrates for many other reactions are also available. How does an enzyme "know" what to do? For example, why does amylase help to break starch molecules into thousands of glucose molecules instead of decomposing hydrogen peroxide molecules into water and oxygen gas?

Figure 7.44 *Without enzymes, this germinating avocado seed would be unable to develop into a mature plant. As the plant grows, it secretes enzymes that catalyze digestion of nutrients stored in the seed. The resulting smaller nutrient molecules are absorbed, thus promoting plant growth.*

and pH can affect enzyme activity. Substances called *inhibitors* interfere with the activity of enzymes by occupying the enzyme's active site, thus blocking substrate access. For example, ACE inhibitors are medicines that slow (inhibit) the activity of the enzyme responsible for initiating blood-

vessel contraction. Individuals with high blood pressure may have ACE inhibitors prescribed; this medication causes blood vessels to enlarge, making it is easier for the heart to pump blood through the body and reducing blood pressure.

The answers to these questions are the same: The active site of a given enzyme has a three-dimensional shape that allows only certain properly shaped molecules or functional groups to occupy it. Some enzymes are much more selective than others. Each enzyme catalyzes only one particular class or type of reaction. Because of the lock-and-key interaction of an enzyme with its substrate or substrates, cells can precisely control which reactions take place.

Scientific American Conceptual Illustration

Figure 7.45 Enzyme Action *An enzyme is a molecule produced by a living organism that catalyzes a specific chemical reaction. An active site within each enzyme accommodates (fits) only certain molecules, called substrates, depicted here in green. As the substrate binds to the enzyme's active site (upper left), the enzyme lowers the energy needed to break chemical bonds in the substrate and facilitates new bond formation. After a substrate is chemically altered, it detaches from the enzyme (lower right) and the enzyme is available to catalyze the transformation of more substrate molecules. Some enzymes can transform over 100 thousand substrate molecules per second. The enzyme's entire three-dimensional structure maintains the shape and specificity of its active site. Thus, an enzyme's effectiveness depends upon careful control of surrounding factors that can alter its shape, such as pH and temperature. The shapes of most enzymes are significantly altered (denatured) under extreme conditions. In some cases, the enzyme becomes permanently denatured and is consequently unable to catalyze its specific reaction even if surrounding conditions later return to normal. While enzymes are not altered as they catalyze reactions, they are subject to degradation by certain reactions. Thus, they must be continually synthesized by cells that depend on their role as biochemical catalysts.*

Scientific American **Conceptual Illustration**

Remind students that proteins are polymers of amino acids. To review the levels of structure (primary, secondary, tertiary) responsible for protein shapes, ask students to consider how the protein depicted is able to maintain its shape. The schematic representation here does not provide detail necessary to visualize the levels of structure; its purpose is to highlight the active site. Review the general steps of the catalytic cycle— (a) the substrate binds to the active site; (b) the enzyme facilitates breaking old bonds and forming new bonds; (c) the products move from the active site. Also note that enzymes are remarkably sensitive to the stereochemistry of substrates on which they act. Like a hand fitting a glove, only the proper positioning of atoms in a substrate molecule will be "recognized" by a particular enzyme.

ChemQuandary 3

A Problem to Chew On

The cracker tastes sweeter after extended chewing. Amylase, an enzyme in saliva, decomposes starch to glucose, which is sweeter than starch.

Investigating Matter

C.7 Amylase Tests

 C.7 Amylase Tests Student Worksheet and Data Table

Students evaluate how temperature and pH affect amylase activity via the reaction of released glucose and Benedict's reagent.

Time

Day 1: 30 min; Day 2: 45 min

Materials

(For 12 student pairs)

60 test tubes (16 × 125 mm)
60 stoppers for test tubes
12 10-mL graduated cylinders
12 hot plates
12 250-mL beakers
Boiling chips
12 test tube holders
150 mL 0.1% starch suspension
 (see below; refrigerate)
300 mL Benedict's reagent (see below)
150 mL 0.5% amylase solution
 (2.3 g amylase in 150 mL sol'n)
Buffer solutions, 60 mL each,
 pH 2, 4, 7, 8, 10 (see below)

Safety

Students should wear protective goggles and aprons. They should respect buffers—they are acidic and alkaline. Tell students *never* to add boiling chips to boiling or very hot water—the solution may "bump" as a burst of hot vapor, carrying scalding water with it.

614

ChemQuandary 3

A PROBLEM TO CHEW ON

Chew an *unsalted* cracker for a minute or two before swallowing. How would you describe the taste when you first begin to chew? How would you describe the taste a minute or two later? If you noted a change, what causes the cracker flavor to change over time? What's happening at the particulate level?

Your body's enzymes help convert large molecules into many smaller molecules, releasing energy in the process. Each smaller molecule stores chemical energy that is released by your cells through other enzyme-catalyzed reactions. In the next investigation, you will explore the performance of an enzyme involved in this process.

Investigating Matter

Lab Video:
Amylase Tests

Amylase: A Biological
Protein Catalyst

C.7 AMYLASE TESTS

Introduction

In this investigation, you will explore how temperature and pH affect the performance of the enzyme amylase. Amylase contained in saliva helps to break down starch molecules into individual glucose molecules.

Glucose reacts with Benedict's reagent to produce a yellow-to-orange precipitate. The color and amount of precipitate formed is a direct indication of the glucose concentration generated by the enzyme-catalyzed reaction.

Your laboratory team will investigate the performance of amylase either at room temperature or at a lower temperature. Read the following procedure. Prepare a data table with appropriately labeled columns specifying data to be collected by each group member.

Procedure

Day 1: Preparing the Samples

1. Label five test tubes near the top with the temperature your group is assigned to investigate and with pH values of 2, 4, 7, 8, and 10. Also mark each label so that your test tubes can be distinguished from those of other groups (see Figure 7.46).
2. Using the pH solutions provided by your teacher, add 5 mL of pH 2, 4, 7, 8, and 10 solution to the appropriate test tubes.

Advance Preparation

Buffer solutions:

You can buy pre-measured powder for buffer solutions. Otherwise, use these reagents:

Sol'n A: Dissolve 12.4 g anhydrous boric acid (H_3BO_3) and 10.5 g citric acid hydrate ($C_6H_8O_7\cdot H_2O$) in water to make 1.00 L sol'n.

Sol'n B: Dissolve 38.0 g trisodium phosphate dodecahydrate ($Na_3PO_4\cdot 12\ H_2O$) in water to make 1.00 L sol'n.

To prepare 200 mL of each buffer, mix solutions as shown below.

BUFFER SOLUTIONS		
pH	mL SOL'N A	mL SOL'N B
2.0	195	5
4.0	155	45
7.0	99	101
8.0	85	115
10.0	54	146

3. Add 2.5 mL of starch suspension to each tube.

4. Add 2.5 mL of 0.5% amylase solution to each tube.

5. Insert a stopper into each tube. Hold the stopper in place with your thumb or finger and shake each tube well for several seconds.

6. Leave the room-temperature test tubes in the laboratory overnight as directed by your teacher.

7. Give your teacher the test tubes that are to be refrigerated.

8. Wash your hands thoroughly before leaving the laboratory.

Day 2: Evaluating the Results

9. Prepare a hot-water bath by adding about 100 mL of tap water to a 250-mL beaker. Add a boiling chip. Warm the beaker on a hot plate. (Heat to just below boiling—hot, but not boiling.)

10. Add 5 mL of Benedict's reagent to each tube. Replace each stopper, being careful not to mix the stoppers. Hold the stopper in place with a thumb or finger and shake each tube well for several seconds.

11. Ensure that all tubes are still clearly labeled. Remove the stoppers and place the test tubes into the hot-water bath.

12. Heat the test tubes in the hot-water bath until the solution in at least one tube has turned yellow or orange. Then continue heating for two to three more minutes.

13. Use tongs to remove the test tubes from the hot-water bath. Arrange them in a test-tube rack in order of increasing pH.

14. Observe and record the color of the contents of each tube.

15. Share your data with your classmates, as directed by your teacher.

16. Wash your hands thoroughly before leaving the laboratory.

Questions

1. a. At which general temperature range (cooled, room temperature, or heated) did the enzyme perform most effectively?

   b. At which pH value did the enzyme perform most effectively?

2. Write a summary statement about the effects of temperature and pH on this enzyme-catalyzed reaction.

Your cells synthesize many enzymes and other kinds of proteins to keep you alive. The amino acids used to synthesize these proteins are best obtained through a diet that provides appropriate amounts of protein. You will now decide whether a particular diet meets those protein needs.

Figure 7.46 *Remember to label all test tubes, so that you can identify them later in the investigation.*

Benedict's reagent also provides a test for the presence of glucose in urine, a symptom of diabetes.

Section C   Proteins, Enzymes, and Chemistry   **615**

that room temperature and neutral pH are most effective for catalysis.

Approve students' labeled data tables before starting.

Amylase breaks glucose linkages within starch, yielding glucose molecules:

$$starch \xrightarrow{amylase} glucose\ (C_6H_{12}O_6)$$

The aldehyde group within glucose is oxidized; Cu^{2+} is reduced. This creates Cu_2O, an orange precipitate.

$$C_6H_{12}O_6 + 2\ Cu^{2+}(blue) + 2\ OH^- \longrightarrow C_6H_{12}O_7 + Cu_2O(orange)$$

Lab Tips

If storing test tubes is a problem, have students work in groups of four. Remind them to label test tubes clearly on Day 1. Refrigerate freshly prepare starch suspension.

Expected Results

In the presence of simple sugars, Benedict's reagent forms a yellow, orange, or reddish Cu_2O precipitate when heated. The color intensity is related to the amount of sugar present. When Benedict's reagent is added and heated, room-temperature samples of pH 2, 4, and 10 usually form blue solutions, while pH 7 and 8 samples form orange solutions.

Answers

1. a. Room temperature, b. pH 7
2. Enzymes work best at body temperature. If temperatures are too low, little happens; if too high, enzymes are denatured. Enzymes work best at a pH similar to that of body tissues.

Post-Lab Discussion

Amylase in saliva is at relatively neutral pH. Chewing one's food thoroughly helps mix amylase with starch, starting digestion. Some enzymes work optimally at non-neutral pHs. *Pepsin*, for protein digestion in the stomach, works best at pH 2.

Benedict's reagent:

Buy prepared Benedict's reagent or:

• Dissolve 100 g sodium carbonate monohydrate ($Na_2CO_3 \cdot H_2O$) and 173 g sodium citrate dihydrate ($Na_3C_6H_5O_7 \cdot 2H_2O$) in 800 mL water. Warm slightly to hasten dissolving.

• Dissolve 17.3 g copper(II) sulfate pentahydrate ($CuSO_4 \cdot 5H_2O$) in 100 mL water. Slowly add to the first solution; stir constantly. Cool; add water to make 1.00 L sol'n.

To prepare 0.1% starch suspension, mix 0.15 g powdered starch in a small volume of cold water, producing a slurry. Slowly add this to the rest of 150 mL water, heated to near boiling. Remove from heat before adding slurry. Cool before use.

Pre-Lab Discussion

Ask students to predict ideal conditions for optimal enzyme activity. Some may guess

C.8 Protein Content

Students will analyze their three-day inventories for proteins. Give students reference materials listed for Making Decisions A.9, page 580.

SECTION C SUMMARY

 Section C Supplement

Reviewing the Concepts

1. Skin, hair, nails, muscles
2. Proteins build the body and regulate and facilitate chemical reactions.
3. Transport, muscle contraction, support, catalysis, and control of metabolism
4. Meats, fish, beans, nuts, egg white, gelatin
5. They are large molecules made of repeating units of amino acids.
6. C, O, N, and H; some proteins may have small amounts of S.
7. 3.6 g protein $\times$ 4 Cal/g = 14.4 Cal $\approx$ 14 Cal
8. Enzymes are proteins. They have C, O, N, and H and may contain small amounts of S.
9. Proteins may have different numbers of amino-acid monomers and can differ from each other in the type and sequencing of specific amino acids.
10. A peptide bond, between a carboxyl group and an amino group, links amino acids together.

$$-\underset{\underset{O}{\|}}{C}-\underset{\underset{H}{|}}{N}-$$

11. The number ranges from about 50 to more than 10 000 units.
12. a. 9.1 g/day
    b. 56 g/day

C.8 PROTEIN CONTENT

You have analyzed the three-day food inventory in terms of energy that the diet provides and fat and carbohydrate molecules that it delivers. Now consider whether the food provided supplies the recommended amounts of a key building block of living material—protein.

Use the food inventory to answer the following questions. Refer to Table 7.4 (page 609), if necessary.

1. What is the average total mass of protein (in grams) consumed daily?
2. What other information would you need to know regarding the person who follows this food-intake pattern to evaluate the appropriateness of the protein supplied by these foods?
3. a. Does the person consume a good balance of essential amino acids? Explain your answer.
   b. What types of snack foods are high in protein (especially types that might be included in the vending machines at Riverwood High School)?

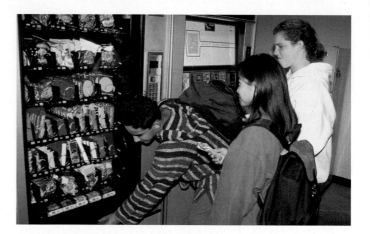

---

13. a. Either of these structures is possible (Gly-Cys or Cys-Gly):

$$H-\underset{}{N}-\underset{\underset{CH_2}{|}}{\underset{|}{C}}-\underset{\underset{O}{\|}}{C}-\underset{}{N}-\underset{\underset{H}{|}}{C}-\underset{\underset{O}{\|}}{C}-O-H$$

$$|$$
$$SH$$

SECTION C SUMMARY
Reviewing the Concepts

Proteins, major structural components of living creatures, fulfill many cellular roles.

1. Name three types of tissue in your body for which protein is the main structural component.

2. The name *protein* comes from a Greek word that means "of prime importance." Why is this name appropriate?

3. List five cellular functions in which proteins are particularly important.

4. Name three food items composed primarily of protein.

5. Why are proteins considered polymers?

6. What chemical elements do proteins contain?

7. How many Calories would be provided by the metabolism of 3.6 g protein? (Recall that 1 g protein = 4 Cal.)

8. What is the chemical composition of an enzyme?

Amino acids are the chemical subunits that make up proteins.

9. How does the relatively small number of different amino acids account for the vast variety of proteins found in nature?

10. What is a *peptide bond*? Use structural formulas to illustrate your answer.

11. How does the total number of amino acids vary within protein molecules?

12. What is the protein DRI value for
    a. a 4-month-old infant?
    b. a 36-year-old male?

13. Write structural formulas for the following molecules:
    a. a dipeptide of glycine and cysteine
    b. a tripeptide abbreviated Asp–Ala–Cys

14. Explain the meaning of the following terms:
    a. complete protein
    b. essential amino acid
    c. complementary proteins

15. On which two functional groups is the name "amino acid" based?

Some protein molecules function as enzymes, that is, biological catalysts that speed up cellular reactions.

16. a. How are enzymes similar to other catalysts?
    b. How are enzymes different from other catalysts?

17. What would be the effect if all enzyme activity in the human body suddenly stopped? Explain.

18. Describe how high temperatures affect the ability of most enzymes to function.

19. Explain why enzymes can speed up only certain chemical reactions.

20. a. Explain the interaction of an active site and a substrate in terms of a lock-and-key analogy.
    b. Describe at least one limitation to the lock-and-key analogy for enzyme activity.

Section Summary 617

14. a. Contains adequate amounts of all essential amino acids
    b. Cannot be synthesized by the body but must be obtained from proteins in the diet
    c. A combination of foods that provides all essential amino acids

15. A carboxylic acid (carboxyl group) at one end of the molecule and an amino (NH_2) group at the other

16. a. They speed up a chemical reaction without being consumed in the reaction.
    b. A specific enzyme can catalyze only one type or class of reaction. Its function depends on temperature and pH.

17. The rates of all enzyme-catalyzed reactions would slow to the point that life would not be possible.

18. Excessively high temperatures can denature enzymes, rendering them inactive.

19. The three-dimensional shape of enzymes determines their function. Only certain substrate molecules fit into the binding site of a particular enzyme.

20. a. Only the correct substrate can fit into the active site, just as only one key can open a lock.
    b. The substrate changes from start to finish, but in the analogy the key doesn't change.

Connecting the Concepts

21. a. All contain C, H, and O.
b. Protein's properties and functions are different, and they contain N and sometimes S.

22. It contains C.

23. a. They consume foods that "complement" each other's amino acid deficiencies.
b. Of the 20 amino acids needed by the human body, 9 must come from the diet. Most animal sources of protein contain all 9; they are *complete*. Plant protein sources are *incomplete*, so a variety must to be consumed to ensure that all 9 essential amino acids are available for protein synthesis.

24.

a

b

c

25. 55 g fat × 9 Cal/g = 495 Cal
75 g protein × 4 Cal/g = 300 Cal
85 g carbohydrate × 4 Cal/g = 340 Cal

Connecting the Concepts

21. a. In what ways are proteins similar to carbohydrates and fats?
b. In what ways are proteins different?

22. If a steak is left on a barbecue grill too long, it turns black. What does that observation suggest about the chemical composition of protein in the meat?

23. Although many plants contain high levels of protein, vegetarians must be more concerned than nonvegetarians about including adequate protein in their diets.
a. How can vegetarians ensure that they obtain all the chemical building blocks needed to build required proteins?
b. Explain your answer.

Extending the Concepts

28. The genetic code in DNA carries blueprints for making proteins in the human body. Explain how DNA helps determine the body's physical development and functioning.

29. The phrase "form follows function" is particularly applicable to enzymes. Explain how form and function are closely related for enzyme molecules.

30. Obtain information on the condition known as *ketosis.* What are its causes and effects? How can a high-protein diet lead to ketosis?

24. Using simple diagrams, including structural formulas, sketch how an enzyme might help form a peptide bond between two amino acids.

25. If a person followed a daily diet of 55 g fat, 75 g protein, and 85 g carbohydrate, how much energy would be provided through the metabolism of each? Show your calculations.

26. In Unit 1, you learned that fish species need a water pH range within which they can live. Given what you know about enzymes from the amylase tests in this section, explain why this is so.

27. Explain how the protein that you eat—whether from beef, turkey, beans, nuts, or tofu—is transformed into human-body proteins.

31. Explain why hydrogen peroxide is an effective antiseptic. How does your answer relate to enzyme action?

32. Research and report on chemical and physical properties of one or more amino acids used by the human body in building protein molecules.

33. What is a *zwitterion?* Under what conditions do amino acids become zwitterions?

26. Enzymes in the fish optimally function within a narrow range of pH.

27. It is broken into its constituent amino acids by enzymes in the stomach and small intestine. The amino acids are absorbed through the wall of the intestines and move through the body. Cells use the amino acids as building blocks for protein syntheses.

Extending the Concepts

28. By coding for structural proteins it determines the body's physical appearance and properties. By specifying enzymes it controls which chemical reactions occur.

29. As the lock-and-key analogy illustrates, an enzyme's shape controls how it interacts with particular substrate molecules.

Other Substances in Foods

The focus of this unit thus far has been on macronutrients in foods: proteins, carbohydrates, and fats. However, there are other substances in food, often in trace amounts: *vitamins, minerals,* and sometimes *additives*. Dietary guidelines imply that vitamins and minerals play vital roles within your body. These micronutrients occur naturally in many foods and may also be added to foods, such as cereal or bread, to improve their quality as sources of various micronutrients. Food manufacturers use food additives for different reasons, as you will soon learn. What do vitamins and minerals do in your body? What purposes do food additives serve?

D.1 VITAMINS

Vitamins are biomolecules necessary for growth, reproduction, health, and life. Each vitamin is required in only a tiny amount. The total quantity of *all* vitamins required daily by an adult is only about 0.2 g; "a little goes a long way" with vitamins (see Figures 7.47 and 7.48). How much is "enough"? The actual quantity depends on age and gender, as is suggested by Table 7.5 (page 620).

Vitamins perform very specialized tasks. Vitamin D, for example, helps move calcium ions from your intestines into the bloodstream. Without vitamin D, your body would not use much of the calcium you ingest. Some vitamins function as **coenzymes,** which are organic molecules that interact with enzymes and enhance their activity. For example, the B-vitamins act as coenzymes in releasing energy from food molecules. Figure 7.49 illustrates how a coenzyme functions.

Figure 7.47 *Vitamin supplements are useful whenever sufficient vitamins are not provided in one's diet.*

Figure 7.48 *Many foods such as leafy greens, liver, milk, eggs, and whole grains are rich in vitamins.*

Coenzyme in place

A

B

Enzyme

Enzyme

Figure 7.49 *A vitamin serving as a coenzyme.*

---

nated ($-NH_3^+$), and the carboxyl group is not protonated ($-COO^-$). Amino acids typically become zwitterions at neutral pH.

Other Substances in Foods

Students explore chemical composition, properties, and functions of vitamins, minerals, and food additives. They investigate the classification of vitamins as water-soluble or fat-soluble and consider the implications of this property difference. Students compare the amounts of vitamin C in beverages through titration. Minerals are discussed briefly in terms of their roles in the body. Additives in processed foods are examined and their benefits and risks considered. Finally, sudents analyze the vitamin and mineral content of their three-day food inventories.

At the close of the unit, students write their report for the Riverwood PTSA. Encourage students to begin thinking about recommendations for the Vending Machine Policy Planning Committee.

D.1 Vitamins

 D.1 and D.4 Content Reading Guide

Vitamins are required in much smaller quantities than fats, carbohydrates, and protein. Some vitamins are produced in our bodies, such as vitamin K, which comes from bacteria within our intestines, and vitamin D, which is produced in skin with help from ultraviolet radiation.

Using the Figures

Figure 7.49: Ask students to distinguish *enzymes* from *coenzymes*. As part of this exercise, suggest that they compare **Figure 7.45** (page 613) with 7.49.

---

30. Ketosis is a metabolic state in which the liver has been depleted of its glycogen stores, so the body uses fat stores as fuel. Fatty acids are converted to glucose to provide energy for the brain. Ketones are also produced and burned. During ketosis, individuals may lose weight, since fat stores are being depleted. A high-protein (and low-carbohydrate) diet can lead to ketosis as blood glucose is used first, then glycogen stores are depleted, and the body is forced to use its fat stores for energy.

31. Hydrogen peroxide kills cells through oxidation. The human body has the enzyme catalase, which decomposes hydrogen peroxide.

32. Answers will vary.

33. Zwitterions are dipolar ions. In the case of amino acids, the amino group is proto-

Most animals produce their own vitamin C, but humans, primates, and guinea pigs cannot. The text examines daily recommended intakes for selected vitamins and health effects of consuming too much or too little.

One health effect of vitamin deficiency is scurvy, a condition once common among sailors due to lack of vitamin C. Although they were unaware of its underlying cause, sailors learned to prevent scurvy by eating citrus fruit on long voyages. Another important food for seafarers was sauerkraut. It is high in vitamin C, and, because it is fermented, it can be stored for a long time. This presented a distinct advantage over citrus fruits.

DIETARY REFERENCE INTAKES (DRIs) FOR SELECTED VITAMINS

Age or Condition	Vit A (μg/d)	Vit D (μg/d)	Vit E (mg/d)	Vit K (μg/d)	Vit C (mg/d)	Thiamin (B₁) (mg/d)	Riboflavin (B₂) (mg/d)	Niacin (mg/d)	Vit B₆ (mg/d)	Vit B₁₂ (μg/d)	Folate (μg/d)
Males											
9–13 yrs	**600**	5*	**11**	60*	**45**	**0.9**	**0.9**	**12**	**1.0**	**1.8**	**300**
14–18 yrs	**900**	5*	**15**	75*	**75**	**1.2**	**1.3**	**16**	**1.3**	**2.4**	**400**
19–30 yrs	**900**	5*	**15**	120*	**90**	**1.2**	**1.3**	**16**	**1.3**	**2.4**	**400**
31–50 yrs	**900**	5*	**15**	120*	**90**	**1.2**	**1.3**	**16**	**1.3**	**2.4**	**400**
50–70 yrs	**900**	10*	**15**	120*	**90**	**1.2**	**1.3**	**16**	**1.7**	**2.4**	**400**
>70 yrs	**900**	15*	**15**	120*	**90**	**1.2**	**1.3**	**16**	**1.7**	**2.4**	**400**
Females											
9–13 yrs	**600**	5*	**11**	60*	**45**	**0.9**	**0.9**	**12**	**1.0**	**1.8**	**300**
14–18 yrs	**700**	5*	**15**	75*	**65**	**1.0**	**1.0**	**14**	**1.2**	**2.4**	**400**
19–30 yrs	**700**	5*	**15**	90*	**75**	**1.1**	**1.1**	**14**	**1.3**	**2.4**	**400**
31–50 yrs	**700**	5*	**15**	90*	**75**	**1.1**	**1.1**	**14**	**1.3**	**2.4**	**400**
50–70 yrs	**700**	10*	**15**	90*	**75**	**1.1**	**1.1**	**14**	**1.5**	**2.4**	**400**
>70 yrs	**700**	15*	**15**	90*	**75**	**1.1**	**1.1**	**14**	**1.5**	**2.4**	**400**
Pregnant	**770**	5*	**15**	90*	**85**	**1.4**	**1.4**	**18**	**1.9**	**2.6**	**600**
Nursing	**1300**	5*	**19**	90*	**120**	**1.6**	**1.6**	**17**	**2.0**	**2.8**	**500**

Note: Recommended Dietary Allowances (RDAs) are in **bold type**. RDAs are established to meet the needs of almost all (97 to 98%) individuals in a group. Adequate Intakes (AIs) are followed by an asterisk (*). AIs are believed to cover the needs of all individuals in the group, but a lack of data prevent being able to specify with confidence the percent of individuals covered by this intake.

Source: Food and Nutrition Board, National Academy of Sciences: National Research Council, *Dietary Reference Intakes 2004.*

| **Table 7.5**

Vitamins and Solubility

Recall that "like dissolves like." See page 72.

Long before the term *vitamin* was introduced early in the last century, people discovered that small quantities of certain substances were necessary to maintain health. One example of vitamin deficiency is *scurvy*, which once was common among sailors; this condition is characterized by swollen joints, bleeding gums, and tender skin. Although early seafarers (in the 1700s and 1800s) did not know what caused scurvy, they commonly loaded citrus fruit onboard, which they ate during long voyages to prevent scurvy. Scurvy is now known to be caused by vitamin C deficiency, a vitamin supplied by citrus fruit. In addition to vitamin C, about a dozen different vitamins have been identified over the past century, each critical to reactions occurring within the human body. Table 7.6 documents how some of those vitamins support human life.

Vitamins are classified as either *fat-soluble* or *water-soluble* (see Table 7.6). Water-soluble vitamins with polar functional groups pass directly into the bloodstream. They are not stored in the body; they must be ingested daily. Some water-soluble vitamins, including the B vitamins and vitamin C, are also destroyed by heat in cooking.

VITAMINS BY CATEGORY, SHOWING SOURCES AND DEFICIENCY CONDITIONS

Vitamin	Main Sources	Deficiency Condition
Water-soluble		
B_1 (thiamin)	Liver, milk, pasta, bread, wheat germ, lima beans, nuts	Beriberi: nausea, severe exhaustion, paralysis
B_2 (riboflavin)	Red meat, milk, eggs, pasta, bread, beans, dark green vegetables, peas, mushrooms	Severe skin problems
Niacin	Red meat, poultry, enriched or whole grains, beans, peas	Pellagra: weak muscles, loss of appetite, diarrhea, skin blotches
B_6 (pyridoxine)	Muscle meats, liver, poultry, fish, whole grains	Depression, nausea, vomiting
B_{12} (cobalamin)	Red meat, liver, kidneys, fish, eggs, milk	Pernicious anemia, exhaustion
Folic acid	Kidneys, liver, leafy green vegetables, wheat germ, peas, beans	Anemia
Pantothenic acid	Plants, animals	Anemia
Biotin	Kidneys, liver, egg yolk, yeast, nuts	Dermatitis
C (ascorbic acid)	Citrus fruits, melon, tomatoes, green peppers, strawberries	Scurvy: tender skin; weak, bleeding gums; swollen joints
Fat-soluble		
A (retinol)	Liver, eggs, butter, cheese, dark green and deep orange vegetables	Inflamed eye membranes, night blindness, scaling of skin, faulty teeth and bones
D (calciferol)	Fish-liver oils, fortified milk	Rickets: soft bones
E (tocopherol)	Liver, wheat germ, whole-grain cereals, margarine, vegetable oil, leafy green vegetables	Breakage of red blood cells in premature infants, oxidation of membranes
K (menaquinone)	Liver, cabbage, potatoes, peas, leafy green vegetables	Hemorrhage in newborns; anemia

| Table 7.6

Your body absorbs fat-soluble vitamins into the blood from the intestine with assistance from fats in the food you eat. Because the nonpolar structures of fat-soluble vitamins allow them to be stored in body fat, it is not necessary to consume fat-soluble vitamins daily. In fact, because fat-soluble vitamins accumulate within the body, they can build up to toxic levels if ingested in excessively large quantities (megadoses).

Using the Figures

Table 7.6: Invite students to research the molecular structures of vitamins in this table (assign one water-soluble or fat-soluble vitamin to each student or group of students). Then ask students to identify common structural features they can observe in water-soluble vitamins and compare them to common structural features of fat-soluble vitamins. Water-soluble vitamins tend to have polar groups, such as —OH, that allow them to interact with and dissolve in water. (See the structure of vitamin C (ascorbic acid) in **Figure 7.52,** page 623.) Fat-soluble vitamins tend to have long carbon chains—much like fat molecules—that make them largely nonpolar.

D.2 Vitamins in the Diet

In this activity, students practice interpreting data from tables and applying it to their own situations.

Answers

1. a. B$_{12}$ (cobalamin) deficiency causes pernicious anemia and exhaustion; D (calciferol) deficiency results in rickets.
   b. Take a vitamin supplement.
2. See below
   a. Vitamin B$_1$ entries
   b. No single food contains adequate quantities of all vitamins. Dietary variety ensures consumption of proper kinds and quantities of vitamins.
   c. Vitamin deficiencies come from lack of food variety.
3. a. Vitamins can decompose as food ages (due to oxidation) or as food is processed.
   b. Water-soluble vitamins, which are more readily removed in canning and boiling processes
   c. Yes. Fresh fruits and raw or lightly steamed vegetables retain maximum vitamin concentrations.

Developing Skills

D.2 VITAMINS IN THE DIET

1. Carefully planned vegetarian diets are nutritionally balanced. Individuals who follow a *vegan* diet do not consume any animal products, including eggs and milk. Because of their dietary limitations, vegans must ensure that they obtain the recommended daily allowances of two particular vitamins.

   a. Use Table 7.6 (page 621) to identify these two vitamins and briefly describe the effect of their absence in the diet.
   b. How might individuals following a vegan diet avoid this problem?

2. Complete the following table about yourself, using data from Tables 7.5 (page 620) and 7.7.

Figure 7.50 *How does the vitamin content of raw and steamed broccoli compare?*

Vegetable (one-cup serving)	Your RDA		Total Servings to Supply Your RDA	
	B$_1$	C	B$_1$	C
Green peas				
Broccoli				

SAMPLE FOR REFERENCE ONLY

   a. Would any of your entries change if you were of the opposite gender? If so, which entry or entries?
   b. Based on your completed table, why do you think variety is essential in a person's diet?
   c. Why might vitamin deficiencies pose problems even if people received adequate supplies of food Calories?

3. Nutritionists recommend eating fresh fruit rather than canned fruit and raw or steamed vegetables instead of canned or boiled vegetables (see Figures 7.50 and 7.51).

   a. What does food freshness have to do with vitamins?
   b. To what type of vitamins might nutritionists be referring?
   c. Is such advice sound? Explain.

Figure 7.51 *Why do dietary guidelines usually favor raw fruit over canned fruit?*

VITAMIN B$_1$ AND C CONTENT OF SOME VEGETABLES		
	Vitamin (in mg)	
Vegetable (1-cup serving)	B$_1$ (thiamin)	C (ascorbic acid)
Green peas	0.387	58.4
Lima beans	0.238	17
Broccoli	0.058	82
Potatoes	0.15	30

| Table 7.7

VEGETABLE	YOUR RDA		TOTAL SERVINGS	
	B$_1$	C	B$_1$	C
Green peas				
Male 14–18	1.2	75	3.1	1.3
Female 14–18	1.0	65	2.6	1.1
Broccoli				
Male 14–18	1.2	75	21	0.91
Female 14–18	1.0	65	17	0.79

D.3 VITAMIN C

Lab Video: Vitamin C

Introduction

Vitamin C, also called *ascorbic acid,* is a water-soluble vitamin. It is among the least stable vitamins because it reacts readily with oxygen gas, and exposure to light or heat can decompose it. In this investigation, you will find out how much vitamin C is contained in some popular beverages, including fruit juices, milk, and soft drinks.

This investigation is based on a chemical reaction of ascorbic acid (vitamin C) with iodine (I_2). A colored solution of iodine oxidizes ascorbic acid, forming the colorless products dehydroascorbic acid, hydrogen ions, and iodide ions:

$$I_2 + C_6H_8O_6 \longrightarrow C_6H_6O_6 + 2\,H^+ + 2\,I^-$$

Iodine Ascorbic acid Dehydroascorbic Hydrogen Iodide
(vitamin C) acid ion ion

Figure 7.52 shows the structures of ascorbic and dehydroascorbic acid.

You will complete a **titration** (Figure 7.53), a common laboratory procedure used to determine concentrations of substances in solution. This investigation involves adding a known amount of one reactant (iodine solution) slowly from a Beral pipet to a second reactant (ascorbic acid in the beverage) in a wellplate until just enough has been added for a complete reaction. The completion of the reaction, the **endpoint,** is signaled by a color change. Knowing the chemical equation for this reaction, you can then calculate the unknown amount of the second reactant (ascorbic acid) from the measured volume and known concentration of the the iodine-solution *titrant.*

The titration endpoint in the beverage-containing well of the wellplate is the point where a dark blue–black color appears and does not disappear with additional stirring. This color is due to the reaction of excess iodine with starch. First, you add a starch suspension to the beverage sample to be tested. Next, an iodine solution of known concentration is added drop by drop from a Beral pipet.

As long as ascorbic acid is present, the added iodine is quickly converted to colorless iodide ions; you will observe no bluish black iodine-starch product. When all the available ascorbic acid has been oxidized to colorless dehydroascorbic acid, the next drop of added iodine solution reacts with the starch, producing the bluish black color that signals the endpoint.

Figure 7.53 *Material needed for fruit-juice titration.*

Ascorbic acid

Dehydroascorbic acid

Figure 7.52 *Molecular structures of ascorbic and dehydroascorbic acid.*

Investigating Matter

D.3 Vitamin C

D.3 Vitamin C Student Worksheet and Data Table

Students employ microscale laboratory techniques and subsequent calculations to determine how much vitamin C is contained in several beverage samples. Beral pipets and wellplates enable student teams to analyze several different samples in 50 min.

Time

50 min

Materials

(For 12 student pairs)

12 10-mL graduated cylinders
12 Beral pipets
12 Beral pipets containing iodine solution
12 Beral pipets containing 1% starch suspension
Vitamin C solution, 0.100 g/100 mL water
Beral pipets containing beverage samples
Toothpicks for stirring
12 24-well wellplates
1 g potassium iodate (KIO_3)
1 g potassium iodide (KI)

Safety

Students should wear protective goggles and aprons throughout the investigation.

Investigating Matter continues on page 624.

SECTION D

Advance Preparation

Iodine solution: Dissolve 1.0 g potassium iodide and 0.053 g potassium iodate in 25 mL water. Add 6 mL 3 M sulfuric acid. Then add water to make the total volume 100 mL. Fill 12 pipets shortly before class time and provide a capped bottle for refills. The iodine pipets cannot be cleaned, so use the same pipets for every class. The reaction in the iodine solution: $IO_3^- + 5 I^- + 6 H^+ \longrightarrow 3 I_2 + 3 H_2O$.

Starch suspension: Mix 1 teaspoon of liquid laundry starch in 100 mL hot (not boiling) water. Fill 12 pipets and provide a capped bottle for refills.

Vitamin C solution: Crush a 100-mg vitamin-C tablet and dissolve in water. Dilute to 100 mL. (This is much more than you need, but it is difficult to work with smaller quantities of the tablet.) The vitamin C in solution is prone to oxidation, so use it the same day you prepare it.

Beverage samples: Choose five or more beverages to test. Beverages vary considerably in vitamin C content. Use beverages that are *not* fortified with vitamin C. The color of dark juices and sodas obscures the titration endpoint, so try to avoid them. Remove any pulp from juices by filtering through cheesecloth before placing in pipets. The relative vitamin C content of some typical beverages is listed below.

> Ascorbic acid is the limiting reactant in this titration.

You will begin by completing a titration involving a solution of known vitamin C concentration. The data will allow you to find the mass of ascorbic acid that reacts with one drop of iodine solution. You can then calculate the mass (in milligrams) of vitamin C present in a 25-drop sample of each beverage. This information will allow you to rank the tested beverages in terms of the mass of vitamin C that each beverage contains.

Before starting this investigation, prepare a suitable data table. Leave room in the data table to record the total drops of vitamin C solution in 1.0 mL (Step 1) and the total drops of iodine needed to reach the endpoint (Step 5). Provide a horizontal row for each beverage that you investigate.

Procedure

Part 1: Investigating the Iodine Solution

1. Fill a Beral pipet with vitamin C solution. Then determine how many drops of vitamin C solution delivered by that pipet represent a volume of 1.0 mL.

2. Fill a second Beral pipet with iodine solution. Determine the total drops delivered by that pipet to equal 1.0 mL, just as in Step 1.

3. Add 25 drops vitamin C solution into a well of a clean 24-well wellplate. This vitamin C solution has a known concentration of 1.0 mg vitamin C per milliliter of solution.

4. Add 1 drop of starch suspension to the same well.

5. Place a sheet of white paper underneath the wellplate; it will help you detect the appearance of color. Add iodine solution one drop at a time, carefully counting drops, to the well that contains the starch and vitamin C mixture. After adding each drop of iodine solution, use a toothpick to gently stir the resulting mixture. Add and count the iodine solution drop by drop, with stirring, until the solution in the well remains bluish black for 20 s. If the color fades before 20 s have elapsed, add another drop of iodine solution. Record the total drops of iodine solution needed to reach the endpoint (the appearance of the first permanent bluish-black color).

6. The concentration of the vitamin C solution used is 1.0 mg/mL.
   a. What total volume of vitamin C solution did you test?
   b. How many milligrams of vitamin C did that volume contain?
   c. How many total drops of iodine did you use?

   Use that information to calculate how many milligrams of vitamin C react with 1 drop of iodine solution:

$$25 \text{ drops vitamin C} \times \frac{1 \text{ mL vitamin C}}{?? \text{ drops vitamin C}} \times \frac{1 \text{ mg vitamin C}}{1 \text{ mL vitamin C}} \times \frac{1}{?? \text{ drops } I_2} = \underline{\quad} \text{ mg vitamin C per drop } I_2 \text{ solution}$$

(Step 1) (Step 5)

VITAMIN C CONTENT	BEVERAGE
Very high	Pineapple juice, orange juice
High	White grape juice, grapefruit juice, Hi-C
Medium	V-8 juice
Low	Apple juice, milk, Tang
Very low or none	Gatorade, Sprite, 7-Up

Suppose there were 30 drops of vitamin C solution in 1.0 mL (Step 1) and that it took 22 drops of iodine solution to reach the endpoint (Step 5). These data lead to the result that 0.038 mg vitamin C reacts with 1 drop iodine solution. Complete calculations to confirm this result.

Part 2: Analyzing Beverages for Vitamin C

7. Using a Beral pipet, add 25 drops of the beverage to be tested to a clean well of a wellplate.

8. Add one drop of starch suspension to the same well.

9. With a Beral pipet, slowly add iodine solution one drop at a time to the well containing the beverage and starch mixture (see Figure 7.54). After each addition, stir the resulting mixture with a toothpick. Count the total drops of iodine solution that are added to reach the endpoint. (*Note:* Colored beverages may not produce a true bluish-black endpoint color. For example, red beverages may make the endpoint appear purple.)

10. Continue adding iodine solution drop by drop, with stirring, until the solution in the well remains bluish black for 20 s. If the color fades before 20 s have elapsed, add another drop of iodine solution. Record the total drops of iodine solution needed to reach the endpoint.

| **Figure 7.54** *Proper technique for a wellplate titration.*

11. Repeat Steps 7–10 for each beverage you have been assigned to investigate.

12. Use your data from Step 10 and the results from Step 6 to calculate the milligrams of vitamin C contained in 25 drops of each assigned beverage.

13. Rank the tested beverages in terms of how much vitamin C each contains, from the highest quantity to the lowest.

14. Wash your hands thoroughly with soap and water before leaving the laboratory.

Questions

1. Among the beverages tested, in your opinion, were any vitamin C levels
   a. unexpectedly low? If so, explain.
   b. unexpectedly high? If so, explain.

2. Imagine that you added too many drops of iodine solution during the titration and missed the true endpoint. Will this procedural error increase or decrease your calculated value of milligrams of vitamin C in the sample? Explain.

Answers

1. a. & b. Answers will vary. Some students may be surprised that Gatorade does not contain vitamin C.

2. Increase; it will appear that there is more vitamin C in the beverage than it actually contains.

Post-Lab Discussion

Students may have some difficulty with calculations. Depending on their mathematical ability, they may need help devising and determining the conversion factor. Model a sample calculation for students, similar to Step 6.

Although student data may not be very accurate, results should allow them to rank beverages quite reliably in terms of vitamin-C levels.

Relate this investigation to text materials by discussing how much of each drink would supply the recommended RDA for vitamin C.

Extensions

If time permits, some teams can investigate the quantity of vitamin C in other foods. Use a blender to extract the juice. Another interesting investigation is to explore the effect on vitamin C content of heating or microwaving a sample. Students can also compare milligrams of Vitamin C obtained experimentally to the milligrams of Vitamin C on beverage labels.

Pre-Lab Discussion

Students probably have heard of vitamin C as a component of various juices and some soft drinks. Name some foods that are high in vitamin C. Students may be surprised to find that broccoli and green and red peppers contain appreciable quantities of vitamin C. (See *ChemMatters*, April 1995.)

Demonstrate correct use of Beral pipets and wellplates in titration. While titrating with a Beral pipet, the angle at which the pipet is held should stay the same (as close to vertical as possible) so that drop size remains constant. Doing otherwise will greatly affect laboratory results.

D.4 Minerals: Essential Within All Diets

Minerals are essential to health as cofactors in biochemical catalysis and as structural components. Some minerals help maintain the health of various organs. Minerals are classified as either *macrominerals* or *trace minerals*. Although people need only small quantities of trace minerals, those minerals still can act as limiting reagents. Health problems occur with either too much or too little of any mineral.

Additional Background: Minerals

Calcium: Necessary for blood clotting, muscle contraction, enzyme-catalyzed reactions, cellular communication, and skin differentiation. Gives bones and teeth strength. Vitamin D regulates absorption of calcium in the body.

Phosphorus: Present in the body as inorganic phosphate or phosphate esters. On the cellular level, energy is stored as adenosine triphosphate (ATP, see pages 574–575). Phosphorus is present in nucleic acids and as a structural component of bones and teeth. Regulation of the narrow pH range within the body depends in part on the phosphate-based buffer system.

When speaking in nutritional terms, *minerals* refer to elements (including calcium, sodium, chlorine, selenium, and zinc in ionic form) necessary to sustain life.

D.4 MINERALS: ESSENTIAL WITHIN ALL DIETS

Minerals in ionic form are essential for life support. Some are quite common; others are likely to be found in large quantities only on research-laboratory shelves.

Some minerals become part of the body's structural material, such as bones and teeth. Others help enzymes do their jobs. Still others help maintain the health of the heart and other organs. The thyroid gland, for example, uses a miniscule quantity of iodine (only millionths of a gram daily) to produce the vital hormone *thyroxine* (Figure 7.55). The rapidly growing field of *bioinorganic chemistry* explores how minerals function within living systems.

Of the more than 100 known elements, only 32 are believed essential to support human life. For convenience, essential minerals are divided into **major minerals** (also called **macrominerals**), and **trace minerals** (also called **microminerals**).

Your body contains rather large quantities, at least 100 mg per kilogram of body mass, of each of the seven macrominerals. Each trace mineral is present in relatively small quantities, less than 100 mg per kilogram of body mass in an average adult. However, trace minerals are just as essential in a human diet as are macrominerals. Any essential mineral, whether a macromineral or a trace mineral, can become a limiting reactant if it is not present in sufficient quantity.

Figure 7.55 *The thyroid gland does not function properly without proper levels of iodine in one's body. Iodine deficiency causes goiter (depicted here).*

The essential minerals and their dietary sources, functions, and deficiency conditions are listed in Table 7.8. Several other minerals, including arsenic (As), cadmium (Cd), and tin (Sn), are known to be needed by laboratory test animals. These minerals and perhaps other trace minerals may also be essential to *human* life. You may be surprised to learn that the widely known poison arsenic might be an essential mineral. In fact, many substances beneficial in low doses become toxic in higher doses. Table 7.9 (page 628) summarizes the recommended daily doses for several macrominerals and trace minerals.

ESSENTIAL DIETARY MINERALS

Mineral	Typical Food Sources	Deficiency Conditions
Macrominerals		
Calcium (Ca)	Milk, dairy products, canned fish	Rickets in children; osteomalacia and osteoporosis in adults
Chlorine (Cl)	Table salt, meat, salt-processed foods	–
Magnesium (Mg)	Seafood, cereal grains, nuts, dark green vegetables, cocoa	Heart spasms, anxiety, disorientation
Phosphorus (P)	Meat, dairy products, nuts, seeds, beans	Blood cell disorders, gastrointestinal tract and renal dysfunction
Potassium (K)	Orange juice, bananas, dried fruits, potatoes	Poor nerve function, irregular heartbeat, sudden death during fasting
Sodium (Na)	Table salt, meat, salt-processed foods	Headache, weakness, thirst, poor memory, appetite loss
Sulfur (S)	Protein (e. g. meat, eggs, legumes)	Conditions related to deficiencies in sulfur-containing essential amino acids
Trace minerals		
Chromium (Cr)	Animal and plant tissue, liver	Loss of insulin efficiency with age
Cobalt (Co)	Animal protein, liver	Conditions related to deficiencies in cobalt-containing vitamin B_{12}
Copper (Cu)	Egg yolk, whole grains, liver, kidney	Anemia in malnourished children
Fluorine (F)	Seafood, fluoridated water	Dental decay
Iodine (I)	Seafood, iodized salt	Goiter
Iron (Fe)	Meats, green leafy vegetables, whole grains, liver	Anemia, tiredness, apathy
Manganese (Mn)	Whole grains, legumes, nuts, tea, leafy vegetables, liver	–
Molybdenum (Mo)	Whole grains, legumes, leafy vegetables, liver, kidney	Weight loss, dermatitis, headache, nausea, disorientation
Selenium (Se)	Meat, liver, organ meats, grains, vegetables	Muscle weakness, Keshan disease (heart-muscle disease)
Zinc (Zn)	Shellfish, meats, wheat germ, legumes, liver	Anemia, growth retardation

| Table 7.8

Magnesium: Works in conjunction with many enzymes involved in energy metabolism, protein synthesis, and nucleic-acid synthesis.

Sodium: Maintains the normal hydration state of bodily fluids; affects movement of water into and out of cells. Plays a role in neuromuscular conduction.

Potassium: Essential to energy metabolism and to glycogen and protein synthesis. Plays a role in neuromuscular conduction.

D.5 Minerals in the Diet

In this activity, students use RDAs and examine a variety of ways to obtain required minerals.

Answers

1. a. Female: 1 slice bread/0.8 mg
   iron × 15 mg iron = 19 slices;
   Male: 1 slice bread/0.8 mg iron ×
   11 mg iron = 14 slices
   b. Anemia, tiredness, apathy

DIETARY REFERENCE INTAKES (DRIs) FOR SELECTED MINERALS						
Age or Condition	Calcium (mg/d)	Phosphorus (mg/d)	Magnesium (mg/d)	Iron (mg/d)	Zinc (mg/d)	Iodine (µg/d)
Males						
9–13 years	1300*	1250	240	8	8	120
14–18 years	1300*	1250	410	11	11	150
19–30 years	1000*	700	400	8	11	150
31–50 years	1000*	700	420	8	11	150
50–70 years	1200*	700	420	8	11	150
> 70 years	1200*	700	420	8	11	150
Females						
9–13 years	1300*	1250	240	8	8	120
14–18 years	1300*	1250	360	15	9	150
19–30 years	1000*	700	310	18	8	150
31–50 years	1000*	700	320	18	8	150
50–70 years	1200*	700	320	8	8	150
> 70 years	1200*	700	320	8	8	150
Pregnant	1000*	700	350	27	11	220
Nursing	1000*	700	310	9	12	290

Recommended Dietary Allowances (RDAs) are in **bold type.** RDAs are established to meet the needs of almost all (97 to 98%) individuals in a group. Adequate Intakes (AIs) are followed by an asterisk (*). AIs are believed to cover the needs of all individuals in the group, but a lack of data prevent being able to specify with confidence the percent of individuals covered by this intake.

Source: Food and Nutrition Board, National Academy of Sciences: National Research Council, *Dietary Reference Intakes 2004.*

| **Table 7.9**

D.5 MINERALS IN THE DIET

Use the values provided in Table 7.9 to answer the following questions.

Sample Problem: *How many cups of broccoli would a 16-year-old female need to eat daily to reach her daily iron allowance? (1 cup broccoli = 1.1 mg iron) Assume that broccoli is her only dietary source of iron.*

The iron DRI for a 16-year-old female is 15 mg per day:

$$15 \text{ mg iron} \times \frac{1 \text{ cup broccoli}}{1.1 \text{ mg iron}} = 14 \text{ cups broccoli}$$

1. One slice of whole-wheat bread contains 0.8 mg iron.
   a. How many slices of whole-wheat bread would supply your daily iron allowance? (Assume that this is your only dietary source of iron.)
   b. Predict health consequences of not consuming an adequate amount of iron.

2. One cup of whole milk contains 288 mg calcium. How much milk would you need to drink daily to meet your daily allowance for that mineral if milk were your only dietary source of calcium?

3. One medium pancake (Figure 7.56) contains about 27 mg calcium and 0.4 mg iron.

   a. Does one pancake provide a greater percent of your DRI for calcium or for iron?

   b. Explain your answer.

4. a. What total mass of each of these minerals do you need to consume daily?
     i. calcium
     ii. phosphorus

   b. Why are the values in your answer to Question 4a higher than DRI values for other listed essential minerals? (*Hint:* Consider how calcium and phosphorus are used in the body.)

   c. List several good dietary sources of
     i. calcium.
     ii. phosphorus.

   d. Predict the health consequences due to a deficiency of
     i. calcium.
     ii. phosphorus.

   e. i. Would a particular age group or gender especially be affected by those consequences?
     ii. If so, which age group or gender and why?

5. Most table salt, sodium chloride (NaCl), includes a small amount of added potassium iodide (KI).

   a. Why do you think KI is added to table salt?

   b. If you do not use iodized salt, what other kinds of food could you use as sources of iodine?

Figure 7.56 *Which foods are good sources of minerals such as calcium?*

"Iodized" salt refers to such products.

Section D Other Substances in Foods **629**

2. Female and male: 1 cup/288 mg Ca × 1300 mg Ca = 4.5 cups

3. a. Iron
   b. The pancake provides 2.1% of the Ca RDA and 3.6% of Fe for males and 2.67% for females. Calculations:
27 mg/1300 mg × 100% = 2.1% of Ca RDA
0.4 mg/11 mg × 100% = 3.6% of Fe RDA (males)
0.4 mg/15mg × 100% = 2.7% of Fe RDA (females)

4. a. i. Ca: 1300 mg/d;
     ii. P: 1250 mg/d
   b. Bones and teeth incorporate large quantities of Ca and P.
   c. i. Ca: milk, dairy products;
     ii. P: animal protein, beans, nuts
   d. i. Ca: rickets, osteomalacia, and osteoporosis;
     ii. P: blood cell disorders, GI tract and renal dysfunction
   e. i. Yes;
     ii. Infants require Ca for proper bone growth, and women are susceptible to osteoporosis resulting from Ca deficiency.

5. a. To prevent goiter
   b. Seafood

Using the Figures

Figure 7.56: Dairy products are all high in Ca. Non-dairy Ca-rich foods include almonds, blackstrap molasses, rhubarb, salmon, and tofu (if prepared with Ca).

D.6 Food Additives

 D.6, D.8 and D.9 Content Reading Guide

Students briefly survey benefits (and some associated risks) involved in contemporary use of food additives.

Demonstration Idea

Prepare 100 mL of approximately 0.2 M sodium sulfite (2.5 g Na_2SO_3/100 mL). Dip a fresh slice of apple into the sulfite bath for one minute. Remove it and place it on a towel near an untreated "control" apple slice. Continue with your lesson and view the slices later in the class period.

The treated slice will continue to look fresh long after the control slice begins to darken. Ask students which apple slice they would more likely choose at a salad bar (assuming they were unaware of the sulfite treatment). Ask students if they think using this additive is justified. Point out that some individuals (a small fraction of the population) suffer serious health consequences if exposed to sulfites.

D.6 FOOD ADDITIVES

Small amounts of vitamins and minerals occur naturally in food. Some foods, especially processed foods such as packaged snacks or frozen entrees, also contain small amounts of **food additives.** Manufacturers add these substances during processing to increase the nutritive value of foods or to enhance their storage life, visual appeal (see Figure 7.57), or ease of production. A food label might provide the ingredient information shown below. Can you guess the identity of the food product from only this label?

> Sugar, bleached flour (enriched with niacin, iron, thiamine, and riboflavin), semisweet chocolate, animal and/or vegetable shortening, dextrose, wheat starch, monocalcium phosphate, baking soda, egg white, modified corn starch, salt, nonfat milk, cellulose gum, soy lecithin, xanthan gum, mono- and diglycerides, BHA, BHT.

This list shows quite a collection of ingredients. You probably recognize the major ingredients, such as sugar, flour, shortening, and baking soda; and some of the additives, such as vitamins (niacin, thiamin, and riboflavin) and minerals (iron and monocalcium phosphate). However, you probably do not recognize the food additives xanthan gum (an *emulsifier* that helps produce uniform, nonseparating water–oil mixtures—see Figure 7.59, page 632) and BHA and BHT (butylated hydroxyanisole and butylated hydroxytoluene, which are antioxidants).

Food additives have been used since ancient times. For example, salt has been used for centuries to preserve foods, and spices disguised the flavor of food that was no longer fresh. To make foods easier and less expensive to distribute and store, most manufacturers, especially manufacturers of processed foods, rely on food preservatives. Table 7.10 summarizes major categories of food additives. The structural formulas of several common additives are shown in Figure 7.58.

Figure 7.57 *Food-coloring additives are often used to make food items more attractive and appetizing.*

Color and taste additives often enhance the commercial appeal of food products. In the following investigation, you will analyze several commonly used food-coloring additives (dyes).

| Table 7.10

FOOD ADDITIVE TYPES, PURPOSES, AND EXAMPLES

Additive Type	Purpose	Examples
Anticaking agents	Keep foods free-flowing	Sodium ferrocyanide
Antioxidants	Prevent fat rancidity	BHA and BHT
Bleaches	Whiten foods (flour, cheese); hasten cheese maturation	Sulfur dioxide (SO$_2$)
Coloring agents	Increase visual appeal	Carotene (natural yellow color); synthetic dyes
Emulsifiers	Improve texture, smoothness; stabilize oil–water mixtures	Cellulose gums, dextrins
Flavoring agents	Add or enhance flavor	Salt, monosodium glutamate (MSG), spices
Humectants	Retain moisture	Glycerin
Leavening agents	Give foods light texture	Baking powder, baking soda
Nutrients	Improve nutritive value	Vitamins, minerals
Preservatives and antimycotic agents (growth inhibitors)	Prevent spoilage, microbial growth	Propionic acid, sorbic acid, benzoic acid, salt
Sweeteners	Impart sweet taste	Sugar (sucrose), dextrin, fructose, aspartame, sorbitol, mannitol

| **Figure 7.58** *The molecular structures of MSG, aspartame, and BHT, a preservative.*

Using the Figures

Table 7.10: Students analyze food labels for additives in Developing Skills D.10 (page 638). However, you may decide to begin this analysis as students first encounter information in this table. Ask each student to bring in one ingredient list from a food package label. Make a list of additive types. Then ask students to identify specific additives they find on their package label and identify the variety of processed foods that contain that particular additive. You may invite students to research additives in their lists that they cannot classify using information in this table. Another approach is to examine ingredient lists from different products within the same food category (such as different cookies, different brands or kinds of peanut butter, and different fruit juices), where some products claim to be "all-natural" or "organic." What does that mean in terms of additives? How might the presence or absence of additives affect such characteristics as flavor, color, consistency, and shelf life?

Scientific American Working Knowledge Illustration

Molecules having similar dual polarity are also found in shampoos, soaps, and detergents as well as in many biological systems, including cell membranes. Once your students have studied the emulsifying properties of lecithin in Figure 7.59, ask them to discuss foods that involve mixing oil and water and whether an emulsifying agent like egg yolk is used. You might also bring to class ingredient labels for cakes, cookies, or ice cream and look for emulsifying agents.

Investigating Matter

D.7 Analyzing Food-Coloring Additives

Students use paper chromatography to separate dyes in commercial candies and compare them to dyes in food coloring. They use the data from the chromatography investigation to calculate R_f values.

Time

50 min

Materials

(For 12 student pairs)

12 wide-mouth bottles or jars
12 stoppers or lids to fit bottles
12 24-well wellplates
36 Beral pipets
Chromatography paper, 1-inch-wide strips
Toothpicks
1 package M&Ms candy
1 package Skittles candy
Red food coloring
Blue food coloring
Yellow food coloring
Green food coloring

Scientific American Working Knowledge Illustration

Figure 7.59 Emulsifier action. *These illustrations depict how lecithin, a molecule contained in egg yolk, emulsifies (mixes together) an oil-water system. In the top view, oil is layered over water. The particulate-level enlargement reveals that oil molecules are long, nonpolar carbon chains quite different in structure and polarity from the small, polar water molecules, also shown. Water-water intermolecular forces are much stronger than are oil-water intermolecular forces. Hence these two liquids do not mix. Each lecithin molecule, the emulsifying agent (middle view), has a long, nonpolar carbon chain and a smaller, polar region involving phosphorus, oxygen, nitrogen, and hydrogen atoms. Lecithin molecules orient themselves so that they simultaneously interact with both oil and water molecules. Once an egg is cracked open and added and the entire mixture is whisked, micelles form (bottom view). Each micelle is a spherical arrangement of oil molecules surrounded by and attracted to the nonpolar region of lecithin molecules. The polar regions of lecithin molecules align at the outside of a micelle, causing the entire sphere to intermingle among polar water molecules. This stable arrangement permits oil molecules to remain evenly dispersed through water. Emulsification is used to make numerous food products, including mayonnaise and ice cream.*

 D.7 Analyzing Food Coloring Additives Student Worksheet and Data Table

D.7 ANALYZING FOOD-COLORING ADDITIVES

Investigating Matter

Introduction

Many candies contain artificial coloring agents to enhance their visual appeal. Colorless candies would be quite dull! In this investigation, you will analyze the food dyes in two commercial candies and compare them with the dyes in food-coloring products.

You will separate and identify the food dyes by **paper chromatography.** This technique uses a solvent (called the *mobile phase*) and paper (the *stationary phase*). Paper chromatography is based on relative differences in attraction between (a) dye molecules and solvent vs. (b) dye molecules and paper. As the solvent and dye mixture moves up the paper, dye molecules that are more strongly attracted to the paper will more readily leave the solvent and separate out onto the paper, leaving a colored spot on the paper. Dye molecules less attracted to paper (and more attracted to solvent) will travel further up the paper before they adhere to the paper later. Thus, characteristic areas representing different dye molecules will appear on the chromatography paper.

To analyze the results of this chromatography investigation, you will calculate the R_f value for each spot. The R_f value, as illustrated in Figure 7.60, is a ratio involving the distance traveled by each dye compared to the distance the solvent has moved up the paper. The actual distance that the dye and solvent travel might vary from trial to trial, but the R_f value will remain constant for a particular dye. Thus chemists use the R_f value, not the actual distance traveled, to identify dye molecules.

Lab Video: Food Coloring Analysis

Calculating R_f for Dye Sample A

$$R_f = \frac{24\ mm}{61\ mm} = 0.39$$

61 mm

24 mm

Dye Sample A

Figure 7.60 *Paper chromatography with R_f values.*

Safety

Students should wear protective goggles and aprons throughout the investigation.

Advance Preparation

Cut 12 strips of chromatography paper, each 15 cm long.

Pre-Lab Discussion

A food product may contain a number of synthetic dyes solely to enhance appearance. Generally, chromatography is used to separate components of a mixture. In this investigation, paper chromatography is used to separate common food coloring into its component dyes. The various dyes in a mixture respond differently based on their relative attractions for paper and solvent. Some dyes are more attracted to paper than to the solvent and travel up the paper *(stationary phase)* only slightly. Some dyes are more attracted to the solvent *(mobile phase)* and will travel up the paper farther. It is difficult to compare results unless all conditions are carefully controlled. Therefore, a standard (known) solution is generally run with an unknown, and then investigators compare R_f values. Other chromatographic methods employ different types of stationary and mobile phases.

Lab Tips

This investigation is not difficult for students. The most common error is allowing spots to be submerged in the solvent. If this happens, the dye merely dissolves in the solvent, and those spots will not appear on the chromatography paper. As an extension, you may decide to invite students to investigate the separation effectiveness of other solvents such as dilute ammonia and dilute vinegar.

SECTION D

Anticipated Results

R_f values are summarized below for red candy and food coloring. Student values may be slightly different. The spots will be in the same order, but actual distances may differ. Many things affect these results: laboratory temperature, small changes in solvent concentration, and even the type of paper employed.

Answers

1. The dyes in pen ink would be separated by paper chromatography.
2. Answers will vary.
3. a. The dye with the smallest R_f value
   b. The dye with the largest R_f value
4. a. Answers will vary.
   b. If different samples contain the same dye, R_f values will be the same in each sample. This is the evidence upon which students should base their answers.
5. a.–c. Answers will vary.

Post-Lab Discussion

Focus on two topics: use of dyes as food additives and the technique of paper chromatography. You can use the answers to questions as prompts in discussing paper chromatography technique. Solicit student opinions on the appropriateness of using dyes to improve food appearance. Examining labels will reveal a somewhat surprising collection of foods that contain dyes.

Procedure

|←2 cm→|

Dye Sample A   Dye Sample B   Dye Sample C

Figure 7.61 *Starting a chromatography investigation.*

Figure 7.62 *Spotting a sample on chromatography paper.*

1. Obtain one piece each of two different commercial candies from your teacher, as well as a food-coloring sample. The food coloring and candies should all be the same color.
2. Put each candy into a separate well of a wellplate. Note which candy is in each well. Add 5–10 drops of water to each well. Stir the mixture in each well with a separate toothpick until the colored coating completely dissolves from the candy. Add 3 to 4 drops of the food coloring sample to a third well. Observe and record the initial colors of each sample.
3. Obtain a strip of chromatography paper, handling it only by its edges. With a pencil (do not use a pen), draw a horizontal line 2 cm from the bottom of the paper strip and another horizontal line 3 cm from the top. Label the strip as shown in Figure 7.61.
4. Next, place a spot of each dye solution on the bottom line; the spots should not be large. To do this, use separate toothpicks for each of the three samples. Place a drop of the first candy's colored solution with a toothpick, as shown in Figure 7.62.
5. Allow the drop of solution to sit until the spot it makes stops spreading out on the paper. Then apply a second drop of the same sample on top of the spot. Repeat this procedure for the second candy's colored solution and also for the food-coloring sample. You will then have three spots along the bottom pencil line on the chromatography paper (Figure 7.61). If the chromatography paper provided is narrow, you may need to use a second piece of paper.
6. Obtain a chromatography chamber. Place a mark on the outside of the chamber approximately 1 cm from the bottom. Fill the chromatography chamber with the solvent (water) to a depth of 1 cm.
7. Lower the spotted chromatography paper's bottom edge into the chromatography chamber until edge rests evenly in the solvent (water). Be sure the colored spots remain above the solvent surface. Cover the chromatography chamber.
8. Allow the solvent to move up the paper until solvent reaches the top penciled line (3 cm from the top). Then remove the paper from the chamber and, using a pencil, mark the farthest point of the solvent's path. Allow the paper to air-dry overnight.
9. After the paper has dried, record the colors observed for the dye sample and candy solutions.
10. Measure the distance (in cm) from the initial pencil line where you placed the spots to the *center* of each dye spot. Record these distances in your data table.
11. Measure and record the distance (in cm) that the solvent moved.
12. Calculate the R_f value of each dye spot you observed. Record these values.

CANDY	DYE COLOR	DISTANCE DYE SPOT MOVED	DISTANCE SOLVENT FRONT MOVED	R_f Value
M&Ms	red component	30 mm	68 mm	0.44
Skittles	red component	25 mm	68 mm	0.37
	yellow component	37 mm	68 mm	0.54
Food Coloring	pink component	22 mm	68 mm	0.33
	red component	45 mm	68 mm	0.66

Questions

1. Why was it important to use a pencil rather than a pen to mark lines on the chromatography paper in Step 3?

2. Which sample solution, if any, created a single spot rather than several spots?

3. Which dye in the sample solutions had the greatest attraction for the

   a. paper?
   b. solvent?

4. a. Based on your data, do any of the three samples contain any of the same dyes?
   b. What evidence did you use to answer Question 4a?

5. The candy and food-coloring packages list each dye that they contain. Compare this information with your experimental results.

   a. What similarities did you find?
   b. What differences did you find?
   c. If you found differences, what are some possible reasons for them?

D.8 REGULATING ADDITIVES

Both processed and unprocessed foods may contain contaminants that were not deliberately added, such as pesticides, mold, antibiotics used to treat animals, insect fragments, food-packaging materials, or dirt. We presume that food purchased in grocery stores and restaurants is safe to eat. In most cases, this is true. Nonetheless, in the past, some food additives and contaminants were identified as or suspected of posing hazards to human health.

Safe food in the United States is required by law—the Federal Food, Drug, and Cosmetic Act of 1938. This act authorized the Food and Drug Administration (FDA) to monitor food's safety, purity, and wholesomeness. This act has been amended to address concerns about pesticide residues; artificial colors and food dyes; potential cancer-causing agents (*carcinogens*); and **mutagens,** which are agents that cause mutations or changes in DNA. Food manufacturers must complete a battery of tests and provide extensive evidence about the safety of any proposed food product or additive. Any new food product must earn FDA approval before it can be marketed.

According to the amended Federal Food, Drug, and Cosmetic Act, ingredients that were known not to be hazardous and were in use for a long time prior to the act were exempted from testing. These substances, rather than legally defined as additives, constitute the "generally recognized as safe" (GRAS) list. The GRAS list, periodically reviewed in light of new findings, includes items such as salt, sugar, vinegar, vitamins (for example, vitamin C and riboflavin), and some minerals.

Section D   Other Substances in Foods   **635**

D.8 Regulating Additives

Students explore various federal regulations associated with using food additives. Discussion of the Delaney Clause (page 636), which requires prospective food additives to be tested on laboratory animals, leads to the ChemQuandary (page 637) on weighing risks and benefits of using nitrites to preserve meats. In 1996, the part of the Delaney Clause relating to pesticide residues was repealed. It was replaced with a new standard of a "reasonable certainty" of no harm. The section also discusses the artificial sweetener aspartame and its relationship to phenylketonuria. It may be useful to discuss the fat substitute Olestra (see **http://chemcases.com/olestra/index.htm**, **http://www.olean.com/**, or **http://www.cspinet.org/olestra/**) at this time. Encourage students to share what they already know about Olestra, its purpose, and its benefits and risks.

It also may be beneficial to emphasize differences between $NaNO_3$ (sodium nit*rate*) and $NaNO_2$ (sodium nit*rite*). Consider discussing the true story *Eleven Blue Men*, a tale of unintentional poisoning in a boarding house. Sodium nitrite was inadvertently substituted for sodium chloride; the boarders developed methemoglobinemia, resulting in reduced oxygen transport in the blood. The story appears in *The Medical Detectives* by B. Roulche, Truman Talley Books/Plume, New York, 1991.

ChemQuandary 4

Nitrite Additives

This ChemQuandary probes benefits and risks of using nitrites as food additives. Some students may feel that benefits of nitrites outweigh their risks. Other students may disagree. Encourage students to explain the rationale behind their personal decisions.

Here are some questions students might pose:

1. How conclusive is evidence that nitrosamines cause cancer in laboratory animals and in humans?

2. How deadly is botulin toxin? Are there antidotes for it?

3. How often does botulism occur, and how often does nitrite cause cancer?

4. What are some possible substitutes for sodium nitrite as a preservative?

5. What is the frequency of *Clostridium botulinum* growth without the use of nitrites?

Testing a new food additive usually requires millions of dollars and years of research.

In accord with the Delaney Clause, which was added to the act in the 1950s, every proposed new food additive must be tested on laboratory animals (usually mice). The Delaney Clause specifies that "no additive shall be deemed to be safe if it is found to induce cancer when it is ingested by man or animal." Thus, approval of a proposed additive is denied if it causes cancer in test animals.

Since the 1950s, great advances have occurred in science and technology. Improvements in chemical-analysis techniques permit scientists to detect even smaller amounts of potentially harmful substances. Consequently, scientists can now detect and study food contaminants that may have always been present but previously were undetected.

This new information has resulted in a greater understanding of potential risks associated with human exposure to particular food additives. People now recognize that amounts of additives comparable to those causing cancer in test animals are often vastly greater than would ever be encountered in a human diet. In light of this, Congress passed the Food Quality and Protection Act in 1996. This legislation, which replaced the Delaney Clause, states that manufacturers may use food additives that present "negligible risk."

Many concerns about food additives still remain. Sodium nitrite ($NaNO_2$), for instance, is a color stabilizer and spoilage inhibitor used in many cured meats, such as hot dogs and lunch meats. Nitrites are particularly effective in inhibiting the growth of the bacterium *Clostridium botulinum,* which produces botulin toxin. This toxin is the cause of botulism, an often fatal disease. Sodium nitrite, however, may be a carcinogen. In the stomach, nitrites are converted to nitrous acid:

$$NaNO_2(aq) + HCl(aq) \longrightarrow HNO_2(aq) + NaCl(aq)$$

| Sodium nitrite | Hydrochloric acid | Nitrous acid | Sodium chloride |

Nitrous acid can then react with compounds formed during protein digestion, producing *nitrosoamines,* known as potent carcinogens. An example of this reaction is shown below: The concentration of carcinogenic compounds produced, however, is generally below the toxic threshold.

$$HNO_2 + R-\underset{\underset{R}{|}}{N}-H \longrightarrow R-\underset{\underset{R}{|}}{N}-N{=}O + H_2O$$

ChemQuandary 4

NITRITE ADDITIVES

Consider the following benefits and risks of using nitrites to preserve meats:

NITRITE RISK TABLE		
	Using Nitrites	**Eliminating Nitrites**
Benefit	Decreases risk of forming botulin toxin	Decreases risk of forming possible carcinogens
Risk	Increases risk of forming possible carcinogens	Increases risk of forming botulin toxin

Based on this information, do you think food manufacturers should use nitrites to preserve meats?

D.9 ARTIFICIAL SWEETENERS

Because many people believe they should reduce the amount of sugar in their diets, many use low-Calorie sweeteners. *Saccharin* (found in Sweet'N Low) was the first sugar substitute used extensively in the United States. There has been some controversy over saccharin use because early investigations conducted with rats suggested that massive amounts of saccharin may cause cancer. Further investigation indicated that the link between saccharin and cancer was very weak. Currently, it is generally believed that saccharin is safe for human consumption. Today, saccharin is used in many candies, baked goods, jellies, and jams.

The sugar-substitute *aspartame* (NutraSweet and Equal) is an ingredient in many diet beverages and in thousands of other food products. Aspartame (Figure 7.63) is a chemical combination of two natural amino acids, aspartic acid and phenylalanine, neither of which, by itself, tastes sweet. One gram of aspartame contains roughly the same food energy as one gram of table sugar (4 Cal), but aspartame tastes 200 times sweeter than sugar. Because we need smaller quantities of aspartame to sweeten a product, it is a low-Calorie alternative to sugar—one that is also safe for people with diabetes. Annually, thousands of tons of aspartame are used in the United States to sweeten diet drinks and foods. Aspartame decomposes at cooking temperatures. However, Splenda, an artificial sweetener based on *sucralose* (a chlorinated carbohydrate; see Figure 7.63), can be used directly in cooking.

Molecular Design of an Artificial Sweetener

Aspartame

Sucralose

| **Figure 7.63** *Molecular structures of aspartame and sucralose.*

D.9 Artificial Sweeteners

Sugar substitutes have gained popularity in many foods and beverages. This material addresses concerns that these additives may also pose health risks.

Using the Figures

Figure 7.63: "Made from sugar so it tastes like sugar." That slogan was used when Splenda (sucralose) was first advertised. Ask students to evaluate the quality of that claim. (Starch and cellulose are also made from sugar, but they don't taste like sugar.) Then ask students to compare the molecular structure of sucralose (this figure) with that of sucrose in **Figure 7.19,** page 584.

Demonstration Idea

Add unopened cans of regular and diet soda to an aquarium or other large, transparent container filled with water. The regular soda cans sink, and the diet soda cans float. Why? It's not due to fewer calories or the fact that diet beverages are sometimes called "lite." Artificial sweeteners are compounds that elicit the same (or a similar) "sweet" flavor we obtain from sugars. In fact, many artificial sweeteners are considerably sweeter than sugar (gram for gram). Therefore, much less sweetener is added to diet sodas than sugar is added to regular soda. This is why diet sodas have much lower densities than their sugar-sweetened counterparts.

Developing Skills

D.10 Food Additive Survey

The purpose of this activity is to increase student awareness of food additives in products they consume daily. Students survey five or six packaged foods and select six additives to describe and investigate.

This activity will require about 30 min to complete. As an alternative, ask each student to investigate only one or two food additives. Then, invite students to share and discuss their findings with the class.

You may find that this activity runs more smoothly if students complete their summary tables at home rather than bring labels to school.

Emphasize risks and benefits of using particular food additives in various products students have selected.

Figure 7.64 *The warning to phenylketonurics found on a can of diet drink containing aspartame.*

Although no serious warning about aspartame has been issued for the general population, aspartame does pose a health hazard to *phenylketonurics*—individuals who cannot properly metabolize phenylalanine. An FDA-required warning, "Phenylketonurics: Contains Phenylalanine," on the label of foods with aspartame highlights the potential risk (see Figure 7.64).

Individuals with specific medical conditions may need to avoid certain foods and food additives. For example, people with diabetes (see Figure 7.65) must regulate their intake of carbohydrates, including sugars. People with high blood pressure (hypertension) must avoid excess sodium. Some people have food allergies. If such restrictions apply to you, you must always read food labels. Sometimes a new ingredient will be used in a food product that you have used safely in the past; this new ingredient may put you at risk.

Figure 7.65 *A diabetic individual checks her blood glucose level.*

Developing Skills

D.10 FOOD ADDITIVE SURVEY

Being aware of what you eat is a wise habit to develop. In this activity, you will investigate food labels and consider additives.

1. Collect the labels from five or six packaged foods in your home. Select no more than two samples of the same type of food. For example, do not select labels from more than two breakfast cereals or two canned soups. Bring your collected labels to class.

2. From the ingredient listings on the labels, select three additives.

3. Complete a summary table with the following format:

   a. List the three additives in a vertical column along the left side.
   b. Make four vertical columns to the right of the listed additives with these headings: "Food Product Where Found," "Purpose of Additive (if known)," "Chemical Formula," and "Other Information."

4. Use Table 7.10 (page 631) to review the purposes of food additives. Then answer the following question for each food additive in your summary table: Why do you think this additive is included in this food?

5. What alternatives to food additives can you propose to prevent food spoilage?

D.11 ANALYZING VITAMINS AND MINERALS

So far, you have analyzed the three-day food inventory in terms of fats, carbohydrates, and proteins. Now decide whether the inventoried foods provide adequate quantities of vitamins and minerals.

1. Your teacher will specify two vitamins and two minerals for you to analyze.

2. Using references provided by your teacher, analyze each food item in your three-day inventory for the presence of these two vitamins and two minerals. Record these values.

3. Determine the average intake of these two vitamins and two minerals over the three days covered in the three-day food inventory. Record these data.

4. a. Does your analyzed food inventory provide enough of each specified vitamin and mineral?
   b. If not, what types of food can be added to increase the intake of these vitamins and minerals? Identify the food groups to which these food types belong.

5. Some people believe that eating a well-balanced diet provides all the vitamins a person needs to remain healthy. Others suggest that vitamin supplements can enhance personal health. Proponents of both opinions have engaged in considerable advertising to promote their viewpoints.

   a. After considering your data, which viewpoint do your results support?
   b. What could you do to help people make more informed decisions about this issue?

Section D   Other Substances in Foods   **639**

Making Decisions

D.11 Analyzing Vitamins and Minerals

Students analyze the three-day diets to decide whether food selections provide adequate quantities of vitamins and minerals. Limiting the analysis to two vitamins (vitamins A and C recommended) and two minerals (Ca and Fe recommended) will help make the assignment manageable.

CHEMISTRY at Work

Keeping Food Supplies Safe for Consumers

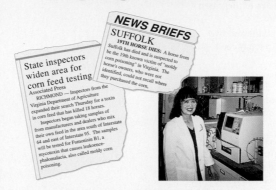

NEWS BRIEFS

SUFFOLK
19TH HORSE DIES: A horse from Suffolk has died and is suspected to be the 19th known victim of "moldy corn poisoning" in Virginia. The horse's owners, who were not identified, could not recall where they purchased the corn.

State inspectors widen area for corn feed testing
Associated Press
RICHMOND — Inspectors from the Virginia Department of Agriculture expanded their search Thursday for a toxin in corn feed that has killed 18 horses.
Inspectors began taking samples from manufacturers and dealers who mix their own feed in the area south of Interstate 64 and east of Interstate 95. The samples will be tested for Fumonisin B1, a mycotoxin that causes leukoencephalomalacia, also called moldy corn poisoning.

These actual newspaper headlines illustrate the deadly effects that certain microscopic toxins can have. The consumers of the food discussed in these articles were horses, but similar toxins can endanger human consumers as well.

Mary Trucksess is a chemist working to understand and eradicate food toxins. She is a research chemist and chief of the Bioanalytical Chemistry Branch in the Division of Natural Food Products, Office of Plant and Dairy Food and Beverages at the U.S. Food and Drug Administration (FDA). Mary and her fellow chemists at the FDA help ensure the quality of foods and drugs (prescription and nonprescription) to protect people from harmful contaminants. Mary is currently investigating *fumonisins*—toxins found mainly in corn that are caused by a common soil fungus. Fumonisins can cause horses to develop a fatal disease of the brain. The FDA is investigating these toxins to make certain that they do not pose a threat to humans.

Mary's office analyzes other foods, such as peanuts and peanut butter, for aflatoxins. Aflatoxins form when certain molds (*Aspergillus flavus* or *Aspergillus para-*

Currently Mary is investigating *fumonisins*— toxins found mainly in corn.

siticus) begin to grow on peanuts. If not controlled, these and other toxins could threaten the health of consumers.

Mary also manages and directs other chemists as they conduct research. The chemists in her branch often discuss with her any problems they encounter in their research. She reviews progress reports from the chemists and recommends different approaches as needed.

For several years, Mary, who holds undergraduate and doctoral degrees in chemistry, has supervised the work of high school honor students who have been selected to intern at the FDA. Mary develops specific projects for the students and trains them in laboratory procedures and data interpretation. Mary has also been a coordinator for Project SEED. This summer program for economically disadvantaged high school students offers them the opportunity to work with a mentor in a chemistry laboratory. For information about this program, visit http://www.acs.org/education/student/projectseed.html

For Research and Practice

1. When preparing food, consumers can unknowingly create conditions in which bacteria thrive.
   a. What should you do to keep your food safe?
   b. What temperature range is the danger zone for food, and why is it called that?
2. According to a CNN report, "A survey by the Centers for Disease Control and Prevention shows that men between the ages of 18 and 29 violate food safety practices more than any other group." Members of this group are also more likely to experience food poisoning than those of any other group. Design a food safety ad campaign that will target men between 18 and 29.

SECTION D SUMMARY

✍ **Section D Supplement**

Reviewing the Concepts

1. Vitamins are needed for growth, reproduction, health, and life.
2. An organic molecule that interacts with enzymes to enhance their activity

3. Some maintain skin and gum health (other answers are possible).
4. a. Anemia, exhaustion
   b. Night blindness, scaling skin
   c. Soft bones, rickets
5. Only a small quantity is required daily, compared to the large required quantity of macronutrients such as fats, carbohydrates, and proteins.

SECTION D SUMMARY
Reviewing the Concepts

Vitamins are organic molecules that are necessary for basic life functions.

1. Vitamins are not considered foods, yet they are vital to healthful diets. Explain.

2. What is a coenzyme?

3. Give an example of a function of a vitamin.

4. List some typical symptoms of dietary deficiency of
   a. vitamin B_{12}.
   b. vitamin A.
   c. vitamin D.

5. Vitamins are regarded as micronutrients. What does this mean regarding the quantity of vitamins required daily?

6. What molecular properties determine whether a vitamin is fat-soluble or water-soluble?

7. Why should people take water-soluble vitamins more regularly than fat-soluble ones?

8. Give two examples of how DRIs for vitamins and minerals vary, based on age and gender.

A titration is a common laboratory procedure to determine the amount of a solute in a particular solution.

9. Describe key steps in a vitamin C titration and explain how this process can determine the quantity of vitamin C in a beverage.

10. What is meant by the *endpoint* of a titration?

11. Vitamin C is colorless in solution, yet you measured its concentration in Investigating Matter D.3. What reactions allowed you to detect its presence in a solution?

12. Suppose you find in a vitamin C titration that 0.035 mg vitamin C reacts with 1 drop iodine solution. How much vitamin C is in a sample that turns bluish black after adding
    a. 1 drop of iodine solution?
    b. 12 drops of iodine solution?

13. For what juices would the vitamin C titration endpoint be difficult to observe? Give examples supporting your answer.

Minerals are elements that are essential for human life.

14. Name three essential minerals.

15. Of the more than 100 known elements, how many are believed essential for human life?

16. What is the difference between a *macromineral* and a *trace mineral*?

17. What roles do minerals play in the body?

18. List a macromineral and a trace mineral and describe a deficiency condition for each.

19. What are some dietary sources of
    a. magnesium?   c. iron?
    b. potassium?   d. molybdenum?

20. Regarding minerals in the diet, some people believe that "if a little is good, more must be better." Evaluate this idea, particularly considering such minerals as arsenic (As) and cadmium (Cd).

---

6. Solubility depends on polarity of its molecules. Polar molecules are water soluble; nonpolar molecules are fat soluble.

7. They cannot be stored in the body.

8. Students should use Tables 7.5 and 7.9 to find examples.

9. Steps are (a) add known amount of one reactant to a second reactant until the reaction reaches an equivalence point (as detected by an indicator); (b) from the titration data, calculate the concentration of unknown reactant based on the concentration of the known reactant.

---

10. The reaction is complete.

11. The iodine reacted with vitamin C (ascorbic acid) until all the ascorbic acid became oxidized to dehydroascorbic acid. When no further vitamin C was available, iodine reacted with starch (blue color).

12. a. $\dfrac{0.035 \text{ mg vitamin C}}{1 \text{ drop } I_2 \text{ solution}} \times 1 \text{ drop}$
    I_2 solution = 0.035 mg vitamin C
    b. $\dfrac{0.035 \text{ mg vitamin C}}{1 \text{ drop } I_2 \text{ solution}} \times$
    12 drops I_2 solution = 0.42 mg vitamin C

13. For grape juice, due to its dark color.

14. Possible answers include Ca, Cl, Mg, K, Na, S, and P.

15. 32

16. Macrominerals are needed in relatively large quantities ($\geq$ 5 g). Trace minerals ($\leq$ 5 g) can act as limiting reactants in biochemical reactions.

17. Roles include controlling heart functions and maintaining healthy bones and teeth.

18. Students should use Table 7.8 to find examples.

19. a. Seafoods, grains
    b. Orange juice, bananas
    c. Liver, meats
    d. Liver, whole grains

20. The total quantity of minerals needed daily is small. The body cannot store excess minerals, so if one consumes more minerals than needed daily, they pass from the body as waste. Excessive mineral consumption can be toxic and—at an extreme—possibly fatal.

21. Basic components are natural substances, such as vitamins and minerals. Additives are added during processing.

22. BHA and BHT are preservatives; carotene improves visual appeal; salt is a preservative. Other answers are possible.

23. a. Vitamins, minerals
    b. Benzoic acid, salt
    c. Carotene
    d. Sodium ferrocyanide

24. a. A cancer-causing agent
    b. An agent that causes mutations

25. The Food Quality and Protection Act stipulates that manufacturers may use food additives that present a "negligible risk." The Delaney Clause states that "no additive may be deemed safe if it is found to induce cancer when ingested by man or animal."

26. Gram for gram, it is much sweeter than sugar, so less is needed to achieve the same degree of sweetness.

27. It decomposes at cooking temperatures.

28. a, b. The R_f value is the ratio of the distances (a) from the starting line to the spot left by a particular colored substance to (b) from the starting line to the farthest point of travel by the solvent.

29. R_f = 3.9 cm/5.8 cm = 0.67

30. Differences between attraction of the dye to the paper and the dye to the solvent. The more strongly the dye is attracted to the solvent, the longer it will travel up the paper.

31. No. Their R_f values differ significantly.
    Sample A: R_f = 4.1 cm/6.2 cm = 0.66
    Sample B: R_f = 4.1 cm/5.3 cm = 0.77

| Food additives are used to increase the nutritive value, storage life, visual appeal, or ease of producing foods.

21. What determines if a substance is considered an additive or a basic component of a food?

22. List two typical food additives and their functions.

23. Give an example of a food additive used to
    a. increase nutritive value.
    b. improve storage life.
    c. enhance visual appeal.
    d. ease production.

24. a. What is a carcinogen?
    b. What is a mutagen?

25. How does the Food Quality and Protection Act differ from the Delaney Clause?

26. Aspartame's energy value is the same as that of sugar, 4 Cal/g. Why, then, is aspartame useful as a low-Calorie artificial sweetener?

27. Explain why aspartame can't be used in baking.

| Paper chromatography is a technique for separating and identifying the components of a solution.

28. a. What is an R_f value?
    b. How is it determined?

29. In a paper-chromatography investigation, the solvent moves 5.8 cm, and a food-dye component moves 3.9 cm. What is the R_f for the food-dye? Show calculations to support your answer.

30. What properties allow chromatography to separate particular components of a solution?

31. A student tests two samples of dye solution with paper chromatography. In A, the solvent moves 6.2 cm, and the dye moves 4.1 cm. In B, the solvent moves 5.3 cm, and the dye moves 4.1 cm. Do these data support that A and B contain the same dye? Explain.

Connecting the Concepts

32. Although high cooking temperatures can destroy some vitamins in foods, they rarely affect the quality of minerals in foods. Explain.

33. Why with certain food additives, do food standards use the term "generally recognized as safe" (GRAS), rather than "always safe" or "100% safe"?

34. Would paper chromatography provide any useful information if one or more sample components were colorless? Explain.

35. How could you modify Investigating Matter D.3 to find out how much vitamin C is lost during cooking a food item?

36. One cup of spinach supplies 51 mg calcium and 1.7 mg iron. Does spinach provide a greater percent of your DRI for calcium or for iron? Show calculations to support your answer.

37. Suppose a government banned all food additives. Overall, do you think the ban would produce positive or negative results? Explain.

38. Suppose one component in a chromatography sample was quite volatile, tending to evaporate when placed on paper. What effect might this property have on the experimental results?

39. All substances described in this unit consist of atoms, molecules, or ions. With that in mind, why do you think some people describe food additives as "chemicals," but do not describe carbohydrates and fats also as chemicals?

40. In a paper chromatography investigation, a sample fails to move up the paper when water is used as a solvent. How could the investigation be modified to address this problem?

Connecting the Concepts

32. Minerals are inorganic substances largely unaffected by heat. Vitamins are organic molecules with covalent bonds that can be broken by excessive heat.

33. GRAS implies that although a substance may be safe for nearly all people under almost all circumstances, there may still be some small risk for a very small fraction of the population.

34. No. It would be impossible to see where the components separated on the chromatography paper.

35. Compare the results from samples of vegetables tested before and after cooking.

Extending the Concepts

41. Investigate some additional types of chromatography, such as gas chromatography and column chromatography. Explain how each type works.

42. Modern food additives are generally safe and healthful. This was not always the case in the past. Research the history of food additives and the unexpected impact of some early additives on human health.

43. When administered in large doses, a prospective food additive is found to cause cancer in laboratory rats. Should this evidence be used to withhold the approval for its use in human foods? Explain your answer.

44. Research some food-preparation methods that tend to preserve vitamin content. Discuss the chemical concepts that can account for the effectiveness of such methods.

45. Liver is a rich source of many trace minerals. Explain this based on liver physiology.

46. Research *goiter*. When and where has it been most prevalent? Why? What specific product makes it much less common today?

47. Some historians claim that the most significant contribution to the success of the British Navy in the 1700s was adding sauerkraut to shipboard food supplies. Investigate and explain the possible connection.

36. Female 14–18: Ca = 51/1300 × 100% = 3.9%; Fe = 1.7/15 × 100% = 11%
    Male 14–18: Ca = 51/1300 × 100% = 3.9%: Fe =1.7 /11 × 100% = 15%
    Spinach provides a greater proportion of the DRI for Fe.

37. Probably negative. Foods without additives would look and taste unfamiliar and have shorter shelf lives than those to which we are accustomed.

38. If one component evaporated, it would not be detected.

39. All foods are composed of chemical substances (*all* matter is composed of "chemicals"). However, if a substance is a natural component of food, people do not commonly consider it a "chemical." This is a quirk of everyday language.

40. By a change in the solvent or the type of paper.

Extending the Concepts

41. Common features of all chromatography methods: They separate substances as they pass through a separation medium. They rely on a *mobile phase* and a *stationary phase;* separation is achieved when each component spends a different amount of time within each phase, depending on its relative attractions to each phase.

42. One hundred fifty years ago it was common to use heavy-metal compounds of mercury, lead, and chromium to add color to food and food containers. Such additives could compromise human health.

43. If the benefit were deemed high, the risk judged low, and no better substitute were available, then the wisest course would be to continue using the additive. Nearly all substances, when consumed in excessive quantities, may produce adverse side effects.

44. Cook at low temperatures, avoid boiling, and eat food fresh and uncooked, if possible. Vitamin solubility and rate of decomposition both increase with increases in temperature.

45. Among its many functions, the liver stores vitamins and minerals.

46. Goiter is an enlargement of the thyroid gland. It has been most prevalent in areas where soil is deficient in iodine. Goiter became rare in the U. S. after the 1920s, when iodized salt was introduced.

47. Sauerkraut has very high vitamin C content, and, because it is prepared by fermentation at room temperature, it is ideal for long sea voyages.

PUTTING IT ALL TOGETHER

School Vending Choices: Guiding PTSA's Decisions

Students serve as members of Riverwood High School's Vending Machine Policy Planning Committee. The committee submits its recommendations to the PTSA in a written report. Students use results of their three-day food inventory analyses completed throughout the unit as a basis for their recommendations. At this point, students have analyzed their food inventories in terms of energy, carbohydrates, fats, proteins, vitamins, and minerals in Making Decisions activities at the close of each section. Students prepare a report that summarizes their analyses and offers recommendations that stem from these results.

Materials

Students will need to access their three-day food inventories and their analyses completed through the unit. They also should have access to reference materials from the library, Internet, and departmental reference books. Give students a bibliographic form they can use as they report on their research. Instruct students about the required format of the final report (for instance, do you want it word-processed?).

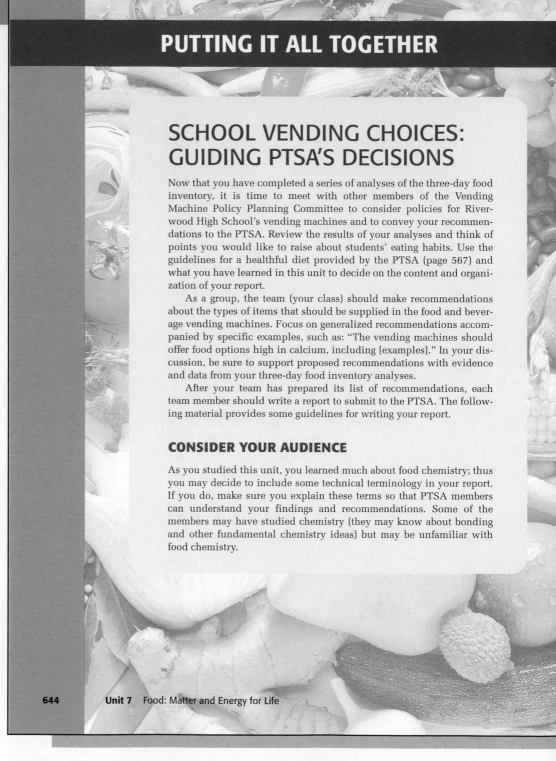

PUTTING IT ALL TOGETHER

SCHOOL VENDING CHOICES: GUIDING PTSA'S DECISIONS

Now that you have completed a series of analyses of the three-day food inventory, it is time to meet with other members of the Vending Machine Policy Planning Committee to consider policies for Riverwood High School's vending machines and to convey your recommendations to the PTSA. Review the results of your analyses and think of points you would like to raise about students' eating habits. Use the guidelines for a healthful diet provided by the PTSA (page 567) and what you have learned in this unit to decide on the content and organization of your report.

As a group, the team (your class) should make recommendations about the types of items that should be supplied in the food and beverage vending machines. Focus on generalized recommendations accompanied by specific examples, such as: "The vending machines should offer food options high in calcium, including [examples]." In your discussion, be sure to support proposed recommendations with evidence and data from your three-day food inventory analyses.

After your team has prepared its list of recommendations, each team member should write a report to submit to the PTSA. The following material provides some guidelines for writing your report.

CONSIDER YOUR AUDIENCE

As you studied this unit, you learned much about food chemistry; thus you may decide to include some technical terminology in your report. If you do, make sure you explain these terms so that PTSA members can understand your findings and recommendations. Some of the members may have studied chemistry (they may know about bonding and other fundamental chemistry ideas) but may be unfamiliar with food chemistry.

644   **Unit 7**   Food: Matter and Energy for Life

 Putting It All Together Supplement

 PTSA Report Rubric

WRITTEN REPORT

Your written report should include the following sections:

1. *Introduction.* The introduction should be a brief summary that highlights the characteristics of the three-day food inventory. In one or two paragraphs, present an overview of what you found in your food-inventory analyses. In addition, list your top three policy recommendations for the food and beverage vending machines. Do not include detailed explanations in this section.

2. *Background Information.* The background provides information that the PTSA members will need to understand your report. The following questions should be answered in this background section:

   ▶ What are fats, carbohydrates, and proteins? You may include information about each substance's molecular structure, energy content, and function in the human body.

   ▶ Why do humans need fats, carbohydrates, and proteins in their diets?

   ▶ What roles do vitamins and minerals play in the diet?

   ▶ You may include structural formulas and other diagrams; however, remember that you need to guide your readers regarding what to look for in any diagrams.

3. *Data Analysis.* The body of your report should be based on your analysis of the data. In this section, you bring together detailed data that you gathered concerning energy, fats, carbohydrates, proteins, vitamins, and minerals. Organize and present the information so that it will make sense to your readers. If helpful, include graphs and tables.

   In this data analysis section, you may wish to address questions about the food inventory such as the following:

   ▶ What is the average daily Calorie intake of Riverwood High School students? How reasonable is this value? Does the average daily Calorie intake accurately represent each day in the inventory or does it vary widely from day to day?

   ▶ What percent of total Calories are supplied by carbohydrates, fats, and proteins? Are these values consistent with recommendations in the 2005 *Dietary Guidelines for Americans*?

   ▶ What percent of fats are saturated and unsaturated? Do these levels meet *Dietary Guidelines*?

   ▶ Which vitamins and minerals are present at adequate levels? Which are lacking?

Writing

Encourage students to follow the report sequence described in the text. Each report should have an introduction, background information, data analysis, and conclusions. Encourage students to include technical terminology in their reports to accurately describe their findings. Students may need to include definitions for technical terms, since they should assume that PTSA members lack food-chemistry expertise.

Emphasize the conclusion section of this report (see student page 646). Students may need to research nutritional information for representative foods and beverages that should (or should not) be included in the school's vending machines. Also, encourage students to clearly explain *why* they elected to include (or exclude) certain items. Students should also consider the likelihood of students actually deciding to eat or drink a food item that they selected for inclusion.

You may decide to give students a scoring rubric to consult as they prepare their reports, so that they clearly understand expectations for this culminating task.

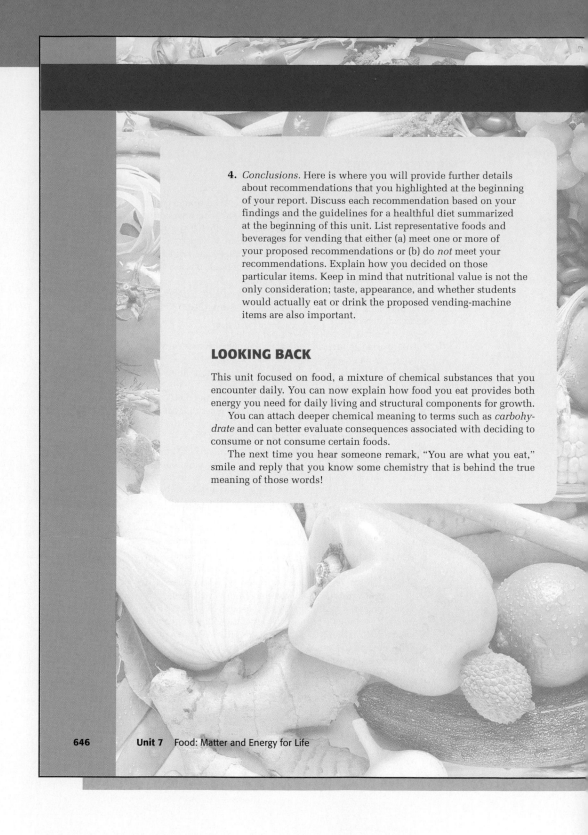

4. *Conclusions.* Here is where you will provide further details about recommendations that you highlighted at the beginning of your report. Discuss each recommendation based on your findings and the guidelines for a healthful diet summarized at the beginning of this unit. List representative foods and beverages for vending that either (a) meet one or more of your proposed recommendations or (b) do *not* meet your recommendations. Explain how you decided on those particular items. Keep in mind that nutritional value is not the only consideration; taste, appearance, and whether students would actually eat or drink the proposed vending-machine items are also important.

LOOKING BACK

This unit focused on food, a mixture of chemical substances that you encounter daily. You can now explain how food you eat provides both energy you need for daily living and structural components for growth. You can attach deeper chemical meaning to terms such as *carbohydrate* and can better evaluate consequences associated with deciding to consume or not consume certain foods.

The next time you hear someone remark, "You are what you eat," smile and reply that you know some chemistry that is behind the true meaning of those words!

THE SCIENTIFIC METHOD VS. SCIENTIFIC METHODS

Scientists deepen their knowledge and understanding of the natural world by observing and manipulating their environment. The inquiry approach used by scientists to solve problems and seek knowledge has led to vast increases in understanding how nature works. Many efforts have been made to formalize and list the steps that scientists use to generate and test new knowledge. You may have been asked to learn the "steps" of the Scientific Method, such as Make Observations, Define the Problem, and so on. But no one comes to an understanding of how scientific inquiry works by simply learning a list of steps or definitions of words.

Although you may not go on to become a research scientist, it is important that all students acquire the ability to conduct scientific inquiry. Why? Everyone is confronted daily with endless streams of facts and claims. What should be accepted as true? What should be discarded? Having well-developed ways to evaluate and test claims is essential in deciding between valid and deceptive information.

What abilities are needed to conduct scientific inquiry? According to the National Science Education Standards (NSES), they include the abilities to

- identify questions and concepts that guide scientific investigations.

- design and conduct scientific investigations.

- use technology and mathematics to improve investigations and communications.

- formulate and revise scientific explanations and models using logic and evidence.

- recognize and analyze alternative explanations and models.

- communicate and defend a scientific argument.

These skills are necessary for both doing and learning science. They are also important skills to evaluate information in daily living. You can only acquire these skills through practice—by doing exercises and investigations such as those contained in this textbook.

Even with all the abilities listed above, doing science is a complex behavior. The NSES outlines the ideas that all students should know and understand about the practices of science:

- Scientists usually inquire about how physical, living, or designed systems function.

- Scientists conduct investigations for a wide variety of reasons.

- Scientists rely on technology to enhance the gathering and manipulation of data.

- Mathematics is essential in scientific inquiry.

- Scientific explanations must adhere to criteria such as: a proposed explanation must be logically consistent; it must abide by the rules of evidence; it must be open to questions and possible modification; and it must be based on historical and current scientific knowledge.

- Results of scientific inquiry—new knowledge and methods—emerge from different types of investigations and public communication among scientists.

The last statement above acknowledges that—despite generalizations that can be listed—there are many paths to gaining new scientific knowledge. That is what makes studying scientific processes so important. Learning how to acquire the abilities to do and understand scientific inquiry may be the most important and useful thing you learn in this course.

NUMBERS IN CHEMISTRY

Chemistry is a quantitative science. Most chemistry investigations involve not only measuring, but also a search for the meaning among the measurements. Chemists learn how to interpret as well as perform calculations using these measurements.

SCIENTIFIC NOTATION

Chemists often deal with very small and very large numbers. Instead of using many zeros to express very large or very small numbers, they often use scientific notation. In scientific notation, a number can be rewritten as the product of a number between 1 and 10 and an exponential term—10^n, where n is a whole number. The exponential term is the number of times 10 would have to be multiplied or divided by itself to yield the appropriate number of digits in the number. For instance, 10^3 is $10 \times 10 \times 10$, or 1000; $3.5 \times 10^3 = 3500$.

> **Sample Problem 1:** *Express the distance between New York City and San Francisco, 4 741 000 meters, using scientific notation.*
>
> 4 741 000 m $= (4.741 \times 1\ 000\ 000)$ m or **4.741×10^6 m**
>
> **Sample Problem 2:** *Express the amount of ranitidine hydrochloride in a Zantac tablet, 0.000 479 mol, using scientific notation.*
>
> 0.000 479 mol $= 4.79 \times 0.0001$ mol or **4.79×10^{-4} mol**

It is easier to assess magnitude and to perform operations with numbers written in scientific notation than with numbers fully written out. As you will see, it is also easier to communicate the precision of the measurements involved.

Rules for adding and subtracting using scientific notation:

> **Step 1.** Convert the numbers to the same power of 10.
>
> **Step 2.** Add (subtract) the non-exponential portion of the numbers. *The power of ten remains the same.*

Example
Add $(1.00 \times 10^4) + (2.30 \times 10^5)$.

> **Step 1.** A good rule to follow is to express all numbers in the problem to the highest power of ten. Convert 1.00×10^4 to 0.100×10^5.
>
> **Step 2.** $(0.100 \times 10^5) + (2.30 \times 10^5) = 2.40 \times 10^5$

Rules for multiplying *using scientific notation:*

Step 1. Multiply the nonexponential numbers.

Step 2. Add the exponents.

Step 3. Convert the answer to scientific notation.

Sample Problem: *Multiply (4.24×10^2) by (5.78×10^4).*

Steps 1 and 2. $(4.24 \times 5.78) \times (10^{2+4}) = 24.5 \times 10^6$

Step 3. Convert to scientific notation $= 2.45 \times 10^7$

Rules for dividing *using scientific notation:*

Step 1. Divide the nonexponential numbers.

Step 2. Subtract the denominator exponent from the numerator exponent.

Step 3. Express the answer in scientific notation.

Sample Problem: *Divide (3.78×10^5) by (6.2×10^8).*

Steps 1 and 2. $\dfrac{3.78}{6.2} \times (10^{5-8}) = 0.61 \times 10^{-3}$

Step 3. Convert to scientific notation $= 6.1 \times 10^{-4}$

Practice Problems*

1. Convert the following numbers to scientific notation.
   a. 0.000 036 9
   b. 0.0452
   c. 4 520 000
   d. 365 000

2. Carry out the following operations:
   a. $(1.62 \times 10^3) + (3.4 \times 10^2)$
   b. $(1.75 \times 10^{-1}) - (4.6 \times 10^{-2})$
   c. $\dfrac{6.02 \times 10^{23}}{12.0}$
   d. $\dfrac{(6.63 \times 10^{-34} \text{ J·s}) \times (3.00 \times 10^8 \text{ m s}^{-1})}{4.6 \times 10^{-9} \text{ m}}$

*Answers to odd-numbered problems can be found on page A-17.

DIMENSIONAL ANALYSIS

Dimensional analysis, also called the *factor-label method,* is used by scientists to keep track of units in calculations and to help guide their work in solving problems. You already used this method to convert from one type of metric unit to another. The method is helpful in setting up problems and also in checking work.

Dimensional analysis consists of three basic steps:

Step 1. Identify equivalence relationships in order to create suitable conversion factors.

Step 2. Identify the given unit(s) and the new unit(s) desired.

Step 3. Arrange each conversion factor so that each unit to be converted can be divided by itself (and thus cancelled).

Sample Problem 1: *In an exercise to determine the volume of a rectangular object, your laboratory partner measured the object's length as 12.2 in (inches). However, measurements of the object's width and height were recorded in centimeters. In order to calculate the object's volume, convert the object's measured length to centimeters.*

Step 1. Find the equivalence relating centimeters and inches.
$$2.54 \text{ cm} = 1 \text{ in}$$

Step 2. Identify the given unit and the new unit.
Given unit = in   new unit = cm

Step 3. Create a fraction so that the "given" unit (in) can be divided and thus cancelled.
$$12.2 \; \cancel{\text{in}} \times \frac{2.54 \text{ cm}}{1 \; \cancel{\text{in}}} = 31.0 \text{ cm}$$

Sample Problem 2: *How many seconds are in 24 hours?*

Step 1. Identify the equivalence:
1 hr = 60 min   1 min = 60 s

Step 2. Given unit: hr   new unit: s

Step 3. Arrange for the given unit to cancel and progress to the desired unit:
$$24 \; \cancel{\text{hr}} \left(\frac{60 \; \cancel{\text{min}}}{1 \; \cancel{\text{hr}}} \right) \times \left(\frac{60 \text{ s}}{1 \; \cancel{\text{min}}} \right) = 86\,400 \text{ s}$$

3. The distance between two European cities is 4 741 000 m. That may sound impressive, but to put all those digits on a car odometer is slightly inconvenient. Kilometers are a better choice for measuring distance in this case. Convert the distance to kilometers.

4. The density of aluminum is 2.70 g/cm³. What is the mass of 234 cm³ of aluminum?

SIGNIFICANT FIGURES

Significant figures are all the digits in a measured or calculated value that are known with certainty plus the first uncertain digit. Numerical measurements have some inherent uncertainty. This uncertainty comes from the measurement device as well as from the human making the measurement. No measurement is exact. When you use a measuring device in the laboratory, read and record each measurement to one digit beyond the smallest marking interval on the scale.

Guidelines for Determining Significant Figures

Step 1. All digits recorded from a laboratory measurement are called significant figures.

The measurement of 4.75 cm has three significant figures.

Note: If you use a measuring device that has a digital readout, such as a balance, you should record the measurement just as it appears on the display.

Measurement	Number of Significant Figures
123 g	3
46.54 mL	4
0.33 cm	2
3 300 000 nm	2
0.033 g	2

Step 2. All non-zero digits are considered significant.

*Answers to odd-numbered problems can be found on page A-17.

A-6   Appendix B: Numbers in Chemistry

Step 3. There are special rules for zeros. Zeros in a measurement or calculation fall into three types: middle zeros, leading zeros, and trailing zeros.

Middle zeros are always significant.

303 mm   a middle zero—always significant. This measurement has three significant figures.

A leading zero is never significant. It is only a placeholder, not a part of the actual measurement.

0.0123 kg   two leading zeros—never significant. This measurement has three significant figures.

A trailing zero is significant when it is to the right of a decimal point. This is not a placeholder. It is a part of the actual measurement.

23.20 mL   a trailing zero—significant to the right of a decimal point. This measurement has four significant figures.

The most common errors concerning significant figures are (1) reporting all digits found on a calculator readout, (2) failing to include significant trailing zeros (14.150 g), and (3) considering leading zeros to be significant—0.002 g has only one significant figure, not three.

Practice Problem*

5. How many significant figures are in each of the following?

    a. 451 000 m   **d.** 0.0065 g

    b. 4056 V   **e.** 0.0540 mL

    c. 6.626×10^{-34} J·s

Using Significant Figures in Calculations

Addition and subtraction: The number of *decimal places* in the answer should be the same as in the measured quantity with the smallest number of *decimal places.*

Sample Problem: *Add the following measured values and express the answer to the correct number of significant figures.*

$$
\begin{array}{r}
1259.1 \text{ g} \\
2.365 \text{ g} \\
+ \ 15.34 \text{ g} \\
\hline
1276.805 \text{ g}
\end{array}
\quad = \textbf{1276.8 g}
$$

*Answers to odd-numbered problems can be found on page A-17.

Multiplication and division: The number of *significant figures* in the answer should be the same as in the measured quantity with the smallest number of *significant figures*.

> **Sample Problem:** *Divide the following measured values and express the answer to the correct number of significant figures.*

$$\frac{13.356 \text{ g}}{10.42 \text{ mL}} = 1.2817658 \text{ g/mL} = \mathbf{1.282 \text{ g/mL}}$$

Practice Problem*

6. Report the answer to each of these using the correct number of significant figures.

    a. $16.27 \text{ g} + 0.463 \text{ g} + 32.1 \text{ g}$

    b. $42.04 \text{ mL} - 3.5 \text{ mL}$

    c. $15.1 \text{ km} \times 0.032 \text{ km}$

    d. $\dfrac{13.36 \text{ cm}^3}{0.0468 \text{ cm}^3}$

Note: Only measurements resulting from scale readings or digital readouts carry a limited number of significant figures. However, values arising from direct counting (such as 25 students in a classroom) or from definitions (such as 100 cm = 1 m, or 1 dozen = 12 things) carry unlimited significant figures. Such "counted" or "defined" values are regarded as exact.

*Answers to odd-numbered problems can be found on page A-17.

CONSTRUCTING GRAPHS

Graphs are of four basic types: pie charts, bar graphs, line graphs, and x-y plots. The type chosen depends on the characteristics of the data displayed.

Pie charts show the relationship of the parts to the whole. This presentation helps a reader visualize the magnitude of difference among various parts. They are made by taking a 360° circle and dividing it into wedges according to the percent of the whole represented by each part.

Bar graphs and **line graphs** compare values within a category or among categories. The horizontal axis (x-axis) is used for the quantity that can be controlled or adjusted. This quantity is the **independent variable.** The vertical axis (y-axis) is used for the quantity that is influenced by the changes in the quantity on the x-axis. This quantity is the **dependent variable.** For example, a bar graph could present a visual comparison of the fat content (dependent variable on the y-axis) of types of cheese (independent variable on the x-axis). Such a graph would make it easy to choose a cheese snack with a low-fat content. Bar graphs can also be useful in studying trends over time.

Graphs involving **x-y plots** are commonly used in scientific work. Sometimes it is difficult to decide if a graph is a line graph or an x-y plot. In an x-y plot, it is possible to determine a mathematical relationship between the variables. Sometimes the relationship is the equation for a straight line ($y = mx + b$), but other times it is more complex and may require transformation of the data to produce a simpler graphical relationship. The first example below refers to a straight-line or direct relationship.

Sample Problem 1: *A group of entrepreneurs was considering investing in a mine that was said to contain gold. To verify this claim, they gave several small, irregular mined particles to a chemist, who was told to use nondestructive methods to analyze the samples.*

The chemist decided to determine the density of the small samples. The chemist found the volume of each particle and determined its mass. The data collected are shown in the table below.

Particle	Volume (mL)	Mass (g)
1	0.006	0.116
2	0.012	0.251
3	0.015	0.290
4	0.018	0.347
5	0.021	0.386

The chemist then used these data to construct an *x-y* plot.

Gold Particle Data

Since the *x-y* plot is linear, the sample materials are likely the same. If point (0, 0) is included (a sample of zero volume has zero mass), the slope is about 19 g/mL, close to gold's density (19.3 g/mL), so these are likely gold particles.

> **Sample Problem 2:** *The graph below is a plot of data gathered at constant temperature involving the volume of 2.00 mol of ammonia (NH₃) gas measured at various pressures. Determine whether the measurements are related by a simple mathematical relationship.*

Volume of 2.00 mol NH₃ at Different Pressures

When the best smooth graph line is not a straight line (or direct relationship), the data can be manipulated to see if any other simple mathematical relationship is possible. Several of the most common types of mathematical relationships are inverse, exponential, and logarithmic. Each relationship has unique characteristics that can often be identified from the graphical presentation. Knowing the mathematical relationship allows scientists to interpret the data. In this case, it appears that as the pressure increases the volume decreases, which is a characteristic of an inverse relationship. In testing this theory, the value of 1/V (the inverse of the volume) can be calculated, recorded in another column of the table, and plotted versus the pressure.

$\dfrac{1}{\text{Volume}}$ of 2.00 mol NH$_3$ at Different Pressures

This graph exhibits a straight line showing that pressure is directly related to the inverse of the volume. This leads to the mathematical result that pressure and volume are inversely related. If this mathematical manipulation had not resulted in a straight line, some other reasonable relationships might have been considered and tested.

EQUATIONS, MOLES, AND STOICHIOMETRY

MOLES AND MOLAR MASS

The **mole** is regarded as a counting number–a number used to specify a certain number of objects. **Pair** and **dozen** are other examples of counting numbers. A mole equals 6.02×10^{23} objects. Most often, things that are counted in units of moles are very small—atoms, molecules, or electrons.

The modern definition of a mole specifies that one mole is equal to the number of atoms contained in exactly 12 g of the carbon-12 isotope. This number is named after Amedeo Avogadro, who proposed the idea, but never determined the number. At least four different types of experiments have accurately determined the value of Avogadro's number—the number of units in one mole. Avogadro's number is known to eight significant figures, but three will be enough for most of your calculations—6.02×10^{23}.

The modern atomic weight scale is also based on C-12. Compared to C-12 atoms with a defined atomic mass of exactly 12, hydrogen atoms have a relative mass of 1.008. Therefore, one mole of hydrogen atoms has a mass of 1.008 g. One mole of oxygen atoms equals 15.9994 g—also called the molar mass of oxygen. The total mass of one mole of a compound is found by adding the atomic weights of all of the atoms in the formula and expressing the sum in units of grams.

Sample Problem: *Calculate the mass of one mole of water.*

$$2 \; \cancel{mol \, H} \times \frac{1.008 \text{ g H}}{1 \; \cancel{mol \, H}} = 2.016 \text{ g H}$$

$$1 \; \cancel{mol \, O} \times \frac{16.00 \text{ g O}}{1 \; \cancel{mol \, O}} = 16.00 \text{ g O}$$

molar mass of water = 2.016 g + 16.00 g = 18.02 g

Practice Problems*

Find the molar mass (in units of g/mol) for each of the following:

1. Acetic acid, CH_3COOH
2. Formaldehyde, $HCHO$
3. Glucose, $C_6H_{12}O_6$
4. 2-Dodecanol, $CH_3(CH_2)_9CH(OH)CH_3$

*Answers to odd-numbered problems can be found on page A-17.

GRAM-MOLE CONVERSIONS

Conversions between grams and moles can be readily accomplished by using the technique of dimensional analysis (see Appendix B).

Sample Problem 1: *What mass (in grams) of water contains 0.25 mol H_2O?* The mass of one mole of water (18.02 g) is found as illustrated earlier. Two factors can be written, based on that relationship:

$$\frac{1 \text{ mol } H_2O}{18.02 \text{ g } H_2O} \quad \text{and} \quad \frac{18.02 \text{ g } H_2O}{1 \text{ mol } H_2O}$$

The second conversion factor is chosen so that each unit to be converted is divided by itself and thus cancelled. Units for the answer are g H_2O, as expected.

$$0.25 \text{ mol } H_2O \times \frac{18.02 \text{ g } H_2O}{1 \text{ mol } H_2O} = 4.5 \text{ g } H_2O$$

Sample Problem 2: *How many moles of water molecules are present in a 1.00-kg sample of water?*

$$1.00 \text{ kg } H_2O \times \frac{1000 \text{ g } H_2O}{1 \text{ kg } H_2O} \times \frac{1 \text{ mol } H_2O}{18.02 \text{ g } H_2O} = 55.5 \text{ mol } H_2O$$

Practice Problems*

5. Acetic acid, CH_3COOH, and salicylic acid, $C_7H_6O_3$, can be chemically combined to form aspirin. If a chemist uses 5.00 g salicylic acid and 10.53 g acetic acid, how many moles of each compound are involved?

6. Calcium chloride hexahydrate, $CaCl_2 \cdot 6H_2O$, can be sprinkled on sidewalks to melt ice and snow. How many moles of that compound are in a 5.0-kg sack of that substance?

A QUANTITATIVE UNDERSTANDING OF CHEMICAL FORMULAS

Calculating percent composition from a formula

The percent by mass of each component found in a sample of material is called its **percent composition.** To find the percent of an element in a particular compound, first calculate the molar mass of the compound. Then find the total mass of the element contained in one mole of the compound. Then divide the mass of the element by the molar mass of the compound and multiply the result by 100%.

Sample Problem 1: *Calculate the molar mass of sucrose, $C_{12}H_{22}O_{11}$.*

$$12 \text{ mol C } (12.01 \text{ g/mol}) = 144.1 \text{ g}$$
$$22 \text{ mol H } (1.008 \text{ g/mol}) = 22.18 \text{ g}$$
$$11 \text{ mol O } (16.00 \text{ g/mol}) = \underline{176.0 \text{ g}}$$
$$\text{Molar mass of } C_{12}H_{22}O_{11} = 342.3 \text{ g}$$

*Answers to odd-numbered problems can be found on page A-17.

Sample Problem 2: *Find the mass percent of each element in sucrose (rounded to significant figures).*

$$\% \text{ C} = \frac{\text{mass C}}{\text{mass C}_{12}\text{H}_{22}\text{O}_{11}} \times 100\% = \frac{144.1 \text{ g C}}{342.3 \text{ g C}_{12}\text{H}_{22}\text{O}_{11}} \times 100\% = 42.10\% \text{ C}$$

$$\% \text{ H} = \frac{\text{mass H}}{\text{mass C}_{12}\text{H}_{22}\text{O}_{11}} \times 100\% = \frac{22.18 \text{ g H}}{342.3 \text{ g C}_{12}\text{H}_{22}\text{O}_{11}} \times 100\% = 6.48\% \text{ H}$$

$$\% \text{ O} = \frac{\text{mass O}}{\text{mass C}_{12}\text{H}_{22}\text{O}_{11}} \times 100\% = \frac{176.0 \text{ g O}}{342.3 \text{ g C}_{12}\text{H}_{22}\text{O}_{11}} \times 100\% = 51.42\% \text{ O}$$

Practice Problems*

7. Barium sulfate, $BaSO_4$, is commonly used to detect gastrointestinal tract abnormalities; it is administered as a water suspension by mouth prior to X-ray imaging. Find the mass percent of each element in barium sulfate.

8. Sodium acetate is a common component in commercial thermal packs. Find the mass percent of each element in sodium acetate, $NaCH_3COO$.

Deriving formulas from percent composition data

An **empirical formula** gives the relative numbers of each element in a substance, using the smallest whole numbers for subscripts. The empirical formula of a compound can be calculated from percent composition data. A formula requires the relative numbers of moles of each element, so percent values must be converted to grams and grams to moles. It is easiest to assume 100 g of compound. Then each percent value is equal to the total grams of that element.

Sample Problem 1: *A hydrocarbon (the only elements in the compound are hydrogen and carbon) consists of 85.7% carbon and 14.3% hydrogen by mass. What is its empirical formula?*

Step 1. Assume 100 g of compound—thus 85.7 g are carbon and 14.3 g are hydrogen.

Step 2. Use dimensional analysis to find the total moles of each element in the compound.

$$85.7 \text{ g C} \times \frac{1 \text{ mol C}}{12.01 \text{ g C}} = 7.14 \text{ mol C}$$

$$14.3 \text{ g H} \times \frac{1 \text{ mol H}}{1.008 \text{ g H}} = 14.2 \text{ mol H}$$

Step 3. Determine the smallest whole-number ratio of moles of elements by dividing all mole values by the smallest value.

$$\frac{7.14 \text{ mol C}}{7.14} = 1 \text{ mol C}$$

$$\frac{14.2 \text{ mol H}}{7.14} = 1.99 \text{ mol H}$$

The ratio of moles C to moles H = 1:2, so the empirical formula for the compound must be CH_2.

*Answers to odd-numbered problems can be found on page A-16.

Sample Problem 2: *The percent composition of one of the oxides of nitrogen is 74.07% oxygen and 25.93% nitrogen. What is the empirical formula of that compound?*

Step 1. 100 g of compound consists of 74.07 g oxygen and 25.93 g nitrogen.

Step 2. $25.93 \text{ g N} \times \dfrac{1 \text{ mol N}}{14.01 \text{ g N}} = 1.851 \text{ mol N}$

$74.07 \text{ g O} \times \dfrac{1 \text{ mol O}}{16.00 \text{ g O}} = 4.629 \text{ mol O}$

Step 3. $\dfrac{1.851 \text{ mol N}}{1.851} = 1 \text{ mol N}$

$\dfrac{4.629 \text{ mol O}}{1.851} = 2.50 \text{ mol O}$

Step 4. This ratio (1:2.5) does not consist entirely of whole numbers. Thus all the numbers in the ratio must be multiplied by a number that converts the decimal to a whole number. In this case the number is 2, and the empirical formula becomes N_2O_5.

Practice Problems*

9. The percent composition by mass of an industrially important substance is 2.04% H, 32.72% S, and 65.24% O. What is the formula of this compound?

10. Determine the empirical formula of a compound that contains (by mass) 38.71% C, 9.71% H, and 51.58% O.

MASS RELATIONSHIPS IN CHEMICAL REACTIONS

Since the total number of atoms is conserved in a chemical reaction, their masses must also be conserved, as expected from the law of conservation of mass. In the equation for the formation of water from the elements hydrogen and oxygen, $2H_2(g) + O_2(g) \rightarrow 2H_2O(l)$, 2 molecules of hydrogen gas and 1 molecule of oxygen gas combine to form 2 molecules of water. One could also interpret the equation this way: 2 mol hydrogen gas react with 1 mol oxygen gas to form 2 mol water. Using the molar mass of each substance, the mass relationships in the table below can be determined. The ratio of moles of hydrogen gas to moles of oxygen gas in forming water will be 2:1. If 10 mol hydrogen gas are available, 5 mol oxygen gas are required.

$2 H_2(g)$	$+$	$O_2(g)$	$\rightarrow$	$2 H_2O(l)$
2 molecules		1 molecule		2 molecules
2 mol		1 mol		2 mol
2 mol × (2.02 g/mol)		1 mol × (32.00 g/mol)		2 mol × (18.02 g/mol)
4.04 g		32.00 g		36.04 g

*Answers to odd-numbered problems can be found on page A-17.

Solving problems involving the masses of products and/or reactants is conveniently accomplished by dimensional analysis. And remember, all numerical problems involving chemical reactions involve a correctly balanced equation.

Sample Problem: *Find the mass of water formed when 10.0 g hydrogen gas completely reacts with oxygen gas.*

$$2 H_2(g) + O_2(g) \rightarrow 2 H_2O(l)$$

Step 1. Find the moles of hydrogen gas represented by 10.0 g, using the molar mass of H_2.

$$10.0 \text{ g } H_2 \times \frac{1 \text{ mol } H_2}{2.02 \text{ g } H_2} = 4.95 \text{ mol } H_2$$

Step 2. Find the total moles of H_2O produced by 4.95 mol H_2. From the balanced equation, you know that for every 2 mol H_2, 2 mol H_2O are produced.

$$4.95 \text{ mol } H_2 \times \frac{2 \text{ mol } H_2O}{2 \text{ mol } H_2} = 4.95 \text{ mol } H_2O$$

Step 3. Find the mass of H_2O that contains 4.95 mol H_2O by using the molar mass of water.

$$4.95 \text{ mol } H_2O \times \frac{18.02 \text{ g } H_2O}{1 \text{ mol } H_2O} = 89.2 \text{ g } H_2O$$

Most chemistry students find it is more convenient to set up all three steps in one extended calculation. Assure yourself that all units divide and cancel except for grams of water (g H_2O)—an appropriate way to express the answer sought in the problem.

$$10.0 \text{ g } H_2 \times \underbrace{\frac{1 \text{ mol } H_2}{2.02 \text{ g } H_2}}_{\substack{\text{Molar mass} \\ \text{of } H_2}} \times \underbrace{\frac{2 \text{ mol } H_2O}{2 \text{ mol } H_2}}_{\substack{\text{Coefficients} \\ \text{in equation}}} \times \underbrace{\frac{18.02 \text{ g } H_2O}{1 \text{ mol } H_2O}}_{\substack{\text{Molar mass} \\ \text{of } H_2O}} = 89.2 \text{ g } H_2O$$

Practice Problems*

11. Find the mass of copper(II) oxide formed if 2.0 g copper metal completely reacts with oxygen gas.

$$2 Cu(s) + O_2(g) \rightarrow 2 CuO(s)$$

12. What mass of water is produced when 25.0 g methane gas reacts completely with oxygen gas?

$$CH_4(g) + 2 O_2(g) \rightarrow 2 H_2O(g) + CO_2(g)$$

*Answers to odd-numbered problems can be found on page A-17.

ANSWERS TO ALL PRACTICE PROBLEMS

Appendix B

1. **a.** 3.69×10^{-5}
   b. 4.52×10^{-2}
   c. 4.52×10^6
   d. 3.65×10^5
2. **a.** 2.0×10^3
   b. 1.3×10^{-1}
   c. 5.02×10^{22}
   d. 4.3×10^{-17}
3. 4741 km
4. *632 g*
5. **a.** 3
   b. 4
   c. 4
   d. 2
   e. 3
6. **a.** *48.8 g*
   b. *38.5 mL*
   c. *0.48 km²*
   d. *285*

Appendix D

1. 60.05 g/mol
2. *30.03 g/mol*
3. 180.16 g/mol
4. *186.33 g/mol*
5. 0.1754 mol acetic acid, 0.0362 mol salicylic acid
6. *23 mol $CaCl_2 \bullet H_2O$*
7. 58.54% Ba, 13.74% S, 27.42% O
8. *28.03% Na, 29.28% C, 3.686% H, 39.01% O*
9. H_2SO_4
10. *CH_3O*
11. 2.5 g CuO
12. *56.2 g H_2O*

The black, odd answers appear in the Student Edition text.
The blue even answers appear only in the Teacher's Edition text.

A

absolute temperature scale
See kelvin temperature scale

absolute zero
the lowest temperature theoretically obtainable, which is 0 K (zero kelvins), or -273 °C

acid–base reaction
See neutralization

acid rain
fog, sleet, snow, or rain with a pH lower than about 5.6 due to dissolved gases such as SO_2, SO_3, and NO_2

acidic solution
an aqueous solution with a pH < 7; it turns litmus from blue to red

acids
ions or compounds that produce hydrogen ions, H^+ (or hydronium ions, H_3O^+), when dissolved in water

activation energy
the minimum energy required for the successful collision of reactant particles in a chemical reaction

active site
the location on an enzyme where a substrate molecule becomes positioned for a reaction

activity series
the ranking of elements in order of chemical reactivity

addition polymer
a polymer formed by repeated addition reactions at double or triple bonds within monomer units

addition reaction
a reaction at the double or triple bond within an organic molecule

adsorb
to take up or hold molecules or particles to the surface of a material

aeration
the mixing of air into a liquid, as in water sprayed into air, or as in water flowing over a dam

alcohol
a nonaromatic organic compound containing one or more –OH groups

alkali metal family
the group of elements consisting of lithium, sodium, potassium, rubidium, cesium, and francium

alkaline
a basic solution containing an excess of hydroxide ions (OH^-)

alkane
a hydrocarbon containing only single covalent bonds

alkene
a hydrocarbon containing one or more double covalent bonds

alkyne
a hydrocarbon containing one or more triple covalent bonds

allotropes
two or more forms of an element in the same state that have distinctly different physical and/or chemical properties

alloy
a solid solution consisting of atoms of two or more metals

alpha decay
the radioactive decay of a nucleus that is accompanied by the emission of an alpha particle

alpha particles (α)
high-speed, positively charged particles emitted during the decay of some radioactive elements; consist of a helium nucleus, ${}_2^4He^{2+}$

amine group
a nitrogen atom (with attached hydrogen atoms) connected to a carbon chain

amino acid
an organic molecule containing a carboxylic acid group and an amine group; serves as a protein building block

anion
a negatively charged ion

anode
an electrode in an electrochemical cell at which oxidation occurs

aqueous solution
a solution in which water is the solvent

aquifer
a structure of porous rock, sand, or gravel that holds water beneath Earth's surface

aromatic compound
a ringlike compound, such as benzene, that can be represented as having alternating double and single bonds between carbon atoms

atmosphere
(a) a unit of gas pressure (atm); (b) the gaseous envelope surrounding Earth, composed of four layers: troposphere, stratosphere, mesosphere, and thermosphere

atom
the smallest particle possessing the properties of an element

atomic mass
the mass of a particular atom of an element

atomic number
the number of protons in an atom; this value distinguishes atoms of different elements

atomic weight
the average mass of an atom of an element as found in nature

average
See mean

Avogadro's law
equal volumes of all gases, measured at the same temperature and pressure, contain the same number of gas molecules

Avogadro's number
6.02×10^{23} particles, which represents one mole of particles

B

background radiation
the relatively constant level of natural radioactivity that is always present

balanced chemical equation
See chemical equation

barometer
a device that measures atmospheric pressure

base unit
an SI unit that expresses a fundamental physical quantity (such as temperature, length, or mass)

bases
ions or compounds that produce OH^- ions when dissolved in water

basic solution
an aqueous solution with a pH > 7; the solution turns litmus from red to blue

batch process
a series of discrete steps or operations involved in producing a substance or other product; *see also* continuous process

battery
a device composed of one or more connected voltaic cells that supplies electrical current

beta decay
the radioactive decay of a nucleus accompanied by the emission of a beta particle

beta particles (β)
negatively charged particles emitted during the decay of some radioactive elements; composed of high-speed electrons

biodiesel
an alternative fuel or fuel additive for diesel engines made from various materials such as new or recycled vegetable oils and animal fats

biomolecules
large organic molecules found in living systems

boiling point
the temperature at which a liquid boils at normal atmospheric pressure

bond, chemical
See chemical bond

Boyle's law
the pressure and volume of a gas sample at constant temperature are inversely proportional; $PV = k$

branched-chain alkane
an alkane in which at least one carbon atom is bonded to three or four other carbon atoms

branched polymer
a polymer formed by reactions that create numerous side chains rather than linear chains

brittle
a property of a material that causes it to shatter under pressure

buffer
a substance or combination of dissolved substances capable of resisting changes in pH when limited quantities of either acid or base are added

C

Calorie (Cal)
a unit of energy; thermal energy required to raise the temperature of one kilogram of water by one degree Celsius; commonly used to express quantity of food energy; informally called *food calorie*; 1 Cal = 1000 cal; 1 kJ = 4.184 Cal

calorie (cal)
a unit of energy; thermal energy required to raise the temperature of one gram of water by one degree Celsius; 1 J = 4.184 cal

carbohydrates
substances such as sugars and starches that are composed of carbon, hydrogen, and oxygen atoms; a main source of energy in foods

carbon chain
carbon atoms chemically linked to one another, forming a chainlike molecular structure

carbon cycle
the movement of carbon atoms within Earth's ecosystems, from carbon storage as plant and animal matter, through release as carbon dioxide due to cellular respiration, combustion, and decay, to reacquisition by plants

carboxylic acid
an organic compound containing the —COOH group

carcinogens
substances known to cause cancer

catalyst
a substance that speeds up a chemical reaction but is itself unchanged

catalytic converter
the reaction chamber in an auto exhaust system designed to accelerate the conversion of potentially harmful exhaust gases to nitrogen gas, carbon dioxide, and water vapor

cathode
an electrode in an electrochemical cell at which reduction occurs

cathode ray
a beam of electrons emitted from a cathode when electricity is passed through an evacuated tube

cation
a positively charged ion

Celsius temperature scale (°C)
SI temperature scale; originally based on the freezing point of water (0 °C) and its normal boiling point (100 °C)

CFCs
See chlorofluorocarbons (CFCs)

chain reaction
in nuclear fission, a reaction that is sustained because it produces enough neutrons to collide with and split additional fissionable nuclei

Charles' law
the volume of a gas sample at constant pressure is directly proportional to its kelvin temperature; $V = kT$

chemical bond
the attractive force that holds atoms or ions together; *see also* covalent bonds; ionic bonds

chemical change
an interaction of matter that results in the formation of one or more new substances

chemical energy
energy stored in the chemical bonds of substances

chemical equation
a symbolic expression summarizing a chemical reaction, such as $2\ H_2(g) + O_2(g) \longrightarrow 2\ H_2O(g)$

chemical formula
a symbolic expression representing the elements contained in a substance, together with subscripts that indicate the relative numbers of atoms of each element

chemical properties
properties only observed or measured by changing the chemical identity of a sample of matter

chemical reaction
the process of forming new substances from reactants that involves the breaking and forming of chemical bonds

chemical species
See species

chemical symbol
an abbreviation of an element's name, such as N for nitrogen or Fe for iron

chemistry
a branch of natural science dealing with the composition of matter and the structures, properties, and reactions of substances

chlorination
adding chlorine (as gas or hypochlorite) in water treatment to kill harmful microorganisms

chlorofluorocarbons (CFCs)
synthetic substances previously used as aerosol propellants, cooling fluids, and cleaning solvents; CFCs lead to stratospheric ozone destruction through production of chlorine radicals

cis–trans isomerism
isomers based on arrangement about a double bond in a molecule; the *cis-* isomer has attachments on the same side of the double bond, while the *trans-* isomer has attachments on opposite sides of double bond

cloud chamber
a container filled with supersaturated air that, when cooled and exposed to ionizing radiation, produces visible trails of condensation, tracing paths taken by radioactive emissions

CNG
See compressed natural gas (CNG)

coating
a treatment in which a material is physically or chemically attached to a product's surface, typically for protection

coefficients
the numbers in a chemical equation that indicate the relative numbers of units of each reactant or product involved in the reaction

coenzyme
an organic molecule that interacts with an enzyme to facilitate or enhance its activity

collision theory
for a reaction to occur, reactant molecules must collide in proper orientation with sufficient kinetic energy

colloid
a mixture containing solid particles small enough to remain suspended and not settle out

color standard
colored solutions of known concentration that allow estimating an unknown solution concentration based on color-intensity comparisons to the color standards

colorimeter
an instrument for determining the concentration of a colored solution based on color-intensity measurements

colorimetry
a chemical analysis method that uses color intensity to determine solution concentration

combustion
a chemical reaction with oxygen gas that produces thermal energy and light; burning

complementary proteins
multiple protein sources that provide adequate amounts of all essential amino acids when consumed together

complete protein
a protein source for humans containing adequate amounts of all essential amino acids

complex ion
a single central atom or ion, usually a metal ion, to which other atoms, molecules, or ions are attached

compound
a substance composed of two or more elements bonded together in fixed proportions; a compound cannot be broken down into simpler substances by physical means

compressed natural gas (CNG)
natural gas condensed under high pressures (160–240 atm) and stored in metal cylinders; CNG can serve as a substitute for gasoline or diesel fuel

concentration
See solution concentration

condensation
converting a substance from its gaseous state to liquid or solid state

condensation polymer
a polymer formed by repeated condensation reactions of one or more monomers

condensation reaction
the chemical combination of two organic molecules, accompanied by the loss of water or other small molecule

condensed formula
a chemical formula that provides additional information about bonding; for example, the condensed formula for propane, C_3H_8, is $CH_3—CH_2—CH_3$ or $CH_3CH_2CH_3$

conductor
a material that allows electricity (or thermal energy) to flow through it

confirming test
a laboratory test giving a positive result if a particular chemical species is present

continuous process
an uninterrupted sequence or flow of operations involved in producing a substance or other product; *see also* batch process

control
in an experiment, a trial that duplicates all conditions except for the variable under investigation

conversion factor
a factor by which a quantity expressed in one set of units is multiplied to convert it to another set of units

corrosion
a chemical action causing the gradual destruction of a metal's surface through oxidation–reduction processes

covalent bond
a linkage between two atoms involving the sharing of one pair (single bond), two pairs (double bond), or three pairs (triple bond) of electrons

cracking
the process by which hydrocarbon molecules from petroleum are converted to smaller molecules, using thermal energy and a catalyst

critical mass
the minimum mass of fissionable material needed to sustain a nuclear chain reaction

cross-linking
polymer chains interconnected by chemical bonds; causes polymer rigidity

crude oil
unrefined liquid petroleum as it is pumped from the ground by oil wells

curie (Ci)
a formerly used expression of a sample's radioactive intensity, equal to radiation emitted by one gram of radium-226, or 37 billion atoms undergoing radioactive decay per second; the corresponding SI unit is the becquerel (Bq), where $1 \text{ Bq} = 2.703 \times 10^{-11}$ Ci

cycloalkane
a saturated hydrocarbon containing carbon atoms joined in a ring

D

data
objective pieces of information, such as information gathered in a laboratory investigation

decant
to pour slowly from the top of a liquid, leaving sediment or other solid material behind in the container

decay
See radioactive decay

decay product
isotopes formed from radioactive decay

decay series
the decay of a particular radioisotope, which yields a different radioisotope that, in turn, decays; this sequential decay process may continue through several more radioisotopes until a stable nucleus is produced

degrees Celsius (°C)
See Celsius temperature scale

density
the mass per unit volume of a given material that is often expressed as g/cm^3

derived unit
an SI unit formed by mathematically combining two or more base units

detergent
a compound or mixture of compounds to assist cleaning that does not form insoluble precipitates with Mg^{2+} or Ca^{2+} as soaps do

diatomic molecule
a molecule made up of two atoms, such as chlorine gas, Cl_2, or carbon monoxide, CO

dimer
a molecule composed of two monomers

dipeptide
a molecule consisting of two amino acids bonded together

direct water use
water consumed by an end user

disaccharide
a sugar molecule (such as sucrose) composed of two monosaccharide units bonded through a condensation reaction

dissolve
the process of a solute interacting with a solvent to form a solution

distillate
the condensed products of distillation

distillation
a process that separates liquid substances based on differences in their boiling points; *see also* fractional distillation

doping
adding impurities to a semiconductor to enhance its electrical conductivity

dot structure
See electron-dot structure

double covalent bond
a bond in which four electrons are shared between two adjacent atoms

ductile (ductility)
a property of a material that permits it to be stretched into a wire without breaking

dynamic equilibrium
see equilibrium

E

electric current
the flow of electrons, as through a wire connecting electrodes in a voltaic cell

electrical conductivity
the ability to transmit an electric current

electrical potential
the tendency for electrical charge to move through an electrochemical cell (based on an element's relative tendency to lose electrons when in contact with a solution of its ions); it is measured in volts (V)

electrochemistry
the study of chemical changes that produce or are caused by electrical energy

electrode
a strip of metal or other conductor serving as a contact between an ionic solution and the external circuit in an electrochemical cell

electrolysis
the process by which a chemical reaction is caused by passing an electrical current through an ionic solution

electrolyte
an ionic solution; dissolved ions allow the passage of an electrical charge through a solution

electromagnetic radiation
radiation ranging from low-energy radio waves to high-energy X-rays and gamma rays; includes visible light

electromagnetic spectrum
comprising the full range of electromagnetic radiation frequencies; *see also* electromagnetic radiation

electrometallurgy
the use of electrical energy to add electrons to metal ions, thus reducing them

electron
a particle possessing a negative electrical charge; electrons surround the nuclei of atoms

electron shell
See shells (electron)

electron-dot formula
See Lewis dot structure

electron-dot structure
See Lewis dot structure

electronegativity
an expression of the tendency of an atom to attract shared electrons within a chemical bond

electroplating
the deposition of a thin layer of metal on a surface by an electrical process involving oxidation-reduction reactions

electrostatic precipitation
a pollution-control method in which combustion waste products are electrically charged and then collected on plates of opposite electric charge

elements
the fundamental chemical substances from which all other substances are made

endothermic
a process that requires the addition of energy

endpoint
point where a titration is stopped, usually because an appropriate indicator just changes color

engineered ceramics
ceramic-based materials with properties designed for particular applications, such as high-temperature stability, wear resistance, electrical insulation, corrosion resistance, high strength and low weight, and thermal insulation

enzymes
biological catalysts present in all cells

equilibrium
the point in a reversible reaction where the rate of products forming from reactants is equal to the rate of reactants forming from products; also called dynamic equilibrium

essential amino acids
amino acids not synthesized in adequate quantities by the human body and that must be obtained from protein in the diet

ester
an organic compound containing the -COOR group, where R represents any stable arrangement of bonded carbon and hydrogen atoms

evaporation
changing from the liquid state to gaseous state

exothermic
a process that involves the release of energy

extrapolation
the process of estimating a value beyond a known range of data points

F

family (periodic table)
See group

fats
energy-storage molecules composed of carbon, hydrogen, and oxygen; they have fewer oxygen atoms and more carbon and hydrogen atoms than do carbohydrates

fatty acids
organic compounds made up of long hydrocarbon chains with carboxylic acid groups at one end

filtrate
the liquid collected after filtration

filtration
the process of separating solid particles from a liquid by passing the mixture through a material that retains the solid particles

fission, nuclear
See nuclear fission

flocculation
a process in which an insoluble material is suspended in or precipitated from a solution; used in water purification

fluorescence
the emission of visible light when exposed to radiant energy (usually ultraviolet radiation)

fluoridation
adding small quantities of fluoride ion (F^-) to treated water supplies with the intended purpose of promoting dental health

food additive
a substance added during food processing that is intended to increase nutritive value or enhance storage life, visual appeal, or ease of production

force
a push or pull exerted on an object; expressed by the newton (N), an SI unit

formula unit
a group of atoms or ions represented by a compound's chemical formula; simplest unit of an ionic compound

fossil fuel
a fuel (such as coal, petroleum, or natural gas) believed formed from plant or animal remains buried under Earth's surface for millions of years

fraction
(a) a mixture of petroleum-based substances with similar boiling points and other properties; (b) one of the distillate portions collected during distillation

fractional distillation
a process of separating a mixture into its components by boiling and condensing the components; *see also* distillation

free radicals
atoms or molecules with unstable arrangements and numbers of electrons

freezing point
the temperature at which a liquid turns into a solid; it is the same value as its melting point

frequency (ν)
the number of waves that pass a given point each second; in other words, the rate of oscillation; for electromagnetic radiation, the product of frequency and wavelength equals the speed of light

fuel cell
a device for directly converting chemical energy into electrical energy by chemically combining a fuel (such as hydrogen gas) with oxygen gas; does not involve combustion

functional group
an atom or a group of atoms that imparts characteristic properties to an organic compound

fusion, nuclear
See nuclear fusion

G

gamma decay
the radioactive decay of a nucleus accompanied by the emission of high-energy gamma rays

gamma radiation
high-energy electromagnetic radiation (gamma rays) emitted during the decay of some radioactive elements

gamma ray (γ)
high-energy electromagnetic radiation emitted during the decay of some radioactive elements

gas constant (R)
the constant used in the ideal gas law, $PV = nRT$; $R = 0.0821$ L·atm/(mol·K)

gaseous state
the state of matter having no fixed volume or shape

geothermal energy
energy extracted from hot water or steam from Earth's crust

gray (Gy)
the unit expressing the quantity of ionizing radiation delivered to tissue; it equals one joule absorbed per kilogram of body tissue

Green Chemistry
the design of chemical products and processes that require fewer resources and less energy and that reduces or eliminates reliance on and generation of hazardous substances

greenhouse effect
the trapping and returning of infrared radiation to Earth's surface by atmospheric substances such as water and carbon dioxide

greenhouse gases
atmospheric substances that absorb infrared radiation, such as CO_2, N_2O, and CH_4

groundwater
water from an aquifer or other underground source

group (periodic table)
a vertical column of elements in the periodic table; also called a family; group members share similar properties

H

Haber-Bosch process
the industrial synthesis of ammonia from hydrogen and nitrogen gases, which involves high pressure and temperature accompanied by a suitable catalyst

half-cell
a metal (or other electrode material) in contact with a solution of ions; forms one-half of a voltaic cell

half-life
the time for a radioactive substance to lose half of its radioactivity from decay; at the end of one half-life, 50% of the original radioisotope remains

half-reaction
a chemical equation explicitly showing either a loss of electrons (oxidation) or a gain of electrons (reduction); any oxidation–reduction reaction can be expressed as the sum of two half-reactions

halogen family
the group of elements consisting of fluorine, chlorine, bromine, iodine, and astatine

hard water
water containing high concentrations of calcium (Ca^{2+}), magnesium (Mg^{2+}), and/or iron(III) (Fe^{3+}) ions

heat
See thermal energy

heat capacity
See specific heat capacity

heat of combustion
the thermal energy released when a specific quantity of a material burns

heavy metals
metallic elements with high atomic weights, such as lead, mercury, and cadmium

heavy-metal ions
ions of heavy metals; these tend to be harmful to living matter

heterogeneous mixture
a mixture that is not uniform throughout

high-level nuclear waste
radioactive waste products associated with nuclear fission or products formed when neutrons are absorbed by nuclear fuel

histogram
a graph indicating the frequency or number of instances of particular values (or value ranges) within a set of related data

homogeneous mixture
a mixture that is uniform throughout; in other words, a solution

hybrid vehicle
a vehicle that combines two or more power sources; the combination of gasoline and electric power is the most common design

hydrocarbon
a molecule composed only of carbon and hydrogen atoms

hydrogenation
a chemical reaction that adds hydrogen atoms to an organic molecule

hydrologic cycle
See water cycle

hydrometallurgy
the industrial extraction of metals from ores at ordinary temperatures by water-based processes

hydrosphere
all parts of Earth where water is found, including oceans, clouds, ice caps, glaciers, lakes, rivers, and underground water supplies

I

ideal gas
a gas sample that behaves under all conditions as described by the kinetic molecular theory or by the ideal gas law

ideal gas law
the mathematical relationship that describes the behavior of an ideal gas sample, $PV = nRT$, where P = gas pressure; V = gas volume; n = moles of gas; R = gas constant, 0.0821 L·atm/(mol·K); and T = kelvin temperature

incomplete combustion
the partial burning of a fuel; the incomplete combustion of carbon, for example, produces carbon monoxide rather than carbon dioxide

indirect water use
water consumed in the preparation, production, or delivery of goods and services

infrared (IR) radiation
electromagnetic radiation just beyond the red (low-energy) end of the visible spectrum

insoluble
cannot dissolve in a particular solvent to any appreciable or directly observable extent

insulator
a material that does not conduct heat or electricity

intermolecular forces
forces of attraction among molecules

International System of Units (SI)
the modernized metric system

ions
electrically charged atoms or groups of atoms; negative ions are called anions, and positive ions are called cations

ion exchange
a process for softening water in which hard-water ions (such as Ca^{2+} and Mg^{2+}) are exchanged for other ions (such as Na^+)

ionic bond
a linkage among anions and cations involving attractions between opposite electrical charges; bonding among anions and cations produces an ionic solid

ionic compound
a substance composed of positive and negative ions

ionize
to become converted to ions

ionizing radiation
nuclear radiation and high-energy electromagnetic radiation with sufficient energy to produce ions by ejecting electrons from atoms and molecules

IR
See infrared (IR) radiation

irradiation
exposure to radiation of any kind, particularly to ionizing radiation

isomer
a molecule that has the same formula as another molecule and differs from it only by the arrangement of atoms or bonds

isomerization
a chemical change involving the rearrangement of atoms or bonds within a molecule without changing its molecular formula

isotopes
atoms of the same element with differing numbers of neutrons

IUPAC
the International Union of Pure and Applied Chemistry, a nongovernmental organization of worldwide chemistry societies; for example, IUPAC is the recognized authority for establishing standards and procedures for naming elements and other substances

K

kelvin temperature scale (K)
the absolute temperature scale, where zero kelvins (0 K) represents the theoretical lowest possible temperature; 0 °C = 273 K

kelvins (K)
See kelvin temperature scale (K)

kilopascal (kPa)
the SI pressure unit equal to 10^3 pascals; *see also* pascal (Pa)

kinetic energy
energy associated with the motion of an object

kinetic molecular theory (KMT)
observed gas behavior and gas laws explained by rapidly moving particles (gas molecules) that are relatively far apart and change direction only through collisions with each other or the container walls

kinetics
the study of reaction rates

L

law of conservation of energy
energy can change form but cannot be created or destroyed in any chemical reaction or physical change

law of conservation of matter
matter is neither created nor destroyed in any chemical reaction or physical change

Le Châtelier's principle
the predicted shift in the equilibrium position that partially counteracts the imposed change in conditions

Lewis dot structure
the representation of atoms, ions, and molecules where valence-electron dots surround each atom's symbol; it is useful for indicating covalent bonding; also called electron-dot structure

limiting reactant
the starting substance that is used up first in a chemical reaction; sometimes called the limiting reagent

liquid state
the state of matter with a fixed volume but no fixed shape

lithosphere
the solid outer layer of Earth, which also includes land areas under oceans and other bodies of water

low-level nuclear waste
radioactive waste products with relatively low levels of radioactivity, such as discarded protective clothing from nuclear laboratories

luster
the reflection of light from the surface of a material

M

macrominerals
minerals essential to human life and occurring in relatively large quantities (at least 5 g) in the body; also called major minerals

macroscopic
large enough to be seen by an unaided eye

magnetic resonance imaging (MRI)
a non-invasive computerized method of imaging soft human tissues by use of a powerful magnet and radio waves

major minerals
See macrominerals

malleable
the property of a material that permits it to be flattened without shattering

mass
the quantity of matter in a object; the kilogram (kg) is the SI base unit of mass

mass number
the sum of the number of protons and neutrons in the nucleus of an atom of a particular isotope

matter
anything that has mass and occupies space

mean
an expression of central tendency obtained by dividing the sum of a set of values by the number of values in the set; also known as the average value

mechanical filtering
a pollution-control method in which the combustion of waste products passes into filters that trap particles too large to pass through

median
within an ascending or descending set of values, the number that represents the middle value with an equal number of values above and below it

melting point
the temperature at which a solid turns into a liquid; it is the same value as its freezing point

mesosphere
the layer of the atmosphere directly above the stratosphere

metal
a material possessing properties such as luster, ductility, conductivity, and malleability

metalloid
a material with properties intermediate between those of metals and nonmetals

meter (m)
the SI base unit of length

microminerals
minerals essential to human life and occurring in relatively small quantities (less than 5 g) in the body; also called trace minerals

microwaves
electromagnetic radiation located between ultrahigh frequency radio waves and infrared radiation

mineral
(a) a naturally occurring solid substance commonly removed from ores to obtain a particular element of interest or value; (b) an inorganic substance needed by the body to maintain good health

mixture
a combination of materials in which each material retains its separate identity

models
tools to understand and interpret natural phenomena that can be physical, mathematical, or conceptual and represent, explain, or predict observed behavior; models are particularly helpful in chemistry to account for molecular-level interactions

molar concentration (M)
See molarity

molar heat of combustion
the quantity of thermal energy released from burning one mole of a substance

molar mass
the mass (usually in grams) of one mole of a substance

molar volume
the volume occupied by one mole of a substance; at 0 °C and 1 atm, the molar volume of any ideal gas is 22.4 L

molarity (M)
the concentration determined by dividing the total moles of solute by the solution volume (expressed in liters); also known as molar concentration

mole (mol)
the SI unit for amount of substance, equal to 6.02×10^{23} units, where the unit may be any specified entity; it is the chemist's "counting" unit

molecule
the smallest particle of a substance retaining all the properties of that substance

molecular formula
a chemical expression indicating the total atoms of each element contained in one molecule of a particular substance

molecular substance
a substance composed of molecules, such as H_2O and CH_4

monomer
a compound whose molecules can react to form the repeating units of a polymer

monosaccharide
a simple sugar (such as glucose or fructose) that cannot be hydrolyzed to produce other sugars

monounsaturated fat
a fat molecule containing one carbon–carbon double bond

mutagen
a material that causes mutations in DNA

mutation
changes in the structure of DNA that may result in production of altered protein material

N

natural water
untreated water gathered from natural sources such as rivers, ponds, or wells

negative oxidation state
the negative number assigned to an atom in a compound when that atom has greater control of bonding electrons than the control exerted by one or more atoms to which it is bonded

neutral solution
a water solution in which H^+ (H_3O^+) and OH^- concentrations are equal; pH = 7 at 25 °C

neutralization
combining an acid and a base in amounts that result in the elimination of all excess acid or base

neutron
a particle without electrical charge; found in the nucleus of an atom

newton (N)
the SI unit of force that is roughly equal to the force exerted by a mass of 100 g at Earth's surface

nitrogen cycle
the movement of atmospheric nitrogen atoms through Earth's ecosystems via collection by bacteria, conversion into ammonia or ammonium ions, conversion into nitrate ions, uptake by plants, passage through the food chain, release as ammonia or ammonium ions, and conversion back into atmospheric nitrogen

nitrogen fixation
chemically converting atmospheric nitrogen gas into nitrogen compounds; this can be done by lightning, by the action of microorganisms, or by industrial means (*see* Haber-Bosch process)

noble gas family
an unreactive element belonging to the last (right-most) group on the periodic table

nonconductor
a material that does not allow electrical current (or thermal energy) to flow through it

nonideal gas
a gas sample that fails to behave as described by the kinetic molecular theory, or a gas sample whose behavior does not follow the ideal gas law; nonideal gas behavior is mainly observed under conditions of low gas temperature and/or high gas pressure

nonionizing radiation
electromagnetic radiation in the visible and lower-energy regions of the electromagnetic spectrum with insufficient energy to form ions when it transfers energy to matter

nonmetal
a material possessing properties such as brittleness, lack of luster, and nonconductivity; nonmetals are often insulators

nonpolar molecule
a molecule that has an even distribution of electrical charge with no regions of partial positive and negative charge

nonrenewable resource
a resource in limited supply that cannot be replenished by natural processes over the time frame of human experience

nuclear fission
splitting a nucleus into two smaller nuclei

nuclear fusion
the combination of two nuclei to form a new, more massive nucleus

nuclear power plant
a facility where thermal energy generated by the controlled fission of nuclear fuel drives a steam turbine, producing electrical power; in other words, a facility that converts nuclear energy into electricity

nuclear radiation
a form of ionizing radiation that results from changes in the nuclei of atoms

nucleus, atomic
the dense, positively charged central region of an atom that contains protons and neutrons

O

octane rating
a measure of the combustion quality of gasoline compared to the combustion quality of isooctane; the higher the number, the higher the octane rating; also called octane number

OIL RIG
a mnemonic device for remembering the processes of *oxidation* and *reduction*: Oxidation Is Loss, Reduction Is Gain (of electrons)

oil shale
sedimentary rock containing a material (kerogen) that can be converted to crude oil

ore
a rock or other solid material from which it is profitable to recover a mineral containing a metal or other useful substances

organic chemistry
the branch of chemistry dealing with hydrocarbons and their derivatives

osmosis
the passage of a solvent from a dilute solution to a more concentrated one through a semipermeable membrane that allows the passage of solvent molecules (such as water) but not solute particles (ions or molecules)

oxidation
any process in which one or more electrons can be considered as lost by a chemical species

oxidation state
the apparent state of oxidation of an atom; also called oxidation number

oxidation–reduction (redox) reaction
a chemical reaction in which oxidation and reduction simultaneously occur

oxidized
see oxidation

oxidizing agent
a species that causes another atom, molecule, or ion to become oxidized; the oxidizing agent becomes reduced in this process

oxygenated fuel
a fuel with oxygen-containing additives, such as methanol, that increase the octane rating and reduce harmful emissions

ozone hole
a region of significant thinning of the stratospheric ozone layer; it occurs seasonally, most prominently over the South Pole

ozone shield
the protective layer of stratospheric ozone that absorbs intense solar ultraviolet radiation that is harmful to living organisms

P

paper chromatography
a method for separating substances that relies on solution components having different attractions to the solvent (mobile phase) and paper (stationary phase)

particle
entities such as alpha particles, atoms, ions, or molecules; *see also* particulates

particulate level
the realm of unseen atoms, molecules, and ions in contrast to observable macroscopic entities

particulate pollution
air contaminants made up of small particles suspended in the atmosphere

particulates
solid particles such as dust, mist, fumes, soot, and smoke that do not settle, but remain in the air; generated by human activities or natural processes

parts per billion (ppb)
an expression of concentration; the number of units of solute found in one billion units of solution

parts per million (ppm)
an expression of concentration; the number of units of solute found in one million units of solution

pascal (Pa)
the SI pressure unit; equal to one newton of force applied per square meter, $1\ Pa = 1\ N/m^2$

peptide bond
the chemical bond that links amino acids together in peptides and proteins

percent composition
the percent by mass of each component in a material; or, specifically, the percent by mass of each element within a compound

percent recovery
the proportion of sought material recovered in a process

period (periodic table)
a horizontal row of elements in the periodic table

periodic relationship
regular patterns among chemical and physical properties of elements arrayed in the periodic table

periodic table of the elements
an arrangement of elements in order of increasing atomic number, such that elements with similar properties are located in the same vertical column (group)

petrochemical
any organic compound produced from petroleum or natural gas

pH
an expression of the acidic or basic character of a solution; at 25 °C, solutions with pH values lower than 7 are acidic, solutions above 7 are basic, and neutral solutions equal 7; pH is based on a solution's hydrogen ion (H^+ or H_3O^+) concentration

photochemical smog
a potentially hazardous mixture of secondary pollutants formed by solar irradiation of certain primary pollutants in the presence of oxygen

photon
an energy bundle of electromagnetic radiation that travels at the speed of light

photosynthesis
the process by which green plants and some microorganisms use solar energy to convert water and carbon dioxide to carbohydrates (stored chemical energy)

physical change
a change in matter in which the identity of the material involved does not change

physical property
a property that can be observed or measured without changing the identity of the sample of matter

polar bond
a covalent bond where electrons are shared unequally due to an electronegativity difference in the bonded atoms

polar molecule
a molecule with regions of partial positive and negative charge resulting from the uneven distribution of electrical charge

pollutant
an undesirable contaminant that adversely affects the chemical, physical, or biological characteristics of the environment

polyatomic ion
an ion composed of two or more atoms, such as the ammonium cation, NH_4^+, or acetate anion, $C_2H_3O_2^-$

polymer
a molecule composed of very large numbers of identical repeating units

polysaccharide
a polymer composed of many monosaccharide units

polyunsaturated fat
a fat molecule containing two or more carbon–carbon double bonds

positive oxidation state
the positive number assigned to an atom in a compound when that atom has less control of its electrons than it has as a free element

positron
a positively charged subatomic particle with the same mass as an electron; the antimatter counterpart to the electron

positron emission tomography (PET)
a technique for examining metabolic activity in tissues (particularly in the brain) by measuring blood flow containing tracers that emit positrons

postchlorination
adding a low level of chlorine to treated water to kill and prevent later bacterial infestation

potable water
water that is safe to drink

potential energy
energy associated with position

prechlorination
a process in which chlorine is added early in water treatment to kill bacterial infestation

precipitate
an insoluble solid substance that has separated from a solution

precipitation
(a) forming a chemical precipitate; (b) moisture falling from the atmosphere as rain, snow, sleet, or hail

pressure
equals force applied per unit area; in SI, pressure is expressed in pascals (Pa)

primary air pollutant
a contaminant that directly enters the atmosphere; it is not initially formed by reactions of airborne substances

products
substances formed in a chemical reaction

protein
a major structural component of living tissue made from many linked amino acids

proton
a particle possessing a positive electrical charge that is found in the nuclei of all atoms; the total protons in an element's atom equals its atomic number

pure substance
See substance

pyrometallurgy
the use of high temperatures (thermal energy) to process metals or their ores

Q

qualitative test
a chemical test indicating the presence or absence of an element, ion, or compound in a sample

quantitative test
a chemical test indicating the amount or concentration of an element, ion, or compound in a sample

R

rad
a unit that expresses the quantity of ionizing radiation absorbed by tissue; 1 rad = 0.01 Gy

radiation
energy emitted in the form of electromagnetic waves or high-speed particles; refers to both ionizing radiation and nonionizing radiation

radioactive decay
a change in an atom's nucleus due to the spontaneous emission of alpha, beta, or gamma radiation

radioactivity
the spontaneous emission of nuclear radiation

radioisotopes
radioactive isotopes

range
the difference between the highest and lowest values in a data set

reactants
starting materials in a chemical reaction

reaction rate
an expression of how fast a particular chemical change occurs

redox reaction
See oxidation–reduction reaction

reduced
See reduction

reducing agent
a species that causes another atom, molecule, or ion to become reduced; the reducing agent, in turn, becomes oxidized in this process

reduction
any process in which one or more electrons can be considered as gained by a chemical species

reference solution
a solution of known composition used as a comparison in chemical tests

reflectivity
the proportion of radiation that a material reflects rather than absorbs

rem
a unit that expresses the ability of radiation to cause ionization in human tissue; 1 rem = 0.01 Sv

renewable resource
a resource that can be replenished by natural processes over the time frame of human experience

reverse osmosis
a water-treatment process involving the separation of dissolved ions by forcing water through a semipermeable membrane under high pressure

reversible reaction
a chemical reaction in which products form reactants at the same time that reactants form products

R_f value
the ratio of the distance a given substance moves to the distance the solvent moves in paper chromatography

S

salt bridge
a connection that allows a voltaic cell's two half-cells to be in electrical contact without mixing; specifically, a tube containing an electrolyte (such as potassium chloride solution) that completes the internal circuit of a voltaic cell

sand filtration
separating solid particles from a liquid by passing the mixture through sand

saturated fat
a fat molecule containing only single carbon–carbon bonds within its fatty acid components

saturated hydrocarbon
a hydrocarbon consisting of molecules in which each carbon atom is bonded to four other atoms

saturated solution
a solution in which the solvent has dissolved as much solute as it can retain stably at a specified temperature

scintillation counter
a detector of ionizing radiation that measures light emitted by atoms that have been excited by ionizing radiation

scrubbing, wet
a pollution-control method involving an aqueous solution that removes particles and sulfur oxides from industrial combustion processes

secondary air pollutant
a contaminant generated in the atmosphere by chemical reactions between primary air pollutants and natural components of air

semiconductor
a solid substance, such as silicon, with electrical conductivity between that of conductors and nonconductors at normal temperatures

shells (electron)
energy levels surrounding an atom's nucleus within which one or more electrons reside; outer-shell electrons are commonly called valence electrons

SI
See International System of Units (SI)

sievert (Sv)
an SI unit that expresses the dose equivalent of absorbed radiation that causes same biological effects as one gray of gamma rays

single covalent bond
a bond in which two electrons are shared by the two bonded atoms

smog
a potentially hazardous combination of smoke and fog; *see also* photochemical smog

soft water
water that is not hard; it contains relatively low concentrations of calcium (Ca^{2+}), magnesium (Mg^{2+}), and iron(III) (Fe^{3+}) ions

solid state
the state of matter having a fixed volume and fixed shape

solid-state detector
a device used to monitor changes in the movement of electrons through semiconductors as they are exposed to ionizing radiation

solubility
the quantity of a substance that will dissolve in a given quantity of solvent to form a saturated solution at a particular temperature

solubility curve
a graph indicating the solubility of a particular solute at different temperatures

solute
the dissolved species in a solution; the solute is usually the smaller component in a solution.

solution
a homogeneous mixture of two or more substances

solution concentration
the quantity of solute dissolved in a specific quantity of solvent or solution

solvent
the dissolving agent in a solution; the solvent is usually the larger component in a solution.

species
a general name used in chemistry for atoms, molecules, ions, free radicals, or other well-defined entities

specific heat capacity
the quantity of thermal energy needed to raise the temperature of 1 g of a material by 1 °C; the expression commonly has units of J/(g °C)

standard temperature and pressure (STP)
conditions of 0 °C and 1 atm

states
see gaseous state, liquid state, and solid state

stoichiometry
the relationships by which quantities of substances involved in a chemical reaction are linked and calculated

STP
See standard temperature and pressure

straight-chain alkane
an alkane consisting of molecules in which each carbon atom is linked to no more than two other carbon atoms

stratosphere
the layer of the atmosphere just above the troposphere

strong acid
an acid that fully ionizes in solution to liberate H^+ (H_3O^+); no molecular form of the acid remains

strong base
a base that fully liberates OH^- in solution

strong force
the force that holds protons and neutrons together in an atom's nucleus

structural formula
a chemical formula showing the arrangement of atoms and covalent bonds in a molecule, in which each electron pair in a covalent bond is represented by a line between the symbols of two atoms

structural isomers
substances involving rearrangement of atoms or bonds within a molecule but sharing a common molecular formula

subatomic particles
particles smaller than an atom; commonly regarded as electrons, protons, and neutrons

subscript
the number printed below the line of type indicating the total atoms of a given element in a chemical formula; in H_2O, for example, the subscript 2 specifies total H atoms

substance
an element or a compound; that is, a material with a uniform, definite composition and distinct properties

substituted alkenes
alkene molecules that contain, in addition to carbon and hydrogen atoms, one or more atoms of other elements, such as oxygen, nitrogen, chlorine, or sulfur

substrate
a molecule that interacts with an enzyme and undergoes a reaction

superconductivity
the ability of a material to conduct an electrical current with zero electrical resistance; with present technology, operating superconductors must be extremely cold

supersaturated solution
a solution containing a higher concentration of solute than a saturated solution at a specified temperature

surface water
water found on Earth's surface, such as oceans, rivers, and lakes

suspension
a mixture containing large, dispersed solid particles that can settle out or be separated by filtration

synergistic interaction
an interaction where the combined effect of several factors is greater than the sum of their separate effects

synthetic radioisotope
a radioactive isotope produced solely by human activity

synthetic substance
a substance produced solely by human activity

T

tap water
water delivered through plumbing lines

temperature
extent of "hotness" or "coldness" of a sample and related to the average kinetic energy of its particles; the SI base unit is the kelvin (K) or degree Celsius (°C)

temperature inversion
an atmospheric condition where a cool air mass is trapped beneath a less-dense warm air mass; it most frequently occurs in a valley or over a city

tetrahedron
a regular triangular pyramid; the four bonds of each carbon atom in an alkane point to the corners of a tetrahedron

thermal energy
the energy a material possesses due to its temperature; also informally called heat

thermoplastics
plastics that soften or melt when heated, and return to their rigid form when cooled, such as nylon, polyvinyl chloride, and polyethylene

thermosphere
the highest layer of the atmosphere

titration
a laboratory procedure for determining the concentrations of dissolved substances

trace minerals
See microminerals

tracer
a readily-identifiable material, such as a radioisotope, used to diagnose disease or to determine how the body is responding to treatment

transmutation
the conversion of one element to another either naturally or artificially

transuranium element
any element with an atomic number greater than 92 (uranium)

triglyceride
a fat molecule composed of a simple three-carbon alcohol (glycerol) and three fatty acid molecules

tripeptide
a molecule composed of three amino acids bonded together

troposphere
the layer of the atmosphere closest to Earth's surface where most clouds and weather are located

turbidity
cloudy conditions caused by suspended solids in a liquid

Tyndall effect
the scattering of a beam of light caused by reflection from suspended particles

U

ultraviolet (UV) radiation
electromagnetic radiation beyond the violet end of the visible spectrum; overexposure to this radiation can cause skin damage

unsaturated fat
a fat molecule containing one or more carbon–carbon double bonds; it is monounsaturated if each fat molecule has a single double bond and polyunsaturated if it has two or more double bonds

unsaturated hydrocarbon
a hydrocarbon molecule containing one or more double or triple bonds

unsaturated solution
a solution containing a lower concentration of solute than a saturated solution contains at a specified temperature

V

valence electrons
electrons in the outermost shell of an atom; these relatively loosely held electrons often participate in bonding with other atoms or molecules

viscous
pertaining to "thick" liquid with resistance to flow; high viscosity

visible radiation
electromagnetic radiation that the human eye can detect; visible radiation has wavelengths from about 400 nm (violet) to 700 nm (red)

vitamin
a biomolecule necessary for growth, reproduction, health, and life

vitrification
the conversion of material into a glassy solid by application of high temperatures

volatile organic compounds (VOCs)
reactive carbon-containing substances that readily evaporate into air, such as components of gasoline and organic solvents

voltaic cell
an electrochemical cell in which a spontaneous chemical reaction produces electricity

W

water cycle
repetitive processes of rainfall (or other precipitation), run-off, evaporation, and condensation that circulate water within Earth's crust and atmosphere; also called the hydrologic cycle

water softener
a device containing an ion-exchange resin that is used to treat water by removing ions causing water hardness

water treatment
refers to cleaning and purification processes applied to water

wavelength (λ)
the distance between corresponding points of two consecutive waves; for electromagnetic radiation, the product of frequency and wavelength equals the speed of light

weak acid
an acid that does not fully ionize in solution to liberate H^+ (H_3O^+) but remains primarily in molecular form

weak base
a base that does not fully liberate OH^- in solution but remains primarily in molecular form

wellplate
a clear, plastic laboratory device containing multiple indentations (wells), where small samples of solutions can be held and tested or chemical reactions studied

wet scrubbing
See scrubbing, wet

X

X-ray
high-energy electromagnetic radiation that cannot penetrate dense materials such as bone or lead but can penetrate less dense materials

Z

zero oxidation state
the value of the oxidation state of an element's atoms when not chemically combined with any other element

ILLUSTRATION AND PHOTO

CHEMCOM PROJECT CREDITS

ChemCom is the product of teamwork involving individuals from all over the United States over more than twenty years. The American Chemical Society is pleased to recognize all who contributed to *ChemCom*.

The team responsible for the fifth edition of *ChemCom* is listed on the copyright page. Individuals who contributed to the initial development of *ChemCom,* to the first edition in 1988, the second edition in 1993, the third edition in 1998, and the fourth edition 2002 are listed below.

Principal Investigator: W. T. Lippincott

Project Manager: Sylvia Ware

Chief Editor: Henry Heikkinen & Conrad L. Stanitski

Contributing Editor: Mary Castellion

Assistant to Contributing Editor: Arnold Diamond

Editor of Teacher's Guide: Thomas O'Brien & Patricia J. Smith

Revision Team: Diane Bunce, Gregory Crosby, David Holzman, Thomas O'Brien, Joan Senyk, Thomas Wysocki

Editorial Advisory Board: Joseph Breen, Glenn Crosby, James DeRose, I. Dwaine Eubanks, Lucy Pryde Eubanks, Regis Goode, Henry Heikkinen (chair), Mary Kochansky, Ivan Legg, W. T. Lippincott (ex officio), Steven Long, Nina McClelland, Lucy McCorkle, Carlo Parravano, Robert Patrizi, Max Rodel, K. Michael Shea, Patricia Smith, Susan Snyder, Conrad Stanitski, Jeanne Vaughn, Sylvia Ware (ex officio)

Writing Team: Rosa Balaco, James Banks, Joan Beardsley, William Bleam, Kenneth Brody, Ronald Brown, Diane Bunce, Becky Chambers, Alan DeGennaro, Patricia Eckfeldt, Dwaine Eubanks (dir.), Henry Heikkinen (dir.), Bruce Jarvis (dir.), Dan Kallus, Jerry Kent, Grace McGuffie, David Newton (dir.), Thomas O'Brien, Andrew Pogan, David Robson, Amado Sandoval, Joseph Schmuckler (dir.), Richard Shelly, Patricia Smith, Tamar Susskind, Joseph Tarello, Thomas Warren, Robert Wistort, Thomas Wysocki

Steering Committee: Alan Cairncross, William Cook, Derek Davenport, James DeRose, Anna Harrison (ch.), W. T. Lippincott (ex officio), Lucy McCorkle, Donald McCurdy, William Mooney, Moses Passer, Martha Sager, Glenn Seaborg, John Truxall, Jeanne Vaughn

Consultants: Alan Cairncross, Michael Doyle, Donald Fenton, Conrad Fernelius, Victor Fratalli, Peter Girardot, Glen Gordon, Dudley Herron, John Hill, Chester Holmlund, John Holman, Kenneth Kolb, E. N. Kresge, David Lavallee, Charles Lewis, Wayne Marchant, Joseph Moore, Richard Millis, Kenneth Mossman, Herschel Porter, Glenn Seaborg, Victor Viola, William West, John Whitaker

Synthesis Committee: Diane Bunce, Dwaine Eubanks, Anna Harrison, Henry Heikkinen, John Hill, Stanley Kirschner, W. T. Lippincott (ex officio), Lucy McCorkle, Thomas O'Brien, Ronald Perkins, Sylvia Ware (ex officio), Thomas Wysocki

Evaluation Team: Ronald Anderson, Matthew Bruce, Frank Sutman (dir.)

Field Test Coordinator: Sylvia Ware

Field Test Workshops: Dwaine Eubanks

Field Test Directors: Keith Berry, Fitzgerald Bramwell, Mamie Moy, William Nevill, Michael Pavelich, Lucy Pryde, Conrad Stanitski

Pilot Test Teachers: Howard Baldwin, Donald Belanger, Navarro Bharat, Ellen Byrne, Eugene Cashour, Karen Cotter, Joseph Deangelis, Virginia Denney, Diane Doepken, Donald Fritz, Andrew Gettes, Mary Gromko, Robert Haigler, Anna Helms, Allen Hummel, Charlotte Hutton, Elaine Kilbourne, Joseph Linker, Larry Lipton, Grace McGuffie, Nancy Miller, Gloria Mumford, Beverly Nelson, Kathy Nirei, Elliott Nires, Polly Parent, Mary Parker, Dicie Petree, Ellen Pitts, Ruth Rand, Kathy Ravano, Steven Rischling, Charles Ross, Jr., David Roudebush, Joseph Rozaik, Susan Rutherland, George Smeller, Cheryl Snyder, Jade Snyder, Samuel Taylor, Ronald Tempest, Thomas Van Egeren, Gabrielle Vereecke, Howard White, Thomas Wysocki, Joseph Zisk

Field Test Teachers: Vincent Bono, Allison Booth, Naomi Brodsky, Mary D. Brower, Lydia Brown, George Bulovsky, Kay Burrough, Gene Cashour, Frank Cox, Bobbie Craven, Pat Criswell, Jim Davis, Nancy Dickman, Dave W. Gammon, Frank Gibson, Grace Giglio, Theodis Gorre, Margaret Guess, Yvette Hayes, Lu Hensen, Kenn Heydrick, Gary Hurst, Don Holderread, Michael Ironsmith, Lucy Jache, Larry Jerdal, Ed Johnson, Grant Johnson, Robert Kennedy, Anne Kenney, Joyce Knox, Leanne Kogler, Dave Kolquist, Sherman Kopelson, Jon Malmin, Douglas Mandt, Jay Maness, Patricia Martin, Mary Monroe, Mike Morris, Phyllis Murray, Silas Nelson, Larry Nelson, Bill Rademaker, Willie Reed, Jay Rubin, Bill Rudd, David Ruscus, Richard Scheele, Paul Shank, Dawn Smith, John Southworth, Mitzi Swift, Steve Ufer, Bob Van Zant, Daniel Vandercar, Bob Volzer, Terri Wahlberg, Tammy Weatherly, Lee Weaver, Joyce Willis, Belinda Wolfe

Field Test Schools: California: Chula Vista High, Chula Vista; Gompers Secondary School, San Diego; Montgomery High, San Diego; Point Loma High, San Diego; Serra Junior-Senior High, San Diego; Southwest High, San Diego. Colorado: Bear Creek Senior High, Lakewood; Evergreen Senior High, Evergreen; Green Mountain Senior High, Lakewood; Golden Senior High, Golden; Lakewood Senior High, Lakewood; Wheat Ridge Senior High, Wheat Ridge. Hawaii: University of Hawaii Laboratory School, Honolulu. Illinois: Project Individual Education High, Oak Lawn. Iowa: Linn-Mar High, Marion. Louisiana: Booker T. Washington High, Shreveport; Byrd High, Shreveport; Caddo Magnet High, Shreveport; Captain Shreve High, Shreveport; Fair Park High, Shreveport; Green Oaks High, Shreveport; Huntington High, Shreveport;

final analysis/report on, 644–646
Venus
    atmosphere of, 342–343
    greenhouse effect on, 342–343
    surface temperature of, 52
Vinegar, 68–69
    as food additive, 635
Vinyl chloride, 270
Visible radiation, 340
Vitamin A, 620–621
Vitamin B complex, 619
Vitamin B$_1$, 620
    diet content of, 622
    food sources of, 621
Vitamin B$_2$, 620–621
Vitamin B$_6$, 620–621
Vitamin B$_{12}$, 620–621
Vitamin C
    beverage analysis for, 625
    deficiency of, health impact of, 620, 621
    diet content of, 622
    Dietary Reference Intakes for, 620
    food sources of, 621–622
    iodine reaction with, 623–625
    molecular structure of, 623
    titration of, 641
Vitamin D, 619–621
Vitamin deficiencies, health impacts of, 620–621
Vitamin E, 620–621
Vitamin K, 620–621
Vitamins
    fat-soluble, 620, 641
    in food, 619–625
        analyzing, 639
        Dietary Reference Intakes for, 620
        functions of, 619–620
        sources of, 619, 621
    as food additives, 635
    megadoses of, 621
    multipurpose, 432
    water-soluble, 620, 623, 641
Vitrification, of nuclear waste, 558–559, 562
Volatile organic compounds (VOCs), as air pollutants, 384–386, 392
Volcanoes, acid precipitation with, 363
Volleyball, energy expended while playing, 576
Voltaic cell(s)
    conceptual applications of, 471–473
    constructing a, 453–454
    diagram of, 453
    electrical potential from, 453
        measurements of, 455
    electrodes in, 453
        size effects of, 455
    electrolysis and, 452–454
    half-reactions and, 456
Volts, in voltaic cells, 453
    measurement of, 455
Volume
    as derived SI unit, 310–311
    in ideal gas behavior, 329–331. See also Pressure-volume behavior; Temperature-volume behavior

conceptual applications of, 333–336
in kinetic molecular theory, 325–326
Vulcanization, 483

W

Walking
    energy expended during, 576
    travel risks with, 556
Warfare. See Weapons
Washing soda, 98
Waste
    from chemical products, 443–444
    municipal
        recycling of, 175
        U.S. generation of, 173–175
    nuclear. See Nuclear waste
    radioactive. See Radioactive waste
Waste Isolation Pilot Plant (Carlsbad), 559
Waste management. See also Resource conservation
    in communities, 175
Waste-to-energy plants, 175
Wastewater
    before and after treatment of, 88–89
    historical treatment of, 86
Water, heat capacity of, 571
Water (H$_2$O)
    black vs. grey, 22
    boiling point of, 52, 216
    from buring gasoline, 153, 161
    in cellular respiration, 574
        limiting reactants in, 598–599
    chemical formula for, 31, 35
    cost of pure vs. unpure, 45, 101
    dynamic equilibrium in, 435
    electrolysis of, 241
    in ethanol, 262–263
    foul, clean up of, 10–15. See also Foul water
    for fruit juice production, 8, 16–17
    gaseous, reaction forming, 157–159
    grey vs. black, 22
    hard, 92–93
        softening of, 93–99
    heat capacity of, 571
    ions found dissolved in, 42–43
    in making acid rain, 368
    as molecular substance, 59, 71
    nuclear power plant use of, 548–549
    one mole of, 162
    particulate view of, 31
    pH of, 363, 371–372
    in photosynthesis, 572–573
    physical properties of, 19, 26–27. See also specific property
    as polar molecule, 59–60, 72
    potable, 22
    radiant energy absorption by, 339–340, 342
    reuse of, 22
    as solvent, 73–75, 83
    specific heat capacity of, 345
Water bath, hot, 58

Water contamination, causing fish kill, 4–6. See also Riverwood water emergency
Water cycle, 15, 23
Water demand. See Water use
Water use diary, 8–9
Water flow
    in nuclear power plant, 547
    in nuclear powered submarines, 551
Water pipes
    acidic water corroding of, 89
    materials for, 66
Water power, 285
Water purification, 10–15
    charcoal absorption and filtration in, 12–13
    conceptual applications of, 24
    cost of, 45, 101
    data analysis for, 13–14
    data table for, 10
    distillation, 15
    earth's system for, 86–87
    economics of, 4–6, 15
    hydrologic cycle process of, 86–87
        municipal system vs., 89, 102
    introduction to, 10
    municipal system for, 88–89
        natural system vs., 89
    oil-water separation in, 11
    osmosis vs. reverse osmosis for, 100–101
    post-lab activities, 14–15
    procedure for, 10
    questions regarding, 15
    sand filtration in, 11–12
    techniques for, 23
Water purity
    in bottled vs. tap water, 91–92
    cost of desired purity, 7–8, 101
    electrical conductivity related to, 14, 30
    light transmission related to, 14–15
    physical characteristics of, 27
Water rationing, daily basis for, 21–22
Water samples, of Snake River, 5. See also Water testing
Water shortage, in Riverwood, 4–5
    townspeople reaction to, 6–7
Water softener, home, 98–99
Water softening, 92–99
    Calgon for, 93, 97
    conceptual applications of, 12–103
    of household hard water, 96–99
    introduction to, 92–94
    ion-exchange for, 93–94, 102
        home units for, 98–99
    procedure for, 94–96
    questions regarding, 96
    sand filtration for, 93
    sodium hexametaphosphate for, 93, 97
Water-soluble vitamins, 620, 623, 641

Water solutions. See Aqueous solutions
Water supply, 15–22
    global distribution of, 18–19
    municipal, 19
    rural, 19
    U.S. use vs., 15–18
Water temperature
    density based on, 27
    maximum tolerance for fish, 77, 84
    oxygen solubility and, 76–79, 83–84
    solubility and, 54–55, 59
Water testing, 42–45
    calcium ion test, 44
    cautions for, 10
    chloride ion test, 44
    conceptual applications of, 52
    data table for, 43
    introduction to, 42–43
    iron ion test, 44
    procedure for, 43–45
    questions regarding, 28, 52
    for Riverwood water mystery, 46–47
    in Snake River fish kill investigations, 79–80
    sulfate ion test, 45
Water treatment
    before and after use, 88–89
    chemical reactions in, 159–160
    evolution of, 86
Water-treatment plants
    chemical reactions in, 159–160
    municipal, 88–89
    water supply for, 19
Water use, 8–9
    direct vs. indirect, 15–16, 23
    in U.S.
        analysis of, 20–21
        categories of, 15–16
        by region, 17
Water vapor
    in air, 18, 303, 304
    greenhouse effectiveness of, 355
    from hydrocarbons, 213
    in photochemical smog, 389
Waves/wavelengths
    in electromagnetic radiation, 338
    parts of, 339
Weak acid, 375
    dilute vs. concentrated, 376–377
Weapons
    in civilization ages, 144
    nitrogen-based explosives as, 440, 443
    nuclear. See Nuclear weapons
Weather
    air pollution reports accompanying, 383, 386–387
    solar radiation and, 343–344
Weighing, of substances, 162–163
Weight control, energy balance and, 578–579
Weight gain, energy intake and, 578–579
Weight lifting, energy expended during, 576

CHART OF THE ELEMENTS

Element	Symbol	Atomic Number	Atomic Weight	Element	Symbol	Atomic Number	Atomic Weight
Actinium	Ac	89	[227]	Mendelevium	Md	101	[258]
Aluminum	Al	13	26.98	Mercury	Hg	80	200.59
Americium	Am	95	[243]	Molybdenum	Mo	42	95.94
Antimony	Sb	51	121.76	Neodymium	Nd	60	144.24
Argon	Ar	18	39.95	Neon	Ne	10	20.18
Arsenic	As	33	74.92	Neptunium	Np	93	[237]
Astatine	At	85	[210]	Nickel	Ni	28	58.69
Barium	Ba	56	137.33	Niobium	Nb	41	92.91
Berkelium	Bk	97	[247]	Nitrogen	N	7	14.01
Beryllium	Be	4	9.012	Nobelium	No	102	[259]
Bismuth	Bi	83	208.98	Osmium	Os	76	190.23
Bohrium	Bh	107	[264]	Oxygen	O	8	16.00
Boron	B	5	10.81	Palladium	Pd	46	106.42
Bromine	Br	35	79.90	Phosphorus	P	15	30.97
Cadmium	Cd	48	112.41	Platinum	Pt	78	195.08
Calcium	Ca	20	40.08	Plutonium	Pu	94	[244]
Californium	Cf	98	[251]	Polonium	Po	84	[209]
Carbon	C	6	12.01	Potassium	K	19	39.10
Cerium	Ce	58	140.12	Praseodymium	Pr	59	140.91
Cesium	Cs	55	132.91	Promethium	Pm	61	[145]
Chlorine	Cl	17	35.45	Protactinium	Pa	91	231.04
Chromium	Cr	24	52.00	Radium	Ra	88	[226]
Cobalt	Co	27	58.93	Radon	Rn	86	[222]
Copper	Cu	29	63.55	Rhenium	Re	75	186.21
Curium	Cm	96	[247]	Rhodium	Rh	45	102.91
Darmstadtium	Ds	110	[281]	Roentgenium	Rg	111	[272]
Dubnium	Db	105	[262]	Rubidium	Rb	37	85.47
Dysprosium	Dy	66	162.50	Ruthenium	Ru	44	101.07
Einsteinium	Es	99	[252]	Rutherfordium	Rf	104	[261]
Erbium	Er	68	167.26	Samarium	Sm	62	150.36
Europium	Eu	63	151.96	Scandium	Sc	21	44.96
Fermium	Fm	100	[257]	Seaborgium	Sg	106	[266]
Fluorine	F	9	19.00	Selenium	Se	34	78.96
Francium	Fr	87	[223]	Silicon	Si	14	28.09
Gadolinium	Gd	64	157.25	Silver	Ag	47	107.87
Gallium	Ga	31	69.72	Sodium	Na	11	22.99
Germanium	Ge	32	72.64	Strontium	Sr	38	87.62
Gold	Au	79	196.97	Sulfur	S	16	32.07
Hafnium	Hf	72	178.49	Tantalum	Ta	73	180.95
Hassium	Hs	108	[277]	Technetium	Tc	43	[98]
Helium	He	2	4.003	Tellurium	Te	52	127.60
Holmium	Ho	67	164.93	Terbium	Tb	65	158.93
Hydrogen	H	1	1.008	Thallium	Tl	81	204.38
Indium	In	49	114.82	Thorium	Th	90	232.04
Iodine	I	53	126.90	Thulium	Tm	69	168.93
Iridium	Ir	77	192.22	Tin	Sn	50	118.71
Iron	Fe	26	55.85	Titanium	Ti	22	47.87
Krypton	Kr	36	83.80	Tungsten	W	74	183.84
Lanthanum	La	57	138.91	Uranium	U	92	238.03
Lawrencium	Lr	103	[262]	Vanadium	V	23	50.94
Lead	Pb	82	207.2	Xenon	Xe	54	131.29
Lithium	Li	3	6.941	Ytterbium	Yb	70	173.04
Lutetium	Lu	71	174.97	Yttrium	Y	39	88.91
Magnesium	Mg	12	24.31	Zinc	Zn	30	65.41
Manganese	Mn	25	54.94	Zirconium	Zr	40	91.22
Meitnerium	Mt	109	[268]				

Note: A value in square brackets is the mass number of the isotope with the longest half-life.